Biology
Volume I

Sixth Edition

Eldra P. Solomon
University of South Florida

Linda R. Berg
St. Petersburg College

Diana W. Martin
Rutgers University

Contents Overview

Contents

PART 2
Energy Transfer Through Living Systems   133

PART **3**

The Continuity of Life:
Genetics *197*

PART 4

The Continuity of Life: Evolution 367

Biologists study the details of living organisms and all of their interactions. The Louisiana heron *(Hydranassa tricolor)* and the Florida red-bellied turtle *(Chrysemys nelsoni)* on which it has perched are complex organisms that make their home in the Florida cypress swamp. *(Mark J. Thomas/Dembinsky Photo Associates)*

The Organization of Life

CHAPTERS

1

A View of Life

Human genome research. Researchers carrying out DNA sequencing at the Joint Genome Institute (JGI). The JGI, a collaboration between three of the U.S. Department of Energy's National Laboratories, is part of the international Human Genome Organization (HUGO) that aims to complete the mapping of the entire human genome, the 3 billion base pairs that form the genetic code, by 2003. HUGO will provide the information needed to discover the genetic cause of many diseases. Computers in the laboratory sit between the large automated sequencers. *(David Parker/Science Photo Library/Photo Researchers, Inc.)*

LEARNING OBJECTIVES

After you have studied this chapter you should be able to

1. Define biology and discuss its applications to human life and society.
2. Distinguish between living and nonliving things by describing the features that characterize living organisms.
3. Relate metabolism to homeostasis and give specific examples of these life processes.
4. Summarize the importance of information transfer to living systems, giving specific examples.
5. Construct a hierarchy of biological organization, including levels of an individual organism and ecological levels.
6. Demonstrate the binomial system of nomenclature using several specific examples, and classify an organism (e.g., a human) in its domain, kingdom, phylum, class, order, family, genus, and species.
7. Contrast the six kingdoms of living organisms and cite examples of each group.
8. Give a brief overview of the theory of evolution and explain why it is the principal unifying concept in biology.
9. Apply the theory of natural selection to any given adaptation, suggesting a logical explanation of how the adaptation may have evolved.
10. Contrast the roles of producers, consumers, and decomposers and cite examples of their interdependence.
11. Design an experiment to test a given hypothesis, using the procedure and terminology of the scientific method.

This is an exciting time to begin your study of **biology,** the science of life. Almost daily, biologists are making remarkable new discoveries about ourselves—the human species—and about the millions of other organisms with which we share our planet. Applications of this basic research have provided us with the technology to transplant kidneys, livers, and hearts, manipulate genes, treat many diseases, and increase world food production. Biology has been a powerful force in providing us with the quality of life that most of us enjoy.

Whatever your college major or career goals, a knowledge of biological concepts is a vital tool for understanding our world

and for meeting many of the personal, societal, and global challenges that confront us. Among these challenges are the expanding human population, diminishing natural resources, decreasing biodiversity, and diseases such as cancer, Alzheimer's disease, malaria, and acquired immunodeficiency syndrome (AIDS). Meeting these challenges will require the combined efforts of biologists and other scientists, politicians, and biologically informed citizens. The debate over genetically modified (GM) crops is an example of the importance of consumer understanding. Scientists have promoted the development of GM crops as a means of increasing yields to meet the needs of growing populations. However, citizens in many countries are fearful of these new methods. In India, farmers recently destroyed fields of GM cotton. In the United States, fear of these new products has kept some off grocery shelves. Consumer demands will affect the course of future research.

Two other remarkable areas of biological investigation, genome research and stem cell studies, have potential applications that could transform health care and many other aspects of our lives during the 21st century. The **Human Genome Project** is mapping the complete set of genes that make up human genetic material (the genome). In 2000 a group of publicly funded scientists led by Francis Collins and a team of privately funded researchers led by J. Craig Venter announced that each had mapped and completed a working draft of the human genome. Their work has been heralded as a brilliant achievement, a big step toward deciphering the "book of life." Locating the genes is just the first step, however. Scientists need to refine what has been done and determine which genes do what and how they function. Detailed analyses of other primate genomes must also be carried out. The Human Genome Project also encompasses the next level of research, studying the proteins for which the genes code. Proteins make up the structural framework of an organism and also serve as enzymes that regulate the biochemical reactions essential to life. Genome research will contribute to the new science of gene therapy and will provide knowledge that will be applied to treatment, and even prevention, of many human disorders.

Stem cells are another exciting focus of biological research. **Stem cells** are cells that are unspecialized and have the capacity to divide, giving rise to more stem cells *and* to one or more specialized types of cell. Stem cells permit the body to repair both normal wear and tear and injury. For example, stem cells in the skin continuously divide, and some differentiate to replace skin cells that are constantly being worn off. Similarly, stem cells in the lining of the intestine reproduce themselves to replace cells that wear out. Stem cells in the bone marrow differentiate to restore the various types of blood cells. Humans and other mammals have an estimated 20 major types of stem cells.

Some tissues in the body, for example the heart, the brain, and the islets of the pancreas that produce insulin, have few or no stem cells and cannot effectively repair themselves. This is why research on embryonic stem (ES) cells is important. ES cells can give rise to all of the types of cells in the body. If ES cells could be cultured in the laboratory and then implanted in damaged hearts, brains, spinal cords, or livers, they could potentially provide the cells needed for repairing injuries or for reversing the ravages of disease processes. Some researchers are confident that stem cells will eventually be used to treat disorders like Parkinson's disease, Alzheimer's disease, multiple sclerosis, diabetes, and spinal cord injury.

In the 1970s and 1980s biologists worked out techniques for culturing ES cells from mouse embryos. Human ES cells were first grown in laboratory cultures in 1998 by two different research teams, one headed by James A. Thomson at the University of Wisconsin and the other led by John D. Gearhart of Johns Hopkins Medical Institutions. Gearhart's team obtained human ES cells from aborted embryos, whereas Thomson's group obtained human ES cells from very early embryos produced in fertility clinics. (After embryos are produced in laboratory glassware and one is implanted in a patient, the unused embryos can be frozen for future implantations, discarded, or donated for this type of ES cell research.) The ethical questions posed by new technology in genetics and developmental biology represent one group of issues that demand a biologically informed society.

The technology being developed for stem cell research is related to the techniques used in cloning animals. **Cloning** is the process of producing genetically identical cells or organisms by asexual reproduction of a single cell or organism. Cloning techniques have been combined with genetic engineering procedures to produce transgenic animals that can produce needed human proteins such as blood clotting factors. Cloning can also be used to improve livestock, to produce animal tissues and organs for transplant into humans, and to reproduce endangered species, pulling them back from the brink of extinction. For example, in 2000 an Iowa cow gave birth to the first cloned endangered species, a baby gaur (an oxlike animal native to India and southeast Asia). In the future, cloning may be used to save cheetahs, giant pandas, ocelots, and many other animals from extinction. In this way cloning can be an important tool in maintaining world biodiversity. The future applications of genetic research, stem cell studies, and cloning research have the potential to enhance our health and well-being and the well-being of our planet.

■ LIFE DEPENDS ON EVOLUTION, TRANSMISSION OF INFORMATION, AND ENERGY

This book is a starting point for your exploration of biology. It will provide you with the basic knowledge and the tools to become a part of this fascinating science and a more informed member of society. In this first chapter we introduce three basic themes of biology: **evolution of life, transmission of information,** and **flow of energy through living systems.** Scientists have accumulated a wealth of evidence showing that the diverse life forms on our planet are related and that organisms have evolved through time from earlier life forms. The process of evolution is the framework for the science of biology and a major theme of this book.

The process of evolution, as well as the survival and function of every organism, depends on the orderly transmission of information. At the molecular level, instructions for producing and maintaining each living organism and each new generation are encoded in the **deoxyribonucleic acid (DNA)** molecules that make up the genes. At higher levels, the activities of organisms are coordinated by many forms of chemical signaling. Animals also use chemical, as well as behavioral, signals to communicate with one another. For example, many female animals release chemical substances that attract males.

Energy is required to maintain the precise order that characterizes living systems. Maintaining the chemical transactions and cellular organization essential to life requires a continuous input of energy. We begin our study of biology by developing a more precise understanding of the fundamental characteristics of living systems.

■ LIFE CAN BE DEFINED IN TERMS OF THE CHARACTERISTICS OF ORGANISMS

We can easily recognize that an oak tree, a butterfly, and a lamb are living, whereas a rock is not. Despite their diversity, the organisms that inhabit our planet share a common set of characteristics

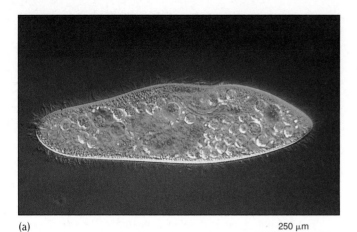

(a)

250 μm

(b)

Figure 1–1 Unicellular and multicellular life forms.
(a) Unicellular organisms are generally smaller than multicellular organisms and consist of one intricate cell that
performs all the functions essential to life. Ciliates, such as
this *Paramecium,* move about by beating their hairlike cilia.
(b) Multicellular organisms, such as this African buffalo
(Syncerus caffer) and the plants on which it grazes, may
consist of billions of cells specialized to perform specific
functions. *(a, Mike Abbey/Visuals Unlimited; b, McMurray
Photography)*

that distinguish them from nonliving things. These features include a precise kind of organization; growth and development;
self-regulated metabolism; movement; the ability to respond to
stimuli; reproduction; and adaptation to environmental change.
We consider each of these characteristics in the following sections.

Organisms are composed of cells

Living organisms are highly organized, and, as discussed later in
this chapter, we can identify a hierarchy of biological organization. As expressed in the **cell theory,** one of the fundamental
unifying concepts of biology, all organisms are composed of basic units called **cells.** Three German scientists are credited with
the cell theory. Matthias Schleiden (in 1838) and Theodor
Schwann (in 1839) were the first to report that plants and animals consist of groups of cells. Later, physician Rudolph Virchow observed cells dividing and giving rise to daughter cells. In
1855, Virchow proposed that new cells are formed only by the
division of previously existing cells. In other words, cells do not
arise by spontaneous generation from nonliving matter, a belief
that had prevailed for centuries.

Although they vary greatly in size and appearance, all organisms are composed of these small building blocks. Some of
the simplest life forms, such as protozoa, are *unicellular,* meaning that each consists of a single cell (Fig. 1–1). In contrast, the
body of a lamb or a maple tree is made of billions of cells. In such
complex *multicellular* organisms, life processes depend on the
coordinated functions of component cells that may be organized
to form tissues, organs, and organ systems.

Organisms grow and develop

Some nonliving things appear to grow. For example, salt crystals
form and enlarge in a supersaturated salt solution. However, this
is not growth in the biological sense. **Biological growth** may involve an increase in the size of individual cells of an organism or
in the number of cells, or both (Fig. 1–2). Growth may be uni-

Figure 1–2 Biological growth. The young African
elephant *(Loxodonta africana)* eats and grows until it
reaches the adult size of its parents, the largest living land
animals. These elephants were photographed in Kenya.
(McMurray Photography)

form in the various parts of an organism, or it may be greater in some parts than in others, causing the body proportions to change as growth occurs.

Some organisms, most trees, for example, continue to grow throughout their lives. Many animals have a defined growth period that terminates when a characteristic adult size is reached. One of the remarkable aspects of the growth process is that each part of the organism typically continues to function as it grows.

Living organisms develop as well as grow. **Development** includes all the changes that take place during the life of an organism. Each human, like many other organisms, begins life as a fertilized egg that then grows and develops. The structures and body form that develop are exquisitely adapted to the functions the organism must perform.

Organisms regulate their metabolic processes

Within all organisms, chemical reactions and energy transformations occur that are essential to nutrition, growth and repair of cells, and conversion of energy into usable forms. The sum of all the chemical activities of the organism is its **metabolism.** Metabolic processes occur continuously in every living organism, and they must be carefully regulated to maintain **homeostasis,** a balanced internal state. When enough of some cellular product has been made, its manufacture must be decreased or turned off. When a particular substance is needed, cellular processes that produce it must be turned on. These **homeostatic mechanisms** are self-regulating control systems that are remarkably sensitive and efficient.

The regulation of glucose (a simple sugar) concentration in the blood of complex animals is a good example of a homeostatic mechanism. Most cells require a constant supply of glucose, which they break down to obtain energy. The circulatory system delivers glucose and other nutrients to all the cells. When the concentration of glucose in the blood rises above normal limits, it is stored in the liver and in muscle cells. When the concentration begins to fall (between meals), stored nutrients are converted to glucose so that the concentration in the blood returns to normal levels. When glucose becomes depleted, we also feel hungry and restore nutrients by eating.

Movement is a basic property of cells

Organisms move as they interact with the environment, and in fact the living material within their cells is in continuous motion. In some organisms, locomotion results from the slow oozing of the cell (a process called *amoeboid motion*). Other organisms beat tiny hairlike extensions of the cell called **cilia** or longer structures called **flagella** (Fig. 1–3). Some bacteria move by means of rotating flagella.

Most animals move very obviously. They wiggle, crawl, swim, run, or fly by contracting muscles. A few animals, such as sponges, corals, and oysters, have free-swimming larval stages

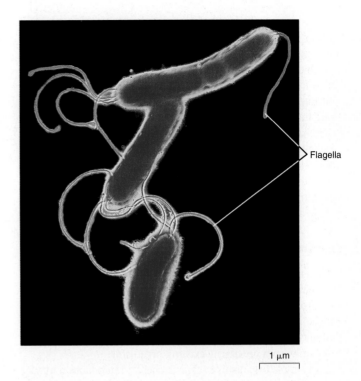

Flagella

1 μm

Figure 1–3 Biological movement. These bacteria *(Helicobacter pylori)*, equipped with flagella for locomotion, have been linked to stomach ulcers. The photograph is a color-enhanced scanning electron micrograph. *(A.B. Dowsett/Science Photo Library/Photo Researchers, Inc.)*

but do not move from place to place as adults. Even though these adults, described as **sessile,** remain firmly attached to some surface, they may have cilia or flagella. These structures beat rhythmically, moving the surrounding water that brings food and other necessities to the organism.

Although plants move more slowly than most animals, they do move. For example, plants orient their leaves to the sun and grow toward light. In some plants, such as the Venus flytrap, movement is obvious, even dramatic (described in the next section).

Organisms respond to stimuli

All forms of life respond to **stimuli,** physical or chemical changes in their internal or external environment. Stimuli that evoke a response in most organisms are changes in the color, intensity, or direction of light; changes in temperature, pressure, or sound; and changes in the chemical composition of the surrounding soil, air, or water.

In simple organisms, the entire individual may be sensitive to stimuli. Certain unicellular organisms, for example, respond to bright light by retreating. In complex animals such as polar bears and humans, certain cells of the body are highly specialized to respond to specific types of stimuli. For example, cells in the retina of the eye respond to light.

Although their responses may not be as obvious as those of animals, plants do respond to light, gravity, water, touch, and other stimuli. Many plant responses involve different rates of growth of various parts of the plant body. A few plants, such as the Venus flytrap of the Carolina swamps (Fig. 1–4), are remarkably sensitive to touch and can catch insects. Their leaves are hinged along the midrib, and they have a scent that attracts insects. Trigger hairs on the leaf surface detect the arrival of an insect and stimulate the leaf to fold. When the edges come together, the hairs interlock, preventing escape of the prey. The leaf then secretes enzymes that kill and digest the insect. The Venus flytrap is usually found in soil that is deficient in nitrogen. The plant obtains part of the nitrogen required for its growth from the insect prey it "eats."

Organisms reproduce

At one time worms were thought to arise spontaneously from horsehair in a water trough, maggots from decaying meat, and frogs from the mud of the Nile. Thanks to the work of several scientists, including Francesco Redi in the 17th century and Louis Pasteur in the 19th century, we now know that an organism can come only from previously existing organisms.

In simple organisms such as amoebas, reproduction may be **asexual,** that is, without the fusion of egg and sperm to form a fertilized egg (Fig. 1–5). When an amoeba has grown to a certain size, it reproduces by splitting in half to form two new amoebas. Before an amoeba divides, its hereditary material (set of genes)

duplicates, and one complete set is distributed to each new cell. Except for size, each new amoeba is similar to the parent cell. The only way that variation occurs among asexually reproducing organisms is by genetic **mutation**, a permanent change in the genes.

In most plants and animals, **sexual reproduction** is carried out by the production of specialized egg and sperm cells that fuse to form a fertilized egg. The new organism develops from the fertilized egg. Offspring produced by sexual reproduction are the product of the interaction of various genes contributed by the mother and the father. Such genetic variation provides raw material for the vital processes of evolution and adaptation.

Populations evolve and become adapted to the environment

The ability of a population to evolve (change over time) and adapt to its environment enables it to survive in a changing world. **Adaptations** are traits that enhance an organism's ability to survive in a particular environment. They may be structural, physiological, behavioral, or a combination of all three (Fig. 1–6). The long, flexible tongue of the frog is an adaptation for catching insects, the feathers and lightweight bones of birds are adaptations for flying, and the thick fur coat of the polar bear is an adaptation for surviving frigid temperatures. Every biologically successful organism is a complex collection of coordinated adaptations produced through evolutionary processes.

(a) (b)

■ **Figure 1–4 Plants respond to stimuli.** **(a)** Hairs on the leaf surface of the Venus flytrap (*Dionaea muscipula*) detect the touch of an insect, and the leaf responds by folding. **(b)** The edges of the leaf come together and interlock, preventing the fly's escape. The leaf then secretes enzymes that kill and digest the insect. *(David M. Dennis/Tom Stack & Associates)*

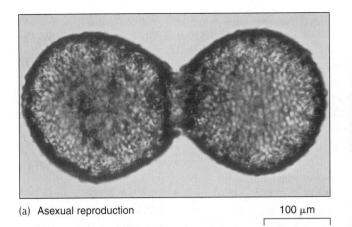

(a) Asexual reproduction

100 μm

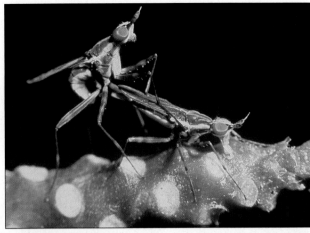

(b) Sexual reproduction

■ **Figure 1–5 Asexual and sexual reproduction.** (a) Asexual reproduction in *Difflugia*, a unicellular amoeba. In asexual reproduction, one individual gives rise to two or more offspring that are similar to the parent. (b) A pair of tropical flies mating. In sexual reproduction, typically two parents each contribute a gamete (sperm or egg). Gametes fuse to produce the offspring, which is a combination of the traits of both parents. *(a, Visuals Unlimited/Cabisco; b, L.E. Gilbert, Biological Photo Service)*

■ **Figure 1–6 Adaptations.** These Burchell's zebras *(Equus burchelli)*, photographed at Ngorongoro Crater in Tanzania, are behaviorally adapted to position themselves to watch for lions and other predators. Stripes are thought to be an adaptation for visually protecting themselves against predators. They serve as camouflage or to break up form when spotted from a distance. The zebra stomach is adapted for feeding on coarse grass passed over by other grazers, an adaptation that helps it survive when food is scarce. *(McMurray Photography)*

■ INFORMATION MUST BE TRANSMITTED WITHIN AND BETWEEN INDIVIDUALS

For an organism to grow, develop, carry on self-regulated metabolism, move, respond, and reproduce, it must have precise instructions. The information an organism needs to carry on these life processes is coded and delivered in the form of chemical substances and electrical impulses.

DNA transmits information from one generation to the next

Humans give birth only to human babies, not to giraffes or rose bushes. In organisms that reproduce sexually, each offspring is a combination of the traits of its parents. In 1953, James Watson and Francis Crick worked out the structure of deoxyribonucleic acid, more simply known as DNA. This chemical substance makes up the **genes,** the units of hereditary material. The work of Watson and Crick led to the understanding of the genetic code that transmits information from generation to generation. This code works somewhat like our alphabet; it can spell an amazing variety of instructions for making organisms as diverse as bacteria, frogs, and redwood trees. The genetic code is a dramatic example of the unity of life because it is used to specify instructions for making every living organism (Fig. 1–7).

Information is transmitted by chemical and electrical signals

Genes control the development and functioning of every organism. DNA contains the "recipes" for making all the **proteins** needed by the organism. Proteins are large molecules that are important in determining the structure and function of cells and tissues. Brain cells are different from muscle cells in large part because they have different types of proteins. Some proteins are important in communication within and among cells. Certain proteins on the surface of a cell serve as markers so that other cells "recognize" them. Other cell surface proteins serve as receptors that combine with chemical messengers.

Cells use proteins and many other types of ions and molecules to communicate with one another. In a multicellular

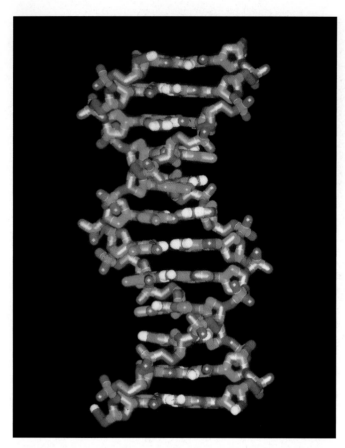

Figure 1-7 DNA. An organism's ability to transmit information from one generation to the next is essential to the continuity of life. In all organisms, the hereditary material is DNA. This computer graphic of a small (12 base-pair) segment of DNA shows its double-helix configuration. The DNA molecule consists of two chains of atoms twisted into a helix. Each chain consists of an outer sugar-phosphate backbone from which nucleotide bases project. The bases are paired in a complementary way. The sequence of bases makes up the genetic code. The atoms are color-coded as follows: carbon, blue; oxygen, red; nitrogen, purple; phosphorus, green; hydrogen, white. *(Jon Wilson/ Science Photo Library/Photo Researchers, Inc.)*

organism, chemical compounds secreted by cells help regulate growth, development, and metabolic processes in other cells. The mechanisms involved in **cell signaling** are complex, often involving multistep biochemical sequences, and cell signaling is currently an area of intense research. A major focus has been the transfer of information among cells of the immune system. A better understanding of how cells communicate promises new insights into how the body protects itself against disease organisms. Learning to manipulate cell signaling may lead to new methods of delivering drugs into cells and new treatments for cancer and other diseases. Examples of cell signaling are discussed throughout this book.

Hormones are molecules that function as chemical messengers that transmit information from one part of an organism to another. A hormone can signal cells to produce or secrete a certain protein or other substance.

Many organisms use electrical signals to transmit information. Most animals have nervous systems that transmit information by way of both electrical impulses and chemical compounds known as **neurotransmitters.** Information transmitted from one part of the body to another is important in regulating life processes. In complex animals, the nervous system transmits signals from sensory receptors such as the eyes and ears to the brain, giving the animal information about its outside environment.

Information must also be transmitted from one organism to another. Mechanisms for this type of communication include release of chemicals, visual displays, and sounds. Typically, organisms use a combination of several types of communication signals. For example, a dog may signal aggression by growling, using a particular facial expression, and positioning its ears back. Many animals perform complex courtship rituals in which they display parts of their bodies, often elaborately decorated, to attract a mate.

■ BIOLOGICAL ORGANIZATION IS HIERARCHICAL

Whether we study a single complex organism or the world of life as a whole, we can identify a hierarchy of biological organization (Fig. 1–8). At every level, structure and function are precisely coordinated. One way to study a particular level is by looking at its components. For example, biologists can learn about cells by studying atoms and molecules. Learning about a structure by studying its parts is known as **reductionism.** However, the whole is more than the sum of its parts. Each level has **emergent properties,** characteristics not found at lower levels. For example, populations have emergent properties such as population density, age structure, and birth and death rates. The individuals that make up a population lack these characteristics.

Organisms have several levels of organization

The **chemical level,** the most basic level of organization, includes atoms and molecules. An **atom** is the smallest unit of a chemical element (fundamental substance) that retains the characteristic properties of that element. For example, an atom of iron is the smallest possible amount of iron. Atoms combine chemically to form **molecules.** Two atoms of hydrogen combine with one atom of oxygen to form a single molecule of water. Although composed of two types of atoms that are gases, water is a liquid with very different properties, an example of emergent properties.

At the **cellular level** many different types of atoms and molecules associate with one another to form cells. However, a cell is much more than a heap of atoms and molecules. Its emergent properties make it the basic structural and functional unit of life, the simplest component of living matter that can carry on all the activities necessary for life. Every cell is surrounded by a **plasma membrane** that regulates the passage of materials between the cell and its surrounding environment. All cells have specialized

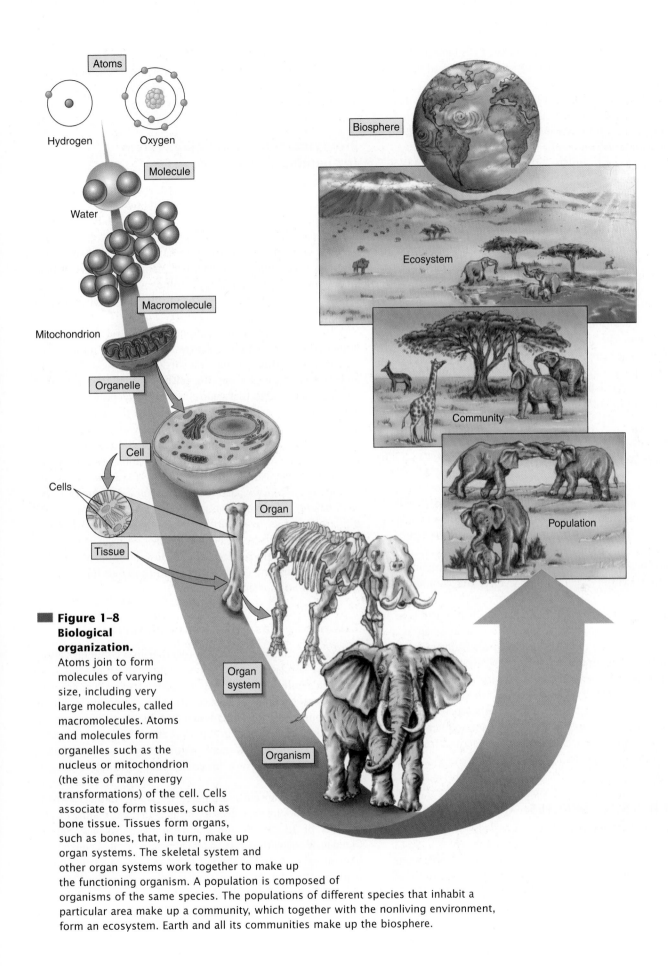

Figure 1-8 Biological organization.
Atoms join to form molecules of varying size, including very large molecules, called macromolecules. Atoms and molecules form organelles such as the nucleus or mitochondrion (the site of many energy transformations) of the cell. Cells associate to form tissues, such as bone tissue. Tissues form organs, such as bones, that, in turn, make up organ systems. The skeletal system and other organ systems work together to make up the functioning organism. A population is composed of organisms of the same species. The populations of different species that inhabit a particular area make up a community, which together with the nonliving environment, form an ecosystem. Earth and all its communities make up the biosphere.

Atoms

Hydrogen   Oxygen

Molecule

Water

Macromolecule

Mitochondrion

Organelle

Cell

Cells

Tissue

Organ

Organ system

Organism

Biosphere

Ecosystem

Community

Population

molecules that contain genetic instructions. Cells typically have internal structures called **organelles** that are specialized to perform specific functions.

Two fundamentally different types of cells are known. Bacteria are **prokaryotic cells.** Their cells lack membrane-bounded organelles. All other organisms are characterized by their **eukaryotic cells.** Unlike the structurally simpler prokaryotic cells, eukaryotic cells typically contain a variety of membrane-bounded organelles, including a **nucleus** that houses DNA.

During the evolution of multicellular organisms, cells associated to form **tissues.** For example, most animals have muscle tissue and nervous tissue, and plants have epidermis, a tissue that serves as a protective covering. In most complex organisms, tissues organize into functional structures called **organs,** such as the heart and stomach in animals and roots and leaves in plants. In animals, each major group of biological functions is performed by a coordinated group of tissues and organs called an **organ system.** The circulatory and digestive systems are examples of organ systems. Functioning together with great precision, organ systems make up a complex, multicellular **organism.** Again, emergent properties are evident. An organism is much more than its component organ systems.

Several levels of ecological organization can be identified

Organisms interact to form still more complex levels of biological organization. All the members of one species that live in the same geographic area at the same time make up a **population.** The populations of organisms that inhabit a particular area and interact with one another form a **community.** A community can consist of hundreds of different types of organisms. As populations within a community evolve, the community changes.

A community together with its nonliving environment is referred to as an **ecosystem.** An ecosystem can be as small as a pond (or even a puddle) or as vast as the Great Plains of North America or the Arctic tundra. All of Earth's ecosystems together are known as the **biosphere.** The biosphere includes all of Earth that is inhabited by living organisms—the atmosphere, the hydrosphere (water in any form), and the lithosphere (Earth's crust). The study of how organisms relate to one another and to their physical environment is called **ecology** (derived from the Greek *oikos,* meaning "house").

■ MILLIONS OF SPECIES HAVE EVOLVED

About 1.8 million species of extant (currently living) organisms have been scientifically identified, and biologists estimate that several million more remain to be discovered. To study life, we need a system for organizing, naming, and classifying its myriad forms. **Systematics** is the field of biology that studies the diversity of organisms and their evolutionary relationships. An aspect of systematics, called **taxonomy,** is the science of naming and classifying organisms. Biologists who specialize in classification are **taxonomists.**

Biologists use a binomial system for naming organisms

In the 18th century Carolus Linnaeus, a Swedish botanist, developed a hierarchical system of naming and classifying organisms that, with some modification, is still used today. The basic unit of classification is the **species.** A species is a group of organisms with similar structure, function, and behavior; in nature they breed only with each other. Members of a species have a common gene pool and share a common ancestry. Closely related species are grouped together in the next higher level of classification, the **genus** (pl. *genera*).

The Linnaean system of naming species is referred to as the **binomial system of nomenclature** because each species is assigned a two-part name. The first part of the name is the genus, and the second part, the **specific epithet,** designates a particular species belonging to that genus. The specific epithet is often a descriptive word expressing some quality of the organism. It is always used together with the full or abbreviated generic name preceding it. The generic name is always capitalized; the specific epithet is generally not capitalized. Both names are always italicized or underlined. For example, the dog, *Canis familiaris* (abbreviated *C. familiaris*), and the timber wolf, *Canis lupus (C. lupus),* belong to the same genus. The cat, *Felis catus,* belongs to a different genus. The scientific name of the American white oak is *Quercus alba,* whereas the name of the European white oak is *Quercus robur.* Another tree, the white willow, *Salix alba,* belongs to a different genus. The scientific name for our own species is *Homo sapiens* ("wise man").

Taxonomic classification is hierarchical

Just as species may be grouped together in a common genus, a number of related genera can be grouped in a more inclusive group, a **family** (Table 1–1; Fig. 1–9). Families are grouped into **orders,** orders into **classes,** and classes into **phyla.** Biologists group phyla into **kingdoms,** and kingdoms are assigned to **domains.** Each formal grouping at any given level is a **taxon.** Note that each taxon is more inclusive than the taxon below it. Together they form a hierarchy ranging from species to domain.

Consider a specific example. The family Canidae, which includes all doglike carnivores (animals that eat mainly meat), consists of 12 genera and about 34 living species. Family Canidae, along with family Ursidae (bears), family Felidae (catlike animals), and several other families that eat mainly meat, is placed in order Carnivora. Order Carnivora, order Primates (the order to which chimpanzees and humans belong), and several other orders belong to class Mammalia (mammals). Class Mammalia is grouped with several other classes that

TABLE 1-1 Classification of Domestic Cat, Human, and White Oak

Category	Cat	Human	White Oak
Domain	Eukarya	Eukarya	Eukarya
Kingdom	Animalia	Animalia	Plantae
Phylum	Chordata	Chordata	Anthophyta
Subphylum	Vertebrata	Vertebrata	None
Class	Mammalia	Mammalia	Dicotyledones
Order	Carnivora	Primates	Fagales
Family	Felidae	Hominidae	Fagaceae
Genus and specific epithet	*Felis catus*	*Homo sapiens*	*Quercus alba*

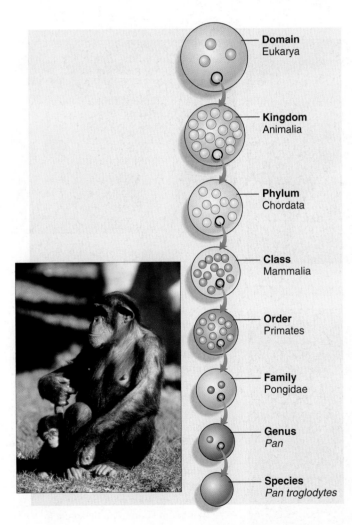

■ **Figure 1–9 Classification of the chimpanzee (Pan troglodytes).** As illustrated by this example, the classification scheme used by biologists is hierarchical. In the series of taxonomic categories from species to domain, each category is more general and more inclusive than the one below it. *(T. Whittaker/ Dembinsky Photo Associates)*

Domain — Eukarya
Kingdom — Animalia
Phylum — Chordata
Class — Mammalia
Order — Primates
Family — Pongidae
Genus — Pan
Species — Pan troglodytes

include fishes, amphibians, reptiles, and birds in subphylum Vertebrata. The vertebrates belong to phylum Chordata, which is part of kingdom Animalia. Animals are assigned to domain Eukarya.

Organisms can be assigned to three domains and six kingdoms

Systematics has itself evolved as new molecular techniques have been developed. As researchers report new data, the classification of organisms changes. Although biologists do not agree on how organisms are related or on how to classify them, many biologists now assign organisms to three domains and six kingdoms.

Bacteria are unicellular prokaryotic cells; they differ from all other organisms in that they are **prokaryotes**. Two distinct groups have been recognized among the prokaryotes, and biologists assign them to two domains: **Archaea** and **Eubacteria** (also called *Bacteria*). The **eukaryotes**, organisms with eukaryotic cells, are classified in domain **Eukarya.**

In the system of classification used in this book, every organism is also assigned to one of six **kingdoms** (Fig. 1–10). Two kingdoms correspond to the prokaryotic domains: **Archaebacteria** corresponds to domain Archaea, and Eubacteria corresponds to domain Eubacteria. Kingdom **Protista** consists of protozoa, algae, water molds, and slime molds. These are unicellular or simple multicellular organisms. Some protists are adapted to carry out **photosynthesis,** the process in which light energy is converted to the chemical energy of food molecules. Kingdom **Fungi** is composed of the yeasts, mildews, molds, and mushrooms. These organisms do not photosynthesize. They obtain their nutrients by secreting digestive enzymes into food and then absorbing the predigested food.

Members of kingdom **Plantae** are complex multicellular organisms adapted to carry out photosynthesis. Among characteristic plant features are the *cuticle* (a waxy covering over aerial parts that reduces water loss), *stomata* (tiny openings in stems and leaves for gas exchange), and multicellular *gametangia* (organs that protect developing reproductive cells). Kingdom Plantae includes both nonvascular plants (mosses) and vascular plants (ferns, conifers, and flowering plants).

Kingdom **Animalia** is made up of multicellular organisms that must eat other organisms for nourishment. Complex animals exhibit considerable tissue specialization and body organization. These characters have evolved along with motility, complex sense organs, nervous systems, and muscular systems.

A more detailed presentation of the kingdoms can be found in Chapters 22 through 30, and classification is summarized in Appendix C. We refer to these groups repeatedly throughout this book as we consider the many kinds of challenges faced by living organisms and the various adaptations that have evolved in response to these challenges.

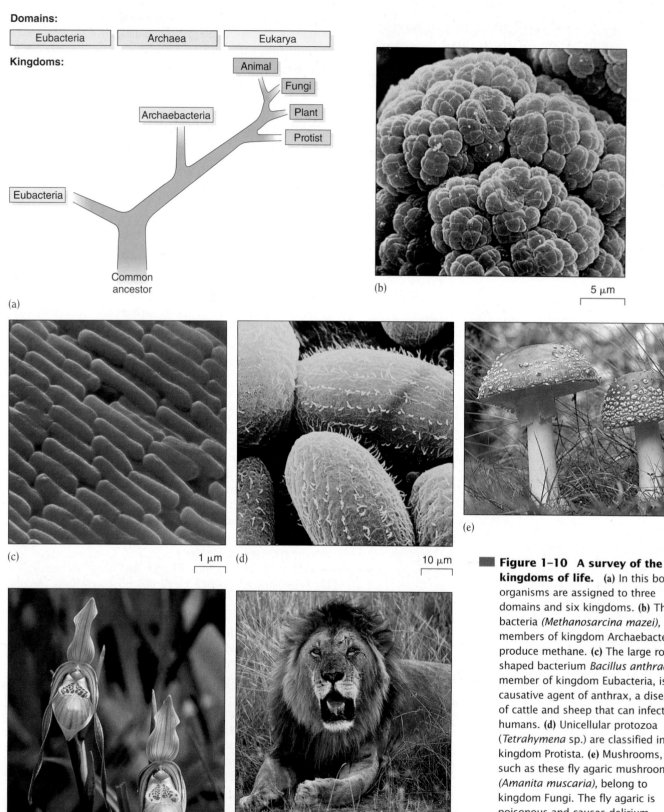

Domains:

Eubacteria | Archaea | Eukarya

Kingdoms:

Animal
Fungi
Plant
Protist

Archaebacteria

Eubacteria

Common ancestor

(a)

(b)

5 μm

(c)

1 μm

(d)

10 μm

(e)

(f)

(g)

■ **Figure 1–10 A survey of the kingdoms of life. (a)** In this book organisms are assigned to three domains and six kingdoms. **(b)** These bacteria *(Methanosarcina mazei)*, members of kingdom Archaebacteria, produce methane. **(c)** The large rod-shaped bacterium *Bacillus anthracis,* a member of kingdom Eubacteria, is the causative agent of anthrax, a disease of cattle and sheep that can infect humans. **(d)** Unicellular protozoa *(Tetrahymena* sp.) are classified in kingdom Protista. **(e)** Mushrooms, such as these fly agaric mushrooms *(Amanita muscaria),* belong to kingdom Fungi. The fly agaric is poisonous and causes delirium, raving, and profuse sweating when ingested. **(f)** The plant kingdom claims many beautiful and diverse forms such as the lady's slipper *(Phragmipedium caricinum).* **(g)** Among the fiercest members of the animal kingdom, lions *(Panthero leo)* are also among the most sociable. The largest of the big cats, lions live in prides (groups).   *(b, R. Robinson/Visuals Unlimited; c, CNRI/ Science Photo Library/Photo Researchers, Inc.; d, David M. Phillips/Visuals Unlimited; e, Ulf Sjostedt/FPG International; f, John Arnaldi; g, McMurray Photography)*

■ EVOLUTION IS THE PRIMARY UNIFYING CONCEPT OF BIOLOGY

The theory of **evolution,** which explains how populations of organisms have changed over time, has become the greatest unifying concept of biology. Some element of an evolutionary perspective is present in every specialized field within biology. Biologists try to understand the structure, function, and behavior of organisms and their interactions with one another by considering them in light of the long, continuing process of evolution. Although evolution is discussed in depth in Chapters 17 through 21, we present a brief overview here to give you the background necessary to understand other aspects of biology.

Species adapt in response to changes in their environment

Every organism is the product of complex interactions between environmental conditions and the genes of its ancestors. If every individual of a species were exactly like every other, any change in the environment might be disastrous to all, and the species would become extinct. Adaptation to changes in the environment involves changes in populations rather than in individual organisms. Such adaptations are the result of evolutionary processes that occur over time and involve many generations.

Natural selection is an important mechanism by which evolution proceeds

Although the concept of evolution had been discussed by philosophers and naturalists through the ages, Charles Darwin and Alfred Wallace first brought the theory of evolution to general attention and suggested a plausible mechanism, **natural selection,** to explain it. In his book *The Origin of Species by Natural Selection,* published in 1859, Darwin synthesized many new findings in geology and biology. He presented a wealth of evidence that the present forms of life descended, with modifications, from previously existing forms. Darwin's book raised a storm of controversy in both religion and science, some of which still lingers.

Darwin's theory of evolution has helped shape the biological sciences to the present day. His work generated a great wave of scientific observation and research that has provided much additional evidence that evolution is responsible for the great diversity of organisms present on our planet. Even today, the details of the process of evolution are a major focus of investigation and debate.

Darwin based his theory of natural selection on the following four observations: (1) Individual members of a species show some variation from one another. (2) Organisms produce many more offspring than will survive to reproduce (Fig. 1–11). (3) Organisms compete for necessary resources such as food, sunlight, and space. Individuals who happen to have characteristics that permit them to effectively use resources are more likely to survive to reproductive maturity and are more likely to leave off-

Figure 1–11 Egg masses of the wood frog (*Rana sylvatica*). Many more eggs are produced than can possibly develop into adult frogs. Random events are largely responsible for determining which of these developing frogs will hatch, reach adulthood, and reproduce. However, certain traits possessed by each organism also contribute to its probability for success in its environment. Not all organisms are as prolific as the frog, but the generalization that more organisms are produced than survive is true throughout the living world. *(J. Serrao/Photo Researchers, Inc.)*

spring. (4) The survivors that reproduce pass their adaptations for survival on to their offspring. Thus, the best adapted individuals of a population leave, on average, more offspring than do other individuals. Because of this differential reproduction, a greater proportion of the population becomes adapted to the prevailing environmental conditions. The environment *selects* the best adapted organisms for survival.

Darwin did not know about DNA or understand the mechanisms of inheritance. We now understand that most variations among individuals are a result of different varieties of genes that code for each characteristic. The ultimate source of these variations is random **mutations,** chemical or physical changes in DNA that persist and can be inherited. Mutations modify genes; by this process they provide the raw material for evolution.

Populations evolve as a result of selective pressures from changes in the environment

All the genes present in a population make up its **gene pool.** By virtue of its gene pool, a population is a reservoir of variation.

(a)

(b)

(c)

■ **Figure 1–12 Adaptation and diversification in Hawaiian honeycreepers.**
(a) The bill of this Akiapolaau male *(Hemignathus munroi)* is adapted for extracting insect larvae from bark. The lower mandible (jaw) is used to peck at and pull off bark, while the upper mandible and tongue remove the prey. **(b)** ʻIʻiwi *(Vestiaria coccinea)* in ʻOhiʻa blossoms. The bill is adapted for feeding on nectar in tubular flowers. **(c)** Palila *(Loxiodes bailleui)* in mamane tree. This finch-billed honeycreeper feeds on immature seeds in pods of the mamane tree. It also eats insects, berries, and young leaves. All three species shown here are endangered. *(a–c, Jack Jeffrey, Inc.)*

Natural selection acts on individuals within a population. Selection favors individuals with genes that specify traits that enable them to cope effectively with pressures exerted by the environment. These organisms are most likely to survive and produce offspring. As these successful organisms pass on their genetic recipe for survival, their traits become more widely distributed in the population. Over time, as organisms continue to change (and as the environment itself changes, bringing different selective pressures), the members of the population become better adapted to their environment and less like their ancestors.

As members of a population adapt to pressures exerted by the environment and exploit new opportunities for finding food or safety, or avoiding predators, the population diversifies and new species may evolve. The Hawaiian honeycreepers, a group of related birds, are a good example. When honeycreeper ancestors first reached Hawaii, few other birds were present and so there was little competition. Honeycreepers moved into a variety of food zones and various types of bills evolved (Figure 1–12; also see discussion in Chapter 19 and Figure 19–17). Some honeycreepers now have long, curved bills, adapted for feeding on nectar from tubular flowers. Others have short, thick bills for foraging for insects, and still others are adapted for eating seeds.

■ LIFE DEPENDS ON A CONTINUOUS INPUT OF ENERGY

A continuous input of energy from the sun enables life to exist. Every activity of a living cell or organism requires energy. Whenever energy is used to perform biological work, some is converted to heat and dispersed into the environment.

Energy flows through cells and organisms

Recall that all the energy transformations and chemical processes that occur within an organism are referred to as me-

tabolism. Energy is necessary to carry on the metabolic activities essential for growth, repair, and maintenance. Each cell of an organism requires nutrients. Some nutrients are used as fuel for **cellular respiration,** a process during which some of the energy stored in the nutrient molecules is released for use by the cells (Fig. 1–13). This energy can be used for cellular work or for synthesis of needed materials such as new cellular components. All cells carry on cellular respiration.

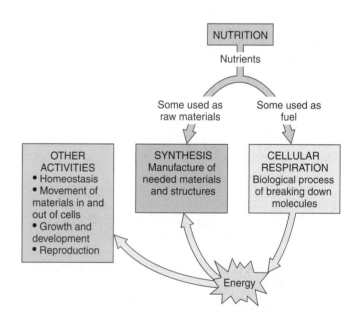

■ **Figure 1–13 Relationships of metabolic processes.**
These processes occur continuously in the cells of living organisms. Some of the nutrients in food are used to synthesize needed materials and cell parts. Other nutrients are used as fuel for cellular respiration, a process that releases energy stored in food. This energy is needed for synthesis and for other forms of cellular work.

Energy flows through ecosystems

Like individual organisms, ecosystems depend on a continuous input of energy. A self-sufficient ecosystem contains three types of organisms—producers, consumers, and decomposers—and has a physical environment appropriate for their survival. These organisms depend on each other and on the environment for nutrients, energy, oxygen, and carbon dioxide. However, there is a one-way flow of energy through ecosystems. Organisms can neither create energy nor use it with complete efficiency. During every energy transaction, some energy is dispersed into the environment as heat and is no longer available to the organism (Fig. 1–14).

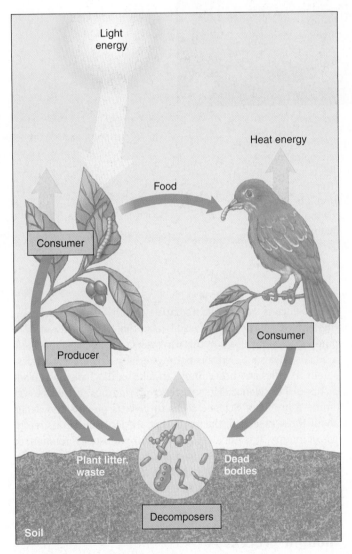

Figure 1–14 Energy flow. Continuous energy input from the sun operates the biosphere. During photosynthesis, producers use the energy from sunlight to make complex molecules from carbon dioxide and water. Consumers obtain energy, carbon, and other needed materials when they eat producers or consumers that have eaten producers. Wastes and dead organic material supply decomposers with energy and carbon. During every energy transaction some energy is lost to biological systems as it is dispersed as heat.

Producers, or **autotrophs,** are plants, algae, and certain bacteria that can produce their own food from simple raw materials. Most of these organisms use sunlight as an energy source and carry out photosynthesis, in which complex molecules are synthesized from carbon dioxide and water. The light energy is transformed into chemical energy, which is stored within the chemical bonds of the food molecules produced. Oxygen, which is required not only by plant cells but also by the cells of most other organisms, is produced as a byproduct of photosynthesis:

Carbon dioxide + Water + Light energy →
 Sugars (food) + Oxygen

Animals are **consumers,** or **heterotrophs,** that is, organisms that depend on producers for food, energy, and oxygen. Consumers obtain energy by breaking down sugars and other food molecules originally produced during photosynthesis. Recall that the biological process of breaking down sugars and other fuel molecules is known as cellular respiration. When chemical bonds are broken during cellular respiration, their stored energy is made available for life processes:

Sugars (and other food molecules) + Oxygen →
 Carbon dioxide + Water + Energy

Consumers contribute to the balance of the ecosystem. For example, consumers produce carbon dioxide needed by producers. The metabolism of consumers and producers helps maintain the life-sustaining mixture of gases in the atmosphere.

Bacteria and fungi are **decomposers,** heterotrophs that obtain nutrients by breaking down wastes, dead leaves, and bodies of dead organisms. In their process of obtaining energy, decomposers make the components of wastes and dead organisms available for reuse. If decomposers did not exist, nutrients would remain locked up in dead bodies, and the supply of elements required by living systems would soon be exhausted.

Process of Science ■ **BIOLOGY IS STUDIED USING THE SCIENTIFIC METHOD**

Biologists work in laboratories and out in the field (Fig. 1–15). Their investigations range from the study of molecular biology and viruses to the interactions of the communities of our biosphere. Perhaps you will decide to become a research biologist and help unravel the complexities of the human brain; discover new hormones that cause plants to flower; identify new species of animals or bacteria; or develop new stem cell strategies to treat cancer, AIDS, or heart disease. Or perhaps you will choose to enter an applied field of biology such as environmental science, dentistry, medicine, pharmacology, or veterinary medicine.

(a)

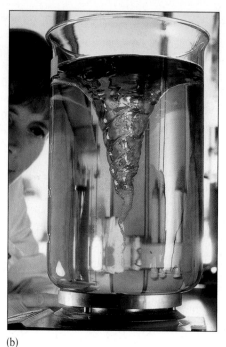
(b)

■ **Figure 1–15 Biologists at work. (a)** This biologist studying the rainforest canopy in Costa Rica is part of an international effort to study and preserve tropical rain forests. Researchers study the interactions of organisms and the effects of human activities on the rain forests. **(b)** This researcher is working on the Human Genome Project at the Sanger Centre in Cambridge, England. She is monitoring a beaker of a yeast-tryptone culture medium that is being prepared for use in growing yeasts or bacteria containing human DNA. As the organisms in the culture medium reproduce, they clone the human DNA. *(a, Mark Moffett/Minden Pictures; b, James King-Holmes/Science Photo Library/Photo Researchers, Inc.)*

A number of interesting careers in the biological sciences are discussed in the Career Visions sections of this book.

Biology is a **science.** The word *science* comes from a Latin word meaning "to know." Science is a way of thinking and a method of investigating the world around us in a systematic manner. Science enables us to uncover ever more about the world we live in and leads us to an expanded appreciation of our universe.

The **process of science** is investigative, dynamic, and often controversial. It changes over time as it is influenced by cultural, social, and historical contexts as well as by the personalities of scientists themselves. The observations made, the range of questions posed, and the design of experiments depend on the creativity of the individual scientist. In contrast, the **scientific method** involves a series of ordered steps and is a framework used by most scientists.

Using the scientific method, scientists make careful observations, ask critical questions, and develop **hypotheses,** which are testable statements. Based on their hypotheses, scientists make predictions that can be tested, and test their predictions by making further observations or by performing experiments (Fig. 1–16). They interpret the results of their experiments and draw conclusions from them. Even results that do not support the hypothesis may be valuable and may lead to new hypotheses. If the results support a hypothesis, a scientist may use them to generate related hypotheses.

Science is systematic. Scientists organize, and often quantify, knowledge, making it readily accessible to all who wish to build on its foundation. In this way science is both a personal and a social endeavor. Science is not mysterious. Anyone who understands its rules and procedures can take on its challenges. What distinguishes science is its insistence on rigorous methods to examine a problem. Science seeks to give us precise knowledge about those aspects of the world that are accessible to its methods of inquiry. It is not a replacement for philosophy, religion, or art. Being a scientist does not prevent one from participating in other fields of human endeavor, just as being an artist does not prevent one from practicing science.

Science requires systematic thought processes

Two types of systematic thought processes used by scientists are deduction and induction. With **deductive reasoning,** we begin with supplied information, called **premises**, and draw conclusions on the basis of that information. Deduction proceeds from general principles to specific conclusions. For example, if we accept the premise that all birds have wings, and the second premise that sparrows are birds, we can conclude deductively that sparrows have wings. Deduction helps us discover rela-

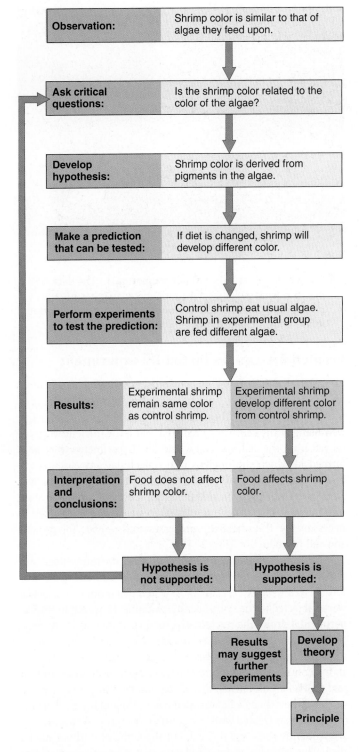

Observation:	Shrimp color is similar to that of algae they feed upon.
Ask critical questions:	Is the shrimp color related to the color of the algae?
Develop hypothesis:	Shrimp color is derived from pigments in the algae.
Make a prediction that can be tested:	If diet is changed, shrimp will develop different color.
Perform experiments to test the prediction:	Control shrimp eat usual algae. Shrimp in experimental group are fed different algae.

Results:	Experimental shrimp remain same color as control shrimp.	Experimental shrimp develop different color from control shrimp.
Interpretation and conclusions	Food does not affect shrimp color.	Food affects shrimp color.
	Hypothesis is not supported:	**Hypothesis is supported:**

Results may suggest further experiments **Develop theory**

Principle

Figure 1–16 The scientific method. Scientists use the scientific method as a framework for their research.

tionships among known facts. The **hypothetico-deductive approach** emphasizes the use of deductive reasoning to test hypotheses.

Scientists also use a **hypothetico-inductive approach** that focuses on discovering new general principles. **Inductive reason-**

ing is the opposite of deduction. We begin with specific observations and draw a conclusion or discover a general principle. For example, if we know that sparrows have wings and are birds, and we know that robins, eagles, pigeons, and hawks have wings and are birds, we might induce that all birds have wings. In this way, the inductive method can be used to organize raw data into manageable categories by answering the question: What do all these facts have in common?

A weakness of inductive reasoning is that conclusions generalize the facts to all possible examples. We go from many observed examples to all possible examples when we formulate the general principle. This is known as the **inductive leap.** Without it, we could not arrive at generalizations. However, we must be sensitive to exceptions and to the possibility that the conclusion is not valid. For example, the kiwi bird of New Zealand does not have functional wings! The generalizations in inductive conclusions come from the creative insight of the human mind, and creativity, however admirable, is not infallible.

Scientists make careful observations and ask critical questions

Chance and luck are often involved in recognizing a phenomenon or problem, but significant discoveries are usually made by those who are in the habit of looking critically at nature. Necessary technology for investigating the problem must also be available. In 1928 the British bacteriologist Alexander Fleming observed that one of his bacterial cultures had become invaded by a blue mold. He almost discarded it, but before he did, he noticed that the area contaminated by the mold was surrounded by a zone where bacterial colonies did not grow well.

The bacteria were disease organisms of the genus *Staphylococcus,* which can cause boils and skin infections. Anything that could kill them was interesting! Fleming saved the mold, a variety of *Penicillium* (blue bread mold). It was subsequently discovered that the mold produced a substance that slowed reproduction of the bacterial population but was usually harmless to laboratory animals and humans. The substance was penicillin, the first antibiotic.

We may wonder how many times the same type of mold grew on the cultures of other bacteriologists who failed to make the connection and simply threw away their contaminated cultures. Fleming benefited from chance, but his mind was prepared to make observations and formulate critical questions, and his pen was prepared to publish them. Still, it was left to others to develop the practical applications. Although Fleming recognized the potential practical benefit of penicillin, he did not develop the chemical techniques needed to purify it, and more than 10 years passed before the drug was put to significant use.

In 1939 Sir Howard Florey and Ernst Boris Chain developed chemical procedures to extract and produce the active agent penicillin from the mold. Florey took the process to laboratories in the United States, and penicillin was first produced to treat wounded soldiers in World War II. In 1945, Fleming, Florey, and Chain shared the Nobel Prize in Medicine.

A hypothesis is a testable statement

In the early stages of an investigation, a scientist typically thinks of many possible hypotheses and hopes that the right one is among them. He or she then decides which, if any, could and should be subjected to experimental test. Why not test them all? Time and money are important considerations in conducting research. We must establish priority among the hypotheses to decide which to test first. Fortunately, some guidelines do exist. A good hypothesis exhibits the following:

1. It is reasonably consistent with well-established facts.
2. It is capable of being tested; that is, it should generate definite predictions, whether the results are positive or negative. Test results should also be repeatable by independent observers.
3. It is falsifiable, which means it can be proved false.

A hypothesis cannot really be proved true, but in theory (though not necessarily in practice) a well-stated hypothesis can be proved false. If one believes in an unfalsifiable hypothesis (e.g., the existence of invisible and undetectable angels), it must be on grounds other than scientific ones.

Consider the following hypothesis: All female mammals (animals that have hair and produce milk for their young) bear live young. The hypothesis was based on the observations that dogs, cats, cows, lions, and humans all are mammals and all bear live young. Consider further that a new species, species X, was identified as a mammal. Biologists predicted that females of species X would bear live young. When a female of the new species gave birth to offspring, this supported the hypothesis. Yet it did not really *prove* the hypothesis.

Before the Southern Hemisphere was explored, most individuals would probably have accepted the hypothesis without question, because all known furry, milk-giving animals did, in fact, bear live young. But it was discovered that two Australian animals (the duck-billed platypus and the spiny anteater) had fur and produced milk for their young but laid eggs (Fig. 1–17). The hypothesis, as stated, was false no matter how many times it had previously been supported. As a result, biologists either had to consider the platypus and the spiny anteater as nonmammals or had to broaden their definition of mammals to include them. (They chose the latter.)

A hypothesis is not true just because some of its predictions (the ones we happen to have thought of or have thus far been able to test) have been shown to be true. After all, they could be true by coincidence. Failure to observe a predicted outcome does not make a hypothesis false, but neither does it show that the hypothesis is true.

A prediction is a logical consequence of a hypothesis

A hypothesis is an abstract idea, so there is no way to test it directly. But hypotheses suggest certain logical consequences, that is, observable things that cannot be false if the hypothesis is true. On the other hand, if the hypothesis is, in fact, false, other definite predictions should disclose that. As used here, then, a **prediction** is a deductive, logical consequence of a hypothesis. It does not have to be a future event.

Figure 1–17 Is this animal a mammal? The duck-billed platypus is classified as a mammal because it has fur and produces milk for its young. However, unlike most mammals, it lays eggs. *(Tom McHugh/Photo Researchers, Inc.)*

Predictions can be tested by experiment

A prediction can be tested by controlled experiments. Early biologists observed that the nucleus was the most prominent part of the cell, and they hypothesized that it might be essential for the well-being of the cell. They predicted that if the nucleus were removed from the cell, the cell would die. Experiments were performed in which the nucleus of a unicellular amoeba was removed surgically with a microloop. After this surgery, the amoeba continued to live and move but it did not grow, and after a few days it died. These results suggested that the nucleus is necessary for the metabolic processes that provide for growth and cell reproduction (Fig. 1–18).

But, the investigators asked, what if the operation itself and not the loss of the nucleus caused the amoeba to die? They performed a *controlled* experiment in which two groups of amoebas were subjected to the same operative trauma. However, in the **experimental group** the nucleus was removed, whereas in the **control group** it was not. An experimental group ideally differs from a control group only with respect to the variable being studied. In the control group, a microloop was inserted into each amoeba and pushed around inside the cell to simulate the removal of the nucleus; then the needle was withdrawn, leaving the nucleus inside. Amoebas treated with such a sham operation recovered and subsequently grew and divided, but the amoebas without nuclei died. This experiment provided data that it was the removal of the nucleus and not simply the operation that caused the death of the amoebas. The data supported the hypothesis that the nucleus is essential for the well-being of the cell.

In scientific studies, care must be taken to avoid **bias.** For example, to prevent bias, most medical experiments today are carried out in a **double-blind** fashion. When a drug is being tested, one group of patients is given the new medication, while a second similar group of patients (the control group) is given a placebo, a harmless starch pill similar in size, shape, color, and

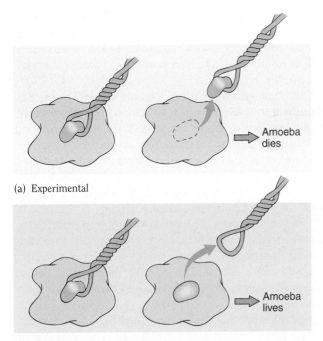

(a) Experimental

(b) Control

■ Figure 1–18 Testing a prediction. An early controlled experiment tested the prediction that if the nucleus is removed from a cell, the cell would die. The data gathered from this and similar experiments provided support for the hypothesis that the nucleus is essential for the well-being of the cell. **(a)** When its nucleus is surgically removed with a microloop, the amoeba dies. **(b)** Control amoebas subjected to similar surgical procedures (including insertion of a microloop), but without actual removal of the nucleus, do not die.

taste to the pill being tested. This is a double-blind study because neither the patient nor the physician knows who is getting the experimental drug and who is getting the placebo. The pills or treatments are coded in some way, and only after the experiment is over and the results are recorded is the code broken. Not all experiments can be so neatly designed; for one thing, it is often difficult to establish appropriate controls.

Scientists interpret the results of experiments and make conclusions

Scientists gather data in an experiment, interpret their results, and then formulate conclusions. For example, in the amoeba experiment described earlier, investigators concluded that the nucleus was essential for the well-being of the cell.

One reason for inaccurate conclusions is **sampling error.** Because *all* cases of what is being studied cannot be observed or tested (scientists cannot study every amoeba), we must be content with a sample, or subset, of them. Yet how can we know whether that sample is truly representative of whatever we are studying? In the first place, if the sample is too small, it may be different owing to random factors. A study with only two, or even nine, amoebas might not yield reliable data that could be gener-

alized to other amoebas. This problem can usually be solved by using large numbers of subjects and applying the mathematics of statistical analysis (Fig. 1–19).

We must also ensure that the sample is typical of the group that we intend to study. Scientists use statistical techniques to ensure that there is no consistent bias in the way that experimental samples are chosen.

Even if a conclusion is based on results from a carefully designed experiment, it is still possible that new observations or results from other experiments can challenge the conclusion. If we test a large number of cases, we are more likely to draw accurate scientific conclusions. The scientist seeks to state with confidence that any specific conclusion has a certain statistical probability of being correct.

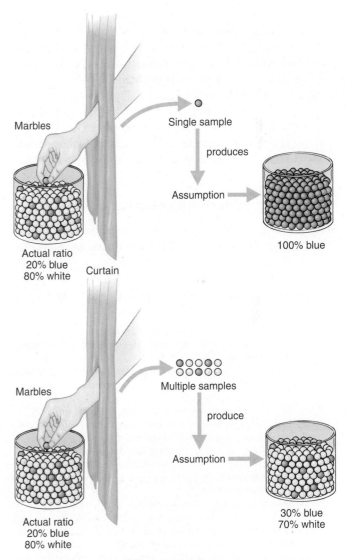

■ Figure 1–19 Statistical probability. Taking a single sample can result in sampling error. If the only marble sampled is blue, we might assume that all the marbles are blue. The greater the number of samples we take of an unknown, the more likely we can make valid assumptions about it.

Experiments must also be replicated. When researchers publish their findings in a scientific journal, they typically include a description of their methods and procedures so that other scientists can repeat the experiments. When the findings are replicated, the conclusions are, of course, strengthened.

A well-supported hypothesis may lead to a theory

Nonscientists often use the word *theory* incorrectly to refer to a hypothesis. A **theory** is actually an integrated explanation of a number of hypotheses, each supported by consistent results from many observations or experiments. A theory relates data that previously appeared to be unrelated. A good theory grows, building on additional facts as they become known. It predicts new facts and suggests new relationships among phenomena. It may even suggest practical applications.

A good theory, by showing the relationships among classes of facts, simplifies and clarifies our understanding of natural phenomena. As Einstein wrote, "In the whole history of science from Greek philosophy to modern physics, there have been constant attempts to reduce the apparent complexity of natural phenomena to simple, fundamental ideas and relations."

A theory that, over a long period, has withstood repeated testing and is almost universally accepted by scientists is referred to as a **scientific principle.** The term **law** is sometimes used for a principle judged to be of great basic importance, such as the law of gravity.

Science has ethical dimensions

Researchers who publish their work in scientific journals describe their experiments in sufficient detail to be independently performed by others. This permits objective observers to detect errors or bias in the original study and helps guard against the occasional odd result caused by random or uncontrolled factors, as well as results tainted by dishonesty on the part of the original researcher.

Scientific investigation depends on commitment to practical ideals such as truthfulness and the obligation to communicate results. Honesty is particularly important in science. Consider the great (though temporary) damage done whenever an unprincipled or even desperate researcher, whose career might depend on publication of a research study, knowingly disseminates false data. Until the deception is uncovered, researchers might devote many thousands of dollars and hours of precious professional labor to futile lines of research inspired by erroneous reports.

Such deception can also be dangerous, especially in medical research. Fortunately, science tends to be self-correcting through the consistent use of the scientific process itself. Sooner or later, someone's experimental results are bound to cast doubt on false data.

In addition to being ethical about their own work, scientists must face many broad ethical issues surrounding areas such as stem cell research, cloning, human and animal experimentation, and applications of genetic engineering. For example, some of the stem cells that show the greatest potential for use in treating human disease are found in early embryos. The cells can be taken from 5- or 6-day-old embryos and then cultured in laboratory glassware. Such cells could be engineered to treat failing hearts or brains harmed by stroke, injury, Parkinson's disease, or Alzheimer's disease. They could save the lives of burn victims and perhaps be engineered to treat specific cancers. Society will need to determine whether the potential benefits of stem cell research outweigh the ethical risks of using these cells.

SUMMARY WITH KEY TERMS

I. **Biology** is the study of life. Basic themes of biology include the evolution of life, the transmission of information, and the flow of energy through organisms.

II. A living organism is able to grow and develop, carry on self-regulated metabolism, move, respond to stimuli, and reproduce. Species evolve and adapt to their environment.
   A. All living organisms are composed of one or more **cells.**
   B. Organisms grow by increasing the size and number of their cells.
   C. **Metabolism** refers to all the chemical activities that take place in the organism, including the chemical reactions essential to nutrition, growth and repair, and conversion of energy to usable forms. **Homeostasis** is the tendency of organisms to maintain a constant internal environment.
   D. Movement, though not necessarily locomotion, is characteristic of living organisms. Some organisms use tiny extensions of the cell, called **cilia,** or longer **flagella** to move from place to place. Other organisms are **sessile** and remain rooted to some surface.
   E. Organisms respond to **stimuli,** physical or chemical changes in their external or internal environment.
   F. In **asexual reproduction,** offspring are typically identical to the single parent; in **sexual reproduction,** offspring are typically the product of the fusion of gametes, and genes are typically contributed by two parents.
   G. Populations evolve and become adapted to their environment. **Adaptations** are traits that increase an organism's ability to survive in its environment.

III. Organisms transmit information chemically, electrically, and behaviorally.
   A. DNA, which makes up the **genes,** contains the instructions for the development of an organism and for carrying out life processes.
      1. Information encoded in **DNA** is transmitted from one generation to the next.
      2. DNA codes for **proteins,** which are important in determining the structure and function of cells and tissues.
   B. **Hormones,** chemical messengers that transmit messages from one part of an organism to another, are one type of **cell signaling.**
   C. Many organisms use electrical signals to transmit information; most animals have nervous systems that transmit electrical impulses and release **neurotransmitters.**

IV. Biological organization is hierarchical.
   A. A complex organism is organized at the **chemical, cellular, tissue, organ,** and **organ system** levels.
   B. The basic unit of ecological organization is the **population.** Various populations form **communities;** a community and its physical environment are referred to as an **ecosystem;** all of Earth's communities and ecosystems together make up the **biosphere.**

V. Millions of species have evolved. A **species** is a group of organisms with similar structure, function, and behavior that, in nature, breed only with each other. Members of a species have a common **gene pool** and share common ancestry.

    A. Taxonomic classification is hierarchical; it includes **species, genus, family, order, class, phylum, kingdom,** and **domain.** Each grouping is referred to as a **taxon.**

    B. Biologists use a **binomial system of nomenclature** in which the name of each species includes a genus name and a **specific epithet.**

    C. Bacteria have **prokaryotic cells;** all other organisms have **eukaryotic cells.**

    D. Organisms can be classified into three domains: **Archaea, Eubacteria,** and **Eukarya,** and six kingdoms: **Archaebacteria, Eubacteria, Protista** (protozoa, algae, water molds, and slime molds), **Fungi** (molds and yeasts), **Plantae,** and **Animalia.**

VI. **Evolution** is the process by which populations change over time in response to changes in the environment.

    A. **Natural selection,** the mechanism by which evolution proceeds, favors individuals with traits that enable them to cope with environmental changes. These individuals are most likely to survive and to produce offspring.

    B. Charles Darwin based his theory of natural selection on his observations that individuals of a species vary; organisms produce more offspring than survive to reproduce; individuals that are best adapted to their environment are more likely to survive and reproduce; as successful organisms pass on their hereditary information, their traits become more widely distributed in the population.

    C. The source of variation in a population is random **mutation.**

VII. Activities of living cells require energy; life depends on continuous energy input from the sun.

    A. During **photosynthesis** plants, algae, and certain bacteria use the energy of sunlight to synthesize complex molecules from carbon dioxide and water.

    B. All cells carry on **cellular respiration,** a biochemical process in which they capture the energy stored in nutrients by producers. Some of that energy is then used to synthesize needed materials or to carry out other cell activities.

    C. A self-sufficient ecosystem includes **producers,** or **autotrophs,** which make their own food; **consumers,** which eat producers or organisms that have eaten producers; and **decomposers,** which obtain energy by breaking down wastes and dead organisms. Consumers and decomposers are **heterotrophs,** which are organisms that depend on producers as an energy source and for food and oxygen.

VIII. The **process of science** is a dynamic approach to investigation. The **scientific method** is a framework that scientists use in their work; it includes observing, recognizing a problem or stating a critical question, developing a hypothesis, making a prediction that can be tested, performing experiments, interpreting results, and drawing conclusions that support or falsify the hypothesis.

    A. Deductive reasoning and inductive reasoning are two categories of systematic thought processes that are used in the scientific method. **Deductive reasoning** proceeds from general principles to specific conclusions and helps us discover relationships among known facts. **Inductive reasoning** begins with specific observations and draws conclusions from them. Inductive reasoning helps us discover general principles.

    B. A **hypothesis** is a testable statement about the nature of an observation or relationship.

    C. A properly designed scientific experiment includes both a **control group** and an **experimental group,** and must be as free as possible from bias. The experimental group differs from a control group only with respect to the variable being studied.

    D. When a number of related hypotheses have been supported by conclusions from many experiments, scientists may develop a **theory** based on them. A well-established and tested theory may be referred to as a **scientific principle.**

    E. Science has important ethical dimensions.

POST-TEST

1. Metabolism (a) is the sum of all the chemical activities of an organism (b) results from an increase in the number of cells (c) is characteristic of plant and animal kingdoms only (d) refers to chemical changes in an organism's environment (e) does not take place in producers

2. Homeostasis (a) is the tendency of organisms to maintain a constant internal environment (b) generally depends on the action of cilia (c) is the long-term response of organisms to changes in their environment (d) occurs at the ecosystem level, not in cells or organisms (e) may be sexual or asexual

3. Structures used by some organisms for locomotion are (a) cilia and nuclei (b) flagella (c) nuclei (d) cilia and sessiles (e) cilia and flagella

4. The splitting of an amoeba into two is best described as an example of (a) locomotion (b) neurotransmission (c) asexual reproduction (d) sexual reproduction (e) metabolism

5. Cells (a) are the building blocks of living organisms (b) always have nuclei (c) are not found among the bacteria (d) answers a, b, and c are correct (e) answers a and b only are correct

6. An increase in the size or number of cells best describes (a) homeostasis (b) biological growth (c) chemical level of organization (d) asexual reproduction (e) adaptation

7. DNA (a) makes up the genes (b) transmits information from one species to another (c) cannot be changed (d) is a neurotransmitter (e) is produced during cellular respiration

8. Cellular respiration (a) is a process whereby sunlight is used to synthesize cellular components with the release of energy (b) occurs in heterotrophs only (c) is carried on by both autotrophs and heterotrophs (d) causes chemical changes in DNA (e) occurs in response to environmental changes

9. Which of the following is a correct sequence of levels of biological organization? (a) cellular, organ, tissue, organ system (b) chemical, cellular, organ, tissue (c) chemical, cellular, tissue, organ (d) tissue, organ, cellular, organ system (e) chemical, cellular, population, species

10. Which of the following is a correct sequence of levels of biological organization? (a) organism, population, ecosystem, community (b) organism, population, community, ecosystem (c) population, biosphere, ecosystem, community (d) species, population, ecosystem, community (e) ecosystem, population, community, biosphere

11. Protozoa are assigned to kingdom (a) Protista (b) Fungi (c) Archaebacteria (d) Animalia (e) Plantae

12. Yeasts and molds are assigned to kingdom (a) Protista (b) Fungi (c) Archaebacteria (d) Animalia (e) Plantae

13. In the binomial system of nomenclature, the first part of an organism's name designates the (a) specific epithet (b) genus (c) class (d) kingdom (e) phylum

14. Which of the following is a correct sequence of levels of classification (a) genus, species, family, order, class, phylum, kingdom (b) genus, species, order, phylum, class, kingdom (c) genus, species, order, family, class, phylum, kingdom (d) species, genus, family, order, class, phylum, kingdom (e) species, genus, order, family, class, kingdom, phylum

15. Darwin suggested that evolution takes place by (a) mutation (b) changes in the individuals of a species (c) natural selection (d) interaction of hormones (e) homeostatic responses to each change in the environment

16. A testable statement is a (an) (a) theory (b) hypothesis (c) principle (d) inductive leap (e) critical question

17. Ideally, an experimental group differs from a control group (a) only with respect to the hypothesis being tested (b) only with respect to the variable being studied (c) by being less subject to bias (d) because it is less vulnerable to sampling error (e) because its subjects are more reliable

REVIEW QUESTIONS

1. Contrast a living organism with a nonliving object.

2. In what ways might the metabolisms of an oak tree and a tiger be similar? Relate these similarities to the biological themes of transmission of information, energy, and evolution.

3. What would be the consequences if an organism's homeostatic mechanisms failed? Explain your answer.

4. What components do you think might be present in a balanced forest ecosystem? In what ways are consumers dependent on producers? On decomposers? Include energy considerations in your answer.

5. Why do you suppose that the binomial system of nomenclature has survived for more than 200 years and is still used by biologists?

6. How might you explain the sharp claws and teeth of tigers in terms of natural selection?

7. What is meant by a "controlled" experiment?

8. Make a prediction and devise a suitably controlled experiment to test each of the following hypotheses: (a) A type of mold found in your garden does not produce an effective antibiotic. (b) The rate of growth of a bean seedling is affected by temperature. (c) Estrogen alleviates the symptoms of Alzheimer's disease in elderly women.

YOU MAKE THE CONNECTION

1. How might a firm understanding of evolutionary processes be helpful to a biologist who is doing research in (a) animal behavior, (b) ecology, or (c) the development of a vaccine against human immunodeficiency virus, the virus that causes AIDS?

2. If you could influence U. S. policy on stem cell research, what position would you take? Explain. What would be your position on the use of genetically modified crops to increase world food supply or the use of genetically modified animals for producing drugs such as insulin and blood-clotting factors?

RECOMMENDED READINGS

Brown, K. "Seeds of Concern." *Scientific American,* Vol. 284, No. 4, Apr. 2001. What are the concerns and what is the evidence regarding genetically modified crops?

Cohen, J. "Can Cloning Help Save Beleaguered Species?" *Science,* Vol. 276, 30 May, 1997. A brief discussion of the benefits and concerns of cloning endangered species.

Lanza, R.P., B.L. Dresser, and P. Damiani. "Cloning Noah's Ark," *Scientific American,* Vol. 283, Nov., 2000. A description of the process and technology used to clone animals on the brink of extinction, and a discussion of some of the attendant controversy.

Mirsky, S., and J. Rennie. "What Cloning Means for Gene Therapy," *Scientific American,* Vol. 276, Jun., 1997. A special report about the benefits of combining cloning technology with other biotechnologies.

Moore, J.A. *Science as a Way of Knowing: The Foundations of Modern Biology.* Harvard University Press, Cambridge, 1993. An account of scientific thought as related to the history of modern biology.

Pedersen, R.A. "Embryonic Stem Cells for Medicine." *Scientific American,* Vol. 280, Apr., 1999. A special report on the potential and ethics of stem cell research.

Pennisi, E. "Human Genome: Finally, the Book of Life and Instructions for Navigating It." *Science,* Vol. 288, 30 Jun., 2000. A brief description of the announcement of the "completion" of the Human Genome Project and its implications.

Science, Vol. 277, 25 Jul., 1997. Special Issue: Human-Dominated Ecosystems. The authors examine the global consequences of human activity on several ecosystems.

Science, Vol. 287, 25 Feb., 2000. Special Section: Stem Cell Research and Ethics. Several articles discuss the state of the art, financial considerations, global issues, and ethical issues.

Scientific American, Vol. 281, Dec., 1999. End of the Millennium Special Issue. Several articles of interest to the beginning biology student, including "Deciphering the Code of Life," which discusses genome research.

Velander, W.H., H. Lubon, and W.N. Drohan. "Transgenic Livestock as Drug Factories," *Scientific American,* Vol. 276, Jan., 1997. A discussion of some exciting new medical applications of genetic techniques.

- Visit our Web site at **http://www.info.brookscole.com/solomonbergmartin** for links to chapter-related resources on the World Wide Web. Additional on-line materials relating to this chapter can also be found on our Web site.

See chapter activity on BioActive Learner CD for additional help in mastering the chapter's material. Icon location in the chapter's margins shows which topics have tutorials or simulations in the CD.

2

Atoms and Molecules: The Chemical Basis of Life

LEARNING OBJECTIVES

After you have studied this chapter you should be able to

1. Name the principal chemical elements in living things and give an important function of each.
2. Compare the physical properties (mass and charge) and the locations of electrons, protons, and neutrons.
3. Distinguish between the atomic number and the mass number of an element.
4. Define the terms *electron orbital* and *electron shell*. Relate electron shells to principal energy levels.
5. Explain how the number of valence electrons of an atom is related to its chemical properties.
6. Distinguish among covalent bonds, hydrogen bonds, and ionic bonds. Compare them in terms of the mechanisms by which they form and their relative bond strengths.
7. Explain how cations and anions form and how they interact.
8. Distinguish between the terms *oxidation* and *reduction* and relate these processes to the transfer of energy.
9. Draw a simple ball-and-stick model of a water molecule, indicating the regions of partial positive and partial negative charge. Show how hydrogen bonds form between adjacent water molecules and explain how these are responsible for many of the properties of water.
10. Contrast acids and bases and discuss their properties.
11. Convert the hydrogen ion concentration (moles per liter) of a solution to a pH value. Describe how buffers help minimize changes in pH.
12. Describe the composition of a salt and explain why salts are important in organisms.

A jaguar, the largest cat in the Western Hemisphere, pauses to drink water from a rainforest stream. Water is a basic requirement for all life. *(Frans Lanting/Minden Pictures)*

Knowledge of chemistry is essential if we are to understand organisms and how they function. This jaguar and the plants of the tropical rain forest, as well as abundant unseen insects and microorganisms, share fundamental similarities in their chemical composition and basic metabolic processes. These chemical similarities provide strong evidence for the evolution of all organisms from a common ancestor and explain why much of what biologists learn from studying bacteria or rats in laboratories can be applied to other organisms, including humans. Furthermore, the basic chemical and physical principles governing organisms are not unique to living things, for they apply to nonliving systems as well.

Today much attention is given to the Human Genome Project, introduced in Chapter 1. The success of this exciting initiative relies heavily on biochemistry and **molecular biology,** the chemistry and physics of the molecules that constitute living things. A biochemist might investigate the precise interactions among a cell's atoms and molecules that maintain the energy flow essential to life, and a molecular biologist might study how proteins interact with deoxyribonucleic acid (DNA) in ways that control the expression of certain genes. However, an understanding of chemistry is essential to *all* biologists. An evolutionary biologist might study evolutionary relationships by comparing the DNA of different types of organisms. An ecologist might study how energy is transferred among the organisms living in an estuary or monitor the biological effects of changes in the salinity of the water. A botanist might study unique compounds produced by plants, and might even be a "chemical prospector," seeking new sources of medicinal agents.

In this chapter we lay a foundation for understanding how the structure of atoms determines the way they form chemical bonds to produce complex compounds. Most of our discussion centers around small, simple substances known as **inorganic compounds.** Among the biologically important groups of inorganic compounds are water, many simple acids and bases, and simple salts. We pay particular attention to water, the most abundant substance on Earth's surface and in organisms, and we examine how its unique properties affect living things as well as their nonliving environment. In Chapter 3 we extend our discussion to **organic compounds,** carbon-containing compounds that are generally large and complex. In all but the simplest organic compounds two or more carbon atoms are bonded to each other to form the backbone, or skeleton, of the molecule.

TABLE 2–1   Functions of Elements that Make Up Two Representative Organisms

Element (Chemical Symbol)	Human: % of Total Mass	Nonwoody Plant: % of Total Mass	Functions
Oxygen (O)	65	78	Required for cellular respiration; present in most organic compounds; component of water
Carbon (C)	18	11	Forms backbone of organic molecules; each carbon atom can form four bonds with other atoms
Hydrogen (H)	10	9	Present in most organic compounds; component of water; hydrogen ion (H^+) is involved in some energy transfers
Nitrogen (N)	3	*	Component of proteins and nucleic acids; component of chlorophyll in plants
Calcium (Ca)	1.5	*	Structural component of bones and teeth; calcium ion (Ca^{2+}) is important in muscle contraction, conduction of nerve impulses, and blood clotting; associated with plant cell wall
Phosphorus (P)	1	*	Component of nucleic acids and of phospholipids in membranes; important in energy transfer reactions; structural component of bone
Potassium (K)	*	*	Potassium ion (K^+) is a principal positive ion (cation) in interstitial (tissue) fluid of animals; important in nerve function; affects muscle contraction; controls opening of stomata in plants
Sulfur (S)	*	*	Component of most proteins
Sodium (Na)	*	*	Sodium ion (Na^+) is a principal positive ion (cation) in interstitial (tissue) fluid of animals; important in fluid balance; essential for conduction of nerve impulses; important in photosynthesis in plants
Magnesium (Mg)	*	*	Needed in blood and other tissues of animals; activates many enzymes; component of chlorophyll in plants
Chlorine (Cl)	*	*	Chloride ion (Cl^-) is principal negative ion (anion) in interstitial (tissue) fluid of animals; important in water balance; essential for photosynthesis
Iron (Fe)	*	*	Component of hemoglobin in animals; activates certain enzymes

*The asterisk indicates that these elements represent less than 1% of the total mass. Other elements found in very small (trace) amounts in animals, plants, or both include iodine (I), manganese (Mn), copper (Cu), zinc (Zn), cobalt (Co), fluorine (F), molybdenum (Mo), selenium (Se), boron (B), silicon (Si), and a few others.

■ ELEMENTS ARE NOT CHANGED IN NORMAL CHEMICAL REACTIONS

Elements are substances that cannot be broken down into simpler substances by ordinary chemical reactions. Scientists have assigned each element a **chemical symbol:** usually the first letter or first and second letters of the English or Latin name of the element. For example, O is the symbol for oxygen, C for carbon, H for hydrogen, N for nitrogen, and Na for sodium (Latin *natrium*).

Just four elements—oxygen, carbon, hydrogen, and nitrogen—are responsible for more than 96% of the mass of most organisms. Others, such as calcium, phosphorus, potassium, and magnesium, are also consistently present but in smaller quantities. Some elements, such as iodine and copper, are known as *trace elements* because they are required only in minute amounts. Table 2–1 lists the elements that make up two representative organisms, a human and a typical nonwoody plant (such as grass), and briefly explains why each is important.

■ ATOMS ARE THE FUNDAMENTAL PARTICLES OF ELEMENTS

An **atom** has been traditionally defined as the smallest portion of an element that retains its chemical properties. Atoms are much smaller than the tiniest particle visible under a light microscope. By scanning tunneling microscopy, with magnifications as high as × 5 million, researchers have been able to photograph the positions of some large atoms in molecules.

Physicists have discovered a number of subatomic particles, but for our purposes we need consider only three: electrons, protons, and neutrons. An **electron** is a particle that carries a unit of negative electrical charge; a **proton** carries a unit of positive charge; and a **neutron** is an uncharged particle. In an electrically neutral atom, the number of electrons is equal to the number of protons.

Clustered together, protons and neutrons compose the **atomic nucleus.** Electrons, however, have no fixed locations and move rapidly through the mostly empty space surrounding the atomic nucleus.

An atom is uniquely identified by its number of protons

Each kind of element has a fixed number of protons in the atomic nucleus. This number, called the **atomic number,** is written as a subscript to the left of the chemical symbol. Thus $_1$H indicates that the hydrogen nucleus contains one proton, and $_8$O means that the oxygen nucleus contains eight protons. It is the atomic number, the number of protons in its nucleus, that determines an atom's identity and defines the element.

The **periodic table** (Fig. 2–1 and Appendix B) is a chart in which elements are arranged in order by atomic number. As will become evident later in this chapter, the periodic table is an extremely useful device because it allows us to simultaneously correlate a great many of the relationships among the various elements.

Figure 2–1 includes representations of the **electron configurations** of several elements important in organisms. These *Bohr models,* which show the electrons arranged in a series of concentric circles around the nucleus, are convenient to use but inaccurate. The space outside the nucleus is actually extremely large compared to the nucleus, and, as we will see, electrons do not actually circle the nucleus in fixed concentric pathways.

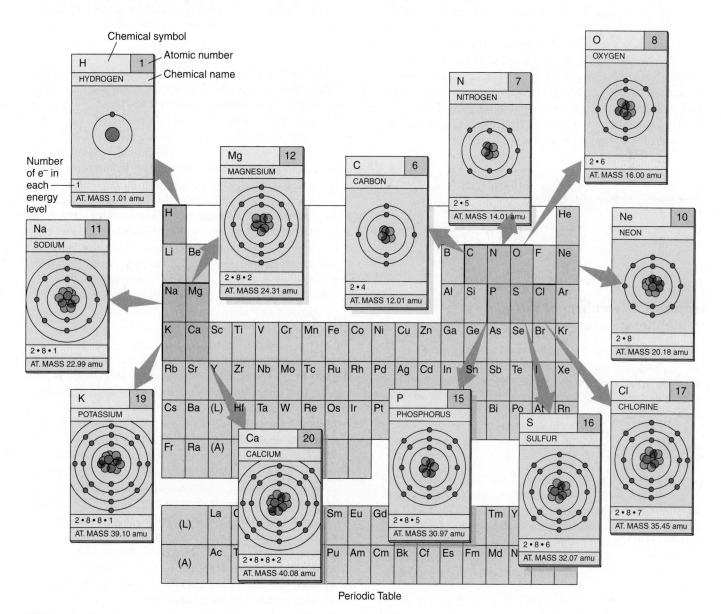

Periodic Table

Figure 2–1   The periodic table.   Note the Bohr models depicting the electron configuration of atoms of some biologically important elements. Although the Bohr model does not depict electron configurations accurately, it is commonly used because of its simplicity and convenience. A complete periodic table is given in Appendix B.

Protons plus neutrons determine atomic mass

The mass of a subatomic particle is exceedingly small, much too small to be conveniently expressed in grams or even micrograms.[1] Such masses are expressed in terms of the **atomic mass unit (amu),** also called the **dalton** in honor of John Dalton, who formulated an atomic theory in the early 1800s. One amu is equal to the approximate mass of a single proton or a single neutron. Protons and neutrons make up almost all the mass of an atom. The mass of a single electron is only about 1/1800 the mass of a proton or neutron.

The **atomic mass** of an atom is a number that indicates approximately how much matter it contains compared with another atom. This value is determined by adding the number of protons to the number of neutrons and expressing the result in atomic mass units or daltons.[2] The mass of the electrons is ignored because it is so small. The atomic mass number is indicated by a superscript to the left of the chemical symbol. The common form of the oxygen atom, with eight protons and eight neutrons in its nucleus, has an atomic number of 8 and a mass of 16 atomic mass units. It is indicated by the symbol $^{16}_{8}O$.

The characteristics of protons, electrons, and neutrons are summarized in the following table:

Particle	Charge	Approximate Mass	Location
Proton	Positive	1 amu	Nucleus
Neutron	Neutral	1 amu	Nucleus
Electron	Negative	Approx. 1/1800 amu	Outside nucleus

Isotopes of an element differ in number of neutrons

Most elements consist of a mixture of atoms with different numbers of neutrons and thus different masses. Such atoms are called **isotopes.** Isotopes of the same element have the same number of protons and electrons; only the number of neutrons varies. The three isotopes of hydrogen, $^{1}_{1}H$ (ordinary hydrogen), $^{2}_{1}H$ (deuterium), and $^{3}_{1}H$ (tritium), contain zero, one, and two neutrons, respectively. Bohr models of two isotopes of carbon, $^{12}_{6}C$ and $^{14}_{6}C$, are illustrated in Figure 2–2. The mass of an element is expressed as an average of the masses of its isotopes (weighted by their relative abundance in nature). For example, the atomic mass of hydrogen is not 1.0 amu, but 1.0079 amu, reflecting the natural occurrence of small amounts of deuterium and tritium in addition to the more abundant ordinary hydrogen.

[1] Tables of commonly used units of scientific measurement are printed inside the back cover of this text.

[2] Unlike weight, mass is independent of the force of gravity. For convenience, however, we consider mass and weight to be equivalent. Atomic weight has the same numerical value as atomic mass, but it has no units.

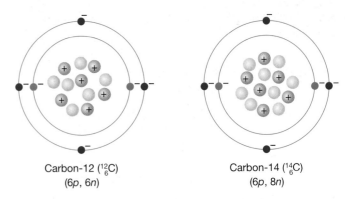

Carbon-12 ($^{12}_{6}C$)
(6p, 6n)

Carbon-14 ($^{14}_{6}C$)
(6p, 8n)

Figure 2–2   Isotopes differ in atomic mass. Carbon-12 ($^{12}_{6}C$) is the most common isotope of carbon. Its nucleus contains six protons and six neutrons, so its atomic mass is 12. Carbon-14 ($^{14}_{6}C$) is a rare radioactive carbon isotope. Because it contains eight neutrons, its atomic mass is 14.

Because they have the same number of electrons, all isotopes of a given element have essentially the same chemical characteristics. However, some isotopes are unstable and tend to break down, or decay, to a more stable isotope (usually becoming a different element). Such unstable isotopes are termed **radioisotopes** because they emit radiation when they decay. For example, the radioactive decay of $^{14}_{6}C$ occurs as a neutron decomposes to form a proton and a fast-moving electron, which is emitted from the atom as a form of radiation known as a beta (β) particle. The resulting stable atom is the common form of nitrogen, $^{14}_{7}N$. Sophisticated instruments allow scientists to detect and measure β particles and other types of radiation. Radioactive decay can also be detected by a method known as **autoradiography,** in which radiation causes the appearance of dark silver grains in photographic film (Fig. 2–3).

Because the different isotopes of a given element have the same chemical characteristics, they are essentially interchangeable in molecules. Molecules containing radioisotopes are usually metabolized and/or localized in the organism in a similar way to their nonradioactive counterparts, and they can be substituted. For this reason, radioisotopes such as ^{3}H (tritium), ^{14}C, and ^{32}P are extremely valuable research tools used in areas such as dating fossils (see Fig. 17–10), tracing biochemical pathways, determining the sequence of genetic information in DNA (see Fig. 14–9), and understanding sugar transport in plants.

In medicine, radioisotopes are used for both diagnosis and treatment. The location and/or metabolism of a sugar, hormone, or drug can be followed in the body by labeling the substance with a radioisotope such as carbon-14 or tritium. For example, the active component in marijuana (tetrahydrocannabinol, or THC) can be labeled and administered intravenously. Then the amount of radioactivity in the blood and urine can be measured at successive intervals. Results of such measurements have determined that for several weeks this compound remains in the blood, and products of its metabolism can be detected in the urine. Radioisotopes are also used to test thyroid gland function, to provide images of blood flow in the arteries supplying the heart muscle, and to study many other aspects of body function and chemistry. Because radiation can interfere with cell division,

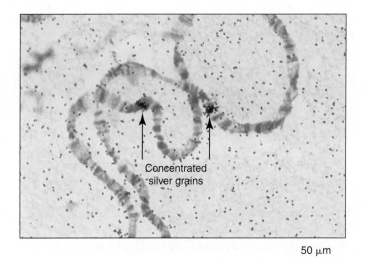

radioisotopes have been used therapeutically in the treatment of cancer (a disease often characterized by rapidly dividing cells).

Electrons move in orbitals corresponding to energy levels

Electrons move through characteristic regions of three-dimensional space, termed **orbitals.** Each orbital contains a maximum of two electrons. Because it is impossible to know an electron's position at any given time, orbitals are most accurately depicted as "electron clouds," shaded areas whose density is proportional to the probability that an electron is present there at any given instant. The energy of an electron depends on the orbital it occupies. Electrons in orbitals with similar energies, said to be at the same **principal energy level,** make up an **electron shell.** These are illustrated in Figure 2–4.

In general, electrons in a shell distant from the nucleus have greater energy than those in a shell close to the nucleus. This is because energy is required to move a negatively charged electron farther away from the positively charged nucleus. The most energetic electrons, known as **valence electrons,** are said to occupy the **valence shell.** The valence shell is represented as the outermost concentric ring in a Bohr model.

■ **Figure 2–3 Autoradiography.** The chromosomes of the fruit fly, *Drosophila melanogaster,* shown in this light micrograph (LM) have been covered with photographic film in which silver grains *(dark spots)* are produced when tritium (^{3}H) that has been incorporated into DNA undergoes radioactive decay. The concentrations of silver grains *(arrows)* mark the locations of specific DNA molecules. *(Peter J. Bryant/Biological Photo Service)*

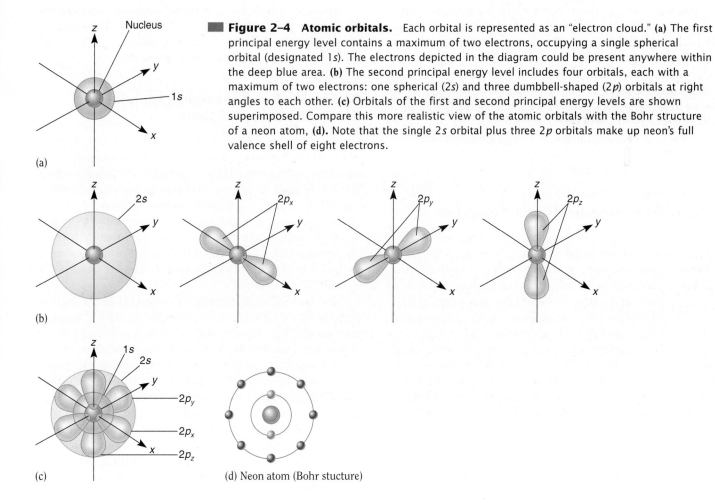

■ **Figure 2–4 Atomic orbitals.** Each orbital is represented as an "electron cloud." **(a)** The first principal energy level contains a maximum of two electrons, occupying a single spherical orbital (designated 1*s*). The electrons depicted in the diagram could be present anywhere within the deep blue area. **(b)** The second principal energy level includes four orbitals, each with a maximum of two electrons: one spherical (2*s*) and three dumbbell-shaped (2*p*) orbitals at right angles to each other. **(c)** Orbitals of the first and second principal energy levels are shown superimposed. Compare this more realistic view of the atomic orbitals with the Bohr structure of a neon atom, **(d).** Note that the single 2*s* orbital plus three 2*p* orbitals make up neon's full valence shell of eight electrons.

An electron can move to an orbital farther from the nucleus by receiving more energy, or it can give up energy and sink to a lower energy level in an orbital nearer the nucleus. Changes in electron energy levels are important in energy conversions in organisms. For example, during photosynthesis light energy absorbed by chlorophyll molecules causes electrons to move to a higher energy level (see Fig. 8–3).

■ VALENCE ELECTRONS PARTICIPATE IN CHEMICAL REACTIONS

The chemical behavior of an atom is determined primarily by the number and arrangement of its valence electrons. The valence shell of hydrogen or helium is full (i.e., stable) when it contains two electrons. The valence shell of any other atom is full when it contains eight electrons. When the valence shell is not full, the atom tends to lose, gain, or share electrons to achieve a full outer shell. The valence shells of all isotopes of an element are identical; this is why they have similar chemical properties and can substitute for each other in chemical reactions (e.g., tritium can substitute for ordinary hydrogen).

Elements that fall into the same vertical column (said to belong to the same *group*) of the periodic table have similar chemical properties because their valence shells have similar tendencies to lose, gain, or share electrons. For example, chlorine and bromine, included in a group commonly known as the *halogens,* are highly reactive. Because their valence shells have seven electrons, they tend to gain an electron in chemical reactions. By contrast, hydrogen, sodium, and potassium each have a single valence electron, which they tend to give up or share with another atom. Helium (He) and neon (Ne) belong to a group referred to as the "noble gases." They are quite unreactive because their valence shells are full. Note the incomplete valence shells of some of the elements important in organisms, including carbon, hydrogen, oxygen, and nitrogen, in Figure 2–1, and compare them with the full valence shell of neon in Figure 2–4d.

Atoms form compounds and molecules

Two or more atoms may combine chemically. When atoms of *different* elements combine, the result is a chemical compound. A **chemical compound** consists of atoms of two or more different elements combined in a fixed ratio. For example, water is a chemical compound composed of hydrogen and oxygen in a ratio of 2:1. Common table salt, sodium chloride, is a chemical compound made up of sodium and chlorine in a 1:1 ratio.

When two or more atoms combine chemically, units called **molecules** can be formed. For example, when two atoms of oxygen combine chemically, a molecule of oxygen is formed. Water is a molecular compound, with each molecule consisting of two atoms of hydrogen and one of oxygen. However, as we shall see, not all compounds are made up of molecules. Sodium chloride is an example of a compound that is not molecular.

Recall from Chapter 1 that emergent properties become evident as a system becomes more complex. Accordingly, a chemical compound has unique properties that are not merely the sum of the properties of its component atoms. For example, at room temperature water is a liquid, whereas hydrogen and oxygen are gases.

Simplest, molecular, and structural chemical formulas give different information

A **chemical formula** is a shorthand expression that describes the chemical composition of a substance. Chemical symbols indicate the types of atoms present, and subscript numbers indicate the ratios among the atoms. There are several types of chemical formulas, each providing specific kinds of information.

In a **simplest formula** (also known as an *empirical formula*), the subscripts give the smallest whole-number ratios for the atoms present in a compound. For example, the simplest formula for hydrazine is NH_2, indicating that there is a 1:2 ratio of nitrogen to hydrogen. (Note that when a single atom of a type is present, the subscript number 1 is never written.)

In a **molecular formula,** the subscripts indicate the actual numbers of each type of atom per molecule. The molecular formula for hydrazine is N_2H_4, which indicates that each molecule of hydrazine consists of two atoms of nitrogen and four atoms of hydrogen. The molecular formula for water, H_2O, indicates that each molecule consists of two atoms of hydrogen and one atom of oxygen.

A **structural formula** shows not only the types and numbers of atoms in a molecule but also their arrangement. From the molecular formula for water, H_2O, you would not know whether the atoms were arranged H—H—O or H—O—H. The structural formula, H—O—H, settles the matter, indicating that the two hydrogen atoms are attached to the oxygen atom.

One mole of any substance contains the same number of units

The **molecular mass** of a compound is the sum of the atomic masses of the component atoms of a single molecule; thus, the molecular mass of water, H_2O, is (hydrogen: 2×1 amu) + (oxygen: 1×16 amu), or 18 amu. (Owing to the presence of isotopes, atomic mass values are not whole numbers. However, for easy calculation each atomic mass value has been rounded off to a whole number.) Similarly, the molecular mass of glucose ($C_6H_{12}O_6$), a simple sugar that is a key compound in cellular metabolism, is (carbon: 6×12 amu) + (hydrogen: 12×1 amu) + (oxygen: 6×16 amu), or 180 amu.

The amount of an element or compound whose mass in grams is equivalent to its atomic or molecular mass is termed 1 **mole (mol).** Thus, 1 mol of water is 18 grams (g), and 1 mol of glucose has a mass of 180 g. As we shall see, the mole is an extremely useful concept because it allows us to make meaningful comparisons between atoms and molecules of very different mass. This is because *1 mol of any substance always has exactly the same number of units,* whether they are small atoms or large molecules. The very large number of units in a mole, 6.02×10^{23}, is known as **Avogadro's number,** named for the Italian physicist Amadeo Avogadro, who first calculated it. Thus 1 mol (180 g) of glucose contains 6.02×10^{23} molecules, as does 1 mol

(2 g) of molecular hydrogen (H_2). Although it is impossible to count atoms and molecules individually, this fact allows a scientist to "count" them simply by weighing a sample. Molecular biologists usually deal with smaller values, either millimoles (a mmol is one-thousandth of a mole) or micromoles (a μmol is one-millionth of a mole).

The mole concept also allows us to make useful comparisons among solutions. A 1-molar solution, represented by 1 *M,* contains 1 mol of that substance dissolved in 1 liter (L) of solution. For example, we can compare 1 L of a 1 *M* solution of glucose with 1 L of a 1 *M* solution of sucrose (table sugar, a larger molecule). They differ in the mass of the dissolved sugar (180 g and 340 g, respectively), but they each contain 6.02×10^{23} sugar molecules.

Chemical equations describe chemical reactions

During any moment in the life of an organism, be it a bacterial cell, a mushroom, or a butterfly, many complex chemical reactions are taking place. Chemical reactions, for example, the reaction between glucose and oxygen, can be described by means of chemical equations:

$$C_6H_{12}O_6 + 6\,O_2 \longrightarrow 6\,CO_2 + 6\,H_2O + \text{Energy}$$

Glucose   Oxygen   Carbon dioxide   Water

In a chemical equation, the **reactants** (the substances that participate in the reaction) are generally written on the left side, and the **products** (the substances formed by the reaction) are written on the right side. The arrow means "yields" and indicates the direction in which the reaction tends to proceed.

Chemical compounds react with each other in quantitatively precise ways. The numbers preceding the chemical symbols or formulas (known as *coefficients*) indicate the relative number of atoms or molecules reacting. For example, 1 mol of glucose burned in a fire or metabolized in a cell reacts with 6 mol of oxygen to form 6 mol of carbon dioxide and 6 mol of water.

Many reactions can proceed simultaneously in the reverse direction (to the left) as well as in the forward direction (to the right); at **dynamic equilibrium** the rates of the forward and reverse reactions are equal (see Chapter 6). Reversible reactions are indicated by double arrows:

$$CO_2 + H_2O \rightleftharpoons H_2CO_3$$

Carbon dioxide   Water   Carbonic acid

In this example, the arrows are drawn in different lengths to indicate that when the reaction reaches equilibrium there will be more reactants (CO_2 and H_2O) than product (H_2CO_3).

■ ATOMS ARE JOINED BY CHEMICAL BONDS

The atoms of a compound are held together by forces of attraction called **chemical bonds.** Each bond represents a certain amount of chemical energy. **Bond energy** is the energy necessary to break a chemical bond. The valence electrons dictate how many bonds an atom can participate in. The two principal types of strong chemical bonds are covalent bonds and ionic bonds.

In covalent bonds electrons are shared

Covalent bonds involve the sharing of electrons between atoms in a way that results in each atom having a filled valence shell. A compound consisting mainly of covalent bonds is called a **covalent compound.** A simple example of a covalent bond is the joining of two hydrogen atoms in a molecule of hydrogen gas, H_2. Each atom of hydrogen has one electron, but two electrons are required to complete its valence shell. The hydrogen atoms have equal capacities to attract electrons, so neither donates an electron to the other. Instead, the two hydrogen atoms share their single electrons so that each of the two electrons is attracted simultaneously to the two protons in the two hydrogen nuclei. The two electrons thus whirl around both atomic nuclei, joining the two atoms.

A simple way of representing the electrons in the valence shell of an atom is to use dots placed around the chemical symbol of the element. Such a representation is called the *Lewis structure* of the atom, named for G.N. Lewis, who developed this type of notation. In a water molecule, two hydrogen atoms are covalently bonded to an oxygen atom:

$$H\cdot + H\cdot + \cdot\ddot{\underset{\cdot\cdot}{O}}\cdot \longrightarrow H\!:\!\ddot{\underset{\cdot\cdot}{O}}\!:\!H$$

Oxygen has six valence electrons; by sharing electrons with two hydrogen atoms, it completes its valence shell of eight. At the same time each hydrogen atom obtains a complete valence shell of two. (Note that in the structural formula H—O—H, each pair of shared electrons constitutes a covalent bond, represented by a solid line. Unshared electrons are usually omitted in a structural formula.)

The carbon atom has four electrons in its valence shell, all of which are available for covalent bonding:

$$\cdot\dot{\underset{\cdot}{C}}\cdot$$

When one carbon and four hydrogen atoms share electrons, a molecule of methane, CH_4, is formed:

$$
\begin{array}{ccc}
\quad H \quad & & \quad H \quad \\
H\!:\!\overset{\cdot\cdot}{\underset{\cdot\cdot}{C}}\!:\!H & \text{or} & H\!-\!C\!-\!H \\
\quad H \quad & & \quad H \quad
\end{array}
$$

Lewis structure   Structural formula

The nitrogen atom has five electrons in its valence shell. Recall that each orbital can hold a maximum of two electrons. Usually two electrons occupy one orbital, leaving three available for sharing with other atoms:

$$\cdot\ddot{N}\cdot$$

When a nitrogen atom shares electrons with three hydrogen atoms, a molecule of ammonia, NH_3, is formed:

$$
\begin{array}{ccc}
H\!:\!\overset{\cdot\cdot}{N}\!:\!H & \text{or} & H\!-\!N\!-\!H \\
\quad H \quad & & \quad H \quad
\end{array}
$$

Lewis structure   Structural formula

When one pair of electrons is shared between two atoms, the covalent bond is referred to as a **single covalent bond** (Fig. 2–5a). Two oxygen atoms may achieve stability by forming covalent bonds with one another. Each oxygen atom has six electrons in its outer shell. To become stable, the two atoms share two pairs of electrons, forming molecular oxygen (Fig. 2–5b). When two pairs of electrons are shared in this way, the covalent bond is called a **double covalent bond,** which is represented by two parallel solid lines. Similarly, a **triple covalent bond** (represented by three parallel solid lines) is formed when three pairs of electrons are shared between two atoms.

The number of covalent bonds usually formed by the atoms commonly present in biologically important molecules is summarized as follows:

Atom	Symbol	Covalent Bonds
Hydrogen	H	1
Oxygen	O	2
Carbon	C	4
Nitrogen	N	3
Phosphorus	P	5
Sulfur	S	2

The function of a molecule is related to its shape

In addition to being composed of atoms with certain properties, each kind of molecule has a characteristic size and a general overall shape. Although the shape of a molecule may change (within certain limits), the functions of molecules in living cells are dictated largely by their geometric shapes. A molecule that consists of two atoms, for example, is linear. Molecules composed of more than two atoms may have more complicated shapes. The geometric shape of a molecule provides the optimal distance between the atoms to counteract the repulsion of electron pairs.

When an atom forms covalent bonds with other atoms, the orbitals in the valence shell may become rearranged in a process known as **orbital hybridization,** thereby affecting the shape of the resulting molecule. For example, when four hydrogen atoms combine with a carbon atom to form a molecule of methane (CH_4), the hybridized valence shell orbitals of the carbon form a geometric structure known as a *tetrahedron*, with one hydrogen atom present at each of its four corners (Fig. 2–6; see Fig. 3–2b).

Covalent bonds can be nonpolar or polar

Atoms of different elements vary in their affinity for electrons. **Electronegativity** is a measure of an atom's attraction for shared electrons in chemical bonds. Very electronegative atoms such as oxygen, nitrogen, fluorine, and chlorine are sometimes called "electron-greedy." When covalently bound atoms have similar electronegativities, the electrons are shared equally, and the covalent bond is described as **nonpolar.** The covalent bond of the hydrogen molecule is nonpolar, as are the covalent bonds of molecular oxygen and methane.

In a covalent bond between two different elements, such as oxygen and hydrogen, the electronegativities of the atoms may be different. If so, electrons are pulled closer to the atomic nucleus of the element with the greater electron affinity (in this case, oxygen). A covalent bond between atoms that differ in elec-

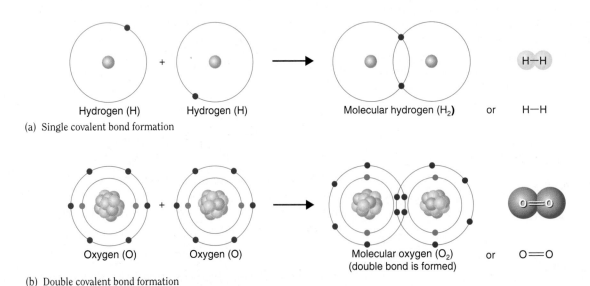

Hydrogen (H) + Hydrogen (H) → Molecular hydrogen (H₂) or H—H

(a) Single covalent bond formation

Oxygen (O) + Oxygen (O) → Molecular oxygen (O₂) (double bond is formed) or O═O

(b) Double covalent bond formation

Figure 2–5 Electron sharing in covalent compounds. (a) Two hydrogen atoms achieve stability by sharing electrons, thereby forming a molecule of hydrogen. In the structural formula shown on the right, the straight line between the hydrogen atoms represents a single covalent bond. (b) In molecular oxygen, two oxygen atoms share two pairs of electrons, forming a double covalent bond.

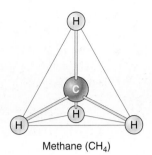

Methane (CH₄)

Figure 2–6 Orbital hybridization in methane. The four hydrogens are located at the corners of a tetrahedron owing to hybridization of the valence shell orbitals of carbon.

tronegativity is called a **polar covalent bond.** Such a bond has two dissimilar ends (or poles), one with a partial positive charge and the other with a partial negative charge. Each of the two covalent bonds in water is polar because there is a partial positive charge at the hydrogen end of the bond and a partial negative charge at the oxygen end, where the "shared" electrons are more likely to be found.

Covalent bonds differ in their degree of polarity, ranging from those in which the electrons are exactly shared (as in the nonpolar hydrogen molecule) to those in which the electrons are much closer to one atom than to the other (as in water). Oxygen is quite electronegative and forms polar covalent bonds with carbon, hydrogen, and many other atoms. Nitrogen is also strongly electronegative, although less so than oxygen.

A molecule with one or more polar covalent bonds can be polar even though it is electrically neutral as a whole. This is because a **polar molecule** has one end with a partial positive charge and another end with a partial negative charge. One example is water (Fig. 2–7). The polar bonds between the hydrogens and the oxygen are arranged in a V shape, rather than linearly. The oxygen end therefore constitutes the negative pole of the molecule, and the end with the two hydrogens is the positive pole.

Ionic bonds form between cations and anions

Some atoms or groups of atoms are not electrically neutral. A particle with one or more units of electrical charge is called an **ion.** An atom becomes an ion if it gains or loses one or more electrons. An atom with one, two, or three electrons in its valence shell tends to lose electrons to other atoms. Such an atom then becomes positively charged because its nucleus contains more protons than the number of electrons orbiting around the nucleus. These positively charged ions are termed **cations.** Atoms with five, six, or seven valence electrons tend to gain electrons from other atoms and become negatively charged **anions.**

The properties of ions are quite different from those of the electrically neutral atoms from which they were derived. For example, although chlorine gas is a poison, chloride ions (Cl^-) are essential to life (see Table 2–1). Because their electrical charges provide a basis for many interactions, cations and anions are involved in energy transformations within the cell, the transmission of nerve impulses, muscle contraction, and many other life processes (Fig. 2–8).

A group of covalently bonded atoms can also become an ion *(polyatomic ion).* Unlike a single atom, a group of atoms can lose or gain protons (derived from hydrogen atoms) as well as electrons. Therefore, a group of atoms can become a cation if it loses one or more electrons or gains one or more protons. A group of atoms becomes an anion if it gains one or more electrons or loses one or more protons.

An **ionic bond** forms as a consequence of the attraction between the positive charge of a cation and the negative charge of an anion. An **ionic compound** is a substance consisting of anions and cations bonded together by their opposite charges.

A good example of how ionic bonds are formed is the attraction between sodium ions and chloride ions. A sodium atom has one electron in its valence shell. It cannot fill its valence shell by obtaining seven electrons from other atoms, for it would then have a large unbalanced negative charge. Instead, it gives up its single valence electron to a very electronegative atom, such as chlorine, which acts as an electron acceptor (Fig. 2–9). Chlorine cannot give up the seven electrons in its valence shell, because it

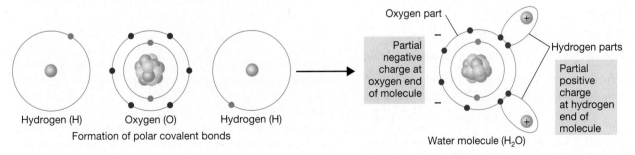

Hydrogen (H)   Oxygen (O)   Hydrogen (H)
Formation of polar covalent bonds

Oxygen part

Partial negative charge at oxygen end of molecule

Hydrogen parts

Partial positive charge at hydrogen end of molecule

Water molecule (H₂O)

Figure 2–7 Water, a polar molecule. Note that the electrons tend to stay closer to the nucleus of the oxygen atom than to the hydrogen nuclei. This results in a partial negative charge on the oxygen portion of the molecule and a partial positive charge at the hydrogen end. Although the water molecule as a whole is electrically neutral, it is a polar covalent compound.

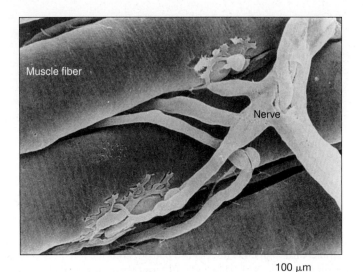

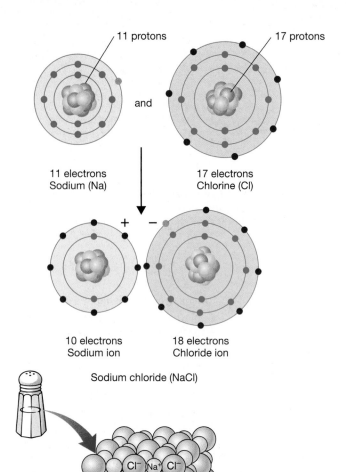

Sodium chloride (NaCl)

Figure 2–8 Ions and biological processes. Sodium, potassium, and chloride ions are essential for this nerve cell to stimulate these muscle fibers, initiating contraction. Calcium ions in the muscle cell are required for muscle contraction. *(D.W. Fawcett)*

would then have a large positive charge. Instead it strips an electron from an electron donor (sodium in this example) to complete its valence shell.

When sodium reacts with chlorine, sodium's valence electron is transferred completely to chlorine. Sodium becomes a cation, with one unit of positive charge (Na^+). Chlorine becomes an anion, a chloride ion with one unit of negative charge (Cl^-). These ions attract each other as a result of their opposite charges. They are held together by this electrical attraction in ionic bonds to form NaCl, sodium chloride,[3] or common table salt.

The term *molecule* does not adequately explain the properties of ionic compounds such as NaCl. When NaCl is in its solid crystal state, each ion is actually surrounded by six ions of opposite charge. The simplest formula, NaCl, indicates that sodium ions and chloride ions are present in a 1:1 ratio, but in the actual crystal, no discrete molecules composed of one Na^+ and one Cl^- ion are present.

Compounds joined by ionic bonds, such as sodium chloride, have a tendency to *dissociate* (separate) into their individual ions when placed in water:

$$NaCl \xrightarrow{\text{in } H_2O} Na^+ + Cl^-$$

Sodium chloride   Sodium ion   Chloride ion

In the solid form of an ionic compound (i.e., in the absence of water), the ionic bonds are very strong. Water, however, is an

Figure 2–9 Ionic bonding. Sodium becomes a positively charged ion when it donates its single valence electron to chlorine, which has seven valence electrons. With this additional electron, chlorine completes its valence shell and becomes a negatively charged chloride ion. These sodium and chloride ions are attracted to one another by their unlike electrical charges, forming the ionic compound sodium chloride.

excellent **solvent;** as a liquid it is capable of dissolving many substances, particularly those that are polar or ionic. This is because of the polarity of water molecules. The localized partial positive charge (on the hydrogen atoms) and partial negative charge (on the oxygen atom) on each water molecule attract and surround the anions and cations on the surface of an ionic solid. As a result, the solid dissolves. A dissolved substance is referred to as a **solute.** In solution, each cation and anion of the ionic compound is surrounded by oppositely charged ends of the water molecules (Fig. 2–10). This process is known as **hy-**

---

[3] In both covalent and ionic binary compounds (*binary* denotes compounds consisting of two elements), the element having the greater attraction for electrons is named second, and an *-ide* ending is added to the stem name, such as sodium chloride and hydrogen fluoride. The *-ide* ending is also used to indicate an anion, as in chloride (Cl^-) and hydroxide (OH^-).

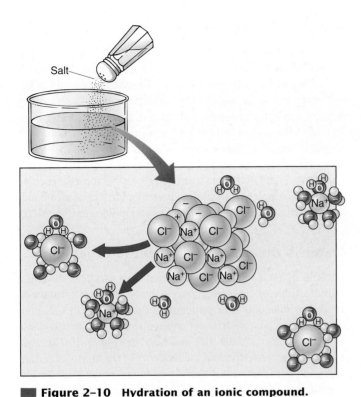

Figure 2–10 Hydration of an ionic compound.
When the crystal of NaCl is added to water, the sodium and chloride ions are pulled apart as the partial negative ends of the water molecules are attracted to the positive sodium ions, and the partial positive ends of the water molecules are attracted to the negative chloride ions. When the NaCl is dissolved, each Na$^+$ and Cl$^-$ is surrounded by water molecules electrically attracted to it.

dration. Hydrated ions still interact with each other to some extent, but the transient ionic bonds formed are much weaker than those in a solid crystal.

Hydrogen bonds are weak attractions

Another type of bond important in organisms is the **hydrogen bond.** When hydrogen combines with oxygen (or with another relatively electronegative atom such as nitrogen), it acquires a partial positive charge because its electron spends more time closer to the electronegative atom. Hydrogen bonds tend to form between an atom with a partial negative charge and a hydrogen atom that is covalently bonded to oxygen or nitrogen (Fig. 2–11). The atoms involved may be in two parts of the same large molecule or in two different molecules. Water molecules interact with each other extensively through hydrogen bond formation.

Hydrogen bonds are readily formed and broken. Although individually relatively weak, hydrogen bonds are collectively strong when present in large numbers. Furthermore, they have a specific length and orientation. As we will see in Chapter 3, these features are very important in determining the three-dimensional structure of large molecules such as DNA and proteins.

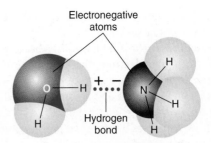

Figure 2–11 Hydrogen bonding. A hydrogen bond (generally indicated by a dotted line) can form between two molecules with regions of unlike partial charge. A hydrogen atom in a water molecule has a partial positive charge because of its polar covalent bond with oxygen. Nitrogen is strongly electronegative and, in molecules like ammonia (NH$_3$), has a partial negative charge because of its polar covalent bonds with hydrogen. Here, the nitrogen atom of the ammonia molecule is joined by a hydrogen bond to a hydrogen atom of a water molecule.

ELECTRONS AND THEIR ENERGY ARE TRANSFERRED IN REDOX REACTIONS

Many of the energy conversions that go on in a cell involve reactions in which an electron is transferred from one substance to another. This is because the transfer of an electron also involves the transfer of the energy of that electron. Such an electron transfer is called an *oxidation-reduction,* or **redox reaction.** Both cellular respiration (Chapter 7) and photosynthesis (Chapter 8) are essentially redox processes.

Rusting, which is the combination of iron (symbol Fe) with oxygen, is a simple illustration of oxidation and reduction:

$$4 \text{ Fe} + 3 \text{ O}_2 \longrightarrow 2 \text{ Fe}_2\text{O}_3$$
$$\text{Iron (III) oxide}$$

Oxidation and reduction always occur together, but initially we will discuss them separately. **Oxidation** is a chemical process in which an atom, ion, or molecule loses electrons. In rusting, each iron atom becomes oxidized as it loses three electrons.

$$4 \text{ Fe} \rightarrow 4 \text{ Fe}^{3+} + 12e^-$$

The e^- is a symbol for an electron; the + superscript in Fe^{3+} represents an electron deficit. (When an atom loses an electron, it acquires one unit of positive charge from the excess of one proton. In our example, each iron atom loses three electrons and acquires three units of positive charge.)

You will recall that the oxygen atom is very electronegative, able to remove electrons from other atoms. In this reaction, oxygen gains electrons from iron.

$$3 \text{ O}_2 + 12e^- \rightarrow 6 \text{ O}^{2-}$$

Oxygen becomes reduced when it accepts electrons from the iron. **Reduction** is a chemical process in which an atom, ion, or molecule *gains* electrons. (The term *reduction* refers to the fact that the gain of an electron results in the reduction of any positive charge that might be present.)

Redox reactions occur simultaneously because one substance must accept the electrons that are removed from the other. In a redox reaction, one component, the *oxidizing agent,* accepts one or more electrons and becomes reduced. Oxidizing agents other than oxygen are known, but oxygen is such a common one that its name was given to the process. Another reaction component, the *reducing agent,* gives up one or more electrons and becomes oxidized.

In our example there was a complete transfer of electrons from iron (the reducing agent) to oxygen (the oxidizing agent). Similarly, in Figure 2–9, an electron was transferred from sodium (the reducing agent) to chlorine (the oxidizing agent).

Electrons are not easily removed from covalent compounds unless an entire atom is removed. In cells, oxidation often involves the removal of a hydrogen *atom* (an electron plus a proton that "goes along for the ride") from a covalent compound; reduction often involves the addition of the equivalent of a hydrogen atom (see Chapter 6).

■ WATER IS ESSENTIAL TO LIFE

A large part of the mass of most organisms is water. In human tissues the percentage of water ranges from 20% in bones to 85% in brain cells; about 70% of our total body weight is water. As much as 95% of a jellyfish and certain plants is water. Water is the source, through photosynthesis (see Chapter 8), of the oxygen in the air we breathe, and its hydrogen atoms become incorporated into many organic compounds. Water is also the solvent for most biological reactions and a reactant or product in many chemical reactions.

Water is not only important as an internal constituent of organisms but also is one of the principal environmental factors affecting them. Many organisms live in the ocean or in freshwater rivers, lakes, or puddles. Water's unique combination of physical and chemical properties is considered to have been essential to the origin of life, as well as to the continued survival and evolution of life on Earth (Fig. 2–12).

Water molecules are polar

As discussed previously, water molecules are polar; that is, one end of each molecule bears a partial positive charge and the other a partial negative charge (see Fig. 2–7). The water molecules in liquid water and in ice associate by hydrogen bonds. The hydrogen atom of one water molecule, with its partial positive charge, is attracted to the oxygen atom of a neighboring water molecule, with its partial negative charge, forming a hydrogen bond. An oxygen atom in a water molecule has two regions of partial negative charge, and each of the two hydrogen atoms has a partial positive charge. Each water molecule can therefore form hydrogen bonds with a maximum of four neighboring water molecules (Fig. 2–13).

Water is the principal solvent in organisms

Because its molecules are polar, water is an excellent solvent, a liquid capable of dissolving many different kinds of substances, especially polar and ionic compounds. Previously in this chapter, we discussed how polar water molecules pull the ions of ionic compounds apart so that they dissociate (see Fig. 2–10). Because of its solvent properties and the tendency of the atoms in certain compounds to form ions when in solution, water plays an important role in facilitating chemical reactions. Substances that interact readily with water are said to be **hydrophilic** ("water-loving"). Examples include table sugar (sucrose, a polar compound) and table salt (NaCl, an ionic compound), which dissolve readily in water. Not all substances in organisms are hydrophilic, however. Many **hydrophobic** ("water-fearing") substances found in living things are especially important because of their ability to form associations or structures that are not disrupted or dissolved by water. Examples, to be discussed more fully in Chapter 3, include fats and other nonpolar substances.

Hydrogen bonding makes water cohesive and adhesive

Water molecules have a strong tendency to stick to each other; that is, they are **cohesive.** This is due to the hydrogen bonds among the molecules. Because of the cohesive nature of water molecules, any force exerted on part of a column of water will be transmitted to the column as a whole. The major mechanism of

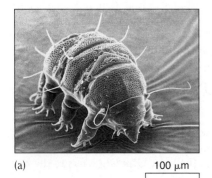
(a)   100 μm

(b)   10 μm

■ **Figure 2–12 Tardigrade. (a)** Commonly known as "water bears," tardigrades such as these members of the genus *Echiniscus* are small (less than 1.2 mm long) animals that normally live in moist habitats, such as thin films of water on mosses. **(b)** When subjected to desiccation, tardigrades assume a barrel-shaped form known as a *tun,* remaining in this state, motionless but alive, for as long as 100 years. When rehydrated they assume their normal appearance and activities. *(a, Diane R. Nelson; b, Robert O. Schuster, courtesy of Diane R. Nelson)*

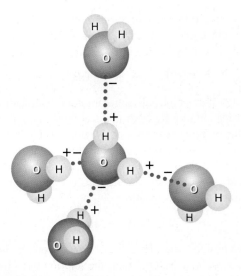

Figure 2-13 Hydrogen bonding of water molecules. Each water molecule can form hydrogen bonds *(dotted lines)* with as many as four neighboring water molecules.

water movement in plants (see Chapter 33) depends on the cohesive nature of water. Water molecules also stick to many other kinds of substances, most notably those with charged groups of atoms or molecules on their surfaces. These **adhesive** forces explain how water makes things wet.

A combination of adhesive and cohesive forces accounts for the phenomenon of **capillary action**, which is the tendency of water to move in narrow tubes, even against the force of gravity (Fig. 2–14). For example, water moves through the microscopic

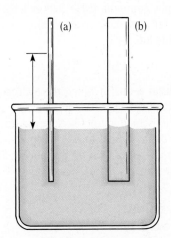

Figure 2-14 Capillary action. (a) In a narrow tube, adhesive forces attract water molecules to the glass wall of the tube. Other water molecules inside the tube are then "pulled along" by cohesive forces, which are due to hydrogen bonds between the water molecules. (b) In the wider tube, a smaller percentage of the water molecules line the glass wall. Because of this, the adhesive forces are not strong enough to overcome the cohesive forces of the water beneath the surface level of the container, and water in the tube rises only slightly.

spaces between soil particles to the roots of plants by capillary action.

Water has a high degree of **surface tension** because of the cohesiveness of its molecules, which have a much greater attraction for each other than for molecules in the air. Thus, water molecules at the surface crowd together, producing a strong layer as they are pulled downward by the attraction of other water molecules beneath them (Fig. 2–15).

Water helps maintain a stable temperature

Raising the temperature of a substance involves adding heat energy to make its molecules move faster, that is, to increase the **kinetic energy** (energy of motion) of the molecules (see Chapter 6). The term **heat** refers to the *total* amount of kinetic energy in a sample of a substance; **temperature** is a measure of the *average* kinetic energy of the particles. Water has a high **specific heat;** that is, the amount of energy required to raise the temperature of water is quite large. A **calorie** (cal) is a unit of heat energy (equivalent to 4.184 joules [J]) that equals the amount of heat required to raise the temperature of 1 g of water 1° Celsius (C). The specific heat of water is therefore 1 cal/g of water per degree Celsius. Most other common substances such as metals, glass, and ethyl alcohol have much lower specific heat values. The specific heat of ethyl alcohol, for example, is 0.59 cal/g/1° C (2.46 J/g/1° C).

The high specific heat of water results from the hydrogen bonding of its molecules. Some of the hydrogen bonds holding the water molecules together must first be broken to permit the molecules to move more freely. Much of the energy added to the system is used up in breaking the hydrogen bonds, and only a portion of the heat energy is available to speed the movement of the water molecules (thereby increasing the temperature of the water). Conversely, when liquid water changes to ice, additional

Figure 2-15 Surface tension of water. Hydrogen bonding between water molecules is responsible for the surface tension of water, which is strong enough to support these water striders, and causes the dimpled appearance of the surface. Although water striders are denser than water, these insects can walk on the surface of a pond because fine hairs at the ends of their legs spread their weight over a large area. *(Dennis Drenner)*

hydrogen bonds must be formed, liberating a great deal of heat into the environment.

Because so much heat input is required to raise the temperature of water (and so much heat is lost when the temperature is lowered), the ocean and other large bodies of water have relatively constant temperatures. Thus, many organisms living in the ocean are provided with a relatively constant environmental temperature. The properties of water are crucial in stabilizing temperatures on the Earth's surface. Although surface water is only a thin film relative to Earth's volume, the quantity is enormous compared to the exposed land mass. This relatively large mass of water resists both the warming effect of heat and the cooling effect of low temperatures.

Hydrogen bonding causes ice to have unique properties with important environmental consequences. Liquid water expands as it freezes because the hydrogen bonds joining the water molecules in the crystalline lattice keep the molecules far enough apart to give ice a density about 10% less than the density of liquid water (Fig. 2–16c). When ice has been heated enough to raise its temperature above 0° C (32° F), these hydrogen bonds among the water molecules are broken, freeing the molecules to slip closer together. The density of water is greatest at 4° C, above which water begins to expand again as the speed of its molecules increases. As a result, ice floats on the denser cold water.

This unusual property of water has been important in enabling life as we know it to appear, survive, and evolve on Earth. If ice had a greater density than water, it would sink; eventually all ponds, lakes, and even the ocean would freeze solid from the bottom to the surface, making life impossible. When a deep body of water cools, it becomes covered with floating ice. The ice insulates the liquid water below it, retarding freezing and permitting a variety of organisms to survive below the icy surface.

The high water content of organisms helps them maintain relatively constant internal temperatures. Such minimizing of temperature fluctuations is important because biological reactions can take place only within a relatively narrow temperature range.

Because its molecules are held together by hydrogen bonds, water has a high **heat of vaporization.** To change 1 g of liquid water into 1 g of water vapor, 540 cal of heat are required. The heat of vaporization of most other common liquid substances is much less. As a sample of water is heated, some molecules are moving much faster than others (i.e., they have more heat energy). These faster moving molecules are more likely to escape the liquid phase and enter the vapor phase (see Fig. 2–16a). When they do, they take their heat energy with them (thus lowering the temperature of the sample, a process called **evaporative cooling**). For this reason the human body can dissipate excess heat as sweat evaporates from the skin, and a leaf can keep cool in the bright sunlight as water evaporates from its surface.

■ ACIDS ARE PROTON DONORS; BASES ARE PROTON ACCEPTORS

Water molecules have a slight tendency to **ionize,** that is, to dissociate into hydrogen ions (H^+) and hydroxide ions

(OH^-).[4] In pure water, a small number of water molecules ionize. This slight tendency of water to dissociate is reversible as hydrogen ions and hydroxide ions reunite to form water:

$$HOH \rightleftharpoons H^+ + OH^-$$

Because each water molecule splits into one hydrogen ion and one hydroxide ion, the concentrations of hydrogen ions and hydroxide ions in pure water are exactly equal (0.0000001 or 10^{-7} mol/L for each ion). Such a solution is said to be neutral, that is, neither acidic nor basic (alkaline).

An **acid** is a substance that dissociates in solution to yield hydrogen ions (H^+) and an anion.

$$Acid \rightarrow H^+ + Anion$$

An acid is a proton *donor*. (Recall that a hydrogen ion, or H^+, is nothing more than a proton.) An acidic solution has a hydrogen ion concentration that is higher than its hydroxide ion concentration. Acidic solutions turn blue litmus paper red and have a sour taste. Hydrochloric acid (HCl) and sulfuric acid (H_2SO_4) are examples of inorganic acids. Lactic acid ($CH_3CHOHCOOH$) from sour milk and acetic acid (CH_3COOH) from vinegar are two common organic acids.

A **base** is defined as a proton *acceptor*. Most bases are substances that dissociate to yield a hydroxide ion (OH^-) and a cation when dissolved in water. A hydroxide ion can act as a base by accepting a proton (H^+) to form water. Sodium hydroxide (NaOH) is a common inorganic base.

$$NaOH \rightarrow Na^+ + OH^-$$

$$OH^- + H^+ \rightarrow H_2O$$

Some bases do not dissociate to yield hydroxide ions directly. For example, ammonia (NH_3) acts as a base by accepting a proton from water, producing an ammonium ion (NH_4^+) and releasing a hydroxide ion.

$$NH_3 + H_2O \rightarrow NH_4^+ + OH^-$$

A basic solution is one in which the hydrogen ion concentration is lower than the hydroxide ion concentration. Basic solutions such as household ammonia turn red litmus paper blue and feel slippery to the touch. In later chapters we encounter a number of organic bases, such as the purine and pyrimidine bases that are components of nucleic acids.

pH is a convenient measure of acidity

The degree of a solution's acidity is generally expressed in terms of **pH**, defined as the negative logarithm (base 10) of the hydrogen ion concentration (expressed in moles per liter):

$$pH = -\log_{10}[H^+]$$

[4] The H^+ immediately combines with a negatively charged region of a water molecule, forming a hydronium ion (H_3O^+). However, by convention, H^+, rather than the more accurate H_3O^+, is used.

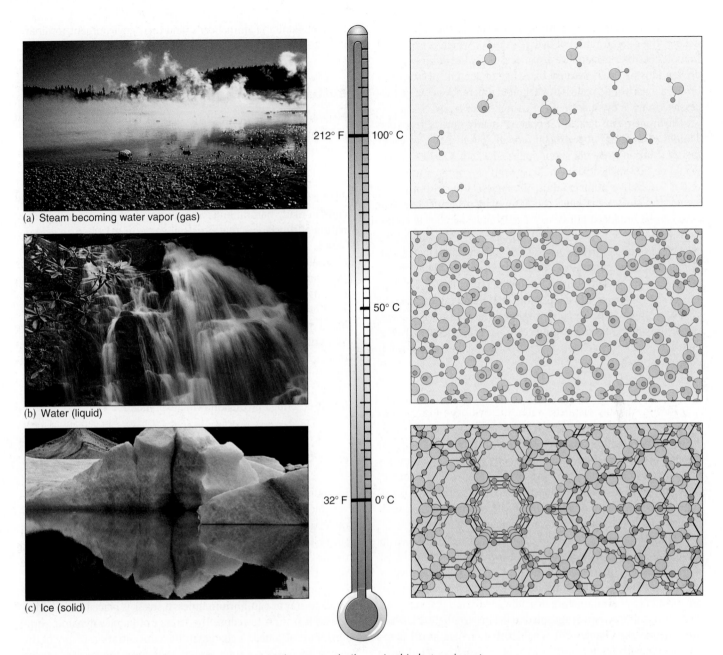

(a) Steam becoming water vapor (gas)

(b) Water (liquid)

(c) Ice (solid)

212° F   100° C

50° C

32° F   0° C

Figure 2–16 Three forms of water. **(a)** When water boils, as in this hot spring at Yellowstone National Park, many hydrogen bonds are broken, causing steam, consisting of minuscule water droplets, to form. If most of the remaining hydrogen bonds are subsequently broken, the molecules begin to move more freely as water vapor (a gas). **(b)** Water molecules in a liquid state continually form, break, and re-form hydrogen bonds with each other. **(c)** In ice, each water molecule participates in four hydrogen bonds with adjacent molecules, resulting in a regular, evenly distanced crystalline lattice structure. Because the water molecules move apart slightly as the hydrogen bonds form, water expands as it freezes; thus ice floats on water. *(a, Woodbridge Wilson/National Park Service; b, Gary R. Bonner; c, Barbara O'Donnell/Biological Photo Service)*

The brackets refer to concentration; therefore, the term [H$^+$] means "the concentration of hydrogen ions," which is expressed in moles per liter because we are interested in the *number* of hydrogen ions per liter. Because the range of possible pH values is broad, a logarithmic scale (with a tenfold difference between successive units) is more convenient than a linear scale.

Hydrogen ion concentrations are nearly always less than 1 mol/L. One gram of hydrogen ions dissolved in 1 L of water (a 1 *M* solution) may not sound impressive, but such a solution would be extremely acidic. The logarithm of a number less than one is a negative number; thus, the *negative* logarithm corresponds to a *positive* pH value. (Solutions with pH values less than zero can be produced but do not occur under biological conditions.)

Whole number pH values are easy to calculate (Table 2–2). For instance, consider our example of pure water, which has a hydrogen ion concentration of 0.0000001 (10^{-7}) mol/L. The logarithm is −7. The negative logarithm is 7; therefore, the pH is 7.

If the hydrogen ion concentration of a solution is known, the hydroxide ion concentration can be easily calculated. The product of the hydrogen ion concentration and the hydroxide ion concentration is 1×10^{-14}:

$$[H^+][OH^-] = 1 \times 10^{-14}$$

In pure (freshly distilled) water, the hydrogen ion concentration is 10^{-7}; therefore, the hydroxide concentration is also 10^{-7}. Such a solution, in which the concentrations are equal, is called a **neutral solution**. **Acidic solutions** (those with an excess of hydrogen ions) have pH values smaller than 7. For example, the hydrogen ion concentration of a solution with pH 1 is ten times that of a solution with pH 2. **Basic solutions** (those with an excess of hydroxide ions) have pH values greater than 7.

The pH values of some common substances are shown in Figure 2–17. Although some very acidic compartments exist within cells (see Chapter 4), most of the interior of an animal or plant cell is neither strongly acidic nor strongly basic but instead an essentially neutral mixture of acidic and basic substances. Although certain bacteria are adapted to life in extremely acidic environments (see Chapter 23), a substantial change in pH is incompatible with life for most cells (Fig. 2–18). The pH of most types of plant and animal cells (and their environment) ordinarily ranges from around 7.2 to 7.4.

Buffers minimize pH change

Many homeostatic mechanisms operate to maintain appropriate pH values. For example, the pH of human blood is about 7.4 and must be maintained within very narrow limits. Should the blood become too acidic (e.g., as a result of respiratory disease), coma and death may result. Excessive alkalinity can result in overexcitability of the nervous system and even convulsions. Organisms contain many natural buffers. A **buffer** is a substance or combination of substances that resists changes in pH when an acid or base is added. A buffering system includes a weak acid or a weak base. A weak acid or weak base does not ionize completely. That is, at any given instant only a fraction of the molecules are ionized; most are not dissociated.

One of the most common buffering systems is found in the blood of vertebrates (see Chapter 44). Carbon dioxide, produced as a waste product of cellular metabolism, enters the blood, the main constituent of which is water. The carbon dioxide reacts with the water to form carbonic acid, a weak acid that dissociates to yield a hydrogen ion and a bicarbonate ion. The buffering system is described by the following expression:

$$\underset{\substack{\text{Carbon} \\ \text{dioxide}}}{CO_2} + \underset{\text{Water}}{H_2O} \rightleftharpoons \underset{\substack{\text{Carbonic} \\ \text{acid}}}{H_2CO_3} \rightleftharpoons H^+ + \underset{\substack{\text{Bicarbonate} \\ \text{ion}}}{HCO_3^-}$$

As indicated by the double arrows, all the reactions are reversible. Because carbonic acid is a weak acid, undissociated molecules are always present, as are all the other components of the system. The expression describes the system when it is at dynamic equilibrium, that is, when the rates of the forward and reverse reactions are equal and the relative concentrations of the components are not changing. A system at dynamic equilibrium tends to stay at equilibrium unless a stress is placed on it, which causes it to shift to reduce the stress until a new dynamic equilibrium is attained. A change in the concentration of any of the components is one such stress. Therefore, the system can be

---

TABLE 2–2 Relationship among pH, Hydrogen Ion, and Hydroxide Ion Concentrations

Substance	[H$^+$]*	log [H$^+$]	pH	[OH$^-$]†
Gastric juice	0.01, 10^{-2}	−2	2	10^{-12}
Pure water, neutral solution	0.0000001, 10^{-7}	−7	7	10^{-7}
Household ammonia	0.00000000001, 10^{-11}	−11	11	10^{-3}

* [H$^+$] = hydrogen ion concentration (mol/L)

† [OH$^-$] = hydroxide ion concentration (mol/L)

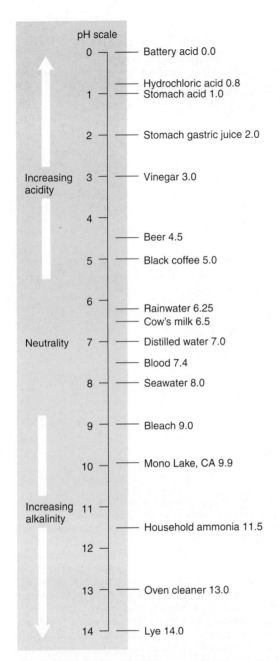

pH scale

0	Battery acid 0.0
1	Hydrochloric acid 0.8 / Stomach acid 1.0
2	Stomach gastric juice 2.0
3	Vinegar 3.0
4	
	Beer 4.5
5	Black coffee 5.0
6	Rainwater 6.25 / Cow's milk 6.5
7	Distilled water 7.0
	Blood 7.4
8	Seawater 8.0
9	Bleach 9.0
10	Mono Lake, CA 9.9
11	
	Household ammonia 11.5
12	
13	Oven cleaner 13.0
14	Lye 14.0

Increasing acidity

Neutrality

Increasing alkalinity

Figure 2–17 pH values of some common solutions. A neutral solution (pH 7) has equal concentrations of H^+ and OH^-. Acidic solutions, which have a higher concentration of H^+ than OH^-, have pH values lower than 7; pH values higher than 7 characterize basic solutions, which have an excess of OH^-.

"shifted to the right" by adding reactants or removing products. Conversely, it can be "shifted to the left" by adding products or removing reactants. Hydrogen ions are the important products to consider in this system.

The addition of excess hydrogen ions temporarily shifts the system to the left, as they combine with the bicarbonate ions to form carbonic acid. Eventually a new dynamic equilibrium is established; at this point the hydrogen ion concentration is similar

Figure 2–18 Acid rain damage. Oxides of sulfur emitted from fossil fuel power plants and other industries, and oxides of nitrogen from automobile exhaust, are converted in the moist atmosphere into acids that become dispersed over wide areas. Unlike unpolluted rain (average pH 5.6), the pH of acid rain has been measured at 4.2 and even lower. Plants, such as these trees photographed in the Black Forest of Germany, may be damaged when the resulting increase in soil acidity causes certain minerals, particularly calcium ions, to leach out of the soil. *(Hans Reinhard/Bruce Coleman)*

to the original concentration, and the product of the hydrogen ion and hydroxide ion concentrations is restored to the equilibrium value of 1×10^{-14}.

If hydroxide ions are added, they combine with the hydrogen ions to form water, effectively removing a product and thus shifting the system to the right. More carbonic acid then ionizes, replacing the hydrogen ions that were removed.

Organisms contain many weak acids and weak bases, thus maintaining an essential reserve of buffering capacity and avoiding pH extremes.

An acid and a base react to form a salt

When an acid and a base are mixed together in water, the H^+ of the acid unites with the OH^- of the base to form a molecule of water. The remainder of the acid (an anion) combines with the remainder of the base (a cation) to form a salt. For example, hydrochloric acid reacts with sodium hydroxide to form water and sodium chloride:

$$HCl + NaOH \rightarrow H_2O + NaCl$$

A **salt** is a compound in which the hydrogen ion of an acid is replaced by some other cation. Sodium chloride, NaCl, is a compound in which the hydrogen ion of HCl has been replaced by the cation Na^+.

When a salt, an acid, or a base is dissolved in water, its dissociated ions can conduct an electrical current; these substances are called **electrolytes.** Sugars, alcohols, and many other substances do not form ions when dissolved in water; they do not conduct an electrical current and are referred to as **nonelectrolytes.**

Cells and extracellular fluids (such as blood) of animals and plants contain a variety of dissolved salts that are the source of the many important mineral ions essential for fluid balance and acid-base balance. The concentrations and relative amounts of the various cations and anions are kept remarkably constant. Any marked change results in impaired cellular functions and may lead to death. Nitrate and ammonium ions from the soil are the important nitrogen sources for plants. In animals, nerve and muscle function, blood clotting, bone formation, and many other aspects of body function depend on ions. Sodium, potassium, calcium, and magnesium are the chief cations present; chloride, bicarbonate, phosphate, and sulfate are important anions (Table 2–3).

TABLE 2–3   Some Biologically Important Ions

Name	Formula	Charge
Sodium	Na^+	1+
Potassium	K^+	1+
Hydrogen	H^+	1+
Magnesium	Mg^{2+}	2+
Calcium	Ca^{2+}	2+
Iron	Fe^{2+} or Fe^{3+}	2+ [iron(II)] or 3+ [iron(III)]
Ammonium	NH_4^+	1+
Chloride	Cl^-	1−
Iodide	I^-	1−
Carbonate	CO_3^{2-}	2−
Bicarbonate	HCO_3^-	1−
Phosphate	PO_4^{3-}	3−
Acetate	CH_3COO^-	1−
Sulfate	SO_4^{2-}	2−
Hydroxide	OH^-	1−
Nitrate	NO_3^-	1−
Nitrite	NO_2^-	1−

SUMMARY WITH KEY TERMS

I. The chemical composition and metabolic processes of all organisms are very similar. The physical and chemical principles that govern nonliving things also govern organisms.

II. Organisms are made up of small, simple, **inorganic compounds** as well as large, complex, carbon-containing **organic compounds.**

III. An **element** is a substance that cannot be decomposed into simpler substances by normal chemical reactions. Four elements—carbon, hydrogen, oxygen, and nitrogen—make up 96% or more of an organism's mass.

IV. Each **atom** is composed of a **nucleus** containing **protons** and **neutrons.** In the space outside the nucleus, **electrons** move rapidly in **orbitals** that correspond to energy levels.
   A. An atom is identified by its number of protons **(atomic number).**
   B. Atoms of the same element with different numbers of neutrons (different **atomic masses**) are **isotopes.** Some isotopes are radioactive **(radioisotopes).**
   C. In an electrically neutral atom, the number of protons equals the number of electrons.
   D. The chemical properties of an atom are determined chiefly by the number and arrangement of its most energetic electrons, known as **valence electrons.**

V. Different atoms are joined by chemical bonds to form **compounds.** A **chemical formula** gives the types and relative numbers of atoms in a substance. A **simplest formula** gives the smallest whole number ratio of the component atoms.
   A. One **mole** (the atomic or molecular mass in grams) of any substance contains 6.02×10^{23} atoms, molecules, or ions. This number is known as **Avogadro's number.**
   B. **Covalent bonds** are strong, stable bonds formed when atoms share **valence electrons,** forming **molecules.** When covalent bonds are formed, the orbitals of the valence electrons may become rearranged in a process known as **orbital hybridization.** A **molecular**

formula gives the actual numbers of each type of atom in a molecule; a **structural formula** shows their arrangement.
   1. Covalent bonds are **nonpolar** if the electrons are shared equally between the two atoms.
   2. Covalent bonds are **polar** if one atom is more **electronegative** (has a greater affinity for electrons) than the other.
   C. An **ionic bond** is formed between a positively charged **cation** and a negatively charged **anion.** Ionic bonds are strong in the absence of water but relatively weak in aqueous solution.
   D. **Hydrogen bonds** are relatively weak bonds formed when a hydrogen atom with a partial positive charge is attracted to an atom (usually oxygen or nitrogen) with a partial negative charge already bonded to another molecule or in another part of the same molecule.

VI. **Oxidation** and **reduction (redox)** reactions are chemical processes in which electrons (and their energy) are transferred from a reducing agent to an oxidizing agent.

VII. Water accounts for a large part of the mass of most organisms. It is important in many chemical reactions within living things and has unique properties that also affect the environment.
   A. Water is a **polar molecule** because one end has a partial positive charge and the other has a partial negative charge.
   B. Because its molecules are polar, water is an excellent **solvent** for ionic or polar **solutes.**
   C. Water molecules are **cohesive** because they form hydrogen bonds with each other; they are also **adhesive** through hydrogen bonding to substances with ionic or polar regions.
   D. Water has a high **specific heat,** which helps organisms maintain a relatively constant internal temperature; this property also helps keep the ocean and other large bodies of water at a constant temperature.
   E. Water has a high **heat of vaporization.** Molecules entering the vapor phase carry a great deal of heat, which accounts for **evaporative cooling.**

F. The fact that ice is less dense than liquid water makes the aquatic environment less extreme than it would be if ice sank to the bottom.

G. Water has a slight tendency to **ionize,** that is, to dissociate to form hydrogen ions (protons, H^+) and hydroxide ions (OH^-).

VIII. **Acids** are proton (H^+) donors; **bases** are proton acceptors. Many bases dissociate in solution to yield hydroxide ions, which then accept protons.

A. The **pH scale** is a logarithmic expression of the hydrogen ion concentration of a solution. A **neutral solution** has a pH of 7; an **acidic** solution has a pH below 7; and a **basic solution** has a pH greater than 7.

B. A buffering system is based on a weak acid or a weak base. A **buffer** resists changes in the pH of a solution when acids or bases are added.

C. A **salt** is a compound in which the hydrogen atom of an acid is replaced by some other cation. Salts provide the many mineral ions essential for life functions.

POST·TEST

1. Which of the following elements is *mismatched* with its properties or function? (a) carbon—forms the backbone of organic compounds (b) nitrogen—component of proteins (c) hydrogen—very electronegative (d) oxygen—can participate in hydrogen bonding (e) all of the above are correctly matched

2. Which of the following applies to a neutron? (a) positive charge and located in an orbital (b) negligible mass and located in the nucleus (c) positive charge and located in the nucleus (d) uncharged and located in the nucleus (e) uncharged and located in an orbital

3. $^{32}_{15}P$, a radioactive form of phosphorus, has (a) an atomic number of 32 (b) an atomic mass of 15 (c) an atomic mass of 47 (d) 32 electrons (e) 17 neutrons

4. Which of the following facts allows you to determine that atom A and atom B are isotopes of the same element? (a) they each have six protons (b) they each have four neutrons (c) in each, the sum of their electrons and neutrons is 14 (d) they each have four valence electrons (e) they each have a mass number of 14

5. Sodium and potassium behave similarly in chemical reactions. This is because (a) they have the same number of neutrons (b) each has a single valence electron (c) they have the same atomic mass (d) they have the same number of electrons (e) they have the same number of protons

6. The orbitals comprising an atom's valence electron shell (a) are arranged as concentric spheres (b) contain the atom's least energetic electrons (c) may change shape when covalent bonds are formed (d) never contain more than one electron each (e) more than one of the above is correct

7. Which of the following bonds and properties are correctly matched? (a) ionic bonds—strong only if the participating ions are hydrated (b) hydrogen bonds—responsible for bonding oxygen and hydrogen to form a single water molecule (c) polar covalent bonds—can occur between two atoms of the same element (d) covalent bonds—may be single, double, or triple (e) hydrogen bonds—stronger than covalent bonds

8. In a redox reaction (a) energy is transferred from a reducing agent to an oxidizing agent (b) a reducing agent becomes oxidized as it accepts an electron (c) an oxidizing agent accepts a proton (d) a reducing agent donates a proton (e) the electrons in an atom move from its valence shell to a shell closer to its nucleus

9. A solution with a pH of 2 has a hydrogen ion concentration that is _____ the hydrogen ion concentration of a solution with a pH of 4. (a) 1/2 (b) 1/100 (c) two times (d) ten times (e) one hundred times

10. The high heat of vaporization of water accounts for (a) evaporative cooling (b) the fact that ice floats (c) the fact that heat is liberated when ice forms (d) the cohesive properties of water (e) capillary action

11. NaOH and HCl react to form Na^+, Cl^-, and water. Which of the following statements is true? (a) Na^+ is an anion, and Cl^- is a cation (b) Na^+ and Cl^- are both anions (c) a hydrogen bond can form between Na^+ and Cl^- (d) Na^+ and Cl^- are electrolytes (e) Na^+ is an acid, and Cl^- is a base

12. Which of the following statements is true? (a) the number of individual particles (atoms, ions, or molecules) contained in one mole varies depending on the substance (b) Avogadro's number is the number of particles contained in one mole of a substance (c) Avogadro's number is 10^{23} particles (d) one mole of ^{12}C has a mass of 12 g (e) both b and d are true

REVIEW QUESTIONS

1. What is the relationship between molecules and compounds? Are all compounds composed of molecules?

2. What are the ways an atom or molecule can become an anion or a cation?

3. What is a radioisotope? Why is it able to substitute for an ordinary (non-radioactive) atom of the same element in a molecule? What are some of the ways radioisotopes are used in biological research?

4. How do ionic and covalent bonds differ?

5. Why does water form hydrogen bonds? List some of the properties of water that result from hydrogen bonding. How do these properties contribute to the role of water as an essential component of organisms?

6. How can weak forces, such as hydrogen bonds, have significant effects in organisms?

7. A solution has a hydrogen ion concentration of 0.01 mol/L. What is its pH? What is its hydroxide ion concentration? How does this solution differ from one with a pH of 1?

8. Why are buffers important in organisms? Give a specific example of how a buffering system works.

9. Differentiate clearly among acids, bases, and salts.

10. Why must oxidation and reduction occur simultaneously? Why are redox reactions important in some energy transfers?

11. Describe a reversible reaction that is at chemical equilibrium. What would be the consequences of adding or removing a reactant or a product?

YOU MAKE THE CONNECTION

1. Element A has two electrons in its valence shell (which is complete when it contains eight electrons). Would you expect element A to share, donate, or accept electrons? What would you expect of element B, which has four valence electrons, and element C, which has seven?

2. A hydrogen bond formed between two water molecules is only about 1/20 as strong as a covalent bond between hydrogen and oxygen. In what ways would the physical properties of water be different if these hydrogen bonds were stronger (e.g., 1/10 the strength of covalent bonds)?

3. Consider the following reaction (in water).

$$HCl \rightarrow H^+ + Cl^-$$

Name the reactant(s) and product(s). Does the expression indicate that the reaction is reversible? Could HCl be used as a buffer?

RECOMMENDED READINGS

Atkins, P.W. *Periodic Kingdom*. Basic Books, Harper Collins, New York, 1995. In this imaginative work the periodic table is described as a landscape inhabited by elements whose properties are determined by the region in which they reside.

Ball, P. *Life's Matrix: A Biography of Water*. Farrar, Straus, & Giroux, New York, 2000. This comprehensive overview of the unique properties of water also provides insight into the process of science by examining some of the major scientific controversies of recent years.

Bettelheim, F.A., W.H. Brown, and J. March. *Introduction to General, Organic, and Biochemistry*, 6th ed. Harcourt College Publishers, Philadelphia, 2001. A very readable reference text for those who would like to know more about the chemistry basic to life.

Hedin, L.O., and G.E. Likens. "Atmosphere Dust and Acid Rain." *Scientific American*, Vol. 275, No. 6, Dec. 1996. This article examines the idea that recent reductions in basic compounds attached to dust particles in the atmosphere may be increasing the environmental damage done by acid rain.

Scerri, E.R. "The Periodic Table and the Electron." *American Scientist*, Vol. 85, No.5, 1997. This article argues that the chemical properties of atoms are only approximately explained by their electron configurations.

Suter, R.B. "Walking on Water." *American Scientist*, Vol. 87, Vol. 2, 1999. The author studies how fishing spiders use the properties of water to their advantage as they propel themselves over the surface.

Zimmer, C. "Wet, Wild and Weird." *Discover*, Dec. 1992. Computer simulations illustrate the many ways water molecules can interact through hydrogen bonding.

- Visit our Web site at **http://www.info.brookscole.com/solomonbergmartin** for links to chapter-related resources on the World Wide Web. Additional on-line materials relating to this chapter can also be found on our Web site.

See chapter activity on BioActive Learner CD for additional help in mastering the chapter's material. Icon location in the chapter's margins shows which topics have tutorials or simulations in the CD.

3

The Chemistry of Life: Organic Compounds

The Atlantic bay scallop, *Argopecten irradians,* like all other living things, contains many types of organic molecules. *(Paul A. Zahl/Photo Researchers, Inc.)*

LEARNING OBJECTIVES

After you have studied this chapter you should be able to

1. Distinguish between organic and inorganic compounds.
2. Describe the properties of carbon that make it the central component of organic compounds.
3. Distinguish among the three principal types of isomers.
4. Identify the major functional groups present in organic compounds and describe their properties.
5. Compare the functions and chemical compositions of the major groups of organic compounds: carbohydrates, lipids, proteins, and nucleic acids.
6. Distinguish among monosaccharides, disaccharides, and polysaccharides. Compare storage polysaccharides with structural polysaccharides.
7. Distinguish among fats, phospholipids, and steroids; describe the composition, characteristics, and biological functions of each.
8. Sketch the structure of an amino acid. Explain how amino acids are grouped into classes based on the characteristics of their side chains.
9. Distinguish among the levels of organization of protein molecules.
10. Describe the components of a nucleotide. Name some nucleic acids and discuss the importance of these compounds in living organisms.

Both inorganic and organic forms of carbon occur widely in nature. The scallop in the photograph contains **organic compounds,** in which carbon atoms are covalently bonded to each other to form the backbone of the molecule. Some very simple carbon compounds are considered inorganic if the carbon is not bonded to another carbon or to hydrogen. Inorganic carbon is represented by the scallop's shell, composed mainly of calcium carbonate. Organic compounds are so named because at one time it was thought that they could be produced only by living (organic) organisms. In 1928 the German chemist Friedrich Wühler synthesized urea, a metabolic waste product. Since that time, scientists have learned to synthesize many organic molecules and have discovered organic compounds not found in any organism.

Organic compounds are extraordinarily diverse; in fact, more than 5 million have been identified. There are many reasons for this diversity. **Hydrocarbons,** organic compounds consisting only of carbon and hydrogen, can be produced in a wide variety of three-dimensional shapes. Furthermore, the carbon atom can form bonds with a greater number of different elements than any other type of atom. The addition of chemical groups containing atoms of other elements, especially oxygen, nitrogen, phosphorus, and sulfur, can profoundly change the properties of an organic molecule.

Further diversity is provided by the fact that a great many organic compounds found in organisms are extremely large **macromolecules.** Cells construct these from simpler modular subunits. For example, protein molecules are built from smaller compounds called *amino acids.*

In this chapter we focus on some of the major groups of organic compounds important in organisms, including carbohydrates, lipids, proteins, and nucleic acids (DNA and RNA). Organic compounds are the main structural components of cells and tissues. They participate in and regulate metabolic reactions, transmit information, and provide energy for life processes. Evolution involves chemical changes in the organic compounds produced by organisms.

■ CARBON ATOMS FORM AN ENORMOUS VARIETY OF STRUCTURES

Carbon has unique properties that permit formation of the carbon backbones of the large, complex molecules essential to life (Fig. 3–1). Because a carbon atom has four valence electrons, it can complete its valence shell by forming a total of four covalent bonds (see Fig. 2–2). Each bond can link it to another carbon atom or to an atom of a different element. Carbon is particularly well suited to serve as the backbone of a large molecule because carbon-to-carbon bonds are strong and not easily broken. However, they are not so strong that it would be impossible for cells to break them. Carbon-to-carbon bonds are not limited to single bonds (based on sharing of one electron pair). Two carbon atoms can share two electron pairs with each other, forming double bonds:

$$>C=C<$$

In some compounds, triple carbon-to-carbon bonds are formed:

$$-C\equiv C-$$

As seen in Figure 3–1, carbon chains can be unbranched or branched, and carbon atoms can also be joined into rings. Rings and chains are joined in some compounds.

The molecules in the cell are analogous to the components of a machine. Each component has a shape that permits it to fill certain roles and to interact with other components (often with a

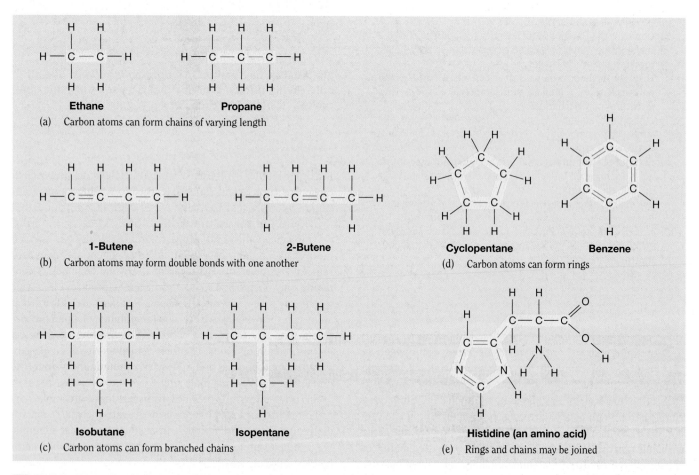

(a) Carbon atoms can form chains of varying length

Ethane   Propane

(b) Carbon atoms may form double bonds with one another

1-Butene   2-Butene

(c) Carbon atoms can form branched chains

Isobutane   Isopentane

(d) Carbon atoms can form rings

Cyclopentane   Benzene

(e) Rings and chains may be joined

Histidine (an amino acid)

■ **Figure 3–1 Organic molecules.** Note that each carbon atom forms four covalent bonds, producing a wide variety of shapes.

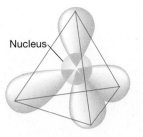

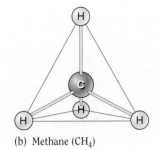

(a) Carbon (C)

(b) Methane (CH$_4$)

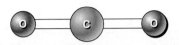

(c) Carbon dioxide (CO$_2$)

complementary shape). Similarly, the shape of a molecule is important in determining its biological properties and function. Carbon atoms are able to link to each other and to other atoms to produce a wide variety of three-dimensional molecular shapes. This is because the four covalent bonds of carbon do not form in a single plane. Instead, as discussed in Chapter 2, the valence electron orbitals become elongated and project from the carbon atom toward the corners of a tetrahedron (Fig. 3–2). The structure is highly symmetrical, with an angle of about 109.5 degrees between any two of these bonds. Keep in mind that, for simplicity, many of the figures in this book are drawn as two-dimensional graphic representations of three-dimensional molecules. Even the simplest hydrocarbon chains, such as those seen in Figure 3–1, are not actually straight but have a three-dimensional zigzag structure.

Generally, there is freedom of rotation around each carbon-to-carbon single bond. This property permits organic molecules to be flexible and to assume a variety of shapes, depending on the extent to which each single bond is rotated. Double and triple bonds do not permit rotation, so regions of a molecule with such bonds tend to be inflexible.

One reason for the great number of possible carbon-containing compounds is the fact that the same components usually can link together in more than one pattern, generating an even wider variety of molecular shapes.

■ ISOMERS HAVE THE SAME MOLECULAR FORMULA, BUT DIFFERENT STRUCTURES

Compounds with the same molecular formulas but different structures and thus different properties are called **isomers.** Isomers do not have identical physical or chemical properties and may have different common names. Cells can distinguish between isomers. Usually, one isomer is biologically active and the other is not. Three types of isomers are structural isomers, geometric isomers, and enantiomers.

Structural isomers are compounds that differ in the covalent arrangements of their atoms. For example, Figure 3–3a illustrates two structural isomers with the molecular formula C$_2$H$_6$O. Similarly, there are two structural isomers of the four-carbon hydrocarbon butane (C$_4$H$_{10}$), one with a straight chain and the other with a branched chain (isobutane). Large compounds have more possible structural isomers. There are only two structural isomers of butane, but there can be up to 366,319 isomers of C$_{20}$H$_{42}$.

Geometric isomers are compounds that are identical in the arrangement of their covalent bonds but different in the spatial arrangement of atoms or groups of atoms. Geometric isomers are present in some compounds with carbon-to-carbon double bonds. Because double bonds are not flexible like single bonds, atoms joined to the carbons of a double bond cannot rotate freely about the axis of the bonds. These *cis-trans* isomers may be drawn as shown in Figure 3–3b. The designation *cis* (Latin, "on this side") indicates that the two larger components are on the same side of the double bond. If they are on opposite sides of the double bond, the compound is designated a *trans* (Latin, "across") isomer.

Enantiomers are molecules that are mirror images of one another (Fig. 3–3c). Recall that the four groups bonded to a single carbon atom are arranged at the vertices of a tetrahedron. If the four bonded groups are all different, the central carbon is described as asymmetrical. Figure 3–3d illustrates that the four groups can be arranged about the asymmetrical carbon in two different ways that are mirror images of each other. The two molecules are enantiomers if they cannot be superimposed on one another no matter how they are rotated in space. Although enantiomers have similar chemical properties and most of their physical properties are identical, cells recognize the difference in shape, and usually only one form is found in organisms.

The existence of isomers is not the only source of variety among organic molecules. The addition of various combinations of atoms, known as *functional groups,* can generate a vast array of molecules with differing properties.

TABLE 3–1   Some Biologically Important Functional Groups

Functional Group	Structural Formula	Class of Compounds Characterized by Group	Description
Hydroxyl	R—OH	Alcohols Ethanol	Polar because electronegative oxygen attracts covalent electrons
Carbonyl	R—C(=O)—H	Aldehydes Formaldehyde	Carbonyl group carbon is bonded to at least one H atom; polar because electronegative oxygen attracts covalent electrons
	R—C(=O)—R	Ketones Acetone	Carbonyl group carbon is bonded to two other carbons; polar because electronegative oxygen attracts covalent electrons
Carboxyl	R—C(=O)—OH (Nonionized) R—C(=O)—O$^-$ + H$^+$ (Ionized)	Carboxylic acids (organic acids) Amino acid	Weakly acidic; can release an H$^+$ ion
Amino	R—N(H)(H) (Nonionized) R—N$^+$(H)(H)(H) (Ionized)	Amines Amino acid	Weakly basic; can accept an H$^+$ ion
Methyl	R—C(H)(H)—H	Component of many organic compounds Ethane	Hydrocarbon; nonpolar

TABLE 3–1 *Continued*

Functional Group	Structural Formula	Class of Compounds Characterized by Group	Description
Phosphate	$$O$$ $$\|\|$$ $$R-O-P-OH$$ $$\|$$ $$OH$$ Nonionized $$O$$ $$\|\|$$ $$*R-O-P-O^- + 2\,H^+$$ $$\|$$ $$O^-$$ Ionized	Organic phosphates $$O$$ $$\|\|$$ $$HO-P-O-R$$ $$\|$$ $$OH$$ Phosphate ester (as found in ATP)	Weakly acidic; one or two H^+ ions can be released
Sulfhydryl	$R-SH$	Thiols $$\begin{array}{ccc} H & H & O \\ \| & \| & \|\| \\ H-C & -C & -C-OH \\ \| & \| & \\ SH & NH_2 & \end{array}$$ Cysteine	Helps stabilize internal structure of proteins

■ FUNCTIONAL GROUPS CHANGE THE PROPERTIES OF ORGANIC MOLECULES

Because covalent bonds between hydrogen and carbon are nonpolar, hydrocarbons lack distinct charged regions. For this reason, hydrocarbons are insoluble in water and tend to cluster together, through **hydrophobic interactions.** "Water fearing," the literal meaning of the term *hydrophobic,* is somewhat misleading. Hydrocarbons can interact with water, but much more weakly than the water molecules cohere to each other through hydrogen bonding. Hydrocarbons do interact weakly with each other, but the main reason for hydrophobic interactions is that they are driven together in a sense, having been excluded by the hydrogen-bonded water molecules.

However, the characteristics of an organic molecule can be changed dramatically by replacing one of the hydrogens with a group of atoms known as a **functional group.** Functional groups help determine the types of chemical reactions in which the compound participates. Most functional groups readily form associations, such as ionic and hydrogen bonds, with other molecules. Polar and ionic functional groups are **hydrophilic** because they associate strongly with polar water molecules.

The properties of the major classes of biologically important organic compounds—carbohydrates, lipids, proteins, and nucleic acids—are largely a consequence of the types and arrangement of functional groups they contain. When we know what kinds of functional groups are present in an organic compound, we can predict its chemical behavior. As you read the rest of this section please refer to Table 3–1 for the complete structural formulas of these groups, as well as additional information. Note that the symbol R is used to represent the *remainder* of the molecule of which each functional group is a part.

The **hydroxyl group** (abbreviated R—OH) must not be confused with the hydroxide ion (OH$^-$) discussed in Chapter 2. The hydroxyl group is polar owing to the presence of a strongly electronegative oxygen atom. If a hydroxyl group replaces one of the hydrogens of a hydrocarbon, the resulting molecule can have significantly altered properties. For example, ethane (see Fig. 3–1a) is a hydrocarbon that is a gas at room temperature. If a hydrogen atom is replaced by a hydroxyl group, the resulting molecule is ethyl alcohol, or ethanol, which is found in alcoholic beverages (Fig. 3–3a). Ethanol is somewhat cohesive because the polar hydroxyl groups of adjacent molecules interact; it is therefore liquid at room temperature. Unlike ethane, ethyl alcohol can dissolve in water because the polar hydroxyl groups interact with the polar water molecules.

The **carbonyl group** consists of a carbon atom that has a double covalent bond with an oxygen atom. This double bond is polar because of the electronegativity of the oxygen; thus, the carbonyl group is hydrophilic. The position of the carbonyl

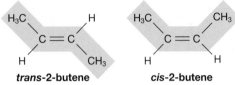

Ethanol (C₂H₆O)   Dimethyl ether (C₂H₆O)

(a)   Structural isomers

trans-2-butene   *cis*-2-butene

(b)   Geometric isomers

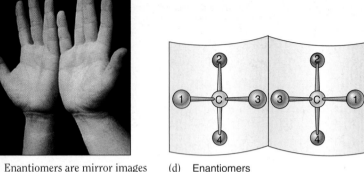

(c)   Enantiomers are mirror images

(d)   Enantiomers

■ **Figure 3–3   Isomers.** Isomers have the same molecular formula, but their atoms are arranged differently. **(a)** Structural isomers differ in the covalent arrangement of their atoms. **(b)** Geometric, or *cis-trans*, isomers have identical covalent bonds but differ in the order in which groups of atoms are arranged in space. **(c and d)** Enantiomers are isomers that are mirror images of one another. The central carbon is asymmetrical because it is bonded to four different groups. Because of their three-dimensional structure the two figures cannot be superimposed no matter how they are rotated. *(c, Dennis Drenner)*

group in the molecule determines the class to which the molecule belongs. An **aldehyde** has a carbonyl group positioned at the end of the carbon skeleton (abbreviated R—CHO); a **ketone** has an internal carbonyl group (abbreviated R—CO—R).

The **carboxyl group** (abbreviated R—COOH) consists of a carbon atom joined by a double covalent bond to an oxygen atom, and by a single covalent bond to another oxygen, which is in turn bonded to a hydrogen atom. Two electronegative oxygen atoms in such close proximity establish an extremely polarized condition, which can cause the hydrogen atom to be stripped of its electron and released as a hydrogen ion (H^+). The carboxyl group then has one unit of negative charge (R—COO⁻):

$$R-C{\overset{O}{\underset{O-H}{}}} \longrightarrow R-C{\overset{O}{\underset{O^-}{}}} + H^+$$

Carboxyl groups are weakly acidic; only a fraction of the molecules ionize in this way. This group can therefore exist in one of two hydrophilic states: ionic or polar. Carboxyl groups are essential constituents of amino acids.

An **amino group** (abbreviated R—NH₂) includes a nitrogen atom covalently bonded to two hydrogen atoms. Amino groups are weakly basic because they are able to accept a hydrogen ion (proton), thus acquiring a unit of positive charge. Amino groups are components of amino acids and of nucleic acids.

A **phosphate group** (abbreviated R—PO₄H₂) is weakly acidic. The attraction of electrons by the oxygen atoms can

result in the release of one or two hydrogen ions, producing ionized forms with one or two units of negative charge. Phosphates are constituents of nucleic acids and certain lipids.

The **sulfhydryl group** (abbreviated R—SH), consisting of an atom of sulfur covalently bonded to a hydrogen atom, is found in molecules called *thiols*. As we will see, amino acids that contain a sulfhydryl group can make important contributions to the structure of proteins.

The **methyl group** (abbreviated R—CH₃), a common hydrocarbon group, is nonpolar.

■ MANY BIOLOGICAL MOLECULES ARE POLYMERS

Many biological molecules such as proteins and nucleic acids are very large, consisting of thousands of atoms. Such giant molecules are known as **macromolecules.** Most macromolecules are **polymers,** produced by linking small organic compounds called **monomers** (Fig. 3–4). Just as all the words in this book have been written by arranging the 26 letters of the alphabet in various combinations, monomers can be grouped together to form an almost infinite variety of larger molecules. Just as we use different words to convey information, cells use different molecules to convey information. The thousands of different complex organic compounds present in organisms are constructed from about 40 small, simple monomers. For example, the 20 monomers called amino acids can be linked end-

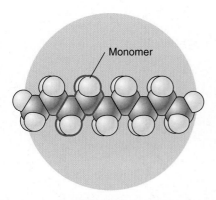

Figure 3–4 A simple polymer. This small polymer of polyethylene is formed by linking two-carbon ethylene (C_2H_4) monomers. One such monomer is outlined in red. The structure is represented by a space-filling model, which accurately depicts the actual three-dimensional shape of the molecule.

to-end in countless ways to form the polymers we know as proteins.

Polymers can be degraded to their component monomers by **hydrolysis** (which means "to break with water"). In a reaction regulated by a specific enzyme,[1] a hydrogen from a water molecule attaches to one monomer, and a hydroxyl from water attaches to the adjacent monomer (Fig. 3–5).

The synthetic process by which monomers are covalently linked is called **condensation.** Because the *equivalent* of a molecule of water is removed during the reactions that combine monomers, the term *dehydration synthesis* is sometimes used to describe the process (see Fig. 3–5). However, in biological systems the synthesis of a polymer is not simply the reverse of hydrolysis, even though the net effect is the opposite of hydrolysis. Synthetic processes such as condensation require energy and are regulated by different enzymes.

In the following sections we examine carbohydrates, lipids, proteins, and nucleic acids. Our discussion begins with the

---

[1] An enzyme is a biological catalyst that accelerates a specific chemical reaction (see Chapter 6). Most enzymes are proteins.

smaller, simpler forms of these compounds and extends to the linking of these monomers to form macromolecules.

◼ CARBOHYDRATES ARE USED FOR FUEL AND STRUCTURAL MATERIALS

Sugars, starches, and cellulose are **carbohydrates.** Sugars and starches serve as energy sources for cells; cellulose is the main structural component of the walls that surround plant cells. Carbohydrates contain carbon, hydrogen, and oxygen atoms in a ratio of approximately one carbon to two hydrogens to one oxygen $(CH_2O)_n$. The term *carbohydrate,* meaning "hydrate (water) of carbon," reflects the 2:1 ratio of hydrogen to oxygen, the same ratio found in water (H_2O). Carbohydrates contain one sugar unit *(monosaccharides),* two sugar units *(disaccharides),* or many sugar units *(polysaccharides).*

Monosaccharides are simple sugars

Monosaccharides typically contain from three to seven carbon atoms. In a monosaccharide, a hydroxyl group is bonded to each carbon except one; that carbon is double-bonded to an oxygen atom, forming a carbonyl group. If the carbonyl group is at the end of the chain, the monosaccharide is an aldehyde; if the carbonyl group is at any other position, the monosaccharide is a ketone. (By convention, the numbering of the carbon skeleton of a sugar begins with the carbon at or nearest the carbonyl end of the open chain.) The large number of polar hydroxyl groups, plus the carbonyl group, gives a monosaccharide hydrophilic properties.

Figure 3–6 shows simplified, two-dimensional representations of some common monosaccharides. The simplest carbohydrates are the three-carbon sugars (trioses): glyceraldehyde and dihydroxyacetone. Ribose and deoxyribose are common pentoses, sugars that contain five carbons; they are components of nucleic acids (DNA, RNA, and related compounds). Glucose, fructose, galactose, and other six-carbon sugars are called **hexoses.** (Note that the names of carbohydrates typically end in *-ose.*)

Glucose ($C_6H_{12}O_6$), the most abundant monosaccharide, is used as an energy source in most organisms. During cellular respiration (see Chapter 7), cells oxidize glucose molecules, converting the stored energy to a form that can be readily used

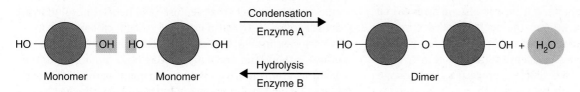

Figure 3–5 Condensation and hydrolysis reactions. Joining two monomers gives a dimer; incorporation of additional monomers produces a polymer. Note that these reactions are catalyzed by different enzymes.

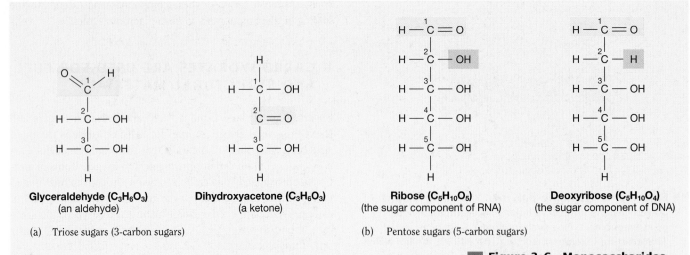

Figure 3–6 Monosaccharides.
Shown are two-dimensional chain structures of **(a)** three-carbon trioses, **(b)** five-carbon pentoses, and **(c)** six-carbon hexoses. Although it is convenient to show monosaccharides in this form, the pentoses and hexoses are more accurately depicted as ring structures, as in Figure 3–7. The carbonyl group *(blue screen)* is terminal in aldehyde sugars and located in an internal position in ketones. Deoxyribose differs from ribose because it has one less oxygen; a hydrogen instead of a hydroxyl group is attached to carbon 2 *(green screen)*. Glucose and galactose are mirror images that differ in the arrangement of the hydroxyl group and hydrogen attached to carbon 4 *(green screen)*.

(a) Triose sugars (3-carbon sugars)

Glyceraldehyde ($C_3H_6O_3$)
(an aldehyde)

Dihydroxyacetone ($C_3H_6O_3$)
(a ketone)

(b) Pentose sugars (5-carbon sugars)

Ribose ($C_5H_{10}O_5$)
(the sugar component of RNA)

Deoxyribose ($C_5H_{10}O_4$)
(the sugar component of DNA)

(c) Hexose sugars (6-carbon sugars)

Glucose ($C_6H_{12}O_6$)
(an aldehyde)

Fructose ($C_6H_{12}O_6$)
(a ketone)

Galactose ($C_6H_{12}O_6$)
(an aldehyde)

for cellular work. Glucose is also used as a component in the synthesis of other types of compounds such as amino acids and fatty acids. So important is glucose in metabolism that its concentration is carefully kept at a homeostatic (relatively constant) level in the blood of humans and other complex animals (see Chapter 47).

Glucose and fructose are structural isomers: They have identical molecular formulas, but their atoms are arranged differently. In fructose (a ketone) the double-bonded oxygen is linked to a carbon within the chain rather than to a terminal carbon as in glucose (which is an aldehyde). Because of these differences, the two sugars have different properties. For example, fructose tastes sweeter than glucose.

Glucose and galactose are both hexoses and aldehydes. However, they are mirror images (enantiomers) because they differ in the arrangement of the atoms attached to asymmetrical carbon atom 4.

The "stick" formulas in Figure 3–6 give a clear but somewhat unrealistic picture of the structures of some common monosaccharides. As has been discussed, molecules are not two-dimensional; in fact, the properties of each compound depend largely on its three-dimensional structure. Thus, three-dimensional formulas are helpful in understanding the relationship between molecular structure and biological function. Molecules of glucose and other pentoses and hexoses in solution are actually rings, rather than extended straight carbon chains.

Glucose in solution (as in the cell) typically exists as a ring of five carbons and one oxygen. It assumes this configuration when its atoms undergo a rearrangement, permitting a covalent bond to connect carbon 1 to the oxygen attached to carbon 5 (Fig. 3–7). When glucose forms a ring, two isomeric forms are possible, differing only in the orientation of the hydroxyl (—OH) group attached to carbon 1. When this hydroxyl group is on the same side of the plane of the ring as the

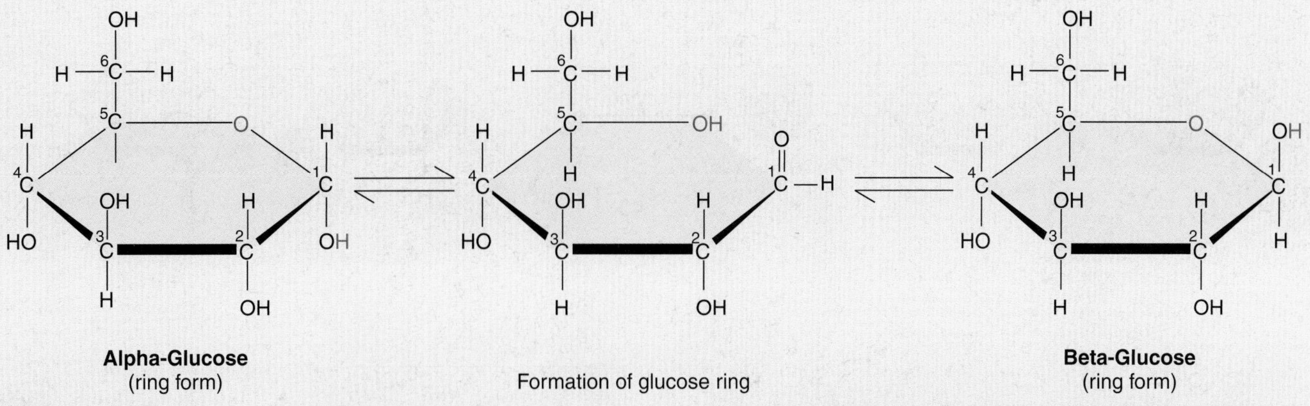

Alpha-Glucose
(ring form)

Formation of glucose ring

Beta-Glucose
(ring form)

(a) Forms of glucose

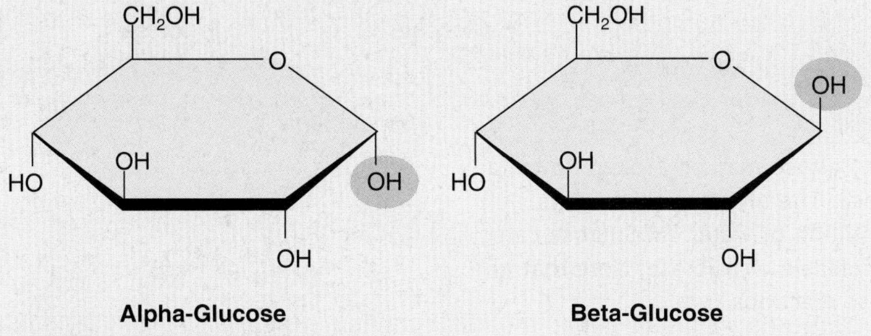

Alpha-Glucose

Beta-Glucose

(b) Simplified ring structure

Figure 3–7 α and β forms of glucose.
(a) When dissolved in water, glucose undergoes a rearrangement of its atoms, forming one of two possible ring structures: α-glucose or β-glucose. Although the drawing does not attempt to show the complete three-dimensional structure, the thick, tapered bonds in the lower portion of each ring represent the part of the molecule that would project out of the page toward you. **(b)** The essential differences between α-glucose and β-glucose are more readily apparent in these simplified structures. By convention, a carbon atom is assumed to be present at each angle in the ring unless another atom is shown. Most hydrogen atoms have been omitted.

—CH_2OH side group, the glucose is designated beta (β)-glucose. When it is on the side (with respect to the plane of the ring) opposite the —CH_2OH side group, the compound is designated alpha (α)-glucose.

Disaccharides consist of two monosaccharide units

A disaccharide (two sugars) contains two monosaccharide rings joined by a **glycosidic linkage,** consisting of a central oxygen covalently bonded to two carbons, one in each ring (Fig. 3–8). The glycosidic linkage of a disaccharide generally forms between carbon 1 of one molecule and carbon 4 of the other molecule. The disaccharide maltose (malt sugar) consists of two covalently linked α-glucose units. Sucrose, common table sugar, consists of a glucose unit combined with a fructose unit. Lactose (the sugar present in milk) is composed of one molecule of glucose and one of galactose.

As shown in Figure 3–8, a disaccharide can be hydrolyzed, that is, split by the addition of water, into two monosaccharide units. During digestion, maltose is hydrolyzed to form two molecules of glucose:

Maltose + Water → Glucose + Glucose

Similarly, sucrose is hydrolyzed to form glucose and fructose:

Sucrose + Water → Glucose + Fructose

Polysaccharides can store energy or provide structure

The most abundant carbohydrates are the **polysaccharides,** a group that includes starches, glycogen, and cellulose. A polysaccharide is a macromolecule consisting of repeating units of simple sugars, usually glucose. Although the precise number of sugar units varies, thousands of units are typically present in a single molecule. The polysaccharide may be a single long chain or a branched chain. Because they are composed of different isomers and because the units may be arranged differently, polysaccharides vary in their properties. Those that can be easily broken down to their subunits are well suited for energy storage, whereas the macromolecular three-dimensional architecture of others makes them particularly well suited to form stable structures.

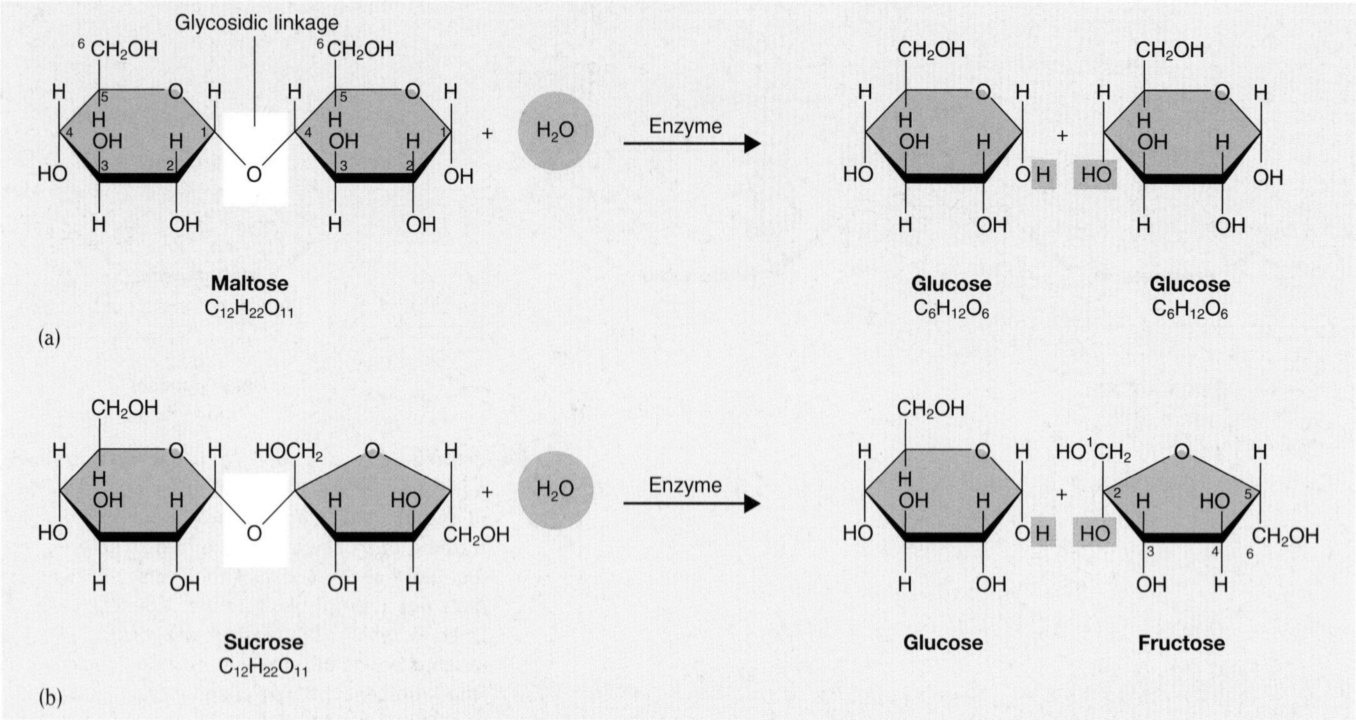

Figure 3–8 Hydrolysis of disaccharides. (a) Maltose may be broken down (as it is during digestion) to form two molecules of glucose. The glycosidic linkage is broken in a hydrolysis reaction, which requires the addition of water. (b) Sucrose can be hydrolyzed to yield a molecule of glucose and a molecule of fructose. Note that an enzyme (a protein catalyst) is needed to promote these reactions.

Starch is the main storage carbohydrate of plants

Starch, the typical form of carbohydrate used for energy storage in plants, is a polymer consisting of α-glucose subunits. These monomers are joined by α 1—4 linkages, which means that carbon 1 of one glucose is linked to carbon 4 of the next glucose in the chain (Fig. 3–9). Starch occurs in two forms: amylose and amylopectin. Amylose, the simpler form, is unbranched. Amylopectin, the more common form, usually consists of about 1000 glucose units in a branched chain.

Plant cells store starch mainly as granules within specialized organelles called **amyloplasts** (Fig. 3–9a). When energy is needed for cellular work, the plant can hydrolyze the starch, releasing the glucose subunits. Humans and other animals that eat plant foods have enzymes to hydrolyze starch.

Glycogen is the main storage carbohydrate of animals

Glycogen (sometimes referred to as *animal starch*) is the form in which glucose is stored as an energy source in animal tissues. It is similar in structure to plant starch but more extensively branched and more water-soluble. Glycogen is stored mainly in liver and muscle cells.

Cellulose is a structural carbohydrate

Carbohydrates are the most abundant group of organic compounds on Earth, and **cellulose** is the most abundant carbohydrate; it accounts for 50% or more of all the carbon in plants (Fig. 3–10). Cellulose is a structural carbohydrate. Wood is about half cellulose, and cotton is at least 90% cellulose. Plant cells are surrounded by strong supporting cell walls consisting mainly of cellulose.

Cellulose is an insoluble polysaccharide composed of many glucose molecules joined together. The bonds joining these sugar units are different from those in starch. Recall that starch is composed of α-glucose subunits, joined by α 1—4 glycosidic linkages. Cellulose contains β-glucose monomers joined by β 1—4 linkages. These bonds cannot be split by the enzymes that hydrolyze the α linkages in starch. Humans, like most organisms, do not have enzymes that can digest cellulose and therefore cannot use it as a nutrient. Because cellulose remains fibrous, it helps keep the digestive tract functioning properly.

Some microorganisms can digest cellulose to glucose. In fact, cellulose-digesting bacteria live in the digestive systems of cows and sheep, enabling these grass-eating animals to obtain nourishment from cellulose. Similarly, the digestive systems of termites contain microorganisms that digest cellulose (see Fig. 24–5a).

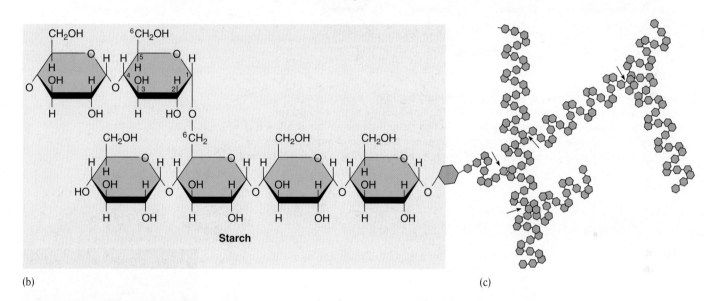

Figure 3–9 Starch, a storage polysaccharide. (a) Starch *(stained purple)* is stored in specialized organelles, called amyloplasts, in these cells of a buttercup root. (b) Starch is composed of α-glucose molecules joined by glycosidic bonds. At the branch points are bonds between carbon 6 of the glucose in the straight chain and carbon 1 of the glucose in the branching chain. (c) Starch is made up of highly branched chains; the arrows indicate the branch points. Each chain is actually in the form of a coil or helix, stabilized by hydrogen bonds between the hydroxyl groups of the glucose subunits. *(a, Ed Reschke)*

Amyloplasts

(a)

100 μm

Starch

(b)

(c)

Cellulose molecules have characteristics that make them well suited for a structural role. The β-glucose subunits are joined in a way that allows extensive hydrogen bonding among different cellulose molecules. Thus, cellulose molecules aggregate in long bundles of fibers, as shown in Figure 3–10a.

Some modified and complex carbohydrates have special roles

Many derivatives of monosaccharides are important biological molecules. Some form important structural components. The amino sugars galactosamine and glucosamine are compounds in which a hydroxyl group (—OH) is replaced by an amino group (—NH₂). Galactosamine is present in cartilage, a constituent of

the skeletal system of vertebrates. *N*-acetyl glucosamine (NAG) subunits, joined by glycosidic bonds, compose **chitin,** a main component of the external skeletons of insects, crayfish, and other arthropods (Fig. 3–11), and of the cell walls of fungi. Chitin forms very tough structures because, as in cellulose, its molecules interact through multiple hydrogen bonds. Some chitinous structures, such as the shell of a lobster, are further hardened by the addition of calcium carbonate.

Carbohydrates may also be combined with proteins to form **glycoproteins,** compounds present on the outer surface of cells other than bacteria. Some of these carbohydrate chains allow cells to adhere to one another, while others provide protection. Most proteins secreted by cells are glycoproteins. These include the major components of mucus, a complex protective material secreted by the mucous membranes of the respiratory and

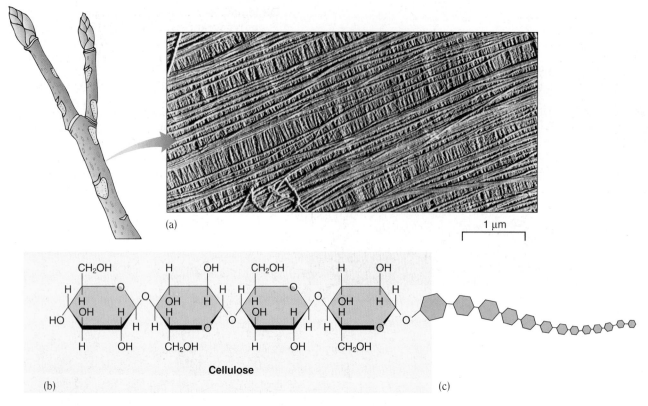

Figure 3–10   Cellulose, a structural polysaccharide. (a) An electron micrograph of cellulose fibers from a cell wall. The fibers visible in the photograph consist of bundles of cellulose molecules, interacting through hydrogen bonds. (b and c) The cellulose molecule is an unbranched polysaccharide composed of approximately 10,000 β-glucose units joined by glycosidic bonds. *(a, Omikron/Photo Researchers, Inc.)*

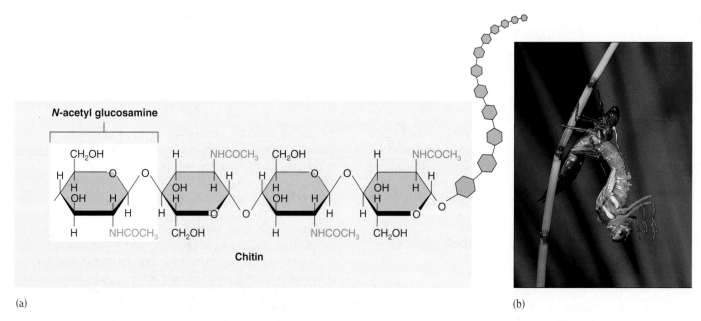

Figure 3–11   Chitin, a structural polysaccharide. (a) Chitin is a polymer composed of *N*-acetyl glucosamine (NAG) subunits. (b) Chitin is an important component of the exoskeleton (outer covering) that this dragonfly is shedding. *(b, Dwight R. Kuhn)*

digestive systems. Carbohydrates can combine with lipids to form **glycolipids,** compounds present on the surfaces of animal cells that are thought to allow cells to recognize and interact with one another.

■ LIPIDS ARE FATS OR FATLIKE SUBSTANCES

Lipids are a heterogeneous group of compounds that are defined, not by their structure, but rather by the fact that they are soluble in nonpolar solvents (such as ether and chloroform) and are relatively insoluble in water. Lipid molecules have these properties because they consist mainly of carbon and hydrogen, with few oxygen-containing functional groups. Hydrophilic functional groups typically contain oxygen atoms; therefore lipids, with little oxygen, tend to be hydrophobic. Among the biologically important groups of lipids are fats, phospholipids, carotenoids (orange and yellow plant pigments), steroids, and waxes. Some lipids are used for energy storage; others serve as structural components of cellular membranes; and some are important hormones.

Triacylglycerol is formed from glycerol and three fatty acids

The most abundant lipids in living organisms are **triacylglycerols,** also known as *triglycerides.* These compounds, commonly known as fats, are an economical form of reserve fuel storage because, when metabolized, they yield more than twice as much energy per gram as do carbohydrates. Carbohydrates and proteins can be transformed by enzymes into fats and stored within the cells of adipose (fat) tissue of animals and in some seeds and fruits of plants.

A **triacylglycerol** molecule consists of glycerol joined to three fatty acids (Fig. 3–12). **Glycerol** is a three-carbon alcohol that contains three hydroxyl (—OH) groups, and a **fatty acid** is a long, unbranched hydrocarbon chain with a carboxyl group (—COOH) at one end. A triacylglycerol molecule is formed by a series of three condensation reactions. In each reaction the equivalent of a water molecule is removed as one of the glycerol's hydroxyl groups reacts with the carboxyl group of a fatty acid, resulting in the formation of a covalent linkage known as an **ester linkage** (Fig. 3–12b). The first reaction yields a **monoacylglycerol** *(monoglyceride),* the second a **diacylglycerol** *(diglyceride),* and the third a triacylglycerol. During digestion triacylglycerols are hydrolyzed to produce fatty acids and glycerol (see Chapter 45). Diacylglycerol is an important molecule used for sending signals within the cell (see Chapter 47).

Saturated and unsaturated fatty acids differ in physical properties

About 30 different fatty acids are commonly found in lipids, and they typically have an even number of carbon atoms. For example, butyric acid, present in rancid butter, has four carbon atoms. Oleic acid, with 18 carbons, is the most widely distributed fatty acid in nature and is found in most animal and plant fats.

Saturated fatty acids contain the maximum possible number of hydrogen atoms. Palmitic acid, a 16-carbon fatty acid, is a common saturated fatty acid (Fig. 3–12c). Fats high in saturated fatty acids, such as animal fat and solid vegetable shortening, tend to be solid at room temperature. This is because even electrically neutral, nonpolar molecules can develop transient regions of weak positive charge and weak negative charge. This occurs as the constant motion of their electrons causes some regions to have a temporary excess of electrons, whereas others have a temporary electron deficit. These slight opposite charges result in attractions, known as **van der Waals forces,** between adjacent molecules. Although van der Waals interactions are individually weak, they can be strong when many occur among long hydrocarbon chains.

Unsaturated fatty acids include one or more adjacent pairs of carbon atoms joined by a double bond. Therefore they are not fully saturated with hydrogen. Fatty acids with one double bond are called **monounsaturated fatty acids,** whereas those with more than one double bond are **polyunsaturated fatty acids.** Oleic acid is a monounsaturated fatty acid, and linoleic acid is a common polyunsaturated fatty acid (Fig. 3–12d and e). Fats containing a high proportion of monounsaturated or polyunsaturated fatty acids tend to be liquid at room temperature. This is because each double bond produces a bend in the hydrocarbon chain that prevents it from aligning closely with an adjacent chain, thereby limiting van der Waals interactions.

At least two unsaturated fatty acids (linoleic acid and arachidonic acid) are essential nutrients that must be obtained from food because the human body cannot synthesize them. However, the amounts required are small, and deficiencies are rarely seen. There is no dietary requirement for saturated fatty acids.

Phospholipids are components of cellular membranes

Phospholipids belong to a group of lipids, called **amphipathic lipids,** in which one end of each molecule is hydrophilic and the other end is hydrophobic. The two ends of a phospholipid differ both physically and chemically. A phospholipid consists of a glycerol molecule attached at one end to two fatty acids, and at the other end to a phosphate group linked to an organic compound such as choline. The organic compound usually contains nitrogen (Fig. 3–13a). (Note that phosphorus and nitrogen are absent in triacylglycerols.) The fatty acid portion of the molecule (containing the two hydrocarbon "tails") is hydrophobic and not soluble in water. However, the portion composed of glycerol, phosphate, and the organic base (the "head" of the molecule) is ionized and readily water-soluble. The amphipathic properties of these lipid molecules cause them to form lipid bilayers in aqueous (watery) solution, making them uniquely suited to function as the fundamental components of cell membranes, structures that are discussed in Chapters 4 and 5 (Fig. 3–13b).

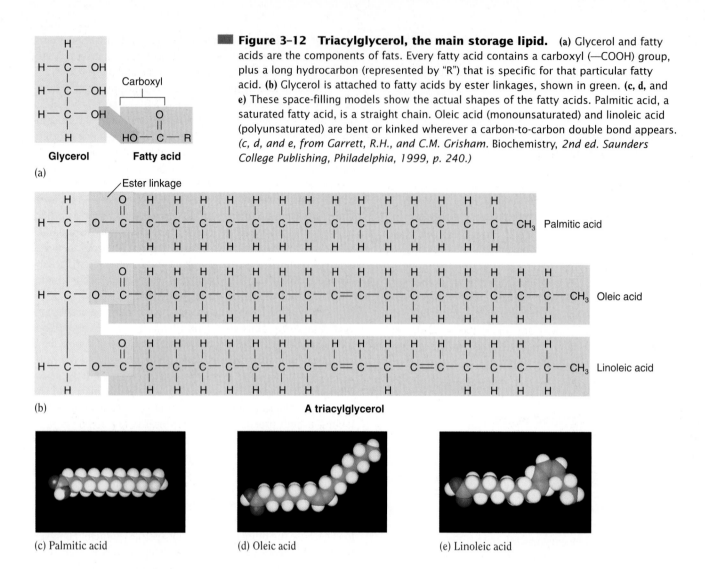

Figure 3–12 Triacylglycerol, the main storage lipid. (a) Glycerol and fatty acids are the components of fats. Every fatty acid contains a carboxyl (—COOH) group, plus a long hydrocarbon (represented by "R") that is specific for that particular fatty acid. (b) Glycerol is attached to fatty acids by ester linkages, shown in green. (c, d, and e) These space-filling models show the actual shapes of the fatty acids. Palmitic acid, a saturated fatty acid, is a straight chain. Oleic acid (monounsaturated) and linoleic acid (polyunsaturated) are bent or kinked wherever a carbon-to-carbon double bond appears. (c, d, and e, from Garrett, R.H., and C.M. Grisham. Biochemistry, 2nd ed. Saunders College Publishing, Philadelphia, 1999, p. 240.)

(a)

(b)

A triacylglycerol

(c) Palmitic acid

(d) Oleic acid

(e) Linoleic acid

Carotenoids and many other pigments are derived from isoprene units

The orange and yellow plant pigments called **carotenoids** are classified with the lipids because they are insoluble in water and have an oily consistency. These pigments, found in the cells of all plants, play a role in photosynthesis. Carotenoid molecules, such as β-carotene, and many other important pigments, consist of five-carbon hydrocarbon monomers known as **isoprene units** (Fig. 3–14).

Most animals can convert carotenoids to vitamin A, which can then be converted to the visual pigment **retinal.** Eyes are found in three different lines of animals—the mollusks, insects, and vertebrates—and all three groups have the same compound involved in the process of light reception, retinal, a molecule that is apparently uniquely fitted for this role.

Notice that carotenoids, vitamin A, and retinal all have a pattern of double bonds alternating with single bonds. The electrons that make up these bonds can move about relatively easily when light strikes the molecule. Such molecules are pigments that

tend to be highly colored because these mobile electrons cause them to strongly absorb light of certain wavelengths and reflect other wavelengths.

Steroids contain four rings of carbon atoms

A **steroid** consists of carbon atoms arranged in four attached rings; three of the rings contain six carbon atoms, and the fourth contains five (Fig. 3–15). The length and structure of the side chains that extend from these rings distinguish one steroid from another. Like carotenoids, steroids are synthesized from isoprene units.

Among the steroids of biological importance are cholesterol, bile salts, reproductive hormones, and cortisol and other hormones secreted by the adrenal cortex. Cholesterol is an essential structural component of animal cell membranes, but when there is excess cholesterol in the blood it forms plaques on artery walls, leading to an increased risk of heart attack (see Chapter 42). Plant cell membranes contain molecules similar to

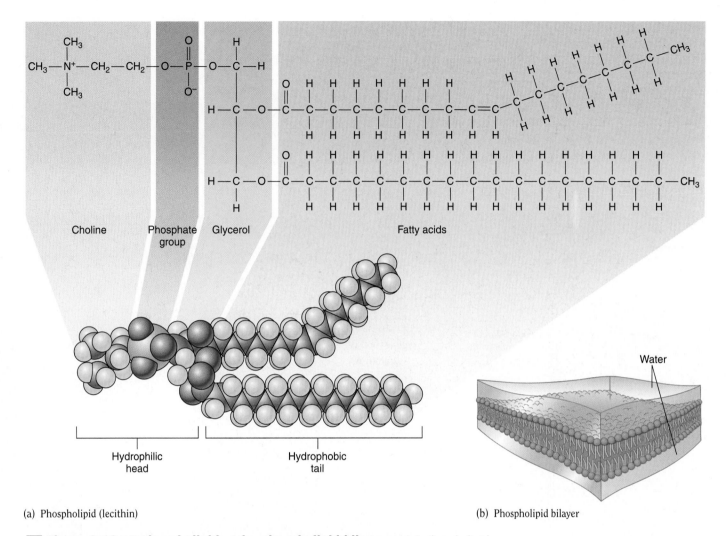

Choline   Phosphate group   Glycerol   Fatty acids

Hydrophilic head   Hydrophobic tail

Water

(a) Phospholipid (lecithin)   (b) Phospholipid bilayer

■ Figure 3–13 A phospholipid and a phospholipid bilayer. (a) A phospholipid consists of a hydrophobic tail, made up of two fatty acids, and a hydrophilic head, which includes a glycerol bonded to a phosphate group, which is in turn bonded to an organic group that can vary. Choline is the organic group in lecithin (or phosphatidylcholine), the molecule shown. The upper fatty acid in the figure is monounsaturated; it contains one double bond that produces a characteristic bend in the chain. (b) Phospholipids form lipid bilayers in which the hydrophilic heads interact with water and the hydrophobic tails are in the bilayer interior.

cholesterol. Interestingly, certain of these plant steroids are able to block the absorption of cholesterol by the intestine. Bile salts emulsify fats in the intestine so that they can be enzymatically hydrolyzed. Steroid hormones regulate certain aspects of metabolism in a variety of animals, including vertebrates, insects, and crabs.

Some chemical mediators are lipids

Animal cells secrete chemicals that permit them to communicate with each other or to regulate their own activities. Some chemical mediators are produced by the modification of fatty acids that have been removed from membrane phospholipids.

These include prostaglandins, which have varied roles, including promoting inflammation and smooth muscle contraction. Certain hormones, such as the juvenile hormone of insects, are also fatty acid derivatives (see Chapter 47).

■ PROTEINS ARE THE MOST VERSATILE CELLULAR COMPONENTS

In June 2000 two groups of scientists, one a government-supported international consortium known as the Human Genome Project, and the other a private company, made a landmark announcement that created great excitement, not only in

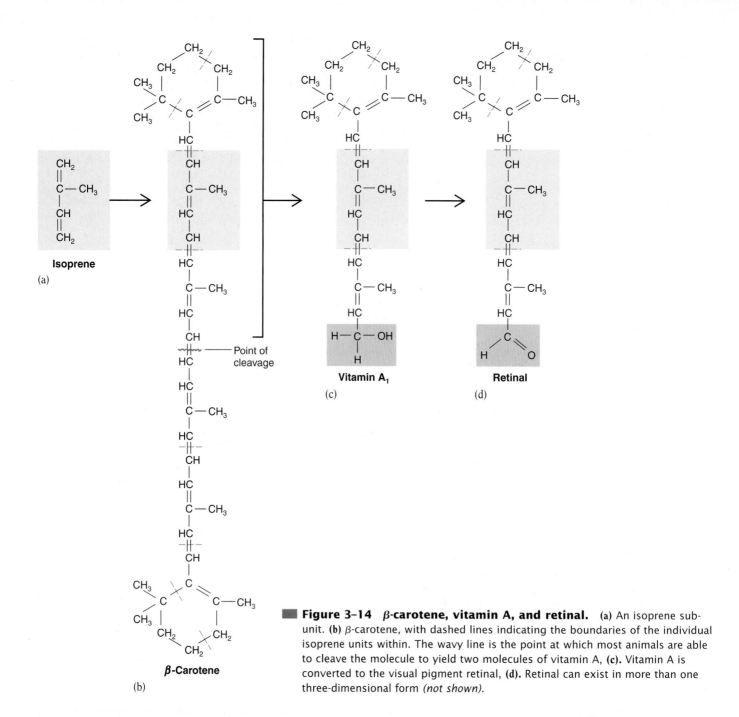

Figure 3–14 β-carotene, vitamin A, and retinal. (a) An isoprene subunit. **(b)** β-carotene, with dashed lines indicating the boundaries of the individual isoprene units within. The wavy line is the point at which most animals are able to cleave the molecule to yield two molecules of vitamin A, **(c).** Vitamin A is converted to the visual pigment retinal, **(d).** Retinal can exist in more than one three-dimensional form *(not shown).*

the scientific community but also among the public. In an immense undertaking they had succeeded in sequencing virtually all the genetic information in a human cell. (See Chapter 15 for additional discussion of the Human Genome Project.)

Some might think that sequencing human genes is the end of the story, but it is actually only the beginning. Most genetic information is used to specify the structure of **proteins,** and it has been predicted that most of the 21st century will be devoted to understanding the functioning of these extraordinarily versatile macromolecules that are of central importance in the chemistry of life. In a real sense, proteins are involved in virtually all aspects of metabolism because most **enzymes** (molecules that regulate the thousands of different chemical reactions that take place in an organism) are proteins. Proteins can be assembled into a variety of shapes, allowing them to serve as major structural components of cells and tissues. For this reason, growth and repair, as well as maintenance of the organism, depend on these compounds. As shown in Table 3–2, proteins serve in a great many other specialized capacities.

The protein constituents of a cell are the clues to its lifestyle. Each cell type contains characteristic forms, distributions, and amounts of protein that largely determine what the cell looks like and how it functions (see Fig. 16–2). A muscle cell contains large amounts of the proteins myosin and actin, which are responsible for its appearance as well as for its ability to contract. The protein hemoglobin, found in red blood

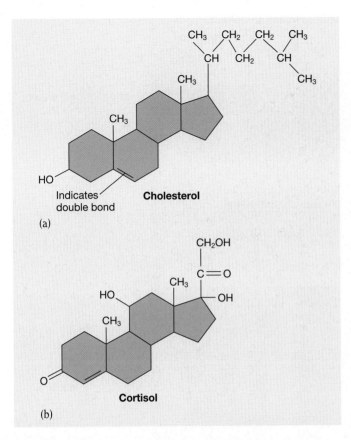

Figure 3–15 Steroids. Four attached rings—three six-carbon rings and one with five carbons—make up the fundamental structure of a steroid *(shown in green)*. Note that some carbons are shared by two rings. In these simplified structures, a carbon atom is present at each angle of a ring; the hydrogen atoms attached directly to the ring have not been drawn. **(a)** Cholesterol is an essential component of animal cellular membranes. **(b)** Cortisol is a steroid hormone secreted by the adrenal glands. Notice that cortisol differs from cholesterol in its attached functional groups.

cells, is responsible for the specialized function of oxygen transport.

Amino acids are the subunits of proteins

Amino acids, the constituents of proteins, have an amino group (—NH_2) and a carboxyl group (—COOH) bonded to the same asymmetrical carbon atom, known as the **alpha carbon.** There are about 20 amino acids commonly found in proteins, each uniquely identified by the variable side chain (R group) bonded to the α carbon (Fig. 3–16). Glycine, the simplest amino acid, has a hydrogen atom as its R group; alanine has a methyl (—CH_3) group.

Amino acids in solution at neutral pH are mainly dipolar ions. This is generally how amino acids exist at cellular pH. Each carboxyl group (—COOH) donates a proton and becomes dissociated (—COO^-), whereas each amino group (—NH_2) accepts a proton and becomes —NH_3^+ (Fig. 3–17). Because of the ability of their amino and carboxyl groups to accept and release protons, amino acids in solution resist changes in acidity and alkalinity and so are important biological buffers.

The amino acids are grouped in Figure 3–16 by the properties of their side chains. These broad groupings actually include amino acids with a fairly wide range of properties. Amino acids classified as having *nonpolar* side chains tend to have hydrophobic properties, whereas those classified as *polar* are more hydrophilic. An acidic amino acid has a side chain that contains a carboxyl group. At cellular pH the carboxyl group is dissociated, giving the R group a negative charge. A basic amino acid becomes positively charged when the amino group in its side chain accepts a hydrogen ion. Acidic and basic side chains are ionic at cellular pH and therefore hydrophilic.

In addition to the 20 common amino acids, some proteins have unusual ones. These rare amino acids are produced by the modification of common ones after they have become part of a protein. For example, lysine and proline may be converted to hydroxylysine and hydroxyproline after they have been incorporated into collagen. These amino acids can form cross links between the peptide chains that make up collagen. Such cross links are responsible for the firmness and great strength of the collagen molecule, which is a major component of cartilage, bone, and other connective tissues.

TABLE 3–2 Some of the Major Classes of Proteins and Their Functions

Protein Types	Some Functions and Examples
Enzymes	Each is responsible for catalyzing a specific chemical reaction
Structural proteins	Strengthen and protect cells and tissues (e.g., collagen strengthens animal tissues)
Storage proteins	Store nutrients; particularly abundant in eggs (e.g., ovalbumin in egg white) and seeds (e.g., zein in corn kernels)
Transport proteins	Transport specific substances between cells (e.g., hemoglobin transports oxygen in red blood cells) Move specific substances (e.g., ions, glucose, amino acids) across cell membranes
Regulatory proteins	Some are protein hormones (e.g., insulin) Some control the expression of specific genes
Motile proteins	Participate in cellular movements (e.g., actin and myosin are essential for muscle contraction)
Protective proteins	Proteins that defend against foreign invaders (e.g., antibodies play a key role in the immune system)

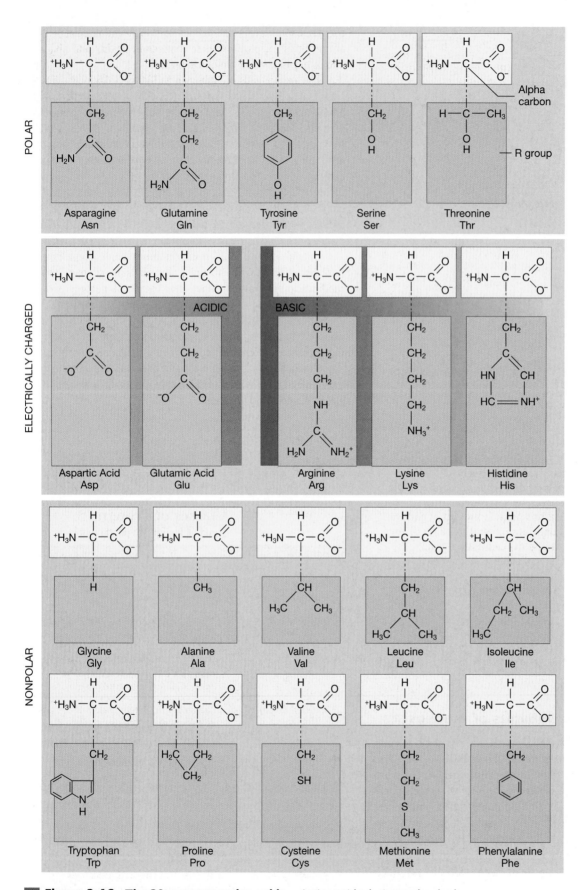

Figure 3–16 The 20 common amino acids. Amino acids designated *polar* have relatively hydrophilic side chains, whereas the side chains of those referred to as *nonpolar* are relatively hydrophobic. Carboxyl groups and amino groups are electrically charged at cellular pH; therefore, acidic and basic amino acids are hydrophilic. The three-letter symbols are the conventional abbreviations for the amino acids.

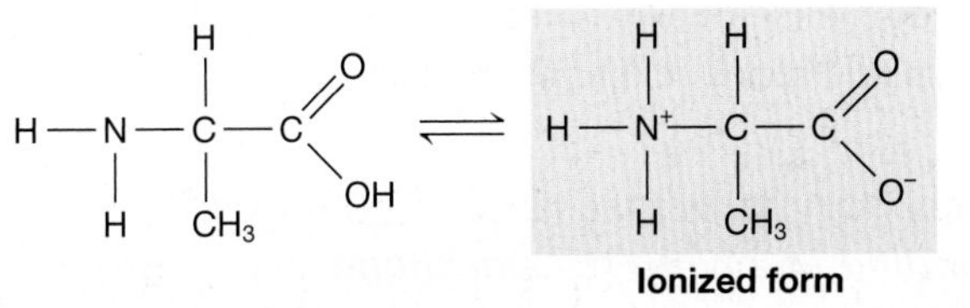

Figure 3-17 An amino acid at pH 7. In living cells, amino acids exist mainly in their ionized form, as dipolar ions.

With some exceptions, bacteria and plants can synthesize all their needed amino acids from simpler substances. If the proper raw materials are available, the cells of humans and animals can manufacture some, but not all, of the biologically significant amino acids. Those that animals cannot synthesize and so must obtain from the diet are known as **essential amino acids.** Animals differ in their biosynthetic capacities; what is an essential amino acid for one species may not be for another. The essential amino acids for humans include isoleucine, leucine, lysine, methionine, phenylalanine, threonine, tryptophan, valine, histidine, and (in children) arginine.

Peptide bonds join amino acids

Amino acids combine chemically with one another by a condensation reaction that bonds the carboxyl carbon of one molecule to the amino nitrogen of another (Fig. 3–18). The covalent car-

bon-to-nitrogen bond linking two amino acids together is called a **peptide bond.** When two amino acids combine, a **dipeptide** is formed; a longer chain of amino acids is a **polypeptide.** A protein consists of one or more polypeptide chains. Each polypeptide has a free amino group at one end and a free carboxyl group (belonging to the last amino acid added to the chain) at the opposite end. The other amino and carboxyl groups of the amino acid monomers (except those in side chains) are part of the peptide bonds. The complex process by which polypeptides are synthesized is discussed in Chapter 12.

A polypeptide may contain hundreds of amino acids joined in a specific linear order. The backbone of the polypeptide chain includes the repeating sequence

$$N-C-C-N-C-C-N-C-C$$

plus all other atoms *except those in the R groups.* The R groups of the amino acids extend from this backbone.

An almost infinite variety of protein molecules is possible, differing from one another in the number, types, and sequences of amino acids they contain. The 20 types of amino acids found in proteins may be thought of as letters of a protein alphabet; each protein is a very long sentence made up of amino acid letters.

Proteins have four levels of organization

The polypeptide chains making up a protein are twisted or folded to form a macromolecule with a specific *conformation,* or

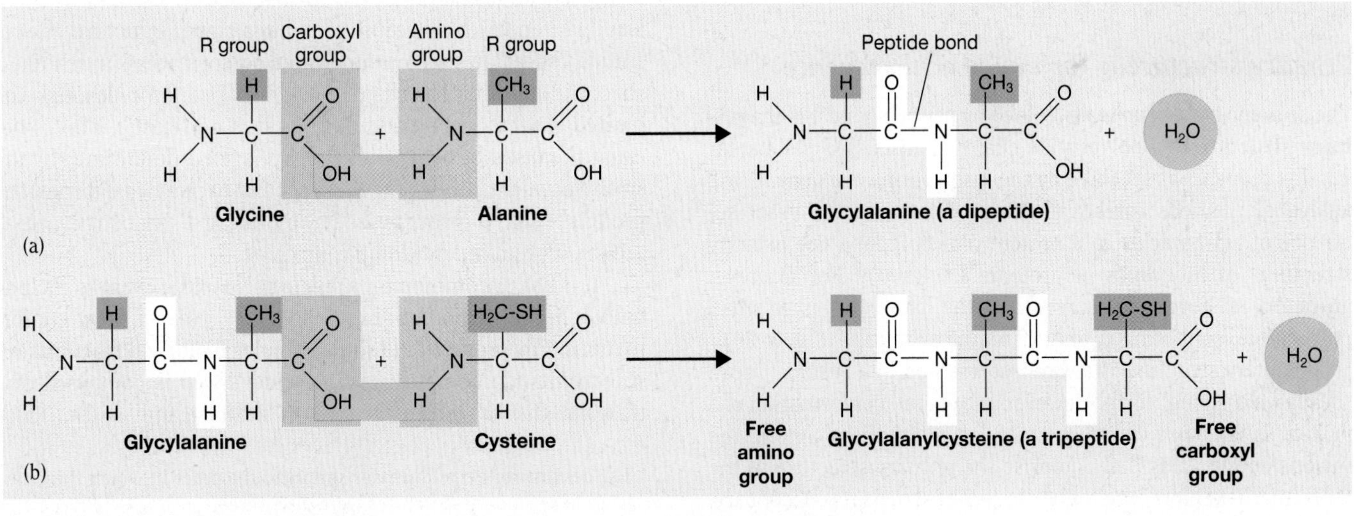

Figure 3-18 Peptide bonds. (a) A dipeptide is formed by a condensation reaction, that is, by the removal of the equivalent of a water molecule from the carboxyl group of one amino acid and the amino group of another amino acid. The resulting peptide bond is a covalent, carbon-to-nitrogen bond. Note that the carbon is also part of a carbonyl group, and that the nitrogen is also covalently bonded to a hydrogen. (b) The carboxyl group of the dipeptide reacts with the amino group of a third amino acid to form a chain of three amino acids (a tripeptide, or small polypeptide). Additional amino acids can be added to form a long polypeptide chain with a free amino group at one end and a free carboxyl group at the other.

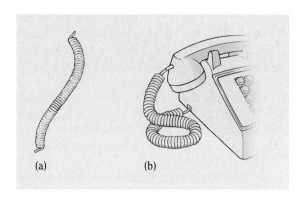

Figure 3–19 Levels of protein structure. A telephone cord provides a familiar analogy for the levels of protein structure. **(a)** Secondary structure, in this case analogous to an α-helix. **(b)** Tertiary structure, in which interactions among side chains cause the molecule to fold back on itself.

three-dimensional shape. Some polypeptide chains form long fibers. **Globular** proteins are tightly folded into compact, roughly spherical shapes. There is a close relationship between a protein's conformation and its function. For example, a typical enzyme is a globular protein with a unique shape that permits it to catalyze a specific chemical reaction. Similarly, the shape of a protein hormone enables it to combine with receptors on its target cell (the cell the hormone acts on).

Four main levels of protein organization can be recognized: primary, secondary, tertiary, and quaternary. An analogy for secondary and tertiary structure is depicted in Figure 3–19.

Primary structure is the amino acid sequence

The sequence of amino acids, joined by peptide bonds, is the **primary structure** of a polypeptide chain. As discussed in Chapter 12, this sequence is specified by the instructions in a gene. Using analytical methods investigators can determine the exact sequence of amino acids in a protein molecule, and the primary structures of thousands of proteins are known. For example, glucagon, a hormone secreted by the pancreas, is a small polypeptide, consisting of only 29 amino acid units (Fig. 3–20).

Primary structure is always represented in a simple, linear, "beads-on-a-string" form. However, the overall conformation of a protein is far more complex, involving interactions among the various amino acids that comprise the primary structure of the molecule. Therefore, the higher orders of structure—secondary, tertiary, and quaternary—ultimately derive from the specific amino acid sequence (i.e., the primary structure).

Secondary structure results from hydrogen bonding involving the backbone

Some regions of a polypeptide exhibit **secondary structure,** which is highly regular. A common secondary structure in protein molecules is the **α-helix,** a region where a polypeptide chain forms a uniform helical coil (Fig. 3–21a). The helical structure is determined and maintained by the formation of hydrogen bonds between the backbones of the amino acids in successive turns of the spiral coil. Each hydrogen bond forms between an oxygen with a partial negative charge and a hydrogen with a partial positive charge. The oxygen is part of the remnant of the carboxyl group of one amino acid; the hydrogen is part of the remnant of the amino group of the fourth amino acid down the chain. Thus 3.6 amino acids are included in each complete turn of the helix. Every amino acid in an α-helix is hydrogen-bonded in this way.

The α-helix is the basic structural unit of some fibrous proteins that make up wool, hair, skin, and nails. The elasticity of these fibers is due to a combination of physical factors (the helical shape) and chemical factors (hydrogen bonding). Although hydrogen bonds maintain the helical structure, these bonds can be broken, allowing the fibers to stretch under tension (like a telephone cord). When the tension is released, the fibers recoil and hydrogen bonds reform. This is why human hairs can stretch to some extent and then snap back to their original length.

Another type of secondary structure is the **β-pleated sheet**[2] (Fig. 3–21b). The hydrogen bonding in a β-pleated sheet takes place between different polypeptide chains, or different regions of a polypeptide chain that has turned back on itself. Each chain is fully extended, but because each has a zigzag structure, the resulting "sheet" has an overall pleated conformation (much like a sheet of paper that has been folded to make a fan). Although the pleated sheet is strong and flexible, it is not elastic. This is because the distance between the pleats is fixed, determined by the strong covalent bonds of the polypeptide backbones. Fibroin, the protein of silk, is characterized by a β-pleated sheet structure, as are the cores of many globular proteins.

It is not uncommon for a single polypeptide chain to include both α-helical regions and regions with β-pleated sheet conformations. The properties of some complex biological materials result from such combinations. A spider's web is composed of a material that is extremely strong, flexible, and elastic. Once

---

[2] The designations α and β refer simply to the order in which these two types of secondary structures were discovered.

+H₃N—His—Ser—Gln—Gly—Thr—Phe—Thr—Ser—Asp—Tyr—Ser—Lys—Tyr—Leu—Asp—Ser—Arg—Arg—Ala—Gln—Asp—Phe—Val—Gln—Trp—Leu—Met—Asn—Thr—COO⁻
 1   2   3   4   5   6   7   8   9 10 11 12 13 14 15 16 17 18 19 20 21 22 23 24 25 26 27 28 29

Figure 3–20 Primary structure of a polypeptide. Glucagon is a very small polypeptide made up of 29 amino acids. The linear sequence of amino acids is indicated by ovals containing their abbreviated names (see Fig. 3–16).

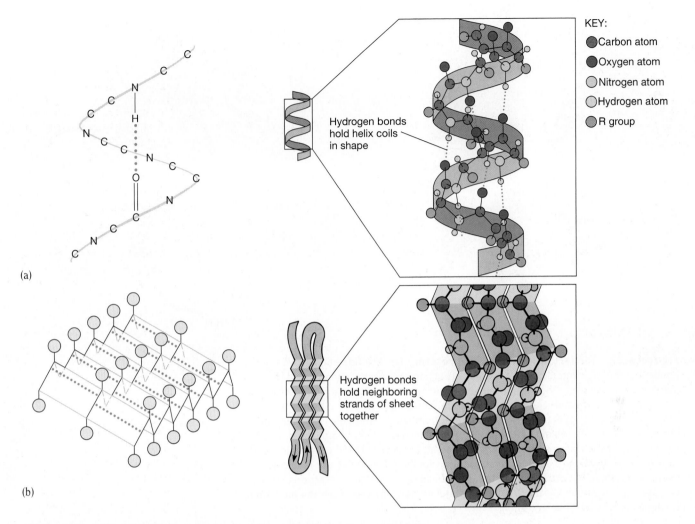

KEY:
- ● Carbon atom
- ● Oxygen atom
- ○ Nitrogen atom
- ○ Hydrogen atom
- ● R group

(a)

Hydrogen bonds hold helix coils in shape

(b)

Hydrogen bonds hold neighboring strands of sheet together

■ Figure 3–21 Secondary structure of a protein. **(a)** Note that the R groups project out from the sides of the α-helix. (The R groups have been omitted in the simplified diagram at left.) **(b)** A β-pleated sheet forms when a polypeptide chain folds back on itself *(arrows);* half the R groups project above the sheet and the other half project below it.

again we see function and structure working together, as these properties derive from the fact that it is a composite of proteins with α-helical conformations (providing elasticity) and others with β-pleated sheet conformations (providing strength).

Tertiary structure depends on interactions among side chains

The **tertiary structure** of a protein molecule is the overall shape assumed by each individual polypeptide chain (Fig. 3–22). This three-dimensional structure is determined by four main factors that involve interactions among R groups (side chains) belonging to the same polypeptide chain. These include both weak interactions (hydrogen bonds, ionic bonds, and hydrophobic interactions) and strong covalent bonds.

1. Hydrogen bonds form between R groups of certain amino acid subunits.

2. Ionic attraction can occur between an R group with a unit of positive charge and one with a unit of negative charge.

3. Hydrophobic interactions result from the tendency of nonpolar R groups to be excluded by the surrounding water and therefore to associate in the interior of the globular structure.

4. Covalent bonds known as disulfide bonds or disulfide bridges (—S—S—) may link the sulfur atoms of two cysteine subunits belonging to the same chain. A disulfide bridge forms when the sulfhydryl groups of two cysteines react; the two hydrogens are removed, and the two sulfur atoms that remain become covalently linked.

Quaternary structure results from interactions among polypeptides

Many functional proteins are composed of two or more polypeptide chains, interacting in specific ways to form the biologically

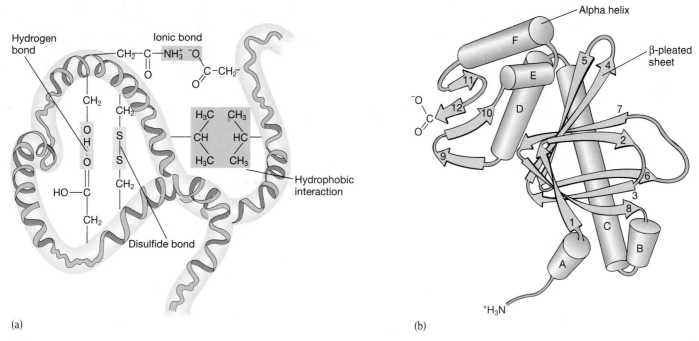

(a)

(b)

■ Figure 3–22 Tertiary structure of a protein. (a) Disulfide bonds, hydrogen bonds, hydrophobic interactions, and ionic attractions between R groups hold the parts of the molecule in the designated shape. (b) Schematic drawing of the tertiary structure of a polypeptide. α-Helical regions are represented as blue tubes lettered A through F; β-pleated sheets are the gray arrows numbered 1 through 12. Green lines represent connecting regions. Although the molecule seems very complicated, it is a single polypeptide chain, starting at the amino end *(bottom left)* and terminating at the carboxyl end *(upper left)*. Most of the bends and foldbacks that give the molecule its overall conformation (tertiary structure) are stabilized by R-group interactions. This polypeptide is a subunit of a DNA-binding protein (known as CAP) from the bacterium *Escherichia coli* (see Chapter 13).

active molecule. **Quaternary structure** is the resulting three-dimensional architecture of these polypeptide chains (each with its own primary, secondary, and tertiary structure). The same types of interactions that produce secondary and tertiary structure can also contribute to quaternary structure; these include hydrogen bonding, ionic bonding, hydrophobic interactions, and disulfide bridges.

For example, a functional antibody molecule consists of four polypeptide chains joined by disulfide bridges (see Chapter 43). Disulfide bridges are a common feature of proteins, such as antibodies, that are secreted from cells; these strong bonds stabilize the molecules in the extracellular environment.

Hemoglobin, the protein in red blood cells that is responsible for oxygen transport, is an example of a globular protein with quaternary structure (Fig. 3–23a). Hemoglobin consists of 574 amino acids arranged in four polypeptide chains: two identical chains called *alpha chains* and two identical chains called *beta chains.*

Collagen, mentioned previously, has a fibrous type of quaternary structure that well suits it to function as the major strengthener of animal tissues. It consists of three polypeptide chains, wound about each other and bound by cross links between their amino acids (Fig. 3–23b).

 The amino acid sequence of a protein determines its conformation

Under defined experimental conditions in vitro (i.e, outside a living cell), a polypeptide can be demonstrated to spontaneously undergo folding processes that allow it to attain its normal, functional conformation. For example, in 1996 researchers at the University of Illinois at Urbana—Champaign conducted an experiment in which they completely unfolded myoglobin, a polypeptide that stores oxygen in muscle cells, and then used sophisticated technology to track the refolding process. They found that within a few fractions of a microsecond the molecule had coiled up to form α-helices, and formation of the tertiary structure was completed within 4 microseconds.

This and other types of evidence support the widely held conclusion that amino acid sequence is the ultimate determinant of protein conformation. However, because conditions in vivo (in the cell) are quite different from defined laboratory conditions, proteins do not necessarily always fold spontaneously. On the contrary, in recent years it has been learned that proteins known as **molecular chaperones** mediate the folding of certain proteins. Chaperones are thought to make the folding process more orderly and efficient and to prevent partially folded proteins from becom-

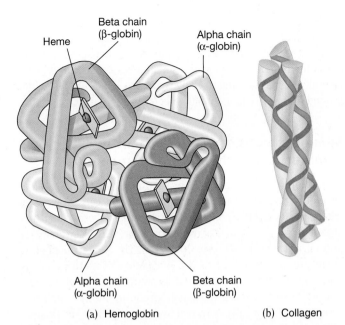

Heme
Beta chain (β-globin)
Alpha chain (α-globin)

Alpha chain (α-globin)
Beta chain (β-globin)

(a) Hemoglobin
(b) Collagen

Figure 3–23 Quaternary structure. (a) Hemoglobin, a globular protein, consists of four polypeptide chains, each joined to an iron-containing molecule, a heme. (b) Collagen, a fibrous protein, is a triple helix consisting of three long polypeptide chains. *(b, from Tobin, A.J. and J. Dusheck. Asking About Life, 2nd ed. Harcourt College Publishers, Philadelphia, 2001, p. 66)*

ing inappropriately aggregated. However, there is no evidence that chaperones actually dictate the folding pattern. For this reason, the existence of chaperones is not an argument against the idea that amino acid sequence determines conformation.

Protein conformation determines function

The overall structure of a protein helps determine its biological activity. A single protein may have more than one distinct structural region, each with its own function. Many proteins are modular, consisting of two or more globular regions, called *domains,* connected by less compact regions of the polypeptide chain. Each domain may have a different function. For example, a protein might have one domain that attaches it to a membrane and another that allows it to act as an enzyme.

The biological activity of a protein can be disrupted by a change in amino acid sequence that results in a change in conformation. For example, the genetic disease known as *sickle cell anemia* is due to a mutation that causes the substitution of the amino acid valine for glutamic acid at position 6 (the sixth amino acid from the amino end) in the beta chain of hemoglobin. The substitution of valine (which has a nonpolar side chain) for glutamic acid (which has a charged side chain) makes the hemoglobin less soluble and more likely to form crystal-like structures. This alteration of the hemoglobin affects the red blood cells, changing them to the crescent or sickle shapes that characterize this disease (see Fig. 15–9).

The biological activity of a protein may be affected by changes in its three-dimensional structure. When a protein is heated, subjected to significant pH changes, or treated with any of a number of chemicals, its structure can become disordered and the coiled peptide chains can unfold to give a more random conformation. This unfolding, which is mainly due to the disruption of hydrogen bonds and ionic bonds, is typically accompanied by a loss of normal function. Such changes in shape and the accompanying loss of biological activity are termed **denaturation** of the protein. For example, a denatured enzyme would lose its ability to catalyze a chemical reaction. An everyday example of denaturation occurs when we fry an egg. The consistency of the egg white protein, known as *albumin,* changes to a solid. Denaturation generally cannot be reversed (you can't "unfry" an egg). However, under certain conditions, some proteins have been denatured and have returned to their original shape and biological activity when normal environmental conditions have been restored.

Process of Science Protein conformation is studied through a variety of methods

The architecture of a protein can be ascertained directly through sophisticated types of analysis, such as the x-ray diffraction studies discussed in Chapter 11. Because these studies are tedious and costly, efforts have been made to develop alternative approaches, which rely heavily on the enormous databases generated by the Human Genome Project and related efforts, many of which are accessible through the Internet. Today a protein's primary structure can be determined rapidly through the application of genetic engineering techniques (see Chapter 14), or by the use of sophisticated technology such as mass spectrometry. A variety of efforts are being made to effectively use these amino acid sequence data to predict a protein's higher levels of structure: secondary, tertiary, and quaternary. As we have seen, side chains can interact in relatively predictable ways, such as through ionic and hydrogen bonds. In addition, regions with certain types of side chains appear more likely to form α-helices or β-pleated sheets. Very complex computer programs are used to make such predictions, but these are imprecise because of the many possible combinations of folding patterns.

Computers are an essential part of yet another strategy. Once the amino acid sequence of a polypeptide has been determined, researchers use computers to search databases to find polypeptides with similar sequences. If the conformations of any of those polypeptides or portions have already been determined by x-ray diffraction or other techniques, this information can be extrapolated to make similar correlations between amino acid sequence and three-dimensional structure for the protein under investigation. These predictions are becoming increasingly reliable as more information is added to the databases on a daily basis.

■ DNA AND RNA ARE NUCLEIC ACIDS

Nucleic acids transmit hereditary information and determine what proteins a cell manufactures. There are two classes of nucleic acids found in cells: **ribonucleic acids (RNAs)** and **deoxyribonucleic**

acids (DNAs). DNA comprises the genes, the hereditary material of the cell, and contains instructions for making all the proteins, as well as all the RNA, needed by the organism. RNA is required as a direct participant in the complex process in which amino acids are linked to form polypeptides. Some types of RNA, known as **ribozymes,** can even act as specific biological catalysts. Like proteins, nucleic acids are large, complex molecules. The name *nucleic acid* reflects the fact that they are acidic and were first identified, by Friederich Miescher in 1870, in the nuclei of pus cells.

Nucleic acids consist of nucleotide subunits

Nucleic acids are polymers of **nucleotides,** molecular units that consist of (1) a five-carbon sugar, either **ribose** (in RNA) or **deoxyribose** (in DNA); (2) one or more phosphate groups, which make the molecule acidic; and (3) a nitrogenous base, a ring compound that contains nitrogen. The nitrogenous base may be either a double-ringed **purine** or a single-ringed **pyrimidine** (Fig. 3–24).

DNA commonly contains the purines adenine (A) and guanine (G), the pyrimidines cytosine (C) and thymine (T), the sugar deoxyribose, and phosphate. RNA contains the purines adenine and guanine, and the pyrimidines cytosine and uracil (U), together with the sugar ribose, and phosphate.

The molecules of nucleic acids are made of linear chains of nucleotides, which are joined by **phosphodiester linkages,** each consisting of a phosphate group and the covalent bonds that attach it to the sugars of adjacent nucleotides (Fig. 3–25). Note that each nucleotide is defined by its particular base and that nucleotides can be joined in any sequence. A nucleic acid molecule is uniquely defined by its specific sequence of nucleotides, which constitutes a kind of code (see Chapter 12). Whereas RNA is usually composed of one nucleotide chain, DNA consists of two nucleotide chains held together by hydrogen bonds and entwined around each other in a double helix (see Fig. 1–7).

Some nucleotides are important in energy transfers and other cellular functions

In addition to their importance as subunits of DNA and RNA, nucleotides serve other vital functions in living cells. **Adenosine triphosphate (ATP),** composed of adenine, ribose, and three phosphates (Fig. 3–26), is of major importance as the primary energy currency of all cells (see Chapter 6). The two terminal phosphate groups are joined to the nucleotide by covalent bonds. These are traditionally indicated by wavy lines, which indicate that ATP can transfer a phosphate group to another molecule, making that molecule more reactive (see Fig. 6–6). In this way ATP is able to donate some of its chemical energy. Most of the readily available chemical energy of the cell is associated with the phosphate groups of ATP.

A nucleotide may be converted to an alternative form with specific cellular functions. ATP, for example, is converted to cyclic adenosine monophosphate **(cyclic AMP)** by the enzyme adenylyl cyclase (Fig. 3–27). Cyclic AMP regulates certain cellular functions and is important in the mechanism by which some hormones act (see Chapters 13, 39, and 47).

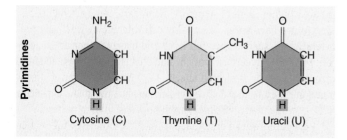

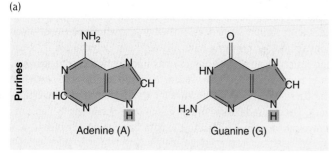

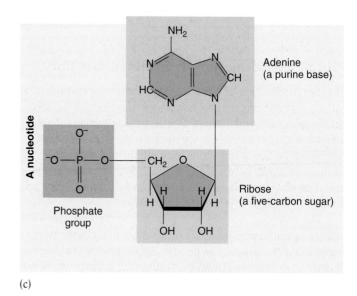

■ **Figure 3–24 Nucleotides.** **(a)** The three major pyrimidine bases found in nucleotides are cytosine, thymine (in DNA only), and uracil (in RNA only). **(b)** The two major purine bases found in nucleotides are adenine and guanine. The hydrogens indicated by the boxes are removed when the base is attached to a sugar. **(c)** A nucleotide, adenosine monophosphate (AMP).

A nucleotide

A phosphodiester linkage

5'

Uracil

Ribose

Adenine

Ribose

Cytosine

Ribose

Guanine

Ribose

3'

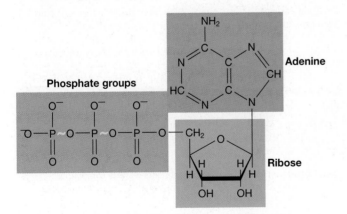

Figure 3–26 Adenosine triphosphate, a nucleotide. The two terminal phosphate groups are joined by covalent bonds (indicated by *wavy lines*) that permit the phosphates to be transferred to other molecules, making them more reactive.

Phosphate groups

Adenine

Ribose

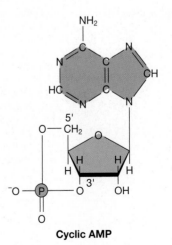

Cyclic AMP

Figure 3–27 Cyclic adenosine monophosphate (cAMP). The single phosphate is part of a ring connecting two regions of the ribose.

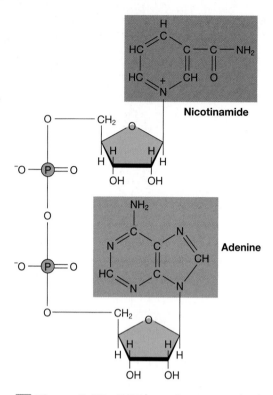

Figure 3–28 NAD⁺, an important hydrogen (electron) acceptor. The nicotinamide portion of the molecule accepts hydrogen and becomes reduced in the process. The resulting reduced molecule, known as *NADH*, is an electron donor.

Cells contain several dinucleotides, which are of great importance in metabolic processes. For example, as discussed in Chapter 6, **nicotinamide adenine dinucleotide** (Fig. 3–28) has a primary role in biological oxidations and reductions within cells. It can exist in an oxidized form (**NAD⁺**) that is converted to a reduced form (**NADH**) when it accepts electrons (in association with hydrogen; see Fig. 6–8). These electrons, along with their energy, can be transferred to other molecules.

■ BIOLOGICAL MOLECULES CAN BE RECOGNIZED BY THEIR KEY FEATURES

Although the fundamental classes of biological molecules may seem to form a bewildering array, one can learn to distinguish them readily by understanding their chief attributes. These are summarized in Table 3–3.

TABLE 3–3   Some of the Groups of Biologically Important Organic Compounds

Class of Compounds	Component Elements	Description	How to Recognize	Principal Function in Living Systems
Carbohydrates	C, H, O	Contain approximately 1 C:2 H:1 O (but make allowance for loss of oxygen and hydrogen when sugar units are linked)	Count the carbons, hydrogens, and oxygens.	Cellular fuel; energy storage; structural component of plant cell walls; component of other compounds such as nucleic acids and glycoproteins
		1. Monosaccharides (simple sugars). Mainly five-carbon (pentose) molecules such as ribose or six-carbon (hexose) molecules such as glucose and fructose	Look for the ring shapes:	Cellular fuel; components of other compounds
		2. Disaccharides. Two sugar units linked by a glycosidic bond, e.g., maltose, sucrose	Count sugar units	Components of other compounds; form of sugar transported in plants
		3. Polysaccharides. Many sugar units linked by glycosidic bonds, e.g., glycogen, cellulose	Count sugar units	Energy storage; structural components of plant cell walls

continued

TABLE 3–3 *Continued*

Class of Compounds	Component Elements	Description	How to Recognize	Principal Function in Living Systems
Lipids	C, H, O (sometimes N, P)	Contain much less oxygen relative to carbon and hydrogen than do carbohydrates		Energy storage; cellular fuel, components of cells; thermal insulation
		1. Neutral fats. Combination of glycerol with one to three fatty acids. Monoacylglycerol contains one fatty acid; diacylglycerol contains two fatty acids; triacylglycerol contains three fatty acids. If fatty acids contain double carbon-to-carbon linkages (C=C), they are unsaturated; otherwise they are saturated	Look for glycerol at one end of molecule:	Cellular fuel; energy storage
		2. Phospholipids. Composed of glycerol attached to one or two fatty acids and to an organic base containing phosphorus	Look for glycerol and side chain containing phosphorus and nitrogen.	Components of cell membranes
		3. Steroids. Complex molecules containing carbon atoms arranged in four attached rings. (Three rings contain six carbon atoms each, and the fourth ring contains five.)	Look for four attached rings:	Some are hormones, others include cholesterol, bile salts, vitamin D, components of cell membranes
		4. Carotenoids. Orange and yellow pigments; consist of isoprene units	Look for isoprene units.	Retinal (important in photo-reception) and vitamin A are formed from carotenoids
Proteins	C, H, O, N. usually S	One or more polypeptides (chains of amino acids) coiled or folded in characteristic shapes.	Look for amino acid units joined by C—N bonds.	Serve as enzymes; structural components; muscle proteins; hemoglobin.
Nucleic acids	C, H, O, N, P	Backbone composed of alternating pentose and phosphate groups, from which nitrogenous bases project. DNA contains the sugar deoxyribose and the bases guanine, cytosine, adenine, and thymine. RNA contains the sugar ribose and the bases guanine, cytosine, adenine, and uracil. Each molecular subunit, called a *nucleotide*, consists of a pentose, a phosphate, and a nitrogenous base.	Look for a pentose-phosphate backbone. DNA forms a double helix.	Storage, transmission, and expression of genetic information

I. An **organic compound** is made up of carbon covalently linked to carbon or to hydrogen. The major groups of biologically important organic compounds are carbohydrates, lipids, proteins, and nucleic acids.

II. The properties of carbon atoms make them extraordinarily versatile, able to form the backbones of the large variety of organic compounds essential to life.

A. Each carbon atom can form four covalent bonds with four other atoms; these can be single, double, or triple bonds.

B. Carbon forms covalent bonds with a greater number of different elements than does any other type of atom. Carbon atoms can form straight or branched chains or can join into rings.

III. **Isomers** are compounds with the same molecular formula but different structures.

A. **Structural isomers** differ in the covalent arrangements of their atoms.

B. **Geometric isomers,** or *cis-trans* isomers, differ in the spatial arrangements of their atoms.

C. **Enantiomers** are isomers that are mirror images of each other. Cells can distinguish between these configurations.

IV. Organic compounds are made up of specific **functional groups** with characteristic properties.

A. **Hydrocarbons,** organic compounds consisting of only carbon and hydrogen, are nonpolar and **hydrophobic.**

B. Polar and ionic functional groups interact with each other and dissolve in water.

C. Partial charges on atoms at opposite ends of a bond are responsible for the polar property of a functional group. **Hydroxyl** and **carbonyl** groups are polar.

D. **Carboxyl** and **phosphate** groups are acidic, becoming negatively charged when they release hydrogen ions. The **amino** group is basic, becoming positively charged when it accepts a hydrogen ion.

V. Long chains of similar organic compounds linked together are called **polymers.** Large polymers such as polysaccharides, proteins, and DNA are referred to as **macromolecules.**

VI. **Carbohydrates** contain carbon, hydrogen, and oxygen in a ratio of approximately one carbon to two hydrogens to one oxygen.

A. **Monosaccharides** are simple sugars such as glucose, fructose, and ribose.

B. Two monosaccharides can be joined by a **glycosidic linkage,** forming a **disaccharide** such as maltose or sucrose.

C. Most carbohydrates are **polysaccharides,** long chains of repeating units of a simple sugar.

1. Carbohydrates are typically stored in plants as **starch** and in animals as **glycogen.**

2. The cell walls of plants are composed mainly of the polysaccharide **cellulose.**

VII. **Lipid** molecules are composed mainly of hydrocarbon-containing regions, with few oxygen-containing (polar or ionic) functional groups. Lipids have a greasy or oily consistency and are relatively insoluble in water.

A. **Triacylglycerol,** the main storage form of fat in organisms, consists of a molecule of **glycerol** combined with three **fatty acids.**

1. **Monoacylglycerols** and **diacylglycerols** contain one and two fatty acids, respectively.

2. A fatty acid can be either **saturated** with hydrogen, or **unsaturated.**

B. **Phospholipids** are structural components of cellular membranes.

C. **Steroid** molecules contain carbon atoms arranged in four attached rings. Cholesterol, bile salts, and certain hormones are important steroids.

VIII. **Proteins** are large, complex molecules made of simpler subunits, called **amino acids,** joined by **peptide bonds.**

A. Proteins are the most versatile class of biological molecules, serving a variety of functions, such as **enzymes,** structural components, and cellular regulators.

B. Proteins are composed of various linear sequences of 20 different amino acids. Two amino acids combine to form a **dipeptide.** A longer chain of amino acids is a **polypeptide.**

1. All amino acids contain an amino group and a carboxyl group, but vary in their side chains. The side chains of amino acids dictate their chemical properties.

2. Amino acids generally exist as dipolar ions at cellular pH and serve as important biological buffers.

C. Four levels of organization can be distinguished in protein molecules.

1. **Primary structure** is the linear sequence of amino acids in the polypeptide chain.

2. **Secondary structure** is a regular conformation, such as an α-**helix** or a β-**pleated sheet;** it is due to hydrogen bonding between elements of the uniform backbone of the polypeptide.

3. **Tertiary structure** is the overall shape of the polypeptide chains, as dictated by chemical properties and interactions of the side chains of specific amino acids. Hydrogen bonding, ionic bonds, hydrophobic interactions, and disulfide bridges contribute to tertiary structure.

4. **Quaternary structure** is determined by the association of two or more polypeptide chains.

IX. The **nucleic acids DNA** and **RNA** store and transfer information that governs the sequence of amino acids in proteins and ultimately the structure and function of the organism.

A. Nucleic acids are composed of long chains of **nucleotide** subunits, each composed of a two-ring **purine** or one-ring **pyrimidine** nitrogenous base, a five-carbon sugar (**ribose** or **deoxyribose**), and a phosphate group.

B. **ATP (adenosine triphosphate)** is a nucleotide of special significance in energy metabolism. **NAD$^+$** is also involved in energy metabolism through its role as an electron (hydrogen) acceptor in biological oxidations.

POST-TEST

1. Which of the following is generally considered an inorganic form of carbon? (a) CO_2 (b) C_2H_4 (c) CH_3COOH (d) b and c (e) all of the above are inorganic

2. Carbon is particularly well suited to be the backbone of organic molecules because (a) it can form both covalent bonds and ionic bonds (b) its covalent bonds are very irregularly arranged in three-dimensional space (c) its covalent bonds are the strongest chemical bonds known (d) it can bond to atoms of a large number of other elements (e) all of the bonds it forms are polar

3. The structures depicted in the right-hand column are

(a) enantiomers (b) different views of the same molecule (c) geometric (*cis-trans*) isomers (d) both geometric isomers and enantiomers (e) structural isomers

4. Which of the following are generally hydrophobic? (a) polar molecules and hydrocarbons (b) ions and hydrocarbons (c) nonpolar molecules and ions (d) polar molecules and ions (e) none of the above

5. Which of the following is a nonpolar molecule? (a) water (H_2O) (b) ammonia (NH_3) (c) methane (CH_4) (d) ethane (C_2H_6) (e) more than one of the above

6. Which of the following functional groups normally acts as an acid? (a) hydroxyl (b) carbonyl (c) sulfhydryl (d) phosphate (e) amino

7. The synthetic process by which monomers are covalently linked is called (a) hydrolysis (b) isomerization (c) condensation (d) glycosidic linkage (e) ester linkage

8. A monosaccharide designated as an aldehyde sugar contains (a) a terminal carboxyl group (b) an internal carboxyl group (c) a terminal carbonyl group (d) an internal carbonyl group (e) a terminal carboxyl group and an internal carbonyl group

9. Structural polysaccharides typically (a) have extensive hydrogen bonding between adjacent molecules (b) are much more hydrophilic than storage polysaccharides (c) have much stronger covalent bonds than do storage polysaccharides (d) consist of alternating α-glucose and β-glucose subunits (e) form helical structures in the cell

10. Fatty acids are components of (a) phospholipids and carotenoids (b) carotenoids and triacylglycerol (c) steroids and triacylglycerol (d) phospholipids and triacylglycerol (e) carotenoids and steroids

11. Saturated fatty acids are so named because they are saturated with (a) hydrogen (b) water (c) hydroxyl groups (d) glycerol (e) double bonds

12. Which pair of amino acid side groups would be most likely to associate with each other by an ionic bond?
    1. $-CH_3$
    2. $-CH_2-COO^-$
    3. $-CH_2-CH_2-NH_3^+$
    4. $-CH_2-CH_2-COO^-$
    5. $-CH_2-OH$
    (a) 1 and 2 (b) 2 and 4 (c) 1 and 5 (d) 2 and 5 (e) 3 and 4

13. Which of the following levels of protein structure may be affected by hydrogen bonding? (a) primary and secondary (b) primary and tertiary (c) secondary, tertiary, and quaternary (d) primary, secondary, and tertiary (e) primary, secondary, tertiary, and quaternary

14. Each phosphodiester linkage in DNA or RNA includes a phosphate joined by covalent bonds to (a) two bases (b) two sugars (c) two additional phosphates (d) a sugar, a base, and a phosphate (e) a sugar and a base

REVIEW QUESTIONS

1. Marble is composed of the carbon-containing compound calcium carbonate ($CaCO_3$). Should calcium carbonate be considered an organic molecule? Why or why not?

2. What are some of the ways that the features of carbon-to-carbon bonds influence the stability and three-dimensional structure of organic molecules?

3. Draw pairs of simple sketches comparing two (a) structural isomers, (b) geometric isomers, and (c) enantiomers.

4. Sketch the following functional groups: methyl, amino, carbonyl, hydroxyl, carboxyl, and phosphate. Classify each as one of the following: nonpolar, polar, acidic, or basic.

5. What features related to hydrogen bonding give storage polysaccharides, such as starch and glycogen, very different properties from structural polysaccharides, such as cellulose and chitin?

6. Draw a structural formula of a simple amino acid and identify the carboxyl group, amino group, and R group.

7. How does the primary structure of a polypeptide influence its secondary and tertiary structures? How can the conformation of a protein be disrupted?

8. Compare the functions of proteins and nucleic acids.

YOU MAKE THE CONNECTION

1. Like oxygen, sulfur forms two covalent bonds. However, sulfur is far less electronegative. In fact, it is approximately as electronegative as carbon. How would the properties of the various classes of biological molecules be altered if you were to replace all the oxygen atoms with sulfur atoms?

2. In what ways are all species alike biochemically? How do species differ from one another biochemically?

RECOMMENDED READINGS

Bettelheim, F.A., W.H. Brown, and J. March. *Introduction to General, Organic and Biochemistry*, 6th ed. Harcourt College Publishers, Philadelphia, 2001. A very readable reference text for those who would like to know more about the chemistry basic to life.

Ezzell, C. "Beyond the Human Genome." *Scientific American*, Vol. 283, No. 1, Jul. 2000. A perspective on the emerging field of proteomics. An outgrowth of the Human Genome Project, proteomics is concerned with understanding the structures and interactions among the thousands of proteins in a cell.

Garrett, R.H., and C.M. Grisham. *Biochemistry*, 2nd ed. Saunders College Publishing, Philadelphia, 1999. A comprehensive, advanced biochemistry text.

Richards, F.M. "The Protein Folding Problem." *Scientific American*, Vol. 264, No. 1, Jan. 1991. A discussion of the mechanisms involved when a protein folds into its biologically active shape.

Strauss, E. "How Proteins Take Shape." *Science News*, 6 Sept. 1997. Chaperones help proteins fold efficiently.

• Visit our Web site at **http://www.info.brookscole.com/solomonbergmartin** for links to chapter-related resources on the World Wide Web. Additional on-line materials relating to this chapter can also be found on our Web site.

See chapter activity on BioActive Learner CD for additional help in mastering the chapter's material. Icon location in the chapter's margins shows which topics have tutorials or simulations in the CD.

4

Organization of the Cell

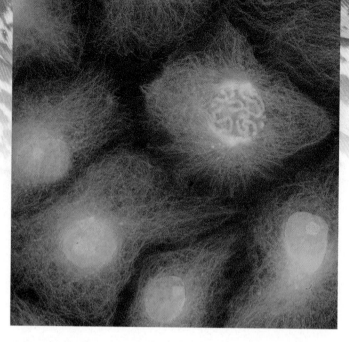

Microtubules, key components of the cytoskeleton.
The cells shown here were stained with fluorescent antibodies (specific proteins) that bound to proteins associated with DNA *(orange)* and to a protein (tubulin) in microtubules *(green)*. This type of microscopy, known as confocal fluorescence microscopy, shows the extensive distribution of microtubules in these cells. *(Courtesy of Dr. John M. Murray, Department of Cell and Developmental Biology, University of Pennsylvania)*

Cells are dramatic examples of the underlying unity of all living things. When we examine a variety of diverse organisms, ranging from simple bacteria to the most complex plants and animals, we find striking similarities at the cellular level. This is a reflection of the evolution of cells from a common ancestor, as well as the fact that living things have many common needs. Careful studies of shared cellular features help us trace the evolutionary history of various groups of organisms and furnish powerful evidence that all organisms alive today had a common origin.

Each cell is a microcosm of life. It is the smallest unit that can carry out all activities we associate with life. When provided with essential nutrients and an appropriate environment, some cells can be kept alive and growing in the laboratory for many years. By contrast, no isolated part of a cell is capable of sustained survival. Composed of a vast array of inorganic and organic ions and molecules including water, salts, carbohydrates, lipids, proteins, and nucleic acids, most cells have all the physical and chemical components needed for their own maintenance, growth, and division. Genetic information is stored in deoxyribonucleic acid (DNA) molecules and is faithfully replicated and passed on to each new generation of cells during cell division. Information in DNA codes for specific proteins that in turn determine cell structure and function. In this chapter and those that follow we discuss how cells use many of the chemical materials introduced in Chapters 2 and 3.

Cells exchange materials and energy with the environment. All living cells need one or more sources of energy, but a cell rarely obtains energy in a form that is immediately usable. Cells convert energy from one form to another, and that energy is used to carry out various activities, ranging from mechanical work to chemical synthesis. Cells convert energy to a convenient form, usually chemical energy stored in adenosine triphosphate (ATP) (see Chapter 3). Although the specifics vary, the basic strategies cells use for energy conversion are very similar. The chemical reactions that convert energy from one form to another are essentially the same in all cells, from bacteria to those of complex plants and animals.

Cells are the building blocks of complex multicellular organisms. Although they are basically similar, cells are also extraordinarily diverse and versatile. They can be modified in a variety of ways to carry out specialized functions. As technology advances, cell biologists have increasingly sophisticated tools to use in their search to better understand the structure and function of cells. For example, investigation of the cytoskeleton (cell skeleton), currently an active and exciting area of research, has been greatly enhanced by advances in microscopy. In the chapter opening illustration, *confocal fluorescence microscopy* was used to show the extensive distribution of microtubules in cells. Microtubules, key components of the cytoskeleton, help maintain cell shape, function in cell movement, and function in transport of materials within the cell.

■ THE CELL IS THE BASIC UNIT OF LIFE

Two German scientists, botanist Matthias Schleiden in 1838 and zoologist Theodor Schwann in 1839, were the first to point out that all plants and animals are composed of cells. Later, Rudolf Virchow, a German scientist and professor of pathology, observed cells dividing and giving rise to daughter cells. In 1855, Virchow proposed that new cells are formed only by the division of previously existing cells.

The work of Schleiden, Schwann, and Virchow gave rise to the **cell theory**, the unifying concept that cells are the basic living units of organization and function in all organisms and that all cells come from other cells. About 1880 another biologist, August Weismann, added an important corollary to Virchow's concept by pointing out that the ancestry of all the cells alive today can be traced back to ancient times. Evidence that all presently living cells have a common origin is provided by the basic similarities in their structures and in the molecules of which they are made.

■ CELL ORGANIZATION AND SIZE PERMIT HOMEOSTASIS

Recall from Chapter 1 that **homeostasis** is the process of maintaining an internal environment that is appropriate and supportive to life. Cells experience constant changes in their environments, including deviations in salt concentration, pH, and temperature. For its biochemical mechanisms to function, the cell must work continuously to restore appropriate conditions.

Organization is basically similar in all cells

Every cell must be able to separate its contents from the external environment. This function is performed by the **plasma membrane,** a structurally distinctive surface membrane that surrounds all cells, whether bacteria, algae, or human cells. The cells must also be able to accumulate materials and energy stores and exchange materials with the environment. These activities are highly regulated, and the plasma membrane must serve as an extremely selective barrier. By making the interior of the cell an enclosed compartment, the plasma membrane permits the chemical composition of the cell to be quite different from that outside the cell.

Typically, cells have internal structures, called **organelles,** specialized to carry on life activities such as converting energy to usable forms, synthesizing needed compounds, and manufacturing structures essential to function and reproduction. Each cell has genetic instructions coded in its DNA, which is concentrated in a limited region of the cell.

Cell size is limited

Although their sizes vary over a wide range (Fig. 4–1), most cells are microscopic, and very small units are required to measure them and their internal structures. The basic unit of linear measurement in the metric system (see inside back cover) is the meter (m), which is just a little longer than a yard. A millimeter (mm) is 1/1000 of a meter and is about as long as the bar enclosed in parentheses (-). The micrometer (μm) is the most convenient unit for measuring cells. A bar 1 μm long is far too short to be seen with the unaided eye, for it is 1/1,000,000 (one-millionth) of a meter, or 1/1000 of a millimeter, long. Most of us have difficulty thinking about units that are too small to see, but it is helpful to remember that a micrometer has the same relationship to a millimeter that a millimeter has to a meter (1/1000).

As small as it is, the micrometer is actually too large to measure most cellular components. For these purposes we use the nanometer (nm), which is 1/1,000,000,000 (one-billionth) of a meter, or 1/1000 of a micrometer. To mentally move down to the world of the nanometer, recall that a millimeter is 1/1000 of a meter, a micrometer is 1/1000 of a millimeter, and a nanometer is 1/1000 of a micrometer.

A good light microscope allows us to see most types of bacterial cells, and some specialized algae and animal cells are large enough to be seen with the naked eye. A human egg cell, for example, is about 130 μm in diameter, or approximately the size of the period at the end of this sentence. The largest cells are birds' eggs, but they are atypical because both the yolk and the egg white consist of food reserves. The functioning part of the cell is a small mass on the surface of the yolk.

Why are most cells so small? If you consider what a cell must do to grow and survive, it may be easier to understand the reasons for its small size. A cell must take in food and other materials and must rid itself of waste products generated by metabolic reactions. Everything that enters or leaves a cell must pass through its plasma membrane. The plasma membrane contains specialized "pumps" and "gates" that selectively regulate the passage of materials into and out of the cell. The plasma membrane must be large enough relative to the cell volume to keep up with the demands of regulating the passage of materials. This means that a critical factor in determining cell size is the ratio of its surface area to its volume (Fig. 4–2).

As a cell becomes larger, its volume increases at a greater rate than its surface area (i.e., its plasma membrane), which

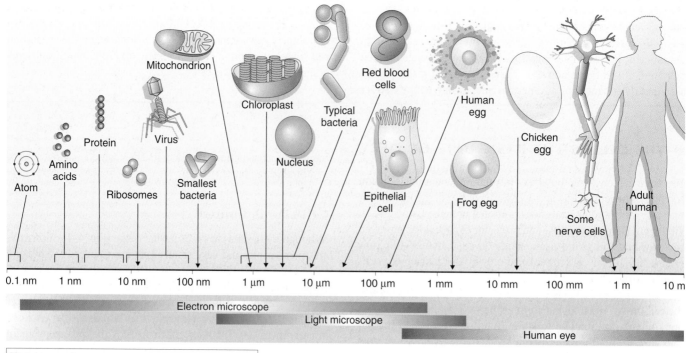

Measurements

1 meter	=	1000 millimeters (mm)
1 millimeter	=	1000 micrometers (μm)
1 micrometer	=	1000 nanometers (nm)

■ **Figure 4–1   Biological size and cell diversity.**   Relative size from chemical to organismic levels is most conveniently compared using a logarithmic scale (multiples of ten). The prokaryotic cells of bacteria typically range in size from less than 1 to 10 μm long; their small size enables them to grow and divide rapidly. Eukaryotic cells are typically 10 to 100 μm in diameter; most are between 10 and 30 μm. The nuclei of animal and plant cells range from about 3 to 10 μm in diameter. Mitochondria are about the size of small bacteria, whereas chloroplasts are usually larger, about 5 μm long. Ova (egg cells) are among the largest cells. Although microscopic, some nerve cells are very long, specialized to transmit messages from one part of the body to another. The cells shown here are not drawn to scale.

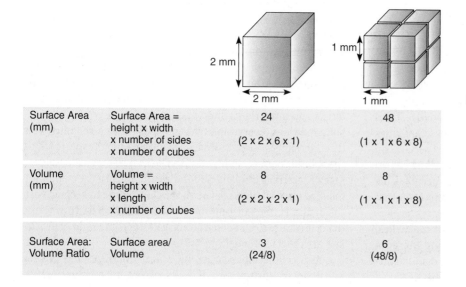

Surface Area (mm)	Surface Area = height x width x number of sides x number of cubes	24 (2 x 2 x 6 x 1)	48 (1 x 1 x 6 x 8)
Volume (mm)	Volume = height x width x length x number of cubes	8 (2 x 2 x 2 x 1)	8 (1 x 1 x 1 x 8)
Surface Area: Volume Ratio	Surface area/ Volume	3 (24/8)	6 (48/8)

■ **Figure 4–2   Surface area–to–volume ratio.**   The surface area of a cell must be large enough relative to its volume to permit adequate exchange of materials with the environment. Although their volumes are the same, eight small cells have a much greater surface area (plasma membrane) in relation to their total volume than does one large cell. In the example shown, the ratio of the total surface area to total volume of eight 1-mm cubes is double the surface-to-volume ratio of the single large cube.

effectively places an upper limit on cell size. Above some critical size, the number of molecules required by the cell could not be transported into the cell fast enough to sustain its needs. In addition, the cell would not be able to regulate its concentration of various ions or efficiently export its wastes.

Of course, not all cells are spherical or cuboidal. Some very large cells have relatively favorable ratios of surface area to volume because of their shapes. In fact, some variations in cell shape represent a strategy for increasing the ratio of surface area to volume. For example, many large plant cells are long and thin, which increases their surface-to-volume ratio. Some cells, such as epithelial cells, have finger-like projections of the plasma membrane, called **microvilli,** that significantly increase the surface area used to absorb nutrients and other materials (see Fig. 45–10c).

Another reason that cells are small is that, once inside, molecules must be transported to the locations where they are converted into other forms. Because cells are small, the distances molecules travel within them are relatively short, which speeds up many cellular activities.

Cell size and shape are related to function

The sizes and shapes of cells are related to the functions they perform. Some cells, such as the amoeba and the white blood cell, can change their shape as they move about. Sperm cells have long, whiplike tails, called *flagella,* for locomotion. Nerve cells possess long, thin extensions that permit them to transmit messages over great distances. The extensions of some nerve cells in the human body may be as long as 1 m. Other cells, such as certain epithelial cells, are almost rectangular in shape and are stacked much like building blocks to form sheetlike structures.

■ CELLS ARE STUDIED BY A COMBINATION OF METHODS

Process of Science One of the most important tools used to study cell structures has been the microscope. In fact, cells were not described until 1665, when Robert Hooke examined a piece of cork using a compound microscope (a microscope with more than one lens) he had made. In his book *Micrographia,* published in 1665, Hooke drew and described what he saw. Hooke chose the term *cell* because the tissue reminded him of the small rooms that monks lived in during that period. What Hooke saw were not actually living cells, but the walls of dead cork cells (Fig. 4–3a). Not until much later was it realized that the interior enclosed by the walls is the important part of living cells.

A few years later, inspired by Hooke's work, the Dutch naturalist Anton van Leeuwenhoek viewed living cells with small lenses that he made. Owing to technical problems in building them, early compound microscopes magnified objects only about 30 times. Leeuwenhoek did not build compound microscopes. He was highly skilled at grinding lenses and was able to magnify images more than 200 times. Among his important discoveries were bacteria, protists, blood cells, and sperm cells. Leeuwenhoek was among the first scientists to report cells in animals.

Leeuwenhoek was a merchant and was not formally trained as a scientist, but his skill, curiosity, and diligence in sharing his discoveries with scientists at the Royal Society of London brought an awareness of microscopic life to the scientific world. He did not share his techniques, however, and it was not until more than a century later, in the late 19th century, that microscopes were sufficiently developed for biologists to seriously focus their attention on the study of cells.

Light microscopes are used to study stained or living cells

The **light microscope (LM),** the type used by most students, consists of a tube with glass lenses at each end. (Because it contains several lenses, the light microscope is referred to as a compound microscope.) Visible light passes through the specimen being observed and through the lenses. Light is refracted (bent) by the lenses, magnifying the image.

Two features of a microscope determine how clearly a small object can be viewed: magnification and resolving power. **Magnification** is the ratio of the size of the image seen with the microscope to the actual size of the object. The best light microscopes usually magnify an object no more than 1000 times. **Resolution,** or **resolving power,** is the capacity to distinguish fine detail in an image. This is defined as the minimum distance between two points at which they can both be seen separately rather than as a single, blurred point. Resolving power depends on the quality of the lenses and the wavelength of the illuminating light. As the wavelength decreases, the resolution increases. The visible light used by light microscopes has wavelengths ranging from about 400 nm (violet) to 700 nm (red); this limits the resolution of the light microscope to details no smaller than the diameter of a small bacterial cell (about 1 μm).

By the early 20th century, refined versions of the light microscope, as well as certain organic compounds that specifically stain different cell structures, became available. These enabled biologists to discover that cells contain a number of different internal structures, the organelles. The contribution of organic chemists in the development of biological stains was essential to this understanding, because the interior of many cells is transparent. Most of the methods used to prepare and stain cells for observation, however, also kill them in the process.

More recently, sophisticated types of light microscopes have been developed that use interfering waves of light to enhance the internal structures of cells. With *phase contrast* and *Nomarski differential interference microscopes,* some internal structures can be seen in unstained living cells (Fig. 4–3d and e). One of the most striking things that can be observed with these microscopes is that living cells contain numerous internal structures that are constantly changing shape and location.

Fluorescence microscopes are used to detect the locations of specific molecules in cells. Fluorescent stains (like paints that glow under black light) are molecules that absorb light energy of one wavelength and then release some of that energy as light of a longer wavelength. One such stain binds specifically to DNA molecules and emits green light after absorbing ultraviolet light.

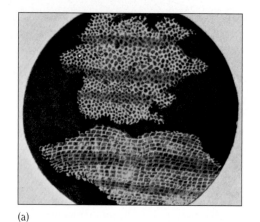

(a)

Figure 4–3 Viewing cells with various types of microscopes. **(a)** Using a crude microscope that he constructed, Robert Hooke looked at a thin slice of cork and drew what he saw. More sophisticated microscopes and techniques permit biologists to view cells in more detail. Unstained epithelial cells from the skin of human cheek are compared using **(b)** bright field (transmitted light), **(c)** dark field, **(d)** phase contrast, and **(e)** Nomarski differential interference microscopy. The phase contrast and differential interference microscopes enhance detail by increasing the differences in optical density in different regions of the cells. *(a, from Hooke's* Micrographica, *1665; b–e, Jim Solliday/Biological Photo Service)*

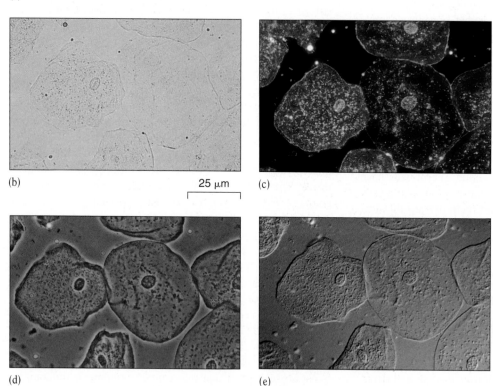

(b)

25 μm

(c)

(d)

(e)

Cells can be stained, and the location of the DNA can be determined, by observing the source of the green fluorescent light within the cell.

Some fluorescent stains can be chemically bonded to *antibodies,* protein molecules important in internal defense. The antibody can then bind to a highly specific region of a molecule in the cell. A single type of antibody molecule binds to only one type of structure, such as a part of a specific protein or some of the sugars in a specific polysaccharide. Purified fluorescent antibodies known to bind to a specific protein isolated from a cell can be used to determine where that protein is located. Powerful computer imaging methods have allowed the development of the *confocal fluorescence microscope,* which greatly improves the resolution of structures labeled by fluorescent dyes (Fig. 4–4 and the micrograph in the chapter introduction).

Cell biologists are developing new techniques for viewing cells using computers, lasers, and photodetectors. Computer-based image processing synthesizes multiple images to produce three-dimensional views.

Electron microscopes provide a high-resolution image that can be greatly magnified

Even with improved microscopes and techniques for staining cells, ordinary light microscopes can distinguish only the gross details of many cell parts. In most cases all that can be seen clearly is the outline of a structure and its ability to be stained by some dyes and not by others. Not until the development of the **electron microscope (EM),** which came into wide use in the 1950s, were researchers able to study the fine details, or **ultrastructure,** of cells.

Whereas light microscopes magnify an object no more than about 1000 times, the electron microscope can magnify it

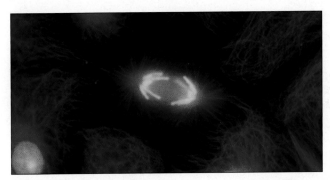

25 μm

■ **Figure 4–4 Confocal fluorescence micrograph of cultured animal cells.** The cell in the center is dividing. The DNA of the chromosomes is yellow; the microtubules are red. The colors are from the fluorescent stain. *(Courtesy of Dr. John M. Murray, Department of Cell and Developmental Biology, University of Pennsylvania)*

250,000 times or more. And while the best light microscopes have about 500 times more resolution than the human eye, the electron microscope multiplies the resolving power by more than 10,000 (Fig. 4–5). This is because electrons have very short wavelengths, on the order of about 0.1 to 0.2 nm. Although such resolution is difficult to achieve with biological material, it can be approached when isolated molecules such as proteins and DNA are examined.

The image formed by the electron microscope cannot be seen directly. The electron beam itself consists of energized electrons, which, because of their negative charge, can be focused by electromagnets just as images are focused by glass lenses in a light microscope (see Fig. 4–5*b*). For **transmission electron microscopy (TEM),** the specimen is embedded in plastic and then cut into extraordinarily thin sections (50 to 100 nm thick) with a glass or diamond knife. A section is then placed on a small metal grid. The electron beam passes through the specimen and then falls onto a photographic plate or a fluorescent screen that works much like a television screen. When you look at TEMs in this chapter (and elsewhere), keep in mind that each represents only a thin cross section of a cell.

To reconstruct a three-dimensional view of the cell, it is necessary to study many consecutive sectional views (called *serial sections*) through the object. To understand the enormity of such a task, try imagining what it would be like to reconstruct an image of the contents of your home from a set of hundreds of consecutive 5-cm sections.

Special methods using antibody molecules that have very tiny gold particles bound to them allow the detection of specific molecules in electron microscope images. The dense gold particles block the electron beam and identify the location of the proteins recognized by the antibodies as precise black spots on the electron micrograph.

In another type of electron microscope, the **scanning electron microscope (SEM),** the electron beam does not pass through the specimen. Instead, the specimen is coated with a thin film of gold or some other metal. When the electron beam strikes various points on the surface of the specimen, secondary electrons are emitted whose intensity varies with the contour of the surface. The recorded emission patterns of the secondary electrons give a three-dimensional picture of the surface (see Fig. 4–5*c*). The SEM provides information about the shape and external features of the specimen that cannot be obtained with the TEM.

Note that the LM, TEM, and SEM are focused by similar principles. A beam of light or an electron beam is directed by the condenser lens onto the specimen and is magnified by the objective lens and the eyepiece in the light microscope or by the objective lens and the projector lens in the TEM. The TEM image is focused onto a fluorescent screen, and the SEM image is viewed on a type of television screen. Lenses in the electron microscopes are actually magnets that bend the beam of electrons.

Process of Science ## Cell fractionation procedures permit study of cell components

The EM is a powerful tool for studying cell structure, but it has limitations. The methods used to prepare cells for electron microscopy kill them and may alter their structure. Furthermore, electron microscopy provides few clues about the functions of organelles and other cell components. To determine what organelles actually do, researchers have to be able to purify different parts of cells so that they can be studied by physical and chemical methods.

Cell fractionation procedures are methods for purifying organelles. Generally, cells are broken apart as gently as possible, and the mixture, referred to as the cell extract, is subjected to centrifugal force by spinning in a device called a **centrifuge.** An ultracentrifuge, a very powerful centrifuge, can spin at speeds exceeding 100,000 revolutions per minute (rpm), generating a centrifugal force of 500,000 × G (a G is equal to the force of gravity). Centrifugal force separates the extract into two fractions: a pellet and a supernatant. The *pellet* that forms at the bottom of the tube contains heavier materials, such as nuclei, packed together. The *supernatant,* the liquid above the pellet, contains lighter particles, dissolved molecules, and ions (Fig. 4–6).

The supernatant can be centrifuged again at a higher speed to obtain a pellet that contains the next heaviest cell components, for example, mitochondria and chloroplasts. In **differential centrifugation,** the supernatant is spun at successively higher speeds, permitting various cell components to be separated on the basis of their different sizes and densities.

Cell components in the resuspended pellets can be further purified by **density gradient centrifugation.** In this procedure, the resuspended pellet is placed in a layer on top of a density gradient, usually made up of a solution of sucrose (table sugar) and water. The concentration of sucrose is highest at the bottom of the tube and decreases gradually so that it is lowest at the top. Because the densities of organelles differ, each will migrate during centrifugation and form a band at the position in the gradient where its own density equals that of the sucrose solution.

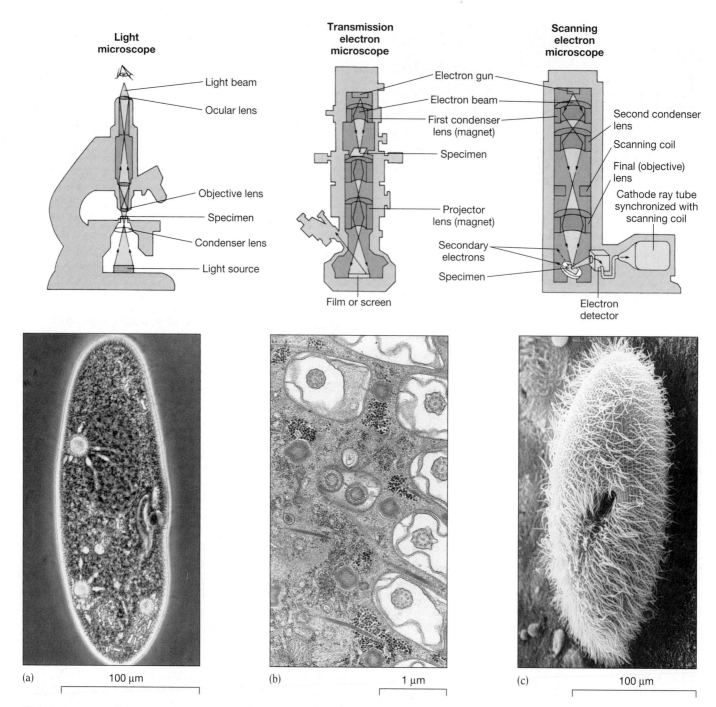

Light microscope

- Light beam
- Ocular lens
- Objective lens
- Specimen
- Condenser lens
- Light source

Transmission electron microscope

- Electron gun
- Electron beam
- First condenser lens (magnet)
- Specimen
- Projector lens (magnet)
- Film or screen

Scanning electron microscope

- Second condenser lens
- Scanning coil
- Final (objective) lens
- Cathode ray tube synchronized with scanning coil
- Secondary electrons
- Specimen
- Electron detector

(a)   100 μm

(b)   1 μm

(c)   100 μm

Figure 4–5 Comparison of light and electron microscopy. Distinctive images of cells, such as the protist *Paramecium* shown in the photomicrographs, are provided by three types of microscopes. **(a)** A phase-contrast light microscope can be used to view stained or living cells, but at relatively low resolution. **(b)** The transmission electron microscope (TEM) produces a high-resolution image that can be greatly magnified. Because of the high magnification, only a small part of the *Paramecium* is shown in the photograph. **(c)** The scanning electron microscope (SEM) is used to provide a clear view of surface features. *(Photos courtesy of T.K. Maugel/University of Maryland)*

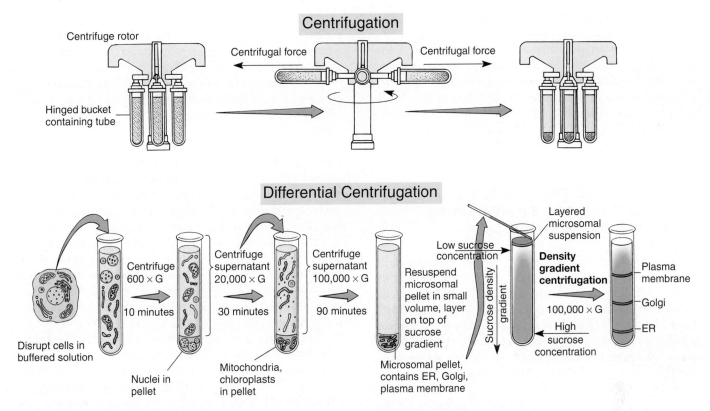

Centrifugation

Centrifuge rotor

Hinged bucket containing tube

Centrifugal force ← → Centrifugal force

Differential Centrifugation

Disrupt cells in buffered solution

Centrifuge 600 × G — 10 minutes

Nuclei in pellet

Centrifuge supernatant 20,000 × G — 30 minutes

Mitochondria, chloroplasts in pellet

Centrifuge supernatant 100,000 × G — 90 minutes

Resuspend microsomal pellet in small volume, layer on top of sucrose gradient

Microsomal pellet, contains ER, Golgi, plasma membrane

Low sucrose concentration

Layered microsomal suspension

Sucrose density gradient

Density gradient centrifugation — 100,000 × G

High sucrose concentration

Plasma membrane

Golgi

ER

Figure 4–6 Cell fractionation. Differential centrifugation permits cell biologists to separate cell structures into various fractions by spinning the suspension at increasing revolutions per minute. Membranes and organelles from the resuspended pellets can then be further purified by density gradient centrifugation, shown as the last step in the figure. G is the force of gravity. ER is the endoplasmic reticulum.

Purified organelles can be examined to determine what kinds of proteins and other molecules they might contain, as well as the nature of the chemical reactions that take place within them. Cell biologists often use a combination of experimental approaches to study the functions of cellular structures.

■ PROKARYOTIC CELLS ARE STRUCTURALLY SIMPLER THAN EUKARYOTIC CELLS

Recall from Chapter 1 that two basic types of cells are known: **prokaryotic** and **eukaryotic.** Bacteria are prokaryotic cells. All other known organisms consist of eukaryotic cells. A major difference between prokaryotic and eukaryotic cells is that the DNA of prokaryotic cells is not enclosed in a nucleus. In fact the term *prokaryotic* means "before the nucleus." In the prokaryotic cell, the DNA is located in a limited region of the cell called a **nuclear area,** or **nucleoid,** which is not enclosed by a membrane (Fig. 4–7). Other types of internal membrane–bounded organelles are also absent in prokaryotic cells. These cells are typically smaller than eukaryotic cells. In fact, the average prokaryotic cell is only about one-tenth the diameter of the average eukaryotic cell.

Like eukaryotic cells, prokaryotic cells have a plasma membrane that confines the contents of the cell to an internal compartment. In some prokaryotic cells the plasma membrane may be folded inward to form a complex of membranes along which many of the cell's metabolic reactions take place. Most prokaryotic cells have **cell walls,** which are extracellular structures that enclose the entire bacterium, including the plasma membrane. Many prokaryotes have **flagella** (sing., *flagellum*), long fibers that

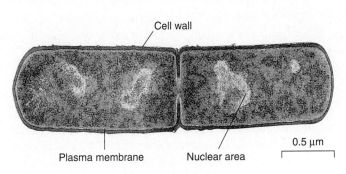

Cell wall

0.5 μm

Plasma membrane

Nuclear area

Figure 4–7 TEM of a prokaryotic cell. This bacterium, *Bacillus subtilis,* which is dividing, has a prominent cell wall surrounding the plasma membrane. The nuclear areas are clearly visible. *(Courtesy of A. Ryter)*

project from the surface of the cell. Prokaryotic flagella operate like propellers and are important in locomotion.

The dense internal material of the bacterial cell contains **ribosomes,** small complexes of ribonucleic acid (RNA) and protein that synthesize polypeptides (discussed later in this chapter). The ribosomes of prokaryotic cells are smaller than those found in eukaryotic cells. Prokaryotic cells also contain storage granules that hold glycogen, lipid, or phosphate compounds. (Prokaryotes are discussed in more detail in Chapter 23.)

■ EUKARYOTIC CELLS ARE CHARACTERIZED BY MEMBRANE-BOUNDED ORGANELLES

Eukaryotic cells are characterized by highly organized membrane-bounded organelles. The most prominent of these is the *nucleus,* which contains the hereditary material DNA. In fact, the name eukaryote means "true nucleus." Table 4–1 summarizes the types of organelles typically found in eukaryotic cells. Some organelles may be found only in specific cells. For example, chloroplasts, structures that trap sunlight for energy conversion, are found only in cells that carry on photosynthesis, such as certain plant cells. The many specialized organelles of eukaryotic cells solve some of the problems associated with large size, permitting eukaryotic cells to be considerably larger than prokaryotic cells. Eukaryotic cells also differ from prokaryotic cells in having a supporting framework, or cytoskeleton, important in maintaining shape and transporting materials within the cell.

Early biologists thought that the cell consisted of a homogeneous jelly, which they called *protoplasm.* With the electron microscope and other modern research tools, perception of the environment within the cell has been greatly expanded. We now know that the cell is highly organized and complex (Figs. 4–8 to 4–11). The eukaryotic cell has its own control center, internal transportation system, power plants, factories for making needed materials, packaging plants, and even a "self-destruct" system. Biologists refer to the part of the cell outside the nucleus as **cytoplasm** and the part of the cell within the nucleus as **nucleoplasm.** Various organelles are suspended within the fluid component of the cytoplasm, which is referred to as the **cytosol.** Therefore, the term *cytoplasm* includes both the cytosol and all the organelles other than the nucleus.

Membranes divide the cell into compartments

Membranes have unique properties that enable membranous organelles to carry out a wide variety of functions. For example, cell membranes never have free ends; therefore, a membranous organelle always contains at least one enclosed internal space or compartment. These membrane-bounded compartments allow certain cell activities to be localized within specific enclosed regions of the cell. Reactants that are located in only a small part of the total cell volume are far more likely to come in contact, and the rate of the reaction can be dramatically increased.

Membrane-bounded compartments keep certain reactive compounds away from other parts of the cell that might be adversely affected by them. Compartmentalizing also permits many different activities to go on simultaneously.

Membranes also allow the storage of energy. The membrane provides a barrier that is analogous to a dam on a river. A difference in the concentration of some substance on the two sides of a membrane is a form of stored energy or *potential energy* (see Chapter 6). As particles of the substance move across the membrane from the side of higher concentration to the side of lower concentration, the cell can convert some of this potential energy to the chemical energy of ATP molecules. This process of energy conversion (discussed in Chapters 7 and 8) is a basic mechanism that cells use to capture and convert energy to sustain life.

Membranes also serve as important work surfaces. For example, many chemical reactions in cells are carried out by enzymes that are bound to membranes. Because the enzymes that carry out successive steps of a series of reactions are organized close together on a membrane surface, certain series of chemical reactions can occur more rapidly.

In a eukaryotic cell several types of membranes are generally considered to be part of the internal membrane system, or **endomembrane system.** Look at Figures 4–8 and 4–9 and notice how membranes divide the cell into many compartments, including the cell itself (bounded by the plasma membrane), the nucleus, endoplasmic reticulum (ER), Golgi complexes, lysosomes, and vesicles and vacuoles. Although it is not internal, the plasma membrane is also included because of its participation in the activities of the endomembrane system. (Mitochondria and chloroplasts are also separate compartments but are not generally considered part of the endomembrane system because they function independently of other membranous organelles.)

Some organelles have direct connections between their membranes and compartments. Others transport materials in **vesicles,** small membrane-bounded sacs formed by "budding" from the membrane of another organelle. Vesicles also carry materials from one organelle to another. Through a complex series of steps, a vesicle can form as a "bud" from one membrane and then be transported to another membrane to which it fuses, thus delivering its contents into another compartment.

The cell nucleus contains DNA

Typically, the **nucleus** is the most prominent organelle in the cell. It is usually spherical or oval in shape and averages 5 μm in diameter. Owing to its size and the fact that it often occupies a relatively fixed position near the center of the cell, some early investigators guessed long before experimental evidence was available that the nucleus served as the control center of the cell (see *Focus On: Acetabularia and the Control of Cell Activities* on page 86). Most cells have one nucleus, although there are exceptions.

The **nuclear envelope** consists of two concentric membranes that separate the nuclear contents from the surrounding cytoplasm (Fig. 4–12 on page 85). These membranes are separated by about 20 to 40 nm. At intervals the membranes come together to form **nuclear pores,** which consist of protein complexes. Nuclear

TABLE 4–1   Eukaryotic Cell Structures and Their Functions

Structure	Description	Function
Cell Nucleus		
Nucleus	Large structure surrounded by double membrane; contains nucleolus and chromosomes	Information in DNA is transcribed in RNA synthesis; specifies cellular proteins
Nucleolus	Granular body within nucleus; consists of RNA and protein	Site of ribosomal RNA synthesis; ribosome subunit assembly
Chromosomes	Composed of a complex of DNA and protein known as chromatin; condense during cell division, becoming visible as rodlike chromosomes	Contain genes (units of hereditary information) that govern structure and activity of cell
Cytoplasmic Organelles		
Plasma membrane	Membrane boundary of cell	Encloses cellular contents; regulates movement of materials in and out of cell; helps maintain cell shape; communicates with other cells (also present in prokaryotes)
Endoplasmic reticulum (ER)	Network of internal membranes extending through cytoplasm	Synthesizes lipids and modifies many proteins; origin of intracellular transport vesicles that carry proteins
Smooth	Lacks ribosomes on outer surface	Lipid biosynthesis; drug detoxification
Rough	Ribosomes stud outer surface	Manufacture of many proteins destined for secretion or for incorporation into membranes
Ribosomes	Granules composed of RNA and protein; some attached to ER, some free in cytosol	Synthesize polypeptides in both prokaryotes and eukaryotes
Golgi complex	Stacks of flattened membrane sacs	Modifies proteins; packages secreted proteins; sorts other proteins to vacuoles and other organelles
Lysosomes	Membranous sacs (in animals)	Contain enzymes to break down ingested materials, secretions, wastes
Vacuoles	Membranous sacs (mostly in plants, fungi, algae)	Store materials, wastes, water; maintain hydrostatic pressure
Peroxisomes	Membranous sacs containing a variety of enzymes	Site of many diverse metabolic reactions
Mitochondria	Sacs consisting of two membranes; inner membrane is folded to form cristae and encloses matrix	Site of most reactions of cellular respiration; transformation of energy originating from glucose or lipids into ATP energy.
Plastids (e.g., chloroplasts)	Double-membraned structure enclosing internal thylakoid membranes; chloroplasts contain chlorophyll in thylakoid membranes	Site of photosynthesis; chlorophyll captures light energy; ATP and other energy-rich compounds are formed and then used to convert CO_2 to glucose
Cytoskeleton		
Microtubules	Hollow tubes made of subunits of tubulin protein	Provide structural support; have role in cell and organelle movement and cell division; components of cilia, flagella, centrioles, basal bodies
Microfilaments	Solid, rodlike structures consisting of actin protein	Provide structural support; play role in cell and organelle movement and cell division
Intermediate filaments	Tough fibers made of protein	Help strengthen cytoskeleton; stabilize cell shape
Centrioles	Pair of hollow cylinders located near nucleus; each centriole consists of nine microtubule triplets (9×3 structure)	Mitotic spindle forms between centrioles during animal cell division; may anchor and organize microtubule formation in animal cells; absent in most plants
Cilia	Relatively short projections extending from surface of cell; covered by plasma membrane; made of two central and nine pairs of peripheral microtubules ($9 + 2$ structure)	Movement of some single-celled organisms; used to move materials on surface of some tissues
Flagella	Long projections made of two central and nine pairs of peripheral microtubules ($9 + 2$ structure); extend from surface of cell; covered by plasma membrane	Cellular locomotion by sperm cells and some unicellular eukaryotes

pores regulate the passage of materials between nucleoplasm and cytoplasm. Just how materials are transported through nuclear pores and how the process is regulated are active areas of research.

Most of the cell's DNA is located inside the nucleus. Recall from Chapter 3 that DNA molecules are composed of sequences of nucleotides called **genes,** which contain the chemically coded

instructions for producing the proteins needed by the cell. The nucleus controls protein synthesis by transcribing and then sending RNA molecules to the cytoplasm (where proteins are manufactured).

DNA is associated with proteins, forming a complex known as **chromatin,** which appears as a network of granules and

(Text continues on page 85)

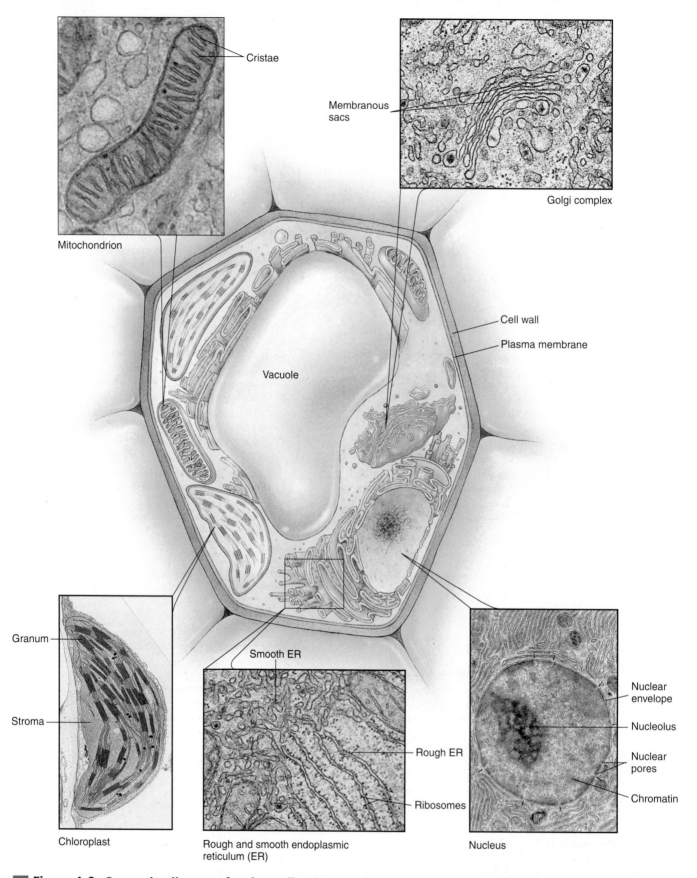

Cristae

Membranous sacs

Golgi complex

Mitochondrion

Cell wall

Plasma membrane

Vacuole

Granum

Stroma

Smooth ER

Nuclear envelope

Nucleolus

Nuclear pores

Chromatin

Rough ER

Ribosomes

Chloroplast

Rough and smooth endoplasmic reticulum (ER)

Nucleus

Figure 4–8 Composite diagram of a plant cell. The TEMs show certain structures or areas of the cell. Some plant cells do not have all the organelles shown. For example, leaf and stem cells that carry on photosynthesis contain chloroplasts, whereas root cells do not. Chloroplasts, a cell wall, and prominent vacuoles are characteristic of plant cells. Many of the other organelles, such as the nucleus, mitochondria, and endoplasmic reticulum (ER), are also found in protist, fungal, and animal cells. *(Clockwise from top left: D.W. Fawcett; D.W. Fawcett and R. Bolender; D.W. Fawcett/Visuals Unlimited; R.Bolender and D.W. Fawcett; E.H. Newcomb and W.P. Wergin, Biological Photo Service)*

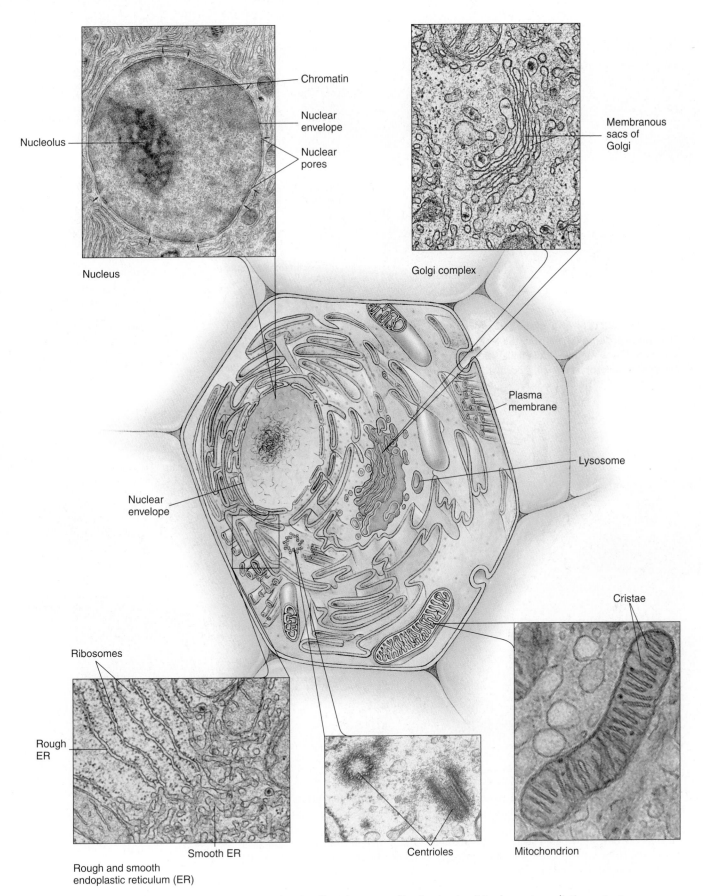

Nucleolus

Chromatin

Nuclear
envelope

Nuclear
pores

Nucleus

Membranous
sacs of
Golgi

Golgi complex

Plasma
membrane

Nuclear
envelope

Lysosome

Cristae

Ribosomes

Rough
ER

Smooth ER

Centrioles

Mitochondrion

Rough and smooth
endoplastic reticulum (ER)

Figure 4–9 Composite diagram of an animal cell. This generalized animal cell is shown in realistic context surrounded by adjacent cells that cause it to be slightly compressed. The TEMs show the structure of various organelles. Depending on the cell type, certain organelles may be more or less prominent. *(Clockwise from top left: D.W. Fawcett; D.W. Fawcett and R. Bolender; D.W. Fawcett; B.F. King, Biological Photo Service; R. Bolender and D.W. Fawcett/Visuals Unlimited)*

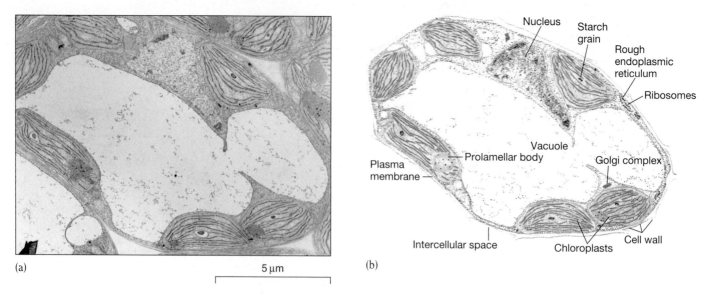

(a)

5 μm

(b)

■ Figure 4–10 TEM of a plant cell paired with interpretive drawing. Most of this cross section of a cell from the leaf of a young bean plant *(Phaseolus vulgaris)* is dominated by a vacuole. Prolamellar bodies are membranous regions typically seen in developing chloroplasts. *(a, Courtesy of Dr. Kenneth Miller, Brown University)*

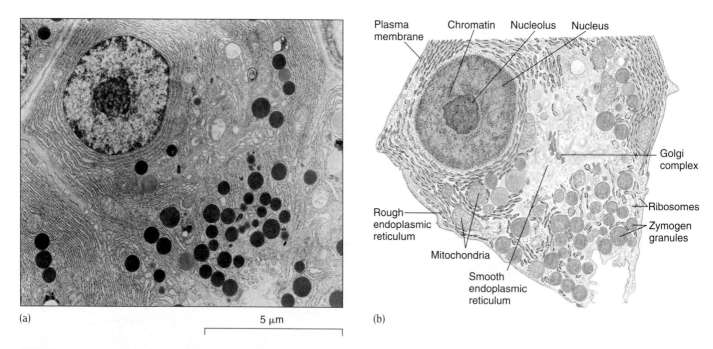

(a)

5 μm

(b)

■ Figure 4–11 TEM of a human pancreas cell paired with interpretive drawing. Most of the structures of a typical animal cell are present. However, like most cells, this one has certain structures associated with its specialized functions. Pancreas cells such as the one shown here secrete large amounts of digestive enzymes. The large, dark, circular bodies in the TEM **(a)** and the corresponding structures in the drawing **(b)** are zymogen granules containing inactive enzymes. When released from the cell, they catalyze chemical reactions such as the breakdown of peptide bonds of ingested proteins in the intestine. Most of the membranes visible in this section are part of the rough endoplasmic reticulum, an organelle specialized to manufacture protein. *(a, Dr. Susumu Ito, Harvard Medical School)*

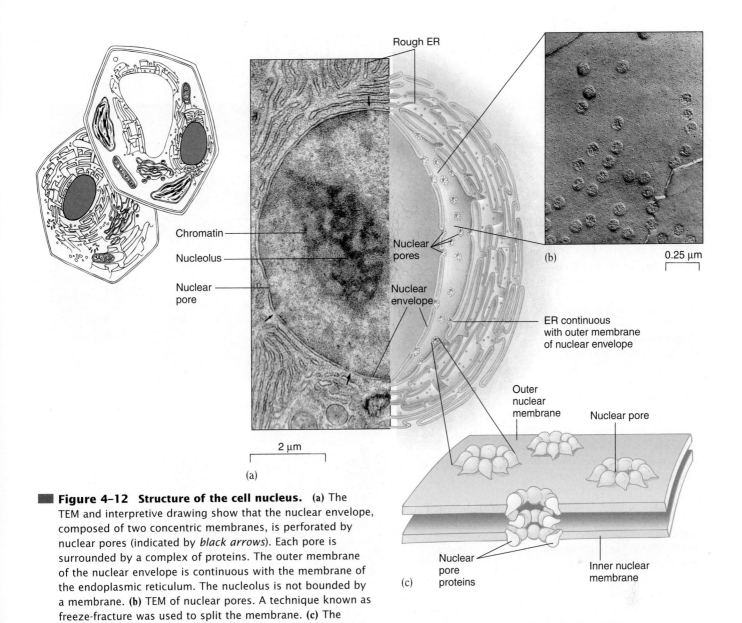

Rough ER

Chromatin

Nucleolus

Nuclear pore

Nuclear pores

Nuclear envelope

(b)

0.25 μm

ER continuous with outer membrane of nuclear envelope

Outer nuclear membrane

Nuclear pore

2 μm

(a)

Nuclear pore proteins

Inner nuclear membrane

(c)

■ Figure 4–12 Structure of the cell nucleus. (a) The TEM and interpretive drawing show that the nuclear envelope, composed of two concentric membranes, is perforated by nuclear pores (indicated by *black arrows*). Each pore is surrounded by a complex of proteins. The outer membrane of the nuclear envelope is continuous with the membrane of the endoplasmic reticulum. The nucleolus is not bounded by a membrane. (b) TEM of nuclear pores. A technique known as freeze-fracture was used to split the membrane. (c) The nuclear pores, which are made up of proteins, form channels between the nucleoplasm and cytoplasm. *(a, D.W. Fawcett; b, R. Kessel-G. Shih/Visuals Unlimited)*

strands in cells that are not dividing. Although chromatin appears disorganized, it is not. Because DNA molecules are extremely long and thin, they must be packed inside the nucleus in a very regular fashion. In dividing cells, the chromatin condenses and becomes visible as distinct threadlike structures called **chromosomes.** If the DNA in the 46 chromosomes of one human cell could be stretched end to end, it would extend for 2 m.

Most nuclei have one or more compact structures called **nucleoli** (sing., *nucleolus*). A nucleolus is *not* membrane-bounded and usually stains differently from the surrounding chromatin. Each nucleolus contains a nucleolar organizer, made up of chromosomal regions containing instructions for making the type of RNA in ribosomes. This ribosomal RNA is synthesized in the nucleolus. The proteins needed to make ribosomes are synthesized in the cytoplasm and imported into the nucleolus. Ribosomal

RNA and proteins are then assembled into ribosomal subunits that leave the nucleus through the nuclear pores.

Ribosomes manufacture proteins

Visible as small granules, ribosomes are molecular structures consisting of RNA and protein. Each eukaryotic ribosome is actually a knot of three RNA strands in association with about 75 different proteins. Free ribosomes are suspended in the cytosol. Other ribosomes are associated with certain internal membranes within the cell. Each ribosome has two main components: a large subunit and a small subunit. In addition to specific ribosomal RNAs, each ribosome contains specific proteins. Ribosomes, which contain the enzyme necessary to form peptide bonds (see Chapter 3), are tiny manufacturing plants that assemble proteins.

(Text continues on page 88)

To the romantically inclined, the little seaweed *Acetabularia* resembles a mermaid's wineglass, although the literal translation of its name, "vinegar cup," is somewhat less elegant (Fig. A). In the 19th century, biologists discovered that this marine eukaryotic alga consists of a single cell. At about 5 cm (2 in) in length, *Acetabularia* is small for a seaweed but gigantic for a cell. It consists of a rootlike **holdfast,** a long cylindrical **stalk,** and a cuplike **cap.** The nucleus is found in the holdfast, about as far away from the cap as it can be. Because it is a single giant cell, *Acetabularia* is easy to manipulate.

■ **Figure A   Light micrograph of *Acetabularia*.** *(L. Sims/Visuals Unlimited)*

Regeneration Experiments Demonstrated that the Cap Shape Is under the Control of Something in the Stalk or the Holdfast

If the cap of *Acetabularia* is removed experimentally, another one grows after a few weeks. Such a response, common among simple organisms, is called **regeneration.** This fact attracted the attention of investigators, especially J. Hämmerling and J. Brachet, who became interested in whether a relationship exists between the nucleus and the physical characteristics of the alga. Because of its great size, *Acetabularia* could be subjected to surgery that would be impossible with smaller cells. During the 1930s and 1940s these researchers performed brilliant experiments that in many ways laid the foundation for much of our modern knowledge of the nucleus. Two species were used for most experiments: *Acetabularia mediterranea,* which has a smooth cap, and *Acetabularia crenulata,* which has a cap divided into a series of finger-like projections.

The kind of cap that is regenerated depends on the species of *Acetabularia* used in the experiment. As you might expect, *A. crenulata* regenerates a "cren" cap, and *A. mediterranea* regenerates a "med" cap. But it is possible to graft together two capless algae of different species. Through this union, they regenerate a common cap that has characteristics intermediate between those of the two species involved (Fig. B).

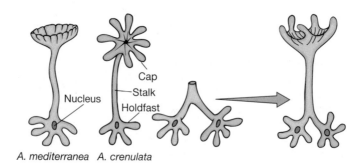

A. mediterranea   A. crenulata

■ **Figure B**

Thus, it is clear that something about the lower part of the cell controls cap shape.

Stalk Exchange Experiments Indicated that Short-Term Control Can Be Exerted by the Stalk, but Long-Term Control Is in the Holdfast

It is possible to attach a section of *Acetabularia* to a holdfast that is not its own by telescoping the cell walls of the two into one another. In this way the stalks and holdfasts of different species may be intermixed.

First, we take *A. mediterranea* and *A. crenulata* and remove their caps. Then we sever the stalks from the holdfasts. Finally, we exchange the parts (Fig. C). What happens? Not, perhaps, what you would expect! The caps that regenerate are characteristic not of the species donating the holdfasts but of those donating the stalks!

However, if the caps are removed once again, this time the caps that regenerate are characteristic of the species that donated the holdfasts. This continues to be the case no matter how many more times the regenerated caps are removed.

From all these results Hämmerling and Brachet deduced that the ultimate control of the *Acetabularia* cell is

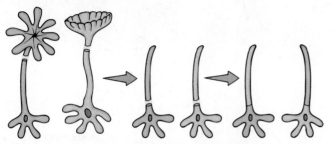

Stalks and holdfasts exchanged

First regenerated caps   Second regenerated caps

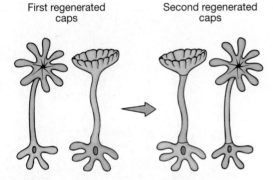

■ **Figure C**

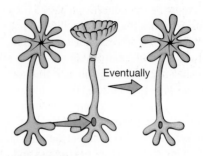

Eventually

■ **Figure E**

associated with the holdfast. Because there is a time lag before the holdfast appears to take over, they hypothesized that it produces some temporary cytoplasmic messenger substance whereby it exerts its control. They further hypothesized that initially the grafted stalks still contain enough of the substance from their former holdfasts to regenerate a cap of the former shape. But this still leaves us with the question of what it is about the holdfast that accounts for its apparent control. An obvious suspect is the nucleus.

inserted and the cap is cut off once again, a new cap regenerates that is characteristic of the species of the nucleus (Fig. E)! If two kinds of nuclei are inserted, the regenerated cap is intermediate in shape between those of the species that donated the nuclei.

As a result of these and other experiments, biologists began to develop some basic ideas about the control of cell activities. The control of the cell exerted by the holdfast is attributable to the

nucleus that is located there. Further, the nucleus is the apparent source of some "messenger substance" that can temporarily exert control but is limited in quantity and cannot be produced without the nucleus (Fig. F). This information helped provide a starting point for research on the role of nucleic acids in the control of all cells.

These ideas have been extended in our modern view of information flow and control in the cell. We now know that the nucleus of eukaryotes controls the cell's activities because it contains DNA, the ultimate source of biological information. DNA can pass on its information to successive generations because it is able to precisely replicate itself. The information in the DNA is used to specify the sequence of amino acids in all the proteins of the cell. To carry out its mission, DNA uses ribonucleic acid (RNA) as a cytoplasmic messenger substance.

Nuclear Exchange Experiments Demonstrated that the Nucleus Is the Ultimate Source of Information for the Control of Cellular Activities

If the nucleus is removed and the cap cut off, a new cap regenerates (Fig. D). *Acetabularia,* however, can usually regenerate only once without a nucleus. If the nucleus of another species is now

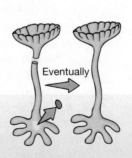

Eventually

■ **Figure D**

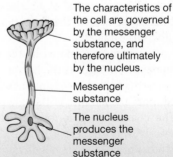

The characteristics of the cell are governed by the messenger substance, and therefore ultimately by the nucleus.

Messenger substance

The nucleus produces the messenger substance

■ **Figure F**

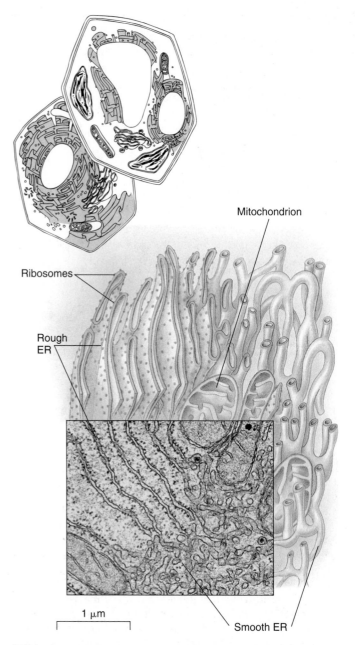

How does a cell store and use genetic information? The cell stores information in the form of DNA. When a cell divides, the information stored in DNA must be reproduced and passed intact to the two daughter cells. DNA has the unique ability to make an exact duplicate of itself through a process called **replication.**

The DNA molecule contains a linear sequence of components called *nucleotides.* In all cells this sequence of nucleotides serves as a code that specifies the amino acid sequence (primary structure) in proteins. Proteins function as structural components of cells and as **enzymes,** molecules that catalyze and regulate virtually every chemical reaction that takes place in the cell. By specifying the structure of enzymes and other proteins, DNA directs the metabolism of the cell.

The cell uses a second nucleic acid, RNA, as a messenger. The sequence of bases in DNA that codes for a specific protein is copied as a sequence of bases called **messenger RNA.** This process is known as **transcription.** In eukaryotic cells, DNA is stored in the nucleus and transcription occurs there.

Messenger RNA leaves the nucleus through nuclear pores and attaches to ribosomes. Two other types of RNA are also involved in protein synthesis: ribosomal RNA (rRNA) and transfer RNA (tRNA). Transfer RNA delivers amino acids to the ribosomes for assembly into proteins. The complex process of assembling a chain of specific amino acids using the code in messenger RNA is called **translation.** After proteins are manufactured, they may be transported to the Golgi complex, where they are modified and sent on to other locations in the cell. (Protein synthesis is discussed in detail in Chapter 12.)

The endoplasmic reticulum is a major manufacturing center

One of the most prominent features in the electron micrograph in Figure 4–11 is a maze of parallel internal membranes that encircle the nucleus and extend into many regions of the cytoplasm. This complex of membranes, the **endoplasmic reticulum (ER),** forms a network that makes up a significant part of the total volume of the cytoplasm in many cells. A higher-magnification TEM of the ER is shown in Figure 4–13. Remember that a TEM represents only a thin cross section of the cell, so there is a tendency to interpret the ER as a series of tubes. In fact, many ER membranes consist of a series of tightly packed and flattened, saclike structures that form interconnected compartments within the cytoplasm.

The internal space enclosed by the membranes is called the **ER lumen.** In most cells the ER lumen forms a single internal compartment that is continuous with the space between outer and inner membranes of the nuclear envelope (see Fig. 4–12). The compartment formed between the two nuclear membranes is thus connected to the ER lumen. The membranes of other organelles are not directly connected to the ER and appear to form distinct and separate compartments within the cytoplasm.

Figure 4–13 The endoplasmic reticulum (ER). The TEM shows both rough and smooth ER in a liver cell. *(R. Bolender and D.W. Fawcett/Visuals Unlimited)*

The ER membranes and lumen contain a large variety of enzymes that catalyze many different types of chemical reactions. In some cases the membranes serve as a framework for systems of enzymes that carry out sequential biochemical reactions. The two surfaces of the membrane contain different sets of enzymes and represent regions of the cell with different synthetic capabilities, just as different regions of a factory are used to make different parts of a particular product. Still other enzymes are located within the ER lumen.

Two distinct regions of the ER can be distinguished in TEMs: rough ER and smooth ER. Although these regions have different functions, their membranes are connected and their internal spaces are continuous. **Rough ER** has ribosomes attached to it and consequently appears rough in electron micrographs. Notice in Figure 4–13 that one membrane face (the lumen side) appears to be bare, while the other membrane face (the cytosolic side) is studded with ribosomes that appear as dark particles.

The rough ER plays a central role in the synthesis and assembly of proteins. Many proteins that are exported from the cell (such as digestive enzymes) and those destined for other organelles are synthesized on ribosomes attached to the ER membrane. The ribosome forms a tight seal with the ER membrane. A tunnel within the ribosome connects to an ER pore, or *translocon*. Proteins are transported through the tunnel and the pore in the ER membrane into the ER lumen. In the ER lumen, proteins may be modified by enzymes that add complex carbohydrates or lipids to them. Other enzymes, called **molecular chaperones,** in the ER lumen catalyze the efficient folding of proteins into proper conformations. The proteins are then transferred to other compartments by small **transport vesicles,** which bud off the ER membrane and then fuse with the membrane of some target compartment.

Smooth ER is more tubular and does not have ribosomes bound to it, so its outer membrane surfaces appear smooth. The smooth ER is the primary site of phospholipid, steroid, and fatty acid metabolism. While the smooth ER may be a minor membrane component in some cells, extensive amounts of smooth ER are present in others. For example, extensive smooth ER is present in human liver cells, where it synthesizes and processes cholesterol and other lipids and serves as a major detoxification site. Enzymes located along the smooth ER of liver cells break down toxic chemicals such as carcinogens (cancer-causing agents). These compounds are then converted to water-soluble products that can be excreted.

The Golgi complex processes and packages proteins

The **Golgi complex** (also known as the *Golgi body* or *Golgi apparatus*) was first described in 1898 by the Italian microscopist Camillo Golgi, who found a way to specifically stain that organelle. In many cells the Golgi complex consists of stacks of flattened membranous sacs called **cisternae** (sing., *cisterna*). In certain regions, cisternae may be distended because they are filled with cellular products (Fig. 4–14). Each of the flattened sacs has an internal space, or lumen. However, unlike the ER, most of these internal spaces of the Golgi complex and the membranes that form them are not continuous. Hence a Golgi complex contains a number of separate compartments, as well as some that are interconnected.

Each Golgi stack has three areas referred to as *cis* and *trans faces,* with a *medial* region between. Typically, the *cis* face is located nearest the nucleus and functions to receive materials from transport vesicles from the ER. The *trans* face, nearest to the plasma membrane, packages molecules in vesicles and transports them out of the Golgi.

In a cross-sectional view like that in the TEM in Figure 4–14, many of the ends of the sheetlike layers of Golgi membranes are distended, an arrangement that is characteristic of well-developed Golgi complexes in many types of cells. In some animal cells the Golgi complex is often located at one side of the nucleus; in other animal cells and in plant cells there are many

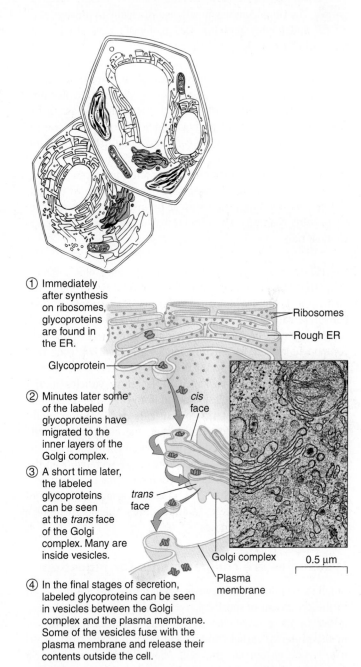

① Immediately after synthesis on ribosomes, glycoproteins are found in the ER.

② Minutes later some of the labeled glycoproteins have migrated to the inner layers of the Golgi complex.

③ A short time later, the labeled glycoproteins can be seen at the *trans* face of the Golgi complex. Many are inside vesicles.

④ In the final stages of secretion, labeled glycoproteins can be seen in vesicles between the Golgi complex and the plasma membrane. Some of the vesicles fuse with the plasma membrane and release their contents outside the cell.

Ribosomes
Rough ER
Glycoprotein
cis face
trans face
Golgi complex
Plasma membrane
0.5 µm

■ **Figure 4–14 TEM and interpretive drawing of the Golgi complex.** Glycoproteins are transported from the rough ER to the Golgi, where they are modified. This diagram shows the passage of glycoproteins through the Golgi complex during the secretory cycle of a mucus-secreting goblet cell that lines the intestine. Mucus is a complex mixture of covalently linked proteins and carbohydrates. (*D.W. Fawcett and R. Bolender*)

Golgi complexes, usually consisting of separate stacks of membranes dispersed throughout the cell. Cells that secrete large amounts of glycoproteins have large numbers of Golgi stacks. Golgi complexes of plant cells produce extracellular polysaccharides that are used as components of the cell wall.

Process of Science The Golgi complex functions principally to process, sort, and modify proteins. Cell biologists have studied the function of the Golgi complex by radioactively labeling newly manufactured amino acids or carbohydrates and observing their movement. Glycoproteins are synthesized and are first located in the rough ER and only later in the Golgi complex. The proteins are transported from the rough ER to the *cis* face of the Golgi complex in small transport vesicles formed from the ER membrane. Until recently, researchers thought that glycoprotein molecules released into the Golgi complex became enclosed in new vesicles that shuttle them from one compartment to another within the Golgi. A competing hypothesis, now the focus of research, holds that the cisternae themselves may move from *cis* to *trans* positions. The vesicles may move backward to recycle materials.

However proteins are moved through the Golgi complex, while there they are modified in different ways, resulting in the formation of complex biological molecules. For example, the carbohydrate part of a glycoprotein (first added to proteins in the rough ER) may be modified. In some cases the carbohydrate component may be a "sorting signal," a kind of zip code that routes the protein to a specific organelle.

Glycoproteins are packaged in secretory vesicles in the *trans* region. These vesicles pinch off from the Golgi membrane and transport their contents to a specific destination. Vesicles transporting products for export from the cell fuse with the plasma membrane. The vesicle membrane becomes part of the plasma membrane, and the glycoproteins are secreted from the cell. Other vesicles may store glycoproteins for secretion at a later time, while still others are routed to various organelles of the endomembrane system. In animal cells, the Golgi complex also manufactures lysosomes.

Lysosomes are compartments for digestion

Small sacs of digestive enzymes called **lysosomes** are dispersed in the cytoplasm of most eukaryotic cells (Fig. 4–15). The enzymes in these organelles break down complex molecules—lipids, proteins, carbohydrates, and nucleic acids—that originate inside or outside the cell. About 40 different digestive enzymes have been identified in lysosomes; most are active under rather acidic conditions (pH 5). Under most normal conditions, the lysosome membrane confines its enzymes and their actions. Some forms of tissue damage have been related to "leaky" lysosomes. The powerful enzymes and low pH maintained by the lysosome provide an excellent example of the importance of separating functions within the cell into different compartments.

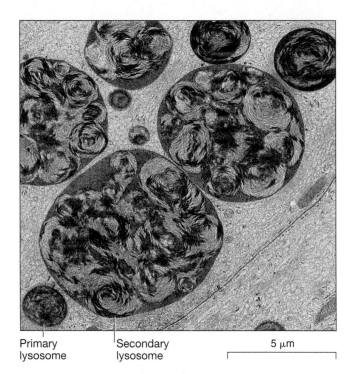

Primary lysosome | Secondary lysosome | 5 μm

Figure 4–15 Lysosomes. The dark vesicles in this TEM are lysosomes. These compartments separate powerful digestive enzymes from the rest of the cell. Primary lysosomes bud off from the Golgi complex. After a lysosome encounters material to be digested, it is known as a secondary lysosome. The large vesicles shown here are secondary lysosomes containing various materials being digested. *(Don Fawcett/Photo Researchers, Inc.)*

Primary lysosomes are formed by budding from the Golgi complex. Their hydrolytic enzymes are synthesized in the rough ER. As these enzymes pass through the lumen of the ER, sugars are attached to each molecule, identifying it as bound for a lysosome. This signal permits the Golgi complex to appropriately sort the enzyme to the lysosomes rather than export it from the cell.

Lysosomes degrade bacteria or debris ingested by scavenger cells. The ingested matter is enclosed in a vesicle formed from part of the plasma membrane. One or more primary lysosomes fuse with the vesicle containing the ingested material, forming a larger vesicle called a *secondary lysosome*. In the secondary lysosome the powerful enzymes come in contact with the ingested molecules and degrade them into their components. Under some conditions lysosomes break down organelles so that their components can be recycled or used as an energy source.

In certain genetic diseases of humans, known as *lysosomal storage diseases,* one of the normally present digestive enzymes is lacking. Its substrate (substance that the enzyme would normally break down) accumulates in the lysosomes, ultimately interfering with cellular activities. An example is Tay-Sachs disease (see Chapter 15), in which a normal lipid cannot be broken down in brain cells. The lipid accumulates in the cells, resulting in mental retardation and death.

Peroxisomes metabolize small organic compounds

Peroxisomes are membrane-bounded organelles containing enzymes that catalyze an assortment of metabolic reactions in which hydrogen is transferred from various compounds to oxygen (Fig. 4–16). During these reactions, hydrogen peroxide (H_2O_2), a substance toxic to the cell, is produced as a byproduct. Peroxisomes contain catalase, an enzyme that splits hydrogen peroxide, rendering it harmless.

Peroxisomes are found in large numbers in cells that synthesize, store, or degrade lipids. In plant seeds, specialized peroxisomes, called *glyoxysomes,* contain enzymes that convert stored fats to sugars. The sugars are used by the young plant as an energy source and as a component needed to synthesize other compounds. Animal cells lack glyoxysomes and cannot convert fatty acids into sugars.

When yeast cells grow in an alcohol-rich medium, they manufacture a large number of peroxisomes. These peroxisomes contain an enzyme that degrades the alcohol. Peroxisomes in human liver and kidney cells detoxify ethanol, the alcohol in alcoholic beverages.

Vacuoles are large, fluid-filled sacs with a variety of functions

Although lysosomes have been identified in almost all kinds of animal cells, their occurrence in plant and fungal cells is open to debate. Many of the functions carried out in animal cells by lysosomes are performed in plant cells by a large, single, membrane-bounded sac referred to as the **vacuole.** The vacuolar membrane, part of the endomembrane system, is referred to as the **tonoplast.** The term *vacuole,* which means "empty," refers to the fact that these organelles have no internal structure. Although the terms vacuole and vesicle are sometimes used interchangeably, vacuoles are usually larger structures, sometimes produced by the merging of many vesicles. As discussed earlier, some biologists now define *vesicle* as a membrane-enclosed structure that holds cargo.

Vacuoles play a significant role in plant growth and development. Immature plant cells are generally small and contain numerous small vacuoles. As water accumulates in these vacuoles, they tend to coalesce, forming a large central vacuole. A plant cell increases in size mainly by adding water to this central vacuole.

As much as 90% of the volume of a plant cell may be occupied by a large central vacuole containing water, as well as stored food, salts, pigments, and metabolic wastes (see Figs. 4–8 and 4–10). The vacuole may serve as a storage compartment for inorganic compounds and for molecules such as proteins in seeds. Plants lack organ systems for disposing of toxic metabolic waste products. Wastes may be recycled in the vacuole, or they may aggregate and form small crystals inside the vacuole. Compounds that are noxious to herbivores (animals that eat plants) may also be stored in some plant vacuoles as a means of defense. Plant vacuoles are lysosome-like in their ability to break down unneeded organelles and other cellular components. The vacuole is also important in maintaining hydrostatic (turgor) pressure in the plant cell.

Vacuoles have numerous other functions and are also present in many types of animal cells and in single-celled protists. Most protozoa have **food vacuoles,** which fuse with lysosomes so that the food they contain can be digested (Fig. 4–17). Many protozoa also have **contractile vacuoles,** which remove excess water from the cell (see Chapter 24).

Mitochondria and chloroplasts are energy-converting organelles

When a cell obtains energy from its environment, it is usually in the form of chemical energy in food molecules (such as glucose) or in the form of light energy. These types of energy must be converted to forms that can be used more conveniently by cells. Some energy conversions go on in the cytosol, but other types take place in mitochondria and chloroplasts, organelles that are specialized to facilitate conversion of energy from one form to another. Chemical energy is most commonly stored in ATP. Recall from Chapter 3 that the chemical energy of ATP can be used to drive a variety of chemical reactions in the cell.

Figure 4–18 summarizes the main activities that take place in mitochondria, found in almost all eukaryotic cells (including algae and plants), and in chloroplasts, found only in algae and certain plant cells. In addition to their central roles in energy metabolism, mitochondria and chloroplasts contain small

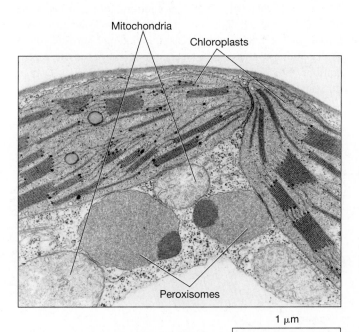

Figure 4–16 Peroxisomes. In this TEM of a tobacco leaf cell, peroxisomes can be seen in close association with chloroplasts and mitochondria. These organelles may cooperate in carrying out some metabolic processes. *(E.H. Newcomb and S.E. Frederick/Biological Photo Service)*

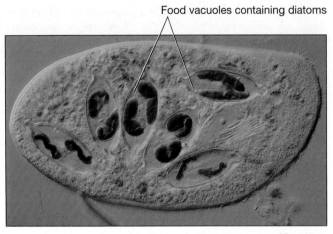

Food vacuoles containing diatoms

15 μm

Figure 4-17 LM of food vacuoles. This protozoon, *Chilodonella*, has ingested many small, photosynthetic protists called diatoms *(dark areas)* that have been enclosed in food vacuoles. From the number of diatoms scattered about its cell, one might judge that *Chilodonella* has a rather voracious appetite. *(M.I. Walker/Photo Researchers, Inc.)*

amounts of DNA that code for some of their proteins. These interesting organelles grow and reproduce themselves.

Mitochondria make ATP through cellular respiration

Virtually all eukaryotic cells (plant, animal, fungal, and protist) contain complex organelles called **mitochondria** (sing., *mitochondrion*). These organelles are the site of **aerobic respiration,** a process that includes most of the reactions that convert the chemical energy present in certain foods to ATP (see Chapter 7). Aero-

bic respiration requires oxygen and results in the release of carbon atoms from food molecules as carbon dioxide (a waste product).

Mitochondria are most numerous in cells that are very active and therefore have high energy requirements. More than 1000 mitochondria have been counted in a single liver cell! Mitochondria vary in size, ranging from 2 to 8 μm in length, and are capable of changing size and shape rapidly. Mitochondria usually give rise to other mitochondria by growth and subsequent division.

Each mitochondrion is bounded by a double membrane, which forms two *different* compartments within the organelle: the intermembrane space and the matrix (Fig. 4–19; see Chapter 7 for more detailed descriptions of mitochondrial structure). The **intermembrane space** is the compartment formed between the outer and inner mitochondrial membranes. The **matrix,** the compartment enclosed by the inner mitochondrial membrane, contains enzymes that break down food molecules and convert their energy to other forms of chemical energy.

The **outer mitochondrial membrane** is smooth and allows many small molecules to pass through it. By contrast, the **inner mitochondrial membrane** has numerous folds and strictly regulates the types of molecules that can move across it. The folds, called **cristae** (sing., *crista*), extend into the matrix. Cristae greatly increase the surface area of the inner mitochondrial membrane, providing a surface for the chemical reactions that transform the chemical energy in food molecules into the energy of ATP. The membrane contains the complex series of enzymes and other proteins needed for these reactions.

In a mammalian cell, each mitochondrion has 5 to 10 identical, circular molecules of DNA, accounting for up to 1% of the total DNA in the cell. Mutations in mitochondrial DNA have been linked with certain genetic diseases, including a form of young adult blindness, and certain types of progressive muscle degeneration. Mitochondrial DNA mutates far more frequently than nuclear DNA, and an accumulation of mutations may interfere

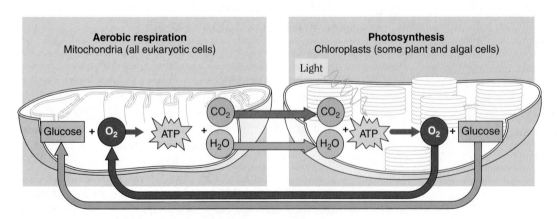

Figure 4-18 Cellular respiration and photosynthesis. Cellular respiration takes place in the mitochondria of eukaryotic cells. In this process, some of the chemical energy in glucose is transferred to ATP. Photosynthesis, which is carried out in chloroplasts in some plant and algal cells, converts light energy to ATP and to other forms of chemical energy. This energy is used to synthesize glucose from carbon dioxide and water.

or activate enzymes that mediate cell destruction. When a mitochondrion is injured, large pores open in its membrane, and cytochrome *c*, a protein important in energy production, is released into the cytoplasm. Cytochrome *c* triggers apoptosis by activating a group of enzymes known as **caspases** that cut up vital compounds in the cell. Inappropriate initiation or inhibition of apoptosis may contribute to a variety of diseases including cancer, acquired immunodeficiency syndrome (AIDS), and Alzheimer's disease. Pharmaceutical companies are developing drugs that block apoptosis. However, cellular dynamics are extremely complex, and blocking apoptosis could lead to a worse fate, including necrosis.

Chloroplasts convert light energy to chemical energy through photosynthesis

Certain plant and algal cells carry out a complex set of energy conversion reactions known as **photosynthesis** (see Chapters 1 and 8). **Chloroplasts** are organelles that contain **chlorophyll,** a green pigment that traps light energy for photosynthesis. Chloroplasts also contain a variety of yellow and orange light-absorbing pigments known as **carotenoids** (see Chapter 3). A unicellular alga may have only a single large chloroplast, whereas a leaf cell may have 20 to 100. Chloroplasts tend to be somewhat larger than mitochondria, with lengths typically ranging from about 5 to 10 μm or longer.

Chloroplasts are typically disc-shaped structures and, like mitochondria, have a complex system of folded membranes (Fig. 4–20; see Chapter 8 for more detailed descriptions of structure). Two membranes, separated by a small space, separate the chloroplast from the cytosol. The inner membrane encloses a fluid-filled space called the **stroma,** which contains enzymes responsible for producing carbohydrates from carbon dioxide and water, using energy trapped from sunlight. A system of internal membranes, suspended in the stroma, consists of an interconnected set of flat, disclike sacs called **thylakoids.** The thylakoids are arranged in stacks called **grana** (sing., *granum*).

The thylakoid membranes enclose a third, innermost compartment within the chloroplast, called the **thylakoid lumen.** The thylakoid membranes, in which chlorophyll is found, are similar to the inner mitochondrial membranes in that they are involved in the formation of ATP. Energy absorbed from sunlight by the chlorophyll molecules is used to excite electrons; the energy in these excited electrons is then used to form ATP and other molecules that can transfer chemical energy. This chemical energy is used to produce carbohydrates from carbon dioxide and water in the stroma.

Chloroplasts belong to a group of organelles known as **plastids** that produce and store food materials in cells of plants and algae. All plastids develop from **proplastids,** precursor organelles found in less specialized plant cells, particularly in growing, undeveloped tissues. Depending on the special functions a cell will eventually have, its proplastids can mature into a variety of specialized mature plastids. These are extremely versatile organelles; in fact, under certain conditions even mature plastids can convert from one form to another.

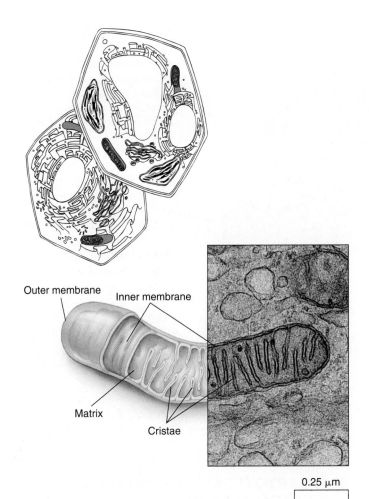

Outer membrane
Inner membrane
Matrix
Cristae

0.25 μm

■ **Figure 4–19 Mitochondria.** Aerobic respiration takes place within mitochondria. Cristae are evident in the TEM as well as in the drawing. The drawing shows the relationship between the inner and outer mitochondrial membranes. *(D.W. Fawcett)*

with mitochondrial function. A diminished capacity to generate energy may contribute to the aging process.

Mitochondria also affect health and aging by leaking electrons. These electrons form **free radicals,** which are toxic, highly reactive compounds that have unpaired electrons. These electrons bond with other compounds in the cell, interfering with normal function.

Mitochondria play an important role in programmed cell death, or **apoptosis.** Unlike **necrosis,** which is uncontrolled cell death that causes inflammation and damages other cells, apoptosis is a normal part of development and maintenance. For example, during the metamorphosis of a tadpole to a frog, the cells of the tadpole tail must die. During human development, the hand is webbed until, through apoptosis, the tissue between the fingers is destroyed. Cell death also occurs in the adult. For example, cells in the upper layer of human skin and in the intestinal wall are continuously destroyed and replaced by new cells.

Mitochondria can initiate cell death in several different ways. For example, they can interfere with energy metabolism

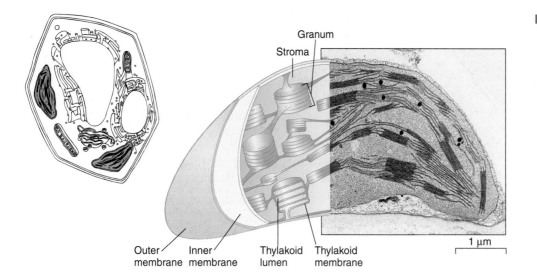

Figure 4–20 The chloroplast, organelle of photosynthesis. The TEM shows part of a chloroplast from a corn leaf cell. Chlorophyll and other photosynthetic pigments are found in the thylakoid membranes. One granum has been cut open to show the thylakoid lumen. The inner chloroplast membrane may or may not be continuous with the thylakoid membrane *(as shown).* *(E.H. Newcomb and W.P. Wergin/Biological Photo Service)*

Granum
Stroma
Outer membrane
Inner membrane
Thylakoid lumen
Thylakoid membrane
1 μm

Chloroplasts are produced when proplastids are stimulated by exposure to light. **Chromoplasts** contain pigments that give certain flowers and fruits their characteristic colors; these attract animals that serve as pollinators or as seed dispersers. **Leukoplasts** are unpigmented plastids; they include **amyloplasts** (see Fig. 3–9), which store starch in the cells of many seeds, roots, and tubers (e.g., white potatoes).

MAKING THE CONNECTION

What is the evolutionary relationship between prokaryotic cells and the more complex cells of eukaryotes? Mitochondria and chloroplasts have provided valuable insights because these organelles have been shown to have many prokaryote features. For example, although most of the DNA in eukaryotic cells resides in the nucleus, both mitochondria and chloroplasts (as well as other plastids) have DNA molecules in their inner compartments. These DNA molecules code for a small number of the proteins found in these organelles. These proteins are synthesized by mitochondrial or chloroplast ribosomes, which are similar to the ribosomes of prokaryotes. Most of the mitochondrial and chloroplast proteins, however, are coded for by nuclear genes, manufactured on free ribosomes in the cytosol, and then transported to their appropriate locations within.

The existence of a separate set of ribosomes and DNA molecules in mitochondria and chloroplasts and their similarity in size to many bacteria, along with other prokaryote-like characteristics, provide support for the **endosymbiont theory** (see Figs. 20–7 and 24–23). According to this theory, mitochondria and chloroplasts evolved from prokaryotic organisms that took up residence inside larger cells and eventually lost the ability to function as autonomous organisms.

Evolutionary biologists are sequencing mitochondrial genes from protists to determine the mitochondrion's evolution from a bacterium to a highly specialized organelle. Evidence suggests that during this process, some genes moved from the early mitochondrion to the nucleus. One such gene codes for a molecular chaperone known as *chaperonin 60,* which helps other proteins fold appropriately. Some investigators think that protists that have retained this gene in their mitochondria evolved earlier than those in which the chaperonin 60 gene is found in the nucleus. The endosymbiont theory is currently being challenged by some investigators who argue that mitochondria evolved in eukaryotic cells.

EUKARYOTIC CELLS CONTAIN A CYTOSKELETON

We have seen that there are many different sizes and shapes of cells. When we watch cells growing in the laboratory, we see that they frequently change shape and that many types of cells move about. The shapes of cells and their ability to move are determined in large part by the **cytoskeleton,** a dense network of protein fibers (Fig. 4–21). In addition to providing mechanical support, the cytoskeleton functions in cell movement, in the transport of materials within the cell, and in cell division.

The cytoskeleton is highly dynamic and constantly changing. Its framework is made of three types of protein filaments: **microtubules, microfilaments** (also known as actin filaments), and **intermediate filaments.** Both microfilaments and microtubules are fibers formed from beadlike, globular protein subunits, which can be rapidly assembled and disassembled. Intermediate filaments are made from fibrous protein subunits and are more stable than microtubules and microfilaments.

Microtubules are hollow cylinders

Microtubules, the thickest filaments of the cytoskeleton, are about 25 nm in outside diameter and up to several micrometers in length. In addition to playing a structural role in the formation of the cytoskeleton, these extremely adaptable structures are involved in the movement of chromosomes during cell division. They serve as tracks for several other kinds of intracellular move-

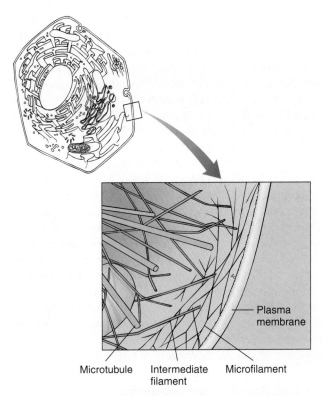

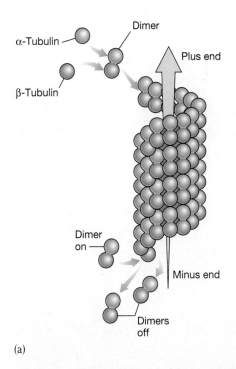

(a)

Figure 4–21 The cytoskeleton. Eukaryotic cells contain a cytoskeleton consisting of networks of several types of fibers, including microtubules, microfilaments, and intermediate filaments. The cytoskeleton contributes to the shape of the cell, anchors organelles, and sometimes rapidly changes shape during cellular locomotion.

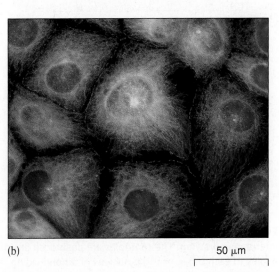

(b)   50 μm

Figure 4–22 Organization of microtubules.
(a) Microtubules are manufactured in the cell by adding dimers of α-tubulin and β-tubulin to an end of the hollow cylinder. Notice that the cylinder has polarity. The end shown at the top of the figure is the fast-growing or plus end; the opposite end is the minus end. Each turn of the spiral requires 13 dimers. **(b)** Confocal fluorescence LM showing microtubules in green. A microtubule-organizing center *(pink dot)* is visible beside or over most of the cell nuclei *(blue)*.   *(b, Nancy Kedersha)*

ment and are the major structural components of cilia and flagella—specialized structures used in some cell movements.

Microtubules consist of two very similar proteins: **α-tubulin** and **β-tubulin.** These proteins combine to form a dimer (recall from Chapter 3 that a dimer forms from the association of two similar, simpler units, referred to as *monomers*). A microtubule elongates by the addition of tubulin dimers (Fig. 4–22). Microtubules are disassembled by the removal of dimers, which can then be recycled to form microtubules in other parts of the cell. Each microtubule has polarity, and its two ends are referred to as *plus* and *minus.* The plus end elongates more rapidly.

For microtubules to act as a structural framework or participate in cell movement, they must be anchored to other parts of the cell. In nondividing cells, the minus ends of microtubules appear to be anchored in regions called **microtubule-organizing centers (MTOCs).** In animal cells, the main MTOC is the cell center or **centrosome,** a structure that is important in cell division. In almost all animal cells, the centrosome contains two structures called **centrioles** (Fig. 4–23). Some other cells also contain centrioles. These structures, which are oriented within the centrosome at right angles to each other, are known as *9 × 3 structures;* they consist of nine sets of three attached microtubules arranged to form a hollow cylinder. The centrioles are

duplicated before cell division and may play a role in some types of microtubule assembly. Most plant cells and fungal cells have an MTOC but lack centrioles. This suggests either that centrioles are not essential to most microtubule assembly processes or that alternative assembly mechanisms are possible.

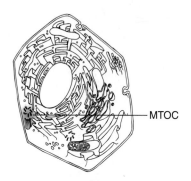

MTOC

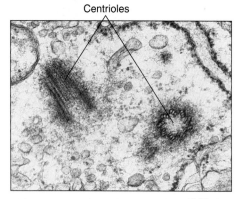

Centrioles

0.25 mm

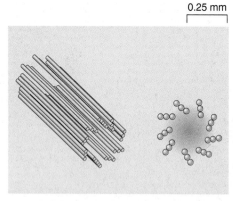

Figure 4–23 Centrioles. The TEM is paired with an interpretive drawing. The centrioles are positioned at right angles to each other, near the nucleus of a nondividing animal cell. Note the 9 × 3 arrangement of microtubules. The centriole on the left has been cut longitudinally and the one on the right transversely. *(B.F. King/Biological Photo Service)*

The ability of microtubules to assemble and disassemble rapidly can be seen during cell division, when much of the cytoskeleton appears to break down (see Chapter 9). Many of the tubulin subunits organize into a structure called the **spindle,** which serves as a framework for the orderly distribution of chromosomes when the cell divides.

Several **microtubule-associated proteins (MAPs)** have been identified and classified into two groups: structural MAPs and motor MAPs. Structural MAPs may help regulate microtubule assembly, and they cross-link microtubules to other cytoskeletal polymers. Motor MAPs use ATP energy to produce movement.

Investigators are studying the mechanisms by which organelles and other materials move within the cell. Nerve cells typically have long extensions called *axons* that transmit signals to other nerve cells, muscle cells, or cells that produce hormones. Because of its length and accessibility and because other cells use similar transport mechanisms, researchers have used the axon as a model system to study the transport of organelles within the cell. They have found that mitochondria, transport and secretory vesicles, and other organelles may attach to microtubules, which then serve as tracks along which organelles can be moved to different cellular locations.

One motor protein, named *kinesin,* moves organelles toward the plus end of a microtubule (Fig. 4–24). *Dynein,* another motor protein, transports organelles in the opposite direction, toward the minus end. This dynein movement is referred to as *retrograde transport.* In 1997, Claire Waterman-Storer of the University of Pennsylvania and her colleagues reported that dynein is necessary but not sufficient for retrograde transport. These investigators determined that a protein complex called *dynactin* is required. Dynactin binds to both microtubules and dynein and appears to function in transport, linking the organelle, microtubule, and dynein.

Cilia and flagella are composed of microtubules

Projecting from surfaces of many cells are thin, movable structures important in cell movement. If a cell has one, or only a few, of these appendages and if they are long (typically about 200 μm) relative to the size of the cell, they are called **flagella** (sing., *flagellum*). If the cell has many short (typically 2–10 μm long) appendages, they are called **cilia** (sing., *cilium*). Both cilia and flagella are used by cells to move through a watery environment, and cilia can be used to pass liquids and particles across the cell surface. These structures are commonly found on unicellular

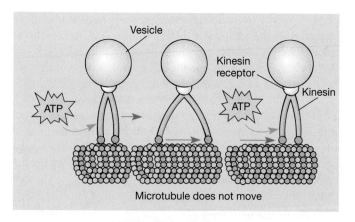

Figure 4–24 Hypothetical model of a kinesin motor. A kinesin molecule attaches to a specific receptor on the vesicle. Energy from ATP allows the kinesin molecule to change its conformation and "walk" along the microtubule, carrying the vesicle along.

and small multicellular organisms. In animals and certain plants, flagella serve as the tails of sperm cells. In animals cilia commonly occur on the surfaces of cells that line internal ducts of the body (e.g., respiratory passageways).

Eukaryotic cilia and flagella are structurally alike (but different from bacterial flagella). Each consists of a slender, cylindrical stalk covered by an extension of the plasma membrane. The core of the stalk contains a group of microtubules arranged so that there are nine attached pairs of microtubules around the circumference and two unpaired microtubules in the center (Fig. 4–25). This *9 + 2* arrangement of microtubules is characteristic of virtually all eukaryotic cilia and flagella, another example of the unity of organisms that reflects their common origin.

The microtubules move by sliding in pairs past each other. The sliding force is generated by dynein proteins, which are attached to the microtubules like small arms. These proteins use the energy from ATP to power the cilia or flagella. The dynein proteins (arms) on one pair of tubules change their shape and "walk" along the adjacent microtubule pair. Thus, the microtubules on one side of a cilium or a flagellum extend farther toward the tip than those on the other side. This sliding of microtubules translates into a bending motion (Fig. 4–25b). Cilia typically move like oars, alternating power and recovery strokes and exerting a force that is parallel to the cell surface. A flagellum moves like a whip, exerting a force perpendicular to the cell surface.

Each cilium or flagellum is anchored in the cell by a **basal body**, which has nine sets of three attached microtubules in a cylindrical array (a 9 × 3 structure). The basal body appears to be the organizing structure for the cilium or flagellum when it first begins to form. However, experiments have shown that as growth proceeds, the tubulin subunits are added much faster to the tips of the microtubules than to the base. Basal bodies and centrioles appear to be functionally related as well as structurally similar. In fact, centrioles are typically found in the cells of organisms that are capable of producing flagellated or ciliated cells; these include animals, certain protists, a few fungi, and a few plants. Both basal bodies and centrioles replicate themselves.

Microfilaments consist of intertwined strings of actin

Microfilaments, also called *actin filaments,* are flexible, solid fibers about 7 nm in diameter. Each microfilament consists of two intertwined polymer chains of beadlike **actin** molecules (Fig. 4–26). Actin filaments are cross-linked with one another and with other proteins by linker proteins. They form bundles of fibers that provide mechanical support for various cell structures. In many cells, a network of microfilaments can be seen in the cytosol just inside the plasma membrane.

In muscle cells, actin is associated with another protein, **myosin,** to form fibers that generate the forces involved in muscle contraction (see Chapter 38). In nonmuscle cells, actin can

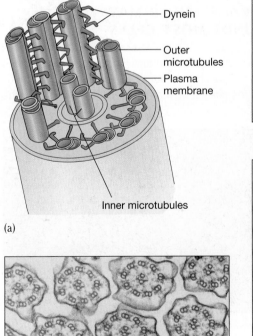

(a)

Dynein
Outer microtubules
Plasma membrane
Inner microtubules

(c)   0.5 μm

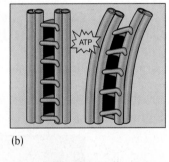

(b)

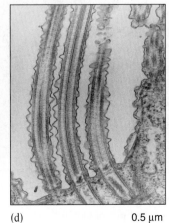

(d)   0.5 μm

■ **Figure 4–25 Structure of cilia.** A cilium (or flagellum) contains microtubules in a 9 + 2 arrangement. **(a)** This three-dimensional representation shows nine attached microtubule pairs (doublets) arranged in a cylinder, with two unattached microtubules in the center. The "arms" are made of dynein, a motor protein that uses energy from ATP to bend the cilia by "walking" up and down the neighboring pair of microtubules. The dynein arms, shown widely spaced for clarity, are actually much closer together along the longitudinal axis. **(b)** The dynein arms move the microtubules by forming and breaking cross bridges on the adjacent microtubules, so that one tubule "walks" along its neighbor. **(c)** TEM of cross sections through cilia showing the 9 + 2 arrangement of microtubules. **(d)** TEM of a longitudinal section of three cilia of the protist *Tetrahymena,* an organism often used in genetic research. Some of the interior microtubules are visible. *(c, d, W.L. Dentler/ Biological Photo Service)*

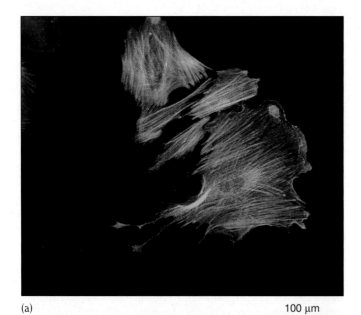

(a)

100 μm

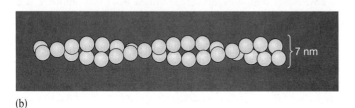

7 nm

(b)

Figure 4–26 Microfilaments (a) Many bundles of aggregated microfilaments *(green)* are evident in this confocal fluorescence LM of fibroblasts (cells found in connective tissue). **(b)** An individual microfilament consists of two intertwined strings of beadlike actin molecules. *(a, Nancy Kedersha/ImmunoGen, Inc.)*

also associate with myosin, forming contractile structures that are involved in various cell movements. Actin filaments themselves cannot contract, but they can generate movement by rapidly assembling and disassembling. Actin filaments associated with myosin are involved in transient functions, such as cell di-

vision in animals, in which contraction of a ring of actin associated with myosin causes the constriction of the cell to form two daughter cells (see Chapter 9). Certain organelles in the giant axons of the squid move along microfilaments. A type of myosin appears to be the motor for this transport.

As mentioned earlier in the chapter, some types of cells have microvilli, projections of the plasma membrane that increase the surface area of the cell for transporting materials across the plasma membrane. Microvilli contain bundles of microfilaments, which extend and retract as a result of the building and breaking down of these microfilaments.

Intermediate filaments help stabilize cell shape

Intermediate filaments are tough fibers, typically 8 to 10 nm in diameter (Fig. 4–27). They vary widely in protein composition and size among different cell types and different organisms. Intermediate filaments function to strengthen the cytoskeleton and stabilize cell shape. They are abundant in parts of a cell that may be subject to mechanical stress applied from outside the cell. Certain proteins cross-link intermediate filaments with other types of filaments and mediate interactions between them.

Intermediate filaments are responsible for formation of a sheath called the **nuclear lamina,** just inside the nuclear envelope. They are important in regulating the timing of the disorganization and initiating the reorganization of the nucleus during division. In humans, more than 50 genes have been identified that code for proteins that assemble into intermediate filaments. Certain mutations in these genes weaken the cell and have been linked to several diseases.

■ AN EXTRACELLULAR MATRIX SURROUNDS MOST CELLS

Most eukaryotic cells are surrounded by a **glycocalyx,** or **cell coat,** formed by polysaccharide side chains of proteins and lipids that are part of the plasma membrane. Certain molecules of the

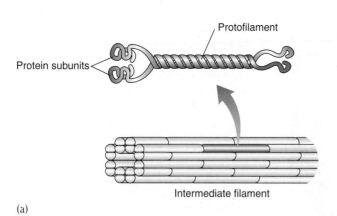

Protofilament

Protein subunits

Intermediate filament

(a)

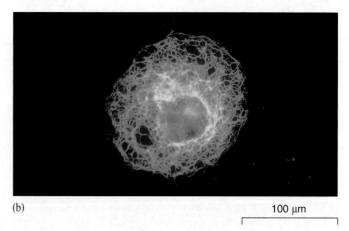

(b)

100 μm

Figure 4–27 Intermediate filaments. (a) Intermediate filaments are flexible rods about 10 nm in diameter. Each intermediate filament consists of components called protofilaments that are made up of coiled protein subunits. **(b)** Intermediate filaments are stained green in this human cell. *(b, K.G. Murti/Visuals Unlimited)*

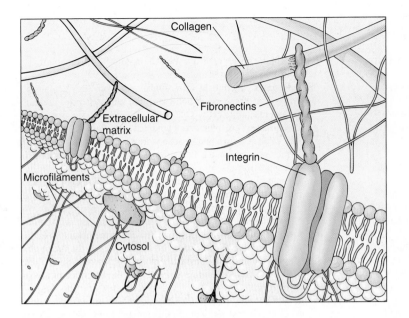

■ **Figure 4–28 Extracellular matrix (ECM).**
Fibronectins, glycoproteins of the ECM, bind to integrins and other receptors in the plasma membrane.

cell coat permit cells to recognize one another, to make contact, and in some cases to form adhesive or communicating associations. Other molecules of the cell coat contribute to the mechanical strength of multicellular tissues.

Many animal cells are also surrounded by an **extracellular matrix (ECM)** which they secrete. It consists of a gel of carbohydrates and fibrous proteins (Fig. 4–28). The main structural protein in the ECM is **collagen,** which forms very tough fibers. Certain glycoproteins of the ECM, called **fibronectins,** bind to protein receptors that extend from the plasma membrane. The main membrane receptors for the ECM are **integrins.** These proteins activate many **cell signaling** pathways and help regulate a variety of cell functions. They appear to be important in cell movement and in organizing the cytoskeleton so that cells assume a definite shape. In many types of cells, integrins anchor the external ECM to the microfilaments of the internal cytoskeleton. When these cells are not appropriately anchored, apoptosis results. Cancer cells apparently lose this requirement to be anchored to the ECM.

Most bacteria, fungi, and plant cells are surrounded by a cell wall and proteins. Plant cells are surrounded by thick cell walls that contain multiple layers of the polysaccharide **cellulose** (see Fig. 3–10). Other polysaccharides in the plant cell wall form cross links between the bundles of cellulose fibers. Each cellulose fiber layer runs in a different direction from the adjacent layer, giving the cell wall great mechanical strength.

A growing plant cell secretes a thin, flexible *primary cell wall,* which can stretch and expand as the cell increases its size (Fig. 4–29). After the cell stops growing, either new wall material is secreted that thickens and solidifies the primary wall or multiple layers of a *secondary cell wall* with a different chemical composition are formed between the primary wall and the plasma membrane. Wood is made mainly of secondary cell walls. Between the primary cell walls of adjacent cells

lies the **middle lamella,** a layer of gluelike polysaccharides called *pectins.* The middle lamella causes the cells to adhere tightly to one another. (See Chapter 31 discussion of the ground tissue system for additional information on plant cell walls.)

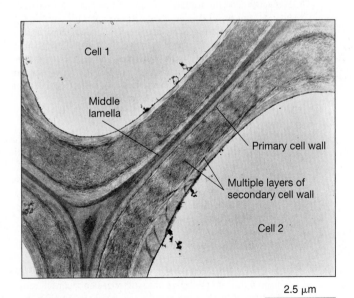

2.5 μm

■ **Figure 4–29 Plant cell walls.** The cell walls of two adjacent plant cells are labeled in this TEM. The cells are cemented together by the middle lamella, a layer of gluelike polysaccharides called pectins. A growing plant cell first secretes a thin primary wall that is flexible and can stretch as the cell grows. The thicker layers of the secondary wall are secreted inside the primary wall after the cell stops elongating. *(Biophoto Associates)*

I. The **cell** is considered the basic unit of life because it is the smallest self-sufficient, self-replicating unit of living material.

II. The **cell theory** states that organisms are composed of cells and that all cells arise by division of preexisting cells.

III. Every cell is surrounded by a **plasma membrane** that forms a cytoplasmic compartment. The plasma membrane serves as a selective barrier between the cell and its surrounding environment.

    A. Cells have genetic instructions coded in **DNA.**

    B. Cells have internal structures called **organelles** that are specialized to carry on specific functions.

    C. A critical factor in determining cell size is the ratio of the plasma membrane (surface area) to the cell's volume; the plasma membrane must be large enough to regulate the passage of materials into and out of the cell.

    D. Cell size and shape are related to function and are limited by the need to maintain homeostasis.

IV. Biologists have learned about cellular structure by studying cells with **light** and **electron microscopes** and by using a variety of chemical methods.

    A. The electron microscope has superior **resolving power,** enabling investigators to see details of cell structures not observable with conventional microscopes.

    B. Cell biologists use **cell fractionation** techniques and other biochemical methods to gain information about the function of cellular structures.

V. **Prokaryotic cells** are bounded by a plasma membrane but have little or no internal membrane organization. They have a **nuclear area** rather than a membrane-bounded nucleus. Prokaryotes typically have a **cell wall** and **ribosomes** and may have propeller-like **flagella.**

VI. **Eukaryotic cells** have a membrane-bounded **nucleus** and **cytoplasm,** which is organized into organelles; the fluid component of the cytoplasm is the **cytosol.**

    A. Plant cells differ from animal cells in that they have rigid cell walls, **plastids,** and large **vacuoles;** cells of most plants lack centrioles.

    B. Membranes divide the cell into membrane-bounded compartments; this allows cells to conduct specialized activities within small areas of the cytoplasm, concentrate molecules, and organize metabolic reactions. A system of interacting membranes forms the **endomembrane system.** Small membrane-bounded sacs, called **vesicles,** transport materials between compartments.

    C. The nucleus, the control center of the cell, contains genetic information coded in DNA.

        1. The nucleus is bounded by a **nuclear envelope** consisting of a double membrane perforated with **nuclear pores** that communicate with the cytoplasm.

        2. DNA in the nucleus associates with protein to form **chromatin.** During cell division, chromatin condenses and the **chromosomes** become visible.

        3. The **nucleolus** is a region in the nucleus that is the site of ribosomal RNA synthesis and ribosome assembly.

    D. The **endoplasmic reticulum (ER)** is a network of folded internal membranes in the cytosol.

        1. **Rough ER** is studded along its outer surface with ribosomes that manufacture proteins. Proteins synthesized on rough ER can be transferred to other cell membranes or secreted from the cells by **transport vesicles,** formed by membrane budding.

        2. **Smooth ER** is the site of lipid synthesis and detoxifying enzymes.

    E. The **Golgi complex** consists of stacks of flattened membranous sacs called **cisternae** that process, sort, and modify proteins synthesized on the ER. The Golgi adds carbohydrates and lipids to proteins and can route proteins, by way of **secretory vesicles,** to the plasma membrane for export from the cell, or to other destinations. The Golgi complex also manufactures lysosomes.

    F. **Lysosomes** function in intracellular digestion; they contain enzymes that break down both worn-out cell structures and substances taken into cells.

    G. **Peroxisomes** are membrane-bounded sacs containing enzymes that catalyze a variety of reactions in which hydrogen peroxide is formed as a byproduct. Peroxisomes contain catalase, an enzyme that splits hydrogen peroxide.

    H. Vacuoles are important in plant growth and development. Many protists have **food vacuoles** and **contractile vacuoles.** Vacuoles may be formed by the merging of many vesicles.

    I. **Mitochondria,** the sites of aerobic respiration, are double-membraned organelles in which the inner membrane is folded, forming **cristae** that increase the surface area of the membrane. The cristae and the compartment enclosed by the inner membrane, the **matrix,** contain enzymes for the reactions of aerobic respiration.

        1. Mitochondria contain DNA that codes for some of its proteins.

        2. Electrons that leak out of mitochondria form free radicals that disrupt cell function.

        3. Mitochondria play an important role in **apoptosis,** or programmed cell death.

    J. Cells of algae and plants contain plastids; **chloroplasts,** the sites of **photosynthesis,** are double-membraned plastids.

        1. Typically, the inner membrane encloses a fluid-filled space, the **stroma. Grana,** stacks of disclike sacs called **thylakoids,** are suspended in the stroma.

        2. **Chlorophyll,** the green pigment that traps light energy during photosynthesis, is found in the thylakoid membranes.

VII. The **cytoskeleton** is a dynamic internal framework made of microtubules, microfilaments, and intermediate filaments. The cytoskeleton provides structural support and functions in various types of cell movement, including transport of materials in the cell.

    A. **Microtubules** are hollow cylinders assembled from subunits of the protein **tubulin.**

        1. In cells that are not dividing, the minus ends of microtubules appear to be anchored in **microtubule-organizing centers (MTOCs).** The main MTOC of animal cells is the **centrosome,** which usually contains two **centrioles.** Each centriole has a 9 × 3 arrangement of microtubules.

        2. **Microtubule-associated proteins (MAPs)** include structural MAPs and motor MAPs. Two motor MAPs are kinesin and dynein.

        3. **Cilia** and **flagella** function in cell movement. Each consists of a 9 + 2 arrangement of microtubules, and each is anchored in the cell by a **basal body** that has a 9 × 3 organization of microtubules.

    B. **Microfilaments,** or **actin filaments,** formed from subunits of the protein **actin,** are important in cell movement.

    C. **Intermediate filaments** are stable structures that strengthen the cytoskeleton and stabilize cell shape.

VIII. Most cells are surrounded by a **glycocalyx,** or **cell coat,** formed by polysaccharides extending from the plasma membrane.

    A. Many animal cells are also surrounded by an **extracellular matrix (ECM)** consisting of carbohydrates and protein. **Fibronectins** are glycoproteins of the ECM that bind to **integrins,** receptor proteins in the plasma membrane.

    B. Most bacteria, fungi, and plant cells are surrounded by a cell wall made of carbohydrates and protein. Plant cells secrete **cellulose** and other polysaccharides to form rigid cell walls.

1. The ability of a microscope to reveal fine detail is known as (a) magnification (b) resolving power (c) cell fractionation (d) scanning electron microscopy (e) phase contrast

2. A plasma membrane is characteristic of (a) all cells (b) prokaryotic cells only (c) eukaryotic cells only (d) animal cells only (e) eukaryotic cells except for plant cells

3. Detailed information about the shape and external features of a specimen can best be obtained by using a (a) differential centrifuge (b) fluorescence microscope (c) transmission electron microscope (d) scanning electron microscope (e) light microscope

4. In eukaryotic cells, DNA is found in (a) chromosomes (b) chromatin (c) mitochondria (d) answers a, b, and c are correct (e) answers a and b only are correct

5. Which of the following structures would *not* be found in prokaryotic cells? (a) cell wall (b) ribosomes (c) nuclear area (d) nucleus (e) propeller-like flagellum

6. Which of the following is/are most closely associated with protein synthesis? (a) ribosomes (b) smooth ER (c) mitochondria (d) microfilaments (e) lysosomes

7. Which of the following is/are most closely associated with the breakdown of ingested material? (a) ribosomes (b) smooth ER (c) mitochondria (d) microfilaments (e) lysosomes

8. Which of the following are most closely associated with photosynthesis? (a) basal bodies (b) smooth ER (c) cristae (d) thylakoids (e) MTOCs

9. A 9 + 2 arrangement of microtubules best describes (a) cilia (b) centrosomes (c) basal bodies (d) microfilaments (e) microvilli

10. Which sequence most accurately describes information flow in the eukaryotic cell? (a) DNA in nucleus → messenger RNA → ribosomes → protein synthesis (b) DNA in nucleus → ribosomal RNA → mitochondria → protein synthesis (c) RNA in nucleus → messenger DNA → ribosomes → protein synthesis (d) DNA in nucleus → messenger RNA → Golgi complex → protein synthesis (e) DNA in nucleus → messenger RNA → smooth ER → protein synthesis

11. Which sequence most accurately describes glycoprotein processing in the eukaryotic cell? (a) smooth ER → transport vesicle → *cis* region of Golgi → *trans* region of Golgi → plasma membrane or other organelle (b) rough ER → transport vesicle → *cis* region of Golgi → *trans* region of Golgi → plasma membrane or other organelle (c) rough ER → transport vesicle → *trans* region of Golgi → *cis* region of Golgi → plasma membrane or other organelle (d) rough ER → nucleus → *cis* region of Golgi → *trans* region of Golgi → plasma membrane or other organelle (e) smooth ER → transport vesicle → *cis* region of Golgi → chloroplast

12. Which of the following is/are part of the cytoskeleton? (a) microfilaments (b) lysosomes (c) peroxisomes (d) ribosomes (e) endoplasmic reticulum

13. Which of the following function(s) in cell movement? (a) microtubules (b) cristae (c) grana (d) smooth ER (e) rough ER

14. Which of the following is/are *not* associated with mitochondria? (a) cristae (b) aerobic respiration (c) apoptosis (d) free radicals (e) thylakoids

15. The extracellular matrix (a) consists mainly of myosin and RNA (b) projects to form microvilli (c) houses the centrioles (d) contains fibronectins that bind to integrins (e) has an elaborate system of cristae

REVIEW QUESTIONS

1. Describe the basic needs of all living things and explain how a cell is able to meet these needs. How does the cell theory help us understand how living things function?

2. Compare and contrast prokaryotic and eukaryotic cells.

3. Draw a chloroplast and a mitochondrion. Label the membranes and their compartments.

4. Describe the functions of each of the following: (a) ribosomes (b) smooth endoplasmic reticulum (c) Golgi complex (d) microtubules

5. Trace the path of a protein from its site of synthesis to its final destination for the following: (a) a secreted protein (b) a protein found inside a lysosome (c) a protein associated with the plasma membrane

6. Contrast microfilaments and microtubules. Compare their structures and the different roles they play in cell structure and function.

7. Describe plant cell walls. How are they formed?

8. Label the diagrams of the animal and plant cells. How is the structure of each organelle related to its function? Use Figures 4–8 and 4–9 to check your answers.

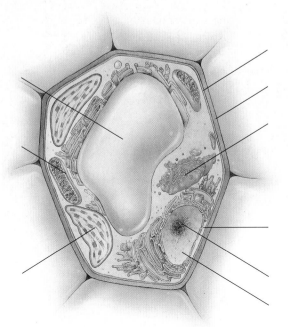
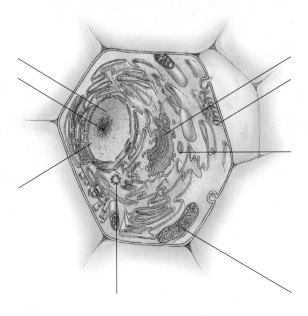

YOU MAKE THE CONNECTION

1. Why does a eukaryotic cell need both membranous organelles and fibrous cytoskeletal components?
2. Describe three examples illustrating the correlation between cell structure and function. (*Hint:* Think of mitochondrial structure.)
3. The *Acetabularia* experiments described in this chapter suggest that DNA is much more stable in the cell than is messenger RNA. Is this advantageous or disadvantageous to the cell? Why? How can *Acetabularia* live for a few days after its nucleus is removed?

RECOMMENDED READINGS

Brown, G.C. "Symbionts and Assassins." *Natural History,* Jul.-Aug. 2000. A highly readable account of the function of mitochondria, including a discussion of their role in apoptosis.

Duke, R.C., D.M. Oljcius, and J. Ding-E Young. "Cell Suicide in Health and Disease." *Scientific American,* Vol. 275, No. 6, Dec. 1996. A discussion of the role of apoptosis in regulation and disease.

Horwitz, A.F. "Integrins and Health." *Scientific American,* Vol. 276, No. 5, May 1997. Integrins are proteins in the plasma membrane that link microtubules of the cytoskeleton to the extracellular matrix.

Ingber, D. "The Architecture of Life." *Scientific American,* Vol. 278, No. 1, Jan. 1998. A discussion of the principles that guide patterns and architecture from cytoskeleton to skeleton.

Special Issue: Frontiers in Cell Biology: The Cytoskeleton. *Science,* Vol. 279, No. 5350, Jan. 1998. Several articles and an editorial discuss cytoskeletal structure and function.

Tobin, A.J., and R.E. Morel. *Asking About Cells.* Saunders College Publishing, Philadelphia, 1997. A clearly written, excellent introduction to cell biology.

Tran, P.B., and R.J. Miller. "Apoptosis: Death and Transfiguration." *Science & Medicine,* Vol. 6, No. 3, May/Jun. 1999. Mitochondria play an important role in programmed cell death.

Wallace, D.C. "Mitochondrial DNA in Aging and Disease." *Scientific American,* Vol. 277, No. 2, Aug. 1997. Mutations in mitochondrial DNA have been linked to several human diseases.

● Visit our Web site at **http://www.info.brookscole.com/solomonbergmartin** for links to chapter-related resources on the World Wide Web. Additional on-line materials relating to this chapter can also be found on our Web site.

See chapter activity on BioActive Learner CD for additional help in mastering the chapter's material. Icon location in the chapter's margins shows which topics have tutorials or simulations in the CD.

5

Biological Membranes

LEARNING OBJECTIVES

After you have studied this chapter you should be able to

1. Evaluate the importance of membranes to the cell, emphasizing their various functions.
2. Make a detailed sketch of the fluid mosaic model of cell membrane structure.
3. Explain how the properties of the lipid bilayer are responsible for many of the physical properties of a cell membrane.
4. Explain how the various classes of membrane proteins associate with the lipid bilayer and discuss the different roles of membrane proteins.
5. Contrast the physical processes of simple diffusion and osmosis with the carrier-mediated physiological processes by which materials are transported across cell membranes.
6. Solve simple problems involving osmosis; for example, predict whether cells will swell or shrink under various osmotic conditions.
7. Summarize the main ways that small hydrophilic molecules can move across membranes.
8. Differentiate between the processes of facilitated diffusion and active transport and discuss the ways in which energy is supplied to active transport systems.
9. Compare endocytotic and exocytotic transport mechanisms.
10. Describe information transfer across the plasma membrane.
11. Describe the structures and compare the functions of desmosomes, tight junctions, gap junctions, and plasmodesmata.

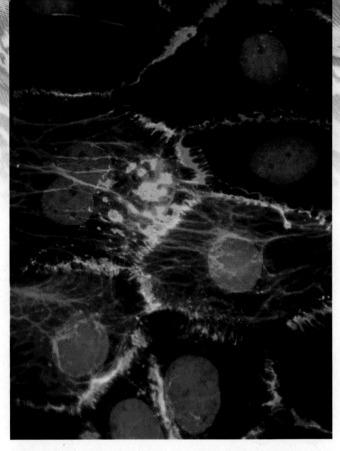

Cadherins. The human skin cells shown in this LM were grown in culture and stained with fluorescent antibodies. Cadherins, a group of membrane proteins, are seen as green belts around each cell in this sheet of cells. The nuclei appear as blue spheres; myosin in the cells appears red. *(Nancy Kedersha)*

To carry out the many chemical reactions necessary to sustain life, a cell must maintain an appropriate internal environment. The plasma membrane that surrounds every cell physically separates the cell from the outside world and defines the cell as a distinct entity. The plasma membrane helps maintain a life-supporting internal environment by regulating the passage of materials into and out of the cell. Many biologists view the evolution of biological membranes as an essential step in the origin of life. One can argue further that membranes made the evolution of complex cells possible because the extensive internal membranes of eukaryotes form multiple compartments with unique environments for highly specialized activities.

Cell biologists have found that biological membranes are not inanimate barriers; they are complex and dynamic structures made from lipid and protein molecules that are in constant motion. The unusual properties of membranes allow them to perform many functions in addition to defining the cell as a compartment and regulating passage of materials. These functions include participating in many chemical reactions, transmitting signals and information between the environment and the interior of the cell, and acting as an essential part of energy transfer and storage systems (see Chapters 7 and 8).

One exciting area of cell membrane research focuses on membrane proteins. Many proteins associated with the plasma membrane are enzymes. Others function in transport of materials or in transfer of information. Still others are important in connecting cells to one another to form tissues. Investigators are studying how membrane proteins function in health and disease. Membrane proteins known as **cadherins** are responsible for calcium-dependent adhesion between cells that form multicellular sheets, for example, the epithelium that makes up human skin (*see LM above*). An absence of these proteins has been observed when cells become malignant. Recent experimental evidence suggests that certain cadherins mediate the way that cells adhere in the early embryo and so are important in development.

In this chapter, we first consider what is known about the composition and structure of biological membranes. We survey how various materials, ranging from simple to complex molecules, and even particles, move across membranes. We then consider how information can cross the plasma membrane through a signal relay system. Finally, specialized structures that permit interactions between membranes of different cells are examined. Although much of our discussion centers on the structure and functions of plasma membranes, many of the concepts are also applicable to other cellular membranes.

■ BIOLOGICAL MEMBRANES ARE LIPID BILAYERS WITH ASSOCIATED PROTEINS

Long before the development of the electron microscope, it was known that membranes are composed of both lipids and proteins. Work by researchers in the 1920s and 1930s had provided clues that the core of cell membranes is composed of lipids, mostly phospholipids (see Chapter 3).

Phospholipids form bilayers in water

Phospholipids are primarily responsible for the physical properties of biological membranes. This is because certain phospholipids have unique attributes, including features that allow them to form bilayered structures. A phospholipid contains two fatty acid chains linked to two of the three carbons of a glycerol molecule (see Fig. 3–13). The fatty acid chains make up the nonpolar, hydrophobic ("water-fearing") portion of the phospholipid. Bonded to the third carbon of the glycerol is a negatively charged, hydrophilic ("water-loving") phosphate group, which in turn is linked to a polar, hydrophilic organic group. Molecules of this type, which have distinct hydrophobic and hydrophilic regions, are called **amphipathic** molecules. All lipids that make up the core of biological membranes have amphipathic characteristics.

Because one end of each phospholipid associates freely with water and the opposite end does not, the most stable orientation for them to assume in water results in the formation of a bilayer structure (Fig. 5–1a). This arrangement allows the hydrophilic heads of the phospholipids to be in contact with the aqueous medium, while their oily tails, the hydrophobic fatty acid chains, are buried in the interior of the structure away from the water molecules.

Amphipathic properties alone do not predict the ability of lipids to associate as a bilayer. Shape is also important. Phospholipids tend to have uniform widths; their roughly cylindrical shapes, together with their amphipathic properties, are responsible for bilayer formation. In summary, phospholipids form bilayers because the molecules have (1) two distinct regions, one strongly hydrophobic and the other strongly hydrophilic (making them strongly amphipathic), and (2) cylindrical shapes that allow them to associate with water most easily as a bilayer structure.

Many common detergents are amphipathic molecules, each containing a single hydrocarbon chain (like a fatty acid) at one end and a hydrophilic region at the other. These molecules are roughly cone-shaped, with the hydrophilic end forming the broad base and the hydrocarbon tail leading to the point. Because of their shapes, these molecules do not associate as bilayers but instead tend to form spherical structures in water (see Fig. 5–1b). Detergents are able to "solubilize" oil because the oil molecules associate with the hydrophobic interiors of the spheres.

Process of Science Current data support a fluid mosaic model of membrane structure

By examining the plasma membrane of the mammalian red blood cell and comparing the surface area of the membrane with the total number of lipid molecules per cell, early investigators were able to calculate that the phospholipids are probably arranged so that the membrane is no more than two phospholipid molecules thick. These findings, together with other data, led H. Davson and J.F. Danielli in 1935 to propose a model in which they envisioned a membrane as a kind of "sandwich" consisting of a *lipid bilayer* (a double layer of lipid) between two protein layers (Fig. 5–2a). This very useful model had a great influence on the direction of membrane research for more than 20 years. Models are important in the scientific process; good ones not only explain the available data but are testable. That is, scientists can use the model to help them develop hypotheses that can be tested experimentally (see Chapter 1).

With the development of the electron microscope in the 1950s, cell biologists were able to see the plasma membrane for the first time. One of their most striking observations was how uniform and thin the membranes are. The plasma membrane is no more than 10 nm thick. The electron microscope revealed a three-layered structure, something like a railroad

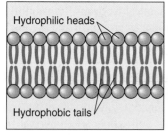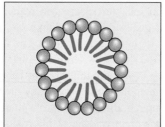

(a) Phospholipids in water   (b) Detergent in water

■ **Figure 5–1 Lipid membranes.** The ability of lipids to associate in water depends on their amphipathic properties and their shapes. (a) Phospholipids associate as bilayers in water because they are roughly cylindrical amphipathic molecules. The hydrophobic fatty acid chains associate with each other and are not exposed to the water. The hydrophilic phospholipid heads are in contact with the water. (b) Detergent molecules are roughly cone-shaped amphipathic molecules that associate in water as spherical structures.

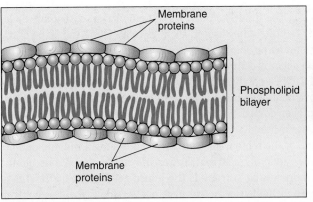

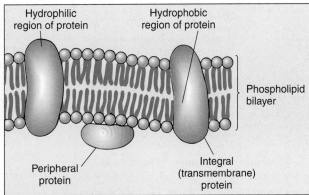

(a) The Davson-Danielli "sandwich" model

(b) Fluid mosaic model

Figure 5–2   Two models of membrane structure. **(a)** According to the Davson-Danielli model, the membrane is a sandwich of phospholipids spread between two layers of protein. Although accepted for more than 20 years, this model was shown to be incorrect. **(b)** According to the fluid mosaic model, a cell membrane is made up of a fluid lipid bilayer with a constantly changing "mosaic pattern" of associated proteins.

track, with two dark layers separated by a lighter layer (Fig. 5–3). Their findings seemed to support the protein-lipid-protein sandwich model.

During the 1960s, a paradox emerged regarding arrangement of the proteins. It was widely assumed that membrane proteins were uniform and had shapes that would allow them to lie like thin sheets on the membrane surface. When proteins

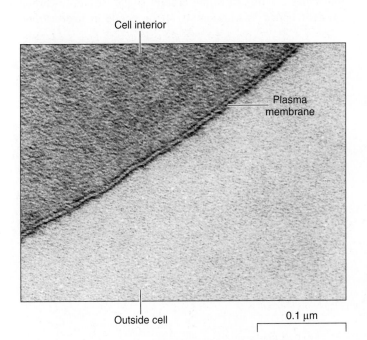

Figure 5–3   TEM of the plasma membrane of a mammalian red blood cell. The plasma membrane separates the cytoplasm *(darker region)* from the external environment *(lighter region)*. The hydrophilic heads of the phospholipids are seen as the parallel dark lines, while the hydrophobic tails are visible as the light zone between them. *(Omikron/Photo Researchers, Inc.)*

from membranes were purified by cell fractionation, however, they were found to be far from uniform; in fact, they varied widely in composition and size. Some proteins were much larger than investigators had imagined. How could these proteins be arranged to fit within a surface layer of a membrane less than 10 nm thick? At first, some investigators attempted to address these objections by modifying the model with the hypothesis that the proteins on the membrane surfaces were a flattened, extended form, perhaps a β-pleated sheet (see Chapter 3).

Other cell biologists found that instead of having sheetlike structures, many membrane proteins are rounded, or globular. Studies of a number of individual membrane proteins showed that one region (or domain) of the molecule could always be found on one side of the bilayer, while another part of the protein might be located on the opposite side. It appeared that, rather than forming a thin surface layer, many membrane proteins extend completely through the lipid bilayer. Thus, membranes appear to contain many different types of proteins of different shapes and sizes that are associated with the bilayer in a mosaic pattern.

In 1972, S.J. Singer and G.L. Nicolson proposed a model of membrane structure that represented a synthesis of the known properties of biological membranes. According to their **fluid mosaic model,** a cell membrane consists of a fluid bilayer of phospholipid molecules in which the proteins are embedded or otherwise associated, much like the tiles in a mosaic picture. This mosaic pattern is not static, however, because the positions of the proteins are constantly changing as they move about like icebergs in a fluid sea of phospholipids. This model has provided great impetus to research; it has been repeatedly tested and has been shown to accurately predict the properties of many kinds of cell membranes. Figure 5–2*b* depicts the plasma membrane of a eukaryotic cell; prokaryotic plasma membranes are discussed in Chapter 23.

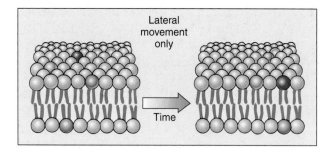

Figure 5–4 Membrane fluidity. The ordered arrangement of phospholipid molecules makes the cell membrane a liquid crystal. However, the hydrocarbon chains are in constant motion, allowing each molecule to move laterally on the same side of the bilayer.

Biological membranes are two-dimensional fluids

An important physical property of phospholipid bilayers is that they behave as *liquid crystals*. The bilayers are crystal-like in that the lipid molecules form an ordered array with the heads on the outside and fatty acid chains on the inside; they are liquid-like in that, despite the orderly arrangement of the molecules, their hydrocarbon chains are in constant motion. Thus, molecules are free to rotate and can move laterally within their single layer (Fig. 5–4). Such movement gives the bilayer the property of a *two-dimensional fluid*. Under normal conditions this means that a single phospholipid molecule can travel laterally across the surface of a eukaryotic cell in seconds.

Process of Science The fluid-like qualities of lipid bilayers also allow molecules embedded in them to move along the plane of the membrane (as long as they are not anchored in some way). This was elegantly demonstrated by David Frye and Michael Ediden in 1970. They conducted experiments in which they followed the movement of membrane proteins on the surface of two cells that had been joined (Fig. 5–5). When the plasma membranes of a mouse cell and a human cell are fused, within minutes at least some of the membrane proteins from each cell migrate and become randomly distributed over the single continuous plasma membrane that surrounds the joined cells. The experiments of Frye and Ediden demonstrated that the fluidity of the lipids in the membrane allows many of the proteins to move, producing an ever-changing configuration.

If a membrane is to function properly, its lipids must be in a state of optimal fluidity. The structure of a membrane is weakened if its lipids are too fluid. On the other hand, it has been shown that many membrane functions, such as the transport of certain substances, are inhibited or cease if the lipid bilayer is too rigid. At normal temperatures, cell membranes are fluid. However, the motion of the fatty acid chains is slowed at low temperatures. If the temperature decreases to a critical point, the membrane is converted to a more solid gel state.

Certain properties of membrane lipids have significant effects on the fluidity of the bilayer. Recall from Chapter 3 that molecules are free to rotate around single carbon-to-carbon covalent bonds. Because most of the bonds in hydrocarbon

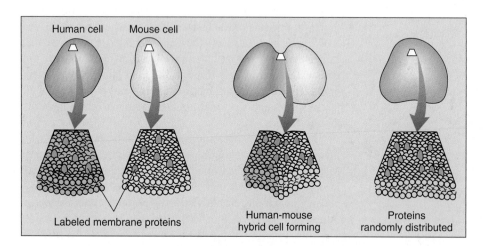

Figure 5–5 Mobility of membrane proteins. An elegant series of experiments by Frye and Ediden demonstrated that at least some membrane proteins are highly mobile entities in a two-dimensional fluid. Membrane proteins of mouse cells and human cells were labeled with fluorescent dye markers in two different colors. When the plasma membranes of a mouse cell and a human cell were fused, mouse proteins were observed migrating to the human side and human proteins to the mouse side. After a short time mouse and human proteins became randomly distributed on the cell surface.

chains are single bonds, the chains themselves can undergo rapid twisting motions that increase as the temperature increases.

The fluid state of the membrane depends on its component lipids. You have probably noticed that when melted butter is left at room temperature, it solidifies. Vegetable oils, however, remain liquid at room temperature. Recall from our discussion of fats in Chapter 3 that animal fats like butter are high in saturated fatty acids that lack double bonds. In contrast, a vegetable oil may be polyunsaturated with most of its fatty acid chains having two or more double bonds. Double bonds produce "bends" in the molecules that prevent the hydrocarbon chains from coming close together and interacting through van der Waals forces (see Chapter 3). In this way unsaturated fats lower the temperature at which oil or membrane lipids solidify.

Many organisms have regulatory mechanisms that allow them to maintain their membranes in an optimally fluid state. For example, some organisms that are unable to maintain a constant internal temperature can compensate for temperature changes by altering the fatty acid content of their membrane lipids. When grown at colder temperatures, such organisms are found to have relatively high proportions of unsaturated fatty acids in their membrane lipids.

Some membrane lipids have the ability to help stabilize membrane fluidity within certain limits. One such "fluidity buffer" is cholesterol, a steroid found in animal cell membranes. A cholesterol molecule is largely hydrophobic but is slightly amphipathic owing to the presence of a single hydroxyl group (see Fig. 3–15a). This hydroxyl group associates with the hydrophilic heads of the phospholipids; the hydrophobic remainder of the cholesterol molecule fits between the fatty acid hydrocarbon chains (Fig. 5–6).

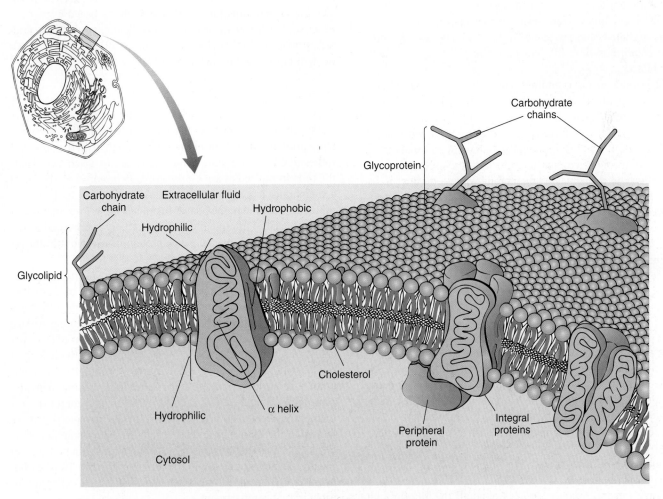

Figure 5–6 Structure of the plasma membrane according to the fluid mosaic model. Although the lipid bilayer consists mainly of phospholipids, other lipids such as cholesterol are present. Peripheral proteins are loosely associated with the bilayer, while integral proteins are tightly bound. The integral proteins shown here are transmembrane proteins that extend through the bilayer. They have hydrophilic regions on both sides of the bilayer, connected by a membrane-spanning α-helix with hydrophobic amino acid side chains *(not shown)*. Glycolipids (carbohydrates attached to lipids) and glycoproteins (carbohydrates attached to proteins) are exposed on the extracellular surface; they play roles in cell recognition and adhesion.

At low temperatures the cholesterol molecules act as "spacers" between the hydrocarbon chains, restricting van der Waals interactions that would promote solidifying. Cholesterol also helps prevent the membrane from becoming weakened or unstable at higher temperatures. This is because the cholesterol molecules interact strongly with the portions of the hydrocarbon chains closest to the phospholipid head. This interaction restricts motion in these regions. Plant cells have steroids other than cholesterol that carry out similar functions.

Biological membranes fuse and form closed vesicles

Lipid bilayers, particularly those in the liquid-crystalline state, have additional important physical properties. Bilayers tend to resist forming free ends; as a result, they are self-sealing and under most conditions spontaneously round up to form closed vesicles. Lipid bilayers are also flexible, allowing cell membranes to change shape without breaking. Finally, under appropriate conditions lipid bilayers have the ability to fuse with other bilayers.

Membrane fusion is an important cellular process. When a vesicle fuses with another membrane, both membrane bilayers and their compartments become continuous. Various transport and secretory vesicles form from and also merge with membranes of the ER and Golgi complex, allowing materials to be transferred from one compartment to another. A secretory vesicle can fuse with the plasma membrane when a product is secreted from the cell. This process is known as *exocytosis*. In *endocytosis,* large molecules are brought into the cell from the outside by the formation of vesicles from the plasma membrane. Both exocytosis and endocytosis are discussed later in this chapter.

Membrane proteins include integral and peripheral proteins

The two major classes of membrane proteins, integral proteins and peripheral proteins, are defined by how tightly they are associated with the lipid bilayer (see Fig. 5–6). **Integral membrane proteins** are firmly bound to the membrane. Cell biologists usually can release them only by disrupting the bilayer with detergents. These proteins are amphipathic. Their hydrophilic regions extend out of the cell or into the cytoplasm, while their hydrophobic regions interact with the fatty acid tails of the membrane phospholipids.

Some integral proteins do not extend all the way through the membrane. Many others, called **transmembrane proteins,** extend completely through the membrane. Some span the membrane only once, while others wind back and forth as many as 24 times. The most common kind of transmembrane protein is an α-helix (see Chapter 3) with hydrophobic amino acid side chains projecting out from the helix into the hydrophobic region of the lipid bilayer.

Peripheral membrane proteins are not embedded in the lipid bilayer. They are located on the inner or outer surfaces of the plasma membrane, usually bound to exposed regions of integral proteins by noncovalent interactions. Peripheral proteins can be easily removed from the membrane without disrupting the structure of the bilayer.

Proteins are oriented asymmetrically across the bilayer

Process of Science One of the most remarkable demonstrations that proteins are actually embedded in the lipid bilayer comes from freeze-fracture electron microscopy (Fig. 5–7), which enables investigators to literally see the membrane from "inside out." When cellular membranes are examined in this way, numerous particles are observed on the fracture faces. These particles are clearly integral membrane proteins because they are never seen in freeze-fractured artificial lipid bilayers. These findings profoundly influenced Singer and Nicolson in their development of the fluid mosaic model.

When the two sides of a membrane are compared (as in Fig. 5–7), large numbers of particles are found on one side and very few on the other. This does not necessarily mean that there are more proteins on one side of the membrane than on the other but rather that most are more firmly attached to a given side. Thus, the protein molecules are *asymmetrically oriented*. Each side of a membrane has different characteristics because each type of protein is oriented in the bilayer in only one way. Proteins are not randomly placed into membranes; asymmetry is produced by the highly specific way in which each protein is inserted into the bilayer.

Membrane proteins that will become part of the inner surface of the plasma membrane are manufactured by free ribosomes and move to the membrane through the cytoplasm. Membrane proteins that will be associated with the cell's outer surface are manufactured like proteins destined to be exported from the cell. As discussed in Chapter 4, these proteins are initially formed by ribosomes on the rough ER. They pass through the ER membrane into the lumen, where sugars are added, making them **glycoproteins.** Only a part of each protein passes through the ER membrane, so each completed protein has some regions that are located in the ER lumen and other regions that remain in the cytosol. Enzymes that attach the sugars to certain amino acids on the protein are found only in the lumen of the ER. Thus, carbohydrates can be added only to the parts of proteins that are located in that compartment.

Follow the vesicle budding and membrane fusion events that are part of the transport process from top to bottom in Figure 5–8. You can see that the same region of the protein that protruded into the ER lumen is also transferred to the lumen of the Golgi complex. There additional enzymes further modify the carbohydrate chains. Within the Golgi complex, the glycoprotein is sorted and directed to the plasma membrane. The modified re-

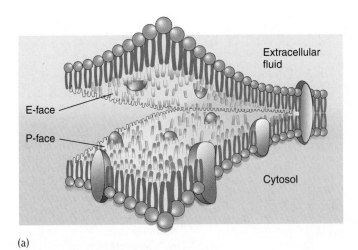

(a)

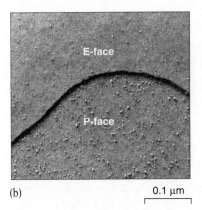

(b)　　　　　　　　0.1 μm

Figure 5–7 Asymmetry of the plasma membrane.
(a) In the freeze-fracture method, the path of membrane cleavage is along the hydrophobic interior of the lipid bilayer, resulting in two complementary fracture faces: (1) an inner half-membrane presenting the P-face (or protoplasmic face), from which project most of the membrane proteins, and (2) a relatively smooth, outer half-membrane presenting the E-face (or external face), which shows fewer protein particles. In a good fracture, particles are visible on both of the inside faces of the fractured membrane, as shown here. These particles are transmembrane proteins inserted into the lipid bilayer. Freeze-fractured bilayers of lipids alone do not have particles on the fracture planes. **(b)** A freeze-fracture TEM. Notice the greater number of proteins on the P-face of the membrane. *(b, D.W. Fawcett)*

gion of the protein remains inside a membrane compartment of a secretory vesicle as it buds from the Golgi complex. When the secretory vesicle fuses with the plasma membrane, the carbohydrate chain becomes the part of the membrane protein that extends to the exterior of the cell surface.

ER lumen ⟶ transport vesicle ⟶ vesicles in Golgi (transport to successive compartments) ⟶ secretory vesicle ⟶ plasma membrane

Membrane proteins function in transport, in information transfer, and as enzymes

Why should a membrane such as the plasma membrane illustrated in Figure 5–6 require so many different proteins? This diversity reflects the multitude of activities that take place in or on the membrane. Generally, plasma membrane proteins fall into several broad functional categories. Some membrane proteins anchor the cell to its substrate. For example, integrins, described in Chapter 4, attach to the extracellular matrix while simultaneously binding to microfilaments inside the cell (Fig. 5–9a). They also serve as receptors, or docking sites, for proteins of the extracellular matrix.

Many membrane proteins are involved in the transport of molecules across the membrane. Some form channels that selectively allow the passage of specific ions or molecules (Fig. 5–9b). Other proteins form pumps that use ATP to actively transport solutes across the membrane (Fig. 5–9c).

Certain membrane proteins are enzymes that catalyze reactions that take place near the cell surface (Fig. 5–9d). In some membranes, for example, mitochondrial or chloroplast membranes, enzymes may be organized in a sequence to regulate a series of reactions such as occurs in cellular respiration or photosynthesis.

Some membrane proteins are receptor proteins that receive information from other cells. For example, cells receive hormonal signals from endocrine cells. This information may be transmitted to the cell interior by *signal transduction,* discussed later in this chapter (Fig. 5–9e).

Membrane proteins can serve as identification tags that permit other cells to recognize them. Cells that recognize one another may connect to form a tissue. Human cells have distinctive major histocompatibility complex (MHC) receptors that identify them as part of a particular individual. Human cells recognize the surface proteins, or antigens, of bacterial cells as foreign. Antigens stimulate immune defenses that destroy the bacteria (Fig. 5–9f). Some membrane proteins form junctions between adjacent cells (Fig. 5–9g). These proteins may also serve as anchoring points for networks of cytoskeletal elements.

■ CELL MEMBRANES ARE SELECTIVELY PERMEABLE

Whether a membrane permits a substance to pass through it depends on the size and charge of the substance and on the composition of the membrane. A membrane is said to be *permeable* to a given substance if it permits that substance to pass through, and impermeable if it does not. A **selectively permeable membrane** allows some but not other substances to pass through it readily. In general, biological membranes are most permeable to small molecules and to lipid-soluble substances able to pass through the hydrophobic interior of the bilayer.

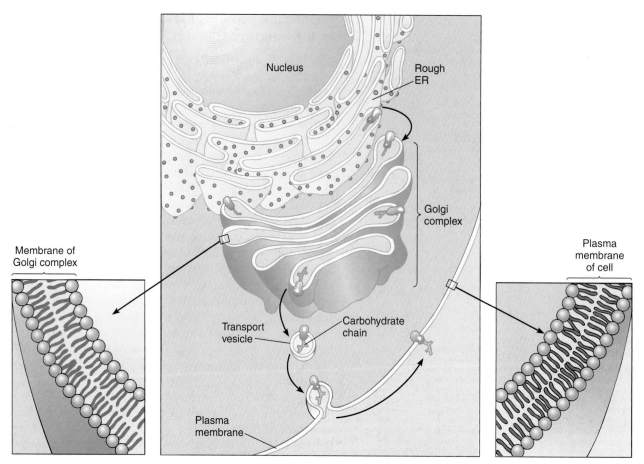

Figure 5–8 Formation of a plasma membrane protein. The surface of the rough ER membrane that faces the lumen of the rough ER also faces the lumen of the Golgi complex and vesicles. When a vesicle fuses with the plasma membrane, its inner surface becomes the extracellular surface of the plasma membrane. Note that the orientation of a protein in the plasma membrane is also a consequence of the pathway of its synthesis and transport in the cell. Carbohydrates added to proteins in the ER and then modified in the Golgi complex are associated with the extracellular surface of the plasma membrane.

Although they are polar (and therefore not lipid-soluble), water molecules can rapidly cross a fluid lipid bilayer. They can pass through a membrane in part because they are small enough to pass through gaps that occur as a fatty acid chain momentarily moves out of the way. Gases such as oxygen, carbon dioxide, and nitrogen; small polar molecules like glycerol; plus larger, nonpolar (hydrophobic) substances such as hydrocarbons also move through the lipid bilayer rapidly. Slightly larger polar molecules, such as glucose, and charged ions of any size pass through the bilayer much more slowly.

Although the bilayer is relatively impermeable to ions, cells must be able to move ions, as well as large and small polar molecules such as amino acids and sugars, across membranes. The permeability of membranes to those substances is due primarily to the activities of specialized membrane proteins. Biological membranes surrounding cells, nuclei, vacuoles, mitochondria, chloroplasts, and other organelles are selectively permeable to different types of molecules.

In response to varying environmental conditions or cellular needs, a plasma membrane may be a barrier to a particular substance at one time and actively promote its passage at another time. Changes in cell volume or ion distribution can critically affect cellular functions. Even routine activity, such as taking in nutrients, can cause chemical imbalance. By regulating chemical traffic across its plasma membrane, a cell can control its volume and its internal ionic and molecular composition, which can be quite different from that on the outside.

In the nonliving world, materials move passively by physical processes such as diffusion. In living cells, some particles cross the bilayer by diffusion. However, complex adaptations have evolved that rapidly move materials in and out of the cell. These physiological transport mechanisms, including active transport, exocytosis, and endocytosis (discussed later in this chapter), require a direct expenditure of metabolic energy by the cell.

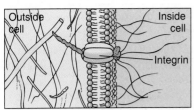

(a) Anchoring cell. Some membrane proteins, for example, integrins, anchor the cell to the extracellular matrix; they also connect to microfilaments within the cell.

Figure 5–9 Functions of membrane proteins.
Membrane proteins function **(a)** in anchoring the cell, **(b)** in passive transport, **(c)** in active transport, **(d)** as enzymes, **(e)** to transmit information into the cell by signal transduction, **(f)** in cell recognition, and **(g)** in forming junctions between cells.

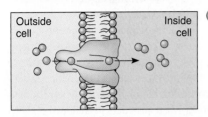

(b) **Passive transport.** Certain proteins form channels that allow selective passage of ions or molecules.

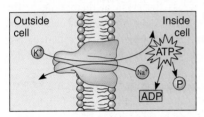

(c) **Active transport.** Some transport proteins pump solutes across the membrane, a process that requires a direct input of energy.

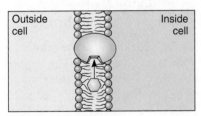

(d) **Enzymatic activity.** Many membrane-bound enzymes catalyze reactions that take place within or along the surface of the membrane.

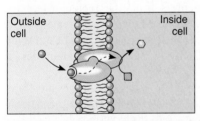

(e) **Signal transduction.** Some receptors bind with signal molecules such as hormones and transmit information into the cell by signal transduction.

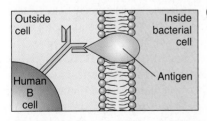

(f) **Cell recognition.** Some receptor proteins function as identification tags. For example, bacterial cells have surface proteins, or antigens, that human cells recognize as foreign. Antigens stimulate immune defenses that destroy the bacteria.

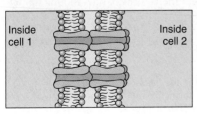

(g) **Junction between cells.** Cell adhesion proteins attach membranes of adjacent cells.

Random motion of particles leads to diffusion

Some substances pass into or out of cells and move about within cells by simple **diffusion,** a physical process based on random motion. All atoms and molecules possess kinetic energy, or energy of motion, at temperatures above absolute zero (0 Kelvin, −273° Celsius, or −459.4° F). Matter may exist as a solid, liquid, or gas, depending on the freedom of movement of its constituent particles. The particles of a solid are closely packed, and the forces of attraction between them allow them to vibrate but not to move around. In a liquid the particles are farther apart; the intermolecular attractions are weaker, and the particles move about with considerable freedom. In a gas the particles are so far apart that intermolecular forces are negligible; molecular movement is restricted only by the walls of the container that encloses the gas. This means that atoms and molecules in liquids and gases move in a kind of "random walk," changing directions as they collide.

Although the movement of the individual particles is undirected and unpredictable, we can nevertheless make predictions about the behavior of groups of particles. If the particles (atoms, ions, or molecules) are not evenly distributed, then at least two regions exist: one with a higher concentration of particles and the other with a lower concentration. Such a difference in the concentration of a substance from one place to another establishes a **concentration gradient.**

In the phenomenon of diffusion, the random motion of particles results in their net movement "down" their own concentration gradient (from the region of higher concentration to the one of lower concentration). This does not mean that individual particles are prohibited from moving "against" the gradient. However, because there are initially more particles in the region of high concentration, it logically follows that more particles move randomly from there into the low-concentration region than vice versa.

Diffusion can occur rapidly over very short distances. The rate of diffusion is determined by the movement of the particles, which in turn is a function of their size and shape, their electrical charges, and the temperature. As the temperature rises, particles move faster and the rate of diffusion increases.

Particles of different substances in a mixture diffuse independently of each other. If particles are not added to or removed from the system, a state of **equilibrium,** a condition of no net change in the system, is ultimately reached. At equilibrium the particles are uniformly distributed.

More commonly in organisms, equilibrium is never attained. For example, carbon dioxide continually forms within a human cell as sugars and other molecules are metabolized during the process of aerobic respiration. Carbon dioxide readily diffuses across the plasma membrane but then is rapidly removed by the blood. This limits the opportunity for the molecules to reenter the cell, so a sharp concentration gradient of carbon dioxide molecules always exists across the membrane. Two special cases of diffusion are dialysis and osmosis.

 How does kidney dialysis depend on diffusion? Dialysis is the diffusion of a solute across a selectively permeable membrane. To demonstrate dialysis, one can fill a cellophane bag[1] with a sugar solution and immerse it in a beaker of pure water (Fig. 5–10). If the cellophane membrane is permeable to sugar as well as to water, both sugar and water molecules will pass through it and the concentrations of sugar molecules in the water on the two sides of the membrane will eventually become equal. Subsequently, both solute and water molecules will continue to cross the membrane, but there will be no net change in their concentrations.

Dialysis has an important practical application in kidney dialysis, a process used to cleanse the blood of wastes when the kidneys do not function properly. Waste products in the form of small molecules diffuse readily across the artificial membrane in the dialysis apparatus. Wastes are removed from the blood, while blood cells, blood proteins, and other large molecules are retained. (See *Focus On: Kidney Disease* in Chapter 46 for a more detailed discussion of dialysis.)

Osmosis is diffusion of water (solvent) across a selectively permeable membrane

The selective permeability of cell membranes results in another special kind of diffusion called **osmosis.** This process involves the movement of *solvent* (in this case, water) molecules through a selectively permeable membrane. The water molecules pass freely in both directions, but, as in all types of diffusion, *net* movement is from the region where the water molecules are more concentrated to the region where they are less concentrated. Most solute molecules cannot diffuse freely through selectively permeable membranes of the cell.

The principles involved in osmosis can be illustrated using an apparatus called a U-tube (Fig. 5–11). The U-tube is divided into two sections by a selectively permeable membrane that allows solvent (water) molecules to pass freely but excludes solute molecules (e.g., sugar, salt). A water/solute solution is placed on one side, and pure water is placed on the other. The side containing the solute dissolved in the water has a lower effective concentration of water than the pure water side. This is because the solute particles, which are charged (ionic) or polar, interact with the partial electrical charges on the polar water molecules. Many of the water molecules are thus "bound up" and no longer free to diffuse across the membrane.

---

[1] Cellophane is often used as an "artificial membrane." It is made from cellulose and can be formed into a thin sheet that allows the passage of water molecules. Such membranes can be constructed with varying permeability to different solutes and can be quite different from biological membranes in their permeability. (When cellophane is used to package foods, it is coated to make it impermeable to air and water.)

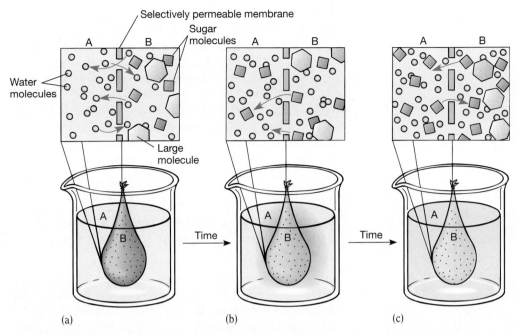

Figure 5-10 Dialysis. **(a)** A cellophane bag, filled with a mixture of sugar, water, and large molecules such as proteins, is immersed in a beaker of pure water. The cellophane acts as a selectively permeable membrane, permitting passage of the sugar and water molecules *(arrows)* but preventing passage of larger molecules. **(b)** The arrows indicate net movement of sugar molecules through the membrane into the water of the beaker. **(c)** Eventually the sugar becomes distributed equally between the two compartments. Although sugar and water molecules continue to diffuse back and forth *(arrows)*, net movement is zero.

Because of the difference in effective water concentration, there is net movement of water molecules from the pure water side (with a high effective concentration of water) to the water/solute side (with a lower effective concentration of water). As a result, the fluid level drops on the pure water side and rises on the water/solute side. Because the solute molecules do not diffuse across the membrane, equilibrium is never attained. Net movement of water continues, and the fluid level continues to rise on the side containing the solute. The weight of the rising column of fluid eventually exerts enough pressure to stop further changes in fluid levels, although water molecules continue to pass through the selectively permeable membrane in both directions.

We define the **osmotic pressure** of a solution as the tendency of water to move into that solution by osmosis. In our U-tube example, we could measure the osmotic pressure by inserting a piston on the water/solute side of the tube and measuring how much pressure must be exerted by the piston to prevent the rise of fluid on that side of the tube. A solution with a high solute concentration has a low effective water concentration and a high osmotic pressure; conversely, a solution with a low solute concentration has a high effective concentration of water and a low osmotic pressure.

Two solutions may be isotonic, or one may be hypertonic and the other hypotonic

Dissolved in the fluid compartment of every living cell are salts, sugars, and other substances that give that fluid a specific osmotic pressure. When a cell is placed in a fluid with exactly the same osmotic pressure, no net movement of water molecules occurs, either into or out of the cell. The cell neither swells nor shrinks. Such a fluid is said to be **isotonic,** of equal solute concentration, to the fluid within the cell (Table 5–1). Normally, our blood plasma (the fluid component of blood) and all our other body fluids are isotonic to our cells; they contain a concentration of water equal to that in the cells. A solution of 0.9% sodium chloride (sometimes called *physiological saline*) is isotonic to the cells of humans and other mammals. Human red blood cells placed in 0.9% sodium chloride neither shrink nor swell (Fig. 5–12*a*).

If the surrounding fluid has a concentration of dissolved substances greater than the concentration within the cell, it has a higher osmotic pressure than the cell and is said to be **hypertonic** to the cell. Because the hypertonic solution has a lower effective water concentration, a cell placed in such a solution shrinks as it loses water by osmosis. Human red blood cells

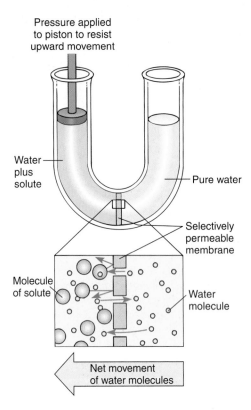

Pressure applied
to piston to resist
upward movement

Water
plus
solute

Pure water

Selectively
permeable
membrane

Molecule
of solute

Water
molecule

Net movement
of water molecules

Figure 5–11   Osmosis. The U-tube contains pure water on the right and water plus a solute on the left, separated by a selectively permeable membrane. Water molecules are able to cross the membrane in both directions *(red arrows)*. Solute molecules are unable to cross *(green arrows)*. The fluid level rises on the left and falls on the right because net movement of water *(blue arrow)* is to the left. The force that must be exerted by the piston to prevent the rise in fluid level is equal to the osmotic pressure of the solution.

sis occurs in plants when the soil or water around them contains high concentrations of salts or fertilizers.

If the surrounding fluid contains a lower concentration of dissolved materials than does the cell, it has a lower osmotic pressure and is said to be **hypotonic** to the cell; water then enters the cell and causes it to swell. Red blood cells placed in a solution of 0.6% sodium chloride gain water, swell (Fig. 5–12c), and may eventually burst. Many cells that normally live in hypotonic environments have adaptations to prevent excessive water accumulation. For example, certain protists such as *Paramecium* have contractile vacuoles that expel excess water (see Fig. 24–6).

Turgor pressure is the internal hydrostatic pressure usually present in walled cells

The relatively rigid cell walls of plant cells, algae, bacteria, and fungi enable these cells to withstand, without bursting, an external medium that is very dilute, containing only a very low concentration of solutes. Because of the substances dissolved in the cytoplasm, the cells are hypertonic to the outside medium (conversely, the outside medium is hypotonic to the cytoplasm). Water moves into the cells by osmosis, filling their central vacuoles and distending the cells. The cells swell, building up a pressure, termed **turgor pressure,** against the rigid cell walls (Fig. 5–13a). The cell walls can be stretched only slightly, and a steady state is reached when their resistance to stretching prevents any further increase in cell size and thereby halts the net movement of water molecules into the cells (although, of course, molecules continue to move back and forth across the plasma membrane). Turgor pressure in the cells is an important factor in providing support for the body of nonwoody plants. Thus, lettuce becomes limp in a salty salad dressing, and a picked flower wilts from lack of water.

Carrier-mediated transport requires special integral membrane proteins

The movement of water through the plasma membrane by osmosis is sometimes insufficient to account for the rapid bulk passage of water that occurs under some conditions. Recently,

placed in a solution of 1.3% sodium chloride shrink and are said to be *crenated* (Fig. 5–12b). If a cell that has a cell wall is placed in a hypertonic medium, it loses water to its surroundings. Its contents shrink, and the plasma membrane separates from the cell wall, a process known as **plasmolysis** (Fig. 5–13). Plasmoly-

TABLE 5–1   Osmotic Terminology

Solute Concentration in Solution A	Solute Concentration in Solution B	Tonicity	Direction of Net Movement of Water
Greater	Less	A hypertonic to B B hypotonic to A	B to A
Less	Greater	B hypertonic to A A hypotonic to B	A to B
Equal	Equal	A and B are isotonic to each other	No net movement

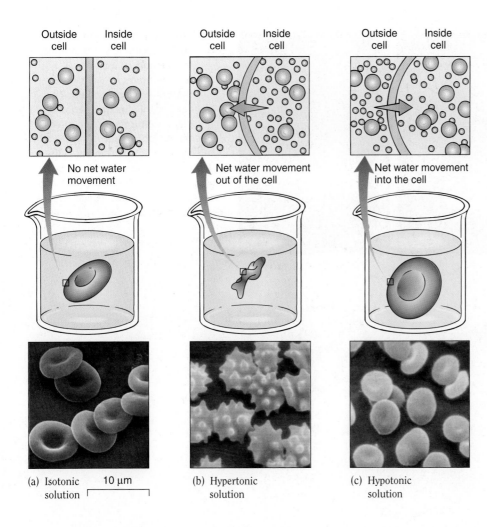

| Outside cell | Inside cell | Outside cell | Inside cell | Outside cell | Inside cell |

No net water movement

Net water movement out of the cell

Net water movement into the cell

(a) Isotonic solution   10 μm

(b) Hypertonic solution

(c) Hypotonic solution

Figure 5–12 How animal cells respond to osmotic pressure differences. (a) When a cell is placed in an isotonic solution, water molecules pass in and out of the cell, but the net movement is zero. (b) When a cell is placed in a hypertonic solution, there is a net movement of water out of the cell *(arrow)*, and the cell becomes dehydrated, crenated (shrunken), and may die. (c) When a cell is placed in a hypotonic solution, there is a net movement of water molecules into the cell *(arrow)*, causing the cell to swell or even burst. *(SEMs of human red blood cells courtesy of Dr. R.F. Baker, University of Southern California Medical School)*

investigators have identified **aquaporin-1,** an integral membrane protein that functions as a gated water channel. In certain types of cells, for example red blood cells, or under certain environmental conditions in plant cells, aquaporin-1 permits the rapid passage of water. The channel formed by aquaporin-1 allows the passage of water molecules, but it excludes protons. In some cells, the number of these channels apparently changes in response to specific signals. Other aquaporins, the focus of current research, appear to regulate the passage of other molecules.

Cells also must continually acquire essential polar nutrient molecules such as glucose and amino acids. The lipid bilayer of the plasma membrane is relatively impermeable to most large polar molecules. This is advantageous to cells for a number of reasons. Most of the compounds required in metabolism are polar, and the impermeability of the plasma membrane prevents their loss by diffusion.

Ions play important roles in many physiological processes. Some ions, such as calcium ions, are used in cell signaling. Changes in their cytoplasmic concentration trigger changes in a number of cellular processes (such as muscle contraction; see Chapter 38). As a cell controls the influx and efflux of ions, it is able to directly or indirectly control many metabolic activities.

Because of their electric charges, ions cannot cross a lipid bilayer by simple diffusion.

To transport ions and nutrients through membranes, systems of carrier proteins apparently evolved early in the origin of cells. This transfer of solutes by proteins located within the membrane is termed **carrier-mediated transport.** The two forms of carrier-mediated transport—facilitated diffusion and carrier-mediated active transport—differ in their capabilities and energy sources.

Facilitated diffusion occurs down a concentration gradient

In all processes in which substances move across membranes by passive diffusion, the net transfer of those molecules from one side to the other occurs as a result of a concentration gradient (see Fig. 6–4). If the membrane is permeable to a substance, there is net movement from the side of the membrane where it is more highly concentrated to the side where it is less concentrated. Such a gradient across the membrane is actually a form of stored energy. A concentration gradient can be established as a result of many different processes that take place in cells. The stored energy of the concentration gradient is released when molecules move from a region of high concentration to one of

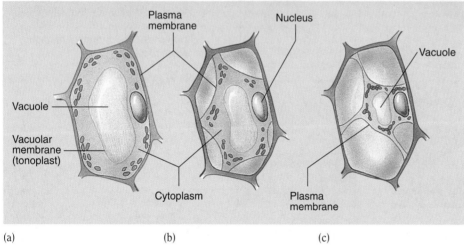

(a)   (b)   (c)

Figure 5–13 Plasmolysis. (a) In hypotonic surroundings, the vacuole of a plant cell fills, but the rigid cell walls prevent the cell from expanding. The cells of this healthy begonia plant are turgid. (b and c) When the begonia plant is exposed to a hypertonic solution, its cells become plasmolyzed as they lose water. The plant wilts and eventually dies. *(Dennis Drenner)*

low concentration; movement down a concentration gradient is therefore spontaneous. (These types of energy and spontaneous processes are discussed in greater detail in Chapter 6.)

In the type of transport known as **facilitated diffusion,** the membrane may be made permeable to a solute, such as an ion or a polar molecule, by a specific carrier or **transport protein** (Fig. 5–14). An important example of a transport protein that works by facilitated diffusion is glucose permease, a transmembrane protein that transports glucose into red blood cells. These cells keep the internal concentration of glucose low by immediately adding a phosphate group to entering glucose molecules, converting them to highly charged glucose phosphates that cannot pass back through the membrane. Because glucose phosphate is a different molecule, it does not contribute to the glucose concentration gradient. Thus, a steep concentration gradient for glucose is continually maintained, and glucose rapidly diffuses into the cell, only to be immediately changed to the phosphorylated form.

The mechanism of facilitated diffusion for glucose has been studied by using **liposomes,** artificial vesicles surrounded by

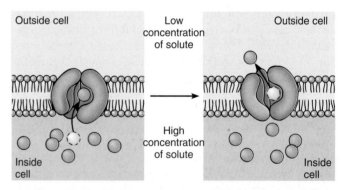

Figure 5–14 Facilitated diffusion. A transport protein in the membrane binds a solute particle. The transport protein changes its shape, opening a channel through the membrane. A specific solute can be transported from the inside of the cell to the outside or from the outside to the inside, but net movement is always from a region of higher solute concentration to a region of lower concentration. Facilitated diffusion requires the potential energy of a concentration gradient.

phospholipid bilayers. The phospholipid membrane of a liposome does not permit the passage of glucose unless researchers introduce the transport protein glucose permease into the membrane. Glucose permease and similar transport proteins temporarily bind to the molecules they transport. This mechanism appears to be similar to the way an enzyme binds with its substrate, the molecule on which it acts (see Chapter 6). In addition, as in enzyme action, binding apparently changes the shape of the transport protein. This change allows the glucose molecule to be released on the inside of the cell. According to this model, when the glucose is released into the cytoplasm, the transport protein reverts to its original shape and is available to bind another glucose molecule on the outside of the cell.

Another similarity to enzyme action is that transport proteins become saturated when the transported molecule is at high concentration. This may be because there are a finite number of transport molecules available and they operate at a defined maximum rate. When the concentration of solute molecules to be transported reaches a certain level, all of the transport molecules are working at their maximum rate.

Some carrier-mediated active transport systems "pump" substances against their concentration gradients

Although adequate amounts of some substances can be transported across cell membranes by diffusion, a cell often needs to move solutes against a concentration gradient. Many substances are required by the cell in concentrations higher than those outside the cell. These molecules are moved across cellular membranes by **carrier-mediated active transport** mechanisms. Because this active transport requires that particles be "pumped" from a region of low concentration to a region of high concentration (i.e., *against a concentration gradient*), transport must be coupled to an energy source such as ATP.

One of the most striking examples of an active transport mechanism is the **sodium-potassium pump** found in virtually all animal cells (Fig. 5–15). The pump is a group of specific proteins in the plasma membrane that uses energy in the form of ATP to exchange sodium ions on the inside of the cell for potassium ions on the outside of the cell. The exchange is unequal, so that usually only two potassium ions are imported for every three sodium ions exported. Because these particular concentration gradients involve ions, an electrical potential (separation of electrical charges) is generated across the membrane, and we say that the membrane is polarized.

Both sodium and potassium ions are positively charged, but because there are fewer potassium ions inside relative to the sodium ions outside, the inside of the cell is negatively charged relative to the outside. The unequal distribution of ions establishes an **electrical gradient** that drives ions across the plasma membrane. The action of sodium-potassium pumps helps maintain a charge separation across the plasma membrane. The separation of charges across a plasma membrane is called a **membrane potential.** Because there is both an electrical charge difference and a concentration difference on the two

sides of the membrane, the gradient is referred to as an **electrochemical gradient.** Such gradients store energy (like water stored behind a dam) that can be used to drive other transport systems. So important is the electrochemical gradient produced by these pumps that some cells (e.g., nerve cells) expend 70% of their total energy just to power this one transport system.

Sodium-potassium pumps (as well as all other ATP-driven pumps) are transmembrane proteins that extend entirely through the membrane. By undergoing a series of conformational changes (i.e., changes in shape), the pumps are able to exchange sodium for potassium across the plasma membrane. Unlike facilitated diffusion, at least one of the conformational changes in the pump cycle requires energy, which is provided by ATP. The shape of the pump protein changes as a phosphate group (from ATP) first binds to it and is subsequently removed later in the pump cycle.

The use of electrochemical potentials for energy storage is not confined to the plasma membranes of animal cells. Plant and fungal cells use ATP-driven plasma membrane pumps to transfer protons from the cytoplasm of their cells to the outside. Removal of positively charged protons from the cytoplasm of these cells results in a large difference in the concentration of protons, such that the outside of the cells is relatively positively charged and the inside of the plasma membrane is relatively negatively charged. The energy stored in these electrochemical gradients can be made available to do many kinds of cell work.

Other proton pumps can be used in "reverse" to synthesize ATP. Bacteria, mitochondria, and chloroplasts use energy from food or light to establish proton concentration gradients (see Chapters 7 and 8). When the protons diffuse through the proton carriers from a region of high proton concentration to one of low concentration, ATP is synthesized. These electrochemical gradients form the basis for the major energy conversion systems in virtually all cells.

Ion pumps have other important roles. For example, they are instrumental in the ability of an animal cell to equalize the osmotic pressures of its cytoplasm and its external environment. If an animal cell does not control its internal osmotic pressure, its contents will become hypertonic relative to the exterior. Water will enter the cell by osmosis, causing it to swell and possibly burst (see Fig. 5–12c). By controlling the ion distribution across the membrane, the cell is able to indirectly control the movement of water, for when ions are pumped out of the cell, water leaves by osmosis.

Linked cotransport systems indirectly provide energy for active transport

The electrochemical concentration gradients generated by the sodium-potassium pump (and other pumps) provide sufficient energy to power the active transport of other essential substances. In these systems a transport protein can **cotransport** the required molecules *against* their concentration gradient, while sodium, potassium, or hydrogen ions move *down* their gradient.

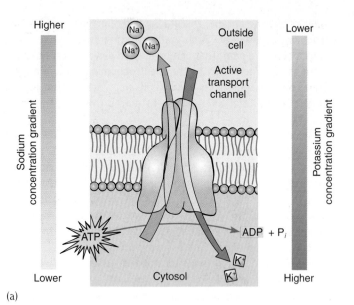

(a)

Figure 5–15 The sodium-potassium pump. (a) The sodium-potassium pump is an active transport system that requires energy from ATP. Each complete pumping cycle uses one molecule of ATP; three sodium ions are exported, and two potassium ions are imported. (b) A model illustrating the sodium-potassium pumping cycle.

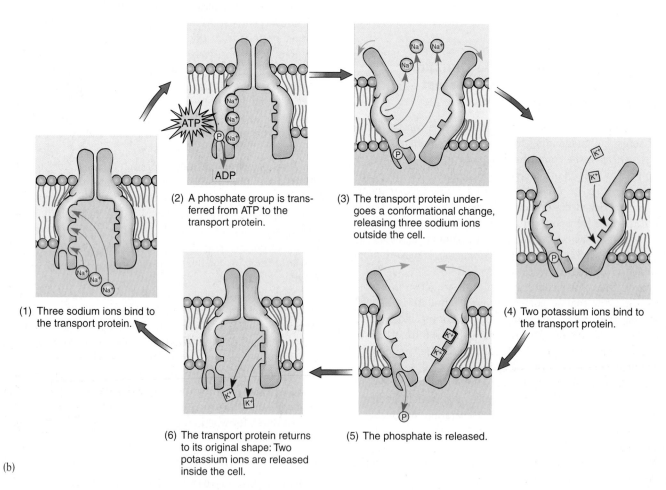

(1) Three sodium ions bind to the transport protein.

(2) A phosphate group is transferred from ATP to the transport protein.

(3) The transport protein undergoes a conformational change, releasing three sodium ions outside the cell.

(4) Two potassium ions bind to the transport protein.

(5) The phosphate is released.

(6) The transport protein returns to its original shape: Two potassium ions are released inside the cell.

(b)

Energy from ATP may be used indirectly in this process. ATP can be used to produce the ion gradient; the energy of this gradient is then used to drive the active transport of a required substance against its gradient.

In some cells more than one system may work to transport a given substance. For example, the transport of glucose from the intestine to the blood occurs through a thin sheet of epithelial cells that line the intestine. The surface that is exposed to the intestine has many **microvilli** (sing., *microvillus*), finger-like extensions that effectively increase the surface area of the membrane available for absorption (see Fig. 45–10c). The glucose transport protein on that region of the cell surface is part of an active transport system for glucose that is "driven" by the cotransport of sodium. The sodium concentration inside the cell is kept low by an ATP-requiring sodium-potassium pump that transports sodium out of the cell and into the blood. Because of its high concentration inside the cell (relative to the blood), glucose can be transported to the blood by facilitated diffusion.

What are the signals that target each transport protein to its appropriate region in the plasma membrane? Some of the current research in cell biology focuses on understanding mechanisms such as those that allow the cell to place different transport proteins in separate regions of the same plasma membrane.

Facilitated diffusion is powered by a concentration gradient; active transport requires another energy source

It is a common misconception that diffusion, whether simple or facilitated, is somehow "free of cost" and that only active transport mechanisms require energy. Because diffusion always involves net movement of a substance down its concentration gradient, we say that the concentration gradient "powers" the process. However, energy is required to do the work of establishing and maintaining the gradient. Think back to the example of facilitated diffusion of glucose. The cell maintains a steep concentration gradient (high outside, low inside) by phosphorylating the glucose molecules once they enter the cell. One ATP molecule is spent for every glucose molecule phosphorylated (not to mention such additional costs as the energy required to make the enzymes that carry out the reaction).

An active transport system can work *against* a concentration gradient, pumping materials from a region of low concentration to a region of high concentration. The energy stored in the concentration gradient is not only unavailable to the system but actually works against it. For this reason some other source of energy must be provided. As we have seen, in many cases ATP energy is used directly. In a cotransport system, energy is provided by a concentration gradient for some other substance (e.g., an ion). ATP may be required indirectly to power the pump that produces the ion gradient.

To summarize, both diffusion and active transport require energy. The energy for diffusion is provided by a concentration

gradient for the substance being transported. Active transport requires some other, usually more direct, expenditure of metabolic energy.

 ## The patch clamp technique has revolutionized the study of ion channels

Because ions cannot cross a lipid bilayer by simple diffusion, every membrane of every cell contains numerous *ion channels*. Movement of ions across a membrane can result in a charge difference, or electrical gradient. If the cell is large enough, this charge difference (usually expressed in millivolts, mV) can be measured by using two microelectrodes connected to an extremely sensitive oscilloscope or voltmeter (Fig. 5–16a). One of the microelectrodes is inserted into the cell and the other is placed just outside the plasma membrane. Although valuable, these techniques have serious limitations, for they cannot be used on smaller cells and do not provide information on the function of individual ion channels.

In the mid 1970s Erwin Neher and Bert Sakmann developed a method, known as the **patch clamp technique,** that allows researchers to study single ion channels of very small cells. In this technique, the tip of a micropipette is tightly sealed to a patch of membrane so small that it generally contains only a single ion channel (Fig. 5–16b). The flow of ions through the channel can be measured using an extremely sensitive recording device.

The patch clamp technique enables neurobiologists to study the action of a single channel over time. They have found that the current flow is intermittent and corresponds to the opening and closing of the ion channel. The permeability of the channel affects the magnitude of the current. This technique has been modified in many ways and has been applied to studies of the roles of ion channels in a wide range of cellular processes in both plants and animals. For example, studies of single ion channels enabled researchers to demonstrate that the genetic disease cystic fibrosis (see Chapter 15) is caused by a defect in a specific type of chloride ion channel. Because of the far-reaching implications of their work, Neher and Sakmann were awarded a Nobel Prize in 1991.

In exocytosis and endocytosis, large particles are transported by vesicles or vacuoles

In both simple and facilitated diffusion, and in carrier-mediated active transport, individual molecules and ions pass through the plasma membrane. Larger quantities of material, such as particles of food and even whole cells, must also be moved into or out of cells. Such work requires that cells expend energy directly, making it a form of active transport.

In **exocytosis,** a cell ejects waste products or specific secretion products such as hormones by the fusion of a vesicle with the plasma membrane (Fig. 5–17). Exocytosis results in the in-

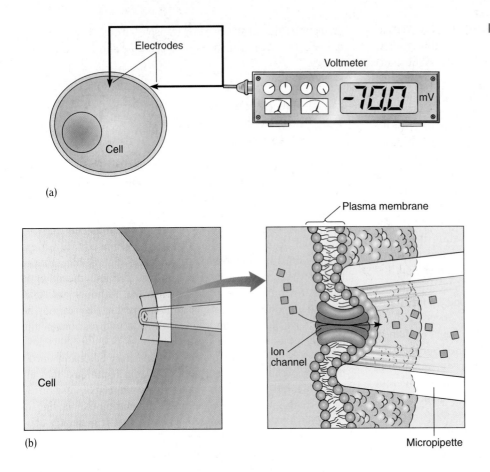

■ **Figure 5–16 Patch clamp technique.** (a) The difference in electrical charge across a membrane can be measured using micro-electrodes and a voltmeter. (b) A micropipette can be used to form a tight seal with a patch of plasma membrane. The membrane can be pulled away from the rest of the cell, and the flow of ions through a single ion channel can be studied.

corporation of the membrane of the secretory vesicle into the plasma membrane, as well as the release of the contents of the vesicle from the cell. This is also the primary mechanism by which plasma membranes grow larger.

In **endocytosis,** materials are taken into the cell. Several types of endocytotic mechanisms operate in biological systems. These mechanisms include phagocytosis, pinocytosis, and receptor-mediated endocytosis. In **phagocytosis** (literally, "cell eating"), the cell ingests large solid particles such as bacteria and food (Fig. 5–18). Phagocytosis is a mechanism used by certain protists and by several types of vertebrate white blood cells to ingest particles, some of which are as large as an entire bacterium. During ingestion, folds of the plasma membrane enclose the particle, which has bound to the surface of the cell, forming a large membranous sac, or vacuole. When the membrane has encircled the particle, it fuses at the point of contact. The vacuole then fuses with lysosomes, and the ingested material is degraded.

In the form of endocytosis known as **pinocytosis** ("cell drinking"), the cell takes in dissolved materials. Tiny droplets of fluid are trapped by folds in the plasma membrane (Fig. 5–19), which pinch off into the cytosol as tiny vesicles. The liquid contents of these vesicles are then slowly transferred into the cytosol; the vesicles may become progressively smaller, to the point that they appear to vanish.

In a third type of endocytosis, called **receptor-mediated endocytosis,** specific molecules combine with *receptor proteins* embedded in the plasma membrane. A molecule that binds specifically to a receptor is called a **ligand.** The receptors are concentrated in *coated pits,* depressed regions on the cytoplasmic surface of the plasma membrane. Each pit is coated by a layer of a protein, called *clathrin,* found just below the plasma membrane. After a ligand binds with a receptor, the coated pit forms a *coated vesicle* by endocytosis.

Cholesterol in the blood is taken up by animal cells by receptor-mediated endocytosis. Much of the receptor-mediated endocytosis pathway was detailed through studies by M. Brown and J. Goldstein on the receptor for low-density lipoprotein (LDL), a primary cholesterol carrier in blood. In 1986 these investigators were awarded the Nobel Prize for their pioneering work. Their findings have important medical implications because cholesterol that remains in the blood instead of entering the cells can become deposited in the artery walls, increasing the risk of heart attack.

In Figure 5–20 the uptake of an LDL particle is shown. Seconds after the vesicle moves into the cytoplasm, the coating dissociates from it, leaving an uncoated vesicle, called an *endosome,* free in the cytoplasm. The endosome typically forms two vesicles. One contains the receptors, the other the LDL particle. The receptors are returned to the plasma membrane, where they are recycled. The remaining vesicle fuses with a lysosome, and its contents are then digested and released into the cytosol.

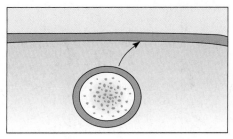

1 A vesicle approaches the plasma membrane,

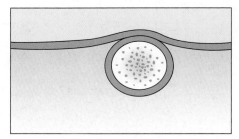

2 fuses with it, and

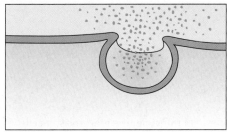

3 releases its contents outside the cell.

(a)

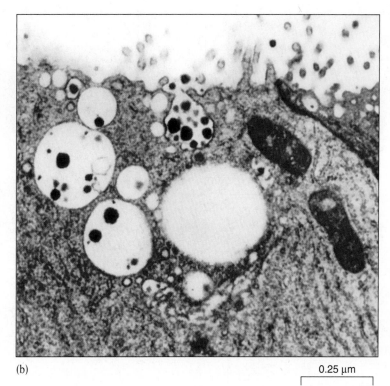

(b)

0.25 μm

Figure 5-17 Exocytosis. (a) The process of exocytosis. (b) TEM showing exocytosis of the protein components of milk by a mammary gland cell. (b, A. Ichikawa/from D.W. Fawcett)

Ligand binds to receptors in coated pits of plasma membrane ⟶ coated vesicle forms by endocytosis ⟶ coating detaches from vesicle ⟶ endosome divides:
⟶ One vesicle returns receptors to plasma membrane, where they are recycled
⟶ Other portion of endosome fuses with lysosome ⟶ contents are digested and released into the cytosol

The recycling of LDL receptors to the plasma membrane through vesicles illustrates a problem common to all cells that employ endocytotic and exocytotic mechanisms. In cells that are constantly involved in secretion, an equivalent amount of membrane must be returned to the interior of the cell for each vesicle that fuses with the plasma membrane; if it is not, the cell surface will keep expanding even though the growth of the cell itself may be arrested. A similar situation exists for cells that use endocytosis. A type of phagocytic cell known as a macrophage, for example, ingests the equivalent of its entire plasma membrane in about 30 minutes, requiring an equivalent amount of recycling or new membrane synthesis for the cell to maintain its surface area.

■ CELL MEMBRANES TRANSFER INFORMATION

Cells communicate with one another and with their external environment mainly by means of proteins that are located in cellular membranes or by chemical compounds that are secreted to the outside of the cell. Unicellular bacteria, protists, and fungi communicate with other members of their species by secreting chemical compounds. For example, when food is scarce, the amoeba-like cellular slime mold *Dictyostelium* secretes **cyclic adenosine monophosphate (cAMP)** (see Fig. 24–20). This chemical compound diffuses through the cell's environment and induces nearby slime molds to come together and form a multicellular slug-shaped colony. Another example is the chemical communication between yeast cells that permits recognition between similar mating types.

About a billion years ago, when cells began to associate to form multicellular organisms, elaborate **cell signaling** systems evolved. The development and functioning of complex organisms require precise internal communication, as well as effective responses to the outside environment. In plants and animals, hormones serve as important chemical signals between

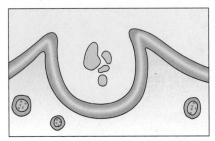

1 Folds of the plasma membrane surround the particle to be ingested, forming a small vacuole around it.

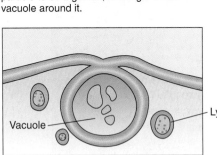

Vacuole —

Lysosome

2 The vacuole then pinches off inside the cell.

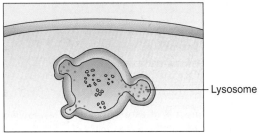

Lysosome

3 Lysosomes may fuse with the vacuole and pour their potent enzymes onto the ingested material.

(a)

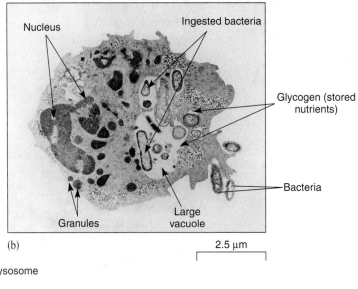

Nucleus

Ingested bacteria

Glycogen (stored nutrients)

Bacteria

Granules

Large vacuole

(b)

2.5 μm

Figure 5–18 Phagocytosis. In this type of endocytosis, a cell ingests relatively large solid particles. **(a)** The process of phagocytosis. **(b)** The white blood cell (known as a *neutrophil*) shown in this TEM is phagocytizing bacteria. The vacuoles contain bacteria that have already been ingested, while other bacteria are still outside the cell. The granules in the cytosol contain digestive enzymes. *(b, D.W. Fawcett)*

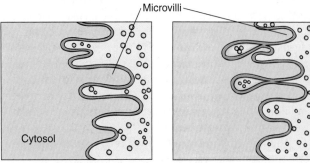

Microvilli

Pinocytotic vesicle

Cytosol

1 Tiny droplets of fluid are trapped by folds of the plasma membrane.

2 These pinch off into the cytosol as small fluid-filled vesicles.

3 The contents of these vesicles are then slowly transferred to the cytosol.

Figure 5–19 Pinocytosis or "cell-drinking."

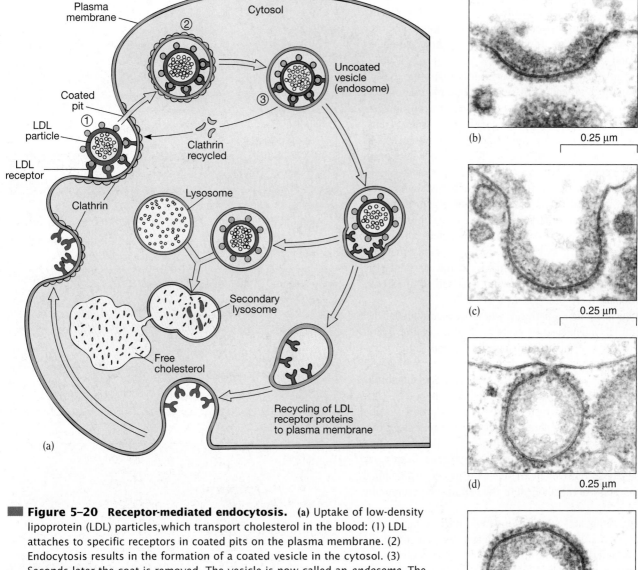

Figure 5–20 Receptor-mediated endocytosis. **(a)** Uptake of low-density lipoprotein (LDL) particles, which transport cholesterol in the blood: (1) LDL attaches to specific receptors in coated pits on the plasma membrane. (2) Endocytosis results in the formation of a coated vesicle in the cytosol. (3) Seconds later the coat is removed. The vesicle is now called an *endosome*. The receptors are returned to the plasma membrane and recycled. The vesicle containing LDL particles fuses with lysosomes to form a secondary lysosome. Hydrolytic enzymes then digest the cholesterol from the LDL particles for use by the cell. **(b** to **e)** Series of TEMs showing the formation of a coated vesicle from a coated pit. *(b to e, from Perry, M.M., and A.B. Gilbert,* J. Cell. Sci. *39:257–272, 1979)*

various cells and organs. Animals have evolved nervous systems in which neurons transmit information electrically and chemically.

The process of information transfer includes (1) **synthesis and release** of the signaling molecules; (2) **transport to target cells,** the cells that can respond to the signal; (3) **reception** of the information by target cells; (4) **signal transduction,** the process in which the cell converts an extracellular signal into an intracellular signal that affects some cell function; (5) **cellular re-**sponse to the information; and (6) **termination** of signaling by destruction of the signaling molecules.

Signaling molecules may be synthesized by neighboring cells or by specialized tissues some distance away from the target cells. Signaling molecules may find their way to target cells by diffusion, by transport in neurons, or via the circulatory system.

Reception is the process of receiving the signal. Target cells are typically equipped with receptor proteins that bind with signaling molecules. The receptor proteins for many chemical signals are specific proteins located in the plasma membrane. A signaling molecule such as a hormone or other regulatory molecule that binds with a receptor protein is called a ligand.

Many regulatory molecules transmit information to the cell interior without physically crossing the plasma membrane. These signal molecules rely on systems of interacting integral membrane proteins to transmit the information by signal transduction. Each component of a signal transduction system acts as a relay "switch," which can be in an activated ("on") state or an inactive ("off") state.

The first component in a signal transduction system is typically the receptor, which may be a transmembrane protein with a domain (a structural/functional component of a protein) exposed on the extracellular surface. A receptor generally has at least three domains. The external domain is a docking site for a signaling molecule. A second domain extends through the plasma membrane, and a third domain is a "tail" that extends into the cytoplasm.

In a typical signaling pathway, when the ligand binds with the receptor, it activates the receptor. Binding of the ligand changes the shape of the receptor tail that extends into the cytoplasm. The activated receptor changes the conformation of a second protein, which then becomes activated. The signal may be relayed through a sequence of proteins (Fig. 5–21). Ultimately these interactions result in the activation of a specific enzyme bound to the membrane. That enzyme may itself catalyze the production of large numbers of intracellular signaling molecules, or it may activate intracellular enzymes. In this way the original signal received by the receptor protein is amplified many times, and the metabolism of the cell may be profoundly altered.

The ligand that acts as a signaling molecule is sometimes referred to as the *first messenger*. Some ligand-receptor complexes bind to and activate specific integral membrane proteins, referred to as **G proteins.** In 1994 Alfred G. Gilman and Martin Rodbell were awarded a Nobel Prize for their research on G proteins. These proteins are so named because the active form is bound to **guanosine triphosphate (GTP),** a molecule similar to ATP but containing the base guanine instead of adenine. G proteins catalyze the hydrolysis of GTP to guanosine diphosphate (GDP), a process that releases energy.

In a complex sequence of events, a G protein relays the message from the receptor to an enzyme that catalyzes the production of a **second messenger.** Often, the enzyme adenylyl cyclase

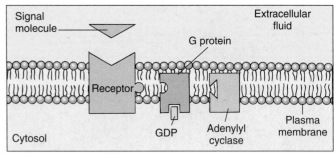
(a)

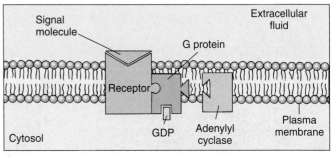
(b)

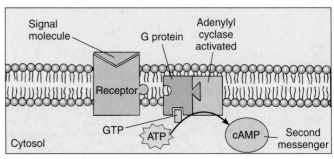
(c)

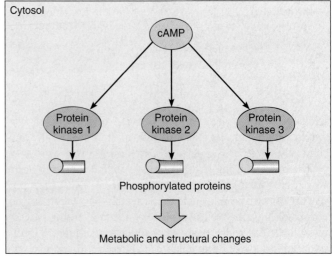
(d)

■ **Figure 5–21 Transfer of information across the plasma membrane.** **(a)** A signal molecule binds with a receptor in the plasma membrane. **(b)** The signal molecule-receptor complex activates a G protein. **(c)** G protein activates an enzyme that catalyzes the production of a second messenger such as cyclic AMP (cAMP). **(d)** cAMP then activates one or more enzymes such as protein kinases. The enzymes may phosphorylate proteins, which then alter the activity of the cell in some way.

catalyzes the formation of the second messenger cyclic AMP. Typically, the second messenger activates **protein kinases,** enzymes that activate specific proteins by transferring phosphate groups to them from ATP. This sequence of reactions, beginning with the binding of the signaling molecule to the receptor, leads to a change in some cell function.

G proteins are involved in a number of important signal transductions, including the action of many hormones (see Chapter 47). Some G proteins regulate channels that allow ions to cross the plasma membrane, and still others play important roles in the senses of sight, smell, and taste (see Chapter 41).

Ras proteins, a group of GTP-binding proteins that function somewhat like G proteins, are thought to be important in signal transduction necessary for many cell activities. Fibroblasts (a type of connective tissue cell) require the presence of two *growth factors,* epidermal growth factor and platelet-derived growth factor, for DNA synthesis. However, when investigators inactivated Ras proteins by injecting antibodies that bind to them into the fibroblasts, the growth factors were no longer effective. Data from this and similar experiments led to the conclusion that Ras proteins are important in signal transduction involving growth factors.

Cell biologists have demonstrated that when certain ligands bind to integrins (transmembrane proteins that connect the cell to the extracellular matrix) in the plasma membrane, certain signal transduction pathways are activated. Growth factors also turn on signaling pathways, and it is thought that growth factors and certain molecules of the extracellular matrix may modulate each other's messages. Integrins also respond to information received from inside the cell. This inside-out signaling affects how selective integrins are with respect to the molecules to which they bind and how strongly they bind to them.

■ JUNCTIONS ARE SPECIALIZED CONTACTS BETWEEN CELLS

Cells in close contact with each other typically develop specialized intercellular junctions. These structures may allow neighboring cells to form strong connections with each other, prevent passage of materials, or establish rapid communication between adjacent cells. Several types of junctions are found connecting animal cells, including anchoring junctions (desmosomes and adhering junctions), tight junctions, and gap junctions. Plant cells are connected by plasmodesmata.

Anchoring junctions connect cells of an epithelial sheet

Adjacent epithelial cells, such as those found in the outer layer of the skin, are so tightly bound to each other by anchoring junctions that strong mechanical forces are required to separate them. Cadherins, transmembrane proteins shown in the chapter opening photograph, are important components

of these junctions. Anchoring junctions do not affect the passage of materials between adjacent cells. Two common types of anchoring junctions are desmosomes and adhering junctions.

Desmosomes are points of attachment between cells (Fig. 5–22). They hold cells together at one point like a rivet or a spot weld. As a result, cells can form strong sheets, and substances can still pass freely through the spaces between the

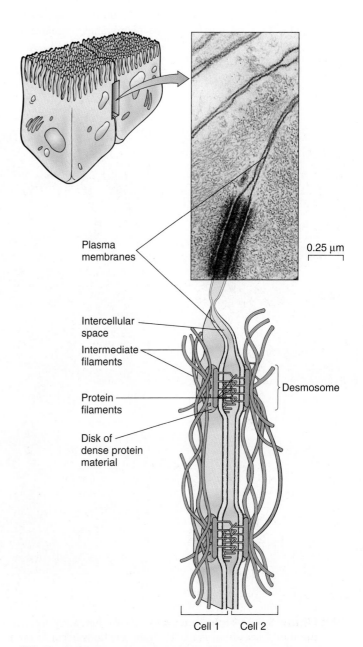

Figure 5–22 Desmosomes. The dense structure in the TEM is a desmosome. Each desmosome consists of a pair of button-like disks associated with the plasma membranes of adjacent cells, plus the intercellular protein filaments that connect them. Intermediate filaments in the cells are attached to the disks and are connected to other desmosomes. *(D.W. Fawcett)*

plasma membranes. Each desmosome is made up of regions of dense material associated with the cytosolic sides of the two plasma membranes, plus protein filaments that cross the narrow intercellular space between them. Desmosomes are anchored to systems of intermediate filaments inside the cells. Thus the intermediate filament networks of adjacent cells are connected so that mechanical stresses are distributed throughout the tissue.

Adhering junctions cement cells together. Cadherins, an important component of these junctions, form a continuous adhesion belt around each cell. These junctions connect to microfilaments that zip up the plasma membranes of adjacent cells.

Tight junctions seal off intercellular spaces between some animal cells

Tight junctions are literally areas of tight connections between the membranes of adjacent cells. These connections are so tight that no space remains between the cells; substances cannot leak between the cells. TEMs of tight junctions show that in the region of the junction the membranes of the two cells are in actual contact with each other, held together by proteins linking the two cells (Fig. 5–23).

Cells connected by tight junctions seal off body cavities. For example, tight junctions between cells lining the intestine prevent substances in the intestine from entering the body or the

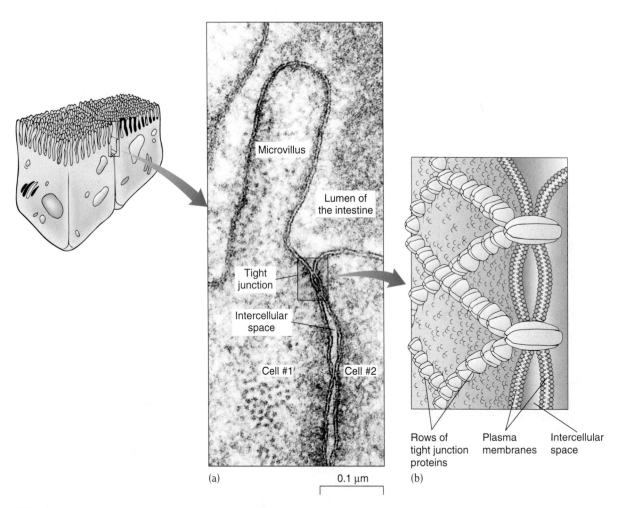

Microvillus

Lumen of the intestine

Tight junction

Intercellular space

Cell #1   Cell #2

(a)   0.1 μm   (b)

Rows of tight junction proteins

Plasma membranes

Intercellular space

Figure 5–23 Tight junctions. These junctions prevent passage of materials through spaces between cells. Tight junctions occur at the points of contact between two cells and extend completely around the cells. **(a)** This TEM shows points of fusion between the plasma membranes of adjacent cells lining the intestine. One tight junction is marked by the box. **(b)** The diagram shows that a tight junction is formed by linkages between rows of proteins of adjacent cells. These proteins are tightly packed in rows that seal off the intercellular space. *(a, G.E. Palade)*

blood by passing around the cells. The sheet of cells thus acts as a selective barrier. Food substances must be transported across the plasma membranes and through the intestinal cells before they enter the blood. This arrangement helps prevent toxins and other unwanted materials from entering the blood, and also prevents nutrients from leaking out of the intestine.

Gap junctions permit transfer of small molecules and ions

The **gap junction** is like the desmosome in that it bridges the space between cells; however, the space it spans is somewhat narrower (Fig. 5–24). Gap junctions also differ in that they are communicating junctions. They not only connect the membranes but also contain channels connecting the cytoplasm of adjacent cells. A gap junction consists of a hexagonal array of proteins (connexins) on adjacent cells that form a channel, about 1 to 1.5 nm in diameter. Small inorganic molecules (e.g., ions) and some biological molecules (e.g., derivatives of ATP)

can pass through the channels, but larger molecules are excluded. When appropriate marker substances are injected into one of a group of cells connected by gap junctions, the marker passes rapidly into the adjacent cells but does not enter the space between the cells.

Cells are able to control the passage of materials through gap junctions by opening and closing the channels (Fig. 5–24d). There is evidence that the open and closed states are regulated mainly by the intracellular concentrations of certain ions, such as Ca^{2+}.

Gap junctions provide for rapid chemical and electrical communication between cells. Cells in the pancreas, for example, are linked together by gap junctions in such a way that if one of a group of cells is stimulated to secrete insulin, the signal is passed through the junctions to the other cells in the cluster, ensuring a coordinated response to the initial signal. Gap junctions allow some nerve cells to be electrically coupled. Heart muscle cells are linked by gap junctions that permit the flow of ions necessary to synchronize contractions.

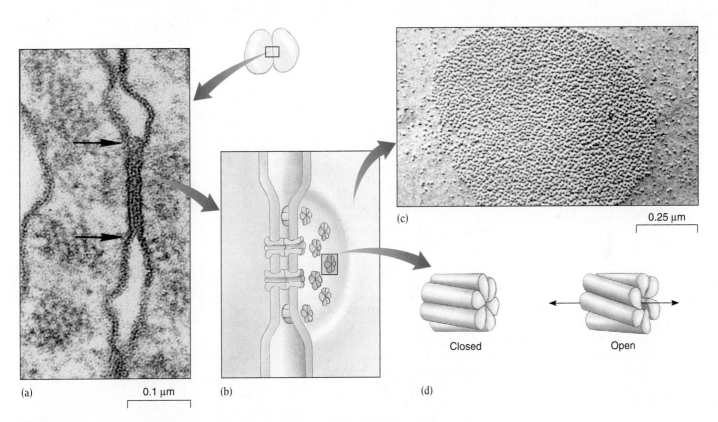

Figure 5–24 Gap junctions. These connections permit transfer of small molecules and ions between adjacent cells. **(a)** A TEM of a gap junction *(between the arrows)*. **(b)** Model of a gap junction based on electron microscopic and x-ray diffraction data. The two membranes contain cylinders composed of six protein subunits. Two cylinders from opposite membranes are joined to form a pore about 1.5 to 2 nm in diameter connecting the cytoplasmic compartments of the two cells. **(c)** Freeze-fracture replica of the P-face of a gap junction between two ovarian cells of a mouse, showing the numerous protein particles present. **(d)** Model illustrating how a gap junction pore might open and close. *(a, D.W. Fawcett; c, E. Anderson, J. Morphol. 156:339–366, 1978)*

Plasmodesmata allow movement of certain molecules and ions between plant cells

Plant cells do not need desmosomes for strength because they have cell walls. However, these same walls would isolate the cells, preventing them from communicating. For this reason, plant cells require connections that are functionally equivalent to the gap junctions of some animal cells. **Plasmodesmata** (sing., *plasmodesma*) are 20- to 40-nm-wide channels through adjacent cell walls connecting the cytoplasm of neighboring cells (Fig. 5–25). The plasma membranes of adjacent cells are therefore continuous with each other through the plasmodesmata. Most plasmodesmata contain a cylindrical membranous structure, called the *desmotubule*, which also runs through the opening and connects the ER of the two adjacent cells.

Plasmodesmata generally allow molecules and ions, but not organelles, to pass through the openings from cell to cell. The movement of ions through the plasmodesmata allows for a very slow type of electrical signaling in plants.

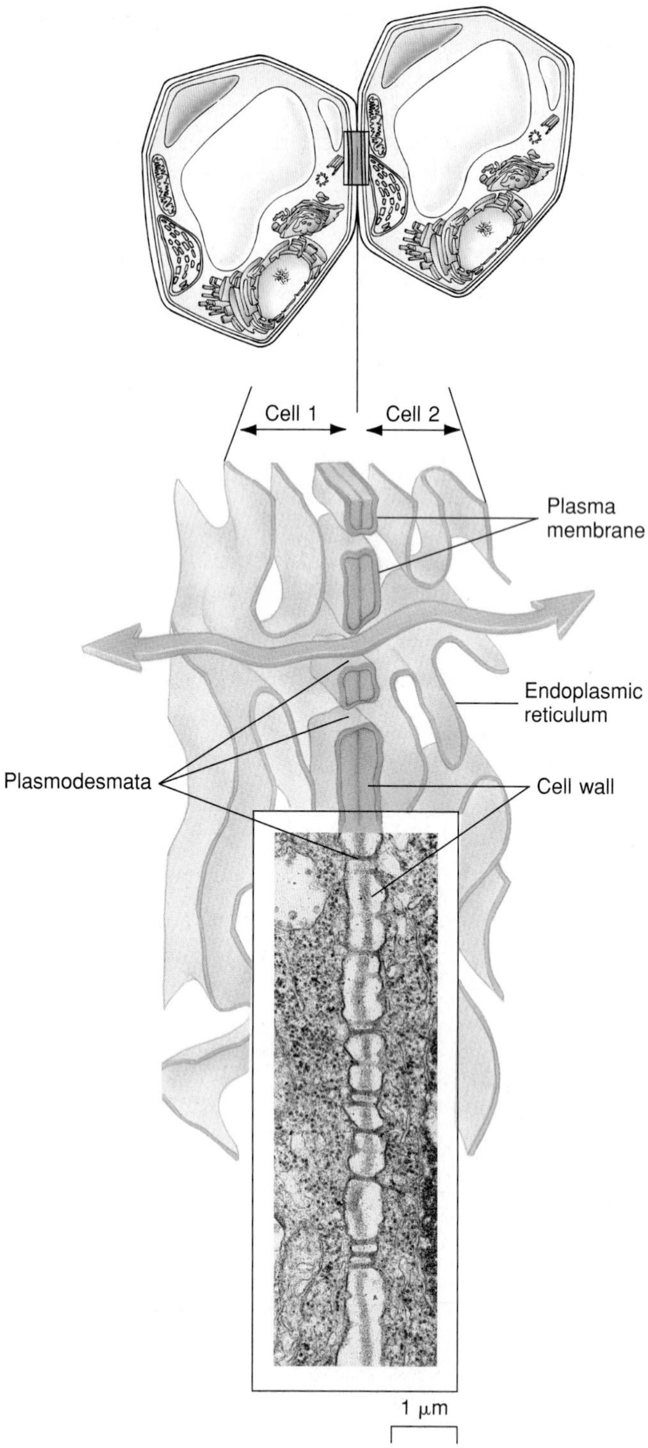

Figure 5–25 Plasmodesmata. TEM and line art of cytoplasmic channels through the cell walls of adjacent plant cells *(wide arrows)* that allow passage of water, ions, and small molecules. The channels are lined with the fused plasma membranes of the two adjacent cells. *(E.H. Newcomb, Biological Photo Service)*

I. Cell membranes are complex structures that (1) physically separate the interior of the cell from the extracellular environment and (2) form compartments within the cells of eukaryotes that allow them to perform complex functions. Membranes have many different structural and functional roles.

   A. They regulate the passage of materials.

   B. They receive information that permits the cell to sense and respond to changes in its environment.

   C. They contain specialized structures that allow specific contacts and communications with other cells.

   D. They participate in and serve as surfaces for biochemical reactions.

II. According to the **fluid mosaic model**, membranes consist of a fluid phospholipid bilayer in which a variety of proteins are embedded.

   A. The phospholipid molecules are **amphipathic:** they have hydrophobic and hydrophilic regions.

   B. The lipid bilayer is arranged in such a way that the hydrophilic heads of the phospholipids are at the two surfaces of the bilayer and their hydrophobic fatty acid chains are in the interior.

   C. In almost all biological membranes, the lipids of the bilayer are in a fluid or liquid-crystalline state, which allows the molecules to move rapidly in the plane of the membrane.

   D. **Integral membrane proteins** are embedded in the bilayer with their hydrophilic surfaces exposed to the aqueous environment and their hydrophobic surfaces in contact with the hydrophobic interior of the bilayer. **Transmembrane proteins** are integral proteins that extend completely through the membrane.

   E. **Peripheral membrane proteins** are associated with the surface of the bilayer, usually bound to integral proteins, and are easily removed without disrupting the structure of the membrane.

   F. Membrane proteins, lipids, and carbohydrates are asymmetrically positioned with respect to the bilayer so that one side of the membrane has a different composition and structure than the other.

   G. Many materials are transported from one part of the cell to another in vesicles that bud from various cell membranes and then fuse with some other membrane.

   H. Membrane proteins have various functions including transport of materials, acting as enzymes or receptors, cell recognition, and structurally linking cells together.

III. Biological membranes are selectively permeable membranes; that is, they allow the passage of some substances but not others.

   A. **Diffusion** is the net movement of a substance down its **concentration gradient** (from a region of greater concentration to one of lower concentration).

   1. **Dialysis** is the diffusion of a solute across a selectively permeable membrane.

   2. **Osmosis** is a kind of diffusion in which molecules of water pass through a selectively permeable membrane from a region where water has a higher effective concentration to a region where its effective concentration is lower.

   3. The **osmotic pressure** of a solution is determined by its concentration of dissolved substances (solutes). Cells regulate their internal osmotic pressures to prevent shrinking or bursting.

   4. An **isotonic** solution has an equal solute concentration to another fluid, for example, the fluid within the cell. When placed in a **hypertonic** solution, one that has a greater solute concentration than the cell, cells lose water to the surroundings; plant cells undergo **plasmolysis,** a process in which the plasma membrane separates from the cell wall. When cells are placed in a **hypotonic** solution, one with a lower concentration of dissolved materials relative to the cell, water enters the cells and causes them to swell.

   5. Plant cells can withstand high internal hydrostatic pressure because their cell walls prevent them from expanding and bursting. When water moves into cells by osmosis, it fills the central vacuoles. The cells swell, building up **turgor pressure** against the rigid cell walls.

   B. In **carrier-mediated transport** special membrane proteins move ions or molecules across a membrane.

   1. Some substances pass through membranes by **facilitated diffusion,** a form of carrier-mediated transport that uses the energy of a concentration gradient for the substance being transported and that cannot work against the gradient.

   2. In **carrier-mediated active transport** the cell expends metabolic energy to move ions or molecules across a membrane *against* a concentration gradient. The **sodium-potassium pump** uses ATP to pump sodium ions out of the cell and potassium ions into the cell.

   C. In **cotransport** an ATP-powered pump such as the sodium-potassium pump transports ions or some other solute and indirectly powers the transport of other solutes by maintaining a concentration gradient.

   D. The **patch clamp technique** allows researchers to study single ion channels.

   E. In **exocytosis,** the cell ejects waste products or secretes substances such as hormones or mucus by fusion of vesicles with the plasma membrane.

   F. In **endocytosis** materials such as food may be moved into the cell; a portion of the plasma membrane envelops the material, enclosing it in a vesicle or vacuole that is then released inside the cell.

   1. In **phagocytosis,** the plasma membrane encloses a particle such as a bacterium or protist, forms a vacuole around it, and moves it into the cell.

   2. In **pinocytosis,** the cell takes in dissolved materials by forming tiny vesicles around droplets of fluid trapped by folds of the plasma membrane.

   3. In **receptor-mediated endocytosis, ligands** bind to specific receptors in coated pits along the plasma membrane. These pits, coated by the protein clathrin, form coated vesicles by endocytosis.

IV. In **signal transduction,** a receptor converts an extracellular signal into an intracellular signal that causes some change in the cell.

   A. Signal transduction typically involves a series of molecules that relay information from one to another.

   B. The signaling pathway often involves activation of **G proteins** by binding of a ligand to a receptor; a second messenger such as **cyclic AMP;** and **protein kinases,** enzymes that activate specific proteins by phosphorylating them. The function of the phosphorylated protein is then altered.

V. Cells in close contact with one another may develop intercellular junctions.

   A. Anchoring junctions include **desmosomes** and **adhering junctions.** Desmosomes spot weld adjacent animal cells together. Desmosomes and adhering junctions are found between cells that form a sheet of tissue.

   B. **Tight junctions** seal membranes of adjacent animal cells together, preventing substances from moving through the spaces between the cells.

   C. **Gap junctions** are protein complexes that form channels in membranes, allowing communication between the cytoplasm of adjacent animal cells.

   D. **Plasmodesmata** are channels connecting adjacent plant cells. Openings in the cell walls allow the plasma membranes and cytoplasm to be continuous, thus permitting certain molecules and ions to pass from cell to cell.

1. Which of the following statements is *not* true? Biological membranes (a) are composed partly of amphipathic lipids (b) have hydrophobic and hydrophilic regions (c) are typically in a fluid state (d) are made mainly of lipids and of proteins that lie like thin sheets on the membrane surface (e) function in signal transduction

2. According to the fluid mosaic model, membranes consist of (a) a lipid-protein sandwich (b) mainly phospholipids with scattered nucleic acids (c) a fluid phospholipid bilayer in which proteins are embedded (d) a fluid phospholipid bilayer in which carbohydrates are embedded (e) a protein bilayer that behaves as a liquid crystal.

3. Transmembrane proteins (a) are peripheral proteins (b) are receptor proteins (c) extend completely through the membrane (d) extend along the surface of the membrane (e) are secreted from the cell

4. Which of the following is *not* a function of the plasma membrane? (a) transports materials (b) helps to structurally link cells together (c) manufactures proteins (d) anchors the cell to the extracellular matrix (e) has receptors that relay signals

5. Which of the following processes requires the cell to expend metabolic energy directly (e.g., from ATP)? (a) active transport (b) facilitated diffusion (c) dialysis (d) osmosis (e) simple diffusion

6. Which of the following is an example of carrier-mediated transport? (a) simple diffusion (b) facilitated diffusion (c) dialysis (d) osmosis (e) osmosis when a cell is in a hypertonic solution

7. Transport of sodium ions by sodium-potassium pumps is an example of (a) active transport (b) pinocytosis (c) dialysis (d) exocytosis (e) facilitated diffusion

8. Which of the following statements is *not* true of the patch clamp technique? (a) It allows researchers to study single ion channels (b) A micropipette is tightly sealed to a patch of membrane that contains a single ion channel (c) The technique can be used to study ion channels in animal cells, but not in plant cells (d) It helped researchers understand the correspondence between electrical current flow and opening of ion channels (e) It was developed by Neher and Sakmann

9. A cell takes in dissolved materials by forming tiny vesicles around fluid droplets trapped by folds of the plasma membrane. This process is (a) active transport (b) pinocytosis (c) receptor-mediated endocytosis (d) exocytosis (e) facilitated diffusion

10. When plant cells are in a hypotonic medium, they (a) undergo plasmolysis (b) build up turgor pressure (c) wilt (d) carry on dialysis (e) lose water to the environment

11. Which sequence most accurately describes receptor-mediated endocytosis? (a) ligand binds to receptors in coated vesicle → vesicle enters cytosol by cotransport mechanisms → clathrin accumulates around vesicle (b) ligands bind to receptors in coated pit → pit forms coated vesicle by endocytosis → clathrin coating detaches from vesicle (c) ATP binds to receptors in coated vesicle → vesicle enters cytosol by facilitated diffusion → protein coat dissolves (d) ligand binds to receptors in coated pit → pit forms coated vesicle by phagocytosis → coating detaches from vesicle (e) clathrin binds to receptors in coated pit → pit forms coated vesicle by endocytosis → protein coating forms around vesicle

12. In signal transduction (a) an extracellular signal is converted to an intracellular signal (b) a signal is relayed through a series of molecules in the membrane (c) signal molecules are destroyed before target cells can respond to the signal (d) answers a, b, and c are correct (e) answers a and b only

13. Anchoring junctions that hold cells together at one point like a spot weld are (a) tight junctions (b) microfilaments (c) desmosomes (d) gap junctions (e) plasmodesmata

14. Junctions that permit the transfer of water, ions, and molecules between adjacent plant cells are (a) tight junctions (b) microfilaments (c) desmosomes (d) gap junctions (e) plasmodesmata

R E V I E W   Q U E S T I O N S

1. What molecules are responsible for the physical properties of a cell membrane?

2. Illustrate how a transmembrane protein might be positioned in a lipid bilayer. How do the hydrophilic and hydrophobic regions of the protein affect its orientation?

3. Describe the pathway used by cells to place carbohydrates on plasma membrane proteins. Explain why this pathway results in the carbohydrate groups being exposed on only one side of the lipid bilayer.

4. What is the source of energy for diffusion? State a rule for predicting the movement of particles along their concentration gradient. Is the rule different for facilitated diffusion compared with simple diffusion?

5. Distinguish between osmosis and dialysis.

6. Predict the consequences if a plant cell were to be placed in a relatively (a) isotonic, (b) hypertonic, or (c) hypotonic environment. How would you modify your predictions for an animal cell?

7. What are some of the functions of the plasma membrane? Discuss the nature of the proteins that carry out those functions and explain how their properties make them especially adapted for their functions.

8. Identify a common energy source for active transport. In what ways are facilitated diffusion and carrier-mediated active transport similar? In what ways do they differ?

9. Draw a diagram illustrating how membrane lipid bilayers fuse during the processes of exocytosis and endocytosis. Is one the exact reverse of the other? Why or why not?

10. Discriminate between the processes of phagocytosis and pinocytosis.

11. How are desmosomes and tight junctions functionally similar? How do they differ? Do they share any structural similarities?

12. What is the justification for considering gap junctions and plasmodesmata to be functionally similar? How do they differ structurally?

13. Label the diagram of a typical plasma membrane. Use Figure 5–6 to check your answers.

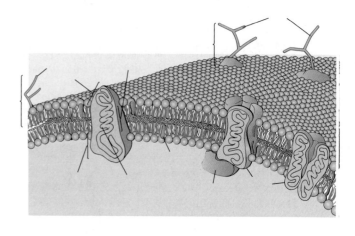

YOU MAKE THE CONNECTION

1. Why can't larger polar molecules and ions cross a lipid bilayer? Would it be advantageous to the cell if they could?
2. Most cells do not actively transport water, yet water is essential to life. How, then, are cells able to control their water content?
3. You prepare a salad with dressing in the morning but find that it is limp and unappetizing by lunch time. Why?
4. Most adjacent living cells in a plant are connected by plasmodesmata. On the other hand, only certain adjacent animal cells are associated through gap junctions. Why?

RECOMMENDED READINGS

Bayley, H. "Building Doors into Cells." *Scientific American,* Vol. 277, No. 3, Sept. 1997. Investigators are using recombinant DNA technology to create artificial pores in cell membranes. The technique has many clinical applications, including delivery of drugs.

Lasic, D.D. "Liposomes," *Science & Medicine,* Vol. 3, No. 3, May/Jun. 1996. Liposomes, artificial vesicles that can be produced commercially, are being investigated as vehicles for delivering drugs to specific cell types in the body.

Linder, M.E., and A. Gilman. "G Proteins." *Scientific American,* Vol. 267, No. 1, Jul. 1992. Pioneers in cell-signaling research discuss the many roles of G proteins.

Neher, E., and B. Sakmann. "The Patch Clamp Technique." *Scientific American,* Vol. 266, No. 3, Mar. 1992. The developers of the patch clamp technique discuss its varied applications.

Rothman, J.E., and L. Orci. "Budding Vesicles in Living Cells." *Scientific American,* Vol. 274, No. 3, Mar. 1996. The authors discuss the exciting process of discovering how cells form transport vesicles.

Scott, J.D. and T. Pawson. "Cell Communication: The Inside Story." *Scientific American,* Vol. 282, No. 6, Jun. 2000. A readable account of the process of signal transduction.

Vogel, S. "Dealing Honestly with Diffusion." *The American Biology Teacher,* Vol. 56, No. 7, Oct., 1994. An explanation of why most macroscopic phenomena attributed to diffusion actually have other explanations. This article emphasizes the fact that diffusion is rapid only over extremely short distances.

Zimmer, C. "Frozen Assets." *Natural History,* Dec. 1999/Jan. 2000. Considers the role of osmosis in protecting plant cells from freezing temperatures.

- Visit our Web site at **http://www.info.brookscole.com/solomonbergmartin** for links to chapter-related resources on the World Wide Web. Additional on-line materials relating to this chapter can also be found on our Web site.

See chapter activity on BioActive Learner CD for additional help in mastering the chapter's material. Icon location in the chapter's margins shows which topics have tutorials or simulations in the CD.

Pharmaceutical Sales Representative

JULIE HUANG

Julie Huang is a pharmaceutical sales representative for Janssen Pharmaceutica, a division of Johnson & Johnson, in Titusville, New Jersey. A native of the Chicago area, Julie graduated with a B.S. in biology and a minor in chemistry from the University of Illinois at Champaign-Urbana in 1997. After graduating, she moved to New York City and earned an M.S. in Biology from New York University in 1998. Julie began working for Janssen in early 1999. In her first position there, she earned a fourth-in-sales ranking among Janssen employees in the United States. Now working in Manhattan, Julie represents medications geared for the elderly. She enjoys the challenges and benefits of working independently and interacting with various medical professionals, and she welcomes the opportunities she has to apply her biology background.

What led you to major in biology and minor in chemistry?

I come from a big family of physicians, and my original intent was to go to medical school. I was also very much interested in biology research. Because I also enjoy chemistry, I eventually found myself one course shy of a minor, so I took that course.

Did you consider a career as a research biologist?

I had actually wanted to get into an M.D.-Ph.D. program, which covers both medicine and research. Then I decided that I wanted to pursue research first. Medical school was not out of the question, but I just wanted to focus on one thing at a time. So I entered the graduate program at New York University.

What type of research did you do for your master's degree?

As an undergraduate, I had done research in the neurosciences, and I decided I wanted to go into that field. My project investigated pain in rats. It involved a drug

that had not been approved by the U.S. Food and Drug Administration for pain. Through the research I identified different neural fibers that caused acute versus chronic pain.

How did you make the leap between basic research and pharmaceutical sales?

I just kind of stumbled on pharmaceutical sales as I was looking for a job, when I was finishing up my master's degree. I attended a job fair put on by NYU, with the intent of pursuing a research position. Janssen had a booth at the fair I attended, although they were looking for someone in marketing and sales, not research. I didn't think that was what I was looking for, but they called me back for an interview. And that's how I came to work at Janssen.

What sort of products do you sell at Janssen?

I'm in an eldercare position. My responsibilities are to make sure our products are represented at nursing homes, and to call on physicians who are focused on geriatrics. This is actually a relatively new division at Janssen. We have a pretty small sales force, but we know that elderly people will make up a greater percentage of the population in the United States as the baby boomers age. We sell an anti-psychotic, which we promote for elderly patients with dementia and psychosis; a patch used for chronic pain; and a drug that is a proton pump inhibitor for heartburn and for ulcers.

Do you have direct professional contact with physicians? With patients?

I don't have direct contact with patients, but I do with physicians. We know that physicians prescribe, so that's who we're out to find. But in eldercare we're more about educating and not so much about pushing our products; that comes secondary to what we do. I interact with physicians to determine their prescribing habits and learn their thoughts about certain types of medications versus ours, provide them with accredited continuing education programs, and consult with them on how to introduce our products to their patients.

Did you receive any business training?

Yes, though not in sales at first. I received four weeks of at-home training in general biology, things like anatomy, then four more weeks of intensive training, this time on the products that I was to sell. I've also gone through some very intensive selling seminars, after first spending time on the job.

Do you think your knowledge of the sciences makes learning about these products, or your ability to speak with physicians, any easier?

Oh, definitely. When we had the home study, I think a lot of people had difficulty with it; they didn't really understand a lot of the information that was given. To me, the at-home training was very straightforward, because that's my field. My background helps me assimilate product information, and it also helps me with study presentations. That's another big part of my job—to look at studies, find out what the key points are, and make those easier for a physician to understand. I feel that one of my strengths is my ability to understand scientific studies and to help others understand them.

What do you like best about your job?

Understanding studies and presenting them, interacting with physicians, and the flexibility of the work.

What advice can you offer biology students interested in pharmaceutical sales?

I would have to say that you should really be sure you like the job. It's a difficult transition; I had a hard time when I first started. It can be very tiring, following up on physicians. Be sure that you like that interaction and that you're willing to be an advocate for both the physicians (and their patients) and your company. You have to represent both interests.

Part

2

Sunlight filters through a forest clearing in West Virginia. Almost all life ultimately depends on solar energy. *(Michael Hubreich/ Photo Researchers, Inc.)*

Energy Transfer Through Living Systems

CHAPTERS

6

Energy and Metabolism

Black-tailed prairie dog (Cynomys ludovicianus). The chemical energy produced by photosynthesis and stored in seeds and leaves is transferred to the black-tailed prairie dog as it eats. *(Barbara Gerlach/Visuals Unlimited)*

LEARNING OBJECTIVES

After you have studied this chapter you should be able to

1. Define *energy,* emphasizing how it is related to work and to heat.
2. Use examples to contrast potential energy and kinetic energy.
3. State the first and second laws of thermodynamics and discuss the implications of these laws as they relate to organisms.
4. Discuss how changes in free energy in a reaction are related to changes in entropy and enthalpy.
5. Compare the energy dynamics of a reaction at equilibrium with the dynamics of a reaction not at equilibrium.
6. Distinguish between exergonic and endergonic reactions and give examples of how they may be coupled.
7. Explain how the chemical structure of ATP allows it to transfer a phosphate group. Discuss the central role of ATP in the overall energy metabolism of the cell.
8. Relate the transfer of electrons (or hydrogen atoms) to the transfer of energy.
9. Explain how an enzyme lowers the required energy of activation for a reaction.
10. Describe specific ways enzymes are regulated.

All living things require energy because life processes involve work. It may seem obvious that cells need energy to grow and reproduce, but even nongrowing cells need energy simply to maintain themselves. The sun is the ultimate source of almost all the energy that powers life; this **radiant energy** flows from the sun as electromagnetic waves. Plants and other photosynthetic organisms capture about 0.02% of the sun's energy that reaches Earth. In the process of photosynthesis, plants convert radiant energy to **chemical energy** in the bonds of organic molecules. The chemical energy captured by photosynthesis and stored in seeds and leaves is transferred to animals, such as the black-tailed prairie dog in the photograph, when they eat. Plants, animals, and other organisms need the energy stored in these or-

ganic molecules, and they commonly use the process of cellular respiration to break them apart and convert their energy to more immediately usable forms.

The first law of thermodynamics states that energy cannot be created or destroyed. A corollary to this in biological terms is that cells have no way to produce new energy. Thus, energy must be captured from the environment, temporarily stored, and then used to perform biological work. However, according to the second law of thermodynamics, not all of the captured energy can be used for work; at every step, some inevitably becomes converted to heat and is dispersed back into the environment.

Cells obtain energy in many forms, but seldom can that energy be used directly to power cellular processes. For this reason, cells have mechanisms that convert energy from one form to another. Because most of the components of these energy-conversion systems evolved very early in the history of life, many aspects of energy metabolism tend to be very similar in a wide range of organisms.

This chapter focuses on some of the basic principles that govern how cells capture, transfer, store, and use energy. We discuss the functions of adenosine triphosphate (ATP) and other molecules used in energy conversions, including those that transfer electrons in oxidation-reduction (redox) reactions. We also pay particular attention to the essential role of enzymes in cellular energy dynamics. In Chapter 7 we will explore some of the main metabolic pathways used in cellular respiration, and in Chapter 8 we will discuss the energy transformations of photosynthesis. The flow of energy in ecosystems is discussed in Chapter 53.

■ BIOLOGICAL WORK REQUIRES ENERGY

Energy, one of the most important concepts in biology, can be understood in the context of **matter,** which is anything that has mass and takes up space. **Energy** can be defined as the capacity to do **work,** which is any change in the state or motion of matter.

Biologists generally express energy in units of work **(kilojoules, kJ)** or units of heat energy **(kilocalories, kcal). (Heat energy** is thermal energy that flows from an object with a higher temperature—the heat source—to an object with a lower temperature—the heat sink.) One kilocalorie equals 4.184 kilojoules. Because heat energy cannot do cellular work, the kilojoule is the unit preferred by most biologists today. However, we will use both units because references to the kilocalorie are common in the scientific literature.

Many of the activities performed by an organism are examples of **mechanical energy,** which is energy in the movement of matter. At this very moment you are expending considerable energy to carry out such activities as breathing and circulating your blood. However, these forms of mechanical energy are the consequence of cellular activities. For example, the cells of the heart muscle use a great deal of energy to contract, thereby pumping the blood through your body. As we will see, however, not all of the work of cells is mechanical. A great deal of it is chemical. For example, heart muscle cells expend energy to synthesize the proteins required for contraction. Energy can be converted to many different forms, including not only mechanical and chemical energy but also heat energy, electrical energy, nuclear energy, and radiant energy.

Organisms carry out conversions between potential energy and kinetic energy

When an archer draws a bow, **kinetic energy,** which is energy of motion, is used and work is done (Fig. 6–1). The resulting tension in the bow and string represents stored energy, or **potential energy.** Potential energy is the capacity to do work owing to position or state. When the string is released, this potential energy is converted to kinetic energy in the motion of the bow, which propels the arrow.

Most of the actions of an organism involve a complex series of energy transformations that occur as kinetic energy is converted to potential energy or as potential energy is converted to kinetic energy. For example, potential energy derived from chemical energy of food molecules is converted to kinetic energy in the muscles of the archer.

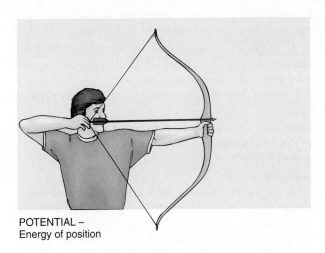

POTENTIAL –
Energy of position

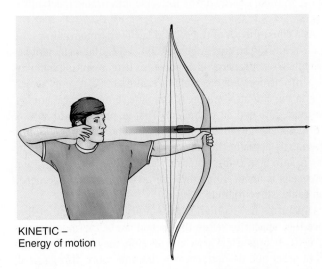

KINETIC –
Energy of motion

■ **Figure 6–1 Potential versus kinetic energy.** The potential chemical energy released by cellular respiration is converted to kinetic energy in the muscles, which do the work of drawing the bow. The potential energy stored in the drawn bow is transformed into kinetic energy as the bowstring pushes the arrow toward its target.

■ TWO LAWS OF THERMODYNAMICS GOVERN ENERGY TRANSFORMATIONS

All the activities of our universe, from the life and death of cells to the life and death of stars, are governed by **thermodynamics,** which is the study of energy and its transformations. When considering thermodynamics, scientists use the term *system* to refer to an object that is being studied, whether a cell, an organism, or planet Earth. The rest of the universe other than the system being studied is known as the *surroundings.* A **closed system** is one that does not exchange energy or matter with its surroundings, whereas an **open system** is one that can exchange matter and energy with its surroundings (Fig. 6–2). Biological systems are open systems.

There are two laws about energy that apply to all things in the universe. These are known as the first and second laws of thermodynamics.

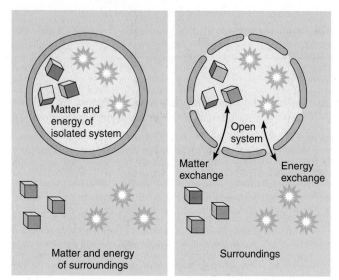

(a) Closed system
(b) Open system

Figure 6–2 Closed and open systems. **(a)** Matter and energy are not exchanged between a closed system and its surroundings. **(b)** Matter and energy are exchanged between an open system and its surroundings. *(Adapted from Tobin, A.J., and R.E. Morel. Asking About Cells. Harcourt College Publishers, Philadelphia, 1997)*

The total energy in the universe does not change

According to the **first law of thermodynamics,** energy cannot be created or destroyed, although it can be transferred or changed from one form to another. As far as we know, the energy present in the universe at its formation, approximately 15 to 20 billion years ago, equals the amount of energy present in the universe today.[1] This is all the energy that can ever be present in the universe. Similarly, the energy of any system and its surroundings is constant. A system may absorb energy from its surroundings, or it may give up some energy to its surroundings, but the total energy content of that system and its surroundings is always the same.

As specified by the first law of thermodynamics, then, organisms cannot create the energy that they require to live. Instead, they must capture energy from the environment to use for biological work, a process involving the transformation of energy from one form to another. In photosynthesis, for example, plants absorb the radiant energy of the sun and convert it into the chemical energy contained in the bonds of carbohydrate molecules. Similarly, some of that chemical energy may later be transformed by the plant to do various types of cellular work, or some animal that eats the plant might convert it to the mechanical energy of muscle contraction or some other needed form.

[1] Technically, mass is a form of energy, and so we should say that the total mass-energy of the universe is a constant. Energy can be produced from mass (recall Einstein's famous equation $E = mc^2$). This is the basis behind the energy generated by the sun and stars. More than 4 billion kilograms of matter per second are converted to energy in our sun.

The entropy of the universe is increasing

As each energy transformation occurs, some of the energy is converted to heat energy that is then given off into the cooler surroundings. This energy can never again be used by any organism for biological work; it is lost, at least from a biological point of view. However, it is not really gone from a thermodynamic point of view because it still exists in the surrounding physical environment. For example, the use of food to enable us to walk or run does not destroy the chemical energy that was once present in the food molecules. After we have performed the task of walking or running, the energy still exists in the surroundings as heat.

The **second law of thermodynamics** can be stated as follows: When energy is converted from one form to another, some usable energy, that is, energy available to do work, is converted into a less usable form, heat, that disperses into the surroundings (see Fig. 53–1). As a result, the amount of usable energy available to do work in the universe decreases over time.

It is important to understand that the second law of thermodynamics is consistent with the first law; that is, the total amount of energy in the universe is *not* decreasing with time. However, the total amount of energy in the universe that is available to do work is decreasing over time.

Less-usable energy is more diffuse, or disorganized. **Entropy (S)** is a measure of this disorder or randomness; organized, usable energy has a low entropy, whereas disorganized energy, such as heat, has a high entropy.

Entropy is continuously increasing in the universe in all natural processes. It may be that at some time, billions of years from now, all energy will exist as heat uniformly distributed throughout the universe. If that happens, the universe will cease to operate because no work will be possible. Everything will be at the same temperature, so there will be no way to convert the thermal energy of the universe into usable mechanical energy.

As a consequence of the second law of thermodynamics, no process requiring an energy conversion is ever 100% efficient because much of the energy is dispersed as heat, resulting in an increase in entropy. For example, an automobile engine, which converts the chemical energy of gasoline to mechanical energy, is between 20% and 30% efficient. That is, only 20% to 30% of the original energy stored in the chemical bonds of the gasoline molecules is actually transformed into mechanical energy; the other 70% to 80% is dissipated as waste heat. Energy utilization in our cells is about 40% efficient, with the remaining energy given to the surroundings as heat.

Organisms have a high degree of organization, and at first glance they appear to refute the second law of thermodynamics (Fig. 6–3). As organisms grow and develop, they maintain a high level of order and do not appear to become more disorganized. However, organisms are able to maintain their degree of order over time only with the constant input of energy from their surroundings. That is why plants must photosynthesize and animals must eat. Although the order within organisms might tend to increase temporarily, the total entropy of the universe (organisms plus surroundings) will increase over time.

In cellular respiration and photosynthesis, the potential energy stored in a concentration gradient of hydrogen ions (H^+) can be transformed into chemical energy in adenosine triphosphate (ATP) as the hydrogen ions pass through a membrane down their concentration gradient. This important concept, known as **chemiosmosis,** will be discussed further in Chapters 7 and 8.

■ METABOLIC REACTIONS INVOLVE ENERGY TRANSFORMATIONS

The chemical reactions that enable an organism to carry on its activities—to grow, move, maintain and repair itself, reproduce, and respond to stimuli—together make up its metabolism. **Metabolism** was defined in Chapter 1 as the sum of all the chemical activities that take place in an organism. An organism's metabolism consists of many intersecting series of chemical reactions, or pathways, which are of two main types: anabolism and catabolism. **Anabolism** refers to the various pathways in which complex molecules are synthesized from simpler substances, such as the linking of amino acids to form proteins. **Catabolism** includes the pathways in which larger molecules are broken down into smaller ones, such as the degradation of starch to form monosaccharides.

As we will see, these changes involve not only alterations in the arrangement of atoms but also various energy transformations. Catabolism and anabolism are complementary processes; catabolic pathways involve an overall release of energy, some of which is used to power the anabolic pathways, which have an overall energy requirement. In the following sections we will discuss how to predict whether a particular chemical reaction requires energy or releases it.

Enthalpy is the total potential energy of a system

In the course of any chemical reaction, including the metabolic reactions of a cell, chemical bonds break, and new and different bonds may form. Every specific type of chemical bond has a certain amount of **bond energy,** defined as the energy required to break that bond. The total bond energy is essentially equivalent to the total potential energy of the system, a quantity known as **enthalpy *(H).***

Free energy is energy that is available to do cellular work

Entropy and enthalpy are related by a third type of energy, termed **free energy *(G),*** which is the amount of energy available to do work under the conditions of a biochemical reaction.[2] Free energy, the only kind of energy that can do cellular work, is the aspect of thermodynamics of greatest interest to a biologist.

[2] The *G* that designates free energy comes from J. Willard Gibbs, one of the founders of thermodynamics.

■ **Figure 6–3 Cutaway view of the shell of the chambered nautilus (*Nautilus* sp.).** The nautilus is a marine animal that lives in the outermost chamber of its shell. As it grows, the nautilus builds a new wall (septum) at the smaller end of the shell, thereby closing it off. The highly organized structure of this coiled shell is developed and maintained only by the constant input of energy from the small, shrimplike animals the nautilus eats. Thus, the high degree of organization of this animal, and of all living things, does not refute the second law of thermodynamics. *(Charles D. Winters)*

MAKING THE CONNECTION Is diffusion related to entropy? In Chapter 5 we saw that randomly moving particles can diffuse down their own concentration gradient (Fig. 6–4). That is, although the movements of the individual particles are random, net movement of the group of particles seems to be directional. What provides energy for this seemingly directed process? A **concentration gradient,** with a region of higher concentration and another region of lower concentration, is an orderly state. A cell must expend energy to produce a concentration gradient. Because work must be done to produce this order, the concentration gradient is a form of potential energy. As the particles move about randomly, disorder increases.

Concentration gradient

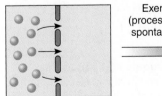
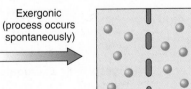

Exergonic (process occurs spontaneously)

Low entropy (*S*)
High free energy (*G*)

High entropy (*S*)
Low free energy (*G*)

■ **Figure 6–4 Entropy and diffusion.** The tendency of entropy to increase can be used to produce work, in this case, diffusion. *(Left)* A concentration gradient is a form of potential energy. *(Right)* When molecules are evenly distributed, they have high entropy.

Enthalpy, free energy, and entropy are related by the following equation:

$$H = G + TS$$

in which H is enthalpy, G is free energy, S is entropy, and T is the absolute temperature of the system, expressed in degrees Kelvin. Disregarding temperature (T) for the moment, enthalpy (the total energy of a system) is equal to free energy (the usable energy) and entropy (the unusable energy).

A rearrangement of the equation shows that entropy and free energy are related inversely; as entropy increases, the amount of free energy decreases:

$$G = H - TS$$

If we assume that entropy is zero, the free energy is simply equal to the total potential energy (enthalpy); an increase in entropy reduces the amount of free energy.

What is the significance of the temperature (T)? Remember that as the temperature increases, there is an increase in random molecular motion that contributes to disorder and multiplies the effect of the entropy term.

Chemical reactions involve changes in free energy

Biologists need ways to analyze the role of energy in the many reactions that comprise metabolism. Although the total free energy of a system (G) cannot be effectively measured, the equation $G = H - TS$ can be extended to predict whether any particular chemical reaction will release energy or require an input of energy. This is because *changes* in free energy can be measured. We use the Greek letter delta (Δ) to denote any change that occurs in the system between its initial state before the reaction and its final state after the reaction. To express what happens with respect to energy in a chemical reaction, the equation becomes:

$$\Delta G = \Delta H - T\Delta S$$

Notice that the temperature does not change; it is held constant during the reaction. Thus the change in free energy (ΔG) during the reaction is equal to the change in enthalpy (ΔH) minus the product of the absolute temperature (T) multiplied by the change in entropy (ΔS). ΔG and ΔH are expressed in kilojoules or kilocalories per mole; ΔS is expressed in kilojoules or kilocalories per degree.

Free energy decreases during an exergonic reaction

An **exergonic reaction** releases energy and is said to be a spontaneous or a "downhill" reaction, from higher to lower free energy (Fig. 6–5a). Because the total free energy in its final state is less than the total free energy in its initial state, ΔG is a negative number for exergonic reactions.

The term *spontaneous* may give the false impression that such reactions are always instantaneous. In fact, spontaneous reactions do not necessarily occur readily; some are extremely slow. This is because energy, known as activation energy, is required to initiate every reaction, even a spontaneous one. Activation energy will be discussed later in the chapter.

Free energy increases during an endergonic reaction

An **endergonic reaction** is a reaction in which there is a gain of free energy (Fig. 6–5b). Because the free energy of the products is greater than the free energy of the reactants, ΔG has a positive value. Such a reaction cannot take place in isolation. Instead, it must occur in such a way that energy can be supplied from the surroundings. Of course, many energy-requiring reactions take place in cells, and as we will see, metabolic mechanisms have evolved that supply the energy needed to "drive" these nonspontaneous cellular reactions in a particular direction.

Free energy changes depend on the concentrations of reactants and products

According to the second law of thermodynamics, any process that increases entropy can do work. Differences in concentration of a substance, for example, between two different parts of a cell, represent a more orderly state than when the substance

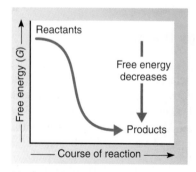

(a) Exergonic reaction
(spontaneous; energy-releasing)

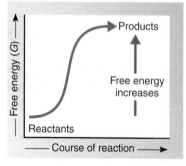

(b) Endergonic reaction
(not spontaneous; energy-requiring)

Figure 6–5 Exergonic and endergonic reactions. (a) In an exergonic reaction there is a net loss of free energy. The products have less free energy than was present in the reactants, and the reaction proceeds spontaneously. (b) In an endergonic reaction there is a net gain in free energy. The products have more free energy than was present in the reactants. An endergonic reaction occurs only if energy is supplied by an exergonic reaction.

is diffused homogeneously throughout the cell (recall the discussion of concentration gradients earlier in the chapter). We have seen that free energy changes in any chemical reaction depend mainly on the difference in bond energies (enthalpy, H) between reactants and products. Free energy also depends on *concentrations* of both reactants and products. The change in molecules from a more concentrated to a less concentrated state increases entropy because it is movement from a more orderly to a less orderly state.

In most biochemical reactions there is little intrinsic free energy difference between reactants and products. Such reactions are reversible, a fact that is indicated by drawing double arrows ($\rightleftharpoons$) between the reactants and the products.

$$A \rightleftharpoons B$$

At the beginning of a reaction, only the reactant molecules (A) may be present. As the reaction proceeds, the concentration of the reactant molecules decreases, and the concentration of the product molecules (B) increases. As the concentration of the product molecules increases, they may have enough free energy to initiate the reverse reaction. The reaction thus proceeds in both directions simultaneously; if undisturbed it could eventually reach a state of **dynamic equilibrium,** in which the rate of the reverse reaction is equal to the rate of the forward reaction. At equilibrium there is no net change in the system; every forward reaction is balanced by a reverse reaction.

At a given temperature and pressure, each reaction has its own characteristic equilibrium. For any given reaction, chemists can perform experiments and calculations to determine the relative concentrations of reactants and products present at equilibrium. If the reactants have much greater intrinsic free energy than the products, the reaction goes almost to completion; that is, it reaches equilibrium at a point at which most of the reactants have been converted to products. Reactions in which the reactants have much less intrinsic free energy than the products reach equilibrium at a point where very few of the reactant molecules have been converted to products.

If we increase the initial concentration of A, then the reaction will "shift to the right," and more A will be converted to B. A similar effect can be obtained if B is removed from the reaction mixture. The reaction always shifts in the direction that reestablishes equilibrium, so that the proportions of reactants and products characteristic of that reaction at equilibrium are restored. The opposite effect occurs if the concentration of B is increased or if A is removed; here the system "shifts to the left." The actual free energy change that occurs during a reaction is defined mathematically to include these effects, which are a consequence of the relative initial concentrations of reactants and products.

Cells manipulate the relative concentrations of reactants and products of almost every reaction. Cellular reactions are virtually never at equilibrium. By displacing their reactions far from equilibrium, cells are able to supply energy to endergonic reactions and direct their metabolism in accordance with their needs (see an example of this in the Chapter 5 discussion of facilitated diffusion of glucose in red blood cells).

Cells drive endergonic reactions by coupling them to exergonic reactions

Many metabolic reactions, such as protein synthesis, are anabolic and endergonic. Because an endergonic reaction cannot take place without an input of energy, endergonic reactions are coupled to exergonic reactions. In **coupled reactions,** the thermodynamically favorable exergonic reaction provides the energy required to drive the thermodynamically unfavorable endergonic reaction. The endergonic reaction can proceed only if it absorbs free energy released by the exergonic reaction to which it is coupled.

Consider the free energy change, ΔG, in the following reaction:

(1) $A \longrightarrow B \qquad \Delta G = +20.9$ kJ/mol ($+5$ kcal/mol)

Because ΔG has a positive value, we know that the product of this reaction has more free energy than the reactant. This is an endergonic reaction. It is not spontaneous and does not take place without an energy source.

By contrast, consider the following reaction:

(2) $C \longrightarrow D \qquad \Delta G = -33.5$ kJ/mol (-8 kcal/mol)

The negative value of ΔG tells us that the free energy of the reactant is greater than the free energy of the product. This exergonic reaction proceeds spontaneously.

We can sum up Reactions 1 and 2 as follows:

(1) $A \longrightarrow B$	$\Delta G = +20.9$ kJ/mol ($+5$ kcal/mol)
(2) $C \longrightarrow D$	$\Delta G = -33.5$ kJ/mol (-8 kcal/mol)
Overall	$\Delta G = -12.6$ kJ/mol (-3 kcal/mol)

Because thermodynamics considers the overall changes in these two reactions, which show a net negative value of ΔG, the two reactions taken together are exergonic.

The fact that we can write reactions this way is a useful bookkeeping device, but it does not mean that an exergonic reaction can mysteriously transfer energy to an endergonic "bystander" reaction. However, these reactions can be coupled if their pathways are altered such that they are linked by a common intermediate. Reactions 1 and 2 might be coupled by an intermediate *(I)* in the following way:

(3) $A + C \longrightarrow I$	$\Delta G = -8.4$ kJ/mol (-2 kcal/mol)
(4) $I \longrightarrow B + D$	$\Delta G = -4.2$ kJ/mol (-1 kcal/mol)
Overall	$\Delta G = -12.6$ kJ/mol (-3 kcal/mol)

Note that Reactions 3 and 4 are sequential. Thus the reaction pathways have changed, but overall the reactants (A and C) and products (B and D) are the same, and the free energy change is the same.

Generally, for each endergonic reaction occurring in a living cell, there is a coupled exergonic reaction to drive it. Often, the exergonic reaction involves the breakdown of ATP. We now examine specific examples of the role of ATP in energy coupling.

■ ATP IS THE ENERGY CURRENCY OF THE CELL

In all living cells, energy is temporarily packaged within a remarkable chemical compound called **adenosine triphosphate (ATP)**, which holds readily available energy for very short periods of time. We may think of ATP as the energy currency of the cell. When you work to earn money, you might say that your energy is symbolically stored in the money you earn. The energy the cell requires for immediate use is temporarily stored in ATP, which is like cash. When you earn extra money, you might deposit some in the bank; similarly, a cell might deposit energy in the chemical bonds of lipids, starch, or glycogen. Moreover, just as you dare not make less money than you spend, so too the cell must avoid energy bankruptcy, which would mean its death. Finally, just as you (alas) do not keep what you make very long, so too the cell continuously spends its ATP, which must be replaced immediately.

ATP is a nucleotide consisting of three main parts: adenine, a nitrogen-containing organic base; ribose, a five-carbon sugar; and three phosphate groups, identifiable as phosphorus atoms surrounded by oxygen atoms (Fig. 6–6). Notice that the phosphate groups are bonded to the end of the molecule in a series, rather like three cars behind a locomotive, and, like the cars of a train, they can be attached and detached.

ATP donates energy through the transfer of a phosphate group

When the terminal phosphate is removed from ATP, the remaining molecule is **adenosine diphosphate (ADP)** (see Fig. 6–6). If the phosphate group is not transferred to another molecule, it is released as inorganic phosphate (P_i). This is an exergonic reaction. ATP is sometimes called a "high-energy" compound because the hydrolysis reaction that releases a phosphate has a relatively large $-\Delta G$. (Calculations of the free energy of ATP hydrolysis vary somewhat, but range between about -28 and -37 kJ/mol, or -6.8 to -8.7 kcal/mol.)

(5) $\text{ATP} + H_2O \longrightarrow \text{ADP} + P_i$

$$\Delta G = -32 \text{ kJ/mol (or } -7.6 \text{ kcal/mol)}$$

Reaction 5 can be coupled to endergonic reactions in cells. Consider the following endergonic reaction in which the disaccharide sucrose is formed from two monosaccharides, glucose and fructose.

(6) $\text{Glucose} + \text{Fructose} \longrightarrow \text{Sucrose} + H_2O$

$$\Delta G = +27 \text{ kJ/mol (or } +6.5 \text{ kcal/mol)}$$

With a free energy change of -32 kJ/mol (-7.6 kcal/mol), the hydrolysis of ATP in Reaction 5 can drive Reaction 6, but only

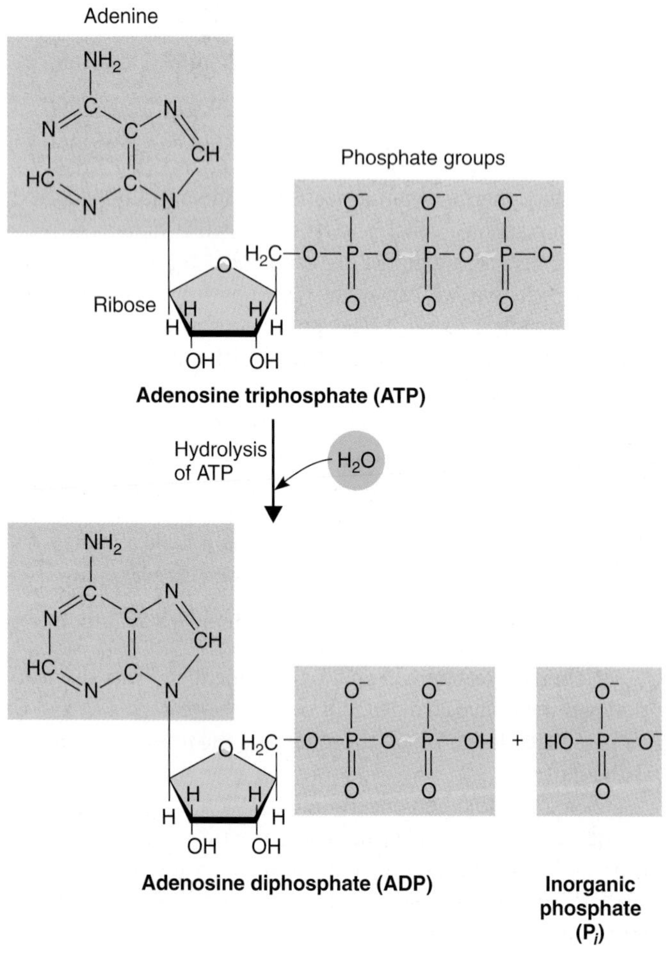

Adenine

Phosphate groups

Ribose

Adenosine triphosphate (ATP)

Hydrolysis of ATP H_2O

Adenosine diphosphate (ADP)   **Inorganic phosphate (P_i)**

■ **Figure 6–6   ATP and ADP**   The energy currency of all living things, ATP is composed of adenine, ribose, and three phosphate groups. The hydrolysis of ATP, an exergonic reaction, yields ADP and inorganic phosphate. (Yellow wavy lines indicate unstable bonds. These bonds permit the phosphates to be transferred to other molecules, making them more reactive.)

if the reactions can be coupled through a common intermediate. The following series of reactions is a simplified version of an alternative pathway used by some bacteria.

(7) Glucose + ATP $\longrightarrow$ Glucose-P + ADP

(8) Glucose-P + Fructose $\longrightarrow$ Sucrose + P$_i$

Reaction 7 is a **phosphorylation reaction,** one in which a phosphate group is transferred to some other compound. Glucose is phosphorylated to form glucose phosphate (glucose-P), the intermediate that links the two reactions. Glucose-P, which corresponds to "I" in Reactions 3 and 4, reacts exergonically with fructose to form sucrose. For energy coupling to work in this way, Reactions 7 and 8 must occur in sequence. It is convenient to summarize the reactions in the following way:

(9) Glucose + Fructose + ATP $\longrightarrow$ Sucrose + ADP + P$_i$

$$\Delta G = -5 \text{ kJ/mol } (-1.2 \text{ kcal/mol})$$

When encountering an equation written in this way, remember that it is actually a summary of a series of reactions and that transitory intermediate products (in this case, glucose-P) are sometimes not shown.

ATP links exergonic and endergonic reactions

We have just discussed how the transfer of a phosphate group from ATP to some other compound can be coupled to endergonic reactions in the cell. Conversely, adding a phosphate group to adenosine monophosphate (AMP; forming ADP) or to ADP (forming ATP) requires coupling to exergonic reactions in the cell.

$$\text{AMP} + \text{P}_i + \text{Energy} \longrightarrow \text{ADP}$$
$$\text{ADP} + \text{P}_i + \text{Energy} \longrightarrow \text{ATP}$$

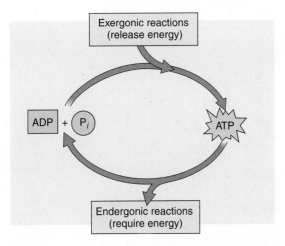

Figure 6–7 ATP links exergonic and endergonic reactions. Because ATP couples many exergonic and endergonic reactions, it is an important link between catabolic reactions, which are exergonic, and anabolic reactions, which are endergonic. Exergonic reactions *(top)* supply the energy to make ATP from ADP, and the hydrolysis of ATP supplies the energy to drive endergonic reactions *(bottom)*.

Thus ATP occupies an intermediate position in the metabolism of the cell and is an important link between exergonic reactions, which are generally components of **catabolic pathways,** and endergonic reactions, which are generally part of **anabolic pathways** (Fig. 6–7).

■ THE CELL MAINTAINS A VERY HIGH RATIO OF ATP TO ADP

The cell maintains a ratio of ATP to ADP far from the equilibrium point. ATP is constantly formed from ADP and inorganic phosphate as nutrients are broken down in cellular respiration or as the radiant energy of sunlight is trapped in photosynthesis. At any point in time, a typical cell contains more than ten ATP molecules for every ADP molecule. The fact that the cell maintains the ATP concentration at such a high level (relative to the concentration of ADP) makes its hydrolysis reaction even more strongly exergonic and more able to drive the endergonic reactions to which it is coupled.

Although the cell maintains a high ratio of ATP to ADP, large quantities of ATP cannot be stored in the cell. The concentration of ATP is always very low, less than 1 mmol/L. In fact, studies suggest that a bacterial cell has no more than a 1-second supply of ATP. Thus, ATP molecules are used almost as quickly as they are produced. A human at rest uses about 45 kg (100 lb) of ATP each day, but the amount present in the body at any given moment is less than 1 g (0.035 oz). Every second in every cell, an estimated 10 million molecules of ATP are made from ADP and phosphate, and an equal number of ATPs transfer their phosphate groups along with their energy to whatever chemical reactions may require them.

■ CELLS TRANSFER ENERGY BY REDOX REACTIONS

We have seen that cells can transfer energy through the transfer of a phosphate group from ATP. Energy can also be transferred through the transfer of electrons. As discussed in Chapter 2, **oxidation** is the chemical process in which a substance loses electrons, whereas **reduction** is the complementary process in which a substance gains electrons. Because electrons released during an oxidation reaction cannot exist in the free state in living cells, every oxidation reaction must be accompanied by a reduction reaction, in which the electrons are accepted by another atom, ion, or molecule. Oxidation and reduction reactions are often called **redox reactions** because they occur simultaneously. The substance that becomes oxidized gives up energy as it releases electrons, and the substance that becomes reduced receives energy as it gains electrons.

Redox reactions often occur in a series as electrons are transferred from one molecule to another. These electron transfers, which are equivalent to energy transfers, are an essential part of cellular respiration, photosynthesis, and many other chemical reactions. Redox reactions, for example, release the energy stored in food molecules so that ATP can be synthesized using that energy.

Most electron carriers transfer hydrogen atoms

Generally it is not easy to remove one or more electrons from a covalent compound; it is much easier to remove a whole atom. For this reason, redox reactions in cells usually involve the transfer of a hydrogen atom rather than just an electron. A hydrogen atom contains an electron, plus a proton that does not participate in the oxidation/reduction.

When an electron, either singly or as part of a hydrogen atom, is removed from an organic compound, it takes with it some of the energy stored in the chemical bond of which it was a part. That electron, along with its energy, is transferred to an acceptor molecule. An electron progressively loses free energy as it is transferred from one acceptor to another.

One of the most frequently encountered acceptor molecules is **nicotinamide adenine dinucleotide (NAD$^+$).** When NAD$^+$ becomes reduced, it temporarily stores large amounts of free energy. Here is a generalized equation showing the transfer of hydrogen from a compound we call X to NAD$^+$:

$$XH_2 + NAD^+ \longrightarrow X + NADH + H^+$$
$$\text{Oxidized} \qquad\qquad \text{Reduced}$$

Note that the NAD$^+$ becomes reduced when it combines with hydrogen. NAD$^+$ is an ion with a net charge of +1. When two electrons and one proton are added, the charge is neutralized and the reduced form of the compound, **NADH,** is produced (Fig. 6–8). (Although the correct way to write the reduced form of NAD$^+$ is NADH + H$^+$, for simplicity we will present the reduced form as NADH in this and succeeding chapters.) Some of the energy stored in the bonds holding the hydrogen atoms to molecule X has been transferred by this redox reaction and is temporarily held by NADH. When NADH transfers the electrons to some other molecule, some of their energy is transferred. This energy is usually then transferred through a complex series of reactions that ultimately result in the formation of ATP (see Chapter 7).

Nicotinamide adenine dinucleotide phosphate (NADP$^+$) is a hydrogen acceptor that is chemically similar to NAD$^+$ but with an extra phosphate group. Unlike NADH, the reduced form of NADP$^+$ (abbreviated **NADPH**) is not involved in ATP synthesis. Instead, the electrons of NADPH are used more directly to provide energy for certain reactions, including certain essential reactions of photosynthesis (see Chapter 8).

Other important hydrogen acceptors or electron acceptors include **flavin adenine dinucleotide (FAD)** and the **cytochromes.**

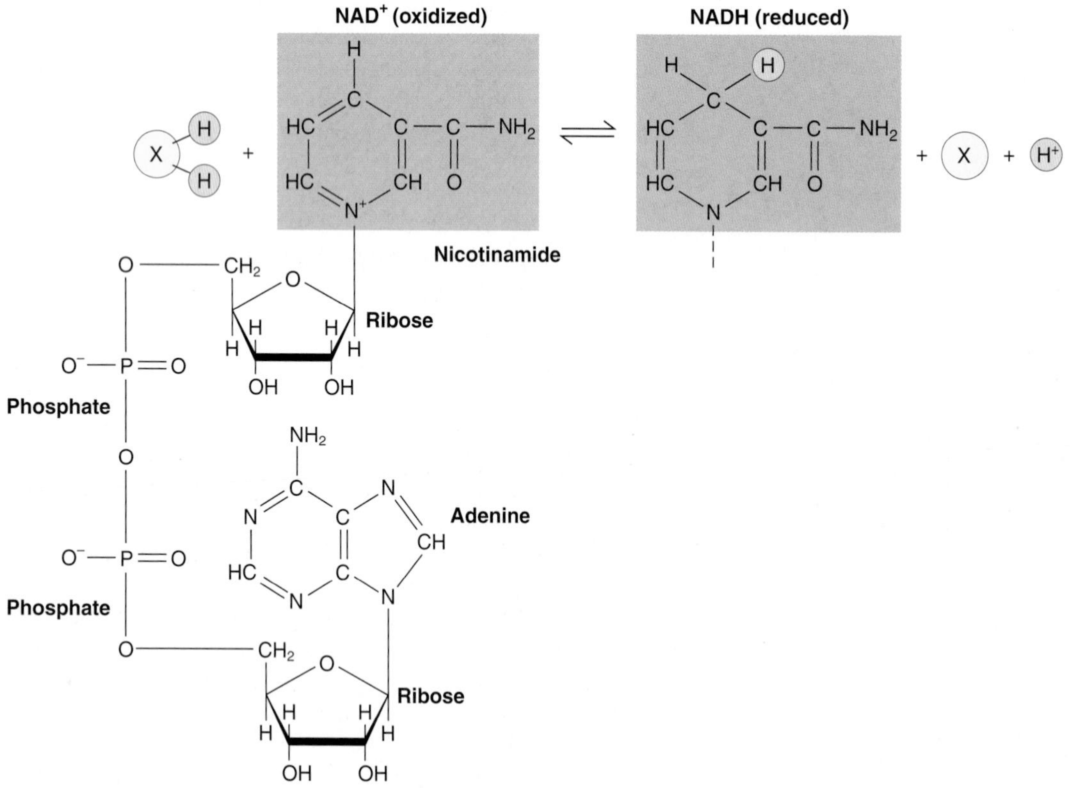

Figure 6–8 NAD$^+$. NAD$^+$ consists of two nucleotides, one with adenine and one with nicotinamide, that are joined at their phosphate groups. The oxidized form (NAD$^+$, *purple screen at top*) becomes reduced (NADH, *pink screen*) by the transfer of two electrons and one proton from another organic compound (XH$_2$), which becomes oxidized (to X) in the process.

FAD is a nucleotide that accepts hydrogen atoms and their electrons; its reduced form is **FADH₂.** The cytochromes are proteins that contain iron; the iron component accepts electrons from hydrogen atoms and then transfers these electrons to some other compound. Like NAD^+ and $NADP^+$, FAD and the cytochromes are electron-transfer agents. Each can exist in a **reduced state,** in which it has more free energy, or in an **oxidized state,** in which it has less. Each is an essential component of many redox reaction sequences in cells.

ENZYMES ARE CHEMICAL REGULATORS

The principles of thermodynamics help us predict whether a reaction can occur, but they tell us nothing about the speed of the reaction. The breakdown of glucose, for example, is an exergonic reaction, yet a glucose solution keeps virtually indefinitely in a bottle if kept free of bacteria and molds and not subjected to high temperatures or strong acids or bases. Cells cannot wait for centuries for glucose to break down, nor can they use extreme conditions to cleave glucose molecules. Cells regulate the rates of chemical reactions with **enzymes,** which are protein **catalysts** that affect the speed of a chemical reaction without being consumed by the reaction.[3]

Cells require a steady release of energy, and they must be able to regulate that release to meet metabolic energy requirements. Metabolism generally proceeds by a series of steps such that a molecule may go through as many as 20 or 30 chemical transformations before it reaches some final state. Even then, the seemingly completed molecule may enter yet another chemical pathway and become totally transformed or consumed to release energy. The changing needs of the cell require a system of flexible metabolic control. The key directors of this control system are enzymes.

The catalytic ability of some enzymes is truly remarkable. For example, hydrogen peroxide (H_2O_2) breaks down extremely slowly if the reaction is uncatalyzed, but a single molecule of the enzyme **catalase** brings about the decomposition of 40 million molecules of hydrogen peroxide per second! Catalase, which has the highest catalytic rate known for any enzyme, protects cells because hydrogen peroxide is a poisonous substance produced as a byproduct of some cellular reactions. The bombardier beetle uses the enzyme catalase as a defense mechanism (Fig. 6–9).

All reactions have a required energy of activation

All reactions, whether exergonic or endergonic, have an energy barrier known as the **energy of activation (E_A),** or **activation energy.** The energy barrier is the energy required to break the existing bonds and begin the reaction. In a population of molecules of any kind, some have a relatively high kinetic energy, while

Figure 6–9 Catalase as a defense mechanism. When threatened, a bombardier beetle uses the enzyme catalase to decompose hydrogen peroxide. The oxygen gas formed in the decomposition ejects water and other chemicals with explosive force. Because the reaction releases a great deal of heat, the water comes out as steam. (A wire attached by a drop of adhesive to the beetle's back immobilizes it. His leg was prodded with the dissecting needle on the left to trigger the ejection.) *(Thomas Eisner and Daniel Aneshansley/Cornell University)*

others have a lower energy content. Only molecules with a relatively high kinetic energy are likely to react to form the product.

Even a strongly exergonic reaction, one that releases a substantial quantity of energy as it proceeds, may be prevented from proceeding by the activation energy required to begin the reaction. For example, molecular hydrogen and molecular oxygen can react explosively to form water:

$$2\,H_2 + O_2 \longrightarrow 2\,H_2O$$

This reaction is spontaneous, yet hydrogen and oxygen can be safely mixed as long as all sparks are kept away. This is because the required energy of activation for this particular reaction is relatively high. A tiny spark provides the activation energy that allows a few molecules to react. Their reaction liberates so much heat that the rest react, producing an explosion. Such an explosion occurred on the space shuttle *Challenger* on January 28, 1986 (Fig. 6–10). The failure of a rubber O-ring to seal properly caused the liquid hydrogen in the tank attached to the shuttle to leak and start burning. When the hydrogen tank ruptured a few seconds later, the resulting force caused the nearby oxygen tank to burst as well, mixing hydrogen and oxygen and igniting a huge explosion.

An enzyme lowers a reaction's activation energy

As do all catalysts, enzymes affect the rate of a reaction by lowering the energy needed to initiate the reaction. An enzyme greatly reduces the activation energy (E_A) necessary to initiate a

---

[3] In recent years scientists have learned that protein enzymes are not the only cellular catalysts; some types of RNA molecules have catalytic activity as well (see Chapter 12).

Figure 6–10 The space shuttle *Challenger* explosion. This disaster resulted from an explosive exergonic reaction between hydrogen and oxygen. All seven crew members died in the accident on January 28, 1986. *(AP Photo/Bruce Weaver)*

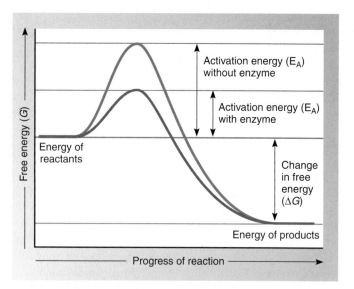

Figure 6–11 Activation energy and enzymes. An enzyme speeds up a reaction by lowering its activation energy (E_A). In the presence of an enzyme, reacting molecules require less kinetic energy to complete a reaction.

action. The enzyme is thought to accomplish this by forming an unstable intermediate complex with the **substrate,** the substance on which it acts. When the **enzyme-substrate complex,** or **ES complex,** breaks up, the product is released; the original enzyme molecule is regenerated and is free to form a new ES complex.

$$\text{Enzyme} + \text{Substrate(s)} \longrightarrow \text{ES complex}$$
$$\text{ES complex} \longrightarrow \text{Enzyme} + \text{Product(s)}$$

The enzyme itself is not permanently altered or consumed by the reaction and can be reused.

As shown in Figure 6–12a, every enzyme contains one or more **active sites,** regions to which the substrate binds, forming the ES complex. The active sites of some enzymes are grooves or cavities in the enzyme molecule, formed by amino acid side chains. The active sites of most enzymes are located close to the surface. During the course of a reaction, substrate molecules occupying these sites are brought close together and react with one another.

The shape of the enzyme does not seem to be exactly complementary to that of the substrate. When the substrate binds to the enzyme molecule, it causes a change, known as **induced fit,** in the shape of the enzyme molecule (Fig. 6–12b). Usually the shape of the substrate also changes slightly, in a way that may distort its chemical bonds. The proximity and orientation of the reactants, together with strains in their chemical bonds, facilitate the breakage of old bonds and the formation of new ones. Thus the substrate is changed into product, which moves away from the enzyme. The enzyme is then free to catalyze the reaction of more substrate molecules to form more product molecules.

chemical reaction (Fig. 6–11). If molecules need less energy to react because the activation barrier is lowered, a larger fraction of the reactant molecules reacts at any one time. As a result, the reaction proceeds more quickly.

Although an enzyme lowers the activation energy for a reaction, it has no effect on the overall free energy change. That is, an enzyme can only promote a chemical reaction that could proceed without it. No catalyst can cause a reaction to proceed in a thermodynamically unfavorable direction or can influence the final concentrations of reactants and products if the reaction goes to equilibrium. Enzymes simply speed up reaction rates.

An enzyme works by forming an enzyme-substrate complex

An uncatalyzed reaction depends on random collisions among reactants. Because of its ordered structure, an enzyme is able to reduce this reliance on random events and thereby control the re-

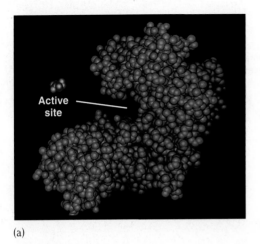
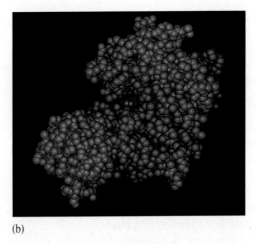

(a)   (b)

Figure 6–12 Active site and induced fit. (a) Computer graphic model of the enzyme hexokinase *(blue)* and its substrate, glucose *(red)*, before forming an ES complex. The active site of the enzyme is the furrow where glucose will bind. (b) The binding of glucose to the active site of hexokinase changes the shape of the enzyme, a phenomenon known as induced fit. Hexokinase, which is involved in cellular respiration, catalyzes the transfer of a phosphate group from ATP to glucose. *(Courtesy of Thomas A. Steitz)*

Most enzyme names end in *-ase*

Enzymes are usually named by the addition of the suffix *-ase* to the name of the substrate. The enzyme sucrase, for example, splits sucrose into glucose and fructose. A few enzymes retain traditional names that do not end in *-ase;* some of these end in *-zyme.* For example, lysozyme (from the Greek *lysis,* "to dissolve") is an enzyme found in tears and saliva; this enzyme breaks down bacterial cell walls. Other examples of enzymes with traditional names include pepsin and trypsin, which break internal peptide bonds in proteins.

Enzymes are specific

Enzymes catalyze virtually every chemical reaction that takes place in an organism. Because there is a close relationship between the shape of the active site and the shape of the substrate, the majority of enzymes are highly specific. Most are capable of catalyzing only a few closely related chemical reactions or, in many cases, only one particular reaction. For example, the enzyme urease, which decomposes urea to ammonia and carbon dioxide, attacks no other substrate. The enzyme sucrase splits only sucrose; it does not act on other disaccharides, such as maltose or lactose. A few enzymes are specific only to the extent that they require the substrate to have a certain kind of chemical bond. For example, lipase, secreted by the pancreas, splits the ester linkages connecting the glycerol and fatty acids of a wide variety of fats.

Enzymes that catalyze similar reactions are classified into groups, although each particular enzyme in the group may catalyze only one specific reaction. The six classes of enzymes that biologists recognize are described in Table 6–1. Each class is divided into many subclasses. For example, sucrase, mentioned

above, is referred to as a *glycosidase* because it cleaves a glycosidic linkage (see Chapter 3). Glycosidases are a subclass of the hydrolases.

Many enzymes require cofactors

Some enzymes consist only of protein. For example, the enzyme pepsin, which is secreted by the animal stomach and digests dietary protein by breaking certain peptide bonds, is exclusively a protein molecule. Other enzymes have two components: a protein referred to as the **apoenzyme** and an additional chemical component called a **cofactor.** Neither the apoenzyme nor the cofactor alone has catalytic activity; only when the two are combined

TABLE 6–1 Some Important Classes of Enzymes

Enzyme Class	Function
Oxidoreductases	Catalyze oxidation-reduction reactions
Transferases	Catalyze the transfer of a functional group from a donor molecule to an acceptor molecule
Hydrolases	Catalyze hydrolysis reactions
Isomerases	Catalyze conversion of a molecule from one isomeric form to another
Ligases	Catalyze certain reactions in which two molecules are joined in a process coupled to the hydrolysis of ATP
Lyases	Catalyze certain reactions in which double bonds are formed or broken.

does the enzyme function. A cofactor may be inorganic, or it may be an organic molecule.

Some enzymes require a specific metal ion as a cofactor. Two very common inorganic cofactors are magnesium ions and calcium ions. Most of the trace elements, such as iron, copper, zinc, and manganese, all of which organisms require in very small amounts, function as cofactors.

An organic, nonpolypeptide compound that binds to the apoenzyme and serves as a cofactor is called a **coenzyme.** Most coenzymes are carrier molecules that transfer electrons or part of a substrate from one molecule to another. Some examples of coenzymes have already been introduced in this chapter. NADH, NADPH, and $FADH_2$ are coenzymes; they transfer electrons. ATP functions as a coenzyme; it is responsible for transferring phosphate groups. Yet another coenzyme, **coenzyme A,** is involved in the transfer of groups derived from organic acids. Most vitamins, which are organic compounds that an organism requires in small amounts but cannot synthesize itself, are coenzymes or components of coenzymes (see Table 45–3).

Enzymes are most effective at optimal conditions

Enzymes generally work best under certain narrowly defined conditions, such as appropriate temperature, pH, and ion concentration. Any departure from optimal conditions adversely affects enzyme activity.

Each enzyme has an optimal temperature

Most enzymes have an optimal temperature, at which the rate of reaction is fastest. For human enzymes, the temperature optima are near the human body temperature (35° to 40° C). Enzymatic reactions occur slowly or not at all at low temperatures. As the temperature increases, molecular motion increases, resulting in more molecular collisions. The rates of most enzyme-controlled reactions therefore increase as the temperature increases, within limits (Fig. 6–13a). High temperatures rapidly denature most enzymes. The molecular conformation (three-dimensional shape) of the protein becomes altered as the hydrogen bonds responsible for its secondary, tertiary, and quaternary structures are broken. Because this inactivation is usually not reversible, activity is not regained when the enzyme is cooled.

Most organisms are killed by even a short exposure to high temperature; their enzymes are denatured, and they are unable to continue metabolism. A few remarkable exceptions to this rule exist. Certain species of bacteria can survive in the waters of hot springs, such as those in Yellowstone Park, where the temperature is almost 100° C; these organisms are responsible for the brilliant colors in the terraces of the hot springs (Fig. 6–14). Still other bacteria live at temperatures much above that of boiling water, near deep-sea vents, where the extreme pressure keeps water in its liquid state (see Chapter 23 and *Focus On: Life Without the Sun* in Chapter 53).

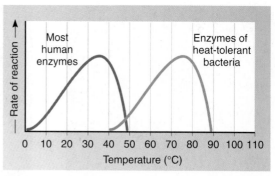

(a)

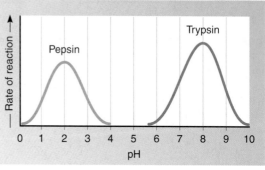

(b)

■ **Figure 6–13 Effect of temperature and pH on enzyme activity.** Substrate and enzyme concentrations are held constant in the reactions illustrated.
(a) Generalized curves for the effect of temperature on enzyme activity. As temperature increases, enzyme activity increases until it reaches an optimal temperature. Enzyme activity abruptly falls after it exceeds the optimal temperature because the enzyme, being a protein, denatures. **(b)** Enzyme activity is very sensitive to pH. Pepsin is a protein-digesting enzyme in the very acidic stomach juice. Trypsin, secreted by the pancreas into the slightly basic small intestine, digests polypeptides.

Each enzyme has an optimal pH

Most enzymes are active only over a narrow pH range and have an optimal pH, at which the rate of reaction is fastest. The optimal pH for most human enzymes is between 6 and 8. (Recall from Chapter 2 that buffers minimize pH changes in cells so that the pH is maintained within a narrow limit.) Pepsin, a protein-digesting enzyme secreted by cells lining the stomach, is remarkable in that it works only in a very acid medium, optimally at pH 2 (Fig. 6–13b). In contrast, trypsin, a protein-splitting enzyme secreted by the pancreas, functions best under the slightly basic conditions found in the small intestine.

The activity of an enzyme may be markedly changed by any alteration in pH, which in turn alters charges on the enzyme. Changes in charge affect the ionic bonds that contribute to tertiary and quaternary structure, thus changing the protein's conformation and activity. Many enzymes become inactive, and usu-

Figure 6–14 Yellowstone National Park's Grand Prismatic Spring. The world's third largest spring, about 61 m (200 ft) in diameter, the Grand Prismatic Spring teems with heat-tolerant bacteria. The rings around the perimeter, where the water is slightly cooler, get their distinctive colors from the various kinds of bacteria living there. *(From Smith, R.B., and L.J. Siegel. Windows into the Earth: The Geologic Story of Yellowstone and Grand Teton National Parks. Oxford University Press, Oxford, 2000)*

ally irreversibly denatured, when the medium is made very acidic or very basic.

Enzymes are organized into teams in metabolic pathways

Enzymes play an essential role in reaction coupling because they usually work in sequence, with the product of one enzyme-controlled reaction serving as the substrate for the next. We can picture the inside of a cell as a factory with many different assembly (and disassembly) lines operating simultaneously. An assembly line is composed of a number of enzymes. Each enzyme carries out one step, such as changing molecule A into molecule B. Then molecule B is passed along to the next enzyme, which converts it into molecule C, and so on. Such a series of reactions is referred to as a **metabolic pathway.**

$$A \xrightarrow{\text{Enzyme 1}} B \xrightarrow{\text{Enzyme 2}} C$$

Each of these reactions is theoretically reversible, and the fact that it is catalyzed by an enzyme does not change that fact. An enzyme does not itself determine the direction of the reaction it catalyzes. However, the overall reaction sequence is portrayed as proceeding from left to right. You will recall that if there is little intrinsic free energy difference between the reactants and products for a particular reaction, its direction will be determined mainly by the relative concentrations of reactants and products.

In biological pathways, both intermediate and final products are often removed and converted to other chemical compounds. Such removal drives the sequence of reactions in a particular direction. Let us assume that Reactant A is being constantly supplied and that its concentration remains constant. Enzyme 1 converts Reactant A to Product B. The concentration of B is always lower than the concentration of A because B is removed as it is converted to C in the reaction catalyzed by Enzyme 2. If C is removed as quickly as it is formed (perhaps by leaving the cell), the entire reaction pathway is "pulled" toward C.

The cell regulates enzymatic activity

Enzymes regulate the chemistry of the cell, but what controls the enzymes? One mechanism depends simply on controlling the amount of enzyme produced. A specific gene directs the synthesis of each type of enzyme. The gene, in turn, may be switched on by a signal from a hormone or by some other type of cellular product. When the gene is switched on, the enzyme is synthesized. The amount of enzyme present then influences the rate of the reaction.

If the pH and temperature are kept constant (as they are in most cells), the rate of the reaction can be affected by the substrate concentration or by the enzyme concentration. If an excess of substrate is present, the enzyme concentration is the rate-limiting factor. The initial rate of the reaction is then directly proportional to the concentration of enzyme (Fig. 6–15a).

If the enzyme concentration is kept constant, the rate of an enzymatic reaction is proportional to the concentration of substrate present. Substrate concentration is the rate-limiting factor at lower concentrations; the rate of the reaction is therefore directly proportional to the substrate concentration. However, at higher substrate concentrations the enzyme molecules become saturated with substrate, that is, substrate molecules are bound to all available active sites of enzyme molecules. In this situation, increasing the substrate concentration does not increase the reaction rate (Fig. 6–15b).

The product of one enzymatic reaction may control the activity of another enzyme, especially in a complex sequence of enzymatic reactions. For example, consider the following metabolic pathway:

$$A \xrightarrow{\text{Enzyme 1}} B \xrightarrow{\text{Enzyme 2}} C \xrightarrow{\text{Enzyme 3}} D \xrightarrow{\text{Enzyme 4}} E$$

A different enzyme catalyzes each step, and the final product E may inhibit the activity of Enzyme 1. When the concentration of E is low, the sequence of reactions proceeds rapidly. However, an increasing concentration of E serves as a signal for Enzyme 1 to slow down and eventually to stop functioning. Inhibition of Enzyme 1 stops the entire reaction sequence. This type of enzyme regulation, in which the formation of a product inhibits an earlier reaction in the sequence, is called **feedback inhibition** (Fig. 6–16).

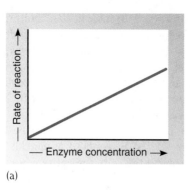
(a)

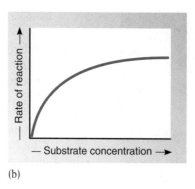
(b)

Figure 6–15 Effect of enzyme concentration and substrate concentration on the rate of a reaction. **(a)** In this example, the rate of reaction is measured at different enzyme concentrations, and an excess of substrate is present at all times. (Temperature and pH are kept at a constant level.) The rate of the reaction is therefore directly proportional to the enzyme concentration. **(b)** In this example, the rate of reaction is measured at different substrate concentrations, and enzyme concentration, temperature, and pH are constant. If the substrate concentration is relatively low, then the reaction rate is directly proportional to substrate concentration. However, higher substrate concentrations do not increase the reaction rate because the enzyme molecules become saturated with substrate.

Another important method of enzymatic control focuses on the activation of enzyme molecules. In their inactive form, the active sites of the enzyme are inappropriately shaped, so that the substrates do not fit. Among the factors that influence the shape of the enzyme are pH, the concentration of certain ions, and the addition of phosphate groups to certain amino acids in the enzyme.

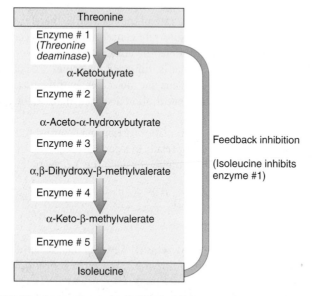

Figure 6–16 Feedback inhibition. Bacteria synthesize the amino acid isoleucine from the amino acid threonine. The isoleucine synthetic pathway involves five steps, each catalyzed by a different enzyme. When enough isoleucine accumulates in the cell, the isoleucine inhibits threonine deaminase, the enzyme that catalyzes the first step in this pathway.

Some enzymes possess a receptor site, called an **allosteric site,** on some region of the enzyme molecule other than the active site. (The word *allosteric* means "another space.") When a substance binds to an enzyme's allosteric site, the conformation of the enzyme's active site is changed, thereby modifying the enzyme's activity. Substances that affect enzyme activity by binding to allosteric sites are called **allosteric regulators.** Some allosteric regulators are inhibitors that keep the enzyme in its inactive shape. Other allosteric regulators are activators that result in an enzyme with a functional active site.

The enzyme **cyclic AMP-dependent protein kinase** is an allosteric enzyme with a regulator that is a protein that binds reversibly to the allosteric site and inactivates the enzyme. Protein kinase is in this inactive form most of the time (Fig. 6–17). When protein kinase activity is needed, the compound cyclic AMP (cAMP; see Fig. 3–27) contacts the enzyme-inhibitor complex and removes the inhibitory protein, thereby activating the protein kinase. Activation of protein kinases by cAMP is an important aspect of the mechanism of action of certain hormones (see Chapters 5 and 47).

Enzymes can be inhibited by certain chemical agents

Most enzymes may be inhibited or even destroyed by certain chemical agents. Enzyme inhibition may be reversible or irreversible. **Reversible inhibition** occurs when an inhibitor forms weak chemical bonds with the enzyme. Reversible inhibition can be competitive or noncompetitive.

In **competitive inhibition,** the inhibitor competes with the normal substrate for binding to the active site of the enzyme (Fig. 6–18*a*). Usually a competitive inhibitor is structurally similar to the normal substrate and so fits into the active site

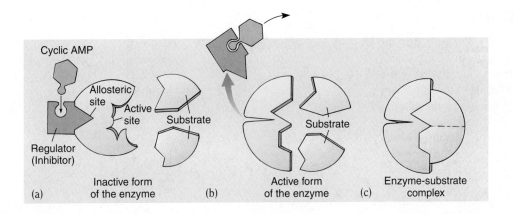

Figure 6–17 Allosteric enzyme. (a) The enzyme protein kinase is inhibited by a regulatory protein that binds reversibly to its allosteric site. When the enzyme is in this inactive form, the shape of the active site is modified so that the substrate cannot combine with it. (b) Cyclic AMP removes the allosteric inhibitor and activates the enzyme. The substrate can then combine with the active site (c).

and combines with the enzyme. However, it is not similar enough to substitute fully for the normal substrate in the chemical reaction, and the enzyme cannot attack it to form product molecules. A competitive inhibitor occupies the active site only temporarily and does not permanently damage the enzyme. In competitive inhibition, an active site is occupied by the inhibitor part of the time and by the normal substrate part of the time. If the concentration of the substrate is increased relative to the concentration of the inhibitor, the active site will usually be occupied by the substrate. Competitive inhibition is demonstrated experimentally by the fact that increasing the substrate concentration reverses competitive inhibition.

In **noncompetitive inhibition,** the inhibitor binds with the enzyme at a site other than the active site (Fig. 6–18b). Such an inhibitor inactivates the enzyme by altering its shape so that the active site cannot bind with the substrate. Many important non-

competitive inhibitors are metabolic substances that regulate enzyme activity by combining reversibly with the enzyme. Noncompetitive inhibition has some features in common with allosteric inhibition, discussed previously.

In **irreversible inhibition,** an inhibitor permanently inactivates or destroys an enzyme when it combines with one of its functional groups, either at the active site or elsewhere. Many poisons are irreversible enzyme inhibitors. For example, heavy metals such as mercury and lead bind irreversibly to and denature many proteins, including enzymes. Certain nerve gases poison the enzyme acetylcholinesterase, which is important to the function of nerves and muscles. Cytochrome oxidase, one of the enzymes that transports electrons in cellular respiration, is especially sensitive to cyanide. Death results from cyanide poisoning because cytochrome oxidase is irreversibly inhibited and can no longer transfer electrons from its substrate to oxygen.

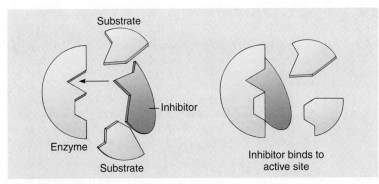

(a) Competitive inhibition

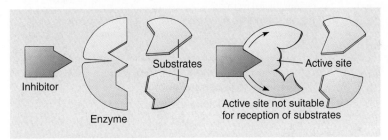

(b) Noncompetitive inhibition

Figure 6–18 Competitive and noncompetitive inhibition. (a) In competitive inhibition, the inhibitor competes with the normal substrate for the active site of the enzyme. A competitive inhibitor occupies the active site only temporarily. (b) In noncompetitive inhibition, the inhibitor binds with the enzyme at a site other than the active site, altering the shape of the enzyme and thereby inactivating it. Noncompetitive inhibition may be reversible.

Some drugs are enzyme inhibitors

Many bacterial infections are treated with drugs that directly or indirectly inhibit bacterial enzyme activity. For example, sulfa drugs have a chemical structure similar to that of the nutrient **para-aminobenzoic acid (PABA)** (Fig. 6–19). When PABA is available, microorganisms can synthesize the vitamin **folic acid,** which is necessary for growth. Humans do not synthesize folic acid from PABA, and that is why sulfa drugs selectively affect bacteria. When a sulfa drug is present, competitive inhibition occurs within the bacterium—that is, the drug competes with PABA for the active site of the bacterial enzyme. When bacteria use the sulfa drug instead of PABA, they synthesize a compound that cannot be used to make folic acid. Therefore, the bacterial cells are unable to grow.

Penicillin and related antibiotics irreversibly inhibit a bacterial enzyme called transpeptidase. This enzyme is responsible for establishing some of the chemical linkages in the bacterial cell wall. Susceptible bacteria cannot produce properly constructed cell walls and are prevented from multiplying effectively. Human cells do not have cell walls and do not employ this enzyme. Thus, except for individuals allergic to it, penicillin is harmless to humans. Unfortunately, during the years since it was introduced, resistance to penicillin has evolved in many bacterial strains. The resistant bacteria fight back with an enzyme of their own, penicillinase, which breaks down the penicillin and renders it ineffective. Because bacteria evolve at such a rapid rate, drug resistance is a growing problem in medical practice (see section in Chapter 17 on infectious disease organisms evolving resistance to drugs). Although new antibacterial drugs are constantly under development, certain serious infections, such as tuberculosis, are becoming increasingly difficult to treat.

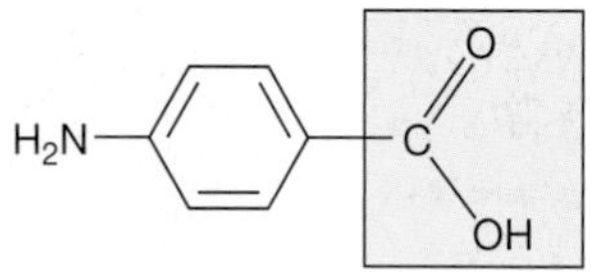

Para-aminobenzoic acid
(PABA)

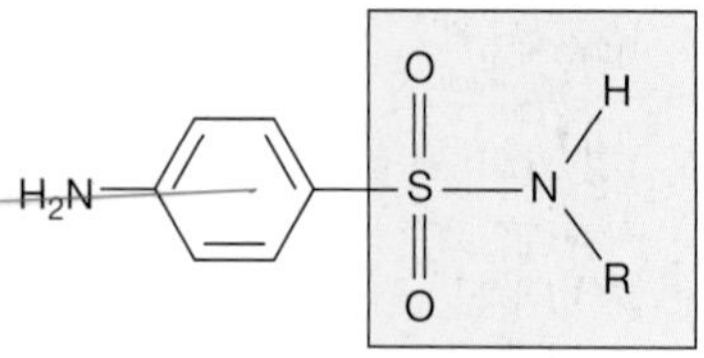

Generic sulfonamide
(Sulfa drug)

■ Figure 6–19 Para-aminobenzoic acid and sulfonamides. Sulfa drugs owe their antibiotic properties to their similarity in structure to para-aminobenzoic acid (PABA), a precursor in the synthesis of folic acid. Sulfa drugs block the synthesis of folic acid, an important vitamin necessary for growth. Animals, including humans, obtain folic acid in their diets, but many bacteria must synthesize it.

SUMMARY WITH KEY TERMS

I. **Energy** can be defined as the capacity to do work (expressed in **kilojoules, kJ**).
   A. All life depends on a continuous input of energy. Most producers capture **radiant energy** during photosynthesis and incorporate some of it into the chemical bonds of organic compounds. Some of this **chemical energy** then becomes available to consumers and decomposers.
   B. All forms of energy are interconvertible.
      1. **Potential energy** is stored energy; **kinetic energy** is energy of motion.
      2. Energy can be conveniently measured as **heat energy,** thermal energy that flows from an object with a higher temperature to an object with a lower temperature; the unit of heat energy is the **kilocalorie (kcal),** which is equal to 4.184 kilojoules. Heat energy cannot do cellular work.

II. The **first law of thermodynamics** states that energy cannot be created or destroyed but can be transferred and changed in form. The **second law of thermodynamics** states that disorder (entropy) in the universe is continuously increasing.
   A. The first law explains why organisms cannot produce energy but must continuously capture it from the surroundings.
   B. The second law explains why no process requiring energy is ever 100% efficient. In every energy transaction, some energy is dissipated as heat, which contributes to **entropy.**

III. When a chemical reaction is in a state of **dynamic equilibrium,** the rate of change in one direction is exactly the same as the rate of change in the opposite direction; the system can do no work because the **free energy** difference between the reactants and products is zero.
   A. As entropy increases, the amount of free energy decreases, as shown in the equation $G = H - TS,$ in which G is the free energy, H is the **enthalpy** (total potential energy of the system), T is the absolute temperature (expressed in degrees Kelvin), and S is entropy.
   B. The equation $\Delta G = \Delta H - T\Delta S$ indicates that the change in free energy (ΔG) during a chemical reaction is equal to the change in enthalpy (ΔH) minus the product of the absolute temperature (T) multiplied by the change in entropy (ΔS).

IV. A spontaneous reaction releases free energy that can perform work.
   A. Free energy decreases in an **exergonic reaction.** Exergonic reactions are spontaneous.
   B. Free energy increases in an **endergonic reaction.** The input of free energy required to drive an endergonic reaction may be supplied by **coupling** it to an exergonic reaction.

V. **Adenosine triphosphate (ATP)** is the immediate energy currency of the cell; it generally transfers energy through the transfer of its terminal phosphate group to acceptor molecules.
   A. ATP is formed by the **phosphorylation** of **ADP,** an endergonic process that requires an input of energy.

B. ATP is the common cellular link between exergonic and endergonic reactions and between **catabolism** (degradation of large complex molecules into smaller, simpler molecules) and **anabolism** (synthesis of complex molecules from simpler molecules).

VI. Energy can be transferred in **oxidation-reduction (redox) reactions.**

A. A substance that becomes oxidized gives up one or more electrons (and energy) to a substance that becomes reduced. Electrons are typically transferred as part of hydrogen atoms.

B. **NAD$^+$** and **NADP$^+$** accept electrons as part of hydrogen atoms and become reduced to form NADH and NADPH, respectively. These electrons (along with some of their energy) can be transferred to other acceptors.

VII. An **enzyme** is a biological **catalyst;** it greatly increases the speed of a chemical reaction without being consumed.

A. An enzyme lowers the **activation energy,** the kinetic energy necessary to get a reaction going.

B. An **active site** of an enzyme is a three-dimensional region where **substrates** come into close contact and thereby react more readily. A substrate binds to an active site, causing an **induced fit,** in which the shapes of the enzyme and substrate change slightly.

C. Some enzymes consist of an **apoenzyme** (its protein component) and a **cofactor.**

1. Most inorganic cofactors are metal ions.
2. A **coenzyme** is an organic cofactor; many coenzymes transfer electrons or part of a substrate from one molecule to another.

D. Enzymes work best at specific temperature and pH conditions.

E. A cell can regulate enzymatic activity by controlling the amount of enzyme produced and by regulating metabolic conditions that influence the shape of the enzyme.

1. Some enzymes have **allosteric sites,** noncatalytic sites to which a substance can bind, changing the enzyme's activity.
2. Allosteric enzymes are subject to **feedback inhibition,** in which the formation of an end product inhibits an earlier reaction in the sequence.

F. Certain chemical substances inhibit most enzymes. Inhibition may be reversible or irreversible.

1. **Reversible inhibition** occurs when an inhibitor forms weak chemical bonds with the enzyme. Reversible inhibition may be **competitive,** in which the inhibitor competes with the substrate for the active site, or **noncompetitive,** in which the inhibitor binds with the enzyme at a site other than the active site.
2. **Irreversible inhibition** occurs when an inhibitor combines with an enzyme and permanently inactivates it.

POST-TEST

1. According to the first law of thermodynamics (a) energy may be changed from one form to another but is neither created nor destroyed (b) much of the work an organism does is mechanical work (c) the disorder of the universe is increasing (d) free energy is available to do cellular work (e) a cell is in a state of dynamic equilibrium

2. According to the second law of thermodynamics (a) energy may be changed from one form to another but is neither created nor destroyed (b) much of the work an organism does is mechanical work (c) the disorder of the universe is increasing (d) free energy is available to do cellular work (e) a cell is in a state of dynamic equilibrium

3. In thermodynamics, _____ is a measure of the amount of disorder in the system. (a) bond energy (b) catabolism (c) entropy (d) enthalpy (e) work

4. The _____ energy of a system is that part of the total energy available to do cellular work. (a) activation (b) bond (c) kinetic (d) free (e) heat

5. A reaction that requires a net input of free energy is described as (a) exergonic (b) endergonic (c) spontaneous (d) both a and c (e) both b and c

6. A reaction that releases energy is described as (a) exergonic (b) endergonic (c) spontaneous (d) both a and c (e) both b and c

7. A spontaneous reaction is one in which the change in free energy *(∆G)* has a _____ value. (a) positive (b) negative (c) positive or negative (d) none of these (∆G has no measurable value)

8. To drive a reaction that requires an input of energy (a) an enzyme-substrate complex must form (b) the concentration of ATP must be decreased (c) the activation energy must be increased (d) some reaction that yields energy must be coupled to it (e) some reaction that requires energy must be coupled to it

9. Which of the following reactions could be coupled to an endergonic reaction with $\Delta G = +3.56$ kJ/mol? (a) A $\rightarrow$ B, $\Delta G = +6.08$ kJ/mol

(b) C $\rightarrow$ D, $\Delta G = +3.56$ kJ/mol (c) E $\rightarrow$ F, $\Delta G = 0$ kJ/mol (d) G $\rightarrow$ H, $\Delta G = -1.22$ kJ/mol (e) I $\rightarrow$ J, $\Delta G = -5.91$ kJ/mol

10. Consider the reaction: Glucose + 6 $O_2 \rightarrow$ 6 CO_2 + 6 H_2O ($\Delta G = -2880$ kJ/mol). Which of the following statements about this reaction is *not* true? (a) the reaction is spontaneous in a thermodynamic sense (b) a small amount of energy (activation energy) must be supplied to start the reaction, which then proceeds with a release of energy (c) the reaction is exergonic (d) the reaction can be coupled to an endergonic reaction (e) the reaction can be coupled to an exergonic reaction

11. The kinetic energy required to initiate a reaction is called (a) activation energy (b) bond energy (c) potential energy (d) free energy (e) heat energy

12. A biological catalyst that affects the rate of a chemical reaction without being consumed by the reaction is a(an) (a) product (b) cofactor (c) coenzyme (d) substrate (e) enzyme

13. The region of an enzyme molecule that combines with the substrate is the (a) allosteric site (b) reactant (c) active site (d) coenzyme (e) product

14. Which inhibitor binds to the active site of an enzyme? (a) noncompetitive inhibitor (b) competitive inhibitor (c) irreversible inhibitor (d) allosteric regulator (e) PABA

15. In the following reaction series, which enzyme(s) is/are most likely to have an allosteric site to which the end product E binds?

Enzyme 1   Enzyme 2   Enzyme 3   Enzyme 4
A ———→ B ———→ C ———→ D ———→ E

(a) enzyme 1 (b) enzyme 2 (c) enzyme 3 (d) enzyme 4 (e) enzymes 3 and 4

REVIEW QUESTIONS

1. You exert tension on a spring and then release it. Explain how these actions relate to work, potential energy, and kinetic energy.
2. Life is sometimes described as a constant struggle against the second law of thermodynamics. How do organisms succeed in this struggle without violating the second law?
3. Consider the free energy change in a reaction in which enthalpy decreases and entropy increases. Is ΔG zero, or does it have a positive value or a negative value? Is the reaction endergonic or exergonic?
4. Why do coupled reactions typically have common intermediates? Give a generalized example involving ATP. Why is ATP able to serve as an important link between exergonic and endergonic reactions?
5. What is activation energy? What effect does an enzyme have on activation energy?
6. Give the function of each of the following: (a) active site of an enzyme (b) coenzyme (c) allosteric site
7. Describe three factors that influence how an enzyme functions.
8. Label the diagram depicting the progress of a chemical reaction with these labels: energy of reactants, energy of products, activation energy with enzyme, activation energy without enzyme, change in free energy. Use Figure 6–11 to check your answers.

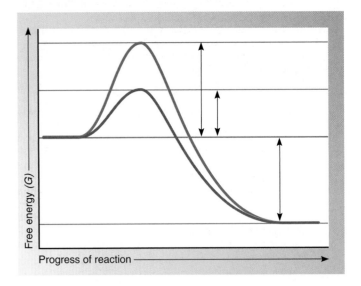

YOU MAKE THE CONNECTION

1. Reaction 1 and Reaction 2 happen to have the same free energy change: $\Delta G = -41.8$ kJ/mol (-10 kcal/mol). Reaction 1 is at equilibrium, but Reaction 2 is far from equilibrium. Is either reaction capable of performing work? If so, which one?
2. You are doing an experiment in which you are measuring the rate at which succinate is converted to fumarate by the enzyme succinic dehydrogenase. You decide to add a little malonate to make things interesting. You observe that the reaction rate slows markedly and conclude that malonate must be acting as an inhibitor. Design an experiment that will help you decide whether malonate is acting as a competitive inhibitor or a noncompetitive inhibitor.
3. Based on what you have learned in this chapter, explain why an extremely high fever (above 105° F or 40° C) is often fatal.

RECOMMENDED READINGS

Adams, S. "No Way Back." *New Scientist,* Oct. 1994. Examines the second law of thermodynamics.

Atkins, P.W. *The Second Law.* W.H. Freeman, San Francisco, 1984. A basic, understandable introduction to thermodynamics with an extensive section devoted to its biological implications.

Deeth, R. "Chemical Choreography." *New Scientist,* Jul. 1997. Reports on the use of computer modeling to study how enzymes function in cells.

Hinrichs, R.A., and M. Kleinbach. *Energy: Its Use and the Environment,* 3rd ed. Harcourt College Publishers, Philadelphia, 2002. This introductory text focuses on the physical principles behind energy use and its effects on the environment.

Tobin, A.J., and R.E. Morel. *Asking About Cells.* Saunders College Publishing, Philadelphia, 1997. A readable cell biology text with excellent coverage of cellular energetics

- Visit our Web site at **http://www.info.brookscole.com/solomonbergmartin** for links to chapter-related resources on the World Wide Web. Additional on-line materials relating to this chapter can also be found on our Web site.

 See chapter activity on BioActive Learner CD for additional help in mastering the chapter's material. Icon location in the chapter's margins shows which topics have tutorials or simulations in the CD.

7

How Cells Make ATP:
Energy-Releasing Pathways

Female gerenuks. Gerenuks *(Litocranius walleri)* live in the dry brush country of East Africa, where they browse on leaves, fruits, and flowers of thorny trees and shrubs. *(Renee Lynn/ Photo Researchers, Inc.)*

LEARNING OBJECTIVES

After you have studied this chapter you should be able to

1. Write a summary reaction for aerobic respiration, showing which reactant becomes oxidized and which becomes reduced.
2. List and give a brief overview of the four stages of aerobic respiration, indicate where each stage takes place in a eukaryotic cell, and add up the energy captured (as ATP, NADH, and FADH$_2$) in each stage.
3. Draw a diagram illustrating chemiosmosis and explain (1) how a gradient of protons is established across the inner mitochondrial membrane and (2) the process by which the proton gradient drives ATP synthesis.
4. Summarize how the products of protein and lipid catabolism enter the same metabolic pathway that oxidizes glucose.
5. Compare and contrast aerobic and anaerobic pathways used by cells to extract free energy from nutrients; include the mechanism of ATP formation, the final electron acceptor, and the end products.
6. Summarize the basic similarities of alcohol and lactate fermentation.

Cells are tiny factories that process materials on the molecular level, through thousands of metabolic reactions. Cells exist in a dynamic state and are continuously building up and breaking down the many different cellular constituents. As you learned in Chapter 6, metabolism has two complementary components: **catabolism,** which releases energy by splitting complex molecules into smaller components, and **anabolism,** the synthesis of complex molecules from simpler building blocks. Anabolic reactions produce proteins, nucleic acids, lipids, polysaccharides, and other complex molecules that help to maintain the cell or the organism of which it is a part. Most anabolic reactions are endergonic and require ATP or some other energy source to drive them.

Every organism must extract energy from the organic food molecules that it either manufactures by photosynthesis or captures from the environment. The gerenuks in the photograph,

for example, eat the leaves of thorny shrubs and trees to obtain energy. In gerenuks and other complex animals, food is first broken down by the digestive system. During digestion, proteins are split into their component amino acids, carbohydrates are digested to simple sugars, and fats are split into glycerol and fatty acids. These nutrients are then absorbed into the blood and transported to all the cells. Each cell converts the energy in the chemical bonds of nutrients to chemical energy stored in ATP in a process known as **cellular respiration.** (The term *cellular respiration* is used to distinguish these cellular processes from *organismic respiration,* the exchange of oxygen and carbon dioxide with the environment by animals that have special organs, such as lungs or gills, for gas exchange.)

Cellular respiration may be either aerobic or anaerobic. **Aerobic** respiration requires molecular oxygen (O$_2$), whereas **anaerobic** pathways, which include anaerobic respiration and fermentation, do not require oxygen. Most cells use aerobic respiration, which is by far the most common pathway and the main subject of this chapter. All three pathways—aerobic respiration, anaerobic respiration, and fermentation—are exergonic and release free energy.

AEROBIC RESPIRATION IS A REDOX PROCESS

Most eukaryotes and prokaryotes carry out **aerobic** respiration, a form of cellular respiration requiring oxygen. During aerobic respiration, nutrients are catabolized to carbon dioxide and water. Most cells of plants, animals, protists, fungi, and bacteria use aerobic respiration to obtain energy from glucose, which enters the cell though a specific transport protein in the plasma membrane (see discussion of facilitated diffusion in Chapter 5). The overall reaction pathway for the aerobic respiration of glucose is summarized as follows:

$$C_6H_{12}O_6 + 6\ O_2 + 6\ H_2O \longrightarrow$$
$$6\ CO_2 + 12\ H_2O + \text{Energy (in the chemical bonds of ATP)}$$

Note that water is shown on both sides of the equation; this is because it is a reactant in some reactions and a product in others.

For purposes of discussion, the equation for aerobic respiration can be simplified to indicate that there is a net yield of water:

$$\overbrace{C_6H_{12}O_6 + 6\ O_2}^{\text{Oxidation}} \rightarrow 6\ CO_2 + \underbrace{6\ H_2O}_{\text{Reduction}} + \text{Energy (in the chemical bonds of ATP)}$$

If we analyze this summary reaction, it appears that CO_2 is produced by the removal of hydrogen atoms from glucose. Conversely, water appears to be formed as the hydrogen atoms are accepted by oxygen. Because the transfer of hydrogen atoms is equivalent to the transfer of electrons, this is a redox process in which glucose becomes **oxidized** and oxygen becomes **reduced** (see Chapter 6).

The products of the reaction would be the same if the glucose were simply placed in a test tube and burned in the presence of oxygen. However, if cells were to burn glucose, its energy would be released all at once as heat, which not only would be unavailable to the cell but also would actually destroy it. For this reason, cells do not transfer hydrogen atoms directly from glucose to oxygen. Aerobic respiration is a redox process in which electrons associated with the hydrogen atoms in glucose are transferred to oxygen in a series of about 30 steps (Fig. 7–1). During this process, the free energy of the electrons is coupled to ATP synthesis.

AEROBIC RESPIRATION HAS FOUR STAGES

The chemical reactions of the aerobic respiration of glucose can be grouped into four stages (Fig. 7–2, Table 7–1, and summary equations at the end of this chapter). In eukaryotes, the first stage (glycolysis) takes place in the cytosol, and the remaining stages take place inside mitochondria. Most bacteria also carry out these processes, but because these cells lack mitochondria, the reactions of aerobic respiration occur in the cytosol and in association with the plasma membrane.

1. **Glycolysis.** A six-carbon glucose molecule is converted to two, three-carbon molecules of pyruvate,[1] and ATP and NADH are formed (see Chapter 6 for a review of ATP and NADH).[2]
2. **Formation of acetyl coenzyme A.** Each pyruvate enters a mitochondrion and is oxidized to a two-carbon group (acetate) that combines with coenzyme A, forming acetyl coenzyme A. NADH is produced, and carbon dioxide is released as a waste product.

[1] Pyruvate and many other compounds in cellular respiration exist as anions at the pH found in the cell. They sometimes associate with H^+ to form acids. For example, pyruvate forms pyruvic acid. In some textbooks these compounds are presented in the acid form.

[2] Although the correct way to write the reduced form of NAD^+ is NADH + H^+, for simplicity we will present the reduced form as NADH throughout the chapter.

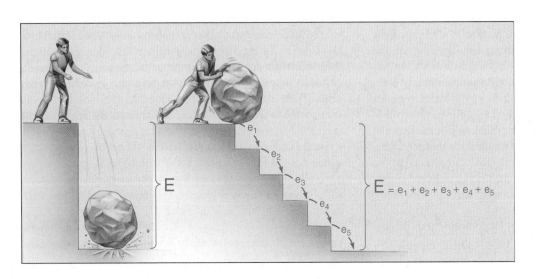

Figure 7–1 Changes in free energy. The release of energy from a glucose molecule is analogous to the liberation of energy by a falling object. The total energy released *(E)* is the same whether it occurs all at once or in a series of steps.

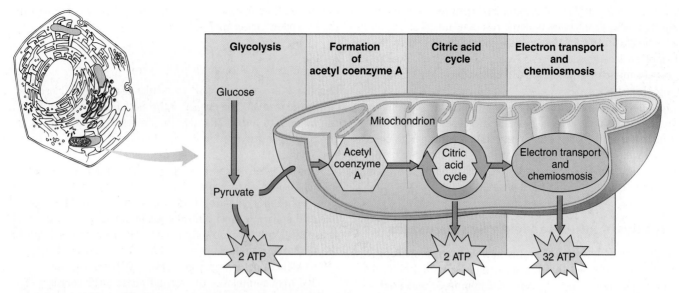

Figure 7-2 The four stages of aerobic respiration. In eukaryotic cells, much of aerobic respiration occurs in mitochondria. Glycolysis, the first stage of aerobic respiration, occurs in the cytosol. Pyruvate, the product of glycolysis, enters a mitochondrion, where cellular respiration continues with the formation of acetyl CoA, the citric acid cycle, and electron transport/chemiosmosis. Most ATP is synthesized by chemiosmosis.

3. **The citric acid cycle.** The acetate group of acetyl coenzyme A combines with a four-carbon molecule (oxaloacetate) to form a six-carbon molecule (citrate). In the course of the cycle, citrate is recycled to oxaloacetate, and carbon dioxide is released as a waste product. Energy is captured as ATP and the reduced, high-energy compounds NADH and $FADH_2$ (see Chapter 6 for a review of $FADH_2$).

4. **The electron transport chain and chemiosmosis.** The electrons removed from glucose during the preceding stages are transferred from NADH and $FADH_2$ to a chain of electron acceptor compounds. As the electrons are passed from one electron acceptor to another, some of their energy is used to move hydrogen ions (protons) across the inner mitochondrial

membrane, forming a proton gradient. In a process known as chemiosmosis, to be described later, the energy of this proton gradient is used to produce ATP.

Most reactions involved in aerobic respiration are one of three types: dehydrogenations, decarboxylations, and those that we will informally categorize as preparation reactions. **Dehydrogenations** are reactions in which two hydrogen atoms (actually, two electrons plus one or two protons) are removed from the substrate and transferred to NAD^+ or FAD. **Decarboxylations** are reactions in which part of a carboxyl group (—COOH) is removed from the substrate as a molecule of CO_2. The carbon dioxide we exhale with each breath is derived from decarboxylations

TABLE 7-1   Summary of Aerobic Respiration

Phase	Summary	Some Starting Materials	Some End Products
1. Glycolysis (in cytosol)	Series of reactions in which glucose is degraded to pyruvate; net profit of 2 ATPs; hydrogen atoms are transferred to carriers; can proceed anaerobically	Glucose, ATP, NAD^+, ADP, P_i	Pyruvate, ATP, NADH
2. Formation of acetyl CoA (in mitochondria)	Pyruvate is degraded and combined with coenzyme A to form acetyl CoA; hydrogen atoms are transferred to carriers; CO_2 is released	Pyruvate, coenzyme A, NAD^+	Acetyl CoA, CO_2, NADH
3. Citric acid cycle (in mitochondria)	Series of reactions in which the acetyl portion of acetyl CoA is degraded to CO_2; hydrogen atoms are transferred to carriers; ATP is synthesized	Acetyl CoA, H_2O, NAD^+, FAD, ADP, P_i	CO_2, NADH, $FADH_2$, ATP
4. Electron transport and chemiosmosis (in mitochondria)	Chain of several electron transport molecules; electrons are passed along chain; released energy is used to form a proton gradient; ATP is synthesized as protons diffuse down the gradient; oxygen is final electron acceptor	NADH, $FADH_2$, O_2, ADP, P_i	ATP, H_2O, NAD^+, FAD

that occur in our cells. The rest of the reactions are preparation reactions in which molecules undergo rearrangements and other changes so that they can subsequently undergo further dehydrogenations or decarboxylations. As we examine the individual reactions of aerobic respiration, we will encounter many examples of these three basic types.

In following the reactions of aerobic respiration, it helps to do some bookkeeping as you go along. Because glucose is the starting material, it is useful to express changes on a per glucose basis. We will be paying particular attention to changes in the number of carbon atoms per molecule and to steps in which some type of energy transfer takes place.

In glycolysis, glucose yields two pyruvates

Glycolysis comes from Greek words meaning "sugar-splitting," which refers to the fact that the sugar glucose is metabolized. Glycolysis does not require oxygen and can proceed under aerobic or anaerobic conditions. Figure 7–3 shows a simple summary of glycolysis, in which a glucose molecule comprising six carbons is converted to two molecules of **pyruvate,** a three-carbon molecule. Some of the energy in the glucose is captured; there is a net yield of two ATP molecules and two NADH molecules. The reactions of glycolysis take place in the cytosol, where the necessary reactants, such as ADP, NAD^+, and inorganic phosphates, float freely and are used as needed.

The glycolysis pathway consists of a series of reactions, each of which is catalyzed by a specific enzyme (Fig. 7–4). Glycolysis is divided into two major phases: The first includes endergonic reactions that require ATP, while the second includes exergonic reactions that yield ATP and NADH.

The first phase of glycolysis requires an investment of ATP

The first phase of glycolysis is sometimes referred to as the "energy-investment" phase. Glucose is a relatively stable molecule and is not easily broken down. In two separate **phosphorylation reactions,** a phosphate group is transferred from ATP to the sugar. The resulting phosphorylated sugar (fructose-1,6-bisphosphate) is less stable and is broken enzymatically into two, three-carbon molecules, dihydroxyacetone phosphate and glyceraldehyde-3-phosphate (G3P); the dihydroxyacetone phosphate is enzymatically converted to G3P, so the products at this point in glycolysis are two molecules of G3P. We may summarize this portion of glycolysis as follows:

$$\text{Glucose} + 2\,\text{ATP} \longrightarrow 2\,\text{G3P} + 2\,\text{ADP}$$

Six-carbon compound   Three-carbon compound

The second phase of glycolysis yields NADH and ATP

Each G3P is converted to pyruvate. In the first step of this process each G3P is oxidized by the removal of two electrons (as

part of two hydrogen atoms). These immediately combine with the hydrogen carrier molecule, NAD^+:

$$NAD^+ + 2\,H \longrightarrow NADH + H^+$$

Oxidized   (From G3P)   Reduced

Because there are two G3P molecules for every glucose, two NADH are formed. The energy of the electrons carried by NADH can be used to form ATP later. The process by which this is accomplished is discussed in conjunction with the electron transport chain.

In two of the reactions leading to the formation of pyruvate, ATP is formed when a phosphate group is transferred to ADP from a phosphorylated intermediate (see Fig. 7–4). This process is called **substrate-level phosphorylation.** Note that in the first phase of glycolysis two molecules of ATP are consumed, but in the second phase four molecules of ATP are produced. Thus, glycolysis yields a net energy profit of *two* ATPs per glucose.

We may summarize the second phase of glycolysis as follows:

$$2\,\text{G3P} + 2\,NAD^+ + 4\,\text{ADP} \longrightarrow$$
$$2\,\text{Pyruvate} + 2\,\text{NADH} + 4\,\text{ATP}$$

Pyruvate is converted to acetyl CoA

In eukaryotes, the pyruvate molecules formed in glycolysis enter the mitochondria, where they are converted to **acetyl coenzyme A (acetyl CoA).** These reactions occur in the cytosol of aerobic prokaryotes. In this series of reactions, pyruvate undergoes a process known as **oxidative decarboxylation.** First, a carboxyl group is removed as carbon dioxide, which diffuses out of the cell (Fig. 7–5 on page 160). Then the remaining two-carbon fragment is oxidized, and NAD^+ accepts the electrons removed during the oxidation. Finally, the oxidized two-carbon fragment, an acetyl group, becomes attached to **coenzyme A,** yielding acetyl CoA. *Pyruvate dehydrogenase,* the enzyme that catalyzes these reactions, is an enormous multienzyme complex consisting of 72 polypeptide chains!

Recall from Chapter 6 that coenzyme A transfers groups derived from organic acids. In this case, coenzyme A transfers an acetyl group, which is related to acetic acid. Coenzyme A is manufactured in the cell from one of the B vitamins, pantothenic acid.

The overall reaction for the formation of acetyl coenzyme A is the following:

$$2\,\text{Pyruvate} + 2\,NAD^+ + 2\,\text{CoA} \longrightarrow$$
$$2\,\text{Acetyl CoA} + 2\,\text{NADH} + 2\,CO_2$$

Note that the original glucose molecule has now been partially oxidized, yielding two acetyl groups and two CO_2 molecules. The electrons removed have reduced NAD^+ to NADH. At this point in aerobic respiration, four NADH molecules have been formed as a result of the catabolism of a single glucose molecule: two during glycolysis and two during the formation of acetyl CoA from pyruvate. Keep in mind that these NADH molecules will be used later (during electron transport) to form additional ATP molecules.

(text continues on page 160)

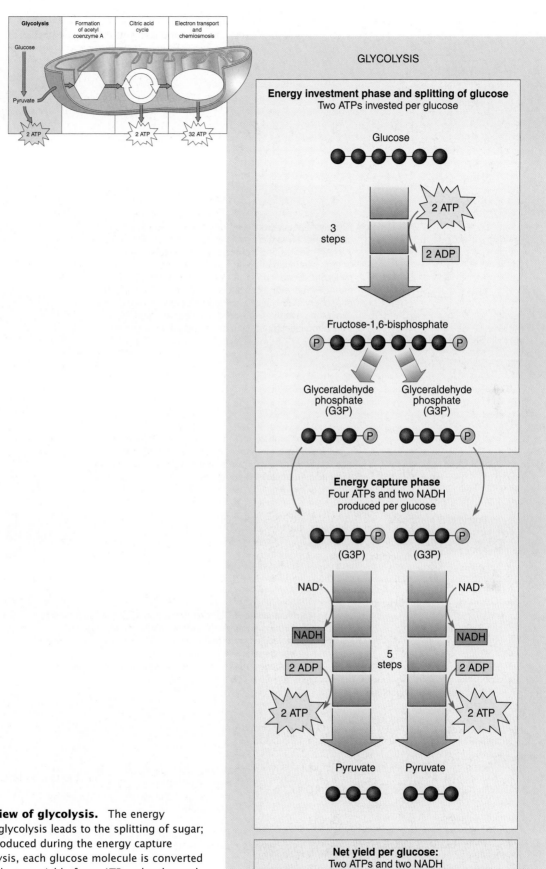

Figure 7–3 Overview of glycolysis. The energy investment phase of glycolysis leads to the splitting of sugar; ATP and NADH are produced during the energy capture phase. During glycolysis, each glucose molecule is converted to two pyruvates, with a net yield of two ATP molecules and two NADH molecules.

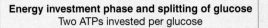

Energy investment phase and splitting of glucose
Two ATPs invested per glucose

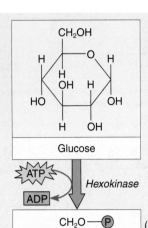

Glucose

Hexokinase

CH₂O—Ⓟ

Glucose-6-phosphate

(1) Glycolysis begins with a preparation reaction in which glucose receives a phosphate group from an ATP molecule. The ATP serves as a source of both phosphate and the energy needed to attach the phosphate to the glucose molecule. (Once the ATP is spent, it becomes ADP and joins the ADP pool of the cell until turned into ATP again.) The phosphorylated glucose is known as glucose-6-phosphate. (Note the phosphate attached to its carbon atom 6.) Phosphorylation of the glucose makes it more chemically reactive.

Phosphoglucoisomerase

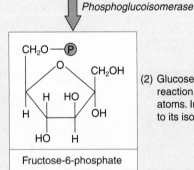

Fructose-6-phosphate

(2) Glucose-6-phosphate undergoes another preparation reaction, the rearrangement of its hydrogen and oxygen atoms. In this reaction glucose-6-phosphate is converted to its isomer, fructose-6-phosphate.

Phosphofructokinase

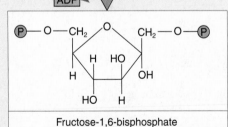

Fructose-1,6-bisphosphate

(3) Next, another ATP donates a phosphate to the molecule, forming fructose-1,6-bisphosphate. So far, two ATP molecules have been invested in the process without any being produced. Phosphate groups are now bound at carbons 1 and 6, and the molecule is ready to be split.

Aldolase

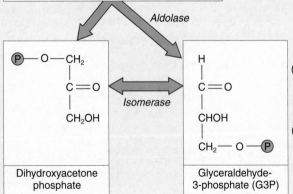

Dihydroxyacetone phosphate

Isomerase

Glyceraldehyde-3-phosphate (G3P)

(4) Fructose-1,6-bisphosphate is then split into two 3-carbon sugars, glyceraldehyde-3-phosphate (G3P) and dihydroxyacetone phosphate.

(5) Dihydroxyacetone phosphate is enzymatically converted to its isomer, glyceraldehyde-3-phosphate, for further metabolism in glycolysis.

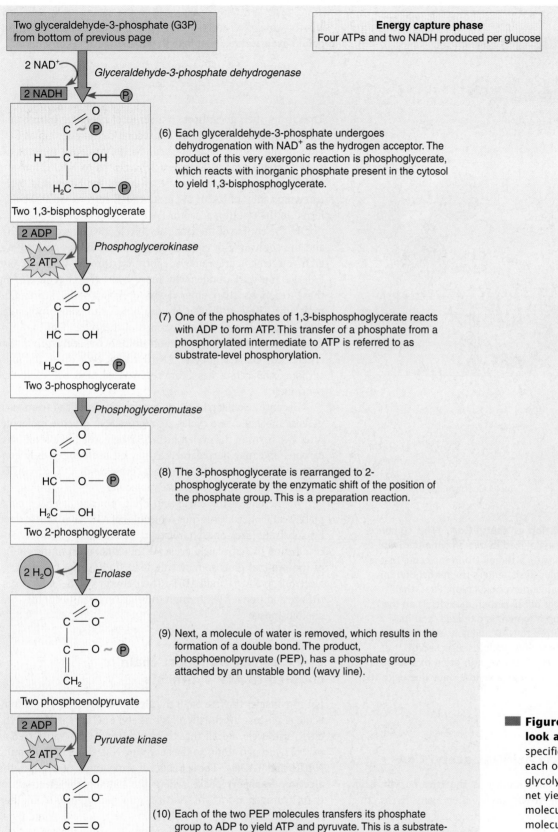

Two glyceraldehyde-3-phosphate (G3P)
from bottom of previous page

Energy capture phase
Four ATPs and two NADH produced per glucose

2 NAD⁺

Glyceraldehyde-3-phosphate dehydrogenase

2 NADH

Ⓟ

Two 1,3-bisphosphoglycerate

(6) Each glyceraldehyde-3-phosphate undergoes dehydrogenation with NAD⁺ as the hydrogen acceptor. The product of this very exergonic reaction is phosphoglycerate, which reacts with inorganic phosphate present in the cytosol to yield 1,3-bisphosphoglycerate.

2 ADP

2 ATP

Phosphoglycerokinase

Two 3-phosphoglycerate

(7) One of the phosphates of 1,3-bisphosphoglycerate reacts with ADP to form ATP. This transfer of a phosphate from a phosphorylated intermediate to ATP is referred to as substrate-level phosphorylation.

Phosphoglyceromutase

Two 2-phosphoglycerate

(8) The 3-phosphoglycerate is rearranged to 2-phosphoglycerate by the enzymatic shift of the position of the phosphate group. This is a preparation reaction.

2 H₂O

Enolase

Two phosphoenolpyruvate

(9) Next, a molecule of water is removed, which results in the formation of a double bond. The product, phosphoenolpyruvate (PEP), has a phosphate group attached by an unstable bond (wavy line).

2 ADP

2 ATP

Pyruvate kinase

Two pyruvate

(10) Each of the two PEP molecules transfers its phosphate group to ADP to yield ATP and pyruvate. This is a substrate-level phosphorylation reaction.

■ **Figure 7–4 A detailed look at glycolysis.** A specific enzyme catalyzes each of the reactions in glycolysis. Note that there is a net yield of two ATP molecules and two NADH molecules. (Yellow wavy lines indicate unstable bonds. These bonds permit the phosphates to be transferred to other molecules, in this case ADP.)

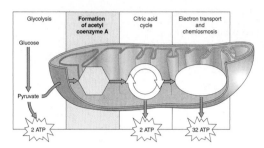

The first reaction of the cycle occurs when acetyl CoA transfers its two-carbon acetyl group to the four-carbon acceptor compound **oxaloacetate,** forming **citrate,** a six-carbon compound:

$$\text{Oxaloacetate} + \text{Acetyl CoA} \longrightarrow \text{Citrate} + \text{CoA}$$

Four-carbon compound   Two-carbon compound   Six-carbon compound

The citrate then goes through a series of chemical transformations, losing first one and then a second carboxyl group as CO_2. Most of the energy made available by the oxidative steps of the cycle is transferred as energy-rich electrons to NAD^+, forming NADH. For each acetyl group that enters the citric acid cycle, three molecules of NADH are produced. Electrons are also transferred to the electron acceptor FAD, forming $FADH_2$.

In the course of the citric acid cycle, two molecules of CO_2 and the equivalent of eight hydrogen atoms (eight protons and eight electrons) are removed, forming three NADH and one $FADH_2$. You may wonder why more hydrogen is generated by these reactions than entered the cycle with the acetyl CoA molecule. These hydrogen atoms come from water molecules that are added during the reactions of the cycle. The CO_2 produced accounts for the two carbon atoms of the acetyl group that entered the citric acid cycle. At the end of each cycle, the four-carbon oxaloacetate has been regenerated, and the cycle can continue.

Because two acetyl CoA molecules are produced from each glucose molecule, two cycles are required per glucose molecule. After two turns of the cycle, the original glucose has lost all of its carbons and may be regarded as having been completely consumed. To summarize, the citric acid cycle yields $4\ CO_2$, 6 NADH, 2 $FADH_2$, and 2 ATP per glucose molecule.

At the end of the citric acid cycle, glucose has been completely catabolized. Only four molecules of ATP have been formed by substrate-level phosphorylation: two during glycolysis and two during the citric acid cycle. At this time, most of the energy of the original glucose molecule is in the form of high-energy electrons in NADH and $FADH_2$. Their energy will be used to synthesize additional ATP through the electron transport chain and chemiosmosis.

The electron transport chain is coupled to ATP synthesis

Let us consider the fate of all the electrons removed from a molecule of glucose during glycolysis, acetyl CoA formation, and the citric acid cycle. Recall that these electrons were transferred as part of hydrogen atoms to the acceptors NAD^+ and FAD, forming NADH and $FADH_2$. These reduced compounds now enter the **electron transport chain,** where the high-energy electrons of their hydrogen atoms are shuttled from one acceptor to another. As the electrons are passed along in a series of exergonic redox reactions, some of their energy is used to drive the synthesis of ATP, which is an endergonic process. Because ATP synthesis (by phosphorylation of ADP) is coupled to the redox reactions in the electron transport chain, the entire process is known as **oxidative phosphorylation.**

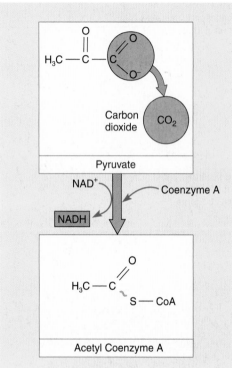

Figure 7–5 Formation of acetyl CoA. This complex series of reactions is catalyzed by the enzyme pyruvate dehydrogenase. Pyruvate, a three-carbon molecule that is the end product of glycolysis, enters the mitochondrion and undergoes oxidative decarboxylation. First, the carboxyl group is split off as carbon dioxide. Then the remaining two-carbon fragment is oxidized, and its electrons are transferred to NAD^+. Finally, the oxidized two-carbon group, an acetyl group, is attached to coenzyme A. Coenzyme A has a sulfur atom that forms a very unstable bond, shown as a yellow wavy line, with the acetyl group.

The citric acid cycle oxidizes acetyl CoA

The **citric acid cycle** is also known as the **tricarboxylic acid (TCA) cycle** and as the **Krebs cycle,** after Hans Krebs, the chemist who assembled the accumulated contributions of many scientists and worked out the details of the cycle in the 1930s. A simple summary of the citric acid cycle, which takes place in the matrix of the mitochondria, is given in Figure 7–6. The eight steps of the citric acid cycle are shown in Figure 7–7. A specific enzyme catalyzes each reaction.

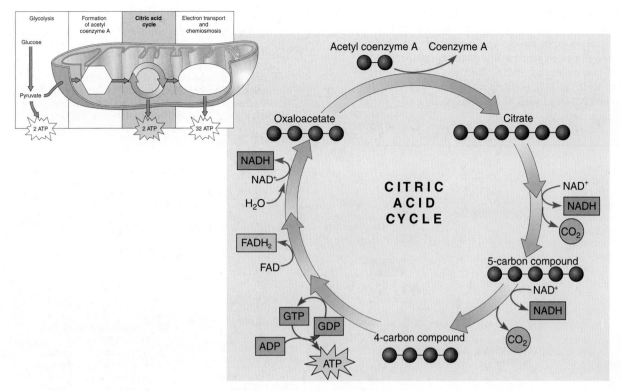

Figure 7–6 Overview of the citric acid cycle. For every glucose, two acetyl groups enter the citric acid cycle *(top)*. Each two-carbon acetyl group combines with a four-carbon compound, oxaloacetate, to form the six-carbon compound citrate. Two CO_2 molecules are removed, and energy is captured as one ATP, three NADH, and one $FADH_2$ per acetyl group (or two ATPs, six NADH, and two $FADH_2$ per glucose molecule).

The electron transport chain transfers electrons from NADH and FADH$_2$ to oxygen

The electron transport chain is a series of electron carriers embedded in the inner mitochondrial membrane of eukaryotes and in the plasma membrane of aerobic prokaryotes. Like NADH and $FADH_2$, each carrier can exist in an oxidized form or a reduced form. Electrons pass down the electron transport chain in a series of redox reactions that works much like a bucket brigade, the old-time chain of people that passed buckets of water from a stream to a building that was on fire. In the electron transport chain, each acceptor molecule is alternately reduced as it accepts electrons and oxidized as it gives up electrons. The electrons entering the electron transport chain have a relatively high energy content. They lose some of their energy at each step as they pass along the chain of electron carriers (just as some of the water spills out of the bucket as it is passed from one person to another).

Members of the electron transport chain include the flavoprotein *flavin mononucleotide (FMN),* the lipid *ubiquinone* (also called *coenzyme Q* or *CoQ*), several *iron-sulfur proteins,* and a group of closely related iron-containing proteins called *cytochromes.* Each of the electron carriers has a different mechanism for accepting and passing electrons. As cytochromes accept and donate electrons, for example, the charge on the iron atom, which is the electron carrier portion of the cytochromes, alternates between Fe^{2+} (reduced) and Fe^{3+} (oxidized).

The electron transport chain has been isolated and purified from the inner mitochondrial membrane as four large, distinct protein complexes, or groups, of acceptors (Fig. 7–8). *Complex I (NADH-ubiquinone oxidoreductase)* accepts electrons from NADH molecules that were produced during glycolysis, the formation of acetyl CoA, and the citric acid cycle. *Complex II (succinate-ubiquinone reductase)* accepts electrons from $FADH_2$ molecules that were produced during the citric acid cycle. Complexes I and II both produce the same product, reduced ubiquinone, which is the substrate of *complex III (ubiquinone-cytochrome c oxidoreductase).* That is, complex III accepts electrons from reduced ubiquinone and passes them on to cytochrome *c. Complex IV (cytochrome c oxidase)* accepts electrons from cytochrome *c* and uses these electrons to reduce molecular oxygen, forming water in the process. The electrons simultaneously unite with protons from the surrounding medium to form hydrogen, and the chemical reaction between hydrogen and oxygen produces water.

Because oxygen is the final electron acceptor in the electron transport chain, organisms that respire aerobically require oxygen. What happens when cells that are strict aerobes are deprived of oxygen? When no oxygen is available to accept them, the last

Figure 7–7 A detailed look at the citric acid cycle.

You should begin in the upper right corner, where acetyl coenzyme A attaches to oxaloacetate. During the citric acid cycle, the entry of a two-carbon acetyl group is balanced by the release of two molecules of CO_2. Electrons are transferred to NAD^+ or FAD, yielding NADH and $FADH_2$, respectively, and ATP is formed by substrate-level phosphorylation.

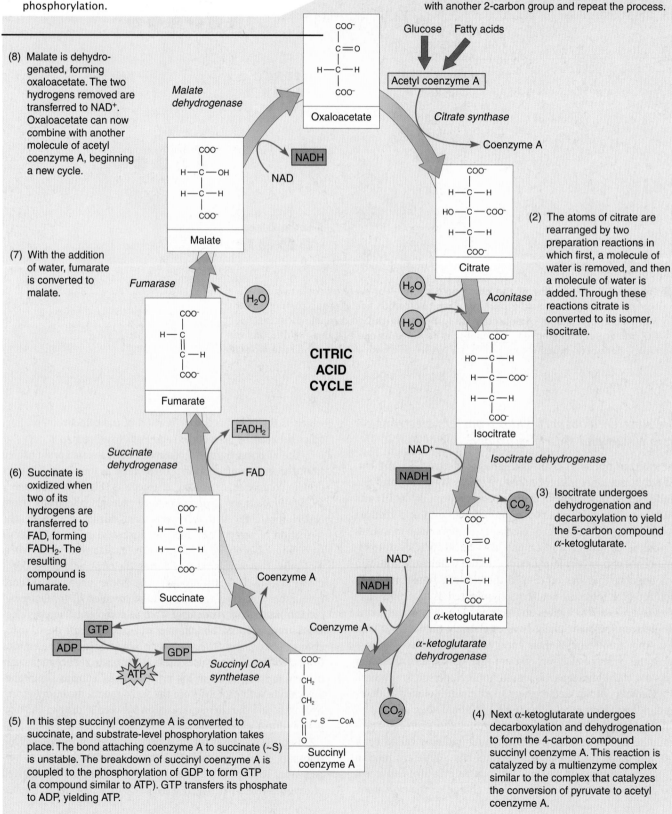

(1) The unstable bond attaching the acetyl group to coenzyme A breaks. The 2-carbon acetyl group becomes attached to a 4-carbon oxaloacetate molecule, forming citrate, a 6-carbon molecule with three carboxyl groups. Coenzyme A is free to combine with another 2-carbon group and repeat the process.

Glucose   Fatty acids

Acetyl coenzyme A

Citrate synthase

Coenzyme A

Oxaloacetate

Malate dehydrogenase

NADH

NAD

(8) Malate is dehydrogenated, forming oxaloacetate. The two hydrogens removed are transferred to NAD^+. Oxaloacetate can now combine with another molecule of acetyl coenzyme A, beginning a new cycle.

Malate

(7) With the addition of water, fumarate is converted to malate.

Fumarase

H_2O

Citrate

H_2O

H_2O

Aconitase

(2) The atoms of citrate are rearranged by two preparation reactions in which first, a molecule of water is removed, and then a molecule of water is added. Through these reactions citrate is converted to its isomer, isocitrate.

CITRIC ACID CYCLE

Fumarate

$FADH_2$

Succinate dehydrogenase

FAD

Isocitrate

NAD^+

NADH

Isocitrate dehydrogenase

CO_2

(3) Isocitrate undergoes dehydrogenation and decarboxylation to yield the 5-carbon compound α-ketoglutarate.

(6) Succinate is oxidized when two of its hydrogens are transferred to FAD, forming $FADH_2$. The resulting compound is fumarate.

Succinate

NAD^+

NADH

Coenzyme A

α-ketoglutarate

α-ketoglutarate dehydrogenase

GTP

ADP

GDP

ATP

Succinyl CoA synthetase

Coenzyme A

Succinyl coenzyme A

CO_2

(5) In this step succinyl coenzyme A is converted to succinate, and substrate-level phosphorylation takes place. The bond attaching coenzyme A to succinate (~S) is unstable. The breakdown of succinyl coenzyme A is coupled to the phosphorylation of GDP to form GTP (a compound similar to ATP). GTP transfers its phosphate to ADP, yielding ATP.

(4) Next α-ketoglutarate undergoes decarboxylation and dehydrogenation to form the 4-carbon compound succinyl coenzyme A. This reaction is catalyzed by a multienzyme complex similar to the complex that catalyzes the conversion of pyruvate to acetyl coenzyme A.

cytochrome in the chain is stuck with its electrons. When that occurs, each acceptor molecule in the chain remains stuck with electrons (i.e., each is reduced), and the entire chain is blocked all the way back to NADH. Because oxidative phosphorylation is coupled to electron transport, no further ATPs are produced by way of the electron transport chain. Most cells of complex organisms cannot live long without oxygen because the small amount of ATP they produce by glycolysis alone is insufficient to sustain life processes.

Lack of oxygen is not the only factor that interferes with the electron transport chain. Some poisons, including cyanide, inhibit the normal activity of the cytochromes. Cyanide binds tightly to the iron in the last cytochrome in the electron transport chain (cytochrome a_3), making it unable to transport electrons on to oxygen. This blocks the further passage of electrons through the chain, halting ATP production.

Although the flow of electrons in electron transport is usually tightly coupled to the production of ATP, some organisms are able to uncouple the two processes to produce heat (see *Focus On: Electron Transport and Heat*).

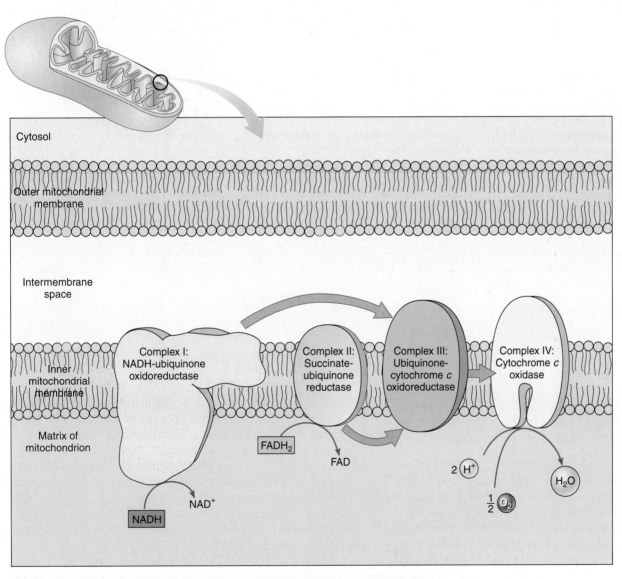

Figure 7–8 Overview of the electron transport chain. Electrons fall to successively lower energy levels as they are passed along the four complexes of the electron transport chain, which are located in the inner mitochondrial membrane. (The orange arrows indicate the pathway of electrons.) The carriers within each complex are alternately reduced and oxidized as they accept and donate electrons. The terminal acceptor is oxygen; one of the two atoms of an oxygen molecule (written as $\frac{1}{2}$ O_2) accepts two electrons, which are added to two protons from the surrounding medium to produce water.

What is the source of our body heat? Essentially, it is a byproduct of various exergonic reactions, especially those involving the electron transport chains in our mitochondria. Some cold-adapted animals, hibernating animals, and newborn animals are able to produce unusually large amounts of heat by uncoupling electron transport from ATP production. These animals have **adipose tissue** (tissue in which fat is stored) that is brown. The brown color comes from the large number of mitochondria found in the brown adipose tissue cells. The inner mitochondrial membranes of these mitochondria contain an *uncoupling protein* that produces a passive proton channel through which protons flow into the mitochondrial matrix. As a consequence, most of the energy of glucose is converted to heat rather than to chemical energy in ATP.

Certain plants, which are not generally considered "warm" organisms, also have the ability to produce large amounts of heat. Skunk cabbage (*Symplocarpus foetidus*), for example,

lives in North American swamps and wet woodlands and generally flowers during February and March when the ground is still covered with snow *(see figure)*. Its uncoupled mitochondria generate large amounts of heat, enabling the plant to melt the snow and attract insect pollinators by vaporizing certain odiferous molecules into the surrounding air. The flower temperature of skunk cabbage is 15° to 22° C (59° to 72° F) when the air surrounding it is −15° to 10° C (5° to 50° F). Skunk cabbage flowers maintain this temperature for two weeks or more. Other plants, such as splitleaf philodendron (*Philodendron selloum*) and sacred lotus (*Nelumbo nucifera*), also generate heat when they bloom and maintain their temperatures within precise limits.

Some plants generate as much or more heat per gram of tissue than animals in flight, which have long been considered the greatest heat producers in the living world. The European plant lords-and-ladies (*Arum maculatum*), for example, produces 0.4 joules (0.1 cal) of

heat per second per gram of tissue, whereas a hummingbird in flight produces 0.24 J (0.06 cal) per second per gram of tissue.

Skunk cabbage (*Symplocarpus foetidus*). This plant not only produces a significant amount of heat when it flowers but also regulates its temperature within a specific range. *(Leonard Lee Rue III /Earth Scenes)*

The chemiosmotic model explains the coupling of ATP synthesis to electron transport in aerobic respiration

For decades scientists were aware that oxidative phosphorylation occurs in mitochondria, and many experiments had shown that the transfer of two electrons from each NADH to oxygen (via the electron transport chain) usually results in the production of up to three ATP molecules. However, for a long time, the connection between ATP synthesis and electron transport remained a mystery.

Then, in 1961 Peter Mitchell proposed the **chemiosmotic model,** based on his experiments with bacteria. Because the respiratory electron transport chain is located in the plasma membrane of an aerobic bacterial cell, the bacterial plasma membrane can be considered comparable to the inner mitochondrial membrane. Mitchell demonstrated that if bacterial cells are placed in an acidic environment (that is, an environment with a high hydrogen ion, or proton, concentration), the cells synthesized ATP even if electron transport was not taking place. On the basis of

these and other experiments, Mitchell proposed that electron transport and ATP synthesis are coupled by means of a proton gradient across the inner mitochondrial membrane in eukaryotes (or across the plasma membrane in bacteria). His model was so radical that it was not accepted immediately. By 1978 so much evidence had accumulated in support of the chemiosmotic model that Peter Mitchell was awarded a Nobel Prize.

The electron transport chain establishes the proton gradient; some of the energy released as electrons pass down the electron transport chain is used to move protons (H^+) across a membrane. In eukaryotes the protons are moved across the inner mitochondrial membrane into the intermembrane space, that is, the space between the inner and outer mitochondrial membranes (Fig. 7–9). Hence the inner mitochondrial membrane separates a space with a higher concentration of protons (the intermembrane space) from a space with a lower concentration of protons (the mitochondrial matrix).

Protons are moved across the inner mitochondrial membrane by three of the four electron transport complexes (com-

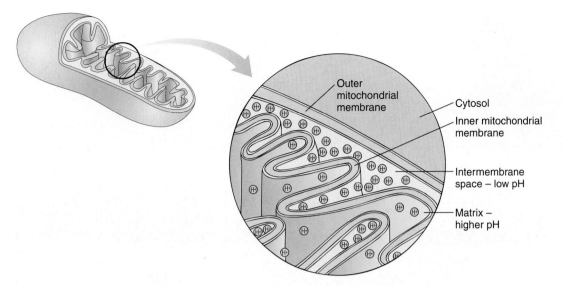

Figure 7–9 Accumulation of protons (H⁺) within the intermembrane space.
As electrons move down the electron transport chain, the electron transport complexes move protons (H^+) from the matrix to the intermembrane space, creating a proton gradient. The high concentration of H^+ in the intermembrane space lowers the pH.

plexes I, III, and IV) (Fig. 7–10). The result is a proton gradient across the inner mitochondrial membrane. Like water behind a dam, the proton gradient is a form of potential energy that can be harnessed to provide the energy for ATP synthesis.

Diffusion of protons from the intermembrane space, where they are highly concentrated, through the inner mitochondrial membrane to the matrix of the mitochondrion is limited to specific channels formed by a fifth enzyme complex, **ATP synthase,** a transmembrane protein. Portions of these complexes project from the inner surface of the membrane (the surface that faces the matrix) and are visible by electron microscopy (Fig. 7–11). Diffusion of the protons down their gradient, through the ATP synthase complex, is exergonic because the entropy of the system increases. This exergonic process provides the energy for ATP production, although the exact mechanism by which ATP synthase catalyzes the phosphorylation of ADP is still incompletely understood. In 1997 Paul Boyer and John Walker shared the Nobel Prize for Chemistry for the discovery that ATP synthase functions in an unusual way. Experimental evidence strongly suggests that ATP synthase acts like a highly efficient molecular motor: During the production of ATP from ADP and inorganic phosphate, a central structure of ATP synthase rotates, possibly in response to the force of protons moving through the enzyme complex. The rotation apparently alters the conformation of the catalytic subunits in a way that allows ATP synthesis.

Chemiosmosis is a fundamental mechanism of energy coupling in cells; it allows exergonic redox processes to drive the endergonic reaction in which ATP is produced by phosphorylating ADP. In photosynthesis (see Chapter 8), ATP is produced by a comparable process.

◼ AEROBIC RESPIRATION OF ONE GLUCOSE YIELDS A MAXIMUM OF 36 TO 38 ATPs

Let us now review where biologically useful energy is captured in aerobic respiration and calculate the total energy yield from the complete oxidation of glucose. Figure 7–12 summarizes the arithmetic involved.

1. In glycolysis, glucose is activated by the addition of phosphates from 2 ATP molecules and converted ultimately to 2 pyruvates + 2 NADH + 4 ATPs, yielding a net profit of 2 ATPs.
2. The 2 pyruvates are metabolized to 2 acetyl CoA + 2 CO_2 + 2 NADH.
3. In the citric acid cycle the 2 acetyl CoA molecules are metabolized to 4 CO_2 + 6 NADH + 2 $FADH_2$ + 2 ATPs.

Because the oxidation of NADH in the electron transport chain yields up to 3 ATPs per molecule, the total of 10 NADH molecules can yield up to 30 ATPs. The 2 NADH molecules from glycolysis, however, yield either 2 or 3 ATPs each. This is because certain types of eukaryotic cells must expend energy to shuttle the NADH produced by glycolysis across the mitochondrial membrane (discussed shortly). Prokaryotic cells lack mitochondria; hence they have no need to shuttle NADH molecules. For this reason, bacteria are able to generate 3 ATPs for every NADH, even those produced during glycolysis. Thus, the maximum number of ATPs formed using the energy from NADH is 28 to 30.

The oxidation of $FADH_2$ yields 2 ATPs per molecule (recall that $FADH_2$ enters the electron transport chain at a different location than NADH), so the 2 $FADH_2$ molecules produced in the citric acid cycle yield 4 ATPs.

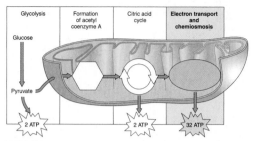

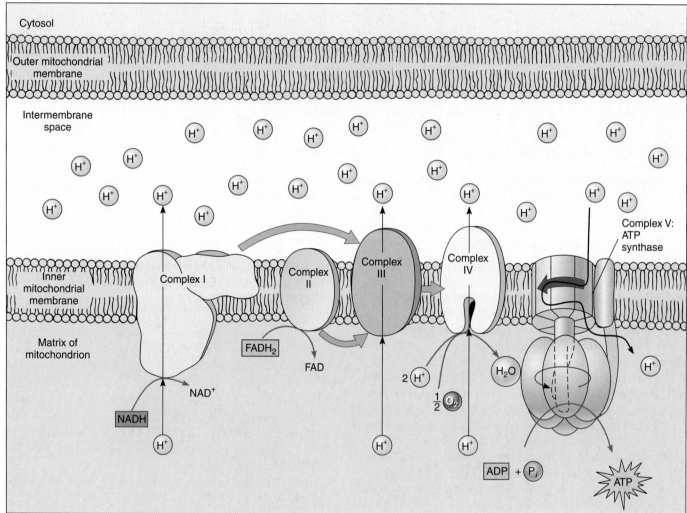

Figure 7–10 A detailed look at electron transport and chemiosmosis.
The electron transport chain in the inner mitochondrial membrane includes
three proton pumps that are located in three of the four electron transport
complexes. (The orange arrows indicate the pathway of electrons.) The energy
released during electron transport is used to transport protons (H^+) from the
mitochondrial matrix to the intermembrane space, where a high concentration
of protons accumulates. The protons are prevented from diffusing back into the
matrix except through special channels in ATP synthase in the inner membrane. The
flow of the protons through ATP synthase provides the energy for generating ATP
from ADP and P_i. In the process, the inner part of ATP synthase rotates *(thick red
arrow)* like a motor.

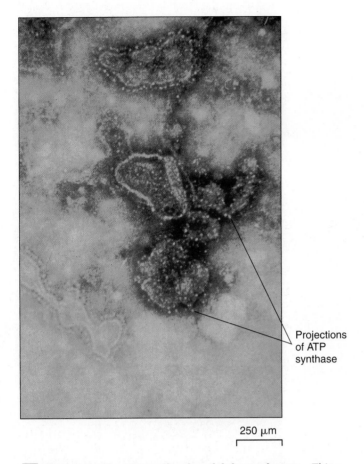

Figure 7–11 **Inner mitochondrial membrane.** This TEM shows hundreds of projections of ATP synthase complexes along the surface of the inner mitochondrial membrane. *(R. Bhatnagar/Visuals Unlimited)*

250 µm

Projections of ATP synthase

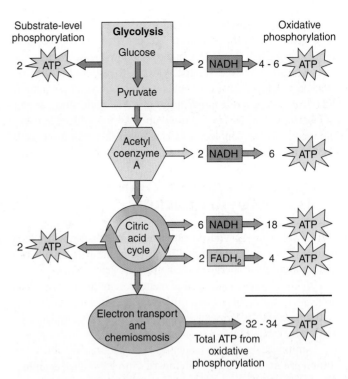

■ Figure 7–12 **Energy yield from the complete oxidation of glucose by aerobic respiration.** A maximum of 36 to 38 ATPs are produced per glucose molecule. Of these ATPs, four are produced by substrate-level phosphorylation, and the remainder by oxidative phosphorylation (that is, electron transport and chemiosmosis).

4. Summing all the ATPs (2 from glycolysis, 2 from the citric acid cycle, and 32 to 34 from electron transport and chemiosmosis), we see that the complete aerobic metabolism of one molecule of glucose yields a maximum of 36 to 38 ATPs. Note that most of the ATPs are generated by oxidative phosphorylation, which involves the electron transport chain and chemiosmosis. Only 4 ATPs are formed by substrate-level phosphorylation in glycolysis and the citric acid cycle.

We can analyze the efficiency of the overall process of aerobic respiration by comparing the free energy captured as ATP to the total free energy in a glucose molecule. You will recall from Chapter 6 that, although heat energy cannot power biological reactions, it is convenient to measure energy as heat. This can be done through the use of a calorimeter, an instrument that measures the heat of a reaction. A sample is placed in a compartment surrounded by a chamber of water. As the sample burns (becomes oxidized), the temperature of the water rises, providing a measure of the heat released during the reaction.

When 1 mol of glucose is burned in a calorimeter, some 686 kcal (2870 kJ) are released as heat. The free energy temporarily held in the phosphate bonds of ATP is about 7.6 kcal (31.8 kJ) per mole. When 36 to 38 ATPs are generated during the aero-

bic respiration of glucose, the free energy trapped in ATP amounts to 7.6 kcal/mol × 36, or about 274 kcal (1146 kJ) per mole. Thus, the efficiency of aerobic respiration is 274/686, or about 40%. (By comparison, a steam power plant has an efficiency of 35% to 36% in converting its fuel energy into electricity.) The remainder of the energy in the glucose is released as heat.

Mitochondrial shuttle systems harvest the electrons of NADH produced in the cytosol

The inner mitochondrial membrane is not permeable to NADH, which is a large molecule. Therefore the NADH molecules produced in the cytosol during glycolysis cannot diffuse into the mitochondria to transfer their electrons to the electron transport chain. Unlike ATP and ADP, NADH does not have a carrier protein to transport it across the membrane. Instead, several systems have evolved to transfer just the *electrons* of NADH, not the NADH molecules themselves, into the mitochondria.

In liver, kidney, and heart cells, a special shuttle system transfers the electrons from NADH through the inner mitochondrial membrane to an NAD^+ molecule in the matrix. These electrons are transferred to the electron transport chain in the inner mitochondrial membrane, and up to three molecules of ATP are produced per pair of electrons.

In skeletal muscle, brain, and some other types of cells, another type of shuttle operates. Because this shuttle requires more energy than the shuttle in liver, kidney, and heart cells, the electrons are at a lower energy level when they enter the electron transport chain. They are accepted by ubiquinone rather than by NAD^+ and so generate a maximum of 2 ATP molecules per pair of electrons. This is why the number of ATPs produced by aerobic respiration of 1 molecule of glucose in skeletal muscle cells is 36 rather than 38.

NUTRIENTS OTHER THAN GLUCOSE ALSO PROVIDE ENERGY

Many organisms depend on nutrients other than glucose as a source of energy. Humans and many other animals usually obtain more of their energy by oxidizing fatty acids than by oxidizing glucose. Amino acids derived from protein digestion are also used as fuel molecules. Such nutrients are transformed into one of the metabolic intermediates that are fed into glycolysis or the citric acid cycle (Fig. 7–13).

Amino acids are metabolized by reactions in which the amino group (—NH_2) is first removed, a process called **deamination.** In mammals and some other animals, the amino group is converted to urea (see Fig. 46–2) and excreted, but the carbon chain is metabolized and eventually is used as a reactant in one of the steps of aerobic respiration. The amino acid alanine, for example, undergoes deamination to become pyruvate, the amino acid glutamate is converted to α-ketoglutarate, and the amino acid aspartate yields oxaloacetate. Pyruvate enters aerobic respiration as the end product of glycolysis, and α-ketoglutarate and oxaloacetate both enter aerobic respiration as intermediates in the citric acid cycle. Ultimately, the carbon chains of all the amino acids are metabolized in this way.

Each gram of lipid in the diet contains 9 kcal (38 kJ), more than twice as much energy as 1 g of glucose or amino acids, which have about 4 kcal (17 kJ) per gram. Lipids are rich in energy because they are highly reduced; that is, they have many hydrogen atoms and few oxygen atoms. When completely oxidized in aerobic respiration, a molecule of a six-carbon fatty acid generates up to 44 ATPs (compared with 36 to 38 ATPs for a molecule of glucose, which also has 6 carbons).

Both the glycerol and fatty acid components of a triacylglycerol (see Chapter 3) are used as fuel; phosphate is added to glycerol, converting it to G3P or another compound that enters glycolysis. Fatty acids are oxidized and split enzymatically into two-carbon acetyl groups that are bound to coenzyme A; that is, fatty acids are converted to acetyl CoA. This process, which occurs in the mitochondrial matrix, is called **beta-oxidation, or β-oxidation.** Acetyl CoA molecules formed by β-oxidation enter the citric acid cycle.

CELLS REGULATE AEROBIC RESPIRATION

Aerobic respiration requires a steady input of fuel molecules and oxygen. Under normal conditions these materials are adequately

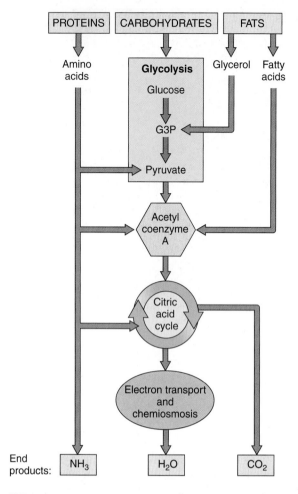

Figure 7–13 Energy from carbohydrates, proteins, and fats. Products of the catabolism of carbohydrates, proteins, and fats enter glycolysis or the citric acid cycle at various points. This diagram is greatly simplified and illustrates only a few of the principal catabolic pathways.

provided and do not affect the rate of respiration. Instead, the rate of aerobic respiration is regulated by how much ADP and phosphate are available. In a resting muscle cell, for example, ATP synthesis continues until most of the ADP has been converted to ATP. At this point oxidative phosphorylation slows considerably. Because electron flow is tightly coupled to oxidative phosphorylation, the flow of electrons also slows, which in turn slows down the citric acid cycle.

When ATP transfers energy to power an energy-requiring process like muscle contraction, many molecules of ATP are hydrolyzed. The ADP molecules produced can then accept phosphate to become ATP once again; aerobic respiration speeds up until most of the ADP has again been converted to ATP.

The control of most metabolic pathways is exerted on a particular enzyme that catalyzes a reaction early in the pathway (see Fig. 6–16 and discussion of feedback inhibition in Chapter 6). The regulated enzyme is usually inhibited by the presence of the end product of the pathway. One of the important control points in aerobic respiration in mammals is phosphofructokinase, an

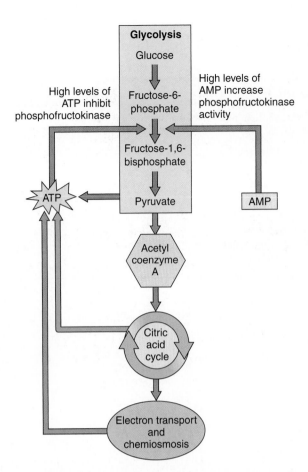

Figure 7–14 Regulation of aerobic respiration.
When enough ATP accumulates in the cell *(left)*, the ATP inhibits phosphofructokinase, an enzyme that catalyzes an early step in glycolysis. Alternatively, when ATP levels are low and AMP levels are correspondingly high *(right)*, phosphofructokinase activity is high. These regulatory controls affect the rate of glycolysis (and therefore of aerobic respiration), matching it to the cell's demands for energy.

enzyme that catalyzes an early reaction of glycolysis (Fig. 7–14; also see Fig. 7–4). The active site of phosphofructokinase binds ATP and fructose-6-phosphate. However, the enzyme is inhibited by the presence of very high levels of ATP and activated by the presence of AMP (adenosine monophosphate, a molecule formed when two phosphates are removed from ATP). Therefore, this enzyme is inactivated when ATP levels are high and activated when they are low.[3] Phosphofructokinase possesses different allosteric sites for both enzyme inhibitors (in this case, ATP) and enzyme activators (in this case, AMP).

When respiration produces more ATP than the cell currently needs, some of the excess ATP binds to the allosteric inhibitor site of phosphofructokinase, changing its conformation so that it is no longer active. Thus, glycolysis and aerobic respiration slow down, and less ATP is produced. As excess ATP is used by the cell, ADP and AMP are produced. Now the allosteric inhibitor site of phosphofructokinase is no longer occupied by ATP. Instead, the allosteric activator sites are filled with AMP. Thus the enzyme becomes activated and respiration proceeds, generating more ATP.

■ ANAEROBIC RESPIRATION AND FERMENTATION DO NOT REQUIRE OXYGEN

Anaerobic respiration, which does not use oxygen as the final electron acceptor, is performed by some types of bacteria that live in such anaerobic environments as waterlogged soil, stagnant ponds, or animal intestines. As in aerobic respiration, electrons are transferred in anaerobic respiration from glucose to NADH; they then pass down an electron transport chain that is coupled to ATP synthesis by chemiosmosis. However, an inorganic substance such as nitrate (NO_3^-) or sulfate (SO_4^{2-}) replaces molecular oxygen as the terminal electron acceptor. The end products of this type of anaerobic respiration are carbon dioxide, one or more reduced inorganic substances, and ATP. One representative type of anaerobic respiration, summarized below, is part of the biogeochemical cycle known as the **nitrogen cycle** (see Chapter 53).

$$C_6H_{12}O_6 + 12\ KNO_3 \longrightarrow$$

Potassium
nitrate

$$6\ CO_2 + 6\ H_2O + 12\ KNO_2 + Energy$$

Potassium
nitrite   (in the chemical
bonds of ATP)

Certain other bacteria, as well as some fungi, regularly use **fermentation,** an anaerobic pathway that does not involve an electron transport chain. During fermentation only two ATPs are formed per glucose (by substrate-level phosphorylation during glycolysis). One might expect that a cell that obtains energy from glycolysis would produce pyruvate, the end product of glycolysis. However, this cannot happen because every cell has a limited supply of NAD$^+$, and NAD$^+$ is required for glycolysis to continue. If virtually all NAD$^+$ becomes reduced to NADH during glycolysis, then glycolysis stops, and no more ATP can be produced.

In fermentation, NADH molecules transfer their hydrogen atoms to organic molecules, thus regenerating the NAD$^+$ needed to keep glycolysis going. The resulting, relatively reduced, organic molecules (commonly, alcohol or lactate) tend to be toxic to the cells and are essentially waste products. Table 7–2 summarizes features of aerobic respiration, anaerobic respiration, and fermentation.

Alcohol fermentation and lactate fermentation are inefficient

Yeasts are **facultative anaerobes.** These eukaryotic, unicellular fungi have mitochondria and carry out aerobic respiration when oxygen is available but switch to **alcohol fermentation** when deprived of oxygen (Fig. 7–15a). They have enzymes that decarboxylate pyruvate, releasing carbon dioxide and forming a two-carbon compound called **acetaldehyde.** NADH produced during glycolysis transfers hydrogen atoms to acetaldehyde, reducing it to form

---

[3] Other materials, including citrate, also affect the activity of phosphofructokinase.

TABLE 7-2 A Comparison of Aerobic Respiration, Anaerobic Respiration, and Fermentation

	Aerobic Respiration	Anaerobic Respiration	Fermentation
Immediate Fate of Electrons in NADH	Transferred to an electron transport chain	Transferred to an electron transport chain	Transferred to an organic molecule
Terminal Electron Acceptor of Electron Transport Chain	O_2	Inorganic substances such as NO_3^- or SO_4^{2-}	No electron transport chain
Reduced Product(s) Formed	Water	Relatively reduced inorganic substances	Relatively reduced organic compounds (commonly, alcohol or lactate)
Mechanism of ATP Synthesis	Oxidative phosphorylation/ chemiosmosis; also substrate-level phosphorylation	Oxidative phosphorylation/ chemiosmosis; also substrate-level phosphorylation	Substrate-level phosphorylation only (during glycolysis)

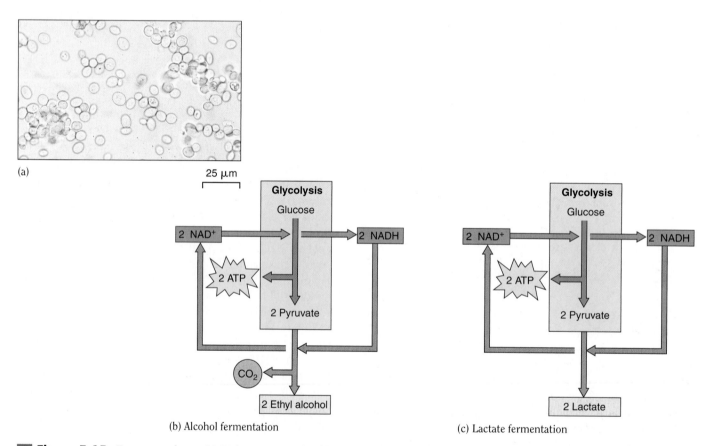

(a)

(b) Alcohol fermentation

(c) Lactate fermentation

Figure 7-15 Fermentation. (a) Light micrograph of live brewer's yeast *(Saccharomyces cerevisiae)*. Yeast cells possess mitochondria and carry on aerobic respiration when O_2 is present. In the absence of O_2, yeasts carry on alcohol fermentation. (b, c) Glycolysis is the first part of fermentation pathways. (b) In alcohol fermentation, CO_2 is split off, and the two-carbon compound ethyl alcohol is the end product. (c) In lactate fermentation, the final product is the three-carbon compound lactate. In both alcohol and lactate fermentation, there is a net gain of only two ATPs per molecule of glucose. Note that the NAD$^+$ used during glycolysis is regenerated during both alcohol fermentation and lactate fermentation. *(a, Dwight R. Kuhn)*

ethyl alcohol (Fig. 7–15b). Alcohol fermentation is the basis for the production of beer, wine, and other alcoholic beverages. Yeast cells are also used in baking to produce the carbon dioxide that causes dough to rise; the alcohol evaporates during baking.

Certain fungi and bacteria perform **lactate (lactic acid) fermentation.** In this alternative pathway, NADH produced during glycolysis transfers hydrogen atoms to pyruvate, reducing it to form **lactate** (Fig. 7–15c). The ability of some bacteria to produce lactate is exploited by humans, who use these bacteria to make yogurt and to ferment cabbage for sauerkraut.

Lactate is also produced during strenuous activity in the muscle cells of humans and other complex animals. If the amount of oxygen delivered to muscle cells is insufficient to support aerobic respiration, the cells shift briefly to lactate fermentation. The shift is only temporary, however, and oxygen is required for sustained work. As lactate accumulates in muscle cells, it contributes to fatigue and muscle cramps.[4] About 80% of the lactate is eventually exported to the liver, where it is used to regenerate more glucose for the muscle cells. The remaining 20% of the lactate is metabolized in muscle cells in the presence of oxygen. This explains why you continue to breathe heavily after you have stopped exercising: The additional oxygen is needed to oxidize lactate, thereby restoring the muscle cells to their normal state.

Although humans can use lactate fermentation to produce ATP for only a few minutes, a few animals can live without oxygen for much longer periods. The red-eared slider can remain under water for as long as two weeks (Fig. 7–16). During this time, it is relatively inactive and therefore does not need to expend a great deal of energy. It relies on lactate fermentation for ATP production.

Both alcohol fermentation and lactate fermentation are highly inefficient because the fuel is only partially oxidized. Alcohol, the end product of fermentation by yeast cells, can be burned and can even be used as automobile fuel; obviously, it

Figure 7–16 Long-term use of lactate fermentation for ATP production. The red-eared slider (*Trachemys scripta*) can stay submerged for as long as two weeks. *(Cleveland P. Hickman, Jr./Visuals Unlimited)*

contains a great deal of energy that the yeast cells are unable to extract using anaerobic methods. Lactate, a three-carbon compound, contains even more energy than the two-carbon alcohol. In contrast, all available energy is removed during aerobic respiration because the fuel molecules become completely oxidized to CO_2. A net profit of only 2 ATPs is produced by the fermentation of one molecule of glucose, compared with up to 36 to 38 ATPs when oxygen is available.

The inefficiency of fermentation necessitates a large supply of fuel. For example, skeletal muscle cells, which often metabolize anaerobically for short periods, store large quantities of glucose in the form of glycogen. To perform the same amount of work, a cell engaged in fermentation must consume up to 20 times more glucose or other carbohydrate per second than a cell using aerobic respiration.

---

[4] Why exercise causes fatigue and muscle cramps is incompletely understood at this time, but these conditions may be related to lactate buildup, insufficient oxygen, and/or the depletion of fuel molecules.

SUMMARY WITH KEY TERMS

I. Metabolism, the total of all the chemical reactions that occur in cells, has two complementary components.
  A. **Catabolism** releases energy by breaking down complex molecules into simpler molecules. Catabolic pathways include aerobic respiration, anaerobic respiration, and fermentation.
  B. **Anabolism** is the synthesis of complex molecules from simpler building blocks. Protein synthesis is an example of anabolism.
II. During **aerobic respiration**, a fuel molecule such as glucose is oxidized to form carbon dioxide and water.
  A. Aerobic respiration is a redox process in which electrons are transferred from glucose (which becomes **oxidized**) to oxygen (which becomes **reduced**).
  B. Up to 36 to 38 ATPs are produced per molecule of glucose.

III. The chemical reactions of aerobic respiration occur in four stages: glycolysis, formation of acetyl CoA, the citric acid cycle, and the electron transport chain/chemiosmosis.
  A. During **glycolysis,** which occurs in the cytosol, a molecule of glucose is degraded to two molecules of **pyruvate.**
    1. Two ATP molecules (net) are produced by **substrate-level phosphorylation** during glycolysis.
    2. Four hydrogen atoms are removed from the fuel molecule and used to produce two NADH.
  B. The two pyruvate molecules each lose a molecule of carbon dioxide, and the remaining acetyl groups each combine with **coenzyme A,** producing two molecules of **acetyl CoA.** One NADH is produced as each pyruvate is converted to acetyl CoA.

C. Each acetyl CoA enters the **citric acid cycle** by combining with a four-carbon compound, **oxaloacetate,** to form **citrate,** a six-carbon compound. Two acetyl CoA molecules enter the cycle for every glucose molecule.
  1. For every two carbons that enter the cycle as part of an acetyl CoA molecule, two leave as carbon dioxide.
  2. For every acetyl CoA, hydrogen atoms are transferred to three NAD^+ and one FAD; only one ATP is produced by substrate-level phosphorylation.
D. Hydrogen atoms (or their electrons) removed from fuel molecules are transferred from one electron acceptor to another down an **electron transport chain** located in the mitochondrial inner membrane.
  1. The electron transport chain is organized as four protein complexes. Complex I accepts electrons from NADH molecules, and complex II accepts electrons from $FADH_2$ molecules; both of these complexes produce reduced ubiquinone. Complex III accepts electrons from reduced ubiquinone and passes them on to cytochrome c. Complex IV accepts electrons from cytochrome c and uses these electrons to reduce molecular oxygen, forming water in the process.
  2. According to the **chemiosmotic model,** some of the energy of the electrons in the electron transport chain is used to establish a proton gradient across the inner mitochondrial membrane.
  3. The diffusion of protons through the membrane from the intermembrane space to the mitochondrial matrix (through channels formed by the enzyme **ATP synthase**) provides the energy needed to synthesize ATP.
  4. The coupling of ATP synthesis to the redox reactions in the electron transport chain is known as **oxidative phosphorylation.**
IV. Organic nutrients other than glucose are converted to appropriate compounds and fed into glycolysis or the citric acid cycle.
  A. Amino acids are **deaminated,** and their carbon skeletons are converted to metabolic intermediates of aerobic respiration.
  B. Both the glycerol and fatty acid components of lipids are oxidized as fuel. Fatty acids are converted to acetyl CoA molecules by the process of **β-oxidation.**
V. In **anaerobic respiration,** electrons are transferred from fuel molecules to an electron transport chain; the final electron acceptor is an inorganic substance such as nitrate or sulfate, not molecular oxygen.
VI. **Fermentation** is an anaerobic process that does not use an electron transport chain. There is a net gain of only two ATPs per glucose; these are produced during glycolysis. To maintain the supply of NAD^+ essential for glycolysis, hydrogen atoms are transferred from NADH to an organic compound derived from the initial nutrient.
  A. Yeast cells carry out **alcohol fermentation,** in which **ethyl alcohol** and carbon dioxide are the final waste products.
  B. Certain fungi, bacteria, and animal cells carry out **lactate fermentation,** in which hydrogen atoms are added to pyruvate to form **lactate,** a waste product.

Summary Reactions for Aerobic Respiration

Summary reaction for the complete oxidation of glucose:

$$C_6H_{12}O_6 + 6\ O_2 + 6\ H_2O \longrightarrow$$
$$6\ CO_2 + 12\ H_2O + \text{Energy (36 to 38 ATP)}$$

Summary reaction for glycolysis:

$$C_6H_{12}O_6 + 2\ ATP + 2\ ADP + 2\ P_i + 2\ NAD^+ \longrightarrow$$
$$2\ \text{Pyruvate} + 4\ ATP + 2\ NADH + H_2O$$

Summary reaction for the conversion of pyruvate to acetyl CoA:

$$2\ \text{Pyruvate} + 2\ \text{Coenzyme A} + 2\ NAD^+ \longrightarrow$$
$$2\ \text{Acetyl CoA} + 2\ CO_2 + 2\ NADH$$

Summary reaction for the citric acid cycle:

$$2\ \text{Acetyl CoA} + 6\ NAD^+ + 2\ FAD + 2\ ADP + 2\ P_i + 2\ H_2O \longrightarrow$$
$$4\ CO_2 + 6\ NADH + 2\ FADH_2 + 2\ ATP + 2\ CoA$$

Summary reactions for the processing of the hydrogen atoms of NADH and $FADH_2$ in the electron transport chain:

$$NADH + 3\ ADP + 3\ P_i + \tfrac{1}{2}\ O_2 \longrightarrow NAD^+ + 3\ ATP + H_2O$$
$$FADH_2 + 2\ ADP + 2\ P_i + \tfrac{1}{2}\ O_2 \longrightarrow FAD + 2\ ATP + H_2O$$

Summary Reactions for Fermentation

Summary reaction for lactate fermentation:

$$C_6H_{12}O_6 \longrightarrow 2\ \text{Lactate} + \text{Energy (2 ATP)}$$

Summary reactions for alcohol fermentation:

$$C_6H_{12}O_6 \longrightarrow 2\ CO_2 + 2\ \text{Ethyl alcohol} + \text{Energy (2 ATP)}$$

POST-TEST

1. The process of splitting larger molecules into smaller ones is an aspect of metabolism called (a) anabolism (b) fermentation (c) catabolism (d) oxidative phosphorylation (e) chemiosmosis

2. The synthetic aspect of metabolism is referred to as (a) anabolism (b) fermentation (c) catabolism (d) oxidative phosphorylation (e) chemiosmosis

3. A chemical process during which a substance gains electrons is called (a) oxidation (b) oxidative phosphorylation (c) deamination (d) reduction (e) dehydrogenation

4. The pathway through which glucose is degraded to pyruvate is referred to as (a) aerobic respiration (b) the citric acid cycle (c) the oxidation of pyruvate (d) alcohol fermentation (e) glycolysis

5. The reactions of _____ take place within the cytosol of eukaryotic cells. (a) glycolysis (b) oxidation of pyruvate (c) the citric acid cycle (d) chemiosmosis (e) the electron transport chain

6. Before pyruvate enters the citric acid cycle, it is decarboxylated, oxidized, and combined with coenzyme A, forming acetyl CoA, carbon dioxide, and one molecule of (a) NADH (b) $FADH_2$ (c) ATP (d) ADP (e) $C_6H_{12}O_6$

7. In the first step of the citric acid cycle, acetyl CoA reacts with oxaloacetate to form (a) pyruvate (b) citrate (c) NADH (d) ATP (e) CO_2

8. Dehydrogenase enzymes remove hydrogen atoms from fuel molecules and transfer them to acceptors such as (a) O_2 and H_2O (b) ATP and FAD (c) NAD^+ and FAD (d) CO_2 and H_2O (e) CoA and pyruvate

9. Which of the following is a major source of electrons for the electron transport chain? (a) H_2O (b) ATP (c) NADH (d) ATP synthase (e) coenzyme A

10. In the process of _____, electron transport and ATP synthesis are coupled by a proton gradient across the inner mitochondrial membrane. (a) chemiosmosis (b) deamination (c) anaerobic respiration (d) glycolysis (e) decarboxylation

11. Which of the following is a common energy flow sequence in aerobic respiration, starting with the energy stored in glucose? (a) glucose $\rightarrow$ NADH $\rightarrow$ pyruvate $\rightarrow$ ATP (b) glucose $\rightarrow$ ATP $\rightarrow$ NADH $\rightarrow$ electron transport chain (c) glucose $\rightarrow$ NADH $\rightarrow$ electron transport chain $\rightarrow$ ATP (d) glucose $\rightarrow$ oxygen $\rightarrow$ NADH $\rightarrow$ water (e) glucose $\rightarrow$ $FADH_2$ $\rightarrow$ NADH $\rightarrow$ coenzyme A

12. Which multiprotein complex in the electron transport chain is responsible for reducing molecular oxygen? (a) complex I (NADH-ubiquinone oxidoreductase) (b) complex II (succinate-ubiquinone reductase) (c) com-

plex III (ubiquinone-cytochrome *c* oxidoreductase) (d) complex IV (cytochrome *c* oxidase) (e) complex V (ATP synthase)

13. A net profit of only 2 ATPs can be produced anaerobically from the _____ of one molecule of glucose, compared with a maximum of 38 ATPs produced in _____. (a) fermentation; anaerobic respiration (b) aerobic respiration; fermentation (c) aerobic respiration; anaerobic respiration (d) dehydrogenation; decarboxylation (e) fermentation; aerobic respiration

14. When deprived of oxygen, yeast cells obtain energy by fermentation, producing carbon dioxide, ATP, and (a) acetyl CoA (b) ethyl alcohol (c) lactate (d) pyruvate (e) citrate

15. During strenuous muscle activity, the pyruvate in muscle cells may accept hydrogen from NADH to become _____. (a) acetyl CoA (b) ethyl alcohol (c) lactate (d) pyruvate (e) citrate

REVIEW QUESTIONS

1. What is the specific role of oxygen in most cells? What happens when cells that can only respire aerobically are deprived of oxygen?

2. Mitochondria are often referred to as the "power plants" of the cell. Justify this with a specific explanation.

3. Refer to Figure 7–7, the diagram of the steps in the citric acid cycle. Look at each reaction and, without reading the description, determine if it is a dehydrogenation, decarboxylation, or preparation reaction.

4. Sketch a mitochondrion and indicate the locations of the electron transport chain and the proton gradient that drives ATP production.

5. Why is each of the following essential to chemiosmotic ATP synthesis? (a) electron transport chain (b) proton gradient (c) ATP synthase complex

6. Explain the roles of the following in aerobic respiration: (a) NAD^+ and FAD (b) oxygen

7. Sum up how much energy (as ATP) is made available to the cell from a single glucose molecule by the operation of (1) glycolysis, (2) the formation of acetyl CoA, (3) the citric acid cycle, and (4) the electron transport chain.

8. Trace the fate of hydrogen atoms removed from glucose during glycolysis when oxygen is present in muscle cells; compare this to the fate of hydrogen atoms removed from glucose when the amount of available oxygen is insufficient to support aerobic respiration.

9. Compare the ATP yields of aerobic respiration and fermentation.

10. Label the ten blank lines in the figure. Use Figure 7–2 to check your answers.

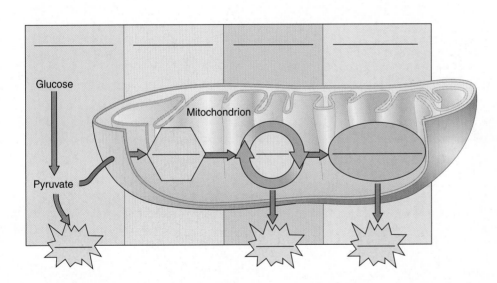

YOU MAKE THE CONNECTION

1. The reactions of glycolysis are identical in *all* organisms—bacteria, protists, fungi, plants, and animals—that obtain energy from glucose catabolism. What does this universality suggest about the evolution of glycolysis?

2. How are the endergonic reactions of the first phase of glycolysis coupled to the hydrolysis of ATP, which is exergonic? How are the exergonic reactions of the second phase of glycolysis coupled to the endergonic synthesis of ATP and NADH?

3. Why is the citric acid cycle also called the Krebs cycle? Why is it known as the tricarboxylic acid cycle? (*Hint:* Examine the chemical structures pictured in Fig. 7–7.)

4. What is the role of the inner mitochondrial membrane in the coupling of electron transport and ATP synthesis?

5. Based on what you have learned in this chapter, explain why a schoolchild can run 17 miles per hour in a 100-meter dash, but a trained athlete can run only about 11.5 miles per hour in a 26-mile marathon.

RECOMMENDED READINGS

Fackelmann, K. "Power Failure." *Science News*, Vol. 152, 27 Sept. 1997. Defects in mitochondria can lead to several different human diseases.

Garrett, R.H., and C.M. Grisham. *Biochemistry*, 2nd ed. Saunders College Publishing, Philadelphia, 1999. A comprehensive biochemistry text with good coverage of cellular respiration and related aspects of metabolism.

Offner, S. "A Plain English Map of the Human Glycolysis Enzymes." *The American Biology Teacher*, Vol. 61, No. 6, June 1999. Every enzyme is a protein coded for by a gene somewhere on the chromosomes. To illustrate this point, the author shows locations on the human chromosomes of the ten enzymes involved in glycolysis.

Seymour, R.S. "Plants That Warm Themselves." *Scientific American*, Vol. 276, No. 3, March 1997. Some plants produce a significant amount of heat when they flower, and a few precisely regulate their temperature.

Tobin, A.J., and R.E. Morel. *Asking About Cells*. Saunders College Publishing, Philadelphia, 1997. Contains a readable and detailed account of cellular energy metabolism.

- Visit our Web site at **http://www.info.brookscole.com/solomonbergmartin** for links to chapter-related resources on the World Wide Web. Additional on-line materials relating to this chapter can also be found on our Web site.

See chapter activity on BioActive Learner CD for additional help in mastering the chapter's material. Icon location in the chapter's margins shows which topics have tutorials or simulations in the CD.

8

Photosynthesis: Capturing Energy

These blue lupines *(Lupinus hirsutus)* and the trees behind them are photoautotrophs. They use CO_2 as a carbon source and light as an energy source. Photographed in Southern Michigan. *(Skip Moody/Dembinsky Photo Associates)*

This chapter deals with photosynthesis, which is the first step in the flow of energy through most living things. To help you appreciate the significance of photosynthesis, consider that all organisms—from microscopic bacteria to dolphins to palm trees—can be classified on the basis of two aspects of their nutrition: their carbon source and their energy source. Carbon atoms are required for the carbon skeletons of an organism's organic molecules, and as we have seen in Chapters 6 and 7, energy powers all life processes, from growth, to movement, to repair of worn or injured tissues.

Organisms obtain carbon in one of two ways. **Autotrophs** (from the Greek *auto,* "self," and *trophos,* "nourishing") are able to carry out carbon fixation; they use carbon dioxide (CO_2) as a carbon source. **Heterotrophs** (from the Greek *heter,* "other," and

trophos, "nourishing") cannot fix carbon; they use organic molecules produced by other organisms as the building blocks from which they synthesize the carbon compounds they need.

Organisms obtain energy in one of two ways. **Phototrophs** are photosynthetic organisms that use light as their energy source. In contrast, **chemotrophs** use organic compounds, such as glucose, or inorganic substances, such as iron, nitrate, ammonia, or sulfur, as sources of energy. Chemotrophs typically obtain energy from these materials by oxidation–reduction reactions (see discussion of redox reactions in Chapters 6 and 7).

By combining both aspects of nutrition—that is, carbon and energy requirements—we find that all organisms fall into one of four groups:

1. Green plants *(see photograph),* algae, and certain bacteria, are **photoautotrophs** (that is, both phototrophs and autotrophs). Photoautotrophs are uniquely capable of absorbing and converting light energy into stored chemical energy of organic molecules by the process of **photosynthesis.** Photoautotrophs use light energy to make ATP and other molecules that temporarily hold chemical energy but are unstable and cannot be stockpiled in the cell. Their energy drives the anabolic pathway by which a photosynthetic cell synthesizes stable organic molecules from the simple inorganic compounds, CO_2 and water. These organic compounds are used not only as starting materials to synthesize all the other organic compounds the photosynthetic organism needs (e.g., complex carbohydrates, amino acids, and lipids) but also for energy storage. Glucose

and other carbohydrates produced during photosynthesis are relatively reduced compounds that can be subsequently oxidized by aerobic respiration or by some other catabolic pathway (see Chapter 7).

2. A few bacteria, known as nonsulfur purple bacteria, are **photoheterotrophs** (i.e., both phototrophs and heterotrophs). Photoheterotrophs are able to use light energy but unable to carry out carbon fixation. Photoheterotrophs must obtain carbon from organic compounds (as "food").

3. **Chemoautotrophs** are bacteria that are both chemotrophs and autotrophs. These bacteria obtain their energy from the oxidation of reduced inorganic molecules such as hydrogen sulfide (H_2S), nitrite (NO_2^-), or ammonia (NH_3). Some of this energy is then used to carry out carbon fixation.

4. All animals, fungi, and most bacteria are **chemoheterotrophs;** that is, they are both chemotrophs and heterotrophs. Chemoheterotrophs use preformed organic molecules as a source of both energy and carbon. Plants and other photosynthetic organisms produce almost all of the preformed organic molecules used by chemoheterotrophs.

From this discussion, it is clear that photosynthesis is the process that captures the vast majority of the energy used by living organisms. Photosynthesis not only sustains plants and other photoautotrophs but also indirectly supports almost all animals and other chemoheterotrophs in the biosphere. Each year plants and other photosynthetic organisms convert CO_2 into billions of tons of organic molecules. The chemical energy stored in these molecules fuels the metabolic reactions that sustain almost all life.

■ LIGHT IS COMPOSED OF PARTICLES THAT TRAVEL AS WAVES

Most life on our planet depends on light, either directly or indirectly, and so it is important to understand the nature of light and how it permits photosynthesis to occur. Visible light represents a very small portion of a vast, continuous range of radiation called the electromagnetic spectrum (Fig. 8–1). All radiation in this spectrum travels as waves. A **wavelength** is the distance from one wave peak to the next. At one end of the electromagnetic spectrum are gamma rays, which have very short wavelengths measured in fractions of nanometers, or nm. (One nanometer equals 10^{-9} m—that is, one billionth of a meter.) At the other end of the spectrum are radio waves, with wavelengths so long they can be measured in kilometers. The portion of the electromagnetic spectrum from 380 to 760 nm is called the visible spectrum because humans can see it. The visible spectrum includes all the colors of the rainbow (Fig. 8–2); violet has the shortest wavelength, and red has the longest.

Light behaves not only as waves do but also as particles. Light is composed of small particles, or packets, of energy called **photons.** The energy of a photon is inversely proportional to its wavelength; shorter wavelength light has more energy per photon than does longer wavelength light.

Why does photosynthesis depend on light detectable by the human eye (visible light) rather than on some other wavelength of radiation? We can only speculate on the answer. Perhaps it is because radiation within the visible light portion of the spectrum excites certain types of biological molecules, moving electrons into higher energy levels. Radiation with wavelengths longer than those of visible light does not possess enough energy to excite these biological molecules. Radiation with wavelengths shorter than those of visible light is so energetic that it disrupts the bonds of many biological molecules. Thus, visible light has just the right amount of energy to be useful in photosynthesis.

When a molecule absorbs a photon of light energy, one of its electrons becomes energized, which means that the electron shifts from a lower energy atomic orbital to a high-energy orbital that is more distant from the atomic nucleus. One of two things then hap-

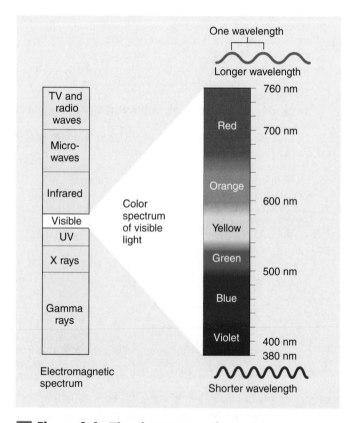

Figure 8–1 The electromagnetic spectrum. Waves in the electromagnetic spectrum have similar properties but different wavelengths and methods of production. Radio waves are the longest (and least energetic) waves, with wavelengths as long as 20 km. Gamma rays are the shortest (and most energetic) waves. Visible light represents a small fraction of the electromagnetic spectrum and consists of a mixture of wavelengths ranging from approximately 380 to 760 nm. The energy from visible light is used in photosynthesis.

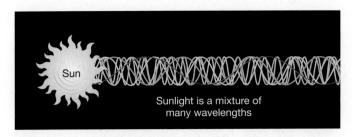

Sun

Sunlight is a mixture of
many wavelengths

Figure 8–2 Visible radiation emitted from the sun.
Electromagnetic radiation from the sun includes ultraviolet
radiation and visible light of varying colors and wavelengths.

pens, depending on the atom and its surroundings (Fig. 8–3). The atom may return to its **ground state,** which is the condition in which all its electrons are in their normal, lowest energy levels. When an electron returns to its ground state, its energy is dissipated as heat or as an emission of light of a longer wavelength than the absorbed light; this emission of light is called **fluorescence.** Alternatively, the energized electron may leave the atom and be ac-

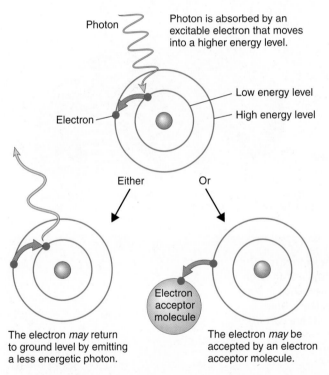

Photon

Photon is absorbed by an
excitable electron that moves
into a higher energy level.

Low energy level

High energy level

Electron

Either   Or

Electron
acceptor
molecule

The electron *may* return
to ground level by emitting
a less energetic photon.

The electron *may* be
accepted by an electron
acceptor molecule.

Figure 8–3 Interactions between light and atoms or molecules. *(Top)* When a photon of light energy strikes an atom, or a molecule of which the atom is a part, the energy of the photon may push an electron to an orbital farther from the nucleus (i.e., into a higher energy level). *(Lower left)* If the electron returns to the lower, more stable energy level, the energy may be released as a less energetic, longer-wavelength photon, known as *fluorescence (shown),* or as heat. *(Lower right)* If the appropriate electron acceptors are available, the electron may leave the atom. During photosynthesis, an electron acceptor captures the energetic electron and passes it to a chain of acceptors.

cepted by an electron acceptor molecule, which becomes reduced in the process; this is what occurs in photosynthesis.

Now that we have an understanding of some of the properties of light, we will consider the cellular location where light is used for photosynthesis.

■ PHOTOSYNTHESIS IN EUKARYOTES TAKES PLACE IN CHLOROPLASTS

When a section of leaf tissue is examined under the microscope, we can see that the green pigment, **chlorophyll,** is not uniformly distributed in the cell but is confined to organelles called chloroplasts (Fig. 8–4). In plants, chloroplasts are located mainly in the cells of the **mesophyll,** a tissue inside the leaf. Each mesophyll cell has 20 to 100 chloroplasts.

The chloroplast, like the mitochondrion, is bounded by outer and inner membranes. The inner membrane encloses a fluid-filled region called the **stroma,** which contains most of the enzymes required to produce carbohydrate molecules. Suspended in the stroma is a third system of membranes that forms an interconnected set of flat, disclike sacs called **thylakoids.** The thylakoid membrane encloses a fluid-filled interior space, the **thylakoid lumen.** In some regions of the chloroplast, thylakoid sacs are arranged in stacks called **grana** (sing., *granum*). Each granum looks something like a stack of coins, with each "coin" being a thylakoid. Some thylakoid membranes extend from one granum to another. These membranes, like the inner mitochondrial membrane (see Chapter 7), are involved in ATP synthesis. (Photosynthetic prokaryotes have no chloroplasts, but thylakoid membranes are often arranged around the periphery of the cell as infoldings of the plasma membrane.)

Chlorophyll is found in the thylakoid membrane

Thylakoid membranes contain several kinds of pigments, which are substances that absorb visible light. Different pigments absorb light of different wavelengths. Chlorophyll, the main pigment of photosynthesis, absorbs light primarily in the blue and red regions of the visible spectrum. Green light is not appreciably absorbed by chlorophyll. Plants usually appear green because some of the green light that strikes them is scattered or reflected.

A chlorophyll molecule (Fig. 8–5) has two main parts, a complex ring and a long side chain. The ring structure, called a *porphyrin ring,* is made up of joined smaller rings composed of carbon and nitrogen atoms; it is the porphyrin ring that absorbs the light energy. The porphyrin ring of chlorophyll is strikingly similar to the heme portion of the red pigment hemoglobin in red blood cells. However, unlike heme, which contains an atom of iron in the center of the ring, chlorophyll contains an atom of magnesium in that position. The chlorophyll molecule also contains a long, hydrocarbon side chain that makes the molecule extremely nonpolar.

All chlorophyll molecules in the thylakoid membrane are associated with specific **chlorophyll-binding proteins.** Biologists have identified about 15 different chlorophyll-binding proteins. Each

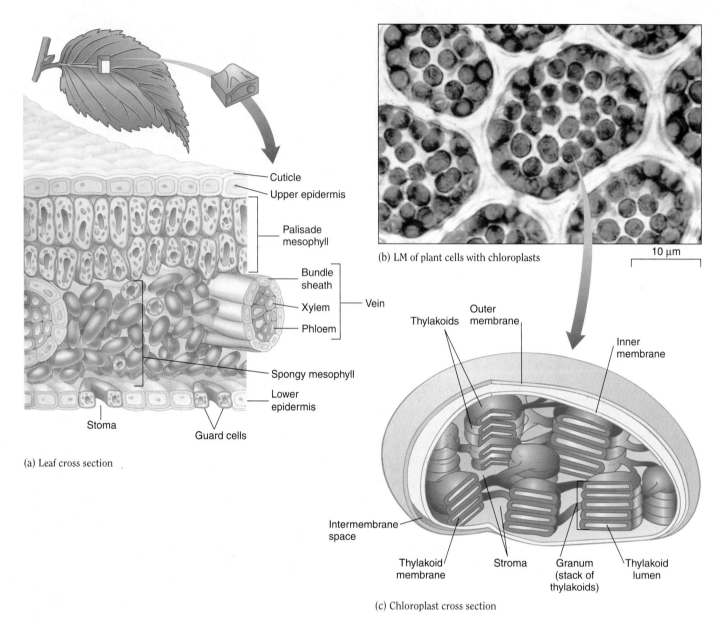

(b) LM of plant cells with chloroplasts

10 μm

(a) Leaf cross section

(c) Chloroplast cross section

Figure 8–4 Where photosynthesis occurs in the plant. **(a)** A leaf cross section reveals that the mesophyll is the photosynthetic tissue. CO_2 enters the leaf through tiny pores called stomata (sing., stoma), and H_2O is carried to the mesophyll in veins. **(b)** LM of plant cells with numerous chloroplasts. **(c)** Chloroplast structure. The pigments necessary for the light-capturing reactions of photosynthesis are part of thylakoid membranes, whereas the enzymes for the synthesis of carbohydrate molecules are in the stroma.   *(b, M. Eichelberger/Visuals Unlimited)*

thylakoid membrane is filled with precisely oriented chlorophyll molecules and chlorophyll-binding proteins, an arrangement that permits transfer of energy from one molecule to another.

There are several kinds of chlorophyll. The most important is **chlorophyll *a***, the pigment that initiates the light-dependent reactions of photosynthesis. **Chlorophyll *b*** is an accessory pigment that also participates in photosynthesis. It differs from chlorophyll *a* only in a functional group on the porphyrin ring: The methyl group ($-CH_3$) in chlorophyll *a* is replaced in chlorophyll *b* by a terminal carbonyl group ($-CHO$). This difference

shifts the wavelengths of light absorbed and reflected by chlorophyll *b*, making it yellow-green, whereas chlorophyll *a* is bright green.

Chloroplasts also have other accessory photosynthetic pigments, such as **carotenoids**, which are yellow and orange (see Fig. 3–14). Carotenoids absorb different wavelengths of light than chlorophyll does and so broaden the spectrum of light that provides energy for photosynthesis. Chlorophyll may be excited by light directly or indirectly, by energy passed to it from accessory pigments that have become excited by light. When a carotenoid

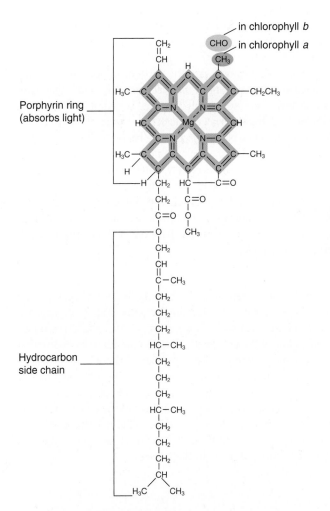

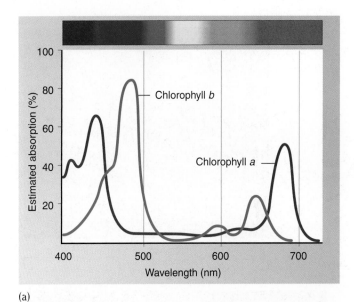

(a)

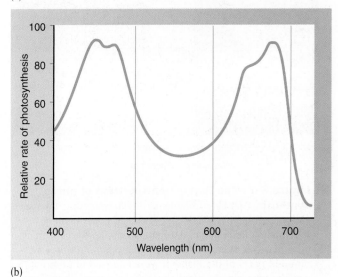

(b)

The relative effectiveness of these different wavelengths of light in photosynthesis is given by an **action spectrum** of photosynthesis. To obtain an action spectrum, the rate of photosynthesis is measured at each wavelength for leaf cells or tissues exposed to monochromatic light (light of one wavelength) (Fig. 8–6b).

Process of Science The first action spectrum was obtained in one of the classic experiments in biology. In 1883 the German biologist T.W. Engelmann carried out an experiment that took advantage of the shape of the chloroplast in a species of *Spirogyra*, a green

Figure 8–5 Chlorophyll structure. Chlorophyll consists of a porphyrin ring and a hydrocarbon side chain. The porphyrin ring, with a magnesium atom in its center, contains a system of alternating double and single bonds; these are commonly found in molecules that strongly absorb visible light. At the top right corner of the diagram, the methyl group (—CH₃) distinguishes chlorophyll *a* from chlorophyll *b*, which has a carbonyl group (—CHO) in this position.

molecule is excited, its energy can be transferred to chlorophyll *a*. Carotenoids also have an indispensable role in protecting chlorophyll and other parts of the thylakoid membrane from excess light energy that could easily damage the photosynthetic components. (High light intensities often occur in nature.)

Chlorophyll is the main photosynthetic pigment

As we have seen, the thylakoid membrane contains more than one kind of pigment. An instrument called a spectrophotometer is used to measure the relative abilities of different pigments to absorb different wavelengths of light. The **absorption spectrum** of a pigment is a plot of its absorption of light of different wavelengths. Figure 8–6a shows the absorption spectra for chlorophylls *a* and *b*.

Figure 8–6 The absorption spectra for chlorophylls *a* and *b* and the action spectrum for photosynthesis. **(a)** Chlorophylls *a* and *b* absorb light mainly in the blue (422 nm to 492 nm) and red (647 nm to 760 nm) regions of visible light. **(b)** The action spectrum of photosynthesis shows how effective various wavelengths of light are in powering photosynthesis. Many plant species, including crop plants, have action spectra for photosynthesis that resemble the generalized action spectrum shown here.

alga that occurs as long, filamentous strands in freshwater habitats, especially slow-moving or still waters (Fig. 8–7a). The individual cells of *Spirogyra* each contain a long, spiral-shaped, emerald-green chloroplast embedded in the cytoplasm. Engelmann exposed these cells to a color spectrum produced by passing light through a prism. He reasoned that if chlorophyll were indeed responsible for photosynthesis, then it would take place most rapidly in the areas where the chloroplast was illuminated by the colors most strongly absorbed by chlorophyll.

Yet how could photosynthesis be measured in those technologically unsophisticated days? Engelmann knew that photosynthesis produces oxygen and that certain motile bacteria are attracted to areas of high oxygen concentration (Fig. 8–7b). He determined the action spectrum of photosynthesis by observing that the bacteria swam toward the portions of *Spirogyra* located in the red and blue regions of the spectrum. How did Engelmann know bacteria were not simply attracted to red or blue light? As a control, Engelmann exposed bacteria to the spectrum of visible light in the absence of *Spirogyra*. The bacteria showed no preference for any particular wavelength of light. Because the action spectrum of photosynthesis closely matched the absorption spectrum of chlorophyll, Engelmann concluded that chlorophyll in the chloroplasts (and not another compound in another organelle) is responsible for photosynthesis. Numerous studies using sophisticated instruments have since confirmed Engelmann's conclusions.

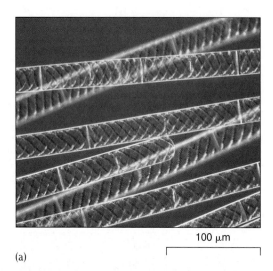

100 μm

(a)

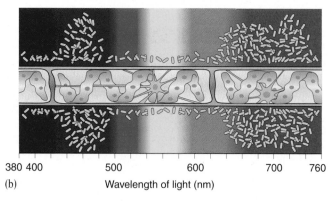

380 400   500   600   700   760

(b)   Wavelength of light (nm)

■■ Figure 8–7 The first action spectrum of photosynthesis. **(a)** LM of filaments of *Spirogyra* sp., the green alga that Engelmann used in his classic experiment. **(b)** Engelmann illuminated a filament of *Spirogyra* with light that had been passed through a prism. In this way, different parts of the filament were exposed to different wavelengths of light. He estimated the rate of photosynthesis indirectly by observing the movement of motile aerobic bacteria toward the portions of the algal filament emitting the most oxygen. Watching through a microscope, Engelmann observed that the bacteria aggregated most densely along the cells in the red and, to a lesser extent, blue portions of the spectrum. This suggested that blue light and red light work most effectively for photosynthesis. *(a, T.E. Adams/Visuals Unlimited)*

The action spectrum of photosynthesis does not parallel the absorption spectrum of chlorophyll exactly (Fig. 8–6). This difference occurs because accessory pigments, such as carotenoids, transfer some of the energy of excitation produced by green light to chlorophyll molecules. The presence of these accessory photosynthetic pigments can be demonstrated by chemical analysis of almost any leaf, although it is obvious in temperate climates when leaves change color in the fall. Toward the end of the growing season, chlorophyll breaks down (and its magnesium is stored in the permanent tissues of the tree), leaving orange and yellow accessory pigments in the leaves.

■ PHOTOSYNTHESIS IS THE CONVERSION OF LIGHT ENERGY TO CHEMICAL BOND ENERGY

During photosynthesis, a cell uses light energy captured by chlorophyll to power the synthesis of carbohydrates. The overall reaction of photosynthesis can be summarized as follows:

$$6\,CO_2 + 12\,H_2O \xrightarrow[\text{Chlorophyll}]{\text{Light energy}} C_6H_{12}O_6 + 6\,O_2 + 6\,H_2O$$

Carbon dioxide   Water   Glucose   Oxygen   Water

The equation is typically written in the form given above, with H_2O on both sides, because water is a reactant in some reactions and a product in others. However, because there is no net yield of H_2O, we can simplify the summary equation of photosynthesis for purposes of discussion:

$$6\,CO_2 + 6\,H_2O \xrightarrow[\text{Chlorophyll}]{\text{Light}} C_6H_{12}O_6 + 6\,O_2$$

When we analyze this process, it appears that hydrogen atoms are transferred from H_2O to CO_2 to form carbohydrate, and so we recognize it as a **redox reaction.** As you learned in Chapter 6, in a redox reaction one or more electrons, usually as part of one or more hydrogen atoms, are transferred from an electron donor (a reducing agent) to an electron acceptor (an oxidizing agent).

$$6\ CO_2 + 6\ H_2O \xrightarrow[\text{Chlorophyll}]{\text{Light}} C_6H_{12}O_6 + 6\ O_2$$

When the electrons are transferred, some of their energy is transferred as well. However, the summary equation of photosynthesis is somewhat misleading because no direct transfer of hydrogen atoms actually occurs. The summary equation describes what happens but not how it happens. The "how" is much more complex and involves multiple steps, many of which are redox reactions.

The reactions of photosynthesis are divided into two parts: the light-dependent reactions (the *photo* part of photosynthesis) and the carbon fixation reactions (the *synthesis* part of photosynthesis). Each set of reactions occurs in a different part of the chloroplast: the light-dependent reactions in association with the thylakoids, and the carbon fixation reactions in the stroma (Fig. 8–8).

ATP and NADPH are the products of the light-dependent reactions: an overview

Light energy is converted to chemical energy in the **light-dependent reactions,** which are associated with the thylakoids. The light-dependent reactions begin as chlorophyll captures light energy, which causes one of its electrons to move to a higher energy state. The energized electron is transferred to an acceptor molecule and is replaced by an electron from H_2O. When this happens, H_2O is split and molecular oxygen is released (Fig. 8–9). Some of the energy of the energized electrons is used

to phosphorylate **adenosine diphosphate (ADP),** forming **adenosine triphosphate (ATP).** In addition, the coenzyme **nicotinamide adenine dinucleotide phosphate (NADP⁺)** becomes reduced, forming NADPH.[1] The products of the light-dependent reactions, ATP and NADPH, are both needed in the endergonic carbon fixation reactions.

Carbohydrates are produced during the carbon fixation reactions: an overview

The ATP and NADPH molecules produced during the light-dependent phase are suited for transferring chemical energy but not for long-term energy storage. For this reason, some of their energy is transferred to chemical bonds in carbohydrates, which can be produced in large quantities and stored for future use. Known as **carbon fixation,** or **CO₂ fixation,** these reactions "fix" carbon atoms from CO_2 to existing skeletons of organic molecules. Because the carbon fixation reactions have no direct requirement for light, they were formerly referred to as the "dark" reactions. However, they certainly do not require darkness; in fact, many of the enzymes involved in carbon fixation are much more active in the light than in the dark. Furthermore, carbon fixation reactions depend on the products of the light-dependent reactions. Carbon fixation reactions take place in the stroma of the chloroplast.

[1] Although the correct way to write the reduced form of NADP⁺ is NADPH + H⁺, for simplicity's sake we present the reduced form as NADPH throughout the chapter

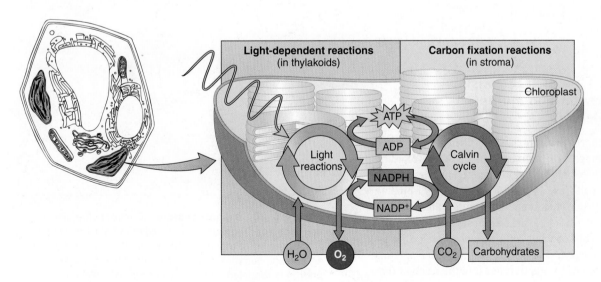

Figure 8–8 Overview of photosynthesis. Photosynthesis consists of light-dependent reactions, which occur in association with the thylakoids, and carbon fixation reactions, which occur in the stroma.

Figure 8–9 Oxygen produced by photosynthesis.
On sunny days the oxygen released by aquatic plants may sometimes be visible as bubbles in the water. This plant (*Elodea* sp.) is actively carrying on photosynthesis. *(Bernd Wittich/Visuals Unlimited)*

Now that we have presented an overview of photosynthesis, let's examine the entire process more closely.

THE LIGHT-DEPENDENT REACTIONS CONVERT LIGHT ENERGY TO CHEMICAL ENERGY

In the light-dependent reactions, the radiant energy from sunlight is used to make ATP and to reduce $NADP^+$, forming NADPH. The light energy captured by chlorophyll is temporarily stored in these two compounds. The light-dependent reactions are summarized as follows:

$$12 \ H_2O + 12 \ NADP^+ + 18 \ ADP + 18 \ P_i \xrightarrow[\text{Chlorophyll}]{\text{Light}}$$
$$6 \ O_2 + 12 \ NADPH + 18 \ ATP$$

Photosystems I and II each consist of a reaction center and multiple antenna complexes

The light-dependent reactions of photosynthesis begin when chlorophyll *a* and/or accessory pigments absorb light. According to the currently accepted model, chlorophylls *a* and *b* and accessory pigment molecules are organized with pigment-binding proteins in the thylakoid membrane into units called **antenna complexes.** The pigments and associated proteins are arranged as highly ordered groups of about 250 chlorophyll molecules associated with specific enzymes and other proteins. Each antenna complex absorbs light energy and transfers it to the **reaction center,** a complex of chlorophyll molecules and proteins, including electron transfer components, that participates directly in photosynthesis (Fig. 8–10). Light energy is converted to chemical

energy in the reaction centers by a series of electron transfer reactions.

Two types of photosynthetic units, designated Photosystem I and Photosystem II, are involved in photosynthesis. Their reaction centers are distinguishable because they are associated with proteins in a way that causes a slight shift in their absorption spectra. Ordinary chlorophyll *a* has a strong absorption peak at about 660 nm. In contrast, the chlorophyll *a* molecule that makes up the reaction center associated with **Photosystem I** has an absorption peak at 700 nm and is referred to as **P700.** The reaction center of **Photosystem II (P680)** is made up of a chlorophyll *a* molecule with an absorption peak of about 680 nm.

When a pigment molecule absorbs light energy, that energy is passed from one pigment molecule to another until it reaches the reaction center. When the energy reaches a molecule of P700 (in a Photosystem I reaction center) or P680 (in a Photosystem II reaction center), an electron is then raised to a higher energy level. As we will see in the next section, this energized electron can be donated to an electron acceptor that becomes reduced in the process.

Noncyclic electron transport produces ATP and NADPH

We begin our discussion of noncyclic electron transport with the events associated with Photosystem I (Fig. 8–11). A pigment molecule in an antenna complex associated with Photosystem I absorbs a photon of light. The absorbed energy is transferred to the reaction center, where it excites an electron in a molecule of

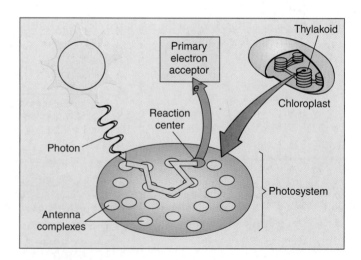

Figure 8–10 A photosystem. Chlorophyll molecules and accessory pigments are arranged in light-harvesting arrays known as antenna complexes. When a molecule in an antenna complex absorbs a photon, the energy of that photon is funneled into the reaction center. When this energy reaches the P700 (or P680) chlorophyll molecule in the reaction center, an electron becomes energized and is accepted by a primary electron acceptor.

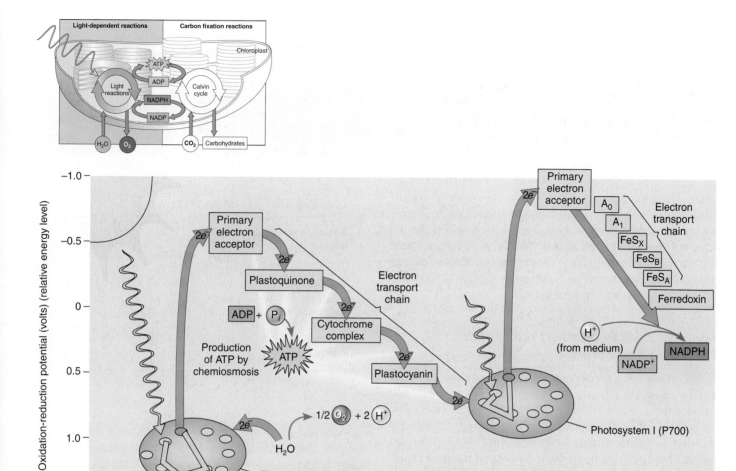

Figure 8–11 Noncyclic electron transport. In noncyclic electron transport, the formation of ATP is coupled to the one-way flow of energized electrons *(orange arrows)* from H_2O *(lower left)* to $NADP^+$ *(middle right)*. Single electrons actually pass down the electron transport chain; two are shown in this figure because two are required to form one molecule of NADPH. Electrons are supplied to the system from the splitting of H_2O by Photosystem II, with the release of O_2 as a byproduct. When Photosystem II is activated by absorbing photons, electrons are passed along an electron transport chain and are eventually donated to Photosystem I. Electrons in Photosystem I are "re-energized" by the absorption of additional light energy and are passed to $NADP^+$, forming NADPH.

P700. This energized electron is transferred to a primary electron acceptor, which is the first of several electron acceptors in a series. (Uncertainty exists regarding the exact chemical nature of the primary electron acceptor for Photosystem I.) The energized electron is passed along an **electron transport chain** from one electron acceptor to another, until it is passed to **ferredoxin,** an iron-containing protein. Ferredoxin transfers the electron to $NADP^+$ in the presence of the enzyme *ferredoxin–$NADP^+$ reductase.* When $NADP^+$ accepts the two electrons, they unite with a proton (H^+); hence the reduced form of $NADP^+$ is NADPH, which is released into the stroma. P700 becomes positively charged when it gives up an electron to the primary electron acceptor; the missing electron is replaced by one donated by Photosystem II.

Like Photosystem I, Photosystem II is activated when a pigment molecule in an antenna complex absorbs a photon of light energy. The energy is transferred to the reaction center, where it causes an electron in a molecule of P680 to move to a higher energy level. This energized electron is accepted by a primary electron acceptor (a highly modified chlorophyll molecule known as pheophytin) and then passes along an electron transport chain until it is donated to P700 in Photosystem I.

A molecule of P680 that has given up an energized electron to the primary electron acceptor is positively charged. This P680 molecule is an oxidizing agent so strong that it is capable of pulling electrons away from an oxygen atom that is part of a H_2O molecule. In a reaction probably catalyzed by a unique, manganese-containing enzyme, the process of **photolysis** (literally "light-splitting") breaks water into its components: two electrons, two protons, and oxygen. Each electron is donated to a P680 molecule, and the protons are released into the thylakoid lumen. Because oxygen does not exist in atomic form, the oxygen produced by splitting one H_2O molecule is written $\frac{1}{2} O_2$. Two water molecules must be split to yield one molecule of oxygen (O_2), which is ultimately released into the atmosphere. This production of oxygen during photosynthesis is the source of almost all of the oxygen in Earth's atmosphere. The photolysis of water is a remarkable reaction, but its name is somewhat misleading because it implies that water is broken by light. Actually, light splits water indirectly, by oxidizing P680.

Noncyclic electron transport is a continuous linear process

In the presence of light, there is a continuous, one-way flow of electrons from the ultimate electron source, H_2O, to the terminal electron acceptor, $NADP^+$. Water undergoes enzymatically catalyzed photolysis to replace energized electrons donated to the electron transport chain by molecules of P680 in Photosystem II. These electrons travel down the electron transport chain that connects Photosystem II with Photosystem I. Thus they provide a continuous supply of replacements for energized electrons that have been given up by P700.

As electrons are transferred along the electron transport chain that connects Photosystem II with Photosystem I, they lose energy. Some of the energy released is used to pump protons across the thylakoid membrane, from the stroma to the thylakoid lumen, producing a proton gradient. The energy of this proton gradient is harnessed to produce ATP from ADP by chemiosmosis, which will be discussed shortly. ATP and NADPH, the products of the light-dependent reactions, are released into the stroma, where both are required in the carbon fixation reactions.

Cyclic electron transport produces ATP but no NADPH

Only Photosystem I is involved in cyclic electron transport, the simplest light-dependent reaction. The pathway is cyclic because energized electrons that originate from P700 at the reaction center eventually return to P700. In the presence of light, there is a continuous flow of electrons through an electron transport chain within the thylakoid membrane. As they are passed from one acceptor to another, the electrons lose energy, some of which is used to pump protons across the thylakoid membrane. An enzyme (ATP synthase, discussed shortly) in the thylakoid membrane uses the energy of the proton gradient to

TABLE 8–1 **A Comparison of Noncyclic and Cyclic Electron Transport**

	Noncyclic Electron Transport	Cyclic Electron Transport
Electron source	H_2O	None — electrons cycle through the system
Oxygen released?	Yes (from H_2O)	No
Terminal electron acceptor	$NADP^+$	None — electrons cycle through the system
Form in which energy is temporarily captured	ATP (by chemiosmosis); NADPH	ATP (by chemiosmosis)
Photosystem(s) required	PS I (P700) and PS II (P680)	PS I (P700) only

manufacture ATP. NADPH is not produced, H_2O is not split, and oxygen is not generated. By itself, cyclic electron transport could not serve as the basis of photosynthesis because, as we explain later in the chapter, NADPH is required to reduce CO_2 to carbohydrate.

The significance of cyclic electron transport to photosynthesis in plants is not yet certain. Cyclic electron transport may occur in plant cells when there is too little $NADP^+$ to accept electrons from ferredoxin. Biologists generally agree that this process was used by ancient bacteria to produce ATP from light energy (see *Focus On: The Evolution of Photosystems I and II*). A reaction pathway analogous to cyclic electron transport in plants is present in some modern photosynthetic bacteria. Noncyclic and cyclic electron transport are compared in Table 8–1.

ATP synthesis occurs by chemiosmosis

Each member of the electron transport chain that links Photosystem II to Photosystem I can exist in an oxidized (lower energy) form and a reduced (higher energy) form. The electron accepted from P680 by the primary electron acceptor is highly energized; it is passed from one carrier to the next in a series of exergonic redox reactions, losing some of its energy at each step. Some of the energy given up by the electron is not lost by the system, however; it is used to drive the synthesis of ATP (an endergonic reaction). Because the synthesis of ATP (that is, the phosphorylation of ADP) is coupled to the transport of electrons that have been energized by photons of light, the process is called **photophosphorylation.**

The Evolution of Photosystems I and II

Photosynthesis is an extremely ancient biological process that has apparently changed a great deal since it first appeared more than 3 billion years ago. The use of light energy to manufacture organic molecules first evolved in ancient bacteria that were similar to the green sulfur bacteria existing today.

Initially there was only one photosystem, Photosystem I, which used a green pigment called *bacteriochlorophyll* to gather light energy. Photosystem I operated alone, generating ATP from light energy by cyclic electron transport. However, cyclic electron transport does not provide the reducing power of NADPH, which is needed to manufacture

carbohydrate molecules from CO_2. (Recall that in cyclic electron transport, the electrons from P700 are not passed to $NADP^+$ but are instead returned to P700.) Ancient photosynthetic bacteria, like some of their modern counterparts, used electron donors such as hydrogen sulfide (H_2S) rather than H_2O to generate the reducing power needed to manufacture carbohydrates in photosynthesis:

$$H_2S \rightarrow S + 2\,H^+ + 2\,e^-$$
$$2\,H^+ + 2\,e^- + NADP^+ \rightarrow NADPH + H^+$$

This process is not very efficient, however; bacteriochlorophyll has enough oxidative potential to extract electrons from H_2S but not sufficient oxidative

potential to extract electrons from H_2O.

Around 3.5 to 3.1 billion years ago, a new group of prokaryotes called **cyanobacteria** evolved (see Chapter 20). These ancient cyanobacteria were probably similar to modern cyanobacteria, which have light-requiring reactions that are similar to those of photosynthetic eukaryotes, including plants. They possess chlorophyll *a* instead of bacteriochlorophyll and can carry out noncyclic electron transport because they have Photosystem II in addition to Photosystem I. Water provides the electrons required to generate NADPH, which in turn provides the reducing power required to manufacture carbohydrate molecules from CO_2.

The chemiosmotic model explains the coupling of ATP synthesis and electron transport

As discussed earlier, the pigments and electron acceptors of the light-dependent reactions are embedded in the thylakoid membrane. Energy released from electrons traveling through the chain of acceptors is used to pump protons from the stroma, across the thylakoid membrane, and into the thylakoid lumen (Fig. 8–12). Thus, the pumping of protons results in the formation of a proton gradient across the thylakoid membrane. Protons also accumulate in the thylakoid lumen as water is split during noncyclic electron transport. Because protons are actually hydrogen ions (H^+), the accumulation of protons causes the pH of the thylakoid interior to fall to a pH of about 5 in the thylakoid lumen, as compared with a pH of about 8 in the stroma. This difference of about 3 pH units across the thylakoid membrane means there is an approximately 1000-fold difference in hydrogen ion concentration.

The proton gradient has a great deal of free energy because of its state of low entropy. How does the chloroplast convert that energy to a more useful form? According to the general principles of diffusion, the concentrated protons inside the thylakoid might be expected to diffuse out readily. However, they are prevented from doing so because the thylakoid membrane is impermeable to H^+ except through certain channels formed by an enzyme called **ATP synthase.** ATP synthase, a transmembrane protein, forms complexes so large they can be seen in electron micrographs; these project into the stroma. As the protons diffuse through an ATP synthase complex, free energy decreases as a consequence of an increase in entropy. Each ATP synthase complex couples this exergonic process of diffusion down a

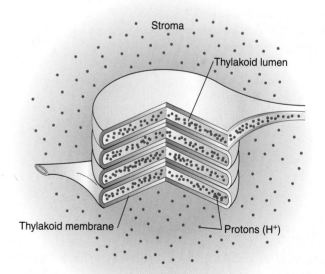

Figure 8–12 Accumulation of protons within the thylakoid lumen. As electrons move down the electron transport chain, protons (H^+) move from the stroma to the thylakoid lumen, creating a proton gradient. The greater concentration of H^+ in the thylakoid lumen lowers the pH.

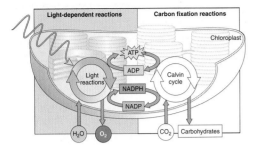

Figure 8–13 A detailed look at electron transport and chemiosmosis. The orange arrows indicate the pathway of electrons along the electron transport chain in the thylakoid membrane. The electron carriers within the membrane become alternately reduced and oxidized as they accept and donate electrons. The energy released during electron transport is used to transport H$^+$ from the stroma to the thylakoid lumen, where a high concentration of H$^+$ accumulates. The H$^+$ are prevented from diffusing back into the stroma except through special channels in ATP synthase in the thylakoid membrane. The flow of the H$^+$ through ATP synthase generates ATP.

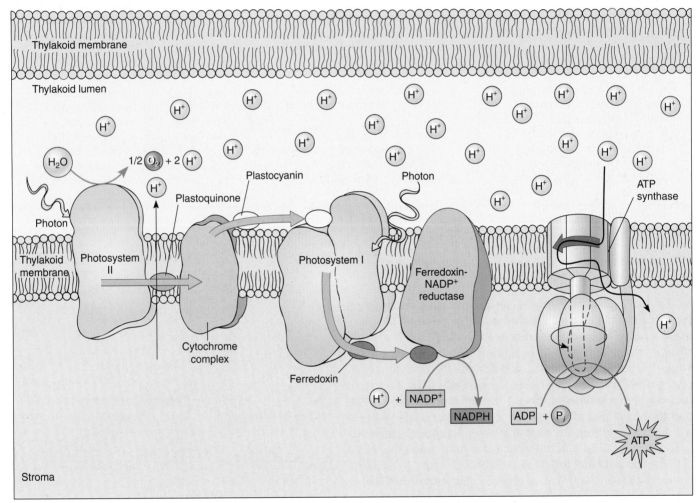

concentration gradient to the endergonic process of phosphorylation of ADP to form ATP, which is released into the stroma (Fig. 8–13). The movement of protons through ATP synthase is thought to induce changes in the conformation of the enzyme that are necessary for the synthesis of ATP. It is estimated that for every four protons that move through ATP synthase, one ATP molecule is synthesized.

The mechanism by which the phosphorylation of ADP is coupled to diffusion down a proton gradient is called **chemiosmosis**. As the essential connection between the electron transport chain and the phosphorylation of ADP, chemiosmosis is a basic mechanism of energy coupling in cells. You may recall from Chapter 7 that chemiosmosis also occurs in aerobic respiration (see Table 8–2).

■ THE CARBON FIXATION REACTIONS REQUIRE ATP AND NADPH

In carbon fixation, the energy of ATP and NADPH is used in the formation of organic molecules from CO$_2$. The carbon fixation reactions may be summarized as follows:

$$12 \text{ NADPH} + 18 \text{ ATP} + 6 \text{ CO}_2 \longrightarrow$$
$$\text{C}_6\text{H}_{12}\text{O}_6 + 12 \text{ NADP}^+ + 18 \text{ ADP} + 18 \text{ P}_i + 6 \text{ H}_2\text{O}$$

TABLE 8–2   A Comparison of Photosynthesis and Aerobic Respiration

	Photosynthesis	Aerobic Respiration
Type of metabolic reaction	Anabolism	Catabolism
Raw materials	CO_2, H_2O	$C_6H_{12}O_6$, O_2
End products	$C_6H_{12}O_6$, O_2	CO_2, H_2O
Which cells have these processes?	Cells that contain chlorophyll (certain cells of plants, algae, and some bacteria)	Every actively metabolizing cell has aerobic respiration or some other energy-releasing pathway
Sites involved (in eukaryotic cells)	Chloroplasts	Cytosol (glycolysis); mitochondria
ATP production	By photophosphorylation (a chemiosmotic process)	By substrate-level phosphorylation and by oxidative phosphorylation (a chemiosmotic process)
Principal electron transfer compound	$NADP^+$ is reduced to form NADPH*	NAD^+ is reduced to form NADH*
Location of electron transport chain	Thylakoid membrane	Mitochondrial inner membrane (cristae)
Source of electrons for electron transport chain	In noncyclic electron transport: H_2O (undergoes photolysis to yield electrons, protons, and oxygen)	Immediate source: NADH, $FADH_2$ Ultimate source: glucose or other carbohydrate
Terminal electron acceptor for electron transport chain	In noncyclic electron transport: $NADP^+$ (becomes reduced to form NADPH)	O_2 (becomes reduced to form H_2O)

*NADPH and NADH are very similar hydrogen (i.e., electron) carriers, differing only in a single phosphate group. However, NADPH generally works with enzymes in anabolic pathways, such as photosynthesis. NADH is associated with catabolic pathways, such as cellular respiration.

Most plants use the Calvin (C₃) cycle to fix carbon

Carbon fixation occurs in the stroma through a sequence of 13 reactions known as the Calvin cycle. Melvin Calvin, Andrew Benson, and others at the University of California were able to elucidate the details of this cycle; for his work, Calvin was awarded a Nobel Prize in 1961 (Fig. 8–14).

The 13 reactions of the Calvin cycle are divided into three phases: CO_2 uptake, carbon reduction, and RuBp regeneration (Fig. 8–15). All 13 enzymes that catalyze steps in the Calvin cycle are located in the stroma of the chloroplast. Ten of the enzymes also participate in glycolysis (see Chapter 7). These enzymes are able to catalyze reversible reactions, degrading carbohydrate molecules in cellular respiration and synthesizing carbohydrate molecules in photosynthesis.

The *CO_2 uptake phase* of the Calvin cycle consists of a single reaction in which a molecule of CO_2 reacts with a phosphorylated five-carbon compound, **ribulose bisphosphate (RuBP).** This reaction is catalyzed by the enzyme **ribulose bisphosphate carboxylase/oxygenase,** also known as **Rubisco.** The Rubisco enzyme is present in the chloroplast in the largest amounts of any protein, and it may be one of the most abundant proteins in the biosphere. The product of this reaction is an unstable, six-carbon intermediate, which immediately breaks down into two molecules of **phosphoglycerate (PGA)** with three carbons each. The carbon that was originally part of a CO_2 molecule is now part of a carbon skeleton; the carbon has been "fixed." The Calvin cycle is also known as the **C₃ pathway** because the product of the initial carbon fixation reaction is a three-carbon compound.

The *carbon reduction phase* consists of two steps in which the energy and reducing power from ATP and NADPH (both produced in the light-dependent reactions) are used to convert the PGA molecules to **glyceraldehyde-3-phosphate (G3P).** As shown in Figure 8–15, for every six carbons that enter the cycle as CO_2, six carbons can leave the system as two molecules of G3P, to be used in carbohydrate synthesis. Each of these three carbon molecules of G3P is essentially half a hexose (six-carbon sugar) molecule. (In fact, you may recall that G3P is a key intermediate in the splitting of sugar in glycolysis; see Figs. 7–3 and 7–4.)

The reaction of two molecules of G3P is exergonic and can lead to the formation of glucose or fructose. In some plants, glucose and fructose are then joined to produce sucrose (common table sugar). Sucrose can be harvested from sugar cane, sugar beets, and maple sap. The plant cell also uses glucose to produce starch or cellulose.

Notice that although 2 G3P molecules are removed from the cycle, 10 G3P molecules remain; this represents 30 carbon atoms in all. Through a complex series of ten reactions that make up the *RuBP regeneration phase* of the Calvin cycle, these 30 carbons and their associated atoms become rearranged into 6 molecules of ribulose phosphate, each of which becomes phosphorylated to produce RuBP, the five-carbon compound with which the cycle started. These RuBP molecules can begin the process of CO_2 fixation and eventual G3P production once again.

In summary, the inputs required for the carbon fixation reactions are six molecules of CO_2, phosphates transferred from

Figure 8–14 Experimental apparatus of Calvin and Benson. The classic experiments carried out by Calvin, Benson, and others in the 1950s elucidated the steps in the carbon fixation reactions of photosynthesis. Calvin and his colleagues grew algae in the green "lollipop." CO_2 labeled with carbon-14 (^{14}C) was bubbled through the algae, which were periodically killed by dumping the "lollipop" contents into a beaker of boiling alcohol. By identifying which compounds in the algae contained the ^{14}C at different times, Calvin was able to determine the steps of carbon fixation in photosynthesis. *(Courtesy of Melvin Calvin, University of California, Berkeley)*

ATP, and electrons (as hydrogen) from NADPH. In the end, the six carbons from the CO_2 can be accounted for by the harvest of a hexose molecule. The remaining G3P molecules are used to synthesize the RuBP molecules with which more CO_2 molecules may combine. (Table 8–3 provides a detailed summary of photosynthesis.)

The initial carbon fixation step differs in C₄ plants and in CAM plants

Because CO_2 is not a very abundant gas (composing only about 0.03% of the atmosphere), it is not easy for plants to obtain the CO_2 they need. This problem is complicated by the fact that gas exchange can occur only across a moist surface. The surfaces of leaves and other exposed plant parts are covered with a waterproof layer that helps prevent excess loss of water vapor. Entry and exit of gases is therefore limited to microscopic pores, called **stomata** (sing., *stoma*), usually concentrated on the undersides of the leaves (see Fig. 8–4a). These openings lead to the interior of the leaf, which is made up of chloroplast-containing cells, known as the **mesophyll**, with many air spaces and a very high concentration of water vapor. The stomata open and close in response to such environmental factors as water content and light intensity. When conditions are hot and dry, the stomata close to reduce the loss of water vapor. As a result, the supply of CO_2 is greatly diminished. Ironically, CO_2 is potentially less available at the very times when maximum sunlight is available to power the light-dependent reactions.

Many plant species living in hot, dry environments have adaptations that allow them initially to fix CO_2 through one of two pathways that help minimize water loss. These pathways, known as the C_4 pathway and the CAM pathway, take place in the cytosol. Both the C_4 and CAM pathways merely precede the Calvin cycle (C_3 pathway); they do not replace it.

The C₄ pathway efficiently fixes CO₂ at low concentrations

Some plants, known as **C_4 plants,** first fix CO_2 into a four-carbon compound, **oxaloacetate,** prior to the C_3 pathway. The C_4 pathway not only occurs before the C_3 pathway, it also occurs in different cells.

Leaf anatomy is usually distinctive in C_4 plants. In addition to having mesophyll cells, C_4 leaves have prominent chloroplast-containing **bundle sheath cells** (Fig. 8–16). These cells tightly encircle the veins of the leaf. The mesophyll cells in C_4 plants are closely associated with the bundle sheath cells. The **C_4 pathway** (also called the **Hatch-Slack pathway,** after M.D. Hatch and C.R. Slack, who worked out many of its steps) occurs in the mesophyll cells, whereas the Calvin cycle takes place within the bundle sheath cells.

The key component of the C_4 pathway is a remarkable enzyme that has an extremely high affinity for CO_2, binding it effectively even at unusually low concentrations. This enzyme, **PEP carboxylase,** catalyzes the reaction by which CO_2 reacts with the three-carbon compound **phosphoenolpyruvate (PEP),** forming oxaloacetate (Fig. 8–17 on page 192).

In a step that requires NADPH, oxaloacetate is converted to some other four-carbon compound, usually malate. The malate then passes to chloroplasts within bundle sheath cells, where a

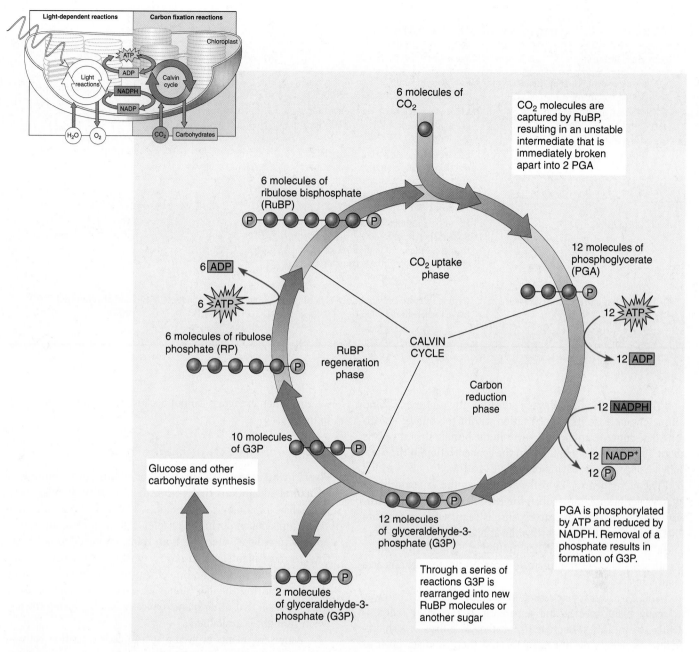

Figure 8–15 A detailed look at the Calvin cycle. This diagram, which shows carbon atoms as black balls, demonstrates that six molecules of CO_2 must be "fixed" (incorporated into preexisting carbon skeletons) to produce one molecule of a six-carbon sugar such as glucose. Two glyceraldehyde-3-phosphate (G3P) molecules "leave" the cycle for every glucose formed. Although these reactions do not require light directly, the energy that drives the Calvin cycle comes from ATP and NADPH, which are the products of the light-dependent reactions.

different enzyme catalyzes the decarboxylation of malate to yield pyruvate (which has three carbons) and CO_2. NADPH is formed, replacing the one used earlier.

$$Malate + NADP^+ \rightarrow Pyruvate + CO_2 + NADPH$$

The CO_2 released in the bundle sheath cell combines with ribulose bisphosphate and goes through the Calvin cycle in the usual manner. The pyruvate formed in the decarboxylation reaction returns to the mesophyll cell, where it reacts with ATP to regenerate phosphoenolpyruvate.

TABLE 8-3 Summary of Photosynthesis

Reaction Series	Summary of Process	Needed Materials	End Products
A. Light-dependent reactions (take place in thylakoid membranes)	Energy from sunlight used to split water, manufacture ATP, and reduce $NADP^+$		
1. Photochemical reactions	Chlorophyll-activated; reaction center gives up photoexcited electron to electron acceptor	Light energy; pigments (chlorophyll)	Electrons
2. Electron transport	Electrons are transported along chain of electron acceptors in thylakoid membranes; electrons reduce $NADP^+$; splitting of water provides some of H^+ that accumulates inside thylakoid space	Electrons, $NADP^+$, H_2O, electron acceptors	NADPH, O_2
3. Chemiosmosis	H^+ are permitted to move across the thylakoid membrane down their gradient; they cross the membrane through special channels in ATP synthase complex; energy released is used to produce ATP	Proton gradient, $ADP + P_i$	ATP
B. Carbon fixation reactions (take place in stroma)	Carbon fixation: carbon dioxide is used to make carbohydrate	Ribulose bisphosphate, CO_2, ATP, NADPH, necessary enzymes	Carbohydrates, $ADP + P_i$, $NADP^+$

The role of the C_4 pathway is to efficiently capture CO_2 and ultimately increase its concentration within the bundle sheath cells. The concentration of CO_2 within the bundle sheath cells is about 10 to 60 times greater than the concentration in the mesophyll cells of plants having only the C_3 pathway.

The combined C_3–C_4 pathway involves the expenditure of 30 ATPs per hexose, rather than the 18 ATPs used by the C_3 pathway alone. The extra energy expense is required to regenerate PEP from pyruvate. It is worthwhile at high light intensities because it ensures a high concentration of CO_2 in the bundle sheath cells and permits them to carry on photosynthesis at a rapid rate.

The C_4 pathway is present in addition to the C_3 pathway in many plant species and apparently has evolved independently several times. Because PEP carboxylase fixes CO_2 so efficiently, C_4 plants do not need to have their stomata open as much. C_4 plants therefore tolerate higher temperatures and greater light intensities, lose less water by transpiration (evaporation), and generally have higher rates of photosynthesis and growth than plants that use only the Calvin cycle. Among the many quick-growing and aggressive plants that use the C_4 pathway are sugar cane, corn, and crabgrass. When sunlight is abundant, the yields of C_4 crop plants can be two to three times greater than those of C_3 plants. If this pathway could be incorporated into more of our crop plants by genetic manipulation, we might be able to greatly increase food production in some parts of the world.

When light is abundant, the rate of photosynthesis is limited by the concentration of CO_2, so C_4 plants, with their higher levels of CO_2 in bundle sheath cells, have the advantage. At lower light intensities and temperatures, C_3 plants are favored. For example, winter rye, a C_3 plant, grows lavishly in cool weather when crabgrass cannot because it requires more energy to fix CO_2.

CAM plants fix CO2 at night

Plants living in very dry, or *xeric*, conditions have a number of structural adaptations that enable them to survive. Many xeric plants have physiological adaptations as well. For example, their stomata may open during the cooler night and close during the hot day to reduce water loss from transpiration. This is in contrast to most plants, which have stomata that are open during the day and closed at night. But xeric plants that have their stomata closed during the day cannot exchange gases for photosynthesis. (Recall that other plants typically fix CO_2 during the day, when sunlight is available.)

Many xeric plants evolved a special carbon fixation pathway called **crassulacean acid metabolism (CAM)** that in effect solves this dilemma. The name comes from the stonecrop plant family (the Crassulaceae), which possesses the CAM pathway, although it has evolved independently in some members of more than 25 other plant families, including the cactus family (Cactaceae), the lily family (Liliaceae), and the orchid family (Orchidaceae) (Fig. 8–18).

CAM plants use the enzyme PEP carboxylase to fix CO_2 during the night when stomata are open, forming oxaloacetate, which is converted to malate and stored in cell vacuoles. During the day, when stomata are closed and gas exchange cannot occur between the plant and the atmosphere, CO_2 is removed from malate by a decarboxylation reaction. Now the CO_2 is available within the leaf tissue to be fixed into sugar by the Calvin cycle (C_3 pathway).

The CAM pathway is very similar to the C_4 pathway but with important differences. C_4 plants initially fix CO_2 into four-carbon organic acids in mesophyll cells. The acids are later decarboxy-

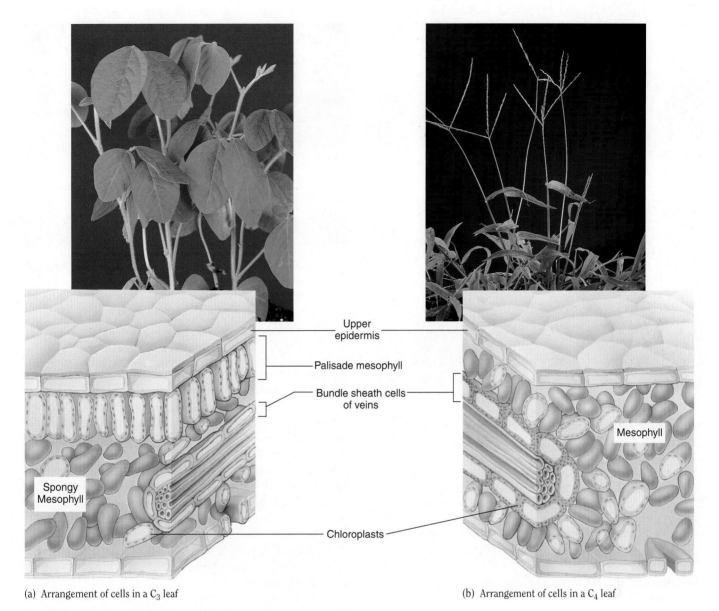

Upper epidermis

Palisade mesophyll

Bundle sheath cells of veins

Spongy Mesophyll

Mesophyll

Chloroplasts

(a) Arrangement of cells in a C₃ leaf

(b) Arrangement of cells in a C₄ leaf

Figure 8-16 Comparison of C₃ and C₄ anatomy. (a) In C₃ plants, such as soybeans, the Calvin cycle takes place in the mesophyll cells, and the bundle sheath cells are nonphotosynthetic. (b) In C₄ plants, such as crabgrass, reactions that fix CO_2 into four-carbon compounds take place in the mesophyll cells. The four-carbon compounds are transferred from the mesophyll cells to the photosynthetic bundle sheath cells, where the Calvin cycle takes place. *(a and b, Dennis Drenner)*

lated to produce CO_2, which is fixed by the C₃ pathway in the bundle sheath cells. In other words, the C₄ and C₃ pathways occur in *different locations* within the leaf of a C₄ plant. In CAM plants, the initial fixation of CO_2 occurs at night. Decarboxylation of malate and subsequent production of sugar from CO_2 by the normal C₃ photosynthetic pathway occur during the day. In other words, the CAM and C₃ pathways occur at *different times* within the same cell of a CAM plant.

Although it does not promote rapid growth the way that the C₄ pathway does, the CAM pathway is a very successful adaptation to xeric conditions. CAM plants are able to exchange gases for photosynthesis and to reduce water loss significantly. Plants

with CAM photosynthesis survive in deserts where neither C₃ nor C₄ plants can.

Photorespiration reduces photosynthetic efficiency

Many C₃ plants, including certain agriculturally important crops such as soybeans, wheat, and potatoes, do not yield as much carbohydrate from photosynthesis as might be expected. This reduction in yield is especially significant during very hot spells in summer. On hot, dry days, plants close their stomata to conserve water. Once the stomata close, photosynthesis rapidly uses up

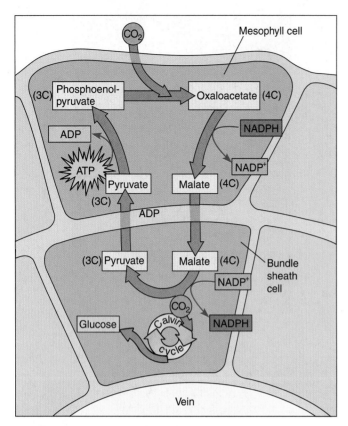

Figure 8–17 Summary of the C₄ pathway. CO_2 combines with phosphoenolpyruvate (PEP) in the chloroplasts of mesophyll cells, forming a four-carbon compound that is converted to malate. Malate goes to the chloroplasts of bundle sheath cells, where it is decarboxylated. The CO_2 thus released in the bundle sheath cell is used to make carbohydrate by way of the Calvin cycle.

the CO_2 remaining in the leaf and produces O_2, which accumulates in the chloroplasts.

Recall that the enzyme RuBP carboxylase/oxygenase (Rubisco) is responsible for CO_2 fixation in the Calvin cycle by attaching CO_2 to RuBP. In addition to this carboxylase activity, Rubisco can also react with O_2, which competes with CO_2 for the active site of Rubisco. The activity of Rubisco toward the substrates CO_2 and O_2 depends on the relative amounts of these two gases in the chloroplast environment. When chloroplast oxygen

Figure 8–18 A typical CAM plant. Prickly pear cactus (*Opuntia* sp.) is a CAM plant. The more than 200 species of *Opuntia* living today originated in various xeric habitats in North and South America. *(Robert W. Domm/Visuals Unlimited)*

levels are high and CO_2 levels are low, Rubisco is more likely to catalyze the reaction of RuBP with O_2 instead of with CO_2. When this occurs, some of the intermediates involved in the Calvin cycle are degraded to CO_2 and H_2O. This process is called **photorespiration** because (1) it occurs in the presence of light; (2) it requires oxygen, like aerobic respiration; and (3) it produces CO_2 and H_2O, like aerobic respiration. Unlike aerobic respiration, however, ATP is not produced during photorespiration. Photorespiration reduces photosynthetic efficiency because it removes some of the intermediates used in the Calvin cycle.

The reasons for photorespiration are incompletely understood, although it is thought to possibly reflect the origin of Rubisco at an ancient time when CO_2 levels were high and molecular oxygen levels were low.

Photorespiration is negligible in C₄ plants because the concentration of CO_2 in bundle sheath cells (where Rubisco is present) is always high. However, many important crop plants are C₃ plants that carry out photorespiration. This is yet another reason that some scientists are attempting to transfer genes for the C₄ pathway to C₃ crops such as soybeans and wheat. If this genetic transfer is accomplished, these plants should be able to produce much more carbohydrate during hot weather.

SUMMARY WITH KEY TERMS

I. Green plants, algae, and certain bacteria are **photoautotrophs** and use light as an energy source for manufacturing organic molecules from CO_2 and H_2O. All animals, fungi, and most bacteria are **chemoheterotrophs** that depend on photoautotrophs for organic molecules.

II. Light behaves as both a wave and a particle. Particles of light energy, called **photons,** can excite biological molecules. The resulting energized electrons may be accepted by electron acceptor compounds.

III. In plants, **photosynthesis** occurs in **chloroplasts,** which are located mainly within **mesophyll** cells inside the leaf. During photosynthesis,

light energy is captured and converted to the chemical energy of carbohydrates; oxygen is released as a byproduct.

A. Chloroplasts are organelles bounded by a double membrane; the inner membrane encloses the **stroma** in which membranous, saclike **thylakoids** are suspended. Thylakoids arranged in stacks are called **grana.**

B. **Chlorophyll** and other photosynthetic pigments are components of the thylakoid membranes of chloroplasts. Each thylakoid encloses a **thylakoid lumen.**

C. The **absorption spectra** of chlorophylls *a* and *b* are similar to the **action spectrum** for photosynthesis.

D. **Photosystems I and II** are the two types of photosynthetic units involved in photosynthesis. Each photosystem includes **antenna complexes** and a **reaction center.**

    1. Chlorophyll molecules and accessory pigments are organized with pigment-binding proteins into antenna complexes.

    2. Only a special chlorophyll *a* in the **reaction center** actually gives up its energized electrons to a nearby electron acceptor.

IV. During the noncyclic **light-dependent reactions,** known as noncyclic electron transport, ATP and NADPH are formed.

A. The electrons in Photosystem I are energized by the absorption of light and passed through an **electron transport chain** to NADP$^+$, forming NADPH.

B. Electrons given up by P700 in Photosystem I are replaced by electrons from P680 in Photosystem II.

C. Electrons given up by P680 in Photosystem II are replaced by electrons made available by the **photolysis** of H$_2$O; oxygen is released in the process.

D. A series of redox reactions takes place as energized electrons are passed along the electron transport chain from Photosystem II to Photosystem I.

    1. Some of the energy is used to pump protons across the thylakoid membrane, providing the energy to generate ATP by **chemiosmosis.**

    2. **Photophosphorylation** is the synthesis of ATP coupled to the transport of electrons energized by photons of light.

    3. As protons diffuse through **ATP synthase,** an enzyme complex in the thylakoid membrane, ADP is phosphorylated to form ATP.

V. During the cyclic light-dependent reactions, known as cyclic electron transport, electrons from Photosystem I are eventually returned to Photosystem I. ATP is produced by chemiosmosis, but no NADPH or oxygen is generated.

VI. During the **carbon fixation reactions,** the energy of ATP and NADPH is used to manufacture carbohydrate molecules from CO$_2$.

A. The carbon fixation reactions proceed by way of the **Calvin cycle,** also known as the **C$_3$ pathway.**

    1. During the CO$_2$ uptake phase of the Calvin cycle, CO$_2$ is combined with **ribulose bisphosphate (RuBP),** a five-carbon sugar, by the enzyme **ribulose bisphosphate carboxylase/oxygenase (Rubisco).**

    2. During the carbon reduction phase of the Calvin cycle, the energy and reducing power of ATP and NADPH are used to convert PGA molecules to **glyceraldehyde-3-phosphate (G3P).**

    3. For every 6 CO$_2$ molecules fixed, 12 molecules of G3P are produced, and 2 molecules of G3P can leave the cycle.

    4. The two G3P molecules are required to produce the equivalent of one molecule of glucose; the remaining G3P molecules are modified to regenerate RuBP during the RuBP regeneration phase of the Calvin cycle.

B. In the **C$_4$ pathway,** the enzyme **PEP carboxylase** binds CO$_2$ effectively, even when CO$_2$ is at a low concentration.

    1. C$_4$ reactions take place within mesophyll cells. The CO$_2$ is fixed in **oxaloacetate,** which is then converted to **malate.**

    2. The malate moves into a **bundle sheath cell,** and CO$_2$ is removed from it. The released CO$_2$ then enters the Calvin cycle.

C. The **crassulacean acid metabolism (CAM)** pathway is similar to the C$_4$ pathway. PEP carboxylase fixes carbon at night in the mesophyll cells, and the Calvin cycle occurs during the day in the same cells.

VII. In **photorespiration,** C$_3$ plants consume oxygen and generate CO$_2$ but do not produce ATP. Photorespiration is significant on bright, hot, dry days when plants close their stomata, conserving water but preventing the passage of CO$_2$ into the leaf.

Summary Reactions for Photosynthesis

The light-dependent reactions (noncyclic electron transport):

$$12\ H_2O + 12\ NADP^+ + 18\ ADP + 18\ P_i \xrightarrow[\text{Chlorophyll}]{\text{Light}}$$
$$6\ O_2 + 12\ NADPH + 18\ ATP$$

The carbon fixation reactions (Calvin cycle):

$$12\ NADPH + 18\ ATP + 6\ CO_2 \longrightarrow$$
$$C_6H_{12}O_6 + 12\ NADP^+ + 18\ ADP + 18\ P_i + 6\ H_2O$$

By canceling out the common items on opposite sides of the arrows in these two coupled equations, we obtain the simplified overall equation for photosynthesis:

$$\underset{\substack{\text{Carbon} \\ \text{dioxide}}}{6\ CO_2} + \underset{\text{Water}}{12\ H_2O} \xrightarrow[\text{Chlorophyll}]{\text{Light energy}} \underset{\text{Glucose}}{C_6H_{12}O_6} + \underset{\text{Oxygen}}{6\ O_2} + \underset{\text{Water}}{6\ H_2O}$$

POST-TEST

1. Where is chlorophyll located in the chloroplast? (a) thylakoid membranes (b) stroma (c) mitochondrial matrix (d) thylakoid lumen (e) between the inner and outer membranes

2. In photolysis, some of the energy captured by chlorophyll is used to split (a) CO$_2$ (b) ATP (c) NADPH (d) H$_2$O (e) both b and c

3. Light is composed of particles of energy called (a) carotenoids (b) reaction centers (c) photons (d) antenna complexes (e) photosystems

4. The relative effectiveness of different wavelengths of light in photosynthesis is demonstrated by (a) an action spectrum (b) photolysis (c) carbon fixation reactions (d) photoheterotrophs (e) an absorption spectrum

5. In plants, the final electron acceptor in the light-dependent reactions is: (a) NADP$^+$ (b) CO$_2$ (c) H$_2$O (d) O$_2$ (e) G3P

6. In addition to chlorophyll, most plants contain accessory photosynthetic pigments such as (a) PEP (b) G3P (c) carotenoids (d) PGA (e) NADP$^+$

7. The part of a photosystem that absorbs light energy is its (a) antenna complexes (b) reaction center (c) terminal quinone electron acceptor (d) pigment-binding protein (e) thylakoid lumen

8. In _____, electrons that have been energized by light contribute their energy to add phosphate to ADP, producing ATP. (a) crassulacean acid metabolism (b) the Calvin cycle (c) photorespiration (d) C$_4$ pathways (e) photophosphorylation

9. In _____, there is a one-way flow of electrons to NADP$^+$, forming NADPH. (a) crassulacean acid metabolism (b) the Calvin cycle (c) photorespiration (d) cyclic electron transport (e) noncyclic electron transport

10. The mechanism by which electron transport is coupled to ATP production by means of a proton gradient is called (a) chemiosmosis (b) crassulacean acid metabolism (c) fluorescence (d) the C$_3$ pathway (e) the C$_4$ pathway

11. In photosynthesis in eukaryotes, the transfer of electrons through a sequence of electron acceptors provides energy to pump protons across the (a) chloroplast outer membrane (b) chloroplast inner membrane (c) thylakoid membrane (d) inner mitochondrial membrane (e) plasma membrane

12. The inputs for _____ are CO$_2$, NADPH, and ATP. (a) cyclic electron transport (b) the carbon fixation reactions (c) noncyclic electron transport (d) Photosystems I and II (e) chemiosmosis

13. The Calvin cycle begins when CO$_2$ reacts with (a) phosphoenolpyruvate

(b) glyceraldehyde-3-phosphate (c) ribulose bisphosphate (d) oxaloacetate (e) phosphoglycerate

14. The enzyme directly responsible for almost all carbon fixation on Earth is (a) Rubisco (b) PEP carboxylase (c) ATP synthase (d) phosphofructokinase (e) ligase

15. In C_4 plants, C_4 and C_3 pathways occur at different _____, whereas in CAM plants, CAM and C_3 pathways occur at different _____. (a) times of day; locations within the leaf (b) seasons; locations (c) locations; times of day (d) locations; seasons (e) times of day; seasons

REVIEW QUESTIONS

1. Why does photosynthesis require light energy?
2. What is the role of chlorophyll in photosynthesis?
3. What is the significance of the fact that the combined absorption spectra of chlorophyll *a* and *b* roughly match the action spectrum of photosynthesis? Why do they not coincide exactly?
4. How is oxygen produced during photosynthesis?
5. In noncyclic electron transport, what molecule becomes phosphorylated? Why is the phosphorylation process referred to as *photo*phosphorylation? Why is it said to be noncyclic?
6. How are ATP and NADPH produced and used in the process of photosynthesis?
7. Describe the three phases of the Calvin cycle.
8. How do the C_4 and CAM pathways improve photosynthesis in hot, dry environments?
9. Label the figure to the right. Use Figure 8–8 to check your answers.

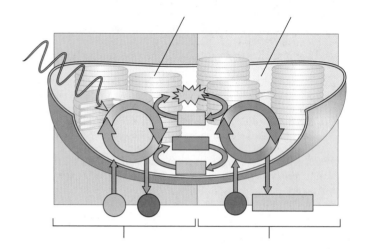

YOU MAKE THE CONNECTION

1. Only some plant cells have chloroplasts, but all actively metabolizing plant cells have mitochondria. Why?
2. Explain why the proton gradient formed during chemiosmosis represents a state of low entropy. (You may wish to refer to the discussion of entropy in Chapter 6.)
3. The electrons in glucose have relatively high free energies. How did they become so energetic?
4. What strategies might be employed in the future to increase world food supply? Base your answer on your knowledge of photosynthesis and related processes.

RECOMMENDED READINGS

Balzani, V. "Greener Way to Solar Power." *New Scientist,* Vol. 12, 12 Nov. 1994. Chemists are imitating the light-gathering photosystems of plants in an attempt to convert solar energy to electricity.

Cline, K. "Gateway to the Chloroplast." *Nature,* Vol. 403, 13 Jan. 2000. Examines recent insights into the process by which proteins are imported during chloroplast development.

Demmig-Adams, B., and W.W. Adams III. "Harvesting Sunlight Safely." *Nature,* Vol. 403, 27 Jan. 2000. A chlorophyll-binding protein within the light-harvesting complexes of the photosynthetic apparatus has a unique, energy-dissipating function, to protect against excess light.

Hendry, G. "Making, Breaking, and Remaking Chlorophyll." *Natural History,* May 1990. Examines the endless process by which plants make chlorophyll in the spring and break it down in the fall.

Moore, P.D. "Mixed Metabolism in Plant Pools." *Nature,* Vol. 399, 13 May 1999. Some aquatic plants use C_4 or CAM photosynthetic pathways, which allow them to coexist and optimize their use of environmental resources.

Riebesell, U. "Carbon Fix for a Diatom." *Nature,* Vol. 407, 21 Jan. 2000. This news article highlights the discovery of a marine diatom (a unicellular alga) that uses the same C_4 pathway as certain terrestrial plants.

Sharkey, T.D. "Some Like It Hot." *Science,* Vol. 287, 21 Jan. 2000. Many plants adapt to colder or warmer temperatures by adjusting the fatty acid content in chloroplast membranes.

Taiz, L., and E. Zeiger. *Plant Physiology,* 2nd edition. Sinauer Associates, Inc., Sunderland, MA, 1998. Chapters 7 through 9 contain an in-depth examination of photosynthesis.

- Visit our Web site at **http://www.info.brookscole.com/solomonbergmartin** for links to chapter-related resources on the World Wide Web. Additional on-line materials relating to this chapter can also be found on our Web site.

See chapter activity on BioActive Learner CD for additional help in mastering the chapter's material. Icon location in the chapter's margins shows which topics have tutorials or simulations in the CD.

CAREER VISIONS

Middle School Science Teacher

CHRISTIE GAYHEART

Christie Gayheart is a middle school science teacher in the Midland Public Schools, Midland, Michigan. Originally from Houghton, Michigan, Christie received her B.S. in biology, with an ecology option, at Michigan Technological University in 1996. After deciding in her senior year that she wanted to become a teacher, she pursued a B.S. in Secondary Education from Central Michigan University, with a major in biology and minor in physical science, completing her degree in 1999. She is currently working toward her M.S. in Educational Administration at Saginaw Valley State University. Christie divides her time between two schools, Central Middle and Northeast Middle, teaching eighth-grade science at both. She encourages her students to think like scientists, to conduct experiments and question their results. She tries to harness the natural enthusiasm of eighth graders—supplementing class work with hands-on experiments, guest speakers, and field trips—to keep science fun but challenging.

Did you have a particular focus in your undergraduate biology coursework?

I started out in a biomedical engineering program, so I was mostly in general engineering classes at first. After taking some of the design courses, and being in the computer lab, the degree work seemed impersonal to me. I decided that was not me, that I needed to be talking to people. I stuck with biology. I was coaching high school golf and high school and college cheerleading at the time, and I decided I liked working with kids. I thought about teaching but I never really pursued it. Instead, I went with an ecology focus, thinking that I wanted to work for the Department of Natural Resources and do some kind of field interpretive work.

What influenced your decision to become a teacher?

The coaching, as well as some tutoring I did as an undergraduate, mostly in high school science. Then, when I started the teaching program, I began working as a substitute teacher, which really convinced me that teaching was what I wanted to do.

Was a second Bachelor of Science degree required for you to become a teacher, or could you have earned a teaching certificate instead?

I could have gotten a certificate, but I felt the bachelor's in education might be more helpful for my future plans—to obtain a master's degree and possibly go on for a doctorate in education.

The best thing about teaching is that it makes you feel good at the end of the day, that you're doing something for people and, hopefully, for humanity in general.

For your secondary education degree, did you have to take additional science courses?

For a secondary education degree, you have to declare a major and a minor, or a double minor, depending on the distinctions in your state. I wanted to be able to teach any secondary-level science course. It made sense to declare a biology major, because I had a lot of those courses. If I took a physical science minor, I could get a distinction called DX, which allows a person to teach any science discipline at the secondary level, 7th through 12th grade. I had to take astronomy and geology, but I had enough credits in the other sciences: chemistry, physics, and biology.

What were your education requirements?

I took education core classes and a two-semester interdisciplinary course in the biology program, "Teaching for Biology Majors," which included an internship in a classroom.

You currently teach eighth-grade science. Is the focus on biology, physical science, or some combination of disciplines?

It's general science. Our seventh- and eighth-grade program is a combination of the different disciplines, so students are exposed to a little bit of earth science, physical science, and life science.

How do you cope with students' differences in abilities?

You really try to vary your teaching style, working with three different approaches: hands-on, visual (giving them visual instruction), and auditory teaching. It is the same with assessment: Not all students are good at tests. You need to vary assessment strategies to meet everyone's needs, so they can all be successful.

Are eighth-grade students typically interested in science? How do you generate or direct their enthusiasm?

I find the students to be very interested. If you give them the right tools and make it meaningful to them, then they are right there with you. I use the word "experimenting," but they think it's play.

That's good, too; I think they should be excited about doing the hands-on activities, but you have to focus this excitement into experimenting, to get them thinking about science process skills. As a new teacher, I am still working on doing inquiry-based learning: giving them a thought question, having them use science process skills to achieve an answer to the problem, and showing them that science isn't always a cookie-cutter method. All of the activities have to be age-appropriate.

How does your biology background affect your approach to teaching?

Because I have a full degree in biology, I have gone through undergraduate research, and my focus is more on the discipline of science—thought processes and problem solving—and on experimentation. I am probably more disciplined and require more in the areas where you have to talk about processes. Also, because I have a varied science background, including coursework in astronomy and geology, I am able to easily connect all the different science disciplines.

What "tools of the trade" have you learned so far?

One is to always be prepared with lesson planning. If you're prepared, you can make it through a lesson. If you feel like you lacked creativity, you can work on that next time. Second, don't beat yourself up if your lesson goes wrong. Just reflect on the strength of the lesson and modify where needed. Finally—and this is important— obtain a mentor and utilize him or her; they are a great resource. Use them to find what works and what doesn't. Most teachers are very supportive of one another.

What are the greatest rewards of your profession? What are the biggest demands you face?

The best thing about teaching is that it makes you feel good at the end of the day, that you're doing something for people and, hopefully, for humanity in general. I like working with kids.

I probably have two big challenges. In the classroom, it's helping kids to feel that they fit in, teaching them that they can be successful in my class. Kids often have preconceived notions, like, "I'm not good in science." It's really hard for them to change that opinion of themselves; they first need to learn that they can be successful.

Another challenge lies with the teaching profession itself, that we are professionals, like any other area, but we aren't always perceived that way. I think that's mostly because salaries have not been in line with other professional areas or degrees, and it is a reason why you don't see a lot of people going into teaching. Young people can make more money elsewhere, but the jobs they choose may not be as rewarding. Many of my friends in engineering or business are making twice what I am, but they are unhappy because it's not rewarding. But when you work in teaching, people generally appreciate everything you do for kids, and the kids appreciate it.

What sort of person makes the best teacher?

Definitely someone who enjoys working with students. That's the number-one

thing. You have to enjoy what you do. Second would be someone who's flexible, yet still firm, disciplined, and principled. Someone who is energetic, because teaching is trying on your body and mind. Definitely friendly. You work with the public and all different kinds of people. You have to be accepting of other people. The last thing I would say is that a teacher should be goal-oriented. Teachers are responsible for furthering their own professional development. You have to set goals and be working toward them all the time.

How would you advise undergraduate biology majors considering a career in teaching?

First, get experience working with students in the classroom. Even when you are working on your biology degree, do something with kids! Make sure you like working with them! Contact a high school; see if they need help with after-school tutoring. Ask to sit in on classes to see how they operate. You really need to know how it is, way before you even start education courses. Even working in after-school programs or church youth groups would be helpful—anything that lets you work with kids. Second, actively learn your subject area. I think it's very important to be sound in your discipline, to be able to explain it to someone else. The last suggestion I have is to network with your college professors and with local high school teachers that you knew in school or in the town where you go to college. Those are people who will be your contacts and your references. If there's a school district that you want to work in, get networking, start substitute teaching, do it all.

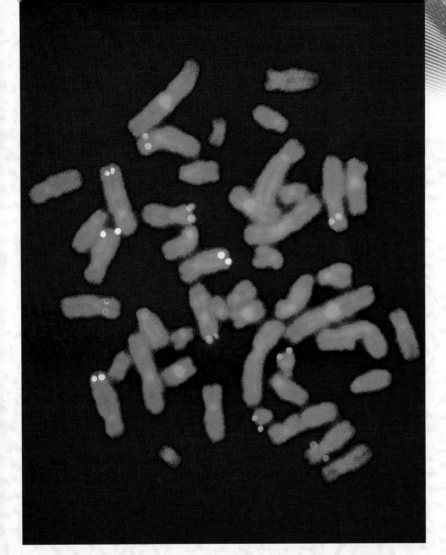

P a r t

3

Researchers in human genetics have identified the genes responsible for many hereditary diseases. The colored dots in this fluorescence micrograph indicate the positions of specific genes on these human chromosomes. *(Drs. T. Ried and D. Ward/Peter Arnold, Inc.)*

The Continuity of Life: Genetics

CHAPTERS

9

Chromosomes, Mitosis, and Meiosis

LEARNING OBJECTIVES

After you have studied this chapter you should be able to

1. Discuss the significance of chromosomes in terms of their information content.
2. Identify the stages in the eukaryotic cell cycle, describe the principal events characteristic of each, and point out some ways in which the cycle is controlled.
3. Illustrate the structure of a duplicated chromosome, labeling the sister chromatids, sister centromeres, and sister kinetochores.
4. Explain the significance of mitosis and diagram the process.
5. Discriminate between asexual and sexual reproduction.
6. Distinguish between haploid and diploid cells and define homologous chromosomes.
7. Explain the significance of meiosis and diagram the process.
8. Contrast mitosis and meiosis, emphasizing how differences in events lead to different outcomes.
9. Compare the roles of mitosis and meiosis and of haploidy and diploidy in various generalized life cycles.

Fluorescence LM of a human lung cell in early mitosis. Computer processing is responsible for this unique three-dimensional view of the mitotic spindle *(green)* and chromosomes *(blue).* *(Alexey Khodjakov, Wadsworth Center, Albany, NY)*

Because all cells are formed by the division of preexisting cells, cells divide to enable the organism to grow, repair damaged parts, or reproduce. Cells can serve as the basic units of life and the essential link between generations because even the simplest contains a massive amount of coded information in the form of DNA, collectively referred to as the organism's **genome.** Today, through the Human Genome Project and related efforts introduced in Chapter 1, we are learning how genomes are organized into informational units called **genes,** which are used to control the activities of the cell and are passed on to its descendants.

When a cell divides, the information contained in the DNA first must be faithfully duplicated and the copies then transmitted to each daughter cell through a precisely choreographed series of steps. However, this presents a problem because DNA is a very long, thin molecule that could easily become tangled and broken. The potential difficulty is especially acute for a eukaryotic cell because its nucleus contains a very large amount of DNA. In this chapter we consider how eukaryotes solve this problem by packaging each DNA molecule with proteins and assembling the resulting complex into a structure called a **chromosome,** each of which contains hundreds or thousands of genes.

We then consider *mitosis,* the process that ensures that a parent cell transmits one copy of every chromosome to each of its two daughter cells. In this way the chromosome number is preserved through successive mitotic divisions. Most of the body cells of eukaryotes divide by mitosis.

Finally we discuss *meiosis,* a special process in which the chromosome number is reduced by half. Meiosis is required in sexual life cycles in eukaryotes. Sexual reproduction is characterized by the fusion of two sex cells, or *gametes,* to form a single cell called a *zygote.* Meiosis makes it possible for each gamete to contain only half the number of parental chromosomes, thereby preventing the zygotes from having twice as many chromosomes as the parents.

Bacterial reproduction is described in Chapter 23. Prokaryotic cells contain much less DNA than eukaryotic cells. Their DNA is usually in the form of a circle and is packaged with very few associated proteins. Although the distribution of genetic material in dividing prokaryotic cells is a simpler process than mitosis, it nevertheless must be very precise if the daughter cells are to be genetically identical to the parent cell.

EUKARYOTIC CHROMOSOMES CONTAIN DNA AND PROTEIN

The major carriers of genetic information in eukaryotes are the chromosomes contained within the cell nucleus. Although the term *chromosome* means "colored body," chromosomes are virtually colorless; the name refers to their ability to be stained by certain dyes.

Chromosomes are made up of **chromatin,** a complex material consisting of proteins and deoxyribonucleic acid (DNA). When a cell is not dividing, the chromosomes are present but in an extended, partially unraveled form. The chromatin consists of long, thin threads that are somewhat aggregated, which gives them a granular appearance when viewed with the electron microscope (see Fig. 4–12). During cell division, the chromatin fibers condense and the chromosomes become visible as distinct structures (Fig. 9–1). The structure of chromatin is described in more detail in Chapter 11.

DNA is organized into informational units called genes

Each chromosome may contain hundreds or even thousands of genes. For example, humans are thought to have about 35,000 to 45,000 genes that code for proteins. The precise number is not known, although scientists are engaged in a massive, coordinated effort to make a precise determination as part of the Human Genome Project (see Chapter 15). As will be evident in succeeding chapters, our concept of the gene has changed considerably since the beginnings of the science of genetics, but our definitions have always centered on the gene as an informational unit. By providing information needed to carry out one or more specific cellular functions, a gene ultimately affects some characteristic of the organism. For example, genes control eye color in humans, wing length in flies, and seed color in peas.

Chromosomes of different species differ in number and informational content

Every individual of a given species has a characteristic number of chromosomes in most nuclei of its body cells. However, it is not the *number* of chromosomes that makes each species unique but rather the *information* specified by the genes in the chromosomes.

Most human body cells have exactly 46 chromosomes, but humans are not humans merely because they have 46 chromosomes. In fact, some humans have abnormal karyotypes (chromosome assortments) with more or fewer than 46 (see Chapter 15). Humans are not unique in having 46 chromosomes; some other species of animals and plants also happen to have 46, whereas others have different chromosome numbers. For example, a certain species of roundworm has only 2 chromosomes in each cell, while some crabs have as many as 200 and some ferns have more than 1000. Most animal and plant species have between 10 and 50 chromosomes. Numbers above and below this are uncommon.

THE CELL CYCLE IS A SEQUENCE OF CELL GROWTH AND DIVISION

Usually when cells reach a certain size, they must either stop growing or divide. Not all cells divide; some, such as nerve, skeletal muscle, and red blood cells, do not normally divide once they are mature. Other cells undergo a sequence of activities required for growth and cell division referred to as the **cell cycle,** which is commonly represented in diagrams as a circle (Fig. 9–2). The **generation time,** the period from the beginning of one division

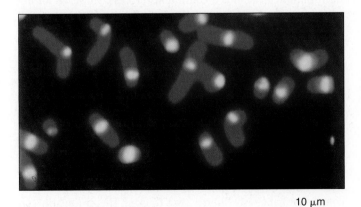

Figure 9–1 Chromosomes. The human chromosomes shown in this confocal fluorescence LM have been stained with a fluorescent antibody that binds to the centromere regions *(yellow). (Courtesy of Oncor, Inc.)*

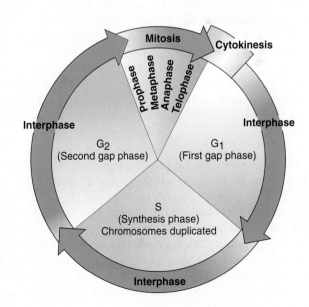

Figure 9–2 The eukaryotic cell cycle. The generation time, the time required to complete one cycle, includes cell division (mitosis and cytokinesis) and interphase. Proportionate amounts of time spent at each stage vary with the species, cell type, and growth conditions.

to the beginning of the next, can vary widely, but in actively growing plant and animal cells it is often about 8 to 20 hours.

Eukaryotic cell division involves two main processes, mitosis and cytokinesis. **Mitosis,** a complex process involving the nucleus, ensures that each new nucleus receives the same number and types of chromosomes as were present in the original nucleus. **Cytokinesis,** which generally begins before mitosis is complete, is the division of the cytoplasm of the cell to form two cells. Multinucleate cells are formed if mitosis is not followed by cytokinesis; this is a normal condition for some kinds of cells.

Chromosomes become duplicated during interphase

Most of the life of a cell is spent in **interphase,** the time when no cell division is occurring. Although the appearance of the nucleus is generally unremarkable (see Fig. 4–12), a cell that is capable of dividing is typically very active during this time, synthesizing needed materials and growing. Most proteins and other materials are synthesized throughout interphase.

Process of Science In the early 1950s, researchers demonstrated that cells preparing to divide synthesize their chromosomes at a relatively restricted interval during interphase and not during early mitosis, as had been previously thought. These investigators used isotopes, such as ^{3}H, to synthesize radioactive thymidine, a nucleotide (see Chapter 3) that is incorporated specifically into DNA as it is synthesized. After the radioactive thymidine had been supplied for a brief period to actively growing cells, a fraction of the cells could be shown by autoradiography (see Chapter 2) to have silver grains over their chromosomes (Fig. 9–3). These labeled cells were those that had been engaged in DNA replication (known as the **synthesis phase,** or **S phase**) during the experiment. The S phase provides the major landmark that is the basis for subdividing interphase (see Fig. 9–2). The proportion of labeled cells out of the total number of cells provides a rough estimate of the length of the S phase relative to the rest of the cell cycle. Other chromosomal constituents, such as the chromosomal proteins, are also synthesized during the S phase. Chromosome duplication is a complex process discussed in Chapter 11.

The time between mitosis and the beginning of the S phase is termed the G_1 **phase** (G stands for *gap,* an interval during which no DNA synthesis occurs). Growth takes place during the G_1 phase, which is usually the most variable in length and also the longest. Toward the end of G_1 there is increased activity of enzymes required for DNA synthesis; these enzymes, along with many other factors, make it possible for the cell to enter the S phase. Cells that are not dividing usually become arrested in the part of the cell cycle prior to the onset of the S phase and are said to be in a state called G_0.

After it completes the S phase, the cell enters a second gap phase, the G_2 **phase.** At this time, increased protein synthesis occurs as the final steps in the cell's preparation for division take place. For many cells, the G_2 phase is short relative to the S and

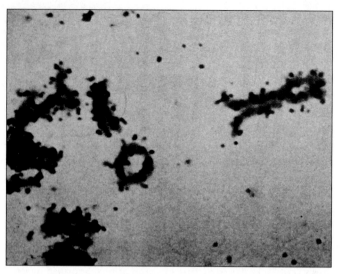

5 μm

Figure 9–3 Detection of the time of DNA synthesis. The silver grains *(black dots)* lying on top of the bean chromosomes in this autoradiogram mark locations where the chromosomes incorporated ^{3}H-labeled thymidine, a DNA precursor, during the S phase of the interphase that preceded mitosis. *(Professor J.H. Taylor,* Proceedings of the National Academy of Science, *Vol. 43,1957, courtesy of New York Academy of Medicine)*

G_1 phases. The completion of the G_2 phase is marked by the beginning of mitosis. The sequence of the substages of interphase is therefore:

$$G_1 \text{ phase} \rightarrow S \text{ phase} \rightarrow G_2 \text{ phase}$$

Mitosis ensures orderly distribution of chromosomes

Each mitotic division is a continuous process. However, for descriptive purposes, mitosis has been divided into stages:

$$\text{Prophase} \rightarrow \text{Metaphase} \rightarrow \text{Anaphase} \rightarrow \text{Telophase}$$

Refer to Figure 9–4 as you read the descriptions of these stages as they would occur in a typical plant or animal cell.

During prophase, duplicated chromosomes become visible with the microscope

The first stage of mitosis, **prophase,** begins when the long chromatin threads begin a coiling process in which chromosomes become simultaneously shorter and thicker. The chromatin can then be distributed to the daughter cells without tangling.

When stained with certain dyes and viewed through the light microscope, chromosomes become visible as darkly staining bodies as prophase progresses. Each chromosome has been duplicated during the preceding S phase and consists of a pair of units, termed **sister chromatids,** which contain identical DNA sequences. Each chromatid includes a constricted region called the **centromere.** Sister chromatids are tightly associated in the vicinity of their centromeres (Fig. 9–5). Although the chemical basis for this close association is not completely understood, evidence suggests that special DNA sequences and special proteins that bind to those DNA sequences are involved. Attached to each centromere is a **kinetochore,** a structure formed from proteins to which microtubules (see Chapter 4) can bind. These microtubules are instrumental to the process by which the chromosomes are distributed during mitosis.

A dividing cell is usually described as a globe, with an equator that determines the midplane, or equatorial plane, and two opposite poles. This terminology is used for all cells regardless of their actual shape. Microtubules radiate from each pole, and some of these protein fibers elongate toward the chromosomes, forming a complex structure known as the **mitotic spindle** (Fig. 9–6). The mitotic spindle is responsible for the separation of the chromosomes during anaphase.

Animal cells differ from the cells of complex plants in the details of mitotic spindle formation. In both types of dividing cells, each pole contains a region, referred to as a **microtubule-organizing center,** from which the microtubules grow outward. When viewed with the electron microscope, microtubule-organizing centers in plant cells consist of fibrils with little or no discernible structure.

In contrast, animal cells and some other cells have a pair of **centrioles** (see Chapter 4) in the middle of each microtubule-organizing center. The centrioles are surrounded by fibrils that make up the **pericentriolar material.** The ends of the spindle microtubules are found in the pericentriolar material, but they do not actually touch the centrioles themselves. Evidence that the pericentriolar material may be functionally similar to the material in the microtubule-organizing centers of plants derives from the fact that they are similar in appearance and in the specific types of proteins present.

Each of the two centrioles becomes duplicated during interphase, yielding two pairs of centrioles. Late in prophase, microtubules radiate from the pericentriolar material surrounding the centrioles, and one pair of centrioles migrates to each pole. The migration of the centrioles to the poles essentially marks the migration of the microtubule-organizing centers. Additional microtubules form clusters extending outward in many directions from the pericentriolar material at the poles; these structures are called **asters.** The function of the asters is not well understood, although there is evidence that these structures play a role in cytokinesis.

It is likely that both plant and animal spindles are organized by similar microtubule organizing centers. Although centrioles were long thought to be required for spindle formation in animal cells, their apparent involvement is probably coincidental. Because centrioles usually arise in association with preexisting centrioles, the localization of the centrioles in the microtubule-organizing center may have evolved to provide for the orderly distribution of these organelles to the daughter cells.

During prophase, the nucleolus (see Chapter 4) diminishes in size and usually disappears. Toward the end of prophase, the nuclear envelope breaks down, and each sister chromatid becomes attached to some of the spindle microtubules at its kinetochore. The chromosomes (each consisting of a pair of sister chromatids connected at their centromeres) undergo a series of movements and finally become aligned along the equatorial plane of the cell.

At metaphase duplicated chromosomes line up on the midplane

The period during which the duplicated chromosomes are lined up along the equatorial plane of the cell constitutes **metaphase.** The mitotic spindle is complete. It is composed of two types of microtubules: polar microtubules and kinetochore microtubules. **Polar microtubules** extend from each pole to the equatorial region, where they generally overlap. **Kinetochore microtubules** extend from each pole and attach to the kinetochores (see Fig. 9–6). At mitotic metaphase the sister chromatids that make up each duplicated chromosome are attached by kinetochore microtubules to *opposite* poles of the cell.

During metaphase each chromatid is completely condensed and appears quite thick and distinct. Because individual chromosomes can be seen more distinctly at metaphase than at any other time, they are usually photographed at this stage to be studied for certain chromosome abnormalities (Fig. 9–7 on page 205; also see Fig. 15–5*b*).

During anaphase chromosomes move toward the poles

Anaphase begins as the protein tethers holding the sister chromatids together in the vicinity of their centromeres are released. Each chromatid is now referred to as an *independent chromosome.* The now separate chromosomes slowly move to opposite poles. The kinetochores, still attached to kinetochore microtubules, lead the way, with the chromosome arms trailing behind. Anaphase ends when all the chromosomes have reached the poles.

The overall mechanism of chromosome movement in anaphase is still poorly understood, although significant progress is being made in this area. Microtubules lack elastic or contractile properties. So how do the chromosomes move apart? Are they pushed or pulled, or do other forces operate?

Process of Science Chromosome movements are studied in a variety of ways. Numbers of microtubules present at a particular stage or after certain treatments can be determined through careful analysis of electron micrographs. It is possible to physically perturb living cells that are dividing, using laser beams or mechanical devices known as *micromanipulators.* Skilled researchers can move chromosomes, break their connections to microtubules, and even remove them from the cell entirely.

Microtubules are constantly changing structures, with tubulin subunits being constantly removed from their ends and others being added, and in fact there is considerable evidence that kinetochore microtubules shorten during anaphase. Therefore, many current hypotheses to explain anaphase movement

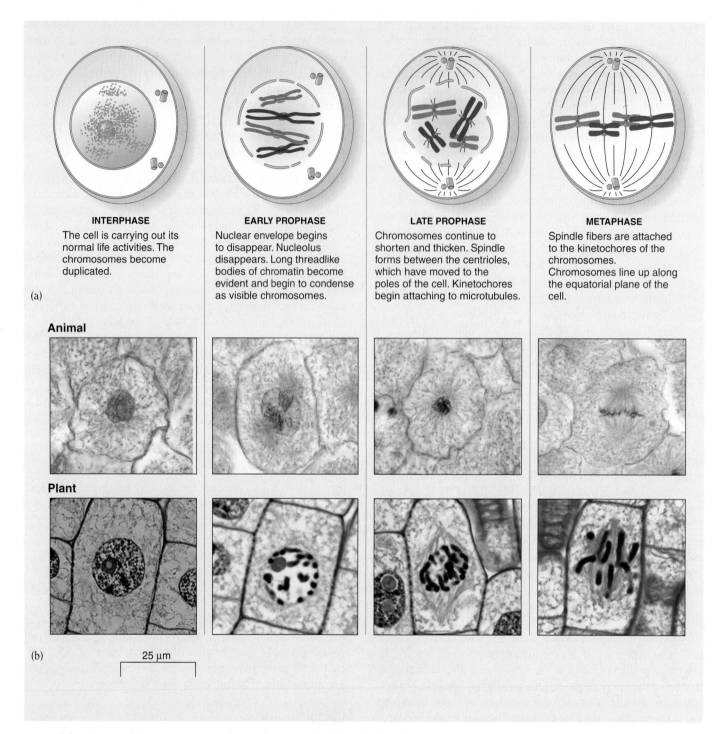

INTERPHASE	EARLY PROPHASE	LATE PROPHASE	METAPHASE
The cell is carrying out its normal life activities. The chromosomes become duplicated.	Nuclear envelope begins to disappear. Nucleolus disappears. Long threadlike bodies of chromatin become evident and begin to condense as visible chromosomes.	Chromosomes continue to shorten and thicken. Spindle forms between the centrioles, which have moved to the poles of the cell. Kinetochores begin attaching to microtubules.	Spindle fibers are attached to the kinetochores of the chromosomes. Chromosomes line up along the equatorial plane of the cell.

(a)

Animal

Plant

(b)   25 μm

■ **Figure 9–4 Cell division.** Interphase and the stages of mitosis are similar in plant and animal cells. Although both types have microtubule organizing centers, the plant cells lack centrioles. **(a)** The drawings depict generalized animal cells with a diploid chromosome number of four. The sizes of the nuclei and chromosomes are exaggerated to show the structures more clearly. **(b)** The upper row of LMs depicts cells of an animal (the whitefish, *Coregonus* sp.). The chromosomes have been stained and the cells flattened on microscope slides. Stained chromosomes in sectioned cells of the onion, *Allium cepa*, are shown in the lower row. *(Animal cells, Michael Abbey/Science Source/Photo Researchers, Inc.; Plant cells, first interphase through telophase, Ed Reschke; second interphase, Carolina Biological Supply Company/Phototake)*

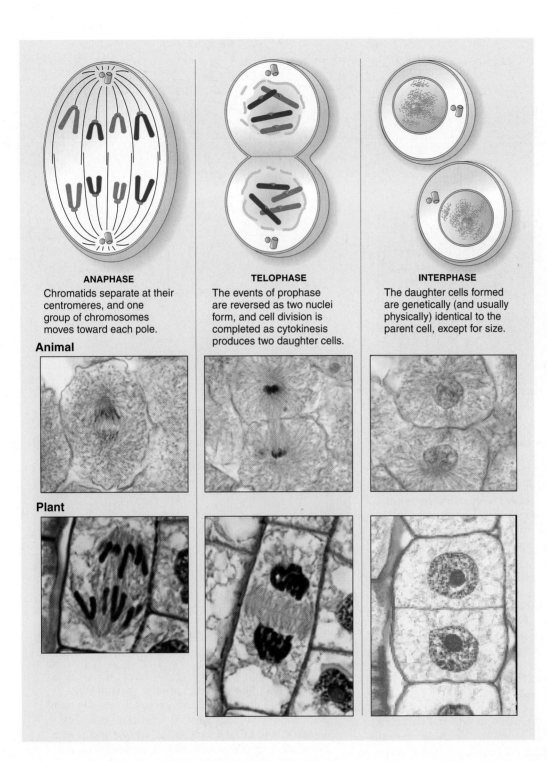

ANAPHASE

Chromatids separate at their centromeres, and one group of chromosomes moves toward each pole.

Animal

Plant

TELOPHASE

The events of prophase are reversed as two nuclei form, and cell division is completed as cytokinesis produces two daughter cells.

INTERPHASE

The daughter cells formed are genetically (and usually physically) identical to the parent cell, except for size.

include the idea that chromosomes are able to move poleward because they are able to remain anchored to the kinetochore microtubules even as tubulin subunits are being removed. There is experimental evidence that multiple types of motor proteins, including forms of kinesin and dynein (see Chapter 4), play a role in this movement.

A second phenomenon also plays a role in chromosome separation. During anaphase the spindle as a whole elongates, at least partly because polar microtubules originating at opposite poles are associated with motors that enable them to slide past one another

at the equator, decreasing the degree to which they are overlapped and thereby "pushing" the poles apart. This mechanism indirectly causes the chromosomes to move apart because they are attached to the poles by kinetochore microtubules.

During telophase two separate nuclei are formed

The final stage of mitosis, **telophase,** is characterized by a return to interphase-like conditions. The chromosomes decondense by uncoiling. A new nuclear envelope forms around each set of

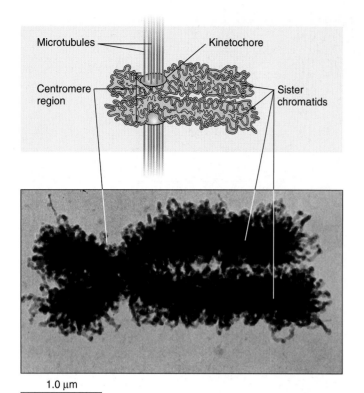

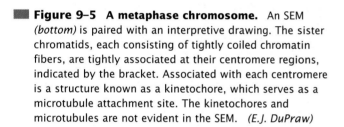

1.0 µm

Figure 9–5   A metaphase chromosome. An SEM *(bottom)* is paired with an interpretive drawing. The sister chromatids, each consisting of tightly coiled chromatin fibers, are tightly associated at their centromere regions, indicated by the bracket. Associated with each centromere is a structure known as a kinetochore, which serves as a microtubule attachment site. The kinetochores and microtubules are not evident in the SEM. *(E.J. DuPraw)*

chromosomes, made at least in part from small vesicles and other components derived from the old nuclear envelope. The spindle microtubules disappear, and the nucleoli reorganize.

Cytokinesis is the formation of two separate daughter cells

Cytokinesis, the division of the cytoplasm to yield two daughter cells, usually overlaps mitosis, generally beginning during telophase. Cytokinesis of an animal cell begins as a ring of actin microfilaments associated with the plasma membrane encircles the cell in the equatorial region, at right angles to the spindle (Fig. 9–8a). The ring contracts, producing a **cleavage furrow** that gradually deepens and separates the cytoplasm into two daughter cells, each with a complete nucleus.

In plant cells, cytokinesis occurs by the formation of a **cell plate** (Fig. 9–8b), a partition constructed in the equatorial region of the spindle and growing laterally toward the cell wall. The cell plate forms as a line of vesicles that originate in the Golgi complex (see Chapter 4). The vesicles contain materials to construct both a primary cell wall for each daughter cell and a middle

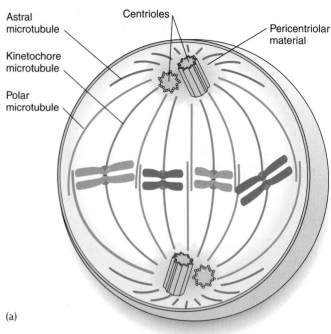

(a)

(b)   10 µm

Figure 9–6   The mitotic spindle. Kinetochore microtubules and polar microtubules are found in both plant and animal cells, whereas most plant cells lack centrioles and astral microtubules. **(a)** One end of each microtubule of this animal cell is associated with one of the poles. Astral microtubules *(green)* radiate in all directions, forming the aster. Kinetochore microtubules *(red)* connect the kinetochores to the poles, and polar microtubules *(blue)* overlap at the midplane. **(b)** Fluorescent-stained LM of animal cell at metaphase with well-defined spindle and asters (chromosomes, *orange;* microtubules, *green*). *(b, CNRI/Phototake, NYC)*

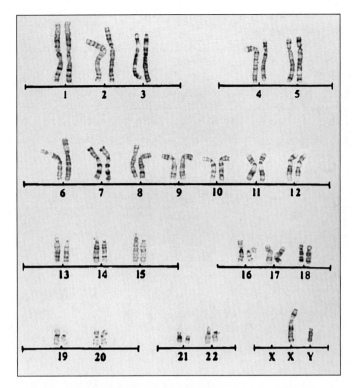

Figure 9–7 A normal human karyotype. Although these are duplicated chromosomes (late prophase), the sister chromatids are not clearly evident because they are closely aligned throughout their lengths. As discussed in Chapter 10, the X and Y chromosomes of this normal male are not strictly homologous; normal females have two X chromosomes and no Y chromosome. The process of karyotyping is discussed in Chapter 15. *(Courtesy of Dr. Leonard Sciorra)*

lamella that will cement the primary cell walls together. The vesicle membranes fuse to become the plasma membrane of each daughter cell.

Mitosis typically produces two cells genetically identical to the parent cell

The remarkable regularity of the process of cell division ensures that each of the daughter nuclei receives exactly the same number and kinds of chromosomes that the parent cell had. Thus, with a few exceptions, every cell of a multicellular organism has exactly the same genetic makeup. If a cell receives more or fewer than the characteristic number of chromosomes through some malfunction of the cell division process, the resulting cell may show marked abnormalities and is often unable to survive.

Most cytoplasmic organelles are distributed randomly to the daughter cells

Mitosis provides for the orderly distribution of chromosomes (and of centrioles, if present), but what about the various cyto-

plasmic organelles? For example, all eukaryotic cells, including plant cells, require mitochondria. Likewise, photosynthetic plant cells cannot carry out photosynthesis without chloroplasts. These organelles contain their own DNA and appear to form by the division of previously existing mitochondria or plastids or their precursors. This nonmitotic division process is similar to prokaryotic cell division (see Chapter 23) and generally occurs during interphase, not when the cell divides. Because many copies of each organelle are present in each cell, organelles are apportioned more or less equally between the daughter cells at cytokinesis.

The cell cycle is controlled by an internal genetic program interacting with external signals

When conditions are optimal, some prokaryotic cells can divide every 20 minutes. The generation times of eukaryotic cells are generally much longer, although the frequency of cell division varies widely among different species and among different tissues of the same species. Some cells in the central nervous system usually cease dividing after the first few months of life, whereas blood-forming cells, digestive tract cells, and skin cells divide frequently throughout the life of the organism. Under optimal conditions of nutrition, temperature, and pH, the eukaryotic cell cycle length is constant for any cell type. Under less favorable conditions, however, the generation time may be longer.

According to a considerable body of evidence that has accumulated in recent years, certain fundamental mechanisms of genetic control of the cell cycle are common to all eukaryotes. The cell cycle is controlled by regulatory molecules that trigger a specific sequence of events. Because a failure to carefully control cell division can have disastrous consequences, checkpoints are built into the program to ensure that all the events of a particular stage have been completed before the next stage begins. Among the key regulatory molecules are **protein kinases,** enzymes that activate or inactivate other proteins by adding phosphate groups (phosphorylation). The particular protein kinases involved in controlling the cell cycle are called **cyclin-dependent protein kinases (Cdk)** because they are only active when they form complexes with regulatory proteins called **cyclins.** The cyclins are so named because their levels fluctuate predictably during the cell cycle (i.e., they "cycle").

When a specific cyclin-dependent protein kinase forms a complex with a specific cyclin, it actively phosphorylates certain cellular proteins. Some of these proteins, including certain enzymes, become activated when they are phosphorylated, and others become inactivated. As some enzymes are activated and others are inactivated by phosphorylation, the activities of the cell change. First, G_1 Cdk complexes prepare the cell for the S phase, and then S-phase Cdk complexes allow the cell to enter the S phase. Mitotic Cdk complexes are responsible for causing chromosome condensation, nuclear envelope breakdown, and mitotic spindle formation. Mitotic Cdk complexes also activate the anaphase-promoting complex (APC) at the end of metaphase. APC initiates anaphase by allowing degradation of the proteins

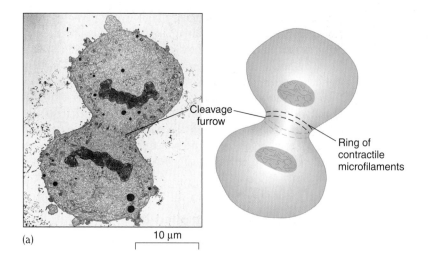

(a)

10 μm

Figure 9–8 Cytokinesis in plant and animal cells. The nuclei in both TEMs are at the telophase stage. Each is accompanied by an interpretive drawing that shows three-dimensional relationships. **(a)** This TEM shows a cleavage furrow forming in the equatorial region of a cultured animal cell undergoing cytokinesis. **(b)** Cytokinesis is occurring by cell plate formation in this TEM of a maple leaf cell, *Acer saccharinum*. *(a, T.E. Schroeder, University of Washington/Biological Photo Service; b, E.H. Newcomb and B.A. Palevitz, University of Wisconsin/Biological Photo Service)*

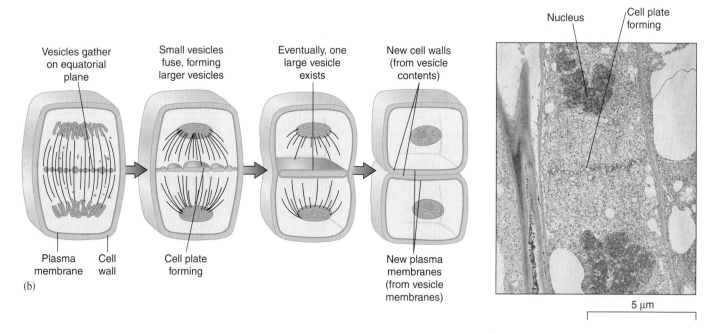

(b)

5 μm

that hold the sister chromatids together. Figure 9–9 illustrates the activities of an important type of mitotic Cdk complex, known as mitosis-promoting factor (MPF). Although not all of the details are understood, these systems of regulating the cell cycle have been highly conserved during the evolution of eukaryotes; they are found in organisms as diverse as yeast (a unicellular fungus), clams, frogs, plants, and humans.

Certain drugs can stop the cell cycle at a specific checkpoint. Some of these prevent DNA synthesis, whereas others inhibit the synthesis of proteins that control the cycle or inhibit the synthesis of structural proteins that contribute to the mitotic spindle. Because one of the distinguishing features of most cancer cells is their high rate of cell division relative to most normal body cells, they can be most affected by these drugs. Many of the side effects of certain anticancer drugs (e.g., nausea, hair loss) are due to the drugs' effects on rapidly dividing normal cells in the digestive system and hair follicles.

Colchicine, a drug used to block cell division in eukaryotic cells, binds with unpolymerized tubulin subunits, preventing them from being added to the spindle microtubules. Under these conditions, the rate of microtubule breakdown far exceeds the rate of microtubule assembly, resulting in the disappearance of the spindle. Although the sister chromatids eventually become detached from one another and each becomes a chromosome, they cannot move to the poles in the absence of the spindle. As a result, a cell may end up with extra sets of chromosomes (a condition known as **polyploidy,** which is discussed in the next section).

In plant cells, certain hormones are known to stimulate mitosis. These include the **cytokinins,** a group of plant hormones that promote mitosis both in normal growth and in wound healing (see Chapter 36). Similarly, hormones such as certain steroid hormones can act as growth stimulators in animals (see Chapter 47).

Protein **growth factors,** which are active at extremely low concentrations, stimulate mitosis in certain animal cells by causing G_1 Cdk complexes to be formed. Of the approximately 50 protein growth factors known, some act only on specific cell classes,

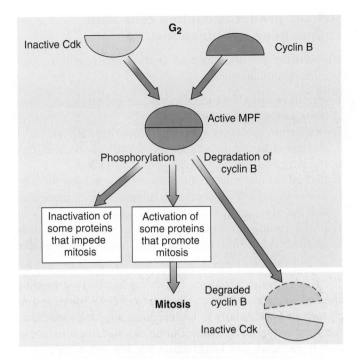

Figure 9–9 Genetic control of the cell cycle. In this example, mitosis-promoting factor (MPF) is required for the cell to pass through the G₂ checkpoint, and make the transition to mitosis. Active MPF is produced when an inactive cyclin-dependent protein kinase (Cdk) becomes complexed with cyclin B. MPF then phosphorylates many proteins, thereby activating those needed for mitosis and inactivating those that would impede mitosis. Later in mitosis, MPF becomes inactive as cyclin B is degraded. These events are repeated when cyclin B levels rise again in G₂ of the next cell cycle.

while others work over a broader range. For example, the effects of the growth factor erythropoietin are limited to cells that will develop into red blood cells, whereas epidermal growth factor stimulates many cell types to divide. Many types of cancer cells divide even in the absence of growth factors.

■ SEXUAL REPRODUCTION REQUIRES A MECHANISM TO REDUCE THE CHROMOSOME NUMBER

Although the details of the reproductive process vary greatly among different kinds of eukaryotes, we can distinguish two basic types of reproduction: asexual and sexual. In **asexual reproduction** a single parent usually splits, buds, or fragments to produce two or more individuals (see Figs. 1–5, 28-8*a*, and 35–19). In most forms of eukaryotic asexual reproduction, all the cells are the result of mitotic divisions, so their genes and inherited traits are like those of the parent. Such a group of genetically identical organisms is termed a **clone.** Asexual reproduction permits organisms well adapted to their environment to produce new generations of similarly adapted organisms. It can occur

rapidly and efficiently, at least in part because time and energy do not need to be expended in finding a mate.

In contrast, **sexual reproduction** involves the union of two specialized sex cells, or **gametes,** to form a single cell called a **zygote.** Usually the gametes are contributed by two different parents, but in some cases a single parent furnishes both gametes. In the case of animals and plants, the egg and sperm cells are the gametes, and the fertilized egg is the zygote. Sexual reproduction results in genetic variation among the offspring. Because they are not genetically identical to their parents or to each other, some may be able to survive environmental changes or other stresses better than either parent. However, some others, with a different combination of traits, may be less likely to survive than their parents.

There is a potential for problems in eukaryotic sexual reproduction: If each gamete has the same number of chromosomes as did the parental cell that produced it, then the zygote would be expected to have twice as many chromosomes. This doubling would occur generation after generation. How do organisms avoid producing zygotes with ever-increasing chromosome numbers? To answer this question, we need more information about the types of chromosomes found in cells.

Each chromosome found in a somatic (body) cell of a higher plant or animal normally has a partner chromosome. The two partners, known as **homologous chromosomes,** are similar in size, shape, and the position of their centromeres. When stained by special techniques, the members of a pair generally share a characteristic pattern of bands. In most species, chromosomes vary enough in their morphological features that cytologists can distinguish the different homologous pairs and match up the partners. The 46 chromosomes in human cells constitute 23 different homologous pairs (see Fig. 9–7). The most important feature of homologous chromosomes is that they carry very similar, but not necessarily identical, genetic information. For example, members of a pair of homologous chromosomes might each carry a gene that specifies hemoglobin structure; however, one member might have the information for the normal hemoglobin β chain (see Fig. 3–23*a*), whereas the other might specify the abnormal form of hemoglobin associated with sickle cell anemia (see Chapter 15). Homologous chromosomes can therefore be contrasted with the two members of a pair of sister chromatids, which are precisely identical to each other.

A *set* of chromosomes has one of each kind of chromosome; in other words, it contains one member of each homologous pair. If a cell or nucleus contains two sets of chromosomes, it is said to have a **diploid** chromosome number. If it has only a single set of chromosomes, it has the **haploid** number. In humans the diploid chromosome number is 46 and the haploid number is 23. When a sperm and egg fuse at fertilization, each gamete is haploid, contributing one set of chromosomes; the diploid number is thereby restored in the fertilized egg (zygote). When the zygote divides by mitosis to form the first two cells of the embryo, each daughter cell receives the diploid number of chromosomes, and this is repeated in subsequent mitotic divisions. Thus, most human body cells are diploid.

If a cell or an individual has three or more sets of chromosomes, we say that it is **polyploid.** Polyploidy is relatively rare among animals but quite common among plants (see Chapter 19). In fact, polyploidy has been an important factor in plant evolution. As many as 80% of all flowering plants are polyploid. Polyploid plants are often larger and hardier than diploid members of the same group. Many commercially important plants, such as wheat and cotton, are polyploid.

The abbreviation for the chromosome number found in the gametes of a particular species is *n,* and the zygotic chromosome number is given as **2n.** If the organism is not polyploid, the haploid chromosome number is equal to n and the diploid number is equal to $2n$. For example, in humans, $n = 23$ and $2n = 46$. For simplicity, in the rest of this chapter we assume that the organisms used as examples are not polyploid. We therefore use the designations diploid and $2n$, and haploid and n, interchangeably, although these terms are not strictly synonymous.

■ DIPLOID CELLS UNDERGO MEIOSIS TO FORM HAPLOID CELLS

We have examined the process of mitosis, which ensures that each daughter cell receives exactly the same number and kinds of chromosomes that the parent cell had. A diploid cell that undergoes mitosis produces two diploid cells; similarly, a mitotic haploid cell produces two haploid cells. A division resulting in a reduction in chromosome number is called **meiosis.** The term *meiosis* means "to make smaller," referring to the fact that the chromosome number is reduced by one-half. In meiosis a diploid cell undergoes two cell divisions, potentially yielding four haploid cells.

Meiosis produces haploid cells with unique gene combinations

The events of meiosis are similar to the events of mitosis, with four important differences:

1. Meiosis involves two successive nuclear and cytoplasmic divisions, producing up to four cells.
2. Despite two successive nuclear divisions, the DNA and other chromosomal components are duplicated only once, during the interphase preceding the first meiotic division.
3. Each of the four cells produced by meiosis contains the haploid chromosome number, that is, only one set containing only one representative of each homologous pair.
4. During meiosis, the genetic information from both parents is shuffled, so each resulting haploid cell has a virtually unique combination of genes.

Meiosis typically consists of two nuclear and cytoplasmic divisions, designated the *first* and *second meiotic divisions,* or simply **meiosis I** and **meiosis II.** Each includes prophase, metaphase, anaphase, and telophase stages. During meiosis I, the members of each homologous pair of chromosomes first join together and then separate and move into different nuclei. In meiosis II, the sister chromatids that make up each chromosome separate and are distributed to two different nuclei. The following discussion describes meiosis in an animal with a diploid chromosome number of four. Refer to Figures 9–10 and 9–11 as you read.

Prophase I includes synapsis and crossing-over

As in mitosis, the chromosomes are duplicated during the S phase of interphase, before meiosis actually begins. Each duplicated chromosome consists of two chromatids. During *prophase*

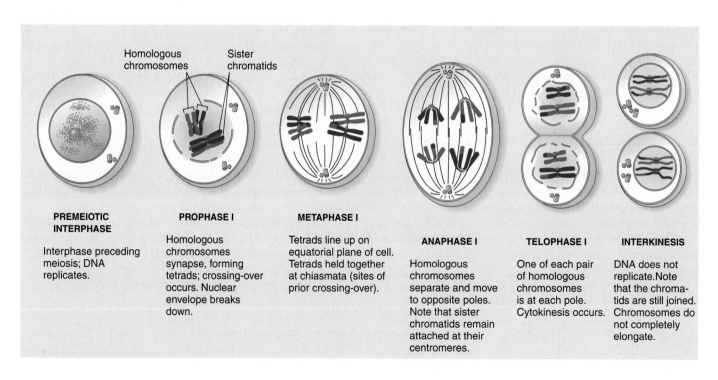

PREMEIOTIC INTERPHASE

Interphase preceding meiosis; DNA replicates.

PROPHASE I

Homologous chromosomes synapse, forming tetrads; crossing-over occurs. Nuclear envelope breaks down.

METAPHASE I

Tetrads line up on equatorial plane of cell. Tetrads held together at chiasmata (sites of prior crossing-over).

ANAPHASE I

Homologous chromosomes separate and move to opposite poles. Note that sister chromatids remain attached at their centromeres.

TELOPHASE I

One of each pair of homologous chromosomes is at each pole. Cytokinesis occurs.

INTERKINESIS

DNA does not replicate. Note that the chromatids are still joined. Chromosomes do not completely elongate.

I, while the chromatids are still elongated and thin, the homologous chromosomes come to lie lengthwise side by side. This process is called **synapsis,** which means "fastening together." In our example, because the diploid number is four, there are two homologous pairs.

It is customary when discussing higher organisms to refer to one member of each homologous pair as a **maternal homologue** because it was originally inherited from the female parent, and to the other as a **paternal homologue** because it was contributed by the male parent during the formation of the zygote. Because each chromosome was duplicated during the premeiotic interphase and now consists of two chromatids, synapsis results in the association of *four* chromatids. The resulting complex is known as a **bivalent** or a **tetrad.** The term bivalent, in which the prefix *bi-* refers to the two homologous chromosomes, is commonly used by cytogeneticists (scientists who study inheritance at the cellular level, particularly through the analysis of chromosomes). The term tetrad (*tetra* means "four") is preferred by some geneticists interested in following the fates of the four chromatids. We will use tetrad in further discussions.

The number of tetrads per prophase I cell is equal to the haploid chromosome number. In our example of an animal cell with a diploid number of four, there are two tetrads; in a human cell at prophase I, there are 23 tetrads (and a total of 92 chromatids).

Homologous chromosomes become closely associated during synapsis. Electron microscopic observations reveal that a characteristic structure, known as the **synaptonemal complex,** forms between the synapsed homologues (Fig. 9–12). This structure holds the synapsed homologues together and is thought to play a role in **crossing-over,** a process in which genetic material is exchanged between homologous (nonsister) chromatids. In crossing-over, enzymes break homologous chromatids and then join them to produce new combinations of genes. The resulting **genetic recombination** greatly enhances the amount of genetic variation among sexually produced offspring. This process is discussed in more detail in Chapter 10.

In many species, prophase I is a lengthy phase during which the cell grows and synthesizes nutrients. This is especially true during the formation of some egg cells because materials need to be made for the benefit of the future embryo. In many types of meiotic cells, the chromosomes assume unusual shapes during this phase. For example, lampbrush chromosomes, found in the female meiotic cells (oocytes) of some amphibians, are composed of hundreds of pairs of loops of chromatin projecting from the chromatid axis. They owe their name to their resemblance to the brushes used to clean old-fashioned oil lamps (Fig. 9–13). The loops are sites of intense synthesis of RNA, which is used to direct the synthesis of specific proteins.

In addition to the unique processes of synapsis and crossing-over, events similar to those seen during mitotic prophase also take place. A spindle composed of microtubules and other components forms. If centrioles are present (as in animal cells), one pair moves to each pole, and astral microtubules are formed. The

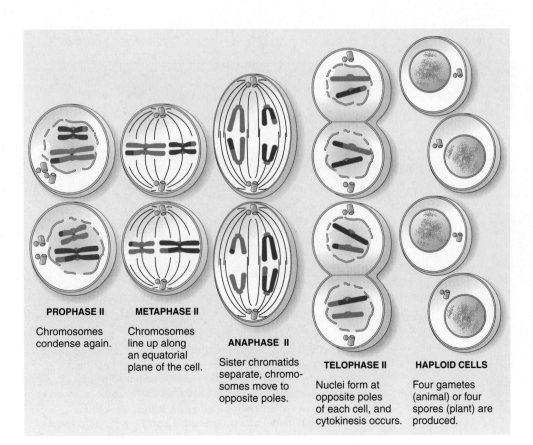

PROPHASE II

Chromosomes condense again.

METAPHASE II

Chromosomes line up along an equatorial plane of the cell.

ANAPHASE II

Sister chromatids separate, chromosomes move to opposite poles.

TELOPHASE II

Nuclei form at opposite poles of each cell, and cytokinesis occurs.

HAPLOID CELLS

Four gametes (animal) or four spores (plant) are produced.

■ **Figure 9–10 Meiosis.**
Two nuclear divisions, meiosis I and meiosis II, are required. In this illustration, the process begins with a cell that has a diploid chromosome number of four and ends with the formation of four haploid cells with two chromosomes each. Centrioles are shown because the example is of an animal cell. The maternal chromosomes are shown in red; the paternal chromosomes are blue.

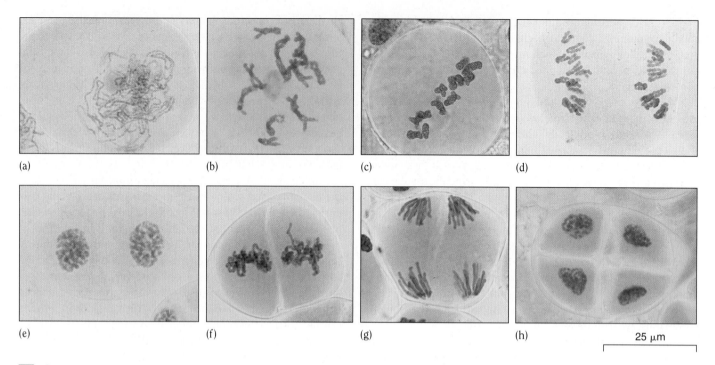

Figure 9–11 Meiosis in the trumpet lily, *Lilium longiflorum*. The chromosomes shown in these LM views have been stained and the cells flattened on microscope slides. (a) Mid-prophase I. (b) Late prophase I. (c) Metaphase I. (d) Anaphase I. (e) Prophase II. (f) Metaphase II. (g) Anaphase II. (h) Four daughter cells. *(Clare Hasenkampf/Biological Photo Service)*

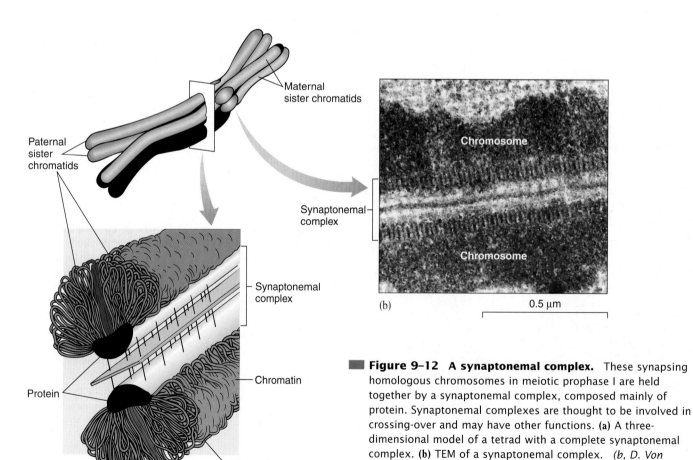

Figure 9–12 A synaptonemal complex. These synapsing homologous chromosomes in meiotic prophase I are held together by a synaptonemal complex, composed mainly of protein. Synaptonemal complexes are thought to be involved in crossing-over and may have other functions. (a) A three-dimensional model of a tetrad with a complete synaptonemal complex. (b) TEM of a synaptonemal complex. *(b, D. Von Wettstein, Proceedings of the National Academy of Science, Vol. 68, 1971, pp. 851–855)*

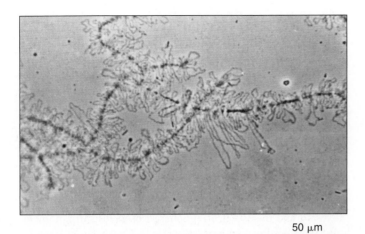

Figure 9–13 Lampbrush chromosomes. This LM shows parts of several tetrads from a female meiotic cell (oocyte) of a newt, *Triturus viridescens*. The loops, composed of chromatin, are sites of intense RNA synthesis. *(Dennis Gould)*

nuclear envelope disappears in late prophase I, and in cells with large and distinct chromosomes the structure of the tetrads can be seen clearly with the microscope (Fig. 9–14). The sister chromatids remain closely aligned along their lengths. However, the centromeres (and kinetochores) of the homologous chromosomes become separated from one another. In late prophase I, the homologous chromosomes are held together only at specialized regions, termed **chiasmata** (sing., *chiasma*). Each chiasma originates at a site of crossing-over, that is, a site at which homologous chromatids were previously broken by enzymes, exchanged genetic material, and rejoined, producing an X-shaped configuration. The genetic consequences of crossing-over will be discussed in Chapter 10.

During meiosis I homologous chromosomes separate

Prophase I ends when the tetrads become aligned on the equatorial plane; the cell is now said to be at **metaphase I.** Both sister kinetochores of one chromosome are attached by spindle fibers to the same pole, and both kinetochores of the homologous chromosome are attached to the opposite pole. (By contrast, in mitosis, sister kinetochores are attached to opposite poles.) During **anaphase I,** the paired homologous chromosomes separate, or disjoin, and move toward opposite poles. Each pole receives a random mixture of maternal and paternal chromosomes, but only one member of each homologous pair is present at each pole. The sister chromatids are united at their centromere regions. Again, this differs from mitotic anaphase, in which the sister chromatids pass to opposite poles.

During **telophase I,** the chromatids generally decondense somewhat, the nuclear envelope may reorganize, and cytokinesis may take place. Each telophase I nucleus contains the haploid number of chromosomes, but each chromosome is a duplicated chromosome (i.e., it consists of a pair of chromatids). In our example, there are two duplicated chromosomes at each pole, for a total of four chromatids; in humans, there are 23 duplicated chromosomes (46 chromatids) at each pole.

An interphase-like stage usually follows. Because it is not a true interphase (i.e., there is no S phase), it is given the name **interkinesis.** Interkinesis is very brief in most organisms and absent in some.

Chromatids separate in meiosis II

Because the chromosomes usually remain partially condensed between divisions, the prophase of the second meiotic division is brief. **Prophase II** is similar to mitotic prophase in many respects. There is no pairing of homologous chromosomes (indeed, only one member of each pair is present in each nucleus) and no crossing-over.

During **metaphase II,** the chromosomes line up on the equatorial planes of their cells. The first and second metaphases can be easily distinguished in diagrams; at metaphase I the chromatids are arranged in bundles of four (tetrads), and at metaphase II they are in groups of two (as in mitotic metaphase). This is not always so obvious in living cells.

During **anaphase II** the chromatids, attached to spindle fibers at their kinetochores, separate and move to opposite poles,

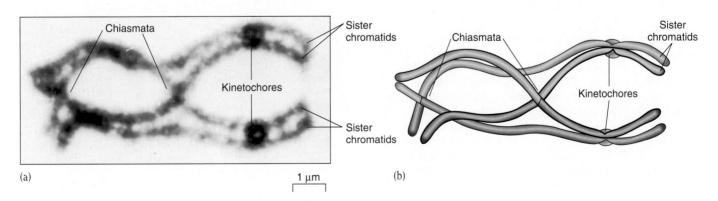

(a)   (b)

Figure 9–14 A meiotic tetrad. **(a)** This LM is of a tetrad during late prophase I of a male meiotic cell (spermatocyte) from a salamander. **(b)** Interpretive drawing indicating the structure of the tetrad. The paternal chromatids are purple, and the maternal chromatids are pink. *(a, Courtesy of J. Kezer)*

just as they would at mitotic anaphase. As in mitosis, each former chromatid is now referred to as a chromosome. Thus, at **telophase II** there is one representative for each homologous pair at each pole. Each is an unduplicated (i.e., single) chromosome. Nuclear envelopes then re-form, the chromosomes gradually elongate to form chromatin threads, and cytokinesis occurs.

The two successive divisions yield four haploid nuclei, each containing *one* of each kind of chromosome. Each resulting haploid cell has a different combination of genes. This genetic variation has two sources: (1) During meiosis the maternal and paternal chromosomes are "shuffled" so that one member of each pair becomes randomly distributed to the poles at anaphase I; (2) DNA segments are exchanged between maternal and paternal homologues during crossing-over.

The important genetic consequences of these events are discussed in more detail in Chapter 10.

■ THE EVENTS OF MITOSIS AND MEIOSIS LEAD TO CONTRASTING OUTCOMES

Although mitosis and meiosis share many similar features, specific distinctions between these processes result in the formation of different types of cells (Fig. 9–15).

Mitosis is a single division in which *sister chromatids* separate from each other. These are distributed to the two daughter cells, which are genetically identical to each other and to the original cell. Homologous chromosomes do not associate physically at any time in mitosis.

In meiosis, a diploid cell undergoes two successive divisions, meiosis I and meiosis II. In prophase I of meiosis, the homologous chromosomes undergo synapsis to form tetrads. If we ignore crossing-over, we can say that *homologous chromosomes* separate during meiosis I, and *sister chromatids* separate during

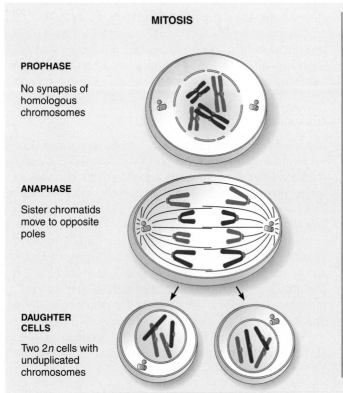

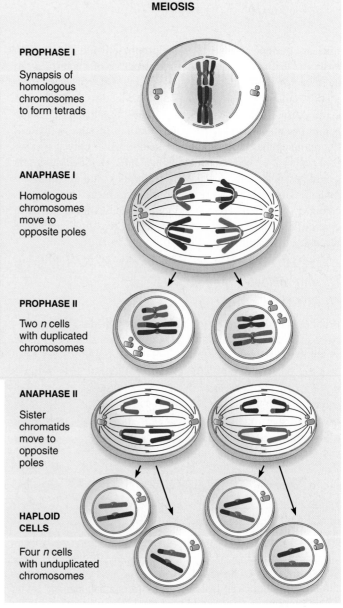

■ Figure 9–15 Mitosis and meiosis. The diagram compares the events and outcomes of mitosis and meiosis, in each case beginning with a diploid cell with four chromosomes (i.e., two pairs of homologous chromosomes). Because the chromosomes were duplicated in the previous interphase, each chromosome consists of two sister chromatids. The chromosomes derived from one parent are shown in blue, and those from the other parent are red. The homologous partner chromosomes can be recognized because they are similar in size and shape. Chiasmata are not shown and some of the stages have been omitted for simplicity.

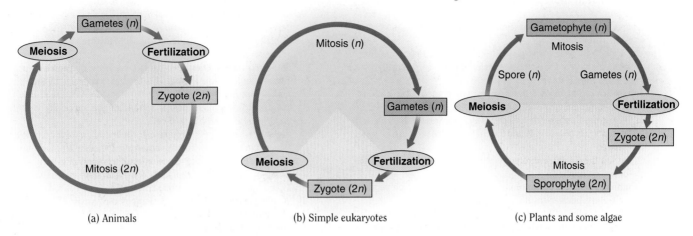

(a) Animals   (b) Simple eukaryotes   (c) Plants and some algae

Figure 9–16 Representative life cycles.

meiosis II. It is also correct to say that homologous centromeres (or kinetochores) separate during meiosis I, and sister centromeres (or kinetochores) disjoin during meiosis II. Meiosis ends with the formation of four, genetically different, haploid daughter cells. The fates of these cells depend on the type of life cycle; in animals they differentiate as gametes, whereas in plants they become spores.

THE POSITION OF MEIOSIS IN THE LIFE CYCLE VARIES AMONG SPECIES

Because sexual reproduction is characterized by the fusion of two haploid sex cells to form a diploid zygote, it follows that, in a sexual life cycle, meiosis must occur before gametes can be produced.

In animals and a few other organisms, meiosis leads directly to gamete formation (Fig. 9–16*a*). The **somatic** (body) cells of an individual organism multiply by mitosis and are diploid; the only haploid cells produced are the gametes. These are formed when certain cells, known as **germ line** cells, undergo meiosis. The formation of gametes is known as **gametogenesis.** Male gametogenesis, termed **spermatogenesis,** results in the formation of four haploid sperm cells for each cell that enters meiosis.

In contrast, female gametogenesis, termed **oogenesis,** results in the formation of a single egg cell, or **ovum,** for every cell that enters meiosis. This is accomplished by a process that apportions virtually all of the cytoplasm to only one of the two nuclei at each of the meiotic divisions. At the end of the first meiotic division, one nucleus is retained and the other, called the first **polar body,** is excluded from the cell and ultimately degenerates. Similarly, at the end of the second division, one nucleus

becomes the second polar body and the other nucleus survives. In this way, one haploid nucleus becomes the recipient of most of the accumulated cytoplasm and nutrients from the original meiotic cell. (See Fig. 48–13 for a more detailed description.)

Although meiosis occurs at some point in a sexual life cycle, it does not always *immediately* precede gamete formation. Many simple eukaryotes (including some fungi and algae) remain haploid (their cells dividing mitotically) throughout most of their lives, with individuals being unicellular or multicellular. Two haploid gametes (produced by mitosis) fuse to produce a diploid zygote that undergoes meiosis to restore the haploid state (Fig. 9–16*b*). Examples of these types of life cycles can be found in Figures 24–15, 24–21, and 25–7.

The most complex life cycles are displayed by plants and some algae (Fig. 9–16*c*). These life cycles, characterized by an **alternation of generations,** consist of a multicellular diploid stage, termed the **sporophyte generation,** and a multicellular haploid stage, termed the **gametophyte generation.** Diploid sporophyte cells undergo meiosis to form haploid spores, each of which then divides mitotically to produce a multicellular haploid gametophyte. Gametophytes produce gametes by mitosis. The female and male gametes (eggs and sperm cells) then fuse to form a diploid zygote that divides mitotically to produce a multicellular, diploid sporophyte.

In higher plants, including flowering plants, the diploid sporophyte—which includes the roots, stems, and leaves of the plant body—is the dominant form. The gametophytes are small and inconspicuous. For example, a microscopic pollen grain contains a haploid male gametophyte that forms haploid sperm by mitosis. More detailed descriptions of alternation of generations can be found in Chapters 26 and 27.

SUMMARY WITH KEY TERMS

I. In the production of a new generation, cells transfer genetic information from parent to offspring.

II. **Genes** are made of DNA, which in eukaryotes is complexed with protein to form the **chromatin** fibers that make up **chromosomes.**

A. A **diploid** organism of a given species has a characteristic number of chromosome pairs per cell.

B. The two members of each chromosome pair, called **homologous chromosomes,** are similar in length, shape, and other structural features and carry genes affecting the same kinds of attributes of the organism.

    C. A **haploid** cell contains only one member of each homologous chromosome pair.

III. The eukaryotic **cell cycle** is the period from the beginning of one division to the beginning of the next; the time required to complete one cycle is the **generation time.**

    A. **Interphase** can be divided into the first gap phase (G_1), the chromosomal synthesis phase (S), and the second gap phase (G_2).

      1. During the **G_1 phase,** the cell grows and prepares for the S phase.

      2. During the **S phase,** DNA and the chromosomal proteins are synthesized.

      3. During the **G_2 phase,** protein synthesis increases in preparation for cell division.

    B. In **mitosis,** identical chromosomes are distributed to each pole of the cell, and a nuclear envelope forms around each set.

      1. During **prophase,** duplicated chromosomes, each composed of a pair of **sister chromatids** associated with each other in the vicinity of their **centromeres,** become visible with the microscope. The nucleolus disappears, the nuclear envelope breaks down, and the **mitotic spindle** begins to form.

      2. During **metaphase,** the chromosomes are aligned on the equatorial plane of the cell; the mitotic spindle is complete and the **kinetochores** of the sister chromatids are attached by microtubules to opposite poles of the cell.

      3. During **anaphase,** the sister chromatids become separated and move to opposite poles. Each former chromatid is now referred to as a chromosome.

      4. During **telophase,** a nuclear envelope re-forms around each set of chromosomes, nucleoli become apparent, the chromosomes uncoil, and the spindle disappears.

    C. During **cytokinesis,** which generally begins in telophase and therefore overlaps mitosis, the cytoplasm divides to form two individual cells.

      1. In animal cells, a ring of microfilaments contracts, producing a **cleavage furrow** that divides the cytoplasm.

      2. In plant cells, the **cell plate** provides materials for new plasma membranes and cell walls.

IV. There are two major forms of reproduction: asexual and sexual.

    A. Offspring produced by **asexual reproduction** usually have hereditary traits identical to those of the single parent. These offspring constitute a **clone.** Usually all the cells involved are produced by mitosis.

    B. In **sexual reproduction,** two haploid sex cells, or **gametes,** fuse to form a single diploid **zygote.** This process is balanced by **meiosis** at some point in the life cycle.

V. A diploid cell undergoing meiosis completes two successive cell divisions to give rise to four haploid cells.

    A. **Meiosis I** begins with **prophase I;** the members of a homologous pair of chromosomes become physically joined by a process known as **synapsis** and undergo **crossing-over,** a process of **genetic recombination** during which segments of DNA strands are exchanged between homologous (nonsister) chromatids.

    B. At **metaphase I, tetrads,** each composed of a pair of homologous chromosomes held together by one or more **chiasmata,** line up on the equatorial plane.

    C. The members of each pair of homologous chromosomes separate during meiotic **anaphase I** and are distributed to different nuclei. Each nucleus contains the haploid number of chromosomes; each chromosome consists of two chromatids.

    D. During **meiosis II,** the two chromatids of each chromosome separate and one is distributed to each daughter cell. Each former chromatid is now referred to as a chromosome.

VI. The position of meiosis in the life cycle varies.

    A. The **somatic** (body) cells of animals are diploid; the only haploid cells are the gametes (produced by **gametogenesis,** which in animals includes meiosis).

    B. Simple eukaryotes may be regularly haploid; the only diploid stage is the zygote, which undergoes meiosis to restore the haploid state.

    C. Plants and some algae have **alternation of generations.** A multicellular diploid **sporophyte** forms haploid spores by meiosis. Each spore divides mitotically to form a multicellular haploid **gametophyte,** which produces gametes by mitosis. Two haploid gametes then fuse to form a diploid zygote, which divides mitotically to produce a new diploid sporophyte.

POST·TEST

1. Chromatin fibers include (a) DNA and structural polysaccharides (b) RNA and phospholipids (c) protein and carbohydrate (d) DNA and protein (e) triacylglycerol and steroids

2. The term *S phase* refers to (a) DNA synthesis during interphase (b) synthesis of chromosomal proteins during prophase (c) active RNA synthesis in lampbrush chromosomes (d) synapsis of homologous chromosomes (e) fusion of gametes in sexual reproduction

3. At which of the following stages do human skin cell nuclei have the same DNA content? (a) early mitotic prophase; mitotic telophase (b) G_1; G_2 (c) G_1; early mitotic prophase (d) G_1; mitotic telophase (e) G_2; mitotic telophase

4. In a cell at _____, each chromosome consists of a pair of attached chromatids. (a) mitotic prophase (b) meiotic prophase II (c) meiotic prophase I (d) meiotic anaphase I (e) all of the above

5. In an animal cell at mitotic metaphase, you would expect to find (a) two pairs of centrioles located on the metaphase plate (b) a pair of centrioles inside the nucleus (c) a pair of centrioles within each microtubule organizing center (d) a centriole within each centromere (e) no centrioles

6. Cell plate formation usually begins during (a) telophase in a plant cell (b) telophase in an animal cell (c) G_2 in a plant cell (d) G_2 in an animal cell (e) a and b are correct

7. The life cycle of a sexually reproducing organism includes (a) mitosis (b) meiosis (c) fusion of sex cells (d) b and c (e) a, b, and c

8. Which of the following are genetically identical? (a) two cells resulting from meiosis I (b) two cells resulting from meiosis II (c) four cells resulting from meiosis I followed by meiosis II (d) two cells resulting from a mitotic division (e) all of the above

9. You would expect to find a synaptonemal complex in a cell at (a) mitotic prophase (b) meiotic prophase I (c) meiotic prophase II (d) meiotic anaphase I (e) meiotic anaphase II

10. A particular plant species has a diploid chromosome number of 20. A haploid cell of that species at mitotic prophase contains a total of _____ chromosomes and _____ chromatids. (a) 20; 20 (b) 20; 40 (c) 10; 10 (d) 10; 20 (e) none of the above because haploid cells cannot undergo mitosis

11. A diploid nucleus at early mitotic prophase has _____ set(s) of chromosomes; a diploid nucleus at mitotic telophase has _____ set(s) of chromosomes. (a) 1; 1 (b) 1; 2 (c) 2; 2 (d) 2; 1 (e) not enough information has been given

12. A chiasma links a pair of (a) homologous chromosomes at meiotic metaphase II (b) homologous chromosomes at meiotic metaphase I (c) sister chromatids at meiotic metaphase II (d) sister chromatids at mitotic metaphase (e) sister chromatids at meiotic metaphase I

REVIEW QUESTIONS

1. Two species may have the same chromosome number and yet have very different attributes. Explain.
2. Sketch a duplicated chromosome and label the sister chromatids, the centromeres, and the kinetochores. What are the functions of centromeres and of kinetochores?
3. How does the DNA content of the cell change from the beginning of interphase to the end of interphase? Does the number of chromatids change? Does the number of chromosomes change?
4. Are homologous chromosomes present in a diploid cell? Are they present in a haploid cell?
5. How does meiosis differ from mitosis? Are there any points of similarity between these two processes? Explain.
6. What kinds of life cycles include a multicellular haploid stage? Can haploid cells divide by mitosis? By meiosis?
7. Assume that an animal has a diploid chromosome number of ten. (a) How many chromosomes would it have in a typical body cell, such as a skin cell? (b) How many chromosomes would be present in a cell at mitotic prophase? How many chromatids? (c) How many chromosomes would be present in each daughter cell produced by mitosis? Are these duplicated chromosomes? (d) How many tetrads would form in prophase I of meiosis? (e) How many chromosomes would be present in each gamete? Are these duplicated chromosomes?

YOU MAKE THE CONNECTION

1. Decide whether each of the following is an example of sexual or asexual reproduction and state why. (a) A diploid queen honeybee produces haploid eggs by meiosis. Some of these eggs are never fertilized and develop into haploid male honeybees (drones). (b) Haploid male honeybees produce haploid sperm by mitosis. These sperm fertilize haploid eggs produced by the queen, resulting in the development of diploid female worker bees. (c) Seeds develop after a flower has been pollinated with pollen from a different plant of the same species. (d) Seeds develop after a flower has been pollinated with pollen from the same plant. (e) A cutting from a plant develops roots after it has been placed in water. The plant survives and grows after it is transplanted to soil.

RECOMMENDED READINGS

Haber, J.E. "Searching for a Partner." *Science,* Vol. 279, 6 Feb. 1998. A discussion of experimental evidence that the order of events in meiotic prophase is not the same in all organisms.

Lodish, H., A. Berk, S.L. Zipursky, P. Matsudaira, D. Baltimore, and J. Darnell. *Molecular Cell Biology,* 4th ed. W.H. Freeman and Co., New York, 2000. An extensive, detailed, and well-written discussion of cell growth and division, covering the control of cell division, the cell cycle, and the events of mitosis and meiosis.

Nasmyth, K. "Viewpoint: Putting the Cell Cycle in Order." *Science,* Vol. 274, 6 Dec. 1996. This overview introduces a series of articles in the same issue that explore various aspects of the cell cycle.

Nicklas, R.B. "How Cells Get the Right Chromosomes." *Science,* Vol. 275, 31 Jan. 1997. A pioneer in the micromanipulation of chromosomes in living cells reviews the mechanisms that ensure proper distribution of chromosomes in mitosis and meiosis.

Sharp, D.J., G.C. Rogers, and J.M. Scholey. "Microtubule Motors in Mitosis." *Nature,* Vol. 407, 7 Sept. 2000. A review of the many types of motor proteins that interact with microtubules during mitosis.

- Visit our Web site at **http://www.info.brookscole.com/solomonbergmartin** for links to chapter-related resources on the World Wide Web. Additional on-line materials relating to this chapter can also be found on our Web site.

 See chapter activity on BioActive Learner CD for additional help in mastering the chapter's material. Icon location in the chapter's margins shows which topics have tutorials or simulations in the CD.

10

The Basic Principles of Heredity

Gregor Mendel. A monk who bred pea plants, Mendel is depicted here in his monastery garden at Brünn, Austria (now Brüno, Czech Republic). *(The Bettmann Archive)*

LEARNING OBJECTIVES

After you have studied this chapter you should be able to

1. Define and use correctly the terms *allele, locus, genotype, phenotype, dominant, recessive, homozygous, heterozygous,* and *test cross.*
2. Apply Mendel's principles to solve genetics problems involving monohybrid and dihybrid crosses.
3. Apply the product rule and sum rule appropriately when predicting the outcomes of genetic crosses.
4. Solve genetics problems involving incomplete dominance, epistasis, polygenes, multiple alleles, and X-linked inheritance.
5. Explain some of the ways in which genes may interact to affect the phenotype; discuss how it is possible for a single gene to affect many features of the organism simultaneously.
6. Analyze data from a test cross involving alleles of two loci. Show how such data can be used to distinguish between independent assortment and linkage. Relate independent assortment and linkage to specific events in meiosis.
7. Discuss the genetic determination of sex and the role of the Y chromosome in determining male sex in humans; contrast the mechanism of sex determination in humans and other mammals with that in various other animals and some plants; compare dosage compensation of X-linked genes in mammals and fruit flies.
8. Assess the effects of inbreeding versus outbreeding on a population; discuss the genetic basis of hybrid vigor.

Heredity, the transmission of genetic information from parent to offspring, is generally a very regular process that follows predictable patterns. The basic rules of inheritance in eukaryotes were first discovered by Gregor Mendel (1822–1884), a monk who bred pea plants. Mendel was the first scientist to effectively apply quantitative methods to the study of inheritance. He did not merely describe his observations; he planned his experiments carefully, recorded the data, and subjected the results to mathematical analysis. Although his work was unappreciated in his lifetime, it was rediscovered in 1900. His major findings, including those now known as Mendel's principles of segregation and independent assortment, became the foundation of the science of **genetics.**

During the decades following the rediscovery of Mendel's findings, geneticists initially extended Mendel's principles by correlating the transmission of genetic information from generation to generation with the behavior of chromosomes during meiosis. They also refined his methods and, through their studies on a variety of organisms, both verified Mendel's findings and added to a growing list of so-called exceptions to his principles. These include such phenomena as linkage, sex linkage, and polygenic inheritance.

Some geneticists were very active in the development of the emerging science of statistical analysis (which had been in its infancy in Mendel's time), thereby providing scientists with increasingly sophisticated ways to analyze and interpret experimental data. These statistical methods were also essential to the study of the genetic makeup of natural populations of organisms. The results of these investigations on the genetics of populations were combined with Charles Darwin's theory of evolution by natural selection to develop a unified modern theory of evolution, firmly based on genetic principles (see Chapters 17 and 18).

Geneticists study not only the transmission of genes but also the expression of genetic information. As you will see in this and succeeding chapters, our understanding of the relationship between an organism's genes and its characteristics has become increasingly sophisticated as we have learned more about the flow of information in cells.

MENDEL FIRST DEMONSTRATED THE PRINCIPLES OF INHERITANCE

Gregor Mendel was not the first plant breeder; at the time he began his work, **hybrid** plants and animals (offspring of two genetically dissimilar parents) had been known for a long time. When Mendel began his breeding experiments in 1856, two main facts about inheritance were widely recognized: (1) All hybrid plants that are offspring of the same kinds of parents are similar in appearance. (2) When these hybrids are mated to each other they do not breed true; their offspring show a mixture of traits. Some look like their parents, and some have features like their grandparents.

Mendel's genius lay in his ability to recognize a pattern in the way the parental traits reappear in the offspring of hybrids. No one before had categorized and counted the offspring and analyzed these regular patterns over several generations.

Just as geneticists do today, Mendel chose the organism for his experiments very carefully. The garden pea, *Pisum sativum,* had several advantages. Pea plants are easy to grow, and many varieties were available through commercial sources. It is impossible to study inheritance without such genetic **variation.** (If every person in the population had blue eyes, it would be impossible to study the inheritance of eye color.) Another advantage of pea plants is that controlled pollinations are relatively easy to conduct. Pea flowers (Fig. 10–1) have both male and female parts, and are naturally self-pollinated. However, the anthers (the male parts of the flower that produce pollen) can be removed to prevent self-fertilization. Pollen from a different source can then be applied to the stigma (receptive surface of the female part). Pea flowers are easily protected from other sources of pollen because the reproductive structures are completely enclosed by the petals. Although Mendel did not mention having done this, plant hybridizers usually cover the flowers with small bags to provide additional protection from pollinating insects.

Although his original pea seeds were obtained from commercial sources, Mendel did some important preliminary work before he started his actual experiments. For several years he worked to develop genetically pure, or **true-breeding,** lines for various inherited features. Today we use the term **phenotype** to refer to the physical appearance of an organism. A true-breeding line produces only offspring expressing the same phenotype (e.g., round seeds or tall plants), generation after generation. During this time he apparently chose those characteristics of his pea strains that could be studied most easily and probably discarded or ignored others. He probably made the initial observations that would later form the basis of his theories.

Mendel eventually chose strains representing seven clearly contrasting pairs of phenotypes: yellow versus green seeds, round versus wrinkled seeds, green versus yellow pods, tall versus short plants, inflated versus constricted pods, white seed coats versus gray seed coats, and flowers borne on the ends of the stems versus flowers appearing all along the stems. Other plant breeders typically studied hybrids between parents that differed in many, often not clearly defined, ways. Mendel's results were much easier to analyze because he chose easily distinguishable phenotypes and limited the genetic variation studied in each experiment.

Mendel began his experiments by crossing plants from two different true-breeding lines with contrasting phenotypes; these genetically pure individuals constituted the **parental,** or **P, generation.** In every case, the members of the first generation of offspring all looked alike and resembled one of the two parents. For example, when he crossed tall plants with short plants, all the progeny were tall (Fig. 10–2). These offspring were the first filial (*filial* comes from Latin for "sons and daughters") generation, or F_1 **generation.** The second filial generation, or F_2 **generation,** was produced by a cross between F_1 individuals, or by self-pollination of F_1 individuals. Mendel's F_2 generation in this experiment included 787 tall plants and 277 short plants.

Most breeders of Mendel's time thought that inheritance was controlled by fluids that blended together when hybrids were formed. One implication of this idea is that a hybrid should be intermediate between the two parents and, in fact, plant breeders had obtained such hybrids. Although Mendel observed some types of hybrids that were intermediate, he chose for further study those F_1 hybrids in which hereditary factors from one of the parents apparently masked expression of the hereditary

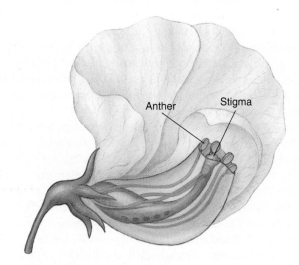

Anther   Stigma

■ Figure 10–1 Reproductive structures of a pea flower. This cutaway view shows the pollen-producing anthers and the stigma, that portion of the female part of the flower that receives the pollen.

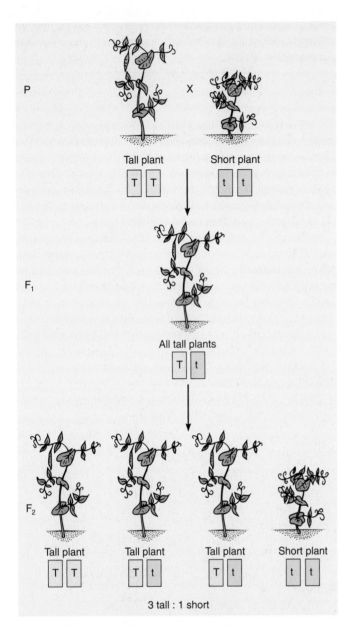

P

Tall plant

T T

X

Short plant

t t

F₁

All tall plants

T t

F₂

Tall plant
T T

Tall plant
T t

Tall plant
T t

Short plant
t t

3 tall : 1 short

■ Figure 10–2 One of Gregor Mendel's many pea plant crosses. Crossing a true-breeding tall pea plant with a true-breeding short pea plant yielded only tall offspring in the F₁ generation. However, when these F₁ individuals self-pollinated, or when two F₁ individuals were crossed, the resulting F₂ generation included tall and short plants in a ratio of about 3:1.

the fact that dominance can occur was not entirely consistent with the notion of blending inheritance.

Mendel's results also argued against blending inheritance in a more compelling way. Once two fluids have blended, it is very difficult to imagine how they can be separated. However, in the example just discussed, in the F₁ generation the hereditary factor(s) that controlled shortness clearly were not lost or blended inseparably with the hereditary factor(s) that controlled tallness because shortness reappeared in the F₂ generation. Mendel was very comfortable with the theoretical side of biology because he was also a student of physics and mathematics. He therefore proposed that each kind of inherited feature of an organism is controlled by two factors that behave like particles and are present in every individual. To Mendel these "hereditary factors" were abstractions, because he knew nothing of chromosomes and DNA. They are essentially what we call **genes** today, so we will use that term in our discussion. Today we know that genes are not particles, but treating them as such allowed Mendel to develop precise mathematical models, testable by experiment, to predict the patterns by which genes are transmitted from generation to generation.

Mendel's experiments led to his discovery and explanation of the major principles of heredity, which we now know as the principles of segregation and independent assortment. We consider the first now and the second later in the chapter.

The principle of segregation states that alleles separate before gametes are formed

Today we use the term **alleles** to refer to the alternative forms of a gene. In the example in Figure 10–2, each F₁-generation tall plant had two different alleles that control plant height: one for tallness (which we designate *T*) and one for shortness (which we designate *t*), but because the tall gene was dominant, these plants were tall. To explain his experimental results, Mendel proposed an idea that we now refer to as the principle of segregation. Using modern terminology, the **principle of segregation** states that, in order for sexual reproduction to occur, the two alleles carried by an individual parent must become separated (segregated). As a result, each sex cell (egg or sperm) formed contains only one allele of each pair. An essential feature of the process is that the alleles remain intact (one does not mix with or eliminate the other); thus, recessive alleles are not lost and so can reappear in the F₂ generation.

In our example, before the F₁ plants formed gametes, the allele for tallness separated (segregated) from the allele for shortness, so that half the gametes contained a *T* allele and the other half a *t* allele. The random process of fertilization led to three possible combinations of alleles in the F₂ offspring: one-fourth with two tallness alleles *(TT)*, one-fourth with two shortness alleles *(tt)*, and one-half with one allele for tallness and one for shortness *(Tt)*. Because both *TT* and *Tt* plants are tall, on average Mendel expected approximately three-fourths (787 of the 1064 plants he obtained) to express the phenotype of the dominant allele (tall) and about one-fourth (277/1064) the phenotype of the recessive allele (short). (The mathematical reasoning behind these predictions will be explained shortly.)

factors from the other parent. These types of hybrids had also been observed by other breeders, but they explained them merely as cases in which the "fluids" from one parent were stronger than those from the other parent. Using modern terminology, the factor expressed in the F₁ generation (tallness in our example) is said to be **dominant;** the one hidden (shortness) is said to be **recessive.** Dominant traits mask recessive ones when both are present in the same individual. Although we know today that dominance is not always observed (exceptions are considered later in this chapter),

Today we know that segregation of alleles is a direct result of the separation of homologous chromosomes during meiosis (Fig. 10–3). (Recall from Chapter 9 that in all sexual life cycles, meiosis must occur at some point prior to gamete formation.) Later, at the time of fertilization, each haploid gamete contributes one chromosome from each homologous pair and therefore one gene for each gene pair (either *T* or *t* in our example). Although gametes and fertilization were known at the time Mendel carried out his research, mitosis and meiosis had not yet been discovered. It is truly remarkable that Mendel was able to formulate his ideas mainly on the basis of mathematical abstractions. Today his principles are much easier to understand because we are able to think about them in concrete terms by relating the transmission of genes to the behavior of chromosomes.

Mendel reported these and other findings (discussed later in this chapter) at a meeting of the Brünn Society for the Study of Natural Science; he published his results in the transactions of that society in 1866. At that time biology was largely a descriptive science, and biologists had little interest in applying quantitative and experimental methods such as Mendel had used. The importance of his results and his interpretations of those results were not appreciated by other biologists of the time, and his findings were neglected for nearly 35 years.

In 1900 Hugo DeVries in Holland, Karl Correns in Germany, and Erich von Tschermak in Austria each rediscovered Mendel's paper and found that it provided explanations for their own research findings. They gave credit to Mendel by naming the basic laws of inheritance after him. By this time biologists had a much greater appreciation of the value of quantitative experimental methods. The details of mitosis, meiosis, and fertilization had been described, and in 1903 W.S. Sutton pointed out the connection between Mendel's segregation of genes and the separation of homologous chromosomes during meiosis. The time was right for wider acceptance and extension of these ideas and their implications.

Alleles occupy corresponding loci on homologous chromosomes

Today we know that each chromatid is made up of one long linear DNA molecule and that each gene is actually a segment of that DNA molecule. We also know that homologous chromosomes are not only similar in size and shape but usually have similar genes located in corresponding positions. The term **locus**[1] (pl., *loci*) was originally coined to designate the location of a particular gene on the chromosome (Fig. 10–4). Of course we are actually referring to a segment of the DNA that has the information required to control some aspect of the structure or function of the organism. One locus may be involved in determining seed color, another seed shape, still another the shape of the pods, and so on. The existence of a particular locus can be inferred (by traditional genetic methods at least) only if at least two allelic variants of that locus, producing contrasting phenotypes (e.g., yellow peas versus green peas) are available for study. In the simplest cases an individual can express one (yellow) or the other (green) but not both.

Thus alleles are genes that govern variations of the same feature (yellow versus green seed color) and occupy corresponding loci on homologous chromosomes. Each allele (variant) of a locus is assigned a single letter (or group of letters) as its symbol. Although more complicated forms of notation are often used by geneticists, it is customary when working simple genetics problems to indicate a dominant allele with a capital letter and a recessive allele with the same letter in lowercase. The choice of the letter is generally determined by the first allelic variant found for that locus. For example, the dominant allele that governs the

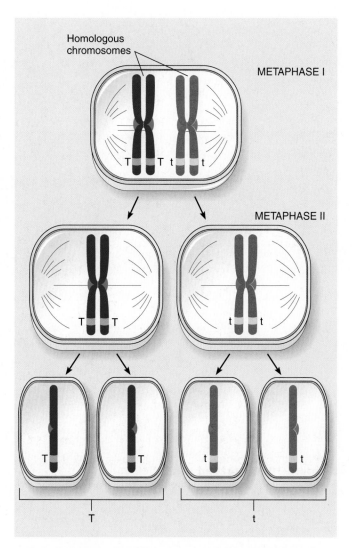

Figure 10–3 The chromosomal basis for segregation. The separation of homologous chromosomes during meiosis results in the segregation of alleles in a heterozygote. Note that half of the gametes will carry *T* and half will carry *t*. See also Figure 9–10.

[1] In mathematics a locus is a dimensionless point; a genetic locus, being a segment of DNA, is obviously not dimensionless!

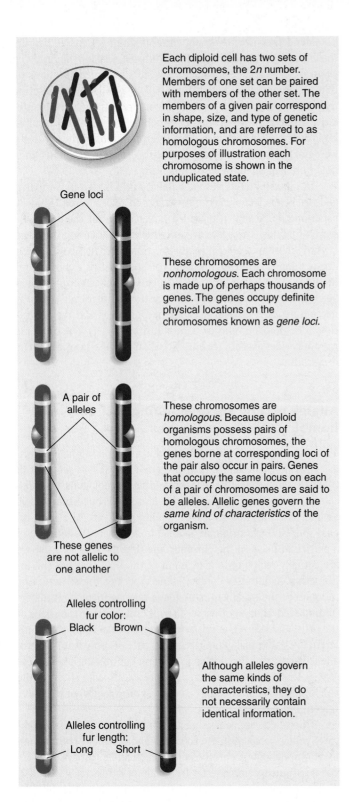

Each diploid cell has two sets of chromosomes, the 2*n* number. Members of one set can be paired with members of the other set. The members of a given pair correspond in shape, size, and type of genetic information, and are referred to as homologous chromosomes. For purposes of illustration each chromosome is shown in the unduplicated state.

Gene loci

These chromosomes are *nonhomologous*. Each chromosome is made up of perhaps thousands of genes. The genes occupy definite physical locations on the chromosomes known as *gene loci*.

A pair of alleles

These chromosomes are *homologous*. Because diploid organisms possess pairs of homologous chromosomes, the genes borne at corresponding loci of the pair also occur in pairs. Genes that occupy the same locus on each of a pair of chromosomes are said to be alleles. Allelic genes govern the *same kind of characteristics* of the organism.

These genes are not allelic to one another

Alleles controlling fur color:
Black   Brown

Although alleles govern the same kinds of characteristics, they do not necessarily contain identical information.

Alleles controlling fur length:
Long   Short

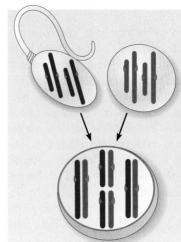

A gamete has one set of chromosomes, the *n* number. It carries *one* chromosome of *each* homologous pair. A given gamete can only possess *one* gene of any particular pair of alleles.

When the gametes fuse, the resulting zygote has homologous pairs of chromosomes. These are shown physically paired for purposes of illustration. One member of each pair is of maternal origin (red) and the other is paternal (blue). Each pair bears allelic genes.

■ **Figure 10–4 Loci and their alleles.**

yellow color of the seed might be designated *Y,* and the recessive allele responsible for the green color would then be designated *y.* Because discovery of the yellow allele made identification of this locus possible, we refer to the locus as the *yellow* locus, although pea seeds are most commonly green.

Remember that the term *locus* designates not only a position on a chromosome but also a type of gene controlling a particular kind of characteristic; thus, *Y* (yellow) and *y* (green) represent a specific pair of alleles of a locus involved in determining seed color in peas. *Although you may initially be uncomfortable* with the fact that geneticists sometimes use the term *gene* to specify a locus and at other times to specify one of the alleles of that locus, the meaning is usually clear from the context.

A MONOHYBRID CROSS INVOLVES INDIVIDUALS WITH DIFFERENT ALLELES OF A GIVEN LOCUS

The basic principles of genetics and the use of genetic terms are best illustrated by examples. In the simplest case, a **monohybrid cross,** the inheritance of two alleles of a single locus is studied. Our first example in this section deals with the expected ratios in the F_2 generation, as did our previous example of Mendel's work on tall and short pea plants.

Heterozygotes carry two different alleles of a locus; homozygotes carry identical alleles

Figure 10–5 illustrates a monohybrid cross featuring a locus that governs coat color in guinea pigs. The female comes from a true breeding line of black guinea pigs. We say that she is **homozygous** for black because the two alleles she carries for this locus are identical. The brown male is also from a true breeding line and is homozygous for brown. What color would you expect the F_1 offspring to be? Dark brown? Spotted? It is impossible to make such a prediction without more information.

In this particular case, the F_1 offspring are black, but they are **heterozygous,** meaning that they carry two different alleles for this locus. The brown allele influences coat color only in a homozygous brown individual; it is referred to as a recessive allele. The black allele influences coat color in both homozygous black and heterozygous individuals; it is a dominant allele. On the basis of this information, we can use standard notation to designate the dominant black allele as *B* and the recessive brown allele as *b*.

During meiosis in the female parent *(BB)*, the two *B* alleles separate according to Mendel's principle of segregation so that each egg has only one *B* allele. In the male *(bb)*, the two *b* alleles separate so that each sperm has only one *b* allele. The fertilization of each *B* egg by a *b* sperm results in heterozygous F_1 offspring, each with the alleles *Bb*. That is, each individual has one allele for brown coat and one for black coat. Because this is the only possible combination of alleles present in the eggs and sperm, all the F_1 offspring are *Bb*.

A Punnett square predicts the ratios of genotypes and phenotypes of the offspring of a cross

During meiosis in heterozygous black guinea pigs *(Bb)*, the chromosome containing the *B* allele becomes separated from its homologue (the chromosome containing the *b* allele), so each normal sperm or egg contains *B* or *b* but never both. Gametes containing *B* alleles and those containing *b* alleles are

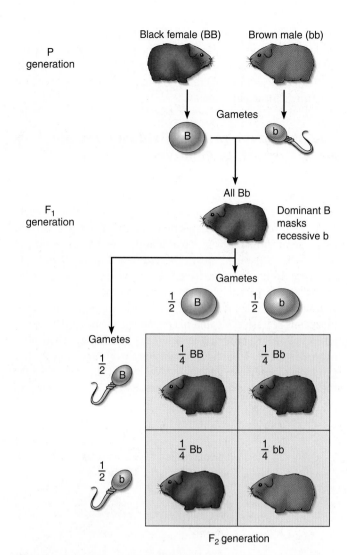

Figure 10–5 A monohybrid cross. In this example, a homozygous black guinea pig is mated with a homozygous brown guinea pig. The F_1 generation includes only black individuals. However, the mating of two of these offspring yields F_2 generation offspring in the expected ratio of 3 black to 1 brown, indicating that the F_1 individuals are heterozygous. The corresponding F_2 genotypic ratio is 1 *BB*:2 *Bb*:1 *bb*.

formed in equal numbers by heterozygous *Bb* individuals. Because no special attraction or repulsion occurs between an egg and a sperm containing the same allele, fertilization is a random process.

As illustrated in Figure 10–5, the possible combinations of eggs and sperm at fertilization can be represented in the form of a "checkerboard" known as a **Punnett square,** devised by an early geneticist, Sir Reginald Punnett. The types of gametes (and their expected frequencies) from one parent are represented across the top, and those from the other parent are indicated along the left side. The squares are then filled in with the resulting F_2 zygote combinations. Three-fourths of all F_2 offspring have the genetic constitution *BB* or *Bb* and are phenotypically black; one-fourth have the genetic constitution *bb* and are phenotypically brown. The genetic mechanism responsible for the approximate 3:1 F$_2$ ratios (called *monohybrid F$_2$ phenotypic ratios*) obtained by Mendel in his pea-breeding experiments is again evident.

The phenotype of an individual does not always reveal its genotype

An organism's phenotype is its appearance (in a given environment) with respect to a certain inherited feature. However, because some alleles may be dominant and others recessive, we cannot always determine which alleles are carried by an organism simply by looking at it. The *genetic constitution* of that organism, most often expressed in symbols, is its **genotype.** In the cross we have been considering, the genotype of the female parent is homozygous dominant, *BB,* and her phenotype is black. The genotype of the male parent is homozygous recessive, *bb,* and his phenotype is brown. The genotype of all the F$_1$ offspring is heterozygous, *Bb,* and their phenotype is black. To prevent confusion we always indicate the genotype of a heterozygous individual by writing the symbol for the dominant allele first and the recessive allele second (always *Bb,* never *bB*).

The phenomenon of dominance partly explains why an individual may resemble one parent more than the other, even if the two parents make equal contributions to their offspring's genetic constitution. Dominance is not predictable and can be determined only by experiment. In one species of animal, black coat may be dominant to brown; in another species, brown may be dominant to black.

A test cross can detect heterozygosity

Guinea pigs with the genotypes *BB* and *Bb* are alike phenotypically; they both have black coats. How, then, can we know the genotype of a black guinea pig? Geneticists can accomplish this by performing a **test cross,** in which an individual of unknown genotype is crossed with a homozygous recessive individual (Fig. 10–6). In a test cross, the alleles carried by the gametes from the parent of unknown genotype are never "hidden" in the offspring by dominant alleles contributed by the other parent. Therefore, one can deduce the genotypes of all the classes of offspring directly from their phenotypes. If all the offspring were black, what inference would you make about the genotype of the black parent? If any of the offspring were brown, what conclusion would you draw regarding the genotype of the black parent? Would you be more certain about one of these inferences than the other?

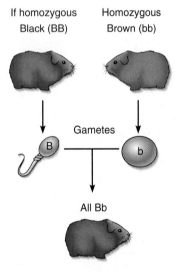

(a)

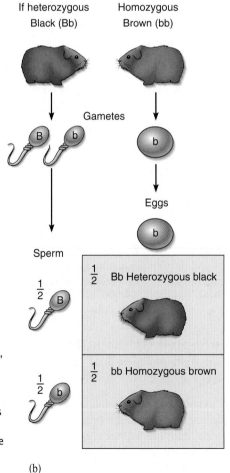

(b)

■ **Figure 10–6 A test cross.** In this illustration, a test cross is used to determine the genotype of a black guinea pig. (**a**) If a black guinea pig is mated with a brown guinea pig and all the offspring are black, the black parent probably has a homozygous genotype. (**b**) If any of the offspring are brown, the black guinea pig must be heterozygous. The expected phenotypic ratio is 1 black to 1 brown.

Mendel conducted numerous test crosses; for example, he bred F$_1$ (tall) pea plants with homozygous recessive *(tt)* short ones. He reasoned that the F$_1$ individuals were heterozygous *(Tt)* and would be expected to produce equal numbers of *T* and *t* gametes. Because the homozygous short parents *(tt)* were expected to produce only *t* gametes, Mendel predicted that he would obtain equal numbers of tall *(Tt)* and short *(tt)* offspring. His results agreed with his predictions, thereby providing additional evidence supporting the hypothesis that there is 1:1 segregation of the alleles of a heterozygous parent. Thus, Mendel's principle of segregation not only explained the known facts, such as the 3:1 monohybrid F$_2$ phenotypic ratio, but also enabled him to successfully anticipate the results of other experiments, in this case the 1:1 test cross phenotypic ratio.

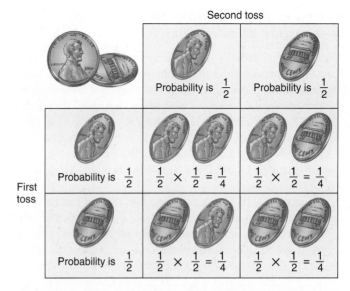

Figure 10–7 The rules of probability. For each coin toss the probability of heads is 1/2 and the probability of tails is also 1/2. Because the outcome of the first toss is independent of the outcome of the second, the combined probabilities of the outcomes of successive tosses are calculated by multiplying their individual probabilities (according to the product rule: 1/2 × 1/2 = 1/4). These same rules of probability are used to predict genetic events.

■ THE RULES OF PROBABILITY PREDICT THE LIKELIHOOD OF GENETIC EVENTS

All genetic ratios are properly expressed in terms of probabilities. In the examples just discussed, among the offspring of two individuals heterozygous for the same gene pair, the expected ratio of the phenotypes of the dominant and recessive alleles is 3:1. The probability of an event is its expected frequency; therefore we can say that there are 3 chances in 4 (3/4) that any particular individual offspring of two heterozygous individuals will express the dominant allele phenotype and 1 chance in 4 (1/4) that it will express the recessive allele phenotype. Although we sometimes speak in terms of percentages, probabilities must always be calculated as fractions (e.g., 3/4) or decimal fractions (e.g., 0.75). If an event is certain to occur, its probability is 1; if it is certain not to occur, its probability is 0. A probability can be 0, 1, or some number between 0 and 1.

Often we wish to *combine* two or more probabilities. The Punnett square, which we use to predict the results of genetic crosses, is a device that allows us to combine probabilities. When we use a Punnett square we are intuitively following two important statistical principles known as the **product rule** and the **sum rule.**

The product rule predicts the combined probabilities of independent events

Events are independent if the occurrence of one does not affect the probability that the other will occur. For example, the probability of obtaining heads on the first toss of a coin is 1/2; the probability of obtaining heads on the second toss (an independent event) is also 1/2. If two or more events are *independent* of each other, the probability of their both occurring is the product of their individual probabilities. If this seems strange to you, keep in mind that when we multiply two numbers that are less than 1, the product is a smaller number. Therefore, the probability of obtaining heads two times in a row is 1/2 × 1/2 = 1/4, or 1 chance in 4 (Fig. 10–7).

Similarly, we can apply the product rule to genetic events. If both parents are *Bb,* what is the probability that they will produce a child who is *bb?* For the child to be *bb,* he or she must receive a *b* gamete from each parent. The probability of a *b* egg is 1/2 and the probability of a *b* sperm is also 1/2. Like the outcomes of the coin tosses, these probabilities are independent, so we combine them by the product rule (1/2 × 1/2 = 1/4). You may wish to check this result using a Punnett square.

The sum rule predicts the combined probabilities of mutually exclusive events

In some cases there is more than one way to obtain a specific outcome. These different ways are called *mutually exclusive* events because no more than one of them can happen; i.e., if one of them occurs, the other(s) cannot. For example, if both parents are *Bb,* what is the probability that their first child will also have the *Bb* genotype? There are two different ways these parents can have a *Bb* child: Either a *B* egg combines with a *b* sperm (probability 1/4), or a *b* egg combines with a *B* sperm (probability 1/4).

Naturally, if there is more than one way to obtain a result, the chances of its being obtained are improved; we therefore combine the probabilities of mutually exclusive events by summing (adding) their individual probabilities. The probability of obtaining a *Bb* child in our example is therefore 1/4 + 1/4 = 1/2. (Because there is only one way these heterozygous parents can produce a homozygous recessive child, *bb,* that probability is only 1/4. The probability of a homozygous dominant child, *BB,* is likewise 1/4.)

The rules of probability can be applied to a variety of calculations

The rules of probability have wide applications. For example, what are the probabilities that a family with two (and only two) children will have two girls, two boys, or one girl and one boy? For purposes of discussion we will assume that male and female births are equally probable. The probability of having a girl first is 1/2, and the probability of having a girl second is also 1/2. These are independent events, so we combine their probabilities by multiplying: $1/2 \times 1/2 = 1/4$. Similarly, the probability of having two boys is also 1/4.

In families with both a girl and a boy, the girl can be born first or the boy can be born first. The probability that a girl will be born first is 1/2, and the probability that a boy will be born second is also 1/2. We use the product rule to combine the probabilities of these two independent events: $1/2 \times 1/2 = 1/4$. Similarly, the probability that a boy will be born first and a girl second is also 1/4. These two kinds of families represent mutually exclusive outcomes, that is, two different ways of obtaining a family with one boy and one girl. Having two different ways of obtaining the desired result improves our chances, so we use the sum rule to combine the probabilities: $1/4 + 1/4 = 1/2$. Notice that the probabilities of the three types of families—both boys (1/4), both girls (1/4), and one girl, one boy (1/2)—add up to 1. This serves as a useful check that the calculations have been done correctly. You may also wish to confirm these results by making a Punnett square.

In working with probabilities, it is important to keep in mind a point that many gamblers forget: Chance has no memory. This means that if events are truly random, past events have no influence on the probability of the occurrence of independent future events. For example, if two brown-eyed people have a child, what is the probability that it will have blue eyes? If their first child has blue eyes, what is the probability that their second child will also have blue eyes? The color of the iris of the human eye is controlled by alleles at several loci, but alleles at one locus are primarily responsible. The allele for brown eye color, *B*, is usually dominant to the allele for blue, *b*. If the two brown-eyed parents are heterozygous, there is 1 chance in 4 that any child of theirs will have blue eyes. Each fertilization is a separate, independent event; its result is not affected by the results of any previous fertilizations. If these two, heterozygous, brown-eyed parents already have three brown-eyed children and are expecting their fourth child, what is the probability that the child will have blue eyes? The uninformed might guess that this one *must* have blue eyes, but in fact there is still only 1 chance in 4 that the child will have blue eyes and 3 chances in 4 that the child will have brown eyes.

If two heterozygous people marry and *plan* to have four children, what is the probability that all four will have brown eyes? The probability of brown eyes for each child is 3/4, so we combine these independent events by the product rule: $3/4 \times 3/4 \times 3/4 \times 3/4 = 81/256$ or 0.32. Why is the answer to this question so different from the answer to the previous question? Remember that for the brown-eyed children that were already born, chance (3/4) is replaced by certainty (1), so the calculation be-

comes $1 \times 1 \times 1 \times 3/4 = 3/4$. The chance that the fourth (as yet unborn) child will have brown eyes is therefore 3/4 (and the chance of blue eyes is 1/4).

When working probability problems, common sense is more important than blindly memorizing rules. Examine your results to see whether they appear reasonable; if they do not, you should reevaluate your assumptions.

■ A DIHYBRID CROSS INVOLVES INDIVIDUALS THAT HAVE DIFFERENT ALLELES AT TWO LOCI

Simple monohybrid crosses each involve a pair of alleles of a single locus. Mendel also analyzed crosses involving alleles of two or more loci. A mating between individuals with different alleles at two loci is called a **dihybrid cross.** Consider the case when two pairs of alleles are located in nonhomologous chromosomes (i.e., one pair of alleles is located in one pair of homologous chromosomes, and the other pair of alleles is located in a *different* pair of homologous chromosomes). Each pair of alleles is inherited independently; that is, each pair segregates during meiosis independently of the other.

An example of a dihybrid cross carried through the F_2 generation is illustrated in Figure 10–8. When a homozygous, black, short-haired guinea pig (*BBSS*, because black is dominant to brown and short hair is dominant to long hair) and a homozygous, brown, long-haired guinea pig *(bbss)* are mated, the *BBSS* animal produces gametes that are all *BS,* and the *bbss* individual produces gametes that are all *bs.* Each gamete contains one and only one allele for each of the two loci. The union of the *BS* and *bs* gametes yields only individuals with the genotype *BbSs.* All these F_1 offspring are heterozygous for hair color and for hair length, and all are phenotypically black and short-haired.

The principle of independent assortment states that alleles on nonhomologous chromosomes are randomly distributed into gametes

Each F_1 guinea pig produces four kinds of gametes with equal probability: *BS, Bs, bS,* and *bs.* Hence, the Punnett square has 16 (4^2) squares representing the zygotes, some of which are genotypically or phenotypically alike. There are 9 chances in 16 of obtaining a black, short-haired individual; 3 chances in 16 of obtaining a black, long-haired individual; 3 chances in 16 of obtaining a brown, short-haired individual; and 1 chance in 16 of obtaining a brown, long-haired individual. This 9:3:3:1 phenotypic ratio is expected in a dihybrid F_2 if the hair color and hair length loci are on nonhomologous chromosomes.

On the basis of similar results, Mendel formulated the principle of inheritance, now called Mendel's **principle of independent assortment,** which states that members of any gene pair segregate from one another independently of the members of the other gene pairs. This occurs in a regular way that ensures that

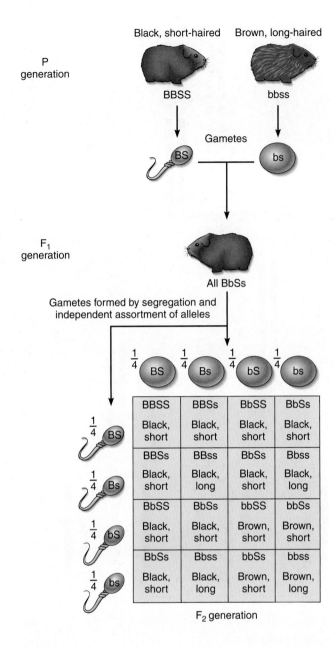

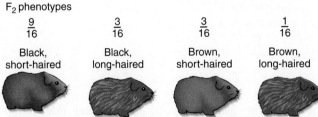

Figure 10–8 A dihybrid cross. When a black, short-haired guinea pig is crossed with a brown, long-haired one, all the offspring are black and have short hair. However, when two members of the F₁ generation are crossed, the ratio of phenotypes is 9:3:3:1. Note that the two pairs of alleles considered here assort independently.

each gamete contains one allele for each locus, but the alleles of different loci are assorted at random with respect to each other in the gametes. (Mendel reported on the results of crosses in which the genes assorted independently. As you will soon see, independent assortment does not always occur.)

Procedures used in solving genetics problems that illustrate Mendel's principles of segregation and independent assortment are summarized at the end of the chapter in *Focus On: Solving Genetics Problems*, and *Focus On: Deducing Genotypes*.

The mechanics of meiosis are the basis for independent assortment

Today we recognize that independent assortment is related to the events of meiosis. It occurs because there are two different ways in which two pairs of homologous chromosomes can be arranged at metaphase I of meiosis. These occur randomly, with approximately half the meiotic cells having one orientation, and the other half having the opposite orientation. The orientation of the homologous chromosomes on the metaphase plate then determines the way they subsequently separate and are distributed into the haploid cells (Fig. 10–9).

Linked genes do not assort independently

Independent assortment does not apply if the two loci are located in the same pair of homologous chromosomes. In fruit flies there is a locus controlling wing shape (the dominant allele *V* for normal wings and the recessive allele *v* for vestigial wings) and another locus controlling body color (the dominant allele *B* for gray and the recessive allele *b* for black). If a homozygous *BBVV* fly is crossed with a homozygous *bbvv* fly, the F₁ flies all have gray bodies and normal wings, and their genotype is *BbVv*.

Because these loci happen to be located in the *same pair* of homologous chromosomes, their alleles do not assort independently; instead they tend to be inherited together and are said to be **linked.** Linkage is most readily observed by analyzing the results of a test cross in which heterozygous F₁ flies *(BbVv)* are mated with homozygous recessive *(bbvv)* flies (Fig. 10–10). Because heterozygous individuals are mated to homozygous recessive individuals, this test cross is similar to the test cross described previously. However, it is called a **two-point test cross** because alleles of two loci are involved.

If the loci governing these characteristics were on different chromosomes (unlinked), the heterozygous parent in a test cross would produce four kinds of gametes (*BV, Bv, bV,* and *bv*) in equal numbers. As a result of this independent assortment, offspring with new gene combinations not present in the parental generation would be produced. Any process that leads to new gene combinations is called **recombination.** In our example, *Bv* and *bV* are both **recombinant gametes.** The other two kinds of gametes, *BV* and *bv,* are called **parental gametes** because they are identical to the gametes produced by the P generation. Of course, the homozygous recessive parent produces only one kind of gamete, *bv.* Thus, if independent assortment were to occur in the F₁ flies, approximately 25% of the test-cross offspring would be gray-bodied

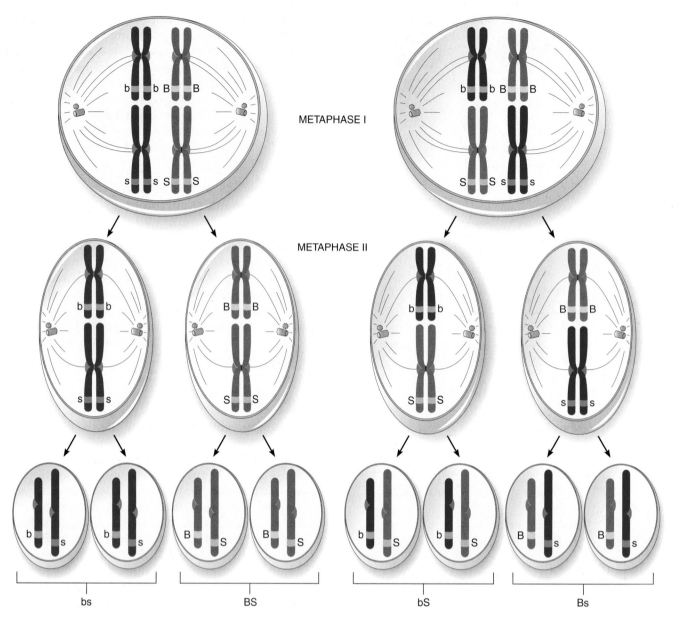

METAPHASE I

METAPHASE II

bs   BS   bS   Bs

Figure 10–9 Meiosis and independent assortment. There are two equally likely ways that two different pairs of homologous chromosomes can line up at metaphase I and be subsequently distributed. A cell with the orientation shown at the left produces half *BS* and half *bs* gametes. Conversely, the cell at the right produces half *Bs* and half *bS* gametes. Because approximately half of the meiotic cells at metaphase I are of each type, the ratio of the four possible types of gametes is 1:1:1:1.

and normal-winged *(BbVv)*, 25% black-bodied and normal-winged *(bbVv)*, 25% gray-bodied and vestigial-winged *(Bbvv)*, and 25% black-bodied and vestigial-winged *(bbvv)*. Notice that the two-point test cross allows us to determine the genotypes of the offspring directly from their phenotypes.

By contrast, the alleles of the loci in our example do not undergo independent assortment because they are linked. Alleles at different loci on a given chromosome tend to be inherited together because chromosomes pair and separate during meiosis as units and therefore tend to be inherited as units. If linkage were complete, only parental type flies would be produced, with approximately 50% having gray bodies and normal wings *(BbVv)*,

and 50% having black bodies and vestigial wings *(bbvv)*. However, in our example, the progeny also include some gray-bodied, vestigial-winged flies and some black-bodied, normal-winged flies. These are recombinant type flies, having received a recombinant gamete from the heterozygous F$_1$ parent. Each recombinant gamete arose by crossing-over between these loci in a meiotic cell of a heterozygous female[2] fly. Recall from Chapter 9 that

[2] Fruit flies are unusual in that crossing-over occurs only in females and not in males. It is far more common for crossing-over to occur in both sexes of a species.

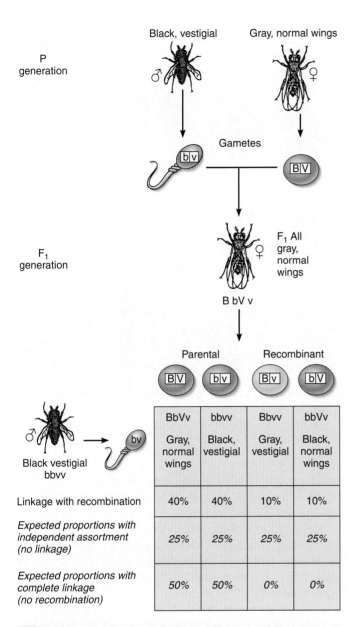

The linear order of linked genes on a chromosome is determined by calculating the frequency of crossing-over

In our example, about 20% of the offspring are recombinant types: gray flies with vestigial wings, *Bbvv* (approximately 10% of the total); and black flies with normal wings, *bbVv* (also about 10% of the total). The remaining 80% are parental types. These data can be used to calculate the percentage of crossing-over between the loci. This is done by adding the number of individuals in the two recombinant classes of offspring (10 + 10), dividing

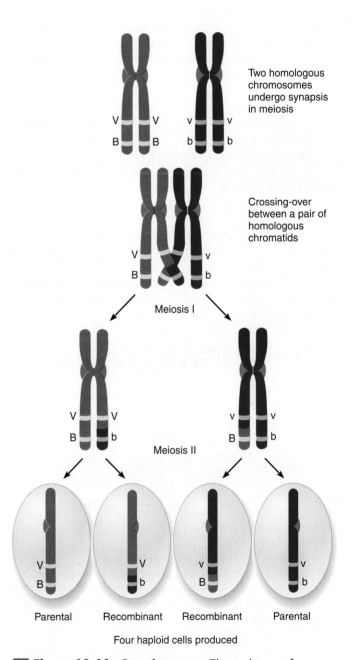

Figure 10–10 A two-point test cross to detect linkage. Linkage can be recognized when an excess of parental type offspring and a deficiency of recombinant type offspring are produced in a two-point test cross. In this example, loci for wing length in fruit flies (vestigial versus normal wings) and for body color (black versus gray body) are linked; they are located on a homologous chromosome pair. This is evident in the proportions of offspring: about 40% of the offspring belong to each of the two parental classes (80% total), and 10% belong to each of the two recombinant classes (20% total). The numbers in italics allow us to contrast this outcome (linkage with recombination), with the expected proportions if either of two other alternatives were true: (1) independent assortment and (2) complete linkage with no recombination.

Figure 10–11 Crossing-over. The exchange of segments between chromatids of homologous chromosomes permits the recombination of linked genes. Genes located far apart on a chromosome have a greater probability of being separated by an exchange of segments than do genes that are closer together.

when chromosomes pair and undergo synapsis, **crossing-over** occurs as homologous (nonsister) chromatids exchange segments of chromosomal material by a process of breakage and rejoining (Fig. 10–11).

by the *total number of offspring* (40 + 40 + 10 + 10), and multiplying by 100. Thus, the *V* locus and the *B* locus have 20% recombination between them.

During a single meiotic division, crossing-over may occur at several different points along the length of each homologous chromosome pair. In general, a crossover is more likely to occur between two loci if they are far apart on the chromosome and less likely to occur if they are close together. Because this rough correlation exists between the frequency of recombination between two loci and the linear distance between them, a genetic map of the chromosome can be generated by converting the percentage of recombination to **map units.** By convention, 1% recombination between two loci equals a distance of 1 map unit, so the loci in our example are 20 map units apart.

The frequencies of recombination between specific linked loci have been measured in many species. All of the experimental results are consistent with the hypothesis that genes are present in a linear order in the chromosomes. Figure 10–12 illustrates the traditional method for determining the linear order of genes in a chromosome.

More than one crossover between two loci in a single tetrad can occur in a given cell undergoing meiosis. (Recall from Chapter 9 that a tetrad is a group of four chromatids that make up a pair of synapsed homologous chromosomes.) We can observe only the frequency of offspring receiving recombinant gametes from the heterozygous parent, not the actual number of crossovers. In fact, the actual frequency of crossing-over is slightly more than the observed frequency of recombinant gametes. This is because the simultaneous occurrence of two crossovers involving the same two homologous chromatids re-

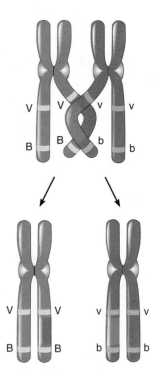

■ Figure 10–13 Double crossing-over. If the same homologous chromatids undergo double crossing-over between the genes of interest, the gametes formed are not recombinant for these genes.

constitutes the original combination of genes (Fig. 10–13). When two loci are relatively close together, the effect of double crossing-over is minimized.

The genes in a particular chromosome tend to be inherited together and therefore are said to constitute a **linkage group.** The number of linkage groups determined by genetic tests is equal to the number of pairs of chromosomes. By putting together the results of many crosses, scientists painstakingly developed detailed linkage maps for many eukaryotes, including the fruit fly (which has four pairs of chromosomes), the mouse, yeast, *Neurospora* (a fungus), and many plants, especially those that are important crops. In addition, special genetic methods have made possible the development of a detailed map for *Escherichia coli,* a bacterium with a single, circular DNA molecule, and many other prokaryotes and viruses. Much more sophisticated maps of chromosomes have been made by means of recombinant DNA technology (see Chapter 14). These methods have been particularly useful in producing maps of human chromosomes through the Human Genome Project (see Chapter 15).

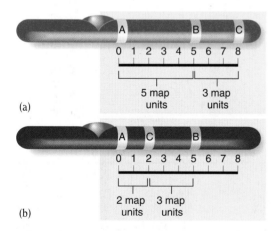

■ Figure 10–12 Gene mapping. Gene order (i.e., which locus lies between the other two) is determined by the percentage of recombination between each of the possible pairs. In this hypothetical example, the percentage of recombination between locus A and locus B is 5% (corresponding to 5 map units) and that between B and C is 3% (3 map units). There are two alternatives for the linear order of these alleles. **(a)** If the recombination between A and C is 8% (8 map units), B must be in the middle. **(b)** If the recombination between A and C is 2%, then C must be in the middle.

■ SEX IS COMMONLY DETERMINED BY SPECIAL SEX CHROMOSOMES

Although in some species sex is controlled mainly by the environment, genes are the most important sex determinants in most organisms. The major sex-determining genes of most animals are carried by sex chromosomes. Typically, members of one sex (the **homogametic** sex) have a pair of similar sex chromosomes and produce gametes that are all identical in sex chromosome constitution. The members of the other sex (the **heterogametic** sex) have two different sex chromosomes and produce two kinds of gametes, each bearing a single kind of sex chromosome.

The females of many animal species (including humans) are homogametic; their cells contain two **X chromosomes.** In contrast, the males are heterogametic, having a single X chromosome and a smaller **Y chromosome.** For example, human males have 22 pairs of **autosomes,** which are chromosomes other than the sex chromosomes, plus one X chromosome and one Y chromosome; females have 22 pairs of autosomes plus a pair of X chromosomes. Domestic cats have 19 pairs of autosomes, to which are added a pair of X chromosomes in females, or an X plus a Y in males.

The Y chromosome determines male sex in most species of mammals

Do male humans have a male phenotype because they have only one X chromosome or because they have a Y chromosome? Much of the traditional evidence bearing on this question comes from studies of persons with abnormal sex chromosome constitutions (see Chapter 15). A person with an XXY constitution is a nearly normal male in external appearance, although his testes are underdeveloped (Klinefelter syndrome). A person with one X but no Y chromosome has the appearance of an immature female (Turner syndrome). An embryo with a Y but no X does not survive. Hence all individuals require at least one X, and the Y is the male-determining chromosome. In fact, several genes on the Y chromosomes that are involved in male determination have been identified. The major male-determining gene on the Y acts as a "genetic switch" that causes the testes to develop in the fetus. The developing testes then secrete testosterone, which causes other features characteristic of males to develop. A small number of other genes on the Y also play a role in sex determination, as do many genes on the X and some on the autosomes, which explains why an XXY individual does not have a completely normal male phenotype.

The X and Y chromosomes are thought to have originated as a homologous pair. However, they are not truly homologous in their present forms because they are not similar in size, shape, or genetic constitution. Nevertheless, they have retained a short homologous "pairing region" that allows them to synapse and separate from one another during meiosis. Half the sperm contain an X chromosome and half contain a Y chromosome. All normal eggs bear a single X chromosome (Fig. 10–14). Fertilization of an X-bearing egg by an X-bearing sperm results in an XX (female) zygote; fertilization by a Y-bearing sperm results in an XY (male) zygote.

We would expect to have equal numbers of X- and Y-bearing sperm and a 1:1 ratio of females to males. In fact, however, in humans more males are conceived than females and more males die before birth. Even at birth the ratio is not 1:1; about 106 boys are born for every 100 girls. It is not known why this occurs, but Y-bearing sperm appear to have some competitive advantage.

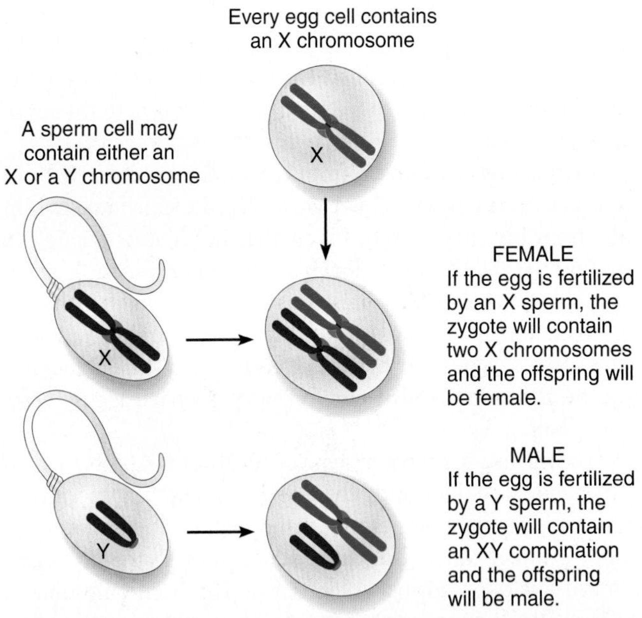

Figure 10–14 Sex is determined by the sperm in mammals. An X-bearing sperm produces a female; a Y-bearing sperm produces a male.

An XX/XY sex chromosome mechanism, similar to that of humans, operates in many species of animals. However, it is not universal, and many of the details may vary. For example, the fruit fly, *Drosophila,* has homogametic (XX) females and heterogametic (XY) males, but the Y is not male-determining; a fruit fly with an X chromosome and no Y chromosome has a male phenotype. In birds and butterflies the mechanism is reversed, with homogametic males (the equivalent of XX) and heterogametic females (the equivalent of XY).

Some organisms are hermaphroditic

In **hermaphroditic** organisms, organs of both sexes are found in the same individual. Hermaphroditic animals (see Chapters 28, 29, and 48) do not have sex chromosomes. Most flowering plants are hermaphrodites. The male and female sexual organs may be in the same flowers. If they are in separate flowers on the same plant, the plants are said to be **monoecious;** corn, walnuts, and oaks are examples. Far fewer flowering plants are not hermaphroditic; they are **dioecious,** having male and female floral organs on separate plants. A few dioecious plants, such as asparagus, apparently have sex chromosomes, although they are not necessarily comparable to those of animals.

X-linked genes have unusual inheritance patterns

The human X chromosome contains many loci that are required in both sexes, whereas the Y chromosome contains only a few genes, including one or more genes for maleness. Genes located in the X chromosome, such as colorblindness and the most common form of hemophilia, are sometimes called **sex-linked** genes. It is more appropriate, however, to refer to them as **X-linked** genes because they follow the transmission pattern of the X chromosome and, strictly speaking, are not linked to the sex of the organism per se.

A female receives one X from her mother and one X from her father. A male receives his Y chromosome, which makes him male, from his father. From his mother he inherits a single X chromosome and therefore all of his X-linked genes. In the male, every X chromosome allele present is expressed, whether that allele was dominant or recessive in the female parent. A male is neither homozygous nor heterozygous for his X-linked loci; instead he is always **hemizygous** for every X-linked locus (*hemi* means "half").

We will use a simple system of notation for problems involving X linkage, indicating the X and incorporating specific alleles as superscripts. For example, the symbol X^c signifies a recessive X-linked allele for colorblindness and X^C the dominant X-linked allele for normal color vision. The Y chromosome is written without superscripts because it does not carry the locus of interest. Two recessive X-linked alleles must be present in a female for the abnormal phenotype to be expressed (i.e., X^cX^c), whereas in the hemizygous male a single abnormal allele is expressed (X^cY). As a practical consequence, these abnormal alleles are much more frequently expressed in male offspring. A heterozygous female may be a *carrier,* an individual who possesses one copy of a mutant recessive allele but does not express it in the phenotype (i.e., X^CX^c).

To be expressed in a female, a recessive X-linked allele must be inherited from both parents. A colorblind female, for example, must have a colorblind father and a mother who is heterozygous or homozygous for colorblindness (Fig. 10–15). Such a combination is unusual because the frequency of the allele for colorblindness is relatively low. In contrast, a colorblind male need only have a mother who is heterozygous for colorblindness; his father can be normal. Hence, X-linked recessive traits are generally much more common in males than in females, a fact that may partially explain why human male embryos are more likely to die.

Dosage compensation equalizes the expression of X-linked genes in males and females

The X chromosome contains numerous genes required by both sexes, yet a normal female has two copies ("doses") for each locus, whereas a normal male has only one. **Dosage compensation** is a mechanism that makes the two doses in the female and the

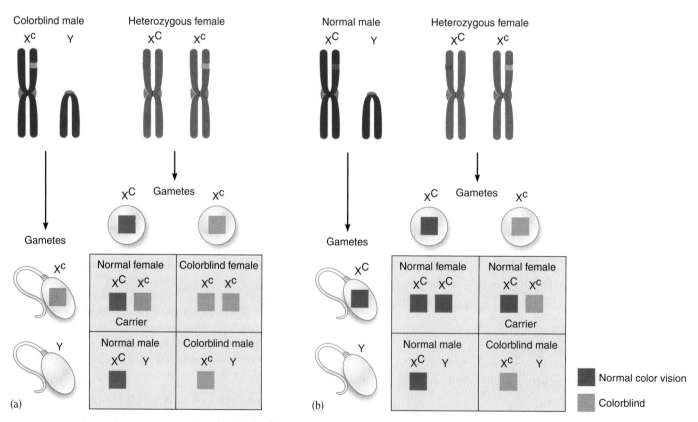

■ **Figure 10–15 X-linked recessive colorblindness.** Note that the Y chromosome does not carry a gene for color vision. **(a)** To be colorblind, a female must inherit alleles for colorblindness from both parents. **(b)** If a normal male mates with a carrier (heterozygous) female, half of their sons would be expected to be colorblind and half of their daughters would be expected to be carriers.

single dose in the male equivalent. Male fruit flies accomplish this by making their single X chromosome more active. In most tissues, the metabolic activity of a single male X chromosome is equal to the combined metabolic activity of the two X chromosomes present in the female.

Dosage compensation in mammals generally involves inactivation of one of the two X chromosomes in the female. During interphase a dark spot of chromatin, called a **Barr body,** is visible at the edge of the nucleus of each female mammalian cell (Fig. 10–16). The Barr body has been found to represent a dense, dark-staining, and metabolically inactive X chromosome. The other X chromosome resembles the metabolically active autosomes; during interphase it is a greatly extended thread that is not evident by light microscopy. From this and other evidence, the British geneticist Mary Lyon hypothesized in 1961 that in any cell of a female mammal, only one of the two X chromosomes is active; the other is inactive and is visible as a Barr body. (Actually, X chromosome inactivation is never complete; a small fraction of the genes are active.)

Because only one X chromosome is active in any one cell and because X chromosome inactivation is a random event, a female mammal that is heterozygous at an X-linked locus expresses one of the alleles in about half her cells and the other allele in the other half. This is sometimes (but not always) evident in the phenotype. Mice and cats have several X-linked genes for certain coat colors. Females that are heterozygous for such genes may show patches of one coat color in the midst of areas of the other coat color. This phenomenon, termed **variegation,** is evident in calico (Fig. 10–17) and tortoiseshell cats. Early in development, when relatively few cells are present, X chromosome inactivation occurs randomly in each cell. When any one of these cells divides by mitosis, the cells of the resulting clone (group of genetically identical cells) all have the same active X chromosome, and, therefore, a patch of cells that all express the same color develops.

Why, you might ask, is variegation not always apparent in females heterozygous at X-linked loci? The answer is that, although variegation usually occurs, we may need to use special techniques to observe it. For example, colorblindness is due to a defect involving the pigments in the cone cells in the retina of the eye (Chapter 41). In at least one type of red-green color-

Figure 10–17 A calico cat. This cat has X-linked genes for both black and yellow (or orange) pigmentation of the fur, but because of random X chromosome inactivation, black is expressed in some groups of cells and yellow (or orange) is expressed in others. Because other genes affecting fur color are also present, white patches are usually evident as well. *(Larime Photographic/Dembinsky Photo Associates)*

blindness, the retina of a heterozygous female actually contains patches of abnormal cones, but the patches of normal cones are sufficient to provide normal color vision. Variegation can be very hard to observe in the cases where cell products become mixed in bodily fluids. For instance, in females heterozygous for hemophilia, only half the cells responsible for producing a specific blood-clotting factor are capable of doing so, but they produce enough to ensure that the blood clots normally.

Sex-influenced genes are autosomal, but their expression is affected by the individual's sex

Not all characteristics that differ in the two sexes are X-linked. Certain **sex-influenced** traits are inherited through autosomal genes, but the *expression* of alleles at these loci can be altered or influenced by the sex of the animal. Therefore, males and females with the same genotype with respect to these loci may have different phenotypes.

Pattern baldness in humans, characterized by premature loss of hair on the front and top of the head, but not on the sides, is far more common among males than among females. It has been proposed that a single pair of autosomal alleles is involved, with the allele responsible for pattern baldness being dominant in males and recessive in females. Because of this unusual situation, we modify our notation, designating the pattern baldness allele as B_1 and the allele for normal hair growth as B_2. Individuals with the genotype B_1B_1 show pattern baldness, regardless of sex. Persons with a B_1B_2 genotype are bald if they are male but

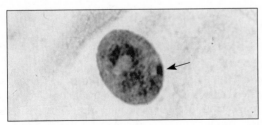

10 μm

Figure 10–16 A Barr body. The darkly stained Barr body *(arrow)* at the edge of the nucleus in this LM is an inactivated X chromosome. The entire cell is not shown. *(Omikron/Photo Researchers, Inc.)*

not bald if they are female. Individuals with the genotype B_2B_2 are not bald, regardless of sex.

Evidence suggests that the expression of most sex-influenced traits is strongly modified by sex hormones. For example, male hormones (see Chapter 48) are strongly implicated in the expression of pattern baldness.

■ THE RELATIONSHIP BETWEEN GENOTYPE AND PHENOTYPE IS OFTEN COMPLEX

The relationship between a given locus and the characteristic it controls may be simple: A single pair of alleles of a locus may regulate the appearance of a single characteristic of the organism (e.g., tall versus short in garden peas). Alternatively, the relationship may be more complex: A pair of alleles may participate in the control of several characteristics, or alleles of many loci may cooperate to regulate the appearance of a single characteristic. Not surprisingly, these more complex relationships are quite common.

We may assess the phenotype on one or many levels. It may be a morphological characteristic, such as shape, size, or color. It may be a physiological characteristic or even a biochemical trait, such as the presence or absence of a specific enzyme required for the metabolism of some specific molecule. In addition, the phenotypic expression of genes may be altered by changes in the environmental conditions under which the organism develops.

Dominance is not always complete

Studies of the inheritance of many traits in a wide variety of organisms have clearly shown that one member of a pair of alleles may not be completely dominant to the other. In such instances it is improper to use the terms *dominant* and *recessive*.

Process of Science For example, the plants commonly known as four o'clocks *(Mirabilis jalapa)* may have red or white flowers. Each color breeds true when these plants are self-pollinated. What flower color might we expect in the offspring of a cross between a red-flowering plant and a white-flowering one? Without knowing which is dominant, we might predict that all would have red flowers or all would have white flowers. This cross was first made by the German botanist Karl Correns (one of the rediscoverers of Mendel's work), who found that all F_1 offspring have pink flowers! Does this result in any way prove that Mendel's assumptions about inheritance are wrong? Did the parental characteristics blend inseparably in the offspring? Quite the contrary, for when two of these pink-flowered plants are crossed, red-flowered, pink-flowered, and white-flowered offspring appear in a ratio of 1:2:1 (Fig. 10–18).

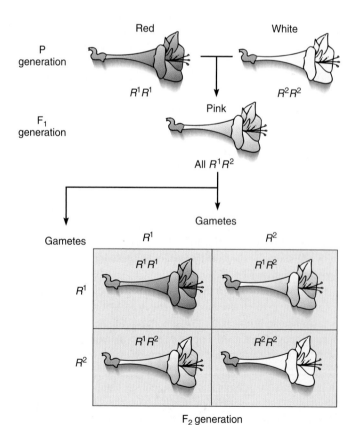

■ **Figure 10–18 Incomplete dominance in four o'clocks.** If a pair of alleles is incompletely dominant to each other, a heterozygote has a phenotype intermediate between its parents. Two incompletely dominant alleles, R^1 and R^2, are responsible for red, white, and pink flower colors. Red-flowered plants are R^1R^1; white-flowered plants are R^2R^2, and heterozygotes (R^1R^2) are pink. Note that uppercase notation is used for both alleles, because neither is recessive to the other.

In this instance, as in all other aspects of the scientific process, results that differ from those predicted prompt scientists to reexamine and modify their assumptions to account for the exceptional results. The pink-flowered plants are clearly the heterozygous individuals, and neither the red allele nor the white allele is completely dominant. When the heterozygote has a phenotype that is intermediate between those of its two parents, the genes are said to show **incomplete dominance.** In these crosses, the genotypic and phenotypic ratios are identical.

Incomplete dominance is not unique to four o'clocks. Numerous additional examples of incomplete dominance are known in both plants and animals. For example, white chickens and black chickens produce gray offspring when crossed.

In both cattle and horses, reddish coat color is not completely dominant to white coat color. Heterozygous individuals have a mixture of reddish hairs and white hairs, which is called roan. If you saw a white mare nursing a roan foal, what would you guess was the coat color of the foal's father? Because the reddish and white colors are expressed independently (hair by hair) in the roan heterozygote, we sometimes refer to this as a case of **codominance.** Strictly speaking, incomplete dominance refers to instances in which the heterozygote is intermediate in phenotype, and codominance refers to instances in which the heterozygote simultaneously expresses the phenotypes of both types of homozygotes.

The human ABO blood group provides a classic case of codominant alleles. Blood types O, A, B, and AB are controlled by three alleles representing a single locus. Allele I^A codes for the synthesis of a specific glycoprotein, antigen A, which is expressed on the surface of red blood cells. (Immunity is discussed in Chapter 43; for now we define antigens simply as substances capable of stimulating an immune response.) Allele I^B leads to the production of a different (but related) glycoprotein, antigen B. Allele i^O does not code for an antigen, although it is allelic to I^A and I^B. As shown in Table 10–1, persons with the genotype $I^A I^A$ or $I^A i^O$

have blood type A; those with genotype $I^B I^B$ or $I^B i^O$ have blood type B; those with genotype $I^A I^B$ have blood type AB; and those with genotype $i^O i^O$ have blood type O. These results show that neither allele I^A nor allele I^B is dominant to the other; they are both expressed phenotypically in the heterozygote and are therefore codominant to each other, although each is dominant to allele i^O.

Determining blood types was one of the traditional ways of settling cases of disputed parentage. While blood type tests can exclude someone as a possible parent of a particular child, they can never prove that a certain person is the parent; they can only determine that he or she *could* be. Could a man with blood type AB be the father of a child with blood type O? Could a woman with blood type O be the mother of a child with blood type AB? Could a type-B child with a type-A mother have a type-A father or a type-O father?[3]

Multiple alleles for a locus may exist in a population

Most of the examples given so far have dealt with situations in which each locus was represented by a maximum of two allelic variants. It is true that a single diploid individual has a maximum of two different alleles for a particular locus and that a haploid gamete has only one allele for each locus. However, if we survey a population, we may find more than two alleles for a particular locus, as we saw with the ABO blood group. If three or more alleles for a given locus exist within the population, we say that locus has **multiple alleles.** A great many loci can be shown to have multiple alleles if the population is surveyed carefully. Some alleles can be identified by the activity of a certain enzyme or by some other biochemical feature but do not produce an obvious phenotype. Others produce a readily recognizable phenotype,

[3] The answer to all these questions is "no."

TABLE 10–1 ABO Blood Types*

Phenotype (blood type)	Genotypes	Antigen on RBC	Antibodies to A or B Antigens in Plasma	Frequency in U.S. Population (%) Western European Descent	Frequency in U.S. Population (%) African Descent
A	$I^A I^A$, $I^A i^O$	A	Anti-B	45	29
B	$I^B I^B$, $I^B i^O$	B	Anti-A	8	17
AB	$I^A I^B$	A, B	None	4	4
O	$i^O i^O$	None	Anti-A, anti-B	43	50

*This table and the discussion of the ABO system have been simplified somewhat. Note that persons produce antibodies against the antigens *lacking* on their own red blood cells (RBCs). Because of their specificity for the corresponding antigens, these antibodies are used in standard tests to determine blood types.

and certain patterns of dominance can be discerned when the alleles are combined in various ways.

In rabbits, for example, a *C* allele causes a fully colored coat. The homozygous recessive genotype, *cc,* causes albino coat color. There are two additional allelic variants of the same locus, c^h and c^{ch}. The genotype $c^h c^h$ causes the "Himalayan" pattern, in which the body is white but the tips of the ears, nose, tail, and legs are colored (similar to the color pattern of a Siamese cat). An individual with the genotype $c^{ch} c^{ch}$ has the "chinchilla" pattern, in which the entire body has a light gray color. On the basis of the results of genetic crosses, these alleles can be arranged in the following series: $C > c^h > c^{ch} > c$. Each allele is dominant to those following it and recessive to those preceding it. For example, a $c^h c^{ch}$ rabbit has the "Himalayan" pattern, whereas a $c^{ch} c$ rabbit has the "chinchilla" pattern. In some other series of multiple alleles, certain alleles may be codominant and others incompletely dominant; hence the heterozygotes commonly have phenotypes intermediate between those of their parents.

A single gene may affect multiple aspects of the phenotype

In the examples presented so far, the relationship between a gene and its phenotype has been direct, precise, and exact, and the loci considered have controlled the appearance of single traits. However, the relationship of gene to characteristic may be quite complex. Most genes probably have many different effects, a quality referred to as **pleiotropy.** Most cases of pleiotropy can be traced to a single fundamental cause. For example, a defective enzyme may affect the functioning of many types of cells. Pleiotropy is evident in many genetic diseases in which multiple symptoms are caused by a single pair of alleles. For example, individuals who are homozygous for the recessive allele that causes cystic fibrosis produce abnormally thick mucus in many parts of the body, including the respiratory, digestive, and reproductive systems (see Chapter 15).

Alleles of different loci may interact to produce a phenotype

Several pairs of alleles may interact to affect a single phenotype, or one pair may inhibit or reverse the effect of another pair. More than 12 pairs of alleles interact in various ways to produce coat color in rabbits, and more than 100 pairs are concerned with eye color and shape in fruit flies.

One type of gene interaction is illustrated by the inheritance of combs in poultry, where two genes may interact to produce a novel phenotype (Fig. 10–19). The allele for a rose comb, *R,* is dominant to that for a single comb, *r.* A second, unlinked pair of alleles governs the inheritance of a pea comb, *P,* versus a single comb, *p.* A single-combed fowl is homozygous for the recessive allele at both loci *(pprr).* A rose-combed fowl is either *ppRR* or *ppRr,* and a pea-combed fowl is either *PPrr* or *Pprr.* When an *R* and *P* occur in the same individual, the phenotype is neither a pea nor a rose comb but a completely different type, called a *walnut comb.* The walnut comb phenotype is produced whenever a fowl has one or two *R* alleles, plus one or two *P* alleles (i.e., *PPRR, PpRR, PPRr,* or *PpRr*). What would you predict about the types of combs among the offspring of two heterozygous walnut-combed fowl, *PpRr?* How does this form of gene interaction affect the ratio of phenotypes in the F_2 generation? Is it the typical Mendelian 9:3:3:1 ratio?

Epistasis is a common type of gene interaction in which the presence of certain alleles of one locus can prevent or mask the expression of alleles of a different locus. (Literally, epistasis means "standing upon.") We have already seen that coat color in guinea pigs can be determined by the *B* and *b* allelic pair, with the *B* allele for black coat dominant to the *b* allele for brown coat. The expression of either phenotype, however, depends on the presence of a dominant allele at yet another locus. This allele, *C,* codes for the enzyme tyrosinase, which converts a colorless precursor to the pigment melanin and hence is required for the production of any kind of pigment. The recessive allele *(c)* codes for an inactive form of the enzyme. Thus, an animal that is homozygous recessive for this allele lacks the enzyme and produces no melanin. It is therefore a white-coated, pink-eyed albino, regardless of the combination of *B* and *b* alleles. Albinism, or lack of melanin pigment, is not restricted to guinea pigs but is found in humans and a variety of other animals (Fig. 10–20).

When an albino guinea pig with the genotype *ccBB* is mated to a brown guinea pig with the genotype *CCbb,* the F_1 generation is black-coated, *CcBb.* When two such animals are mated, their offspring appear black-coated, brown-coated, and albino in a ratio of 9:3:4. (Make a Punnett square to verify this.)

You might wonder why heterozygous *Cc* individuals do not show at least some lightening of the coat color, given the fact

| Single comb
pprr | Pea comb
PPrr or *Pprr* | Walnut comb
PPRR, PpRR,
PPRr, or *PpRr* | Rose comb
ppRR or *ppRr* |

■ **Figure 10–19 Gene interaction.** Two gene pairs govern these types of genetically determined combs in roosters. Note that four different genotypes have walnut combs.

Figure 10–20 Epistasis. Homozygous alleles for albinism exhibit epistasis, masking the expression of alleles of other loci that govern production of melanin pigment. Albino individuals, such as this albino koala, occur occasionally in nature. *(Tom McHugh/Photo Researchers, Inc.)*

that they produce only about half the normal amount of tyrosinase enzyme. It turns out that half the normal amount of enzyme is usually adequate to produce normal amounts of pigment. This type of situation applies to many enzymes and explains many (although certainly not all) cases of dominance.

Polygenes act additively to produce a phenotype

The inherited components of many human characteristics, such as height, body form, and skin color, are not inherited through alleles at a single locus. The same holds true for many commercially important characteristics in domestic plants and animals, such as milk and egg production. Alleles at several, perhaps many, different loci affect each characteristic. The term **polygenic inheritance** is applied when multiple independent pairs of genes have similar and additive effects on the same characteristic.

Polygenes are responsible for the inheritance of skin color in humans. It is now thought that alleles representing three to four different loci are involved in determining skin color. We illustrate the principle of polygenic inheritance with pairs of alleles at three unlinked loci. These can be designated *A* and *a*, *B* and *b*, and *C* and *c* (Fig. 10–21). The capital letters represent incompletely dominant alleles producing dark skin. The more capital letters, the darker the skin, because the alleles affect skin color in an additive fashion. A person with the darkest skin

would have the genotype *AABBCC,* and a person with the lightest skin would have the genotype *aabbcc.* The F_1 offspring of an *aabbcc* person and an *AABBCC* person are all *AaBbCc* and have an intermediate skin color. The F_2 offspring of two such triple heterozygotes would have skin colors ranging from very dark to very light.

Polygenic inheritance is therefore characterized by an F_1 generation that is intermediate between the two completely homozygous parents and by an F_2 generation that shows wide variation between the two parental types. Most of the F_2 generation individuals have one of the intermediate phenotypes; only a few show the extreme phenotypes of the grandparents (P generation). On average, only 1 of 64 is as dark as the very dark grandparent, and only 1 of 64 is as light as the very light grandparent (Fig. 10–22). The alleles *A, B,* and *C* each produce about the same amount of darkening of the skin; hence, the genotypes *AaBbCc, AABbcc, AAbbCc, AaBBcc, AabbCC,* and *aaBbCC* all produce similar intermediate phenotypes.

The model used here for the inheritance of skin color in humans is a rather simple example of polygenic inheritance because only three major allelic pairs are used. The inheritance of height in humans involves alleles representing ten or more loci. Because many allelic pairs are involved and because height is modified by a variety of environmental conditions, the height of adults ranges from perhaps 125 to 215 cm. If we were to measure the heights of 1000 adult American men selected at random, we would find that only a few are as tall as 215 cm or as short as 125 cm. The heights of most would cluster around the mean, about 170 cm. When the number of men at each height is plotted against height (in centimeters) and the points are connected, the result is a bell-shaped curve, called a **normal distribution curve** (Fig. 10–23).

■ SELECTION, INBREEDING, AND OUTBREEDING ARE USED TO DEVELOP IMPROVED STRAINS

How do geneticists go about establishing a breed of cow that will give more milk, a strain of hens that will lay bigger eggs, or a variety of corn with more kernels per ear? By selecting organisms that manifest the desired phenotype and using these individuals in further matings, a true-breeding strain with the commercially advantageous phenotype is gradually developed. Such a strain is expected to be homozygous for all of the genes involved, whether they be dominant, recessive, or additive in their effects.

There is a limit to the effectiveness of breeding by selection. When a strain becomes homozygous for all of the genes involved, further selective breeding cannot increase the desired quality. Moreover, because of **inbreeding**—the mating of two closely related individuals—the strain may become homozygous for multiple undesirable traits as well. Human inbreeding, for example, increases the frequency with which otherwise very rare genetic disorders are observed to occur in the population, although the individual risk is relatively small.

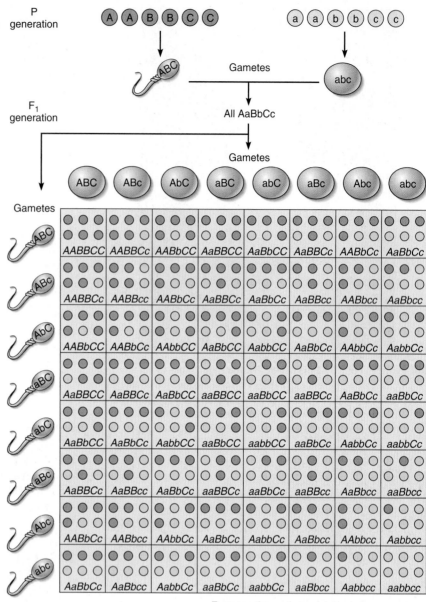

Figure 10–21 Polygenic inheritance. This model assumes that skin color in humans is governed by alleles of three unlinked loci. The alleles producing dark skin (*A, B,* and *C*) are represented by capital letters, but they are not dominant. Instead they have additive effects. If one parent is very dark and the other very light, their children (F₁) are intermediate in skin color. A wide range of skin colors are expected in the F₂. The number of dark dots (each signifying an allele producing dark skin) is counted to determine the phenotype. The results are summarized in Figure 10–22.

The mating of individuals of totally unrelated strains, termed **outbreeding,** frequently leads to offspring much better adapted for survival than either parent. Such improvement reflects a phenomenon called **hybrid vigor.** A large proportion of the corn, wheat, and other crops grown in the United States consists of hybrid strains. Each year the seed to grow these crops must be obtained by mating the original strains. The hybrids are heterozygous at a great many loci and give rise, even when self-fertilized, to a wide variety of forms, few of which are as good as the original hybrid. (The seeds produced by F₁ hybrid corn plants are not normally planted, but eaten instead!)

The reason for hybrid vigor has long been a matter of debate, and, in fact, there may be multiple causes. One explanation may be that each of the parental strains is homozygous for cer-

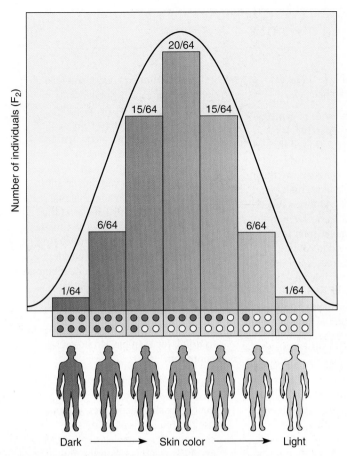

Figure 10–22 Distribution of phenotypes in polygenic inheritance. The bars indicate the expected phenotypic ratios in the F_2 generation shown in Figure 10–21. This expected distribution of phenotypes is consistent with the superimposed normal distribution curve.

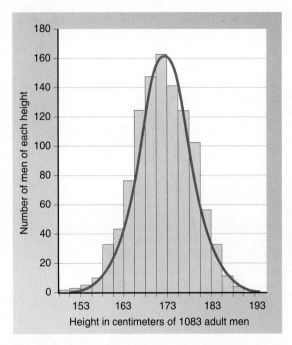

Figure 10–23 Polygenic inheritance in a population. The distribution of heights of 1083 adult males approximates a normal curve, which is consistent with continuous phenotypic variation in the population. The bars indicate the actual number of men whose heights were within the unit range. For example, there were 163 men whose heights were between 170.5 and 173.0 cm.

tain undesirable recessive genes, but any two strains are homozygous for different undesirable genes. Each strain contains dominant genes to make up for the recessive, undesirable genes of the other strain. The hybrid offspring would express all the desirable (dominant) traits and none of the undesirable (recessive) traits of the two parental strains.

Another explanation is that hybrid vigor is due to **heterozygote advantage,** that is, the superiority of the heterozygous genotype to either homozygous genotype. The key may be that a particular allele may have advantages under one set of conditions, but that a different allele may be favored when conditions change. Therefore an individual with two different alleles for a locus may be able to function over a wider range of conditions. This view is supported by experimental evidence that the metabolism of an individual heterozygous at many loci tends to be more stable and less affected by environmental changes.

A case of heterozygote advantage with a rather specific explanation is seen in humans who are heterozygous for the recessive sickle cell anemia allele *(s)* and the normal dominant allele *(S)* (see Chapter 18). These *Ss* individuals appear to have increased resistance to the parasite that lives inside red blood cells and causes malaria. Such resistance is a significant advantage in areas of the world where malaria is still uncontrolled. Homozygous normal individuals *(SS)* appear to be less resistant to malaria; homozygous sickle cell individuals *(ss)* are at a distinct disadvantage due to severe anemia and other serious effects of the sickle cell allele (see Chapter 15).

Simple Mendelian genetics problems are like puzzles. They can be fun and easy to work if you follow certain conventions and are methodical in your approach.

1. Always use standard designations for the generations. The generation with which a particular genetic experiment is begun is called the *P*, or *parental, generation*. Offspring of this generation (the "children") are called the F_1, or *first filial, generation*. The offspring resulting when two F_1 individuals are bred constitute the F_2, or *second filial, generation* (the "grandchildren").

2. Write down a key for the symbols you are using for the allelic variants of each locus. Use uppercase to designate a dominant allele and lowercase to designate a recessive allele. Use the same letter of the alphabet to designate both alleles of a particular locus. If you are not told which is dominant and which is recessive, the phenotype of the F_1 generation is a good clue.

3. Determine the genotypes of the parents of each cross by making use of the following types of evidence:
   a. Are they from true-breeding lines? If so, they should be homozygous.
   b. Can their genotypes be reliably deduced from their phenotypes? This is usually true if they express the recessive phenotype.
   c. Do the phenotypes of their offspring provide any information? *See Focus On: Deducing Genotypes*

for an example of how these determinations can be made.

4. Indicate the possible kinds of gametes formed by each of the parents. It is helpful to draw a circle around the symbols for each kind of gamete.
   a. If it is a monohybrid cross, we must apply the principle of segregation; i.e., a heterozygote *Aa* forms two kinds of gametes: *A* and *a*. Of course a homozygote, such as *aa*, forms only one kind of gamete: *a*.
   b. If it is a dihybrid cross, we must apply both the principle of segregation *and* the principle of independent assortment. For example, an individual heterozygous for two loci would have the genotype *AaBb*. Allele *A* segregates from *a*, and *B* segregates from *b*. The assortment of *A* and *a* into gametes is independent of the assortment of *B* and *b*. Therefore *A* is equally likely to end up in a gamete with *B* or *b*. The same is true for *a*.

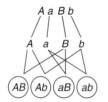

Segregation of the alleles of each locus

Independent assortment of alleles of different loci

5. Set up a Punnett square, placing the possible types of gametes from one parent down the left side and the possible types from the other parent across the top.

6. Fill in the Punnett square and read off (and sum up) the genotypic and phenotypic ratios of the offspring. Avoid confusion by consistently placing the dominant allele first and the recessive allele second in heterozygotes (*Aa*, never *aA*). If it is a dihybrid cross, it is very important to always write the two alleles of one locus first and the two alleles of the other locus second. It does not matter which locus you choose to write first, but once you have decided on the order, it is critical that you maintain it consistently. This means that if the individual is heterozygous for both loci, you will always use the form *AaBb*. Writing this particular genotype as *aBbA*, for example, would cause confusion.

7. If you do not need to know the frequencies of all the expected genotypes and phenotypes, you may use the rules of probability as a shortcut. For example, if both parents are *AaBb*, what is the probability of an *AABB* offspring? To be *AA*, the offspring must receive an *A* gamete from each parent. The probability that a given gamete is *A* is 1/2 and each gamete represents an independent event, so we combine their probabilities by multiplying (1/2 × 1/2 = 1/4). The probability of *BB* is calculated similarly and is also 1/4. The probability of *AA* is independent of the probability of *BB*, so again we use the product rule to obtain their combined probabilities (1/4 × 1/4 = 1/16).

Deducing Genotypes

The science of genetics resembles mathematics in that it consists of a few basic principles, which, once grasped, enable the student to solve a wide variety of problems. Very often the genotypes of the parents can be deduced from the phenotypes of their offspring. In chickens, for example, the allele for rose comb *(R)* is dominant to the allele for single comb *(r)*. Suppose that a cock is mated to three different hens, as shown in the figure. The cock and hens A and C have rose combs; hen B has a single comb. Breeding the cock with hen A produces a rose-combed chick, with hen B a single-combed chick, and with hen C a single-combed chick. What types of offspring can be expected from further matings of the cock with these hens?

Because the allele for single comb, *r,* is recessive, all hens and chicks that are phenotypically single-combed must be *rr.* We can deduce that hen *B* and the offspring of hens *B* and *C* are genotypically *rr.*

All individuals that are phenotypically rose-combed must have at least one *R* allele. The fact that the offspring of the cock and hen B was single-combed proves that the cock is heterozygous *Rr,* because, although the single-combed chick received one *r* allele

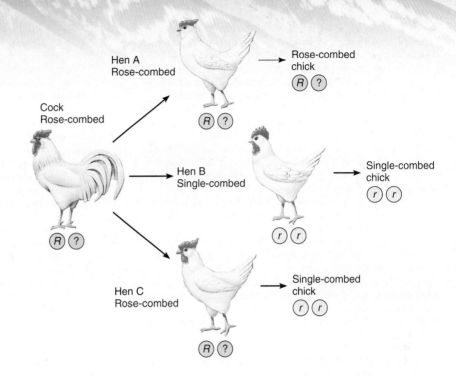

from its mother, it must have received the second one from its father.

The fact that the offspring of the cock and hen C had a single comb proves that hen C is heterozygous, *Rr.* It is impossible to determine from the data given whether hen A is homozygous *RR* or heterozygous *Rr;* further breeding

would be necessary to determine this. (Can you suggest an appropriate mating?)

Additional matings of the cock with hen B should result in half rose-combed and half single-combed individuals; additional matings of the cock with hen C should produce three-fourths rose-combed and one-fourth single-combed chicks.

SUMMARY WITH KEY TERMS

I. **Genetics** is the study of the structure, expression, and transmission of genetic information. The transfer of genetic information from parent to offspring is called **heredity.**

II. Mendel's inferences about inheritance obtained from his garden pea-breeding experiments have been tested repeatedly in all kinds of diploid organisms and found to be generally true. These principles have been extended and now can be stated in a more modern form.

A. Today we know that the **genes** are in chromosomes; the site a gene occupies in the chromosome is its **locus.**

B. Different forms of a particular gene are **alleles;** they occupy corresponding loci on homologous chromosomes. Genes therefore exist as pairs of alleles in diploid individuals.

C. An individual that carries two identical alleles is said to be **homozygous** for that locus. If the two alleles are different, that individual is said to be **heterozygous** for that locus.

D. One allele (the **dominant allele**) may mask the expression of the other allele (the **recessive allele**) in a heterozygous individual. For this rea-

son two individuals with the same appearance **(phenotype)** may differ from each other in genetic constitution **(genotype).**

E. Dominance does not always apply, and alleles can be **incompletely dominant,** in which the heterozygote is intermediate in phenotype, or **codominant,** in which the heterozygote simultaneously expresses the phenotypes of both homozygotes.

F. According to Mendel's **principle of segregation,** during meiosis the alleles for each locus separate, or segregate, from each other as the homologous chromosomes separate. When haploid gametes are formed, each contains only one allele for each locus.

G. According to Mendel's **principle of independent assortment,** alleles of different loci are distributed randomly into the gametes. This can result in **recombination,** that is, production of new gene combinations that were not present in the **parental (P) generation.**

H. Each chromosome behaves genetically as if it were composed of genes arranged in a linear order. Genes in the same chromosome are **linked.**

1. Recombination of linked genes can occur as a result of **crossing-over** (breaking and rejoining of homologous chromatids) in meiotic prophase I.
2. By measuring the frequency of recombination between linked genes, it is possible to construct a linkage map of a chromosome.
I. A cross between homozygous parents (P generation) that differ from each other with respect to their alleles at one locus is called a **monohybrid cross;** if they differ at two loci, it is a **dihybrid cross.**
   1. The first generation of offspring is heterozygous and is called the first filial, or **F_1, generation;** the generation produced by a cross of two F_1 individuals is the second filial, or **F_2, generation.**
   2. A **test cross** is between an individual of unknown genotype and a homozygous recessive individual.
III. Genetic ratios can be expressed in terms of probabilities.
  A. Any probability is expressed as a fraction or decimal fraction, calculated as the number of favorable events divided by the total number of events. This can range from 0 (an impossible event) to 1 (a certain event).
  B. According to the **product rule,** the probability of two independent events occurring together can be obtained by multiplying the probabilities of each occurring separately.
  C. According to the **sum rule,** the probability of an outcome that can be obtained in more than one way can be calculated by adding the separate probabilities.
IV. The sex of humans and many other animals is determined by the **X** and **Y sex chromosomes** or their equivalents. **Autosomes** are chromosomes other than sex chromosomes.
  A. Normal female mammals have two X chromosomes; normal males have one X and one Y.
  B. The fertilization of an X-bearing egg by an X-bearing sperm results in a female (XX) zygote. The fertilization of an X-bearing egg by a Y-bearing sperm results in a male (XY) zygote.

C. The Y chromosome is responsible for determining male sex in mammals.
D. The X chromosome contains many important genes unrelated to sex determination that are required by both males and females. A male receives all his **X-linked** genes from his mother. A female receives X-linked genes from both parents.
E. A female mammal shows **dosage compensation** of X-linked genes. Only one of the two X chromosomes is expressed in each cell; the other is inactive and is seen as a dark-staining **Barr body** at the edge of the interphase nucleus.
V. **Multiple alleles** (three or more alleles that can potentially occupy a particular locus) may exist in a population. A diploid individual has any two of the alleles; a haploid individual or gamete has only one.
VI. The relationship between a gene and its phenotype may be quite complex.
  A. Most genes have many different effects; they are **pleiotropic.**
  B. Many types of gene interactions are known. In **epistasis,** an allele of one locus can mask the expression of alleles of a different locus.
  C. In **polygenic inheritance,** multiple independent pairs of genes may have similar and additive effects on the phenotype.
   1. Many human characteristics showing continuous variation, such as height and skin color, as well as many characteristics in other animals and plants, are inherited through polygenes.
   2. In polygenic inheritance, the F_1 generation is intermediate between the two parental types and shows little variation; the F_2 generation shows wide variation.
VII. **Inbreeding,** the mating of two closely related individuals, greatly increases the probability that an individual offspring will be homozygous for one or more recessive genes. **Outbreeding,** the mating of totally unrelated individuals, increases the probability that the offspring will be heterozygous at many loci and exhibit **hybrid vigor.**

POST-TEST

1. One reason why Mendel was able to discover the basic principles of inheritance is that he (a) understood the behavior of chromosomes in mitosis and meiosis (b) studied a wide variety of experimental organisms (c) began by establishing true-breeding lines (d) studied various types of linkage (e) studied hybrids between parents that differed in many, often not clearly defined, ways

2. One of the autosomal loci controlling eye color in fruit flies has two alleles, one for brown eyes and the other for red eyes. Fruit flies from a true-breeding line with brown eyes were crossed with flies from a true-breeding line with red eyes. The F_1 flies had red eyes. What conclusion can be drawn from this experiment? (a) these alleles underwent independent assortment (b) these alleles underwent segregation (c) these genes are X-linked (d) the allele for red eyes is dominant to the allele for brown eyes (e) all of the above are true

3. The F_1 flies described in question 2 were mated with brown-eyed flies from a true-breeding line. What phenotypes would you expect the offspring to have? (a) all red eyes (b) all brown eyes (c) half red eyes and half brown eyes (d) red-eyed females and brown-eyed males (e) brown-eyed females and red-eyed males

4. The type of cross described in question 3 is a(an) (a) F_2 cross (b) dihybrid cross (c) test cross (d) two-point test cross (e) none of the above

Use the following information to answer questions 5 through 8:

In peas, the allele for round seeds *(R)* is dominant to that for wrinkled seeds *(r);* the allele for yellow seeds *(Y)* is dominant to that for green seeds *(y)*. These loci are unlinked. Plants from a true-breeding line with round, green seeds are crossed with plants from a true-breeding line with wrinkled, yellow seeds. These parents constitute the P generation.

5. The genotypes of the P generation are (a) *RRrr* and *Yyyy* (b) *RrYy* (c) *RRYY* and *rryy* (d) *RRyy* and *rrYY* (e) *RR* and *YY*

6. What are the expected genotypes of the F_1 hybrids produced by the described cross? (a) *RRrr* and *YYyy* (b) all *RrYy* (c) *RRYY* and *rryy* (d) *RRyy* and *rrYY* (e) *RR* and *YY*

7. What kinds of gametes can the F_1 individuals produce? (a) *RR* and *YY* (b) *Rr* and *Yy* (c) *RR, rr, YY,* and *yy* (d) *R, r, Y,* and *y* (e) *RY, Ry, rY,* and *ry*

8. What is the expected proportion of F_2 wrinkled, yellow seeds? (a) 9/16 (b) 1/16 (c) 3/16 (d) 1/4 (e) zero

9. Individuals of genotype *AaBb* were crossed with *aabb* individuals. Approximately equal numbers of the following classes of offspring were produced: *AaBb, Aabb, aaBb,* and *aabb*. These results illustrate Mendel's principle(s) of (a) linkage (b) independent assortment (c) segregation (d) a and c (e) b and c

10. Assume that the ratio of females to males is 1:1. A couple already has two daughters and no sons. If they plan to have a total of six children, what is the probability that they will have a family of all girls? (a) 1/4 (b) 1/8 (c) 1/16 (d) 1/32 (e) 1/64

11. Red-green colorblindness is an X-linked recessive disorder in humans. Your friend is the daughter of a colorblind father. Her mother had normal color vision, but her maternal grandfather was colorblind. What is the probability that your friend is colorblind? (a) 1 (b) 1/2 (c) 1/4 (d) 3/4 (e) zero

12. When homozygous, a particular allele of a locus in rats causes abnormalities of the cartilage throughout the body, an enlarged heart, slow development, and death. This is an example of (a) pleiotropy (b) polygenic inheritance (c) epistasis (d) codominance (e) dosage compensation

1. In peas, yellow seed color is dominant to green. Predict the phenotypes (and their proportions) of the offspring of the following crosses: (a) homozygous yellow X green (b) heterozygous yellow X green (c) heterozygous yellow X homozygous yellow (d) heterozygous yellow X heterozygous yellow

2. If two animals heterozygous for a single pair of alleles are mated and have 200 offspring, about how many would be expected to have the phenotype of the dominant allele (i.e., to look like the parents)?

3. When two long-winged flies were mated, the offspring included 77 with long wings and 24 with short wings. Is the short-winged condition dominant or recessive? What are the genotypes of the parents?

4. A blue-eyed man, both of whose parents were brown-eyed, married a brown-eyed woman whose father was blue-eyed and whose mother was brown-eyed. If brown is dominant to blue, what are the genotypes of the individuals involved?

5. Outline a breeding procedure whereby a true-breeding strain of red cattle could be established from a roan bull and a white cow.

6. What is the probability of rolling a seven with a pair of dice? Which is a more likely outcome, rolling a six with a pair of dice or rolling an eight?

7. In rabbits, spotted coat *(S)* is dominant to solid color *(s)*, and black *(B)* is dominant to brown *(b)*. These loci are unlinked. A brown, spotted rabbit from a pure line is mated to a solid black one, also from a pure line. What are the genotypes of the parents? What would be the genotype and phenotype of an F_1 rabbit? What would be the expected genotypes and phenotypes of the F_2 generation?

8. The long hair of Persian cats is recessive to the short hair of Siamese cats, but the black coat color of Persians is dominant to the brown-and-tan coat color of Siamese. Make up appropriate symbols for the alleles of these two unlinked loci. If a pure black, long-haired Persian is mated to a pure brown-and-tan, short-haired Siamese, what will be the appearance of the F_1 offspring? If two of these F_1 cats are mated, what is the chance that a long-haired, brown-and-tan cat will be produced in the F_2 generation? (Use the shortcut probability method to obtain your answer; then check it with a Punnett square.)

9. Mr. and Mrs. Smith are concerned because their own blood types are A and B respectively, but their new son, Richard, is blood type O. Could Richard be the child of these parents?

10. The expression of an allele called *frizzle* in fowl causes abnormalities of the feathers. As a consequence, the animal's body temperature is lowered, adversely affecting the functions of many internal organs. When one gene affects many characteristics of the organism in this way, we say that gene is _____.

11. A walnut-combed rooster is mated to three hens. Hen A, which is walnut-combed, has offspring in the ratio of 3 walnut : 1 rose. Hen B, which is pea-combed, has offspring in the ratio of 3 walnut : 3 pea : 1 rose : 1 single. Hen C, which is walnut-combed, has only walnut-combed offspring. What are the genotypes of the rooster and the three hens?

12. What kinds of matings result in the following phenotypic ratios? (a) 3:1 (b) 1:1 (c) 9:3:3:1 (d) 1:1:1:1

13. The weight of the fruit in a certain variety of squash is determined by allelic pairs for two loci: *AABB* produces fruits that average 2 kg each, and *aabb* produces fruits that are 1 kg each. Each allele represented by a capital letter adds 0.25 kg. When a plant that produces 2-kg fruits is crossed with a plant that produces 1-kg fruits, all of the offspring produce fruits that are 1.5 kg each. What would be the weights of the fruits produced by the F_2 plants if two of these F_1 plants were crossed?

14. The X-linked *barred* locus in chickens controls the pattern of the feathers, with the alleles *B* for barred pattern and *b* for no bars. If a barred female $(X^B Y)$ is mated to a nonbarred male $(X^b X^b)$, what will be the appearance of the male and female progeny? (Recall that in birds males are homogametic and females are heterogametic.) Do you see any commercial usefulness for this result? (*Hint:* It is notoriously difficult to determine the sex of newly hatched chicks.)

15. Individuals of genotype *AaBb* were mated to individuals of genotype *aabb*. One thousand offspring were counted, with the following results: 474 *Aabb*, 480 *aaBb*, 20 *AaBb*, and 26 *aabb*. What is this type of cross known as? Are these loci linked? What are the two parental classes and the two recombinant classes of offspring? What is the percentage of recombination between these two loci? How many map units apart are they?

16. Genes *A* and *B* are 6 map units apart, and *A* and *C* are 4 map units apart. Which gene is in the middle if *B* and *C* are 10 map units apart? Which is in the middle if *B* and *C* are 2 map units apart?

Answers to these Review Questions are included in Appendix A with the Post-Test answers.

YOU MAKE THE CONNECTION

1. Would the development of the science of genetics in the 20th century have been any different if Gregor Mendel had never lived?

2. Sketch a series of diagrams showing each of the following, making sure to end each series with haploid gametes:
   (a) how a pair of alleles for a single locus segregates in meiosis
   (b) how the alleles of two unlinked loci assort independently in meiosis
   (c) how the alleles of two linked loci undergo genetic recombination

3. Can you always ascertain an organism's genotype for a particular locus if you know its phenotype? Conversely, if you are given an organism's genotype for a locus, can you always reliably predict its phenotype? Explain.

RECOMMENDED READINGS

Corcos, A., and F. Monaghan. *Mendel's Experiments on Plant Hybrids: A Guided Study.* Rutgers University Press, New Brunswick, 1993. This interpretive study of Mendel's paper includes information on his life as a monk and a scientist.

Ganetzky, B. "Tracking Down a Cheating Gene." *American Scientist,* Vol. 88, Mar.-Apr. 2000. An analysis of the *Segregation-Distorter* system in fruit flies, which violates the Mendelian principle of 1:1 segregation of alleles.

Heim, W.G. "What Is A Recessive Allele?" *The American Biology Teacher,* Vol. 53, Feb. 1991. A discussion of the molecular basis for the traits Mendel studied in garden peas.

Mendel, G. "Experiments in plant hybridization." Reprinted in *Genetics: Readings from Scientific American.* W.H. Freeman and Co., San Francisco, 1990. Try reading this translation of Mendel's classic paper from the perspective of other scientists of his time who lacked knowledge of chromosomes, mitosis, and meiosis.

There are several well-written, college-level genetics texts that cover the principles of genetics in eukaryotes. The following are three representative examples:

Atherly, A.G., J.R. Girton, and J.F. McDonald. *The Science of Genetics,* 1st ed. Saunders College Publishing, Philadelphia, 1999.

Griffiths, A.J.F., J.H. Miller, D.T. Suzuki, R.C. Lewontin, and W.M. Gelbart. *An Introduction to Genetic Analysis,* 7th ed. W.H. Freeman, New York, 2000.

Russell, P. *Genetics,* 5th ed. Benjamin/Cummings, Menlo Park, CA, 1998.

● Visit our Web site at **http://www.info.brookscole.com/solomonbergmartin** for links to chapter-related resources on the World Wide Web. Additional on-line materials relating to this chapter can also be found on our Web site.

See chapter activity on BioActive Learner CD for additional help in mastering the chapter's material. Icon location in the chapter's margins shows which topics have tutorials or simulations in the CD.

11

DNA: The Carrier of Genetic Information

LEARNING OBJECTIVES

After you have studied this chapter you should be able to

1. Summarize the evidence that accumulated during the 1940s and early 1950s demonstrating that DNA is the genetic material.
2. Relate the chemical and physical features of DNA to the structure proposed by Watson and Crick.
3. Sketch how nucleotide subunits are linked together to form a single DNA strand.
4. Illustrate how the two strands of DNA are oriented with respect to each other.
5. State the base-pairing rules for DNA and describe how complementary bases bind to each other.
6. Cite experimental evidence that allowed scientists to differentiate between semiconservative replication of DNA and alternative models (conservative and dispersive replication).
7. Summarize how DNA replicates and identify some of the unique features of the process.
8. Explain the special constraints on DNA replication that cause it to be (1) bidirectional and (2) discontinuous in one strand and continuous in the other.
9. Compare the organization of DNA in prokaryotic and eukaryotic cells.

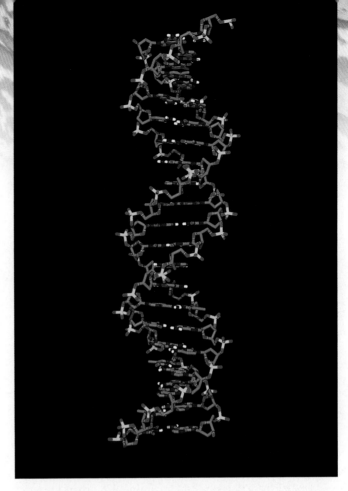

A model showing the structure of DNA (deoxyribonucleic acid). *(Prof. K. Seddon & Dr. T. Evans, Queen University, Belfast, Science Photo Library/Photo Researchers, Inc.)*

Following the rediscovery of Mendel's principles, geneticists conducted a variety of elegant experiments to learn how genes are arranged in chromosomes and how they are transmitted from generation to generation. However, the basic questions remained unanswered through most of the first half of the 20th century: What are genes made of? How do genes work? The studies of inheritance patterns described in Chapter 10 did not answer these questions, but they provided a foundation of knowledge that allowed scientists to make predictions about what the molecular (chemical) nature of genes might be and how genes might function.

Because scientists generally agreed that the function of genes must be to provide information, it followed that the mole-cules of which genes are made should have the ability to store information in a form that could be retrieved and used by the cell. But genes had other properties that had to be accounted for as well. For example, countless genetic experiments on a wide variety of organisms had demonstrated that genes are usually quite stable, being passed unchanged from generation to generation. However, occasionally a gene was observed to convert to a different form; such genetic changes, called **mutations,** were then transmitted unchanged to future generations.

As the science of genetics was developing, the science of biochemistry was flourishing as well. Not surprisingly, there was a growing effort to correlate the known properties of genes with the nature of the various biological molecules. What kind of molecule could store information? How could that information be retrieved and used to direct cellular functions? What kind of molecule could be relatively stable but have the capacity to change, resulting in a mutation, under some circumstances?

Some scientists thought that the problem could never be solved. They thought the information required by a cell to be so complex that no one type of molecule could function as the genetic material. However, as more was learned about the central role that proteins play in virtually every aspect of cellular structure and metabolism, other scientists considered them the prime candidates for the genetic material. However, protein did not turn out to be the molecule responsible for inheritance. In this chapter we discuss how **deoxyribonucleic acid (DNA),** a nucleic acid that was once thought to be dull and uninteresting, was found to be the molecular basis of inheritance, and we examine the unique features of DNA that allow it to carry out this role.

EVIDENCE THAT DNA IS THE HEREDITARY MATERIAL WAS FIRST FOUND IN MICROORGANISMS

During the 1930s and early 1940s, most geneticists and biochemists paid little attention to DNA and RNA, and were convinced that the genetic material must be protein. In light of the accumulating evidence that genes control the production of proteins, discussed in Chapter 12, it certainly seemed likely that genes themselves must also be proteins. Proteins were known to contain more than 20 different kinds of amino acids in many different combinations, allowing each type of protein to have unique properties. Given their complexity and diversity compared with other molecules, proteins seemed to be the "stuff" of which genes are made.

In contrast, it had been established that DNA and other nucleic acids were made of only four nucleotides, and what was known about their arrangement made them seem relatively uninteresting to most scientists. For this reason, several early clues to the role of DNA were not widely recognized.

One of these clues had its origin in 1928, when Frederick Griffith made a curious observation concerning two strains of pneumococcus bacteria (Fig. 11–1). A smooth (S) strain, named for its formation of smooth colonies on a solid growth medium, was known to be **virulent,** or lethal. When living cells of this strain were injected into mice, the animals contracted pneumonia and died. Not surprisingly, the injected animals survived if the cells were first killed with heat. A related rough (R) strain, which forms colonies with a rough surface, was known to be **avirulent,** or nonlethal; mice injected with either living or heat-killed cells of this strain survived. However, when Griffith injected mice with a mixture of *heat-killed,* virulent S-strain cells and live avirulent R-strain cells, a high proportion of the mice died. Griffith was then able to isolate living S-strain cells from the dead mice.

Because neither the heat-killed S strain nor the living R strain could be converted to the living virulent form when injected by itself in the control experiments, something in the heat-killed cells appeared to convert the avirulent cells to the lethal form. This type of permanent genetic change in which the properties of one strain of dead cells are conferred on a different strain of living cells became known as **transformation.** It was widely hypothesized that transformation was caused by some chemical substance (called the "transforming principle") that was transferred from the dead bacteria to the living cells.

In 1944, O.T. Avery, C.M. MacLeod, and M. McCarty of the Rockefeller Institute chemically identified Griffith's transform-

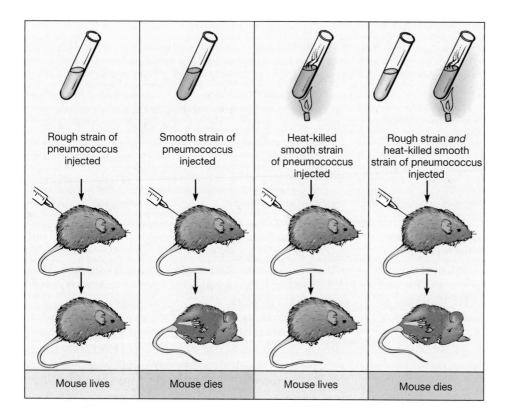

Rough strain of pneumococcus injected — Mouse lives

Smooth strain of pneumococcus injected — Mouse dies

Heat-killed smooth strain of pneumococcus injected — Mouse lives

Rough strain *and* heat-killed smooth strain of pneumococcus injected — Mouse dies

Figure 11–1 Griffith's transformation experiments. Although neither the rough (R) strain nor the heat-killed smooth (S) strain could kill a mouse, a combination of the two did. Autopsy of the dead mouse showed the presence of living, S-strain pneumococci. These results indicated that some substance in the heat-killed S strain was responsible for the transformation of the living R strain to a virulent form. Avery and his colleagues later showed that purified DNA isolated from the S strain confers virulence on the R-strain bacteria, establishing that DNA carries the necessary information for bacterial transformation.

ing principle as DNA. They did this through a series of very careful experiments in which they treated living R cells with highly purified DNA extracted from S cells, causing the R cells to become transformed into S cells. Although today we consider their findings to be the first demonstration that DNA is the genetic material, not all scientists of the time were convinced. One argument given was that the DNA preparations used might have been contaminated with a tiny amount of protein, which might have been responsible for the results. This was not a trivial objection, because it was well known that a very small amount of an enzyme could have significant biological effects. Furthermore, many scientists thought that their findings, even if true, might apply only to bacteria and not have any relevance for the genetics of eukaryotes.

During the next few years, new evidence accumulated that the haploid nuclei of pollen grains and gametes such as sperm contain only half the amount of DNA found in diploid somatic cells of the same species. Because the idea that genes are on chromosomes was generally accepted, these findings correlating DNA content with chromosome number provided strong circumstantial evidence of DNA's importance in inheritance in eukaryotes.

In 1952 Alfred Hershey and Martha Chase performed a series of elegant experiments (Fig. 11–2) on the reproduction of viruses that infect bacteria, known as **bacteriophages** (see Chapter 23). When they planned their experiments, they knew that bacteriophages reproduce inside a bacterial cell, eventually causing the cell to break open, releasing large numbers of new viruses. Because electron microscope studies had shown that only part of an infecting bacteriophage actually enters the cell, they reasoned that the genetic material should be included in that portion. They labeled the viral protein of one sample of bacteriophages with ^{35}S, a radioactive isotope of sulfur, and the viral DNA of a second sample with ^{32}P, a radioactive isotope of phosphorus. (Recall from Chapter 3 that proteins contain sulfur as part of the amino acid cysteine, and nucleic acids contain phosphate groups.) The bacteriophages in each sample were allowed to attach to bacteria and then shaken off by agitating them in a blender. The cells were then subjected to centrifugation (see Chapter 4). In the sample in which the proteins were labeled with ^{35}S, all of the label was subsequently found in the supernatant, indicating that the protein had not entered the cells. In the sample in which the DNA was labeled with ^{32}P, the label was found associated with the bacterial cells (in the pellet), indicating that DNA had actually entered the cells. Hershey and Chase

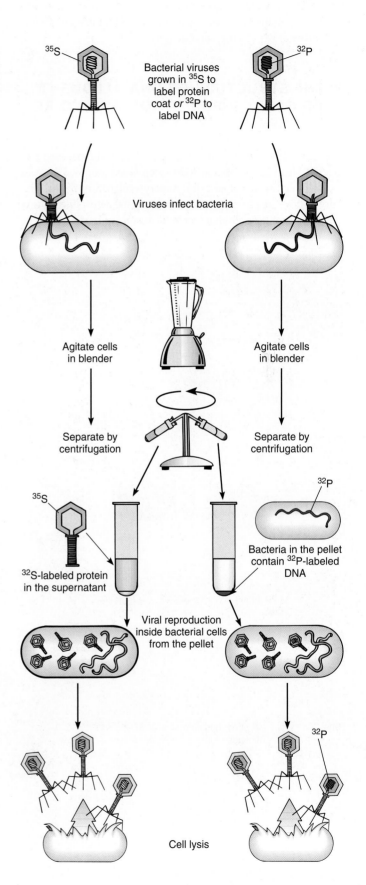

Figure 11–2 The Hershey-Chase experiments. Although bacteriophage protein coats labeled with the radioactive isotope ^{35}S *(left)* could be separated from infected bacterial cells without interfering with viral reproduction, viral DNA labeled with the radioactive isotope ^{32}P *(right)* could not, thus demonstrating that the DNA enters the cells and is required for synthesis of new protein coats and DNA.

concluded that bacteriophages inject their DNA into bacterial cells, leaving most of their protein on the outside. This finding emphasized the significance of DNA in viral reproduction and was seen by many scientists as another important demonstration of the role of DNA as the hereditary material.

THE STRUCTURE OF DNA ALLOWS IT TO CARRY INFORMATION AND TO BE FAITHFULLY DUPLICATED

DNA did not become widely accepted as the genetic material until 1953, when James Watson and Francis Crick proposed a model for its structure that had extraordinary explanatory power. The story of how the structure of DNA came to be determined is one of the most remarkable chapters in the history of modern biology.

As we will see in the subsequent discussion, a great deal was already known about the physical and chemical properties of DNA when Watson and Crick became interested in the problem, and in fact they did not conduct any experiments or gather any new data. Their all-important contribution was to integrate all the available information into a model that demonstrated how the molecule can both carry information for making proteins and serve as its own **template** (pattern or guide) for its duplication.

Nucleotides can be covalently linked in any order to form long polymers

As discussed in Chapter 3, each DNA building block is a **nucleotide** consisting of a pentose sugar **(deoxyribose),** a phosphate, and one of four nitrogenous bases (Fig. 11–3a). It is conventional to number the atoms in a molecule using a system

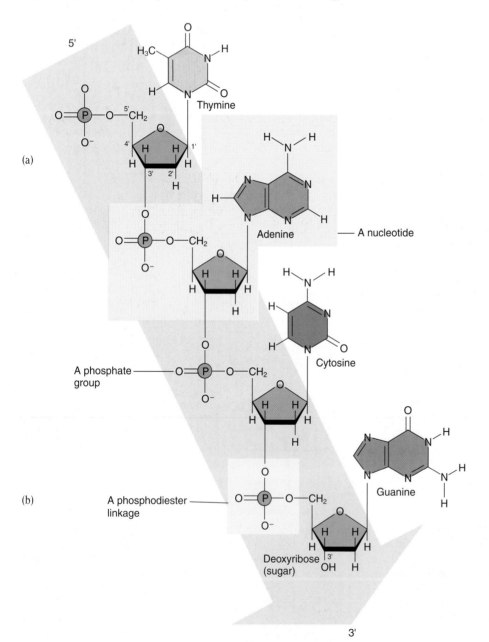

Figure 11–3 The nucleotide subunits of DNA. **(a)** A single strand of DNA consists of a backbone made of phosphate groups alternating with the sugar deoxyribose *(green)*. Linked to the 1' carbon of each sugar is one of four nitrogenous bases. The purine bases, adenine and guanine, have two-ring structures; the pyrimidine bases, thymine and cytosine, have one-ring structures. Note the polarity of the polynucleotide chain, with the 5' end at the top of the figure and the 3' end at the bottom. **(b)** Sugars of adjacent nucleotides are joined by phosphodiester linkages.

devised by organic chemists, and accordingly in nucleic acid chemistry the individual carbons in each sugar and each base are numbered. The carbons in a base are designated by ordinary numerals, but the carbons in a sugar are distinguished from those in the base by "prime" (') designations, such as 2'. The nitrogenous base is attached to the 1' carbon of the sugar, and the phosphate is attached to the 5' carbon. The bases include two **purines—adenine (A)** and **guanine (G)**—and two **pyrimidines—thymine (T)** and **cytosine (C).**

The nucleotides are linked by covalent bonds to form an alternating sugar-phosphate backbone. The 3' carbon of one sugar is bonded to the 5' phosphate of the adjacent sugar to form a 3',5' **phosphodiester linkage** (Fig. 11–3*b*). It is therefore possible to form a polymer of indefinite length, with the nucleotides linked in any order. We now know that most DNA molecules found in cells are millions of bases long. Figure 11–3*a* also illustrates that a single polynucleotide chain is directional. No matter how long the chain may be, one end (the **5' end**) has a 5' carbon attached to a phosphate and the other (the **3' end**) has a 3' carbon attached to a hydroxyl group.

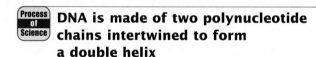

DNA is made of two polynucleotide chains intertwined to form a double helix

Key information about the structure of DNA came from **x-ray diffraction** studies on crystals of purified DNA, carried out by Rosalind Franklin in the laboratory of M.H.F. Wilkins. X-ray diffraction is a powerful method for determining distances between atoms of molecules arranged in a regular, repeating crystalline structure (Fig. 11–4). X rays have such extremely short wavelengths that they can be scattered by the electrons surrounding the atoms in a molecule. Atoms with dense electron clouds (e.g., phosphorus, oxygen) tend to deflect electrons more strongly than do atoms with lower atomic numbers.

When a crystal is exposed to an intense beam of x rays, the regular arrangement of the atoms in the crystal causes the x rays to be diffracted, or scattered, in specific ways. The pattern of diffracted x rays is seen on film as dark spots. Mathematical analysis of the arrangement and distances between the spots can then be used to determine precise distances between atoms and their orientation within the molecules.

Franklin had already produced x-ray crystallographic films of DNA patterns when Watson and Crick began to pursue the problem of DNA structure. The pictures clearly showed that DNA has a type of helical structure, and three major types of regular, repeating patterns in the molecule (with the dimensions 0.34 nm, 3.4 nm, and 2.0 nm) were evident. Franklin and Wilkins had inferred from these patterns that the nucleotide bases (which are flat molecules) are stacked like rungs of a ladder. Using this information, Watson and Crick began to build scale models of the DNA components and then fit them together to agree with the experimental data.

After a number of trials, the two worked out a model that fit the existing data (Fig. 11–5). The nucleotide chains conformed to the dimensions of the x-ray data only if each DNA molecule con-

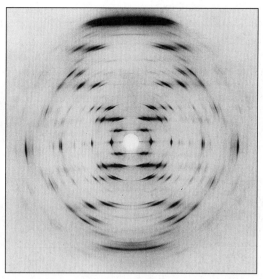

Figure 11–4 X-ray diffraction image of DNA. Important clues about DNA structure are provided by detailed mathematical analysis of measurements of x-ray diffraction images of the lithium salt of DNA. The diagonal pattern of spots stretching from 11 o'clock to 5 o'clock and from 1 o'clock to 7 o'clock provides evidence for the helical structure of DNA. The elongated horizontal patterns at the top and bottom indicate that the purine and pyrimidine bases are stacked 0.34 nm apart and are perpendicular to the axis of the DNA molecule. *(Dr. S.D. Dover, Division of Biomolecular Sciences, Kings College, London)*

sisted of *two* polynucleotide chains arranged in a coiled **double helix.** In their model, the sugar-phosphate backbones of the two chains form the outside of the helix. The bases belonging to the two chains associate as pairs along the central axis of the helix. The reasons for the repeating patterns of 0.34-nm and 3.4-nm measurements are readily apparent from the model: each pair of bases is exactly 0.34 nm from the adjacent pairs above and below. Because exactly ten base pairs are present in each full turn of the helix, each turn constitutes 3.4 nm of length. To fit the data, the two chains must run in opposite directions; therefore, each end of the double helix must have an exposed 5' phosphate on one strand and an exposed 3' hydroxyl group on the other (Fig. 11–6*a*). Because the two strands run in opposite directions, they are said to be **antiparallel** to each other.

In double-stranded DNA, hydrogen bonds form between adenine and thymine and between guanine and cytosine

Other features of the Watson and Crick model integrated critical information about the chemical composition of DNA with the x-ray diffraction data. By 1950, the base composition of DNA from a number of organisms and tissues had been determined by Erwin Chargaff and his coworkers at Columbia University. They found a simple relationship among the bases that turned out to be an important clue to the structure of DNA. Regardless of the

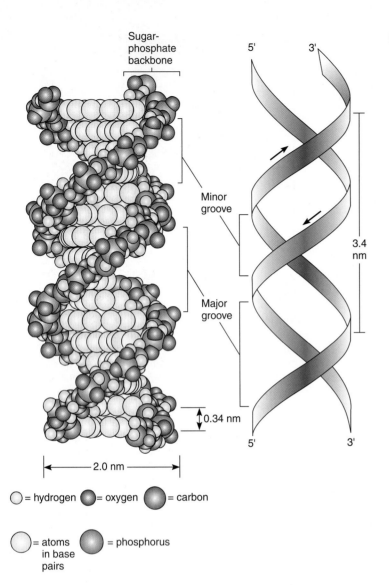

Sugar-phosphate backbone

Minor groove

Major groove

3.4 nm

0.34 nm

2.0 nm

○ = hydrogen ● = oxygen ● = carbon

● = atoms in base pairs ● = phosphorus

Figure 11–5 Structure of the DNA double helix. On the left is a space-filling model of the DNA double helix. The measurements on the diagrammatic model on the right match those derived from x-ray diffraction images. The ribbons represent the sugar-phosphate backbone of each strand; the arrows indicate that the two strands extend in opposite directions.

source of the DNA, in Chargaff's words, the "ratios of purines to pyrimidines and also of adenine to thymine and of guanine to cytosine were not far from 1." In other words, in double-stranded DNA molecules, the number of purines equals the number of pyrimidines, the number of adenines equals the number of thymines (A equals T), and the number of guanines equals the number of cytosines (G equals C).

The x-ray diffraction studies indicated that the double helix has a precise and constant width, as shown by the 2.0-nm measurements. This finding is actually connected to Chargaff's rules. Notice in Figure 11–3 that each pyrimidine (cytosine or thymine) contains only one ring of atoms, whereas each purine (guanine or adenine) contains two rings. Study of the models made it clear to Watson and Crick that if each cross-rung of the ladder were to contain one purine and one pyrimidine, the width of the helix at each base pair would be exactly 2.0 nm; by contrast, the combination of two purines (each of which is 1.2 nm wide) would be wider and that of two pyrimidines would be narrower, so the diameter would not be constant.

Further examination of the model showed that adenine can pair with thymine (and guanine with cytosine) in such a way that hydrogen bonds form between them; the opposite combinations,

cytosine with adenine and guanine with thymine, do not lead to favorable hydrogen bonding.

The nature of the hydrogen bonding between adenine and thymine and between guanine and cytosine is shown in Figure 11–6*b*. Two hydrogen bonds can form between adenine and thymine, and three between guanine and cytosine. This concept of *specific base-pairing* neatly explains Chargaff's rules. The amount of cytosine has to equal the amount of guanine because every cytosine in one chain must have a paired guanine in the other chain. Similarly, every adenine in the first chain must have a thymine in the second chain. Thus, the sequences of bases in the two chains are **complementary** to each other. In other words, the sequence of nucleotides in one chain dictates the complementary sequence of nucleotides in the other. For example, if one strand has the sequence:

3' — AGCTAC —5'

then the other strand has the complementary sequence:

5' — TCGATG — 3'

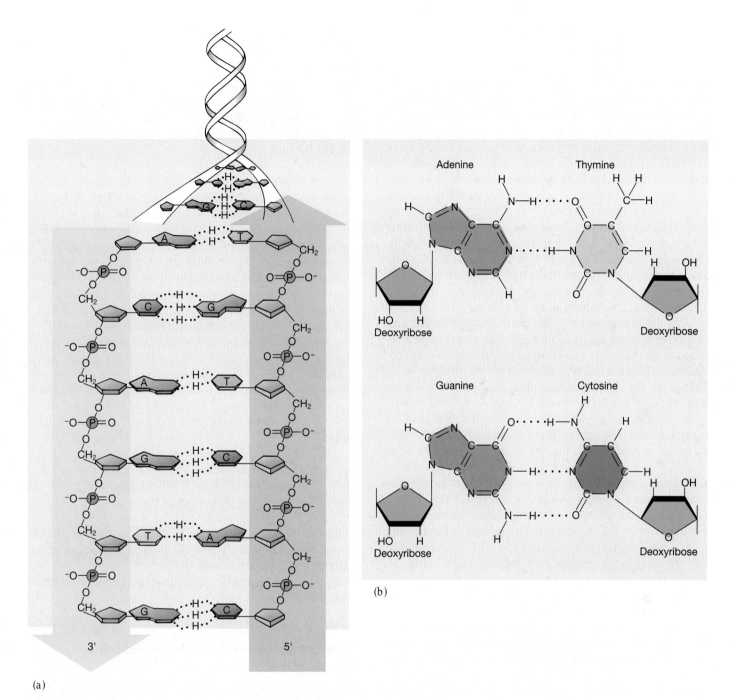

(a)

(b)

Figure 11–6 Hydrogen bonding between bases. The two strands of a DNA double helix are associated by hydrogen bonding between the bases. **(a)** The two sugar-phosphate chains run in opposite directions. This orientation permits the complementary bases to pair. **(b)** Diagram of the hydrogen bonding between base pairs adenine (A) and thymine (T) *(top)* and guanine (G) and cytosine (C) *(bottom)*. The AT pair has two hydrogen bonds; the GC pair has three.

The double-helix model strongly suggested that the sequence of bases in DNA can provide for the storage of genetic information and that this sequence could be ultimately related to the sequences of amino acids in proteins. Although there are restrictions on how the bases pair with each other, the number of possible sequences of bases in a strand is virtually unlimited. Because a DNA molecule in a cell can be millions of nucleotides long, it can store enormous amounts of information, usually comprising a large number of genes.

DNA REPLICATION IS SEMICONSERVATIVE

Two immediately apparent and distinctive features of the Watson-Crick model made it seem more plausible that DNA is the genetic material. We have already mentioned that the sequence of bases in DNA can carry coded information. The model also suggested a way in which the sequence of nucleotides in DNA could be precisely copied, a process known as **DNA replication.** The connection to the behavior of chromosomes in mitosis was obvious to Watson and Crick; just as a chromosome becomes duplicated so that it consists of two identical sister chromatids that later separate at anaphase, so the genetic material must be able to be precisely duplicated and distributed to the daughter cells. They noted in a classic and now famous understatement at the end of their first brief paper, "It has not escaped our notice that the specific pairing we have postulated immediately suggests a possible copying mechanism for the genetic material."

The model suggested that, because the nucleotides pair with each other in a complementary fashion, each strand of the DNA molecule could serve as a template for the synthesis of the opposite strand. It would simply be necessary for the hydrogen bonds between the two strands to break (recall that hydrogen bonds are relatively weak) and the two chains to separate. Each strand of the double helix could then pair with new complementary nucleotides to replace its missing partner. The result would be two DNA double helices, each identical to the original one and consisting of one original strand from the parent molecule and one newly synthesized complementary strand. This type of information copying is known as a **semiconservative replication** mechanism (Fig. 11–7a).

Although the semiconservative replication mechanism suggested by Watson and Crick was (and is) a simple and compelling model, experimental proof was needed to establish that DNA in fact duplicates in that manner. First it was necessary to rule out several other possibilities. For example, with a *conservative replication* mechanism, both parent (or old) strands would remain together, and the two newly synthesized strands would form a second double helix (Fig. 11–7b). As a third alternative, the parental and newly synthesized strands might become randomly mixed during the replication process; this possibility was known as *dispersive replication* (Fig. 11–7c). To discriminate among the semiconservative replication mechanism and the other possibilities, it was necessary to distinguish between old and newly synthesized strands of DNA.

One way to accomplish this is to use a heavy-nitrogen isotope, ^{15}N (ordinary nitrogen is ^{14}N), to label the bases of the DNA strands, making them more dense. Using the technique known as **density gradient centrifugation** (a technique that had been recently developed at that time), large molecules such as DNA can be separated on the basis of differences in their density. When DNA is mixed with a solution containing cesium chloride (CsCl) and centrifuged at high speed, the solution forms a density gradient in the centrifuge tube, ranging from a region of lowest density at the top to one of highest density at the bottom. During centrifugation, the DNA molecules migrate to the region of the gradient identical to their own density.

 In 1957, Matthew Meselson and Franklin Stahl grew the bacterium *Escherichia coli* on a medium that contained ^{15}N in the form of ammonium chloride (NH_4Cl). The cells used the ^{15}N to synthesize bases, which then became incorporated into DNA (Fig. 11–7d). The resulting heavy nitrogen–containing DNA molecules were extracted from some of the cells. When they were subjected to density gradient centrifugation, they accumulated in the high-density region of the gradient. The rest of the bacteria (which also contained ^{15}N-labeled DNA) were transferred to a different growth medium in which the NH_4Cl contained the naturally abundant, lighter ^{14}N isotope; they were then allowed to undergo additional cell divisions.

The newly synthesized DNA strands were expected to be less dense because they incorporated bases containing the lighter ^{14}N isotope. Indeed, double-stranded DNA from cells isolated after one generation had an intermediate density, indicating that they contained half as many ^{15}N atoms as the "parent" DNA. This finding supported the semiconservative model, which predicted that each double helix should contain a previously synthesized strand (heavy in this case) and a newly synthesized strand (light in this case). It was also consistent with the dispersive model, which would also yield one class of molecules, all with intermediate density. It was inconsistent with the conservative model, which predicted that there should be two classes of double-stranded molecules, those with two heavy strands and those with two light strands.

After another cycle of cell division in the medium with the lighter ^{14}N isotope, two types of DNA appeared in the density gradient. One consisted of "hybrid" DNA helices (with one ^{15}N strand and one ^{14}N strand), whereas the other contained only DNA with the naturally occurring light isotope. This finding refuted the dispersive model, which predicted that all strands should have intermediate density. Instead, each strand of the parental double-helix molecule was conserved, but in a *different* daughter molecule, exactly as predicted by the semiconservative replication model.

Semiconservative replication explains the stability of mutations

The recognition that DNA could be copied by a semiconservative mechanism suggested how DNA could fulfill a third essential characteristic of genetic material—the ability to mutate.

It was long known that mutations, or genetic changes, could arise in genes and then be transmitted faithfully to succeeding generations. When the double-helix model was proposed, it seemed plausible that mutations could represent a change in the sequence of bases in the DNA. One could predict that if DNA is copied by a mechanism involving complementary base pairing, any change in the sequence of bases on one strand would result in a new sequence of complementary bases during the next replication cycle. The new base sequence would then be passed on to daughter molecules by the same mechanism used to copy the original genetic material, as if no change had occurred.

(a) Hypothesis 1: Semiconservative replication

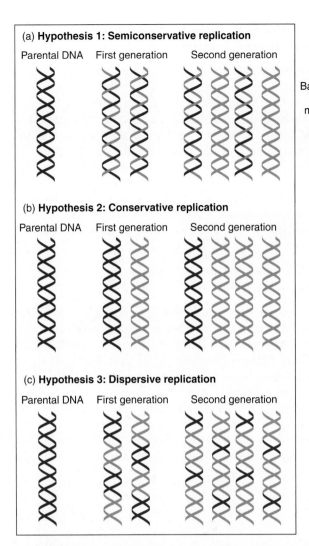

Parental DNA   First generation   Second generation

(b) Hypothesis 2: Conservative replication

Parental DNA   First generation   Second generation

(c) Hypothesis 3: Dispersive replication

Parental DNA   First generation   Second generation

Figure 11–7 Testing the mechanism of DNA replication. The predicted arrangement of old *(dark blue)* and newly synthesized *(light blue)* DNA strands after one and two generations, according to **(a)** the semiconservative model, **(b)** the conservative model, or **(c)** the dispersive model. **(d)** Meselson and Stahl tested the mechanism of DNA replication in an elegant series of experiments. They grew the bacterium *Escherichia coli* in heavy-nitrogen (^{15}N) growth medium for many generations. Some of the cells were then transferred to light-nitrogen (^{14}N) medium. DNA was isolated from cells after growth on ^{15}N medium one generation after transfer to ^{14}N medium, and two generations after transfer to ^{14}N medium. **(e)** The density of the molecules in each group matches the labeling pattern expected if DNA is replicated according to the semiconservative model depicted in part a.

(d) Hypothesis testing

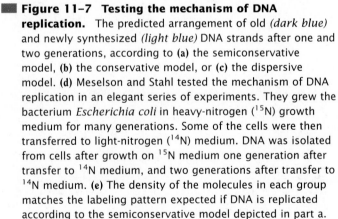

Bacteria are grown in ^{15}N (heavy) medium. All DNA is heavy.

Some cells are transferred to ^{14}N (light) medium.

Some cells continue to grow in ^{14}N medium.

First generation   Second generation

Cesium chloride (CsCl)

DNA

DNA is mixed with CsCl solution, placed in an ultracentrifuge, and centrifuged at very high speed for about 48 hours.

High density   Low density

The greater concentration of CsCl at the bottom of the tube is due to sedimentation under centrifugal force.

^{14}N (light) DNA ^{14}N -^{15}N hybrid DNA ^{15}N (heavy) DNA

DNA molecules move to positions where their density equals that of the CsCl solution.

(e) Results

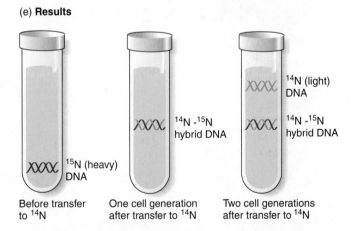

^{14}N (light) DNA

^{14}N -^{15}N hybrid DNA

^{14}N -^{15}N hybrid DNA

^{15}N (heavy) DNA

Before transfer to ^{14}N

One cell generation after transfer to ^{14}N

Two cell generations after transfer to ^{14}N

The location of DNA molecules within the centrifuge tube can be determined by UV optics. DNA solutions absorb strongly at 260 nm.

In the example shown in Figure 11–8, an adenine base in one of the DNA strands has been changed to guanine. This could occur by a rare error in DNA replication or by one of several other known mechanisms. (There are systems of enzymes that repair errors when they occur, but not all mutations are corrected properly.) When the DNA molecule is replicated again, one of the strands gives rise to a molecule exactly like the parent strand; the other (mutated) strand gives rise to a molecule with a new combination of bases that will be stably transmitted generation after generation.

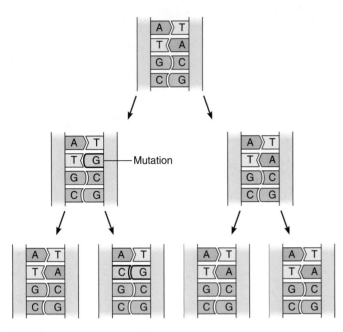

DNA replication is complex and has several unique features

Although semiconservative replication is a simple and straightforward prediction from the Watson-Crick model, the process actually requires a complex "replication machine" containing a large number of proteins and enzymes. Many of the essential features of DNA replication are universal, although some differences exist between prokaryotes and eukaryotes because their DNA is organized differently. In most bacterial cells, such as *E. coli*, most or all of the DNA is in the form of a single, *circular*, double-stranded DNA molecule. Each unreplicated eukaryotic chromosome contains a single, *linear*, double-stranded molecule associated with at least as much protein (by mass) as DNA.

DNA strands must be unwound during replication

Watson and Crick recognized that in their double-helix model the two DNA strands are wrapped around one another like the strands of a rope. If we try to pull the strands apart, the rope must either rotate or twist into tighter coils. We would expect similar things to happen when complementary DNA strands are separated for replication. Separating the two strands of DNA is accomplished by **DNA helicase enzymes** that travel along the helix, opening the double helix as they move. Once the strands are separated, **helix-destabilizing proteins** bind to single DNA strands, preventing re-formation of the double helix until the

Figure 11-8 Perpetuation of a mutation. The process of DNA replication can stabilize a mutation *(bright yellow)* so that it will be passed to future generations.

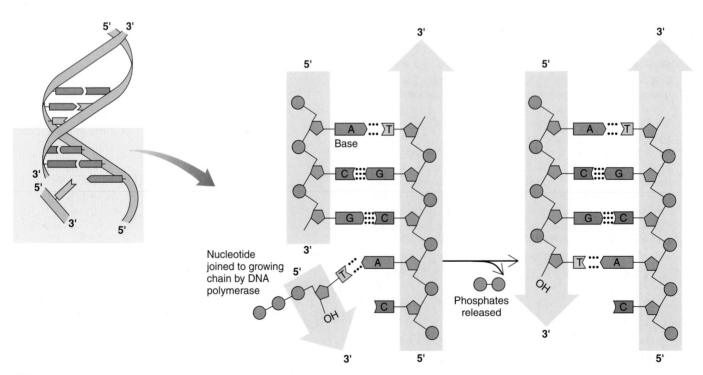

Figure 11-9 A simplified view of DNA replication. The polymerase enzymes that catalyze the polymerization reactions add one nucleotide at a time to the 3' end of a growing chain.

strands are copied. Enzymes called **topoisomerases** produce breaks in the DNA molecules and then rejoin the strands, relieving strain and effectively preventing the formation of knots during replication.

DNA synthesis always proceeds in a 5' → 3' direction

The enzymes that catalyze the linking together of the nucleotide subunits are called **DNA polymerases.** They have several limitations that contribute to the complexity of the replication process. They are able to add nucleotides only to the 3' end of a growing polynucleotide strand, and this strand must be paired with the strand being copied (Fig. 11–9). Nucleotides with three phosphate groups are used as substrates for the polymerization reaction. As the nucleotides are linked together, two of the phosphates are removed. Like the hydrolysis of ATP, these reactions are strongly exergonic (see Chapter 6) and do not require additional energy. Because the new polynucleotide chain is elongated by the linkage of the 5' phosphate group of the next nucleotide subunit to the 3' hydroxyl group of the sugar at the end of the preexisting strand, the new strand of DNA always grows in the 5' → 3' direction.

DNA synthesis requires an RNA primer

A second limitation of the DNA polymerases is that they can add nucleotides only to the 3' end of an *existing* polynucleotide strand. So how can DNA synthesis be initiated once the two strands are separated? The answer is that a short piece (usually about 5–14 nucleotides) of an **RNA primer** is first synthesized at the point of initiation of replication (Fig. 11–10).

RNA, or **ribonucleic acid** (see Chapters 3 and 12), is a nucleic acid polymer consisting of nucleotide subunits that can associate by complementary base-pairing with the single-stranded DNA template. The RNA primer is synthesized by **primase,** an enzyme that is able to start a new strand of RNA opposite a DNA strand. After a few nucleotides have been added, the primase is displaced by DNA polymerase, which can then add subunits to the 3' end of the short RNA primer. The primer is later degraded by specific enzymes, and the space is filled in with DNA.

DNA replication is discontinuous in one strand and continuous in the other

A major obstacle in understanding DNA replication was the fact that the complementary DNA strands are antiparallel. Because DNA synthesis proceeds only in the 5' → 3' direction, which

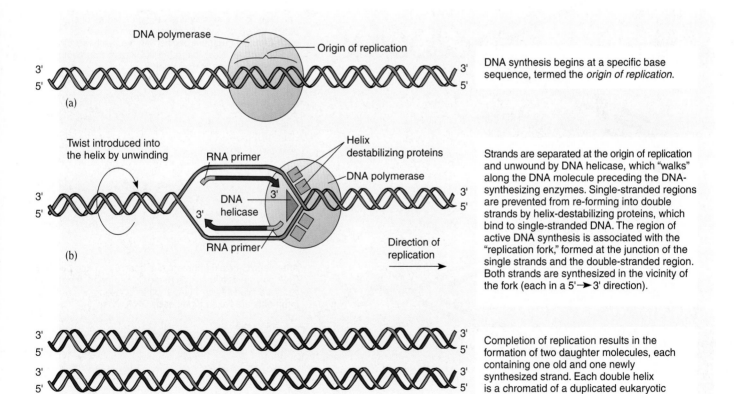

DNA synthesis begins at a specific base sequence, termed the *origin of replication*.

Strands are separated at the origin of replication and unwound by DNA helicase, which "walks" along the DNA molecule preceding the DNA-synthesizing enzymes. Single-stranded regions are prevented from re-forming into double strands by helix-destabilizing proteins, which bind to single-stranded DNA. The region of active DNA synthesis is associated with the "replication fork," formed at the junction of the single strands and the double-stranded region. Both strands are synthesized in the vicinity of the fork (each in a 5'→3' direction).

Completion of replication results in the formation of two daughter molecules, each containing one old and one newly synthesized strand. Each double helix is a chromatid of a duplicated eukaryotic chromosome.

■ **Figure 11–10 Overview of DNA replication.** This process requires a number of steps involving several enzymes and RNA primers.

means that the strand being copied is being read in a 3' → 5' direction, it would seem necessary to copy one of the strands starting at one end of the double helix and the other strand starting at the opposite end. Such a solution to this, the most difficult replication problem, would be extremely awkward at best, and probably completely unworkable; thus a very different mechanism has evolved.

DNA replication begins at specific sites on the DNA molecule, termed **origins of replication,** and both strands are replicated at

the same time at a Y-shaped structure called the **replication fork** (Fig. 11–11). The position of the replication fork is constantly moving as replication proceeds. Two identical DNA polymerase molecules are responsible for replication. One of these adds nucleotides to the 3' end of the new strand that is always growing *toward* the replication fork. Because this strand can be formed smoothly and continuously, it is called the **leading strand.**

A separate (but identical) DNA polymerase molecule adds nucleotides to the 3' end of the other new strand, termed the **lag-**

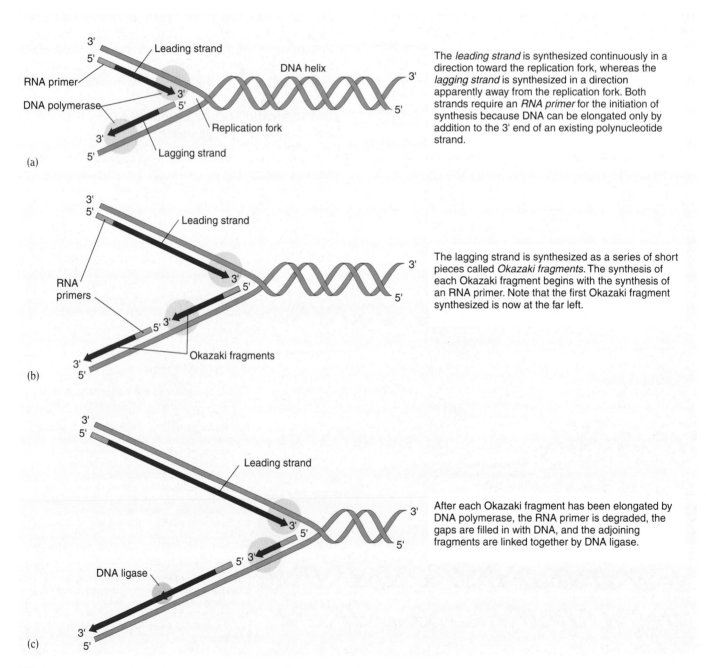

The *leading strand* is synthesized continuously in a direction toward the replication fork, whereas the *lagging strand* is synthesized in a direction apparently away from the replication fork. Both strands require an *RNA primer* for the initiation of synthesis because DNA can be elongated only by addition to the 3' end of an existing polynucleotide strand.

The lagging strand is synthesized as a series of short pieces called *Okazaki fragments.* The synthesis of each Okazaki fragment begins with the synthesis of an RNA primer. Note that the first Okazaki fragment synthesized is now at the far left.

After each Okazaki fragment has been elongated by DNA polymerase, the RNA primer is degraded, the gaps are filled in with DNA, and the adjoining fragments are linked together by DNA ligase.

Figure 11–11 Leading and lagging DNA strands. Because elongation can proceed only in a 5' → 3' direction, the two strands at the replication fork are copied in different ways, each by a separate DNA polymerase molecule.

ging strand. The lagging strand is always growing *away* from the replication fork. Only short pieces can be synthesized because the DNA polymerase enzyme would need to move far away from the fork if it were to add continuously to the 3' end of that strand. These 100- to 2000-nucleotide pieces are called **Okazaki fragments** after their discoverer, Reijii Okazaki.

Each Okazaki fragment is initiated by a separate RNA primer and is then extended toward the 5' end of the previously synthesized fragment by DNA polymerase. When the RNA primer of the previously synthesized fragment is reached, the primer is degraded and replaced with DNA by DNA polymerase. The fragments are then joined together by **DNA ligase,** an enzyme that links the 3' OH of one DNA fragment to the 5' phosphate of another immediately adjacent, forming a phosphodiester linkage.

It has been suggested that simultaneous synthesis of both the leading and lagging strands is possible because the lagging strand (and the DNA strand from which it is copied) forms a loop. This loop allows DNA polymerase to synthesize the lagging strand while remaining close to the replication fork as it works.

Most DNA synthesis is bidirectional

When double-stranded DNA is separated, two replication forks are formed, allowing the molecule to be replicated in both directions from the origin of replication. Prokaryotic cells usually have only one origin of replication on each circular DNA molecule (Fig. 11–12a), so the two replication forks proceed around the circle and eventually meet at the other side to complete the formation of two new DNA molecules.

A eukaryotic chromosome is composed of one, extremely long, linear DNA molecule, so the process is speeded up by having multiple origins of replication (Fig. 11–12b–d). Synthesis continues at each replication fork until it meets one coming from the opposite direction, resulting in the formation of a chromosome containing two DNA double helices (each of which corresponds to a chromatid). The ends of eukaryotic chromosomes present special problems in replication. For this reason, they are capped by special regions known as **telomeres** (see *On the Cutting Edge: Telomerase, Cellular Aging, and Cancer*).

■ DNA IS PACKAGED IN A HIGHLY ORGANIZED WAY IN CHROMOSOMES

Prokaryotic and eukaryotic cells differ markedly in their DNA content as well as in the organization of DNA molecules. An *E. coli* cell normally contains about 4×10^6 base pairs (almost 1.35 mm) of DNA in its single circular DNA molecule. In fact, the total length of the DNA is about 1000 times greater than the length of the cell itself. Therefore, the DNA molecule must, with the help of special proteins, be twisted and folded compactly to fit inside the bacterial cell.

A typical eukaryotic cell contains much more DNA than a bacterium does, and it is organized in the nucleus as multiple chromosomes; these vary widely in size and number among different species. Although a human cell nucleus is about the size

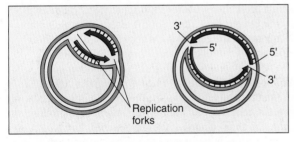

(a)

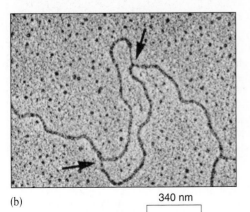

(b)

340 nm

Figure 11–12 Bidirectional DNA replication. The leading strands and lagging strands are not represented in the illustrations. **(a)** The circular DNA in *E. coli* has only one origin of replication. Because DNA synthesis proceeds from that point in both directions, two replication forks are formed, travel around the circle, and eventually meet *(not shown)*. **(b)** This TEM shows two replication forks *(arrows)* in a segment of a eukaryotic chromosome that has been partly replicated. **(c)** Eukaryotic chromosomal DNA contains multiple origins of replication. DNA synthesis proceeds in both directions from each origin until adjacent "replication bubbles" eventually merge **(d)**. *(b, Kriegstein, H.J. and D.S. Hogness, 1974, Proc. Nat. Acad. Sci. USA, 71:135–139.)*

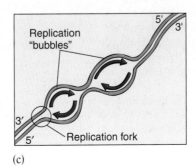

(c)

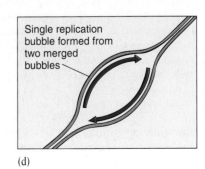

(d)

Telomerase, Cellular Aging, and Cancer

HYPOTHESIS: The number of cell divisions that normal human somatic cells can undergo when grown in culture is limited by the length of their telomeric DNA.

METHOD: To test the prediction that cells will be able to undergo more divisions if their telomeric DNA is lengthened, researchers used a virus to introduce the gene coding for the catalytic subunit of telomerase into cultured normal human cells, which normally lack telomerase activity.

RESULTS: The cells produced active telomerase, which elongated the telomeres. The cells continued to actively proliferate for many cell cycles beyond the point at which cell division would normally cease.

CONCLUSION: The life spans of cells can be extended by lengthening the telomeric DNA of their chromosomes.

Unlike prokaryotic DNA, which is circular, eukaryotic chromosomes have free ends. This simple fact has far-reaching consequences. Because DNA replication is discontinuous in the lagging strand, DNA polymerases are unable to complete replication of the strand neatly. When they reach the end of the DNA, they leave a small portion unreplicated, causing a small single-stranded segment of the DNA to be lost with each cell cycle. This situation is less dangerous than it sounds because chromosomes have end caps (telomeres) that do not contain protein-coding genes, but instead consist of short, simple, noncoding DNA sequences that are repeated many times. Therefore, although a small amount of telomeric DNA fails to replicate each time the cell divides, a cell can divide many times before it starts losing essential genetic information.

It has been suggested that the progressive loss of DNA at the telomeres could contribute to the phenomenon known as **cellular aging.** Cellular aging has been analyzed since the 1960s, following the pioneering studies of Leonard Hayflick, who showed that when normal cells of the human body, known as *somatic cells,* are grown in culture, they lose their ability to divide after a limited number of cell divisions. Furthermore, the number of cell divisions is determined by the age of the individual from whom the cells were taken. Cells from a 70-year-old can divide only 20 to 30 times, as compared with those from an infant, which can divide 80 to 90 times.

Telomeric DNA can be lengthened by **telomerase,** a special DNA replication enzyme. This enzyme, which was discovered in 1984 by Carol W. Greider and Elizabeth H. Blackburn, is typically present in cells that can divide an unlimited number of times, including unicellular organisms and many types of cancer cells. In animals such as humans, active telomerase is usually present in germ line cells (the cells that give rise to eggs and sperm) but not in somatic cells. It is these somatic cells that typically show evidence of cellular aging when placed in culture.

Although correlations between the ability of cells to undergo unlimited divisions and the presence of telomerase activity were repeatedly noted by different investigators, this connection remained controversial. Proof of a causal relationship was lacking until Andrea G. Bodnar and her colleagues at the Geron Corporation teamed up with researchers from the University of Texas Southwestern Medical Center to conduct a direct test.[*] Using the techniques of recombinant DNA technology (see Chapter 14), they infected cultured normal human cells with a virus that carried the genetic information coding for the catalytic subunit of telomerase. Not only did the infected cells produce active telomerase, which elongated the telomeres significantly, but the cells continued to divide long past the point at which cell divisions would normally cease.

These findings have revived interest in telomeres, both for theoretical and practical reasons. The ability to give cells the capacity to divide many times more than they would ordinarily has many potential therapeutic applications, especially if lost or injured cells need to be replaced. However, cancer cells also have the ability to divide many times in culture; in fact, they are virtually immortal. Would cells with active telomerase behave like cancer cells if transplanted into the human body?

To obtain a preliminary answer to this question, scientists at Geron and the University of Texas Southwestern Medical Center independently tested the cells to see if they behaved like cancer cells in other ways.[†,‡] Unlike cultured normal cells, cultured cancer cells fail to stop dividing when they touch other cells, can form tumor-like aggregations when grown under certain conditions, and are still able to divide if their DNA is damaged. By contrast, the cells that had been given the ability to produce active telomerase showed none of these properties. These results are reassuring, but of course they do not prove that there would be no risk for cancer from these cells if they were transplanted.

[*] Bodnar, A.G., M. Ouellette, M. Frolkis, S.E. Holt, C.P. Chiu, G.B. Morin, C.B. Harley, J.W. Shay, S. Lichsteiner, and W.E. Wright. "Extension of Life-Span by Introduction of Telomerase into Normal Human Cells." *Science,* Vol. 279, 16 Jan. 1998.

[†] Jiang, X., G. Jimenez, E. Chang, M. Frolkis, B. Kusler, M. Sage, M. Beeche, A.G. Bodnar, G.M. Wahl, T.D. Tisty, and C. Chiu. "Telomerase Expression in Human Somatic Cells Does Not Induce Changes Associated With a Transformed Phenotype." *Nature Gen.,* Vol. 21, pp. 111–114, 1999.

[‡] Morales, C.P., S.E. Holt, M. Ouellette, K.J. Kaur, Y. Yan, K.S. Wilson, M.A. White, W.E. Wright, and J.W. Shay. "Absence of Cancer-Associated Changes in Human Fibroblasts Immortalized With Telomerase." *Nature Gen.,* Vol. 21, pp. 115–118, 1999.

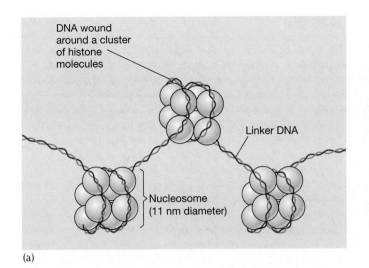

DNA wound around a cluster of histone molecules

Linker DNA

Nucleosome (11 nm diameter)

(a)

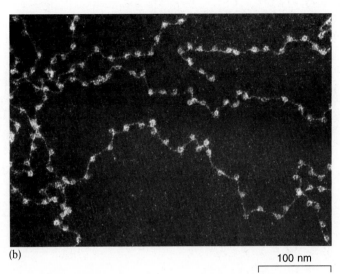

(b)

100 nm

Figure 11–13 Nucleosomes. (a) A model for the structure of a nucleosome. Each nucleosome bead contains a set of eight histone molecules; these form a protein core around which the double-stranded DNA is wound. The DNA surrounding the histones consists of 146 nucleotide pairs; another segment of DNA, about 60 nucleotide pairs long, links nucleosome beads. (b) TEM of nucleosomes from the nucleus of a chicken red blood cell. Normally nucleosomes are packed more closely together, but the preparation procedure has spread them apart, revealing the DNA linkers. *(b, Courtesy of D.E. Olins and A.L. Olins)*

of a large bacterial cell, it contains almost 1000 times the amount of DNA found in *E. coli*. The haploid DNA content of a human cell is about 3×10^9 base pairs; if stretched end to end, it would be almost 1 m long.

So how does a eukaryotic cell pack its DNA into the chromosomes? It does so with the help of certain proteins known as **histones.**[1] Histones are positively charged because they have a high proportion of amino acids with basic side chains (see Chapter 3). The positively charged histones are able to associate with DNA, which is negatively charged due to its phosphate groups, to form structures called **nucleosomes.** The fundamental unit of each nucleosome complex consists of a beadlike structure with 146 base pairs of DNA wrapped around a disc-shaped core of eight histone molecules (two each of four different histone types) (Fig. 11–13). Although the nucleosome was originally defined as a bead plus a DNA segment that links it to an adjacent bead, today the term more commonly refers only to the bead itself (i.e., the eight histones and the DNA wrapped around them).

The nucleosomes are part of the **chromatin,** the complex of nucleic acids and protein that makes up the chromosomes. The higher order structures of chromatin leading to the formation of a highly condensed metaphase chromosome are illustrated in Figure 11–14. The nucleosomes themselves are 11 nm in diameter. The packed nucleosome state occurs when a fifth type of histone, known as histone H1, associates with the linker DNA, packing adjacent nucleosomes together to form a 30-nm-diameter thread. In extended chromatin, these 30-nm-diameter threads form large coiled loops held together by a set of nonhistone **scaffolding proteins.** The loops then interact in complex ways to form the condensed chromatin found in a metaphase chromosome.

Nucleosomes function like tiny spools, thereby preventing DNA strands from becoming tangled. The importance of this role is underscored by Figure 11–15, which illustrates the enormous number of DNA fibers that unravel from a mouse chromosome after the histones have been removed. However, their role is more than structural, for their arrangement also affects the activity of the DNA with which they are associated (Chapter 13).

[1] A few types of eukaryotic cells lack histones. Conversely, histones do occur in one group of prokaryotes, the Archaebacteria (Chapter 23).

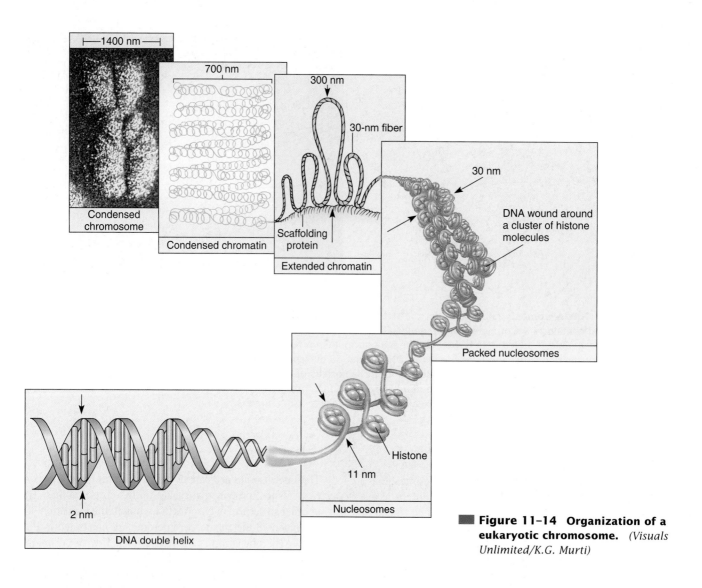

Figure 11-14 Organization of a eukaryotic chromosome. *(Visuals Unlimited/K.G. Murti)*

- 1400 nm — Condensed chromosome
- 700 nm — Condensed chromatin
- 300 nm / 30-nm fiber — Scaffolding protein — Extended chromatin
- 30 nm — DNA wound around a cluster of histone molecules — Packed nucleosomes
- 11 nm — Histone — Nucleosomes
- 2 nm — DNA double helix

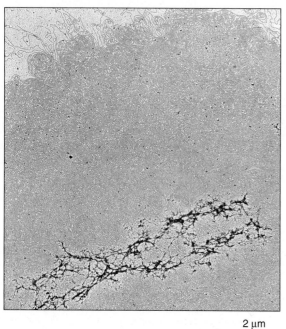

2 μm

Figure 11-15 A chromosome depleted of histones. Note how densely packed the DNA fibrils are in this TEM of a mouse metaphase chromosome, even though they have been released from the histone proteins that organize them into tightly coiled structures. The dark structure extending from left to right across the bottom of the photograph is composed of scaffolding proteins. *(Courtesy of U. Laemmli, from* Cell, *Vol. 12, p. 817, 1988. Copyright by Cell Press)*

I. Many early geneticists thought that genes were made of proteins. Proteins were known to be complex and variable, whereas nucleic acids were thought of as rather simple molecules with a limited ability to store information.

II. Several lines of evidence supported the idea that **DNA** is the genetic material.

   A. In **transformation** experiments, the DNA of one strain of bacteria can endow related bacteria with new genetic characteristics.

   B. When a bacterial cell becomes infected with a **bacteriophage** (virus), only the DNA from the virus enters the cell; this DNA is sufficient for the virus to reproduce and form new virus particles.

   C. Watson and Crick's studies on the structure of DNA demonstrated how information can be stored in the molecule's structure and how DNA molecules can serve as **templates** for their own duplication.

III. DNA is a very regular polymer of **nucleotides.**

   A. Each nucleotide subunit contains a nitrogenous base, which may be one of the **purines (adenine or guanine)** or one of the **pyrimidines (thymine or cytosine).** Each base is covalently linked to a five-carbon sugar, **deoxyribose,** which is covalently bonded to a phosphate group.

   B. The backbone of each single DNA chain is formed by alternating sugar and phosphate groups, joined by covalent **phosphodiester linkages.** Each phosphate group is attached to the 5' carbon of one deoxyribose and to the 3' carbon of the neighboring deoxyribose.

   C. Each DNA molecule is composed of two polynucleotide chains that associate as a **double helix.** The two chains are **antiparallel** (meaning they run in opposite directions); at each end of the DNA molecule one chain has a phosphate attached to a 5' deoxyribose carbon (the **5' end**), and the other has a hydroxyl group attached to a 3' deoxyribose carbon (the **3' end**).

   D. The two chains of the helix are held together by hydrogen bonding between specific base pairs. Adenine (A) forms two hydrogen bonds with thymine (T); guanine (G) forms three hydrogen bonds with cytosine (C).

      1. **Complementary** base-pairing between A and T and between G and C is the basis of Chargaff's rules, which state that A equals T and G equals C.

      2. Because the two strands of DNA are held together by complementary base-pairing, it is possible to predict the base sequence of one strand if one knows the base sequence of the other strand.

IV. During **DNA replication,** the two strands of the double helix unwind. Each strand serves as a template for the formation of a new, complementary strand.

   A. DNA replication is **semiconservative;** that is, each daughter double helix contains one strand from the parent molecule and one newly synthesized strand.

   B. DNA replication is a complex process requiring a number of different enzymes.

      1. The enzyme that adds new deoxyribonucleotides to a growing DNA strand is a **DNA polymerase.**

      2. Additional enzymes and other proteins are required to unwind and stabilize the separated DNA helix and to form **RNA primers. Topoisomerases** prevent tangling and knotting, and **DNA ligase** links together fragments of newly synthesized DNA.

   C. DNA synthesis always proceeds in a 5' $\longrightarrow$ 3' direction. This requires that one DNA strand (the **lagging strand**) be synthesized discontinuously, as short **Okazaki fragments.** The opposite strand (the **leading strand**) is synthesized continuously.

   D. DNA replication is bidirectional, starting at the **origin of replication** and proceeding in both directions from that point. A eukaryotic chromosome may have multiple origins of replication and may be replicating at many points along its length at any one time.

   E. Eukaryotic chromosome ends, known as **telomeres,** shorten slightly with each cell cycle but can be extended by the enzyme **telomerase.** The absence of telomerase activity in certain cells may be a cause of **cellular aging.**

V. DNA molecules have to be organized in a cell because they are much longer than the nuclei or the cells that contain them.

   A. Prokaryotic cells usually have circular DNA molecules.

   B. The organization of eukaryotic DNA into chromosomes allows the DNA to be accurately replicated and segregated into daughter cells without tangling. Chromosomes have several levels of organization.

      1. The DNA is associated with **histones** (basic proteins) to form **nucleosomes,** each of which consists of a histone bead with DNA wrapped around it.

      2. The nucleosomes are organized into large coiled loops held together by nonhistone **scaffolding proteins.**

POST-TEST

1. Which of the following inspired Avery and his coworkers to do the experiments that demonstrated that the transforming principle in bacteria is DNA? (a) the fact that A is equal to T, and G is equal to C (b) Watson and Crick's model of DNA structure (c) Meselson and Stahl's studies on DNA replication in *E. coli* (d) Griffith's experiments on smooth and rough strains of pneumococci (e) Hershey and Chase's experiments on the reproduction of bacteriophages

2. In the Hershey-Chase experiment with bacteriophages (a) harmless bacterial cells became permanently transformed into virulent cells (b) DNA was demonstrated to be the transforming principle of earlier bacterial transformation experiments (c) the replication of DNA was conclusively shown to be semiconservative (d) viral DNA was shown to enter bacterial cells and be responsible for the production of new viruses within the bacteria (e) the viruses injected proteins, not DNA, into bacterial cells

3. The experiments in which Meselson and Stahl grew bacteria in heavy nitrogen conclusively demonstrated that DNA (a) is a double helix (b) replicates semiconservatively (c) consists of repeating nucleotide subunits (d) has complementary base pairing (e) is always synthesized in a 5' to 3' direction

4. The statement "DNA replicates by a semiconservative mechanism" means that (a) only one DNA strand is copied (b) first one DNA strand is copied, and then the other strand is copied (c) the two strands of a double helix have identical base sequences (d) some portions of a single DNA strand are old, and other portions are newly synthesized (e) each double helix consists of one old and one newly synthesized strand

5. Multiple origins of replication (a) speed up replication of eukaryotic chromosomes (b) allow the lagging strands and leading strands to be synthesized at different replication forks (c) help to relieve strain as the double helix is unwound (d) prevent mutations (e) are necessary for the replication of a circular DNA molecule in bacteria

6. Topoisomerases (a) synthesize DNA (b) synthesize RNA primers (c) join Okazaki fragments (d) break and rejoin DNA to resolve knots that have formed (e) prevent single DNA strands from joining to form a double helix

7. A phosphate in DNA is (a) hydrogen-bonded to a base (b) covalently linked to two bases (c) covalently linked to two deoxyriboses (d) hydrogen-bonded to two additional phosphates (e) covalently linked to a base, a deoxyribose, and another phosphate

8. Which of the following depicts the relative arrangement of the complementary strands of a DNA double helix?

(a) 5' — 5'   (b) 3' — 5'   (c) 3' — 3'   (d) 5' — 5'   (e) 3' — 5'
    3' — 3'   3' — 5'   3' — 3'   5' — 5'   5' — 3'

9. A lagging strand is formed by (a) joining primers (b) joining Okazaki fragments (c) joining leading strands (d) breaking up a leading strand (e) joining primers, Okazaki fragments, and leading strands

10. The immediate source of energy for DNA replication is (a) the hydrolysis of the nucleotides, with the release of two phosphates (b) the oxidation of NADPH (c) the hydrolysis of ATP (d) electron transport (e) the breaking of hydrogen bonds

11. A nucleosome consists of (a) DNA and scaffolding proteins (b) scaffolding proteins and histones (c) DNA and histones (d) DNA, histones, and scaffolding proteins (e) histones only

REVIEW QUESTIONS

1. How did the experiments of Avery and coworkers point to DNA as the essential genetic material? Did the Hershey-Chase experiment establish that DNA is the genetic material in all organisms? Did either of these experiments demonstrate how DNA could function as the chemical basis of genes?

2. Sketch the structure of a single strand of DNA. What types of subunits make up the chain? How are they linked?

3. Describe the structure of double-stranded DNA as determined by Watson and Crick.

4. Does a single strand of DNA obey Chargaff's rules? How do Chargaff's rules relate to the structure of DNA?

5. What are some of the mechanical problems encountered in DNA replication? How are they dealt with by the cell?

6. Why is DNA replication continuous for one strand but discontinuous for the other?

7. Compare the structures of a bacterial DNA molecule and a eukaryotic chromosome. What effects do these differences have on replication?

8. Describe how both prokaryotic and eukaryotic cells cope with the large discrepancy between the length of their DNA molecules and the size of the cell or nucleus.

YOU MAKE THE CONNECTION

1. What characteristics must a molecule have if it is to serve as genetic material?

2. What important features of the structure of DNA are consistent with its role as the chemical basis of heredity?

RECOMMENDED READINGS

Greider, C.W., and E.H. Blackburn. "Telomeres, Telomerase, and Cancer." *Scientific American,* Vol. 274, No. 2, Feb. 1996. The discoverers of telomerase discuss the possible roles of telomere shortening and lengthening in cancer and aging.

Judson, H.F. *The Eighth Day of Creation: Makers of the Revolution in Biology.* Simon & Schuster, New York, 1979. A beautifully written and fascinating account of the early history of molecular biology.

Lodish, H., A. Berk, S.L. Zipursky, P. Matsudaira, D. Baltimore, and J. Darnell. *Molecular Cell Biology,* 4th ed. W.H. Freeman and Co., New York, 2000. An extensive, detailed, and well written discussion of DNA structure and replication.

Pool, R. "Dr. Tinkertoy." *Discover,* Feb. 1997. Chemist Ned Seeman uses short DNA molecules as construction components that join together by complementary base-pairing.

Rennie, J. "DNA's New Twists." *Scientific American,* Mar. 1993. A fascinating summary of novel studies in genetics that challenge previous ideas and open the way for a new understanding of the role of DNA in evolution and in genetic diseases.

Rebek, J., Jr. "Synthetic Self-Replicating Molecules." *Scientific American,* Jul. 1994. Experiments on certain molecules fabricated in the laboratory demonstrate that self-duplication is not unique to DNA.

Watson, J.D. *The Double Helix.* Atheneum, New York, 1968. Watson's view of the discovery of the structure of DNA. Somewhat controversial, but entertaining and insightful reading.

Watson, J.D., and F.H.C. Crick. "Molecular Structure of Nucleic Acids: A Structure for Deoxyribose Nucleic Acid." *Nature,* Vol. 171, 1953. Watson and Crick's original report—a simple, clearly written two-page paper that shook the scientific world.

● Visit our Web site at **http://www.info.brookscole.com/solomonbergmartin** for links to chapter-related resources on the World Wide Web. Additional on-line materials relating to this chapter can also be found on our Web site.

See chapter activity on BioActive Learner CD for additional help in mastering the chapter's material. Icon location in the chapter's margins shows which topics have tutorials or simulations in the CD.

12

RNA and Protein Synthesis: The Expression of Genetic Information

LEARNING OBJECTIVES

After you have studied this chapter you should be able to

1. Summarize the early evidence that most genes specify the structure of proteins.
2. Outline the flow of genetic information in cells, from DNA to protein.
3. Compare the structures of DNA and RNA and explain how the structure of each is related to its role in the cell.
4. Compare the processes of transcription and replication, identifying both similarities and differences.
5. Identify the features of tRNA that are important in decoding genetic information and converting it into "protein language."
6. Explain how the ribosome functions in protein synthesis.
7. Diagram the processes of initiation, chain elongation, and chain termination in protein synthesis.
8. Compare eukaryotic and prokaryotic mRNAs and explain the functional significance of their structural differences.
9. Analyze the differences in translation in prokaryotic and eukaryotic cells.
10. Explain why the genetic code is said to be redundant and virtually universal. Discuss how these features may reflect the evolutionary history of the code.
11. Give examples of the different classes of mutations that affect the base sequence of DNA and demonstrate the effects that each has on the protein produced.

Visualization of transcription. In this TEM, RNA molecules *(lateral strands)* are being synthesized as complementary copies of a DNA template *(central axis)*. *(Professor Oscar Miller/Science Photo Library/Photo Researchers, Inc.)*

I n Chapter 11 we saw that the sequence of nucleotides in DNA is replicated extremely accurately by a cell so that it can be passed unaltered to its descendants. The basic features of the DNA double helix originally described by Watson and Crick are now known to be the same in all cells studied to date, from those of humans to bacteria.

By the mid-1950s it became evident that the sequence of bases in DNA contains the information required to specify all the proteins needed by the cell. However, more than a decade of intense investigation by many scientists was required before a fundamental understanding could be developed of how cells are able to convert DNA information into amino acid sequences of pro-

teins. Much of that understanding came from studying the functions of bacterial genes. After the discovery of the structure of DNA, prokaryotic cells quickly became the organisms of choice for these investigations because they could be grown quickly and easily and because they seemed to contain only the minimal amount of DNA needed for growth and reproduction. The validity, as well as the utility, of this approach has been repeatedly confirmed, as researchers have learned that all organisms share fundamental genetic similarities.

In this chapter we first examine the evidence that accumulated in the first half of the 20th century that most genes specify the structure of proteins. We then consider at the molecular level how DNA is able to affect the phenotype of the organism through a process known as **gene expression.** Gene expression is accomplished by a complex series of events in which the information contained in the sequence of bases in DNA is used to specify the makeup of the proteins in the cell. The proteins produced then affect the phenotype in some way; these effects can range from readily observable visible physical traits to subtle changes detectable only at the biochemical level. The first major step of gene expression is **transcription,** the synthesis of RNA molecules complementary to the DNA. The second key event is **translation,** in which RNA is used as a coded template to direct protein synthesis. In Chapter 13 we consider some of the ways the entire process of gene expression is controlled.

We first focus our attention on gene expression in prokaryotes because these cells are best understood. We then extend our discussion to include eukaryotic cells. Our understanding of these cells is improving rapidly as a result of groundwork laid by study of the simpler bacterial systems.

MOST GENES CARRY INFORMATION FOR MAKING PROTEINS

The idea that there is a connection between proteins and genes had its inception early in the 20th century, soon after the rediscovery of Mendel's principles. In the first edition of his book, *Inborn Errors of Metabolism* (1908), Archibald Garrod, an English physician, discussed a genetic disease called **alkaptonuria,** which was known to have a simple recessive inheritance pattern. The condition involves the metabolic pathway that breaks down the amino acids phenylalanine and tyrosine, ultimately converting them to carbon dioxide and water. The urine of affected individuals contains an intermediate in this pathway, homogentisic acid, which turns black when exposed to air (Fig. 12–1).

At that time, enzymes were known, but the protein nature of enzymes was yet to be established. Garrod hypothesized that persons with alkaptonuria lack the enzyme that normally oxidizes homogentisic acid and that this metabolic block causes homogentisic acid to accumulate in their tissues and blood, and to be excreted in their urine. Before the second edition of his book had been published in 1923, it was found that affected persons do indeed lack the enzyme that oxidizes homogentisic acid. Garrod's hypothesis was correct: A mutation in this specific gene is associated with the absence of a specific enzyme. The first clear identification of an enzyme as a protein came shortly thereafter, in 1926, when James Sumner purified a different enzyme, urease, and showed it to be a protein.

Given the hindsight we have today, we might say that, taken together, these findings demonstrated that a mutation in a specific gene can cause a change in a specific protein. However, despite the implications, little work was done in this area, primarily because genetically transmitted errors in metabolism appeared to be rare. The lack of experimental subjects made genetic testing and statistical analysis very difficult.

A major advance in understanding the relationship between genes and enzymes came in the early 1940s, when George Beadle and Edward Tatum developed a new approach to the problem. Most efforts until that time had centered on studying known loci and attempting to determine what biochemical reactions they affected. Experimenters examined previously identified loci, such as those controlling eye color in *Drosophila* or pigments in plants. They found that specific phenotypes are controlled by a series of biosynthetic reactions, but it was not clear to the investigators whether the genes themselves were acting as enzymes or if they determined the workings of the enzymes in more complex ways.

Beadle and Tatum decided to take the opposite approach. Rather than try to identify the enzymes affected by single genes, they decided to look for mutations interfering with the known metabolic reactions that produce essential molecules such as amino acids and vitamins. They chose a fungus, *Neurospora,* which is a common bread mold, as an experimental organism for several important reasons. First, wild-type[1] *Neurospora* is easy to grow in culture. It can make all of its essential biological molecules when it is grown on a simple minimal growth medium containing only sugar, salts, and the vitamin biotin. However, a mutant *Neurospora* strain that cannot make a substance such as an amino acid can still grow if that substance is simply added to the growth medium.

Second, the life cycle of *Neurospora* includes both sexual and asexual reproduction, a fact that facilitates certain types of manipulations and genetic analysis. Third, *Neurospora* grows primarily as a haploid organism, allowing a recessive mutant al-

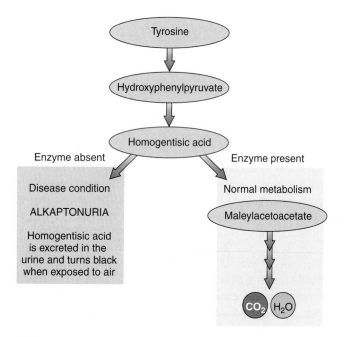

Figure 12–1 An "inborn error of metabolism."
Garrod proposed that the alkaptonuria allele causes the absence of a specific enzyme, one that is part of the pathway by which the amino acid tyrosine is catabolized. That enzyme normally converts homogentisic acid to maleylacetoacetate. Homogentisic acid thus accumulates in the blood and is excreted through the urine. When the homogentisic acid in the urine comes in contact with air, it oxidizes and turns black.

[1] *Wild type* refers to the genotypes and phenotypes most commonly found in natural populations of a particular species. Wild-type alleles are generally thought of as "normal," or nonmutant, alleles.

lele to be immediately identified because there is no homologous chromosome that could carry a dominant allele that would mask its expression. (For an illustration of the generalized life cycles of simple organisms such as fungi, see Figure 9–16b; a more detailed life cycle of organisms similar to *Neurospora* is given in Figure 25–9.)

Beadle and Tatum began by exposing thousands of haploid wild-type *Neurospora* asexual spores to x rays or ultraviolet radiation to induce mutant strains. Each irradiated strain was first grown on a complete growth medium, which contained all the amino acids and vitamins normally made by *Neurospora*. Each strain was then tested on the standard minimal growth medium described previously. About 1% to 2% of the strains that grew on the complete medium failed to grow after transfer to the minimal medium. Beadle and Tatum reasoned that such a strain carried a mutation that made it unable to produce one of the compounds essential for growth. Further testing of the mutant strain on media containing different combinations of amino acids, purines, vitamins, and so on enabled the investigators to determine the exact compound that was required (Fig. 12–2).

Their findings can be illustrated with a class of mutants that require the amino acid arginine. Beadle and Tatum found that some of the arginine-requiring mutants could grow on ornithine or citrulline, as well as arginine; others could grow on citrulline or arginine; and still others could grow only on arginine (Fig. 12–3a). This information was then used to deduce the order of these intermediates in the biochemical pathway leading to arginine (Fig. 12–3b).

Using this approach, Beadle and Tatum analyzed mutants affecting several metabolic pathways. Each mutant strain was verified by special genetic crossing experiments to have a mutation in only one gene locus. They found that for each individual gene locus identified, only one enzyme was affected. This one-to-one correspondence between genes and enzymes was succinctly stated as the *one gene, one enzyme hypothesis*.

Through the discoveries of Beadle and Tatum and others, the sciences of genetics and biochemistry became ever more closely allied, leading to an evolution of the definition of the gene and additional predictions regarding its chemical nature. The idea that a gene encodes the information required to produce a single enzyme held for almost a decade, until additional findings required a modification of this definition.

In the late 1940s it became evident that genes control not only enzymes, but other proteins as well. In 1949 Linus Pauling and his coworkers were able to demonstrate that the structure of hemoglobin can be altered by a mutation of a single locus. This particular mutant form of hemoglobin is associated with the genetic disease sickle cell anemia (Chapter 15). In addition, various studies showed that many proteins are constructed from two or more polypeptide chains, each of which may be controlled by a different locus. For example, hemoglobin was shown to contain two types of polypeptide chains, the α and β subunits (see Fig. 3–23a). Sickle cell anemia results from a mutation affecting the β subunits.

The definition of a gene was therefore extended to state that one gene is responsible for one polypeptide chain. Even this def-

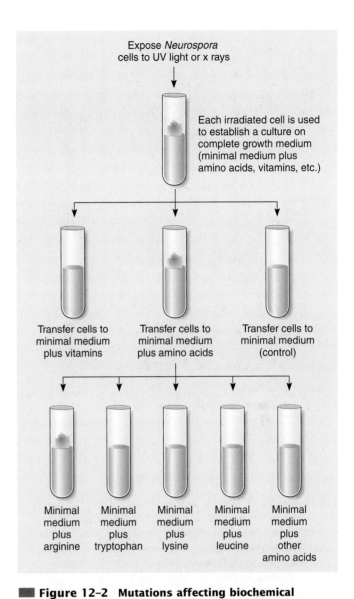

Figure 12–2 Mutations affecting biochemical pathways. Beadle and Tatum irradiated *Neurospora* cells in an effort to induce mutations. Cultures derived from these cells were first established on a complete growth medium, one that contained all the amino acids, vitamins, and so on that *Neurospora* normally makes for itself. Any strain that subsequently failed to grow when transferred to a simple minimal growth medium was thought to carry a mutation causing a block at a step in a biochemical pathway. The specific nutritional requirement in the mutant strain was determined by testing for growth on minimal media supplemented with individual vitamins or amino acids. In this example, only the medium containing the amino acid arginine supports growth, indicating that the mutation affects some part of the arginine biosynthetic pathway.

inition has proved to be only partially correct, although as we will see later in this chapter, we still define a gene in terms of its product.

Although the elegant work of Beadle and Tatum and others demonstrated that genes code for proteins, the mechanism by

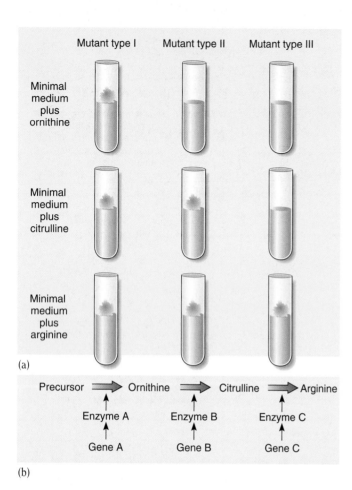

(a)

Precursor ⟹ Ornithine ⟹ Citrulline ⟹ Arginine

Enzyme A   Enzyme B   Enzyme C

Gene A   Gene B   Gene C

(b)

Figure 12–3 Genes and enzymes. **(a)** In this example, Beadle and Tatum tested different mutant strains that require the amino acid arginine. These were grouped (Types I, II, or III in the figure) by their response to various intermediates in the metabolic pathway leading to arginine, which were provided as supplements to the minimal growth medium. **(b)** Analysis of the experimental results led to this model for a portion of the arginine biosynthetic pathway (which is actually a cycle). Because type I mutant strains grew on minimal medium supplemented with ornithine, citrulline, or arginine, they were thought to be missing enzyme A, required for formation of all three compounds. Type II mutant strains were thought to be missing enzyme B because they were unable to grow on minimal medium supplemented with ornithine but allowed the conversion of citrulline to arginine. Type III mutant strains were thought to be missing enzyme C because they grew on minimal medium to which only arginine had been added. Special genetic crosses (*not shown*) were conducted to verify that there was a one-to-one correspondence between each specific enzyme and a specific gene locus.

which this could occur was completely unknown. After Watson and Crick's discovery of the structure of DNA, a great many scientists worked to understand gene expression in terms of the basic flow of information in the cell. We will begin with an overview of gene expression and then consider the various processes in more detail.

■ OVERVIEW: INFORMATION FLOWS FROM DNA TO RNA TO PROTEIN

Although the sequence of bases in DNA determines the sequence of amino acids in polypeptides, the information in DNA is not used directly. Instead, a related nucleic acid, **ribonucleic acid (RNA),** serves as an intermediary between DNA and protein. When a protein-coding gene is expressed, first an RNA copy is made of the information in the DNA. It is this RNA copy that provides the information to direct protein synthesis.

Like DNA, RNA is a polymer of nucleotides, but it has some important differences (Fig. 12–4). RNA is usually single-stranded, although internal regions of some RNA molecules may have complementary sequences that allow the strand to fold back and pair to form short, double-stranded segments. As shown in Figure 12–4, the sugar in RNA is **ribose,** which is similar to deoxyribose of DNA, but with an extra hydroxyl group at the 2' position. (Compare ribose with the deoxyribose of DNA, shown in Fig. 11–3, which has only a hydrogen at the 2' position.) The base **uracil** substitutes for thymine and, like thymine, is a pyrimidine that can form two hydrogen bonds with adenine. Hence, uracil and adenine are a complementary pair.

DNA is transcribed to form RNA

The process by which RNA is synthesized resembles DNA replication in that the sequence of bases in the RNA strand is determined by complementary base-pairing with one of the DNA strands, referred to as the *transcribed strand,* or *template strand* (Fig. 12–5). Because RNA synthesis involves taking the information in one kind of nucleic acid (DNA) and copying it in the form of another nucleic acid (RNA), we refer to this process as **transcription** ("copying"). The type of RNA that carries the specific information for making a protein is called **messenger RNA,** or **mRNA.**

RNA is translated to form a polypeptide

Figure 12–5 also shows the second stage of gene expression, in which the transcribed information in the mRNA is used to specify the amino acid sequence of a polypeptide. This process is called **translation** because it involves conversion of the "nucleic acid language" in the mRNA molecule into the "amino acid language" of protein.

A sequence of three consecutive bases in mRNA, called a **codon,** specifies one amino acid. For example, one codon that corresponds to the amino acid threonine is 5'— ACG — 3'. Because each codon requires three nucleotides, the code is referred to as a **triplet code.** Taken together, all of the assignments of codons to amino acids or to punctuation (stop and start signals) are referred to collectively as the **genetic code** (Table 12–1). Various aspects of the genetic code are discussed later in this chapter.

Transfer RNAs (tRNAs) are critical parts of the decoding machinery because they act as "adapters" that provide a connection between amino acids and nucleic acids. This is possible because each tRNA can (1) link with a specific amino acid and (2) recognize the appropriate mRNA codon for that particular amino acid. A particular tRNA can recognize a specific codon because it

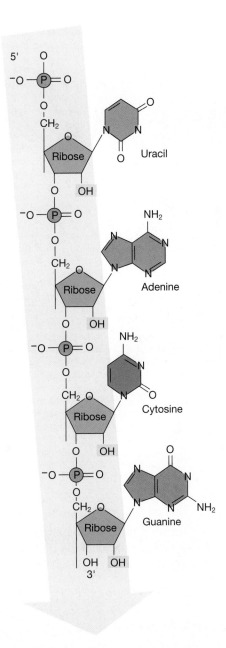

has a sequence of three bases, called the **anticodon,** that hydrogen bonds with the mRNA codon by complementary base-pairing. The exact anticodon that is complementary to the codon for threonine in our example is 3' — UGC — 5'.

Translation requires that (1) each tRNA anticodon be hydrogen bonded to the complementary mRNA codon and (2) the amino acids carried by the tRNAs be linked together in the order specified by the order of the codons in the mRNA. This is accomplished by **ribosomes** (see Chapter 4), complex organelles composed of two different subunits, each containing more than 50 proteins and **ribosomal RNA (rRNA).** Ribosomes attach to one end of the mRNA and travel along it, thereby allowing the tRNAs to attach sequentially to the codons of mRNA. In this way the amino acids carried by the tRNAs become properly positioned to be joined by peptide bonds in the correct sequence to form a polypeptide.

Now that we have presented an overview of information flow from DNA to proteins, let us examine the entire process more closely.

■ TRANSCRIPTION IS THE SYNTHESIS OF RNA FROM A DNA TEMPLATE

Three main kinds of RNA are transcribed from DNA: ribosomal RNA (rRNA) and transfer RNA (tRNA), as well as messenger RNA (mRNA). Most RNA is synthesized by **DNA-dependent RNA polymerases,** enzymes that are present in all cells. These enzymes require DNA as a template and have many similarities to the DNA polymerases discussed in Chapter 11. Like DNA polymerases, they carry out synthesis in a 5' ⟶ 3' direction; that is, they begin at the 5' end of the RNA molecule being synthesized and then continue to add nucleotides at the 3' end until the molecule is complete (Fig. 12–6). They use nucleotides with three phosphate groups as substrates, removing two of the phosphates as the nucleotides are covalently linked to the 3' end of the RNA. Like DNA replication and the hydrolysis of ATP, these reactions are strongly exergonic (see Chapter 6).

Whenever nucleic acid molecules associate by complementary base-pairing, the two strands are antiparallel. Just as the two paired strands of DNA are antiparallel (see Chapter 11), the transcribed strand of the DNA and the complementary RNA strand are also antiparallel. Therefore, as shown in Fig 12–6, when transcription takes place, as RNA is being synthesized in its 5' → 3' direction, the DNA template is being read in its 3' → 5' direction.

It is conventional to refer to a sequence of bases in a gene or the mRNA sequence transcribed from it as *upstream* or *downstream* of some reference point. **Upstream** means toward the 5' end of the mRNA sequence or the 3' end of the transcribed DNA strand. **Downstream** means toward the 3' end of the RNA or the 5' end of the transcribed DNA strand.

Upstream	Downstream
5'—A—T—G—A—C—T—3'	(nontranscribed DNA strand)
3'—T—A—C—T—G—A—5'	(transcribed DNA strand)

Direction of transcription →

Triphosphate 5'—A—U—G—A—C—U—3' OH (RNA)

Messenger RNA synthesis includes several steps

In both prokaryotes and eukaryotes, the DNA sequence to which RNA polymerase initially binds is called the **promoter.** Because

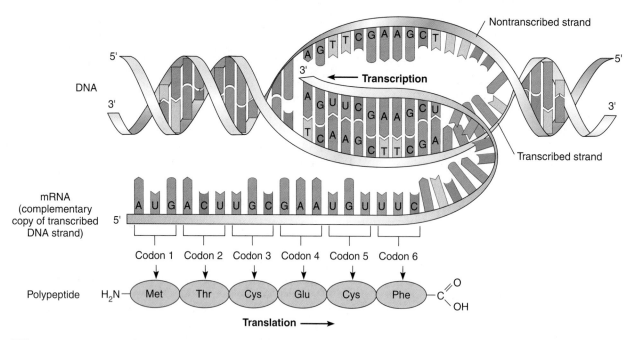

Figure 12–5 Overview of transcription and translation. In transcription, messenger RNA is synthesized as a complementary copy of one of the DNA strands, the transcribed strand. Messenger RNA carries genetic information in the form of sets of three bases called codons, each of which specifies one amino acid. Messenger RNA codons are translated consecutively, thus specifying the linear sequence of amino acids in the polypeptide chain. Translation requires transfer RNA and ribosomes *(not shown)*. The figure depicts transcription and translation in prokaryotes. In eukaryotes transcription takes place in the nucleus and translation occurs in the cytoplasm.

the promoter is not transcribed, the RNA polymerase must move past the promoter to begin transcription of the protein-coding sequence of DNA. Different genes may have slightly different promoter sequences, so the cell can direct which genes are transcribed at any one time (Chapter 13). Bacterial promoters are usually about 40 bases long and are positioned in the DNA just upstream of the point at which transcription will begin. Once the polymerase has recognized the correct promoter, it unwinds the helix and begins transcription.

Unlike DNA synthesis, RNA synthesis does not require a primer. However, transcription requires several proteins in addition to RNA polymerase; these are discussed in Chapter 13.

As illustrated in Figure 12–6, the first nucleotide at the 5' end of a new mRNA chain retains its triphosphate group, but as each additional nucleotide is incorporated at the 3' end of the growing RNA molecule, two of its phosphates are removed in an exergonic reaction that leaves the remaining phosphate to become part of the sugar-phosphate backbone (as in DNA replication). The last nucleotide to be incorporated has an exposed 3' hydroxyl group.

The termination of transcription, like its initiation, is controlled by a set of specific base sequences. These termination signals at the end of the gene cause transcription to stop.

Usually only one of the strands in a protein-coding region of

DNA is transcribed (Fig. 12–7a). For example, consider a segment of DNA that contains the following DNA base sequence in the transcribed strand:

3' — TAACGGTCT — 5'

If the complementary DNA strand

5' — ATTGCCAGA — 3'

were to be transcribed, a message specifying an entirely different (and generally nonfunctional) protein would be produced. However, the fact that only one strand is transcribed does not mean that the same strand is always the template throughout the length of a chromosome-sized DNA molecule. Instead, a particular strand may serve as the transcribed strand for some genes and the nontranscribed strand for others (Fig. 12–7b).

Messenger RNA contains additional base sequences that do not directly code for protein

A completed messenger RNA contains more than the nucleotide sequence that codes for a protein. A typical bacterial messenger

TABLE 12–1 The Genetic Code: Codons of mRNA that Specify a Given Amino Acid

First Position (5' end)	Second Position	Third Position (3' end)			
		U	C	A	G
U	U	UUU UUC Phenylalanine		UUA UUG Leucine	
	C	UCU UCC UCA UCG Serine			
	A	UAU UAC Tyrosine		UAA (Stop)	UAG (Stop)
	G	UGU UGC Cysteine		UGA (Stop)	UGG Tryptophan
C	U	CUU CUC CUA CUG Leucine			
	C	CCU CCC CCA CCG Proline			
	A	CAU CAC Histidine		CAA CAG Glutamine	
	G	CGU CGC CGA CGG Arginine			
A	U	AUU AUC AUA Isoleucine			AUG (start) Methionine
	C	ACU ACC ACA ACG Threonine			
	A	AAU AAC Asparagine		AAA AAG Lysine	
	G	AGU AGC Serine		AGA AGG Arginine	
G	U	GUU GUC GUA GUG Valine			
	C	GCU GCC GCA GCG Alanine			
	A	GAU GAC Aspartic acid		GAA GAG Glutamic acid	
	G	GGU GGC GGA GGG Glycine			

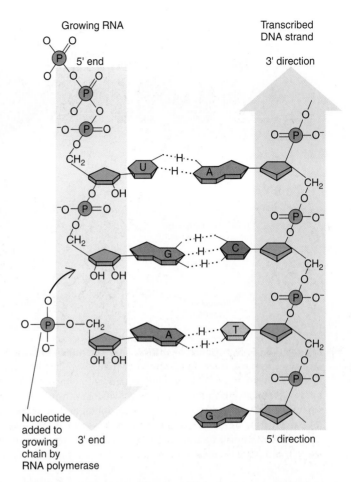

Figure 12–6 Transcription. Incoming nucleotides with three phosphates pair with complementary bases on the transcribed DNA strand *(right)*. RNA polymerase cleaves two phosphates *(not shown)* from each nucleotide and covalently links the remaining phosphate to the 3' end of the growing RNA chain. Thus, RNA, like DNA, is synthesized in a 5' → 3' direction.

RNA is shown in Figure 12–8. (The unique features of eukaryotic messenger RNA and transcription in eukaryotes are discussed later in the chapter.) In both prokaryotes and eukaryotes, RNA polymerase starts transcription of a gene well upstream of the protein-coding DNA sequence. As a result, the mRNA has a non-coding **leader sequence** at its 5' end. The leader contains recognition signals for ribosome binding, which allow the ribosomes to be properly positioned to translate the message. The leader sequence is followed by the **coding sequence,** which contains the actual messages for the proteins. Unlike eukaryotic cells, it is common for one or more polypeptides to be encoded by a single mRNA molecule in bacterial cells (see Chapter 13). At the end of each coding sequence is a special **termination,** or **stop, codon.** The stop codons—UAA, UGA, or UAG (see Table 12–1)— are present in both prokaryotic and eukaryotic messages. They do not code for amino acids but instead specify the end of the protein. These are followed by noncoding 3' trailing sequences, which can vary in length.

■ DURING TRANSLATION, THE NUCLEIC ACID MESSAGE IS DECODED

In eukaryotes, messenger RNA must move from the nucleus, the site of transcription, to the cytoplasm, the site of **translation,** or

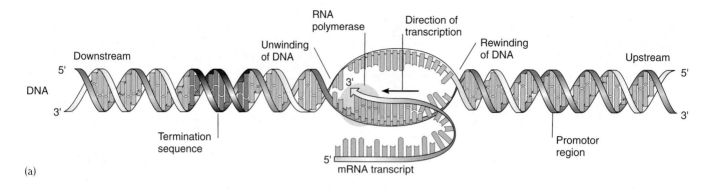

(a)

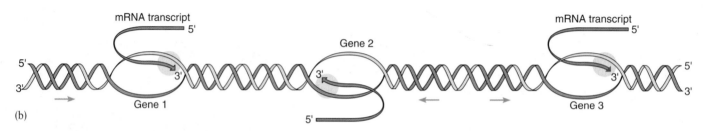

(b)

■ **Figure 12–7 Synthesis of mRNA.** **(a)** The mRNA is synthesized in a 5' ⟶ 3' direction from the transcribed strand of the DNA molecule. Transcription starts downstream from a DNA promoter sequence, to which the RNA polymerase initially binds. Termination sequences, found downstream from the protein-coding sequences, signal the RNA polymerase to stop transcription and be released from the DNA. **(b)** Usually only one of the two strands is transcribed for a given gene, but the opposite strand may be transcribed for a neighboring gene. Each transcript starts at its own promoter *(orange region)*.

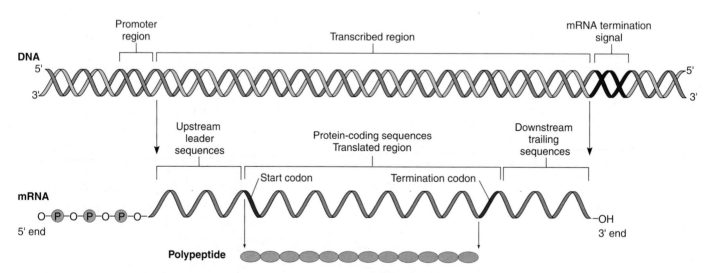

■ **Figure 12–8 Bacterial mRNA.** This figure compares a bacterial mRNA with the region of DNA from which it was transcribed. RNA polymerase recognizes, but does not transcribe, promoter sequences in the DNA. Initiation of RNA synthesis occurs five to eight bases downstream from the promoter. Ribosome-recognition sites are located in the 5' mRNA upstream leader sequences. Protein-coding sequences begin at a start codon, which follows the leader sequences, and end at a downstream termination codon near the 3' end of the molecule. Noncoding trailing sequences, which can vary in length, follow the protein-coding sequences.

protein synthesis. No such movement occurs in prokaryotes, which lack a nucleus. Translation adds another level of complexity to the process of information transfer because it involves the conversion of the triplet nucleic acid code to the 20-amino acid alphabet of proteins. The structural differences between a polynucleotide chain and a polypeptide chain are so great that no simple way exists for amino acids to interact directly with an mRNA molecule to make a protein. Translation therefore requires the coordinated functioning of more than 100 kinds of macromolecules, including the protein and RNA components of the ribosomes, mRNA, and amino acids linked to tRNAs.

An amino acid is attached to transfer RNA before becoming incorporated into a polypeptide

Amino acids are joined together by peptide bonds to form proteins (see Chapter 3). This joining involves linking the amino and carboxyl groups of adjacent amino acids. The translation process ensures that not only are peptide bonds formed but that the amino acids are linked in the correct sequence specified by the codons in the mRNA. How do the amino acids become aligned in the proper sequence so they can become linked?

Francis Crick, one of the codiscoverers of the structure of DNA (see Chapter 11), recognized this problem and proposed that a molecule was needed to serve as an "adapter" in protein synthesis and bridge the gap between mRNA and proteins. Crick's adapters turned out to be transfer RNA (tRNA) molecules. DNA contains special tRNA genes that are transcribed to form the tRNAs. Each kind of tRNA molecule binds to a specific amino acid. Amino acids are covalently linked to their respective tRNA molecules by specific enzymes called **aminoacyl-tRNA synthetases,** which use ATP as an energy source (Fig. 12–9). The resulting complexes, called **aminoacyl-tRNAs,** are able to bind to the mRNA coding sequence so as to align the amino acids in the correct order to form the polypeptide chain.

Transfer RNA molecules have specialized regions with specific functions

Although tRNA molecules are considerably smaller than mRNA or rRNA molecules, they have a complex structure. A tRNA molecule must have several properties:

1. It must have an **anticodon,** a specific complementary binding sequence for the correct mRNA codon.
2. It must be recognized by a specific aminoacyl-tRNA synthetase that adds the correct amino acid.
3. It must have a region that serves as the attachment site for the specific amino acid specified by the anticodon.
4. It must be recognized by ribosomes.

The tRNAs are polynucleotide chains 70 to 80 nucleotides long, each with several unique base sequences, as well as some sequences that are common to all (Fig. 12–10). Complementary base-pairing within each tRNA molecule causes it to be doubled back and folded. Three or more loops of unpaired nucleotides are

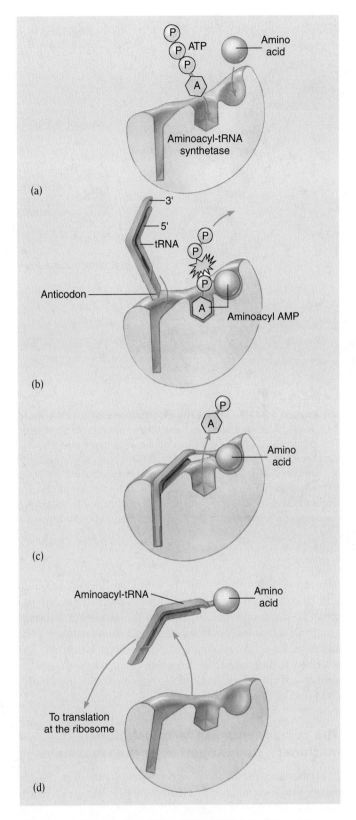

Figure 12–9 Formation of aminoacyl-tRNA. (a) A specific aminoacyl-tRNA synthetase is responsible for catalyzing the attachment of an amino acid to its correct tRNA. (b,c) In an ATP-requiring reaction, the carboxyl group of the amino acid becomes attached to the 3' end of the tRNA. (d) The resulting aminoacyl-tRNA complex is released.

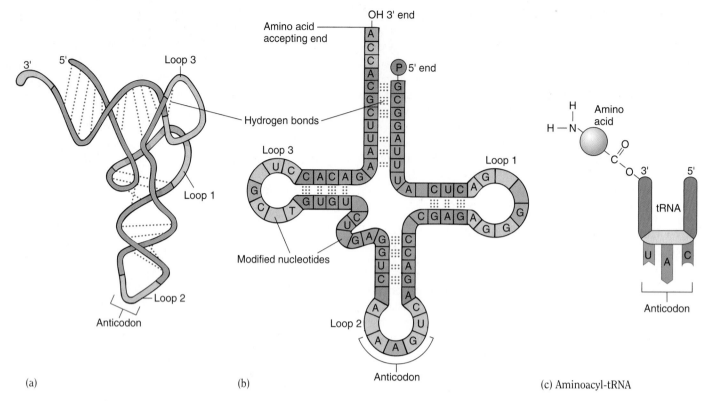

(a)   (b)   (c) Aminoacyl-tRNA

■ **Figure 12–10 Three representations of a tRNA molecule.** The genetic code is "read" by tRNA molecules, which have characteristic structures. **(a)** The three-dimensional shape of a tRNA molecule is determined by hydrogen bonds that form between complementary bases. **(b)** One loop contains the triplet anticodon; these unpaired bases can pair with a complementary mRNA triplet codon. The amino acid is attached to the terminal nucleotide at the OH 3' end. **(c)** This schematic diagram of an aminoacyl tRNA shows an amino acid attached to its tRNA by its carboxyl group, leaving its amino group exposed for peptide bond formation.

formed, one of which contains the anticodon triplet. The amino acid binding site is at the 3' end of the molecule. The carboxyl group of the amino acid is bound to the exposed 3' hydroxyl group of the terminal nucleotide, leaving the amino group of the amino acid free to participate in peptide bond formation. The pattern of folding results in a constant distance between the anticodon and amino acid in all tRNAs examined, allowing for precise positioning of the amino acids during translation.

The components of the translational machinery come together at the ribosomes

The importance of ribosomes and of protein synthesis in cellular metabolism is exemplified by a rapidly growing *E. coli* cell, which contains some 15,000 ribosomes—nearly one-third of the total mass of the cell. Although prokaryotic and eukaryotic ribosomes are not identical, ribosomes from all organisms share a great many fundamental features and basically work in the same way. All are composed of two subunits made up of protein and ribosomal RNA, which is transcribed from DNA. Unlike messenger RNA and transfer RNA, ribosomal RNA does not transfer specific in-

formation but instead has catalytic functions. The ribosomal proteins do not appear to be catalytic but instead contribute to the overall structure of the ribosome.

Each ribosomal subunit can be isolated intact in the laboratory and then separated into each of its RNA and protein constituents. For example, it has been found that in bacteria the smaller of these subunits contains 21 proteins and one ribosomal RNA molecule, and the larger contains 35 proteins and two ribosomal RNA molecules. Under certain conditions it is possible to reassemble each subunit into a functional form by adding each component in its correct order. Through this approach, together with sophisticated electron microscopic studies, it has been possible to determine the three-dimensional structure of the ribosome (Fig. 12–11*a*), as well as how it is assembled in the living cell. The large subunit contains a depression on one surface into which the small subunit fits. During translation, the mRNA fits in a groove formed between the contact surfaces of the two subunits.

The structure of the ribosome allows it to hold not only the mRNA template but also the aminoacyl-tRNA molecules and the growing peptide chain in the correct orientation so that the genetic code can be read and the next peptide bond formed. Trans-

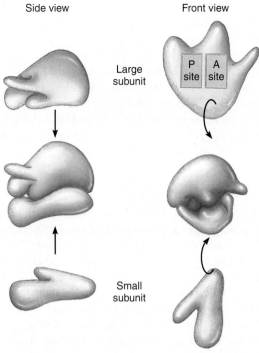

Side view | Front view

Large subunit

Small subunit

P site | A site

(a) This model of a ribosome is based on three-dimensional reconstruction of electron microscopic images.

▪ **Figure 12–11 Ribosome structure.** (a) A ribosome consists of two subunits, one larger and one smaller. (b) Each ribosome contains two binding sites for aminoacyl tRNA molecules.

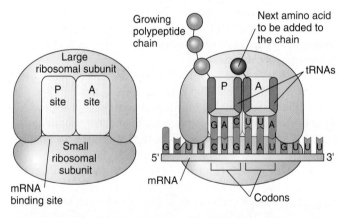

(b) The mRNA passes through a groove formed between the two ribosomal subunits. A ribosome contains two binding sites for tRNAs that recognize adjacent codons. The A site (aminoacyl-tRNA site) binds an aminoacyl-tRNA that will be used to add an amino acid to the growing chain. The P site (polypeptide-tRNA site) binds the tRNA that is linked to the growing polypeptide chain.

fer RNA molecules attach to two depressions on the ribosome, the **A** and **P** binding sites (Fig. 12–11*b*). The tRNA holding the growing **p**olypeptide chain occupies the P site and is bound to an mRNA codon. The A site is so named because the **a**minoacyl-tRNA delivering the next amino acid in the sequence binds at this location, positioning it at the next codon to be read. Following peptide bond formation between the amino acid at the A site and the end of the growing polypeptide chain, the tRNA (now with the entire polypeptide chain attached) then moves to the P site

of the ribosome, leaving the A site available for the next aminoacyl-tRNA molecule.

Translation includes initiation, elongation, and termination

For purposes of discussion, the process of protein synthesis is generally divided into three distinct stages: **initiation,** repeating cycles of **elongation,** and **termination.**

The initiation process (Fig. 12–12) consists of several steps and requires proteins called **initiation factors,** which become attached to the small ribosomal subunit, allowing it to bind to a special **initiator tRNA.**

Once the initiator tRNA is loaded on the small subunit, the resulting initiation complex binds to the special **ribosome-** recognition sequences near the 5' end of the mRNA, upstream of the coding sequences. The initiation complex then slides along the mRNA until it reaches a special codon known as the **initiation codon.** In all organisms, the initiation codon is AUG, which codes for the amino acid methionine. The initiation factors dissociate, the anticodon of the initiator tRNA binds to the initiation codon, and the large ribosomal subunit attaches to the complex, forming the completed ribosome. At this point, the initiator tRNA is bound to the P site of the ribosome, leaving the A site unoccupied so that it can be filled by the aminoacyl-tRNA specified by the next codon.

Figure 12–13 outlines the events involved in **elongation,** the addition of other amino acids to the growing polypeptide. The appropriate aminoacyl-tRNA binds to the A site by specific base-pairing of its anticodon with the complementary mRNA codon. This binding step requires energy, in this case supplied by GTP (guanosine triphosphate, an energy transfer molecule similar to ATP).

The amino group of the amino acid at the A site is now aligned with the carboxyl group of the preceding amino acid at the P site. Peptide bond formation then takes place between the amino group of the new amino acid and the carboxyl group of the preceding amino acid. In this process, the amino acid attached at the P site is released from its tRNA and becomes attached to the aminoacyl-tRNA at the A site. This reaction is spontaneous (i.e., it does not require additional energy) because energy was transferred from ATP during the formation of the aminoacyl-tRNA. It does, however, require an enzyme (known as *peptidyl transferase*). Remarkably, this enzyme is not a protein, but an rRNA component of the large ribosomal subunit. Such an RNA catalyst is known as a **ribozyme.**

Recall from Chapter 3 that polypeptide chains have direction, or polarity. The amino acid on one end has a free amino group (the amino end), and the amino acid at the other end has a free carboxyl group (the carboxyl end). Protein synthesis always proceeds from the amino end to the carboxyl end of the growing peptide chain.

After the peptide bond is formed, the tRNA molecule in the P site is released. The growing peptide chain, which is now attached to the tRNA in the A site, is then translocated to the P site, leaving the A site open for the next aminoacyl tRNA. This **translocation** process requires energy, which is again supplied by GTP.

During translocation, the ribosome and the mRNA move in relation to each other so that the mRNA codon specifying the next amino acid in the polypeptide chain becomes positioned in the unoccupied A site. This process involves movement of the ribosome in the 3' direction along the mRNA molecule; thus, translation of the mRNA always proceeds in a 5' to 3' direction. The end of the mRNA molecule that is synthesized first during transcription is also the first to be translated to form a polypeptide. Formation of each peptide bond requires a fraction of a second; by repeating the elongation cycle, an average-sized protein of about 360 amino acids can be assembled by a prokaryotic cell in about 18 seconds, and by a eukaryotic cell in a little over a minute.

The synthesis of the polypeptide chain is terminated by "release factors" that recognize the termination, or stop, codon at

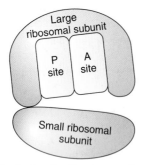

(a) Before translation begins, the ribosomes are dissociated into small and large subunits.

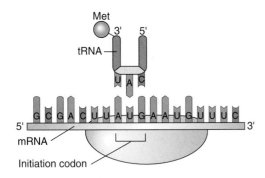

(b) An initiation complex forms, consisting of the small ribosomal subunit, mRNA, and formylated methionine (the initiator tRNA).

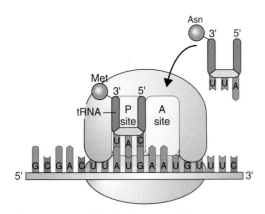

(c) The large ribosomal subunit binds to the initiation complex. The process of peptide elongation begins with the addition of the second tRNA with its amino acid.

■ **Figure 12–12 Initiation of protein synthesis.** The small ribosomal subunit participates in the formation of an initiation complex, which then associates with the large subunit. The initiation complex shown is found in *E. coli.* Initiation factors are not shown.

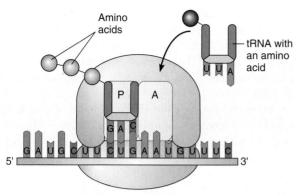

(a) The polypeptide chain is attached to the tRNA that carries the amino acid most recently added to the chain. This tRNA is in the P site of the ribosome.

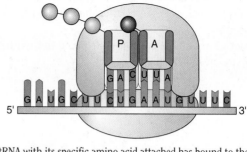

(b) A tRNA with its specific amino acid attached has bound to the A site. Base pairs have formed between the anticodon of tRNA and the codon of mRNA.

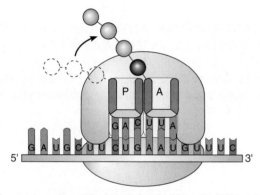

(c) The growing polypeptide chain is detached from the tRNA molecule in the P site and joined by a peptide bond to the amino acid linked to the tRNA at the A site.

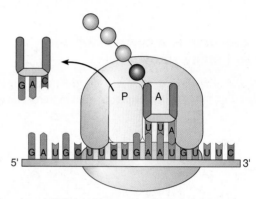

(d) The released tRNA joins the cytoplasmic pool of tRNA and can bind with another amino acid.

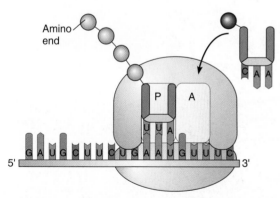

(e) In the translocation step the mRNA and tRNA move in one direction and the ribosome moves in the opposite direction. In this way the growing polypeptide chain is transferred to the P site.

■ **Figure 12–13 Elongation.** Each repetition of the elongation process adds one amino acid to the growing polypeptide chain. This illustration begins after a short chain of amino acids has formed.

the end of the coding sequence. The release factors release the newly made protein, the mRNA, and the last tRNA used, and then cause the ribosome to dissociate into its two subunits, which can then be used to form a new initiation complex with another mRNA molecule.

The relative orientations of the mRNA and the synthesized polypeptide are given below:

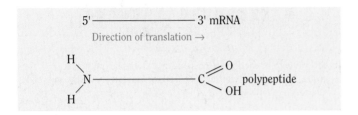

A polyribosome is a complex of one mRNA and many ribosomes

In *E. coli* and other prokaryotes, transcription and translation are *coupled* (Fig. 12–14). Ribosomes can bind to the 5' end of the growing mRNA and initiate translation long before the synthesis of the message is completed. As many as 15 ribosomes may be bound to a single mRNA molecule. Messenger RNA molecules bound to clusters of ribosomes are referred to as **polyribosomes,** or sometimes **polysomes.** Polyribosomes also occur in eukaryotic cells.

Although many polypeptide chains can be actively synthesized on a single messenger RNA at any one time, the half-life (the time it takes for half of the molecules to be degraded) of mRNA molecules in bacterial cells is only about 2 minutes. Usually, degradation of the 5' end of the mRNA begins even before the first polypeptide has been completed. Once the ribosome recognition sequences at the 5' end of the mRNA have been degraded, no more ribosomes can attach and initiate protein synthesis.

■ TRANSCRIPTION AND TRANSLATION ARE COMPLEX IN EUKARYOTES

Although the basic mechanisms of transcription and translation are quite similar in all organisms, some significant differences

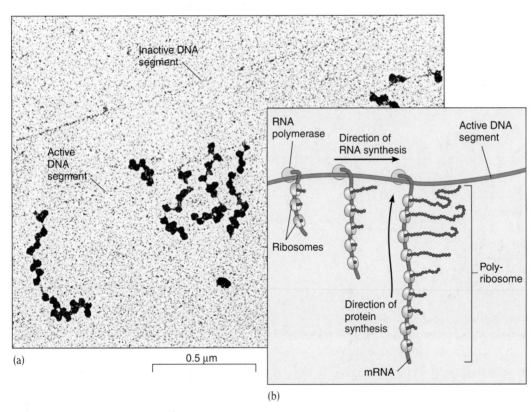

(a)

0.5 μm

(b)

Figure 12–14 Coupled transcription and translation in bacteria. (a) TEM of two strands of *E. coli* DNA, one inactive and the other actively producing mRNA. Protein synthesis begins while the mRNA is being completed, as multiple ribosomes attach to the mRNA to form a polyribosome. **(b)** Diagram showing a sequence of coupled transcription and translation.   *(Courtesy of Dr. Barbara Hamkalo, University of California, Irvine)*

exist between eukaryotes and prokaryotes. Some of these are a consequence of differences in cell structure. Bacterial mRNA is translated as it is being transcribed from the DNA. This cannot occur in eukaryotes because eukaryotic chromosomes are confined to the cell nucleus, and protein synthesis takes place in the cytoplasm. Therefore, eukaryotic mRNA must be transported through the nuclear envelope and into the cytoplasm before it can be translated.

There are many other differences between eukaryotic and prokaryotic mRNA. Bacterial mRNAs are used immediately after transcription without further processing. In eukaryotes, the original transcript, known as **precursor mRNA,** or **pre-mRNA,** must be modified in several ways while it is still in the nucleus. These **posttranscriptional modification and processing** activities are required to form mature mRNA that is competent for transport and translation.

Modification of the eukaryotic message begins when the growing RNA transcript is about 20 to 30 nucleotides long. At that point, enzymes add a **cap** to the 5' end of the mRNA chain. The cap is in the form of an unusual nucleotide, 7-methylguanylate, which is guanosine monophosphate with a methyl group added to one of the nitrogens in the base. Eukaryotic ribosomes cannot bind to an uncapped message.

Capping may also protect the RNA from certain types of degradation and may therefore be partially responsible for the fact that eukaryotic mRNAs are much more stable than prokaryotic mRNAs. Eukaryotic mRNAs have half-lives ranging from 30 minutes to as long as 24 hours; the average half-life of an mRNA molecule in a mammalian cell is about 10 hours (compared with 2 minutes in a bacterial cell).

A second modification of eukaryotic mRNA occurs at the 3' end of the molecule. Near the 3' end of a completed message there is usually a sequence of bases that serves as a signal for the addition of a "tail" with many adenines, known as a **polyadenylated** (or **poly-A) tail.** Within about 1 minute of completion of the transcript, enzymes in the nucleus recognize this **polyadenylation signal** and cut the mRNA molecule at that site. This is followed by the enzymatic addition of a string of 100 to 250 adenine nucleotides to the 3' end. The function of polyadenylation is not completely understood, although there is evidence that it helps in the export of the mRNA from the nucleus, stabilizes some mRNAs against degradation in the cytoplasm, and makes initiation of translation more efficient.

Both noncoding and coding sequences are transcribed from eukaryotic genes

One of the greatest surprises in the history of molecular biology was the finding that most eukaryotic genes have **interrupted coding sequences;** that is, there are long sequences of bases within the protein-coding sequences of the gene that do not code for amino acids in the final protein product! The noncoding regions within the gene are called **introns** (**in**tervening sequences), as opposed to **exons** (**ex**pressed sequences) which are parts of the protein-coding sequence.

A typical eukaryotic gene may have multiple exons and introns, although the number is quite variable. For example, the β-globin gene, which produces one component of hemoglobin, contains 2 introns; the ovalbumin gene of egg white contains 7; and the gene specifying another egg-white protein, conalbumin, contains 16. In many cases, the combined lengths of the introns are much greater than those of the exon sequences. For instance, the ovalbumin gene contains about 7700 base pairs, whereas the total of all the exon sequences is only 1859 base pairs.

When a gene that contains introns is transcribed, the entire gene is copied as a large RNA transcript, the precursor mRNA, or pre-mRNA (Fig. 12–15). A pre-mRNA molecule contains both exon and intron sequences. (Note that the terms *intron* and *exon* refer to corresponding nucleotide sequences in both DNA and RNA.) For the pre-mRNA to be made into a functional message, not only must it be capped and have a poly-A tail added, but also the introns must be removed and the exons spliced together to form a continuous protein-coding message. The splicing reactions are mediated by special base sequences within and to either side of the introns. Splicing itself can occur by several different mechanisms. In many instances it involves the association of **small nuclear ribonucleoprotein complexes (snRNPs)** which bind to the introns and catalyze the excision and splicing reactions. In some cases, the RNA within the intron acts as a ribozyme, splicing itself without the use of protein enzymes.

The evolution of eukaryotic gene structure is incompletely understood

The reason for the complex structure of eukaryotic genes is a matter of ongoing debate among molecular biologists. Why do introns occur in most eukaryotic nuclear genes but not in the genes of most prokaryotes (or of mitochondria and chloroplasts)? How did this remarkable genetic system involving interrupted coding sequences ("split genes") evolve, and why has it survived? It seems incredible that as much as 75% of the original transcript of a eukaryotic nuclear gene has to be removed to make a working message.

In the early 1980s, Walter Gilbert of Harvard University proposed that exons are nucleotide sequences that code for **protein domains,** regions of protein tertiary structure that may have specific functions. For example, the active site of an enzyme might comprise one domain. A different domain might enable that enzyme to bind to a particular cellular structure, and yet another might be a site involved in allosteric regulation (see Chapter 6). Analyses of the DNA and amino acid sequences of a great many eukaryotic genes have shown that most exons are too small to code for an entire protein domain, although a block of several exons can code for a domain.

Gilbert further postulated that new proteins with new functions can emerge rapidly when novel combinations of exons are produced by genetic recombination within intron regions of genes that code for different proteins. This hypothesis has become known as *evolution by "exon shuffling."* It has been

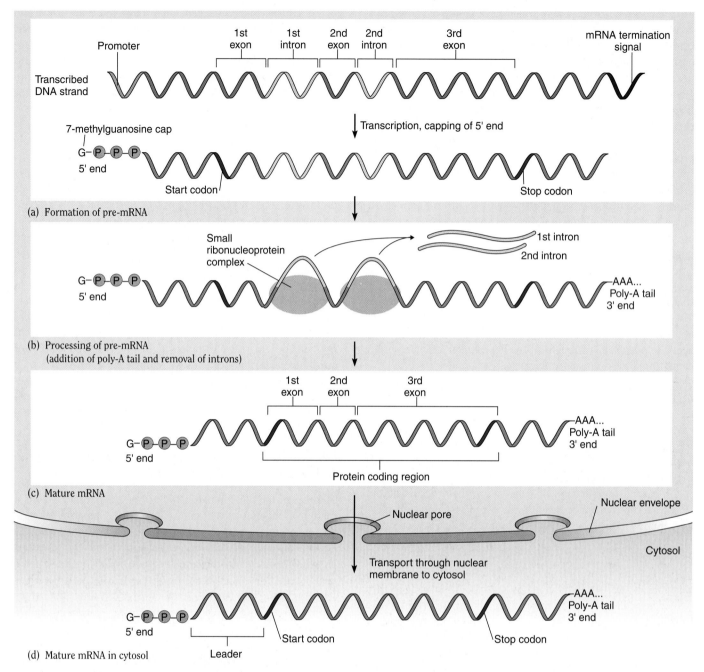

(a) Formation of pre-mRNA

(b) Processing of pre-mRNA
(addition of poly-A tail and removal of introns)

(c) Mature mRNA

(d) Mature mRNA in cytosol

Figure 12–15 Posttranscriptional modification of eukaryotic RNA. **(a)** A DNA sequence containing both exons and introns is transcribed by RNA polymerase to make the primary transcript, or mRNA precursor. As it is synthesized, the pre-mRNA is "capped" by the addition of a modified base attached "backwards" (by a 5'–5' linkage) to its 5' end. **(b)** A poly-A tail (100–250 nucleotides long) is added to the 3' end; introns are removed, and the exons are spliced together. **(c)** The mature mRNA is transported through the nuclear envelope and into the cytosol **(d)** to be translated.

supported by examples such as the low-density lipoprotein (LDL) receptor protein, a protein found on the surface of human cells that binds to cholesterol transport molecules (see Chapter 5). The LDL receptor protein has several domains that are related to parts of several other proteins with totally different functions.

However, many other genes and their corresponding proteins show no evidence of exon shuffling.

Some scientists think that introns first evolved in the nucleus of an early eukaryote and were propagated as mobile genetic elements, known as *transposons* (discussed later in this chapter). Regardless of how split genes originated, intron excision provides one of the many ways in which present-day eukaryotes regulate the expression of their genes (see Chapter 13). This opportunity for control, together with the fact that eukaryotic RNAs are far more stable than those of prokaryotes, may balance the energy cost of maintaining a large load of noncoding DNA.

■ THE GENETIC CODE HAS SPECIAL FEATURES

Process of Science Before the genetic code was deciphered, scientists had become interested in how a genetic code might work. The Watson and Crick model of DNA showed it to be a linear sequence of four nucleotides. If each nucleotide were to code for a single amino acid, it would be possible to specify only 4 amino acids, not the 20 found in the vast variety of proteins in the cell. Scientists saw that the DNA bases could serve as a four-letter "alphabet" and hypothesized that three-letter combinations of the four bases (4^3) would make it possible to form a total of 64 "words," more than sufficient to specify all the naturally occurring amino acids. In 1961, Francis Crick and his coworkers concluded from a mathematical analysis that the code was based on nonoverlapping triplets of bases. They predicted that the code is read, one triplet at a time, from a fixed starting point that establishes the **reading frame.** Because there are no "commas" separating the triplets, an alteration in the reading frame would result in the incorporation of incorrect amino acids.

Experimental evidence allowing the assignment of specific triplets to specific amino acids was first obtained by Marshall Nirenberg and Heinrich Matthaei. By constructing artificial mRNA molecules with known base sequences, they were able to determine which amino acids would be incorporated into protein in purified in vitro protein synthetic systems derived from *E. coli.* For example, when the synthetic mRNA polyuridylic acid (UUUUUUUU . . .) was added to a mixture of purified ribosomes, aminoacyl tRNAs, and essential cofactors needed to synthesize protein, only phenylalanine was incorporated into the resulting polypeptide chain. The inference that UUU is the triplet that codes for phenylalanine was inescapable. Similar experiments showed that polyadenylic acid (AAAAAAAAA . . .) codes for a polypeptide of lysine, and polycytidylic acid (CCCCCCCCC . . .) codes for a polypeptide of proline.

By using mixed nucleotide polymers (e.g., a random polymer of A and C) as artificial messengers, it became possible to assign the other nucleotide triplet codons to specific amino acids. However, three of the codons, UAA, UGA, and UAG, were not found to specify any amino acid. These codons (the stop, or termination, codons mentioned earlier) are now known to be the signals that specify the end of the coding sequence for a polypeptide chain.

By 1967 the "cracking" of the genetic code was completed, and the coding assignments of all 64 possible codons listed in Table 12–1 were known. Investigators were also able to demonstrate conclusively that the code is a nonoverlapping triplet code.

Remember that the genetic code we define and use is an mRNA code. The tRNA anticodon sequences as well as the DNA sequence from which the message is transcribed are complementary to the sequences shown in Table 12–1. For example, the mRNA codon for the amino acid methionine is 5' — AUG — 3'. It is transcribed from the DNA base sequence 3' — TAC — 5', and the corresponding tRNA anticodon is 3' — UAC — 5'.

The genetic code is universal

This chapter has only one table to represent the genetic code. This is because of the single most remarkable feature of the code: *It is essentially universal!* Over the years, the genetic code has been examined in a diverse array of species and found to be the same in organisms as different as *E. coli,* redwood trees, and humans. These findings strongly suggest that the code is an ancient legacy that evolved very early in the history of life (see Chapter 20) and has been retained as a kind of "frozen accident" because all but the most minimal changes would be lethal.

Recently some very minor exceptions to the universality of the genetic code have been discovered. In several unicellular protozoa, two of the stop codons, UAA and UGA, code for the amino acid glutamine. The other exceptions are found in mitochondria, which contain their own DNA and protein-synthesis machinery for a small number of genes (see Chapters 4 and 20). These slight coding differences vary with the organism, but it is important to keep in mind that in each case all of the other coding assignments are identical to the standard genetic code.

The genetic code is redundant

Given that there are 64 possible codons and that there are only 20 common amino acids, it is not surprising that certain amino acids are specified by more than one codon. The genetic code is said to be degenerate because of this redundancy in the code, which has certain characteristic patterns. The codons CCU, CCC, CCA, and CCG are synonymous in that they all code for the amino acid proline. The only difference among the four codons involves the nucleotide at the 3' end of the triplet. Although the code may be read three nucleotides at a time, only the first two nucleotides appear to contain specific information for proline. A similar pattern can be seen for many other amino acids. Only methionine and tryptophan have single-triplet codes. All other amino acids are specified by two to six different codons.

Process of Science There are 61 codons that specify amino acids. Although most cells contain only about 40 different tRNA molecules, some of these tRNAs can pair with more than one codon, so all the codons can still be used. This apparent breach of the base-pairing rules was first proposed by Francis Crick as the **wobble hypothesis.** Crick reasoned that the third nucleotide of a tRNA anticodon (which is the 5' base of the anticodon sequence) may sometimes be capable of forming hydrogen bonds with more than one kind of third nucleotide (the 3' base) of a codon. Investigators later established this experimentally by determining the anticodon sequences of tRNA molecules and testing their specificities in artificial systems. Some tRNA molecules can recognize as many as three separate codons differing in their third nucleotide, but specifying the same amino acid.

A GENE IS DEFINED AS A FUNCTIONAL UNIT

At the beginning of this chapter, we traced the development of ideas regarding the nature of the gene. For a time it was useful to define a gene as a sequence of nucleotides that codes for one polypeptide chain. As we have continued to learn more about how genes work, we have revised our definition. We now know that some genes are transcribed to produce RNA molecules such as rRNA and tRNA, whereas others specify the RNA component of the small nuclear ribonucleoprotein complexes used to modify complex mRNA molecules. Studies have also shown that in eukaryotic cells a single gene may be capable of producing more than one polypeptide chain by modifications in the way the mRNA is processed (see Chapter 13).

It is perhaps most useful to define a gene in terms of its product. A **gene** can therefore be thought of as a nucleotide sequence that carries the information needed to produce a specific RNA or protein product. As we will see in Chapter 13, a gene includes noncoding regulatory sequences, as well as coding sequences.

THERE ARE EXCEPTIONS TO THE USUAL DIRECTION OF FLOW OF GENETIC INFORMATION

For several decades, one of the central premises of molecular biology was that genetic information always flows from DNA to RNA to protein. An important exception to this rule was discovered by Howard Temin in 1964 through his studies of certain viruses. Although viruses are noncellular, they contain a single type of nucleic acid and are capable of reproducing in a host cell. Temin was studying certain unusual, cancer-causing tumor viruses that have RNA, rather than DNA, as their genetic material. He found that infection of a host cell by one of these particular viruses is blocked by inhibitors of DNA synthesis and also by inhibitors of transcription. These findings suggested that DNA synthesis and transcription are required for the multiplication of RNA tumor viruses and that there must be a way for information to flow in the "reverse" direction (that is, from RNA to DNA).

Temin proposed that a **DNA provirus** is formed as an intermediary in the replication of RNA tumor viruses. This hypothesis required a new kind of enzyme that would synthesize DNA using RNA as a template. In 1970 Temin and David Baltimore discovered just such an enzyme, and in 1975 they shared the Nobel Prize for their discovery. This RNA-directed DNA polymerase, also known as **reverse transcriptase,** was found in all RNA tumor viruses. (Some RNA viruses that do not produce tumors, however, are replicated directly without using a DNA intermediate.) The steps of RNA tumor virus reproduction are shown in Figure 12–16. Because of their reversal of the usual direction of information flow, viruses that require reverse transcriptase have become known as **retroviruses.** The virus (HIV-1) that causes AIDS is the most widely known retrovirus. As we will see in Chapter 14, the reverse transcriptase enzyme has become an extremely important research tool for molecular biologists.

MUTATIONS ARE CHANGES IN DNA

One of the first major discoveries about genes was that they can undergo **mutations,** changes in the nucleotide sequence of the DNA. However, the overall observed mutation rate is much lower than the frequency of damage to DNA, because all organisms have special systems of enzymes that can repair certain kinds of alterations in the DNA.

As explained in Chapter 11, once the DNA sequence has been changed, DNA replication copies the altered sequence just as it would copy a normal sequence, making the mutation stable over an indefinite number of generations. In most cases, the mutant allele has no greater tendency than does the original allele to mutate again. Mutations provide the diversity of genetic material that makes it possible to study inheritance and the molecular nature of genes. As we will see in later chapters, mutations also provide the variation necessary for evolution to occur within a given species.

Genes can be altered by mutation in several ways (Fig. 12–17). It is now possible to determine where a specific mutation occurs in a gene by using recombinant DNA methods to isolate the gene and determine its sequence of bases (see Chapter 14).

Base substitution mutations result from the exchange of one base pair for another

The simplest type of mutation, called a **base substitution mutation,** involves a change in only one pair of nucleotides. Often these mutations result from errors in base pairing that occurred during the replication process. For example, an AT base pair might be replaced by a GC, CG, or TA pair. Such a mutation may cause the altered DNA to be transcribed as an altered mRNA. The altered mRNA may then be translated into a peptide chain with only one amino acid different from the normal sequence.

Base substitutions that result in the replacement of one amino acid by another are sometimes referred to as **missense mutations.** Missense mutations can have a wide range of effects. If the amino acid substitution occurs at or near the active site of an enzyme, the activity of the altered protein may be decreased or even destroyed. Some missense mutations involve a change in an amino acid that is not part of the active site. Others may result in the substitution of a closely related amino acid (one with very similar chemical characteristics). Such mutations may be *silent* (undetectable) if one simply examines its effects on the whole organism. Because silent mutations occur relatively frequently, the true number of mutations in an organism or a species is much greater than what is actually observed.

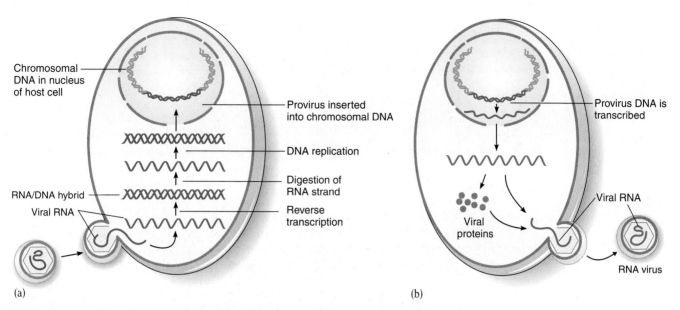

(a)

(b)

■ **Figure 12–16 Infection cycle of an RNA tumor virus.** **(a)** After an RNA tumor virus enters the host cell, the viral reverse transcriptase synthesizes a DNA strand that is complementary to the viral RNA. Next, the RNA strand is degraded and a complementary DNA strand is synthesized, thus completing the double-stranded DNA provirus, which is then integrated into the host cell's DNA. **(b)** The provirus DNA is transcribed, and the resulting viral mRNA is translated to form specific viral proteins. Additional viral RNA molecules are produced and then incorporated into mature virus particles enclosed by protein coats.

Nonsense mutations are base substitutions that convert an amino acid–specifying codon to a termination codon. A nonsense mutation usually destroys the function of the gene product; in the case of a protein-specifying gene, the part of the polypeptide chain that follows the termination codon is missing.

Frameshift mutations result from the addition or deletion of base pairs

In **frameshift mutations,** one or two nucleotide pairs are inserted into or deleted from the molecule, causing an alteration of the *reading frame.* As a result of this shift, codons downstream of the insertion or deletion site specify an entirely new sequence of amino acids. Depending on where the insertion or deletion occurs in the gene, different effects can be generated. In addition to producing an entirely new polypeptide sequence immediately after the change, frameshift mutations usually produce a stop or termination codon within a short distance of the mutation. This codon terminates the already altered polypeptide chain. A frame shift in a gene specifying an enzyme usually results in a loss of enzyme activity. If the enzyme is an essential one, the effect on the organism can be disastrous.

Some mutations involve larger DNA segments

Some types of mutations are due to a change in chromosome structure (see Chapters 13, 15, and 16). These changes usually have a wide range of effects because they involve large numbers of genes.

Process of Science One type of mutation is caused by DNA sequences that "jump" into the middle of a gene. These movable sequences of DNA not only disrupt the functions of some genes, but under some conditions also activate previously inactive genes. Jumping genes, now known as **mobile genetic elements, transposable elements,** or **transposons,** were discovered in maize (corn) by Barbara McClintock in the 1950s. She observed that certain genes appeared to be "turned off" and "turned on" spontaneously. She deduced that the mechanism involved a gene that moved from one region of a chromosome to another, where it would either activate or inactivate genes in that vicinity. It was not until the development of recombinant DNA methods (see Chapter 14) and the discovery of transposons in a wide variety of organisms that this phenomenon began to be understood. We now know that transposons are segments of DNA that range from a few hundred to several thousand bases. The elements themselves seem to require a special **transposase** enzyme in order to be incorporated into a new location within the chromosome. The longer transposable elements may contain other genes that "go along for the ride." In recognition of her insightful findings, McClintock was awarded a Nobel Prize in 1983.

Mutations have varied causes

Most types of mutations occur infrequently but spontaneously as a consequence either of mistakes in DNA replication or of defects in the mitotic or meiotic separation of chromosomes. Some regions of DNA, known as mutational **hot spots,** are much more

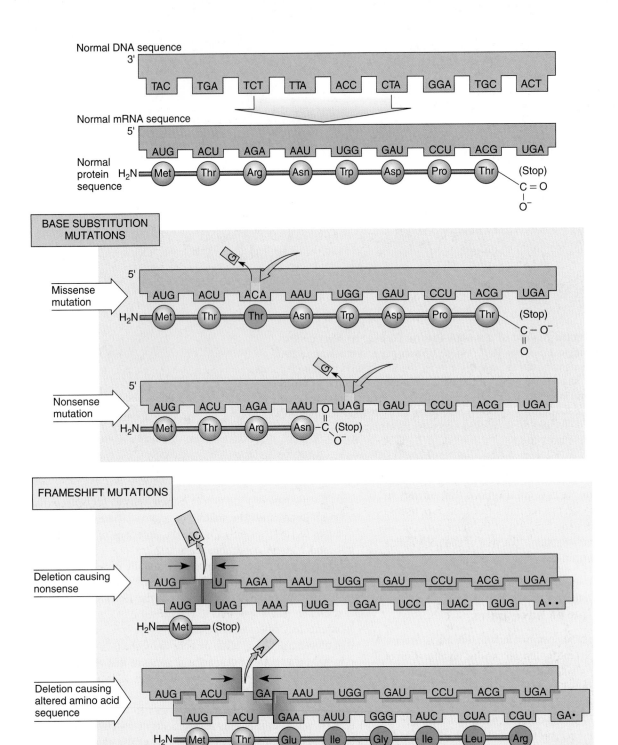

Figure 12–17 Mutations. Missense and nonsense mutations are types of base substitutions. A missense mutation results in a protein of normal length, but with an amino acid substitution. A nonsense mutation, caused by conversion of an amino acid–specifying codon to a termination (stop) codon, results in the production of a truncated (shortened) protein, which is usually not functional. A frameshift mutation, which results from the insertion *(not shown)* or deletion of one or two bases, causes the base sequence following the mutation to shift to a new reading frame. A frame shift may produce a termination codon downstream of the mutation (which would have the same effect as a nonsense mutation caused by base substitution), or it may produce an entirely new amino acid sequence.

likely than others to undergo mutation. An example would be a short stretch of repeated nucleotides, which can cause DNA polymerase to "slip" while reading the template during replication.

Mutations in certain genes can increase the overall mutation rate. For example, a mutation in a gene coding for DNA polymerase might make DNA replication less precise, or a mutation in a gene coding for a repair enzyme might cause more mutations to persist rather than to be repaired.

Not all mutations occur spontaneously; many of the types of mutations discussed previously can also be caused by agents known as **mutagens.** Among these are various types of radiation, including x rays, gamma rays, cosmic rays, and ultraviolet rays. Some chemical mutagens react with and modify specific bases in the DNA, leading to mistakes in complementary base pairing when the DNA molecule is replicated. Other mutagens are inserted into the DNA molecule and change the normal reading frame during replication.

Despite the presence of enzymes that repair mutations, some new mutations do persist. In fact, each of us is very likely to have some mutant allele that was not present in either of our parents. Although some of these mutations can produce an altered phenotype, most are not noticeable because they are recessive.

Mutations that occur in the cells of the body (somatic cells) are not passed on to the offspring. However, these mutations are of concern because there is a close relationship between somatic mutations and cancer. Many mutagens are also **carcinogens,** agents that produce cancer.

SUMMARY WITH KEY TERMS

I. Garrod's early work on inborn errors of metabolism and that of Beadle and Tatum in the 1940s with *Neurospora* mutants provided strong evidence that genes specify proteins.

II. The mechanism by which information encoded in DNA is used to specify the sequences of amino acids in proteins involves two processes: transcription and translation.

A. During **transcription,** an RNA molecule that is complementary to the transcribed or template DNA strand is synthesized. **Messenger RNA (mRNA)** molecules contain information that specifies the amino acid sequences of polypeptide chains.

B. During **translation,** a polypeptide chain specified by the mRNA is synthesized.

1. Each **triplet** (three-base sequence) in the mRNA constitutes a **codon,** which specifies one amino acid in the polypeptide chain, or a stop or start signal.

2. Translation requires tRNAs and complex cell machinery, including ribosomes.

III. Messenger RNA is synthesized by **DNA-dependent RNA polymerase** enzymes.

A. RNA is formed from nucleotide subunits, each of which contains the sugar ribose, a base (uracil, adenine, guanine, or cytosine), and three phosphates.

B. RNA polymerase initially binds to a special DNA sequence called the **promoter** region.

C. Like DNA, RNA subunits are covalently joined by a 5' — 3' linkage to form an alternating sugar-phosphate backbone. The same base-pairing rules are followed as in DNA replication, except that uracil is substituted for thymine.

D. RNA synthesis proceeds in a 5' → 3' direction, which means that the template DNA strand is "read" in a 3' → 5' direction.

IV. **Transfer RNAs (tRNAs)** are the "decoding" molecules in the translation process.

A. Each tRNA molecule is specific for only one amino acid.

1. One part of the molecule contains a three-base **anticodon,** which is complementary to a codon of the mRNA.

2. Attached to one end of the tRNA molecule is the amino acid specified by the complementary mRNA codon.

B. Amino acids are covalently bound to tRNA by **aminoacyl-tRNA synthetase** enzymes.

V. **Ribosomes** bring together all the mechanical machinery necessary for translation. They couple the tRNAs to their proper codons on the mRNA, facilitate the formation of peptide bonds between amino acids, and translocate the mRNA so that the next codon can be read.

A. Each ribosome is made of a large and a small subunit; each subunit contains **ribosomal RNA (rRNA)** and over 50 proteins.

B. **Initiation** is the first stage of translation. The small ribosomal subunit protein, plus **initiation factors** and the **initiator tRNA,** binds to AUG, the **initiation codon,** in the 5' region of the mRNA, followed by binding of the large ribosomal subunit.

C. **Elongation** is a cyclic process in which amino acids are added one by one to the growing polypeptide chain.

1. Elongation proceeds in a 5' → 3' direction along the mRNA.

2. The polypeptide chain grows from its amino end to its carboxyl end.

D. **Termination,** the final stage of translation, occurs when the ribosome reaches one of three special **termination,** or **stop, codons,** which triggers release of the completed polypeptide chain.

VI. In bacterial cells, transcription and translation are coupled. Translation of the mRNA molecule usually begins before the 3' end of the transcript is completed. A single mRNA molecule can be translated by groups of ribosomes called **polyribosomes.**

VII. The basic features of transcription and translation are the same in prokaryotic and eukaryotic cells, but eukaryotic genes and their mRNA molecules are more complex than those of bacteria.

A. After transcription, eukaryotic mRNA molecules are **capped** at the 5' end with a modified guanosine triphosphate. Many also have a **poly-A tail** composed of adenine-containing nucleotides added at the 3' end. These modifications appear to protect eukaryotic mRNA molecules from degradation, giving them longer lifetimes than bacterial mRNA.

B. In many eukaryotic genes the coding regions, called **exons,** are interrupted by noncoding regions, called **introns.** Both introns and exons are transcribed, but the introns are later removed from the **mRNA precursor,** and the exons are spliced together to produce a continuous protein-coding sequence.

VIII. The **genetic code** is defined at the mRNA level. There are 61 codons that code for amino acids, plus three codons that serve as stop signals.

A. The start signal for all proteins is the codon AUG, which also specifies the amino acid methionine.

B. The genetic code is read from mRNA as a series of nonoverlapping triplets that specify a single sequence of amino acids.

C. The genetic code is said to be degenerate because it is redundant; that is, some amino acids are specified by more than one codon.

D. The genetic code is virtually universal, strongly suggesting that all organisms are descended from a common ancestor. Only a few minor variations are exceptions to the standard code.

IX. A **gene** can be defined as a sequence of nucleotides (plus closely associated regulatory sequences) that can be transcribed to yield a specific protein or RNA product.

X. The flow of genetic information can be reversed by **reverse transcriptase,** an enzyme associated with RNA tumor viruses that can synthesize DNA from an RNA template.

XI. Types of **mutations** range from disruption of the structure of a chromosome to a change in only a single pair of nucleotide bases.

A. A **base substitution** can destroy the function of a protein if a codon is altered such that it specifies a different amino acid **(missense mutation)** or becomes a termination codon **(nonsense mutation).** A base substitution has minimal effects if the amino acid is not altered or if the codon is changed to specify a chemically similar amino acid.

B. Insertion or deletion of one or two base pairs in a gene invariably destroys the function of that protein because it results in a **frameshift mutation** that changes the codon sequences downstream from the mutation.

C. Mutations can be produced by errors in DNA replication, by physical agents such as x rays or ultraviolet rays, or by chemical **mutagens.** Mutations can also occur through **transposons** or **mobile genetic elements,** which move from one part of a chromosome to another, disrupting the function of a part of the DNA. Some damage to DNA can be repaired by special systems of enzymes.

POST-TEST

1. Beadle and Tatum (a) predicted that tRNA molecules would have anticodons (b) discovered the genetic disease alcaptonuria (c) showed that the genetic disease sickle cell anemia is due to a change in a single amino acid in a hemoglobin polypeptide chain (d) worked out the genetic code (e) studied the relationship between genes and enzymes in *Neurospora*

2. The genetic code is defined as a series of _____ in _____. (a) anticodons; tRNA (b) codons; DNA (c) anticodons; mRNA (d) codons; mRNA (e) codons and anticodons; rRNA

3. Transcription is the process by which _____ is/are synthesized. (a) mRNA (b) mRNA and tRNA (c) mRNA, tRNA, and rRNA (d) protein (e) mRNA, tRNA, rRNA, and protein

4. RNA differs from DNA in that the base _____ is substituted for _____. (a) adenine; uracil (b) uracil; thymine (c) guanine; uracil (d) cytosine; guanine; uracil (e) guanine; adenine

5. RNA grows in the _____ direction, as DNA-dependent RNA polymerase moves along the template DNA strand in the _____ direction. (a) $5' \longrightarrow 3'$; $3' \longrightarrow 5'$ (b) $3' \longrightarrow 5'$; $3' \longrightarrow 5'$ (c) $5' \longrightarrow 3'$; $5' \longrightarrow 3'$ (d) $3' \longrightarrow 3'$; $5' \longrightarrow 5'$ (e) $5' \longrightarrow 5'$; $3' \longrightarrow 3'$

6. Which of the following is/are *not* found in a prokaryotic mRNA molecule? (a) protein termination codon (b) upstream leader sequences (c) downstream trailing sequences (d) start codon (e) promoter sequences

7. Which of the following is/are typically removed from pre-mRNA during nuclear processing in eukaryotes? (a) upstream leader sequences (b) poly-A tail (c) introns (d) exons (e) all of the above are removed

8. Which of the following is a spontaneous process, with no direct requirement for ATP or GTP? (a) formation of a peptide bond (b) translocation of the ribosome (c) formation of aminoacyl-tRNA (d) a and b (e) all of the above are spontaneous processes

9. Select the events of the elongation cycle of protein synthesis from the following list and place them in the proper sequence.

1. peptide bond formation
2. binding of the small ribosomal subunit to the 5' end of the mRNA
3. binding of aminoacyl-tRNA to the A site
4. translocation of the ribosome

(a) $1 \longrightarrow 3 \longrightarrow 2 \longrightarrow 4$ (b) $3 \longrightarrow 1 \longrightarrow 4$ (c) $3 \longrightarrow 1 \longrightarrow 3 \longrightarrow 2$ (d) $1 \longrightarrow 3 \longrightarrow 4$ (e) $4 \longrightarrow 2 \longrightarrow 1 \longrightarrow 3$

10. The statement "the genetic code is redundant" or "degenerate" means that (a) some codons specify punctuation (stop and start signals) rather amino acids (b) some codons specify more than one amino acid (c) certain amino acids can be specified by more than one codon (d) in some cases, the third nucleotide of an anticodon may be able to pair with more than one kind of base in a codon (e) all organisms have essentially the same genetic code

11. A nonsense mutation (a) causes one amino acid to be substituted for another in a polypeptide chain (b) results from the deletion of one or two bases, leading to a shift in the reading frame (c) results from the insertion of one or two bases, leading to a shift in the reading frame (d) results from the insertion of a transposon (e) usually results in the formation of an abnormally short polypeptide chain

REVIEW QUESTIONS

1. A certain transcribed DNA strand has the following nucleotide sequence:

3' — TACTGCATAATGATT — 5'

What would be the sequence of codons in the mRNA transcribed from this strand? What would be the nucleotide sequence of the complementary nontranscribed DNA strand? What would be the exact anticodon for each codon? Use Table 12–1 to determine the amino acid sequence of the polypeptide. Be sure to label the 5' and 3' ends of the nucleic acids and the carboxyl and amino ends of the polypeptide.

2. What are ribosomes made of? Do ribosomes themselves carry information to specify the amino acid sequence of proteins?

3. In what ways are DNA polymerase and RNA polymerase similar? How do they differ?

4. Describe initiation, elongation, and termination of protein synthesis.

5. Explain how the genetic code was deciphered. What experimental procedures needed to be developed before this could be accomplished?

6. What are the main types of mutations? What effects does each have on the protein product produced?

7. Why can't amino acids become incorporated into polypeptides without the aid of tRNA?

YOU MAKE THE CONNECTION

1. In Chapter 10 we discussed the fact that heritable variation is essential for the study of inheritance. What role did mutant strains play in Beadle and Tatum's development of the one gene, one enzyme hypothesis?

2. How many amino acids could be specified if two bases coded for one amino acid? Why is redundancy or degeneracy important to the idea of wobble? If you could "reinvent" the genetic code, would you make any changes? Why or why not?

3. Compare and contrast the formation of mRNA in prokaryotic and eukaryotic cells. How do the differences affect the way in which each type of mRNA is translated? Does one system have any obvious advantage in terms of energy cost? Which system offers greater opportunities for control of gene expression?

RECOMMENDED READINGS

Craig, P.P. "Jumping Genes: Barbara McClintock's Scientific Legacy." *Carnegie Institution of Washington Perspectives in Science,* No. 6, 1994. A fascinating illustrated essay on the life of Barbara McClintock and the far-reaching implications of her work. Copies may be obtained for $1.00 each by calling 202-939-1121 or by writing The Carnegie Institution of Washington, 1530 P Street NW, Washington, DC, 20005–1910.

Dahlberg, A.E. "The Ribosome in Action." *Science,* Vol. 292, 4 May 2001. This perspective introduces two articles that present new images of the bacterial ribosome, with an emphasis on interactions with tRNA and mRNA, and the mechanism by which certain antibiotics disrupt ribosome function.

Frank, J. "How the Ribosome Works." *American Scientist,* Vol. 86, No. 5, Sept.–Oct. 1998. Sophisticated methods are producing clear three-dimensional maps of ribosomes that permit function to be explained in terms of structure.

Hayes, B. "The Invention of the Genetic Code." *American Scientist,* Vol. 86, No. 1, Jan.–Feb. 1998. This article relates the history of early conjectures regarding the nature of the genetic code and how the genetic code was finally solved.

Lodish, H., A. Berk, S.L. Zipursky, P. Matsudaira, D. Baltimore, and J. Darnell. *Molecular Cell Biology,* 4th ed. W.H. Freeman and Co., New York, 2000. Contains an extensive, detailed, and well written discussion of transcription and translation.

Moffat, A.S. "Transposons Help Sculpt a Dynamic Genome." *Science,* Vol. 289, 1 Sept., 2000. Genomic restructuring caused by transposons is apparently common in both plants and animals and may have evolutionary significance.

Ochert, A. "Transposons." *Discover,* Dec. 1999. Transposons alter patterns of gene expression in ways that can cause genetic disease but also may foster evolutionary change.

Strasser, B.J. "Sickle Cell Anemia: A Molecular Disease." *Science,* Vol. 286, 19 Nov., 1999. The title of this perspective is taken from the famous 1949 *Science* paper by Linus Pauling et al., linking the genetic disease sickle cell anemia to abnormal hemoglobin (a protein).

• Visit our Web site at **http://www.info.brookscole.com/solomonbergmartin** for links to chapter-related resources on the World Wide Web. Additional on-line materials relating to this chapter can also be found on our Web site.

See chapter activity on BioActive Learner CD for additional help in mastering the chapter's material. Icon location in the chapter's margins shows which topics have tutorials or simulations in the CD.

13

Gene Regulation: The Control of Gene Expression

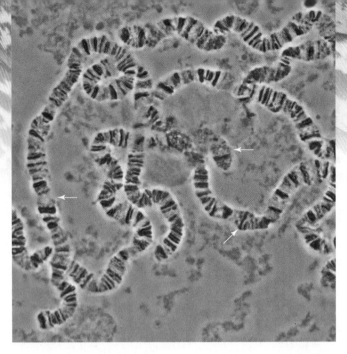

Regulated gene expression. LM of chromosomes from a cell in the salivary gland of the larva of the fruit fly, *Drosophila*. The expanded "puffed" chromosomal regions *(arrows)* contain genes that are actively transcribed in that cell, while the more compact banded regions include genes that are transcribed at very low rates, at different times, or not at all. *(Peter J. Bryant/Biological Photo Service)*

LEARNING OBJECTIVES

After you have studied this chapter you should be able to

1. Explain why the organization of genes into operons is advantageous to bacteria. Explain why some genes, such as those of the lactose operon, are inducible, while others, such as those of the tryptophan operon, are repressible.
2. Sketch the main elements of an inducible operon, such as the lactose operon, and explain the functions of the operator and promoter regions.
3. Diagram the major components of an mRNA molecule produced by the lactose operon, and relate that structure to the organization of the operon.
4. Differentiate between positive and negative control, and show how both types of control operate in the regulation of the lactose operon.
5. Sketch the structure of a typical eukaryotic gene and the DNA sequences involved in the regulation of that gene.
6. Give examples of some of the ways eukaryotic DNA-binding proteins bind to DNA.
7. Illustrate how a change in chromosome structure might affect the activity of a gene.
8. List two ways that a gene in a multicellular organism might be able to produce different products in different types of cells.
9. Identify some of the types of regulatory controls that can be exerted in eukaryotes after mature mRNA is formed.

Each type of cell in a multicellular organism has a characteristic shape, carries out very specific activities, and makes a distinct set of proteins. Yet, with few exceptions, they all contain the same genetic information. Why, then, are they not identical in structure and molecular composition? This is because gene expression is regulated; i.e., only certain subsets of the total genetic information are expressed in any given cell *(see photograph)*.

What are the mechanisms controlling the expression of a gene? Let us consider a gene that codes for a protein that is an enzyme. Expression of that gene involves not only transcription to form messenger ribonucleic acid (mRNA); the mRNA must be translated into protein, and the protein must actively catalyze a specific reaction. Gene expression, then, is the result of a series of processes, each of which can be controlled in many different ways. The control mechanisms require information in the form of various signals (some originating within the cell and others coming from other cells or from the environment) that interact with deoxyribonucleic acid (DNA), RNA, or protein.

Some of the main strategies used to regulate gene expression include controlling (1) the amount of mRNA that is available, (2) the rate of translation of the mRNA, and (3) the activity of the protein product. This can be done in a variety of ways. For example, the amount of mRNA available can be controlled by regulating the rate of mRNA degradation as well as the rate of transcription.

Although bacteria are not multicellular, they still need to regulate the expression of their genes. Energy efficiency and economical use of resources are usually of primary importance to bacterial cells. As a result, most gene regulation in prokaryotes involves transcriptional level control of genes whose products are involved in resource utilization. In eukaryotes there is a much greater emphasis on fine-tuning the control systems, which is consistent with the greater complexity of these cells and the need to control development in multicellular organisms (see Chapter 16). Consequently, eukaryotic gene regulation occurs at many levels.

GENE REGULATION IN PROKARYOTES IS ECONOMICAL

Escherichia coli is a bacterium that is a common inhabitant of the intestine. It has 4288 genes that code for proteins, approximately 62% of which have known functions. Some of these genes encode proteins that are always needed (e.g., enzymes involved in glycolysis). These genes, which are constantly transcribed, are called **constitutive genes.** Other proteins are needed only when the bacterium is growing under special conditions.

For instance, the bacteria living in the colon of an adult cow are not normally exposed to the milk sugar lactose, a disaccharide (see Chapter 3). If those cells were to end up in the colon of a calf, however, they would have lactose available as a source of energy. This poses a dilemma. Should a bacterial cell invest energy and materials to produce lactose-metabolizing enzymes just in case it ends up in the digestive system of a calf? Given that the average lifetime of an actively growing *E. coli* cell is about 30 minutes, such a strategy appears wasteful. Yet if *E. coli* cells do not have the capacity to produce those enzymes, they might starve in the midst of an abundant food supply. *E. coli* handles this problem by regulating many of its enzymes to efficiently use available organic molecules.

Cells have two basic ways of controlling their metabolic activity. They can regulate the *activity* of certain enzymes (how effectively an enzyme molecule works), and/or they can control the *number* of enzyme molecules present in each cell. Some enzymes may be regulated in both ways in the same type of cell. An *E. coli* cell growing on glucose is estimated to need about 800 different enzymes. Some of these must be present in large numbers, whereas only a few molecules of others are required. For the cell to function properly, the quantity of each enzyme must be efficiently controlled.

Operons in prokaryotes permit coordinated control of functionally related genes

The French researchers François Jacob and Jacques Monod are credited with the first demonstration, in 1961, of how some genes are regulated at the biochemical level. They studied the genes that code for the enzymes that metabolize lactose. For *E. coli* to use lactose as an energy source, the sugar must be cleaved into the monosaccharides glucose and galactose by the enzyme β-galactosidase. Galactose is then converted to glucose by another enzyme, and the resulting two glucose molecules are further broken down by enzymes in the glycolysis pathway (see Chapter 7).

E. coli cells growing on glucose contain very little of the β-galactosidase enzyme, perhaps no more than one to three molecules per cell. However, cells grown on lactose have as many as 3000 β-galactosidase molecules per cell, accounting for about 3% of total cellular protein. Levels of two other enzymes, galactose permease and galactoside transacetylase, also increase when the cells are grown on lactose. The permease is needed to transport lactose efficiently across the bacterial plasma membrane; without it, only small amounts of lactose can enter the cell. The transacetylase may be involved in a minor aspect of lactose metabolism, although its function is not clear.

Jacob and Monod were able to identify mutant strains of *E. coli* in which a single genetic defect resulted in the loss of all three enzymes. This finding, along with other information, led them to the conclusion that the coding DNA sequences for all three enzymes are linked together as a unit on the bacterial DNA and are subject to a common control mechanism. Each protein coding sequence is known as a **structural gene.** Jacob and Monod coined the term **operon** to refer to a gene complex consisting of a group of structural genes with related functions, plus the closely linked DNA sequences responsible for controlling them. The structural genes of the lactose operon—*lac Z, lac Y,* and *lac A*—code for β-galactosidase, galactose permease, and galactoside transacetylase, respectively (Fig. 13–1).

Transcription of the lactose operon begins as RNA polymerase binds to a single **promoter** site upstream from the coding sequences. It then proceeds to transcribe the DNA, forming a single mRNA molecule that contains the coding information for all three enzymes. Between the enzyme-coding sequences this mRNA contains a translation termination codon for the previous sequence and a translation initiation codon for the sequence to follow; hence it is translated to form three separate protein molecules. Because all three enzymes are translated from the same mRNA molecule, their synthesis can be coordinated by turning a single molecular "switch" off or on.

The switch that controls mRNA synthesis is called the **operator;** it is a sequence of bases that overlaps part of the promoter region and is upstream from the first structural gene in the operon. In the absence of lactose, a **repressor protein** called the **lactose repressor** binds tightly to the operator region. Because the repressor protein is large enough to cover part of the promoter sequence, RNA polymerase is unable to bind to the lactose promoter site, and transcription of the lactose operon is effectively blocked.

The lactose repressor protein is encoded by a **regulatory gene,** which in this case is an adjacent structural gene located upstream from the promoter site. Unlike the lactose operon genes, the repressor gene is always "on," so small amounts of the repressor protein are produced continuously. Such a gene that is not regulated and is therefore constantly transcribed is said to be constitutive. The repressor protein binds specifically to the lactose operator sequence. When cells are grown in the absence of lactose, the operator site is nearly always occupied by a repressor molecule. A very small amount of mRNA can be synthesized when the operator site is briefly free of the repressor, but very few enzyme molecules are synthesized because *E. coli* mRNA is rapidly degraded (having a half-life of about 2 to 4 minutes).

Lactose is able to "turn on," or *induce,* the transcription of the lactose operon because the lactose repressor protein contains a second functional region separate from its DNA binding site; this is an allosteric binding site for allolactose, a structural isomer made from lactose. (Recall from Chapter 6 that an **allosteric regulator,** such as allolactose in this case, binds to a site in a protein other than its active site, changing its conformation and thereby altering its function.) If lactose is present in the growth medium, a few molecules are able to enter the cell and are converted to allolactose by the few β-galactosidase molecules

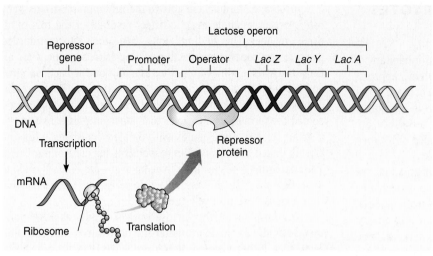

(a) In the absence of lactose, a repressor protein, encoded by an adjacent gene, binds a region known as the operator. By preventing RNA polymerase from binding to the promotor, the bound repressor protein blocks transcription of the structural genes.

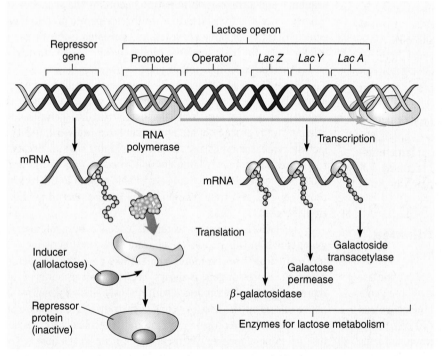

(b) When lactose is present, it is converted to allolactose, which binds to the repressor at an allosteric site, altering the structure of the protein so that it can no longer bind to the operator. This allows RNA polymerase to bind to the promoter and transcribe the structural genes.

Figure 13–1 Lactose operon. The structural genes coding for the three enzymes used by *E. coli* to metabolize the disaccharide lactose are transcribed as part of a single mRNA molecule.

present. When a molecule of allolactose binds to the repressor at the allosteric site, it alters the conformation of the protein so that its DNA-binding site can no longer recognize the operator. When all the repressor molecules have allolactose bound to them and are therefore inactivated, RNA polymerase binds to the unblocked promoter, and the operon is actively transcribed.

The *E. coli* cell continues to produce β-galactosidase and the other lactose operon proteins until virtually all of the lactose is used up. When intracellular levels of lactose drop, allolactose dissociates from the repressor proteins, which then assume a conformation that allows them to bind to the operator region and shut down transcription of the operon.

Jacob and Monod isolated genetic mutants to study the lactose operon

How were Jacob and Monod able to dissect the functioning of the lactose operon? Their approach centered around the use of mutant strains, which even today play an essential role in allowing researchers to unravel the components of a regulatory system. Mutant strains permit investigators to carry out genetic crosses to determine the map positions (linear order) of the genes on the DNA (see Chapter 10) and to infer normal gene functions by studying what happens when they are missing or altered. This information is usually combined with results of direct biochemical studies.

To understand the reasoning behind Jacob and Monod's experiments, follow the branching steps in Figure 13–2 as you read. They were able to divide their mutant strains into two groups based on whether a particular mutation affected only one enzyme or all three. In one group only one enzyme of the three—β-galactosidase, galactose permease, or galactoside transacetylase—was affected. Subsequent gene mapping studies showed that these were mutations in structural genes located next to each other in a linear sequence.

Jacob and Monod also studied strains they classified as regulatory mutants because a single mutation coordinately affected the expression of all three enzymes. Some of these regulatory mutants were constitutive; in these the structural genes of the lactose operon were always transcribed at a significant rate, even in the absence of lactose, causing the cell to waste energy producing unneeded enzymes. One group of constitutive mutations had map positions just outside the lactose operon itself. Using special genetic strains, it was possible to show that these particular mutations always caused constitutive expression, regardless of their location in the genome. On the basis of these findings, Jacob and Monod hypothesized the existence of a repressor gene that codes for a repressor molecule (later found to be a protein). Although the specific defect may vary, the members of this group of constitutive mutants do not produce active repressor proteins; hence, no binding to the lactose operator and promoter takes place, and the lactose operon is transcribed constitutively.

The genes responsible for the behavior of a second group of constitutive mutants had map positions within the lactose operon but did not directly involve any of the three structural genes. The members of this group were found to produce normal repressor molecules but to have abnormal operator sequences incapable of binding the repressor.

In contrast to the constitutive mutants, other mutants failed to transcribe the lactose operon even when lactose was present. Some of these abnormal genes had the same map position as the hypothesized regulatory gene. They were eventually found to have an altered binding site on the repressor protein that prevented allolactose from binding, although the ability of the repressor to bind to the operator was unaffected. Once bound to the operator, such a mutant repressor remains bound, keeping the operon "turned off."

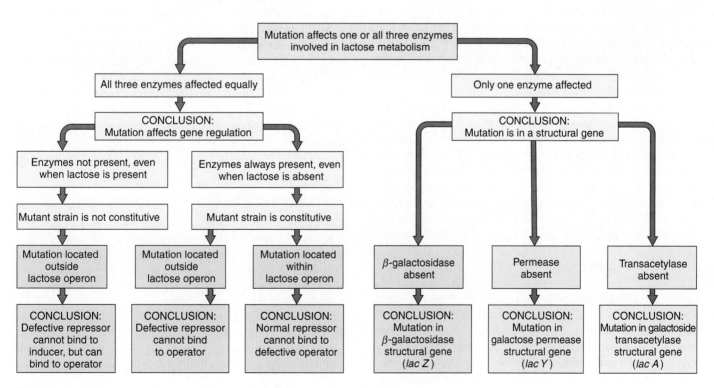

■ **Figure 13–2 Genetic and biochemical characterization of the lactose operon.** Jacob and Monod analyzed the properties of various mutant strains of *E. coli* to deduce the structure and function of the lactose operon.

An inducible gene is not transcribed unless a specific inducer inactivates its repressor

The lactose operon is called an **inducible** system. An inducible gene or operon is usually controlled by a repressor that keeps it in the "off" state. The presence of an **inducer molecule** (in this case allolactose) renders the repressor inactive so that the gene or operon is turned on. Inducible genes or operons usually code for enzymes that are part of catabolic pathways, which are responsible for breaking down molecules to provide both energy and components for anabolic reactions. This type of regulatory system enables the cell to save the energy costs of making enzymes when no substrates are available upon which they can act.

A repressible gene is transcribed unless a specific repressor-corepressor complex is bound to the DNA

Another type of gene regulation system in bacteria is associated mainly with anabolic pathways in which amino acids, nucleotides, and other essential molecules are synthesized from simpler precursors. Regulation of these pathways normally involves repressible enzymes, which are coded for by **repressible** genes.

Repressible genes and operons are usually on; they are turned off only under special conditions. In most cases the molecular signal used to regulate these genes is the end product of the anabolic pathway. When the supply of the end product (e.g., an amino acid) is low, all enzymes in the pathway are actively synthesized. When intracellular levels of the end product are high, enzyme synthesis is repressed. Because compounds such as amino acids are continuously needed by the growing cell, the most effective strategy is to keep the genes that control their production on except when a large supply of the amino acid is available. The ability to turn the genes off allows cells to avoid overproduction of amino acids and other molecules that are essential but energetically expensive to make.

The tryptophan operon is an example of a repressible system. In both *E. coli* and a related bacterium, *Salmonella*, the operon consists of five structural genes that code for the enzymes required for synthesis of the amino acid tryptophan; these are clustered together as a transcriptional unit with a single promoter and a single operator (Fig. 13–3). A distant repressor gene codes for a diffusible repressor protein, which differs from the lactose repressor in that it is synthesized in an inactive form that is unable to bind to the operator region of the tryptophan operon.

The DNA-binding site of the repressor becomes effective only when tryptophan, its **corepressor,** binds to an allosteric site on the repressor. When intracellular tryptophan levels are low, the repressor protein is inactive and unable to bind to the operator region of the DNA. The enzymes required for tryptophan synthesis are produced, and the concentration of tryptophan increases. As the concentration of intracellular tryptophan rises, some tryptophan binds to the allosteric site of the repressor, altering its conformation so that it binds tightly to the operator. This has the effect of switching the operon off, thereby blocking transcription.

Negative regulators repress transcription; positive regulators activate transcription

The features of the lactose and tryptophan operons described so far are examples of **negative control.** Systems under negative control are those in which the DNA-binding regulatory protein is a repressor that turns off transcription of the gene. Some regulatory systems involve **positive control,** that is, regulation by **activator proteins** that bind to DNA and thereby stimulate transcription of a gene. The lactose operon is controlled by both a negative regulator (the lactose repressor protein) and a positively acting activator protein (Fig. 13–4).

Positive control of the lactose operon requires that the cell be able to sense the absence of the sugar glucose, which is the initial substrate in the glycolysis pathway (see Chapter 7). Lactose, like glucose, can undergo stepwise breakdown to yield energy. However, because glucose is a product of the catabolic hydrolysis of lactose, it is most efficient for *E. coli* cells to use the available supply of glucose first, sparing the cell the considerable energy cost of making additional enzymes such as β-galactosidase.

The lactose operon has a very inefficient promoter sequence; that is, it has a low affinity for RNA polymerase even when the repressor protein is inactivated. However, a DNA sequence adjacent to the promoter site is a binding site for another regulatory protein, the **catabolite gene activator protein (CAP).**

In its active form CAP has **cyclic AMP**, or **cAMP,** an alternative form of adenosine monophosphate (see Fig. 3–27), bound to an allosteric site.[1] As the cells become depleted of glucose, cAMP levels increase. The cAMP molecules bind to CAP, and the resulting active complex then binds to the CAP-binding site near the lactose operon promoter. This binding of active CAP causes the double helix to bend (Fig. 13–5) and increases the affinity of the promoter region for RNA polymerase such that the rate of transcription initiation is increased in the presence of lactose. Thus, the lactose operon is fully active only if lactose is available and intracellular glucose levels are low. The properties of negative and positive control systems are summarized in Table 13–1.

A regulon is a group of functionally related operons controlled by a common regulator

CAP differs from the lactose and tryptophan repressors in that it can control transcription of operons involved in the metabolism of several catabolites, such as the sugars galactose, arabinose, and maltose, as well as of lactose. A group of operons coordinately controlled by a single regulator is generally referred to as a **regulon** (Fig. 13–6 on page 292).

Other multigene systems in bacteria are also controlled in this manner. For example, genes involved in nitrogen and phosphate metabolism are organized into regulons that consist of multiple sets of operons controlled by one or more combinations

---

[1] For this reason, CAP is also known as CRP, which stands for **c**AMP **r**eceptor **p**rotein.

(text continues on page 291)

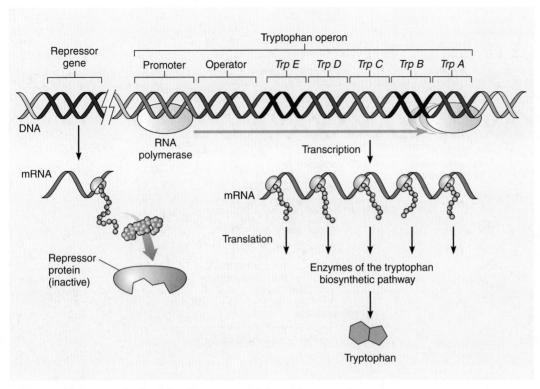

(a) **Intracellular tryptophan levels low.** Repressor protein is unable to prevent transcription because it cannot bind to the operator.

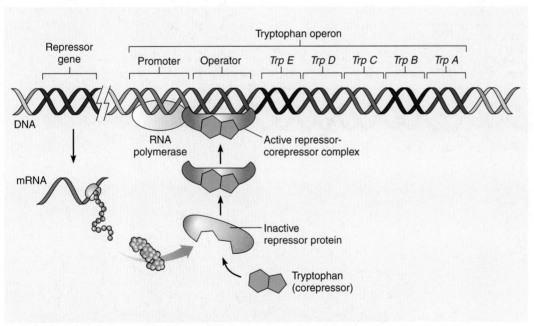

(b) **Intracellular tryptophan levels high.** The amino acid tryptophan binds to an allosteric site on the repressor protein, changing its conformation. The resulting active form of the repressor binds to the operator region, blocking transcription of the operon until tryptophan is again required by the cell.

Figure 13–3 Tryptophan operon. Genes coding for enzymes that synthesize the amino acid tryptophan are organized in a repressible operon.

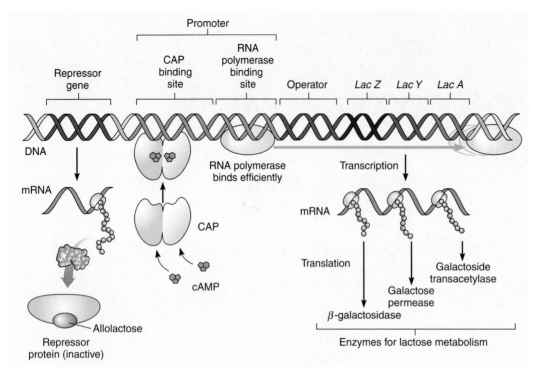

(a) **Lactose high, glucose low, cAMP high.** When glucose concentrations are low, each CAP polypeptide has cAMP bound to its allosteric site. CAP can bind to the DNA sequence and transcription becomes activated.

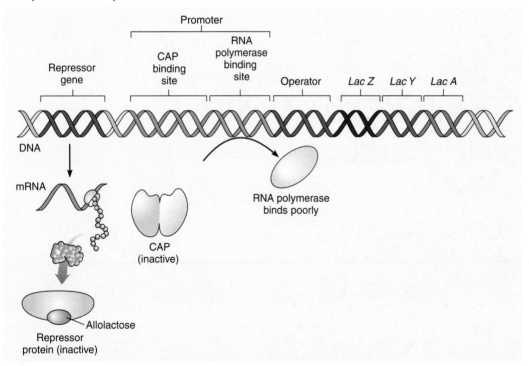

(b) **Lactose high, glucose high, cAMP low.** When glucose levels are high, cAMP is low. CAP is in an inactive form and cannot stimulate transcription. Transcription occurs at a low level or not at all.

Figure 13–4 Positive control of the lactose operon. The lactose promoter by itself is weak and binds RNA polymerase inefficiently even when the lactose repressor is inactive. The CAP is an allosteric regulator that can bind to a sequence of bases in the promoter, allowing RNA polymerase to bind efficiently, thereby stimulating transcription of the operon. The CAP molecule contains two polypeptides that can each bind to cAMP at allosteric sites. The cell's cAMP concentration is inversely proportional to the glucose concentration.

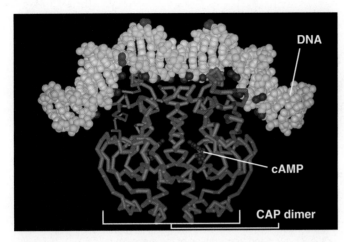

Figure 13–5 Binding of CAP to DNA. This computer-generated picture illustrates the bend formed in the DNA double helix when it binds to CAP. CAP is a dimer consisting of two identical polypeptide chains, each of which binds one molecule of cAMP. *(Courtesy of S.C. Schultz, G.C. Shields, and T.A. Steitz, Yale University)*

of regulatory genes. Other complex multigene systems respond to changes in environmental conditions, such as rapid shifts in temperature, exposure to radiation, changes in osmotic pressure, and changes in oxygen levels. Specific mutants often provide clues to the existence of a regulon system. A single mutation that destroys the activity of CAP, for example, prevents the cell from

efficiently metabolizing not only lactose but many other sugars also regulated by CAP.

Not all constitutive genes are transcribed at the same rate

Many of the gene products encoded by the *E. coli* DNA are needed only under certain environmental or nutritional conditions. As we have seen, these genes are generally regulated at the level of transcription. They can be turned on and off as metabolic and environmental conditions change. By contrast, constitutive genes are continuously transcribed, but they are not necessarily transcribed (or their mRNAs translated) at the same rate. Some enzymes work more effectively or are more stable than others and consequently need to be present in smaller amounts. Constitutive genes that encode proteins required in large amounts are generally transcribed more rapidly than genes coding for proteins required at lower levels. The transcription rate of these genes is controlled by their promoter sequences. Constitutive genes with efficient ("strong") promoters bind RNA polymerase more frequently and consequently transcribe more mRNA molecules than those with inefficient ("weak") promoters.

Genes coding for repressor or activator proteins that regulate metabolic enzymes are usually constitutive and produce their protein products constantly. Because each cell usually needs relatively few molecules of any specific repressor or activator protein, promoters for those genes tend to be relatively weak.

TABLE 13–1   Types of Transcriptional Control in Prokaryotes*

Negative Control	Result
Inducible genes	
Repressor protein alone	**Active repressor "turns off" regulated gene(s)**
Lactose repressor alone	Lactose operon not transcribed
Repressor protein + inducer	**Inactive repressor-inducer complex fails to "turn off" regulated gene(s)**
Lactose repressor + allolactose	Lactose operon transcribed
Repressible genes	
Repressor protein alone	**Inactive repressor fails to "turn off" regulated gene(s)**
Tryptophan repressor alone	Tryptophan operon transcribed
Repressor protein + corepressor	**Active repressor-corepressor complex "turns off" regulated gene(s)**
Tryptophan repressor + tryptophan	Tryptophan operon not transcribed

Positive Control	Result
Activator protein alone	**Activator alone cannot stimulate transcription of regulated gene(s)**
CAP alone	Transcription of lactose operon not stimulated
Activator protein + coactivator	**Functional activator-coactivator complex stimulates transcription of regulated gene(s)**
CAP + cAMP	Transcription of lactose operon stimulated

*A general description of each type is followed by a specific example. A negative regulator is a repressor that "turns off" transcription of the regulated gene(s). Conversely, a positive regulator is an activator that stimulates transcription.

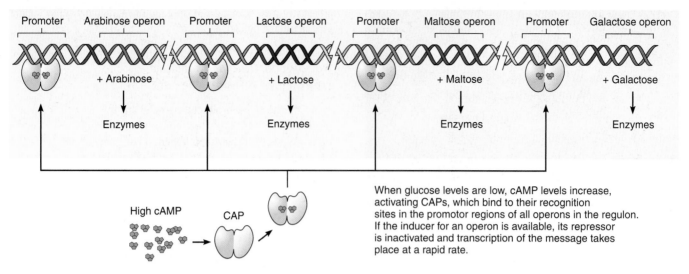

When glucose levels are low, cAMP levels increase, activating CAPs, which bind to their recognition sites in the promotor regions of all operons in the regulon. If the inducer for an operon is available, its repressor is inactivated and transcription of the message takes place at a rapid rate.

Figure 13–6 Regulon. Operons that convert several different sugars to glucose in *E. coli* make up a regulon that is under positive control by CAP.

Some posttranscriptional regulation occurs in prokaryotes

As we have seen, much of the variability in protein levels in *E. coli* is determined by **transcriptional level control.** However, regulatory mechanisms that operate after transcription, known as **posttranscriptional controls,** also occur, operating at various levels of gene expression.

Translational controls are posttranscriptional controls that regulate the rate at which a particular mRNA molecule is translated. Because the lifetime of an mRNA molecule in a bacterial cell is very short, an mRNA that is translated rapidly can produce more proteins than one that is translated slowly. Some mRNA molecules in *E. coli* are translated as much as 1000 times faster than others. Most of the differences appear to be due to the rate at which ribosomes can attach to the mRNA and begin translation.

Posttranslational controls generally act as switches that activate or inactivate one or more existing enzymes. These systems allow the cell to respond to changes in the intracellular concentrations of essential molecules, such as amino acids, by rapidly adjusting the activities of its enzymes. A common posttranslational control adjusts the rate of synthesis in a metabolic pathway through **feedback inhibition,** also known as **end product inhibition** (see Fig. 6–17). The end product binds to the first enzyme in the pathway at an allosteric site, temporarily inactivating the enzyme. When the first enzyme in the pathway does not function, all of the succeeding enzymes are deprived of substrates. Notice that feedback inhibition differs from the repression caused by tryptophan discussed previously. In that case, the end product of the pathway (tryptophan) prevented the formation of new enzymes. Feedback inhibition acts as a fine-tuning mechanism that regulates the activity of the existing enzymes in a metabolic pathway.

GENE REGULATION IN EUKARYOTES IS MULTIFACETED

Like bacteria, eukaryotic cells must respond to changes in their environment. In addition, multicellular eukaryotes require modes of regulation that permit individual cells to become committed to specialized roles and groups of cells to organize into tissues and organs (see *Focus On: Regulation in Prokaryotes and Eukaryotes*). This is mainly accomplished by transcriptional regulation, but posttranscriptional (translational and posttranslational) controls are also important. In previous chapters we observed that all aspects of information transfer, including replication, transcription, and translation, are far more complicated in eukaryotes. Not surprisingly, this complexity provides additional opportunities for control of gene expression.

Unlike many of the prokaryotic genes, most eukaryotic genes are not found in operon-like clusters. However, each eukaryotic gene has specific regulatory sequences that are essential in the control of transcription.

Many of the "housekeeping" enzymes (those needed by all cells) appear to be encoded by constitutive genes, which are expressed in all cells at all times. Some inducible genes have also been found; these respond to environmental threats or stimuli such as heavy metal ingestion, viral infection, and heat shock. For example, when a cell is exposed to high temperature, many proteins fail to fold properly. The presence of these unfolded proteins elicits a survival response in which genes known as heat-shock genes are transcribed, and heat-shock proteins are formed. Although the functions of most of the heat-shock proteins are not known, some are **molecular chaperones,** which are responsible for helping other proteins attain their proper conformation.

Some genes appear to be inducible only during certain periods in the life of the organism; they are thought to be controlled by **temporal regulation** mechanisms. Finally, a number of genes

Regulation in Prokaryotes and Eukaryotes

Why do prokaryotic and eukaryotic cells have distinctly different strategies for regulating the activity of their genes? In large part these differences reflect the ways in which the organisms make their living. Bacterial cells exist independently, and each cell must be able to perform all its own essential functions. Because they grow rapidly and have relatively short lifetimes, bacterial cells carry little excess baggage.

The dominant theme of prokaryotic gene regulation is *economy,* and controlling transcription is usually the most cost-effective way to regulate gene expression. The organization of related genes into operons and regulons that can be rapidly turned on and off as units allows these cells to synthesize only the gene products needed at any particular time. This type of regulation requires rapid turnover of mRNA molecules to prevent messages from accumulating and continuing to be translated when they are not needed. Bacteria rarely

regulate enzyme levels by degrading proteins. Once the synthesis of a protein ends, the previously synthesized protein molecules are diluted so rapidly in subsequent cell divisions that breaking them down is usually not necessary. Only when cells are starved or deprived of essential amino acids are protein-digesting enzymes used to recycle amino acids by breaking down proteins no longer needed for survival.

Eukaryotic cells have different regulatory requirements. In multicellular organisms, groups of cells cooperate with each other in a division of labor. Because a single gene may need to be regulated in different ways in different types of cells, eukaryotic gene regulation is complex. Although transcriptional level control predominates, especially in multicellular eukaryotes, control of other levels of gene expression is also very important. Eukaryotic cells usually have long lifetimes during which they may need to respond repeatedly to many different stimuli. Rather than synthesize new

enzymes each time they respond to a stimulus, these cells make extensive use of preformed enzymes and other proteins that can be rapidly converted from an inactive to an active state. Some cells have a large store of inactive messenger RNA; for example, the mRNA of an egg cell becomes activated when it is fertilized.

Much of the emphasis of gene regulation in multicellular organisms is on *specificity* in the form and function of the cells in each tissue. Each type of cell has certain genes that are active and others that may never be used (see Chapter 16). Apparently the adaptive advantages of cellular cooperation in eukaryotes far outweigh the detrimental effects of carrying a load of inactive genes through many cell divisions. For example, developing red blood cells produce the oxygen transport protein hemoglobin, whereas muscle cells never produce hemoglobin but instead produce myoglobin, a related protein that stores oxygen in muscle tissues.

---

are under the control of **tissue-specific regulation.** For example, a gene involved in the production of a particular enzyme may be regulated by one stimulus (e.g., a hormone) in muscle tissue, by an entirely different stimulus in pancreatic cells, and by a third stimulus in liver cells. These types of regulation are explored in more detail in Chapter 16.

Eukaryotic transcription is controlled at many sites and by many different regulatory molecules

Most genes of multicellular eukaryotes are controlled at the transcriptional level. As we see in the following discussion, various base sequences in the DNA are important in transcriptional control. In addition, the rate of transcription is affected by regulatory proteins and by the way the DNA is organized in the chromosome.

Eukaryotic promoters vary in efficiency, depending on their upstream promoter elements

In eukaryotic as well as prokaryotic cells, the transcription of any gene requires a base pair where transcription begins, known as the **transcription initiation site,** plus a promoter to which RNA polymerase binds. A prokaryotic promoter (Fig. 13–7a) includes certain characteristic base sequences, known as a *Pribnow box*

and a *-35 box,* located 35 base pairs upstream from the transcription initiation site.[2] In multicellular eukaryotes, RNA polymerase binds to a sequence of bases known as a **TATA box,** about 25 to 35 base pairs upstream from the transcription initiation site (Fig. 13–7b). A eukaryotic promoter generally contains one or more sequences of 8 to 12 bases within a short distance upstream of the RNA polymerase–binding site. These have been given various names; we will refer to them as **upstream promoter elements (UPEs).** Efficient initiation of transcription seems to be related to the number and type of UPEs. Thus, a constitutive gene containing only one UPE is generally weakly expressed, whereas one containing five or six UPEs is usually transcribed much more actively (Fig. 13–7c and d).

Enhancers are DNA sequences that increase the rate of transcription

Regulated eukaryotic genes commonly require not only the upstream promoter elements but also DNA sequences called **enhancers.** Whereas the promoter elements are required for

---

[2] By convention, the base pair that serves as the transcription initiation site is given the designation +1; upstream base pairs are given negative numbers, and downstream base pairs are given positive numbers.

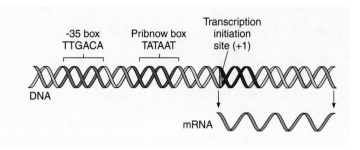

(a) **A prokaryotic promoter.** A typical prokaryotic promoter contains a "Pribnow box" and a "-35 box," usually found, respectively, 10 and 35 base pairs upstream from the transcription initiation site (the +1 base pair). The base sequences shown are those most commonly found.

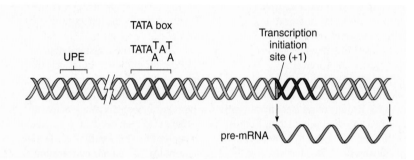

(b) **Eukaryotic promoter elements.** A eukaryotic promoter usually contains a "TATA box" located 25 to 35 base pairs upstream from the transcription initiation site. The most commonly found base sequence is shown (either T or A can be present at the positions where they appear together). One or more upstream promoter elements (UPEs) are usually present.

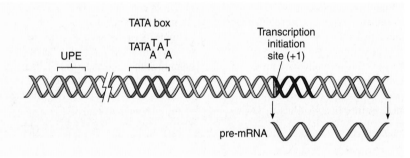

(c) **A weak eukaryotic promoter.** A weakly expressed gene contains only one UPE.

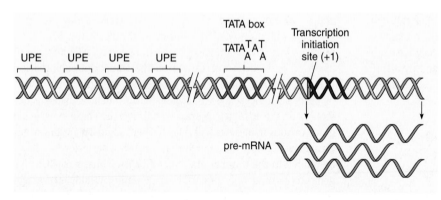

(d) **A strong eukaryotic promoter.** A strongly expressed gene is likely to contain several UPEs.

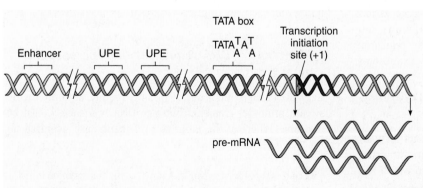

(e) **A strong eukaryotic promoter plus an enhancer.** Transcription of this eukaryotic gene is stimulated by an enhancer, located several thousand bases from the promoter.

Figure 13-7 Control of transcription. The DNA double helix and other elements are not drawn to scale.

accurate and efficient initiation of mRNA synthesis, enhancers increase the *rate* of RNA synthesis after initiation, often by several orders of magnitude (Fig. 13–7e).

Enhancer sequences are remarkable in many ways. Although present in all cells, a particular enhancer is functional only in certain types of cells. An enhancer can regulate a gene on the same DNA molecule from very long distances (up to thousands of base pairs away from the promoter) and can be either upstream or downstream of the promoters it controls. Furthermore, if an enhancer sequence is experimentally cut out of the DNA and inverted, it still regulates the gene it normally controls. As we shall see, evidence suggests that at least some enhancers work by interacting with proteins that regulate transcription.

Transcription factors are regulatory proteins that have several functional domains and may work in various combinations

We previously discussed some DNA-binding proteins that regulate transcription in prokaryotes. These include the lactose repressor, the tryptophan repressor, and the catabolite gene activator protein (CAP). Similarly, many regulators of transcription have been identified in eukaryotes; these eukaryotic proteins are known as **transcription factors.**

It is useful to compare transcriptional regulators in prokaryotes and eukaryotes. Many transcriptional regulators are modular molecules; that is, they have more than one **domain** (region with its own tertiary structure), and each domain has a different function. Each eukaryotic transcription factor, like the transcriptional regulators of prokaryotes, has a DNA-binding domain, plus at least one other domain, and may be either an activator or a repressor.

Many prokaryotic regulators and some eukaryotic transcription factors contain a *helix-turn-helix* motif, consisting of two α-helical segments. One of these, known as the *recognition helix,* is inserted into the major groove of the DNA without unwinding the double helix. The second helps to hold the first in place. (Fig. 13–8a). The "turn" is a sequence of amino acids that forms a sharp bend in the molecule.

Some other regulators have multiple "zinc fingers," loops of amino acids held together by zinc ions. Each loop includes an α-helix that fits into the major groove of the DNA (Fig. 13–8b). Certain amino acid functional groups exposed in each finger have been shown to recognize specific DNA sequences.

Many regulatory proteins are functional only as pairs, or *dimers,* and these have special domains required for dimer formation. Many of these transcription factors are known as **leucine zipper proteins** because they are held together by the side chains of leucine and other hydrophobic amino acids (Fig. 13–8c). In some cases the two polypeptides that make up the dimer may be identical and form a *homodimer.* In other instances they are different, and the resulting *heterodimer* may have very different regulatory properties. For a simple and speculative example, let us assume that three regulatory proteins—A, B, and C—are involved in controlling a particular set of genes. These three proteins might associate as dimers in six different ways: three kinds of homodimers (AA, BB, and CC) and three kinds of heterodimers (AB, AC, and BC). Such multiple combinations of regulatory

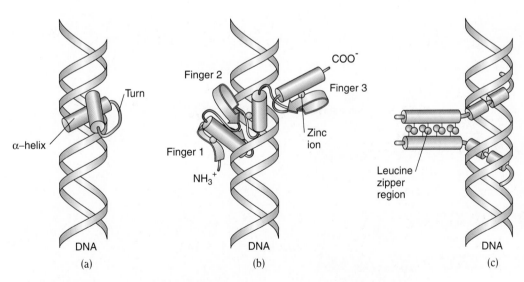

■ **Figure 13–8 Regulatory proteins.** In these illustrations, α-helical regions are shown as barrel shapes and β-pleated sheets are shown as ribbons. **(a)** A portion of a regulatory protein containing the helix-turn-helix arrangement. The recognition helix is inserted into the major groove of the DNA and is connected to a second helix that helps hold it in place by a sequence of amino acids that form a sharp bend. **(b)** Regions of certain transcription factors form projections known as "zinc fingers," which can insert into the grooves of the DNA and bind to specific base sequences. **(c)** This leucine zipper protein is a dimer, held together by hydrophobic interactions involving side chains of leucine and other amino acids.

proteins have the potential to greatly increase the number of possible ways that transcription can be controlled.

Transcription factors interact with the general transcription machinery

Transcription in eukaryotes requires multiple regulatory proteins that are bound to different parts of the promoter. The "general transcription machinery" is a protein complex that binds to the TATA region of the promoter near the transcription initiation site. That complex is required for RNA polymerase to bind and initiate transcription.

Both enhancers and UPEs apparently become functional when specific transcription factors are bound to them. Figure 13–9 illustrates interactions involving an enhancer and a transcription factor that acts as an activator. Each activator must have at least two functional domains: a DNA recognition site that usually binds to an enhancer or UPE, and a "gene activation site" that contacts the target in the general transcriptional machinery. The DNA between the enhancer and promoter sequences is thought to form a loop that allows an activator bound to an enhancer to come in contact with one or more target proteins associated with the general transcriptional machinery. When this occurs, the rate of transcription is increased.

The organization of the chromosome may affect the expression of some genes

A chromosome is not simply a bearer of genes. Various arrangements of its ordered components can result in increased or decreased expression of the genes it contains.

MULTIPLE COPIES OF GENES   A single gene cannot always provide enough copies of its mRNA to meet the cell's needs. The requirement for high levels of certain products may be met if multiple copies of the genes that encode them are present in the chromosome. Genes of this type, whose products are essential for all cells, may be present as multiple copies arranged one after another along the chromosome. These are known as *tandemly repeated gene sequences.* Other genes, which may be required by only a small group of cells, may be selectively replicated in those cells in a process called **gene amplification** (see Chapter 16).

Within an array of repeated genes, each copy is almost identical to the others. Histone genes, which code for the proteins that associate with DNA to form nucleosomes (see Chapter 11), are usually found as multiple copies of 50 to 500 genes in cells of multicellular organisms. Similarly, multiple copies (150 to 450) of genes for rRNA and tRNA occur in all cells.

GENE INACTIVATION BY CHANGES IN CHROMATIN STRUCTURE   In multicellular eukaryotes, only a subset of the genes present in a cell are active at any one time. The inactivated genes differ among cell types and in many cases seem to be irreversibly dormant.

Some of the inactive genes appear to be found in highly compacted chromatin, which can be seen as densely staining regions of chromosomes during cell division. These regions of chromatin remain tightly coiled throughout the cell cycle, and even during interphase are visible as darkly staining fibers called **heterochromatin** (Fig. 13–10). Evidence suggests that the DNA of heterochromatin is not transcribed. When one of the two X chromosomes is inactivated in female mammals, most of the inactive X chromosome

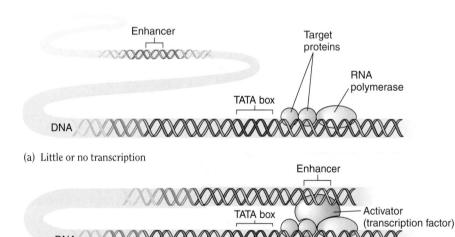

(a) Little or no transcription

(b) High rate of transcription

■ **Figure 13–9 Stimulation of transcription by an enhancer.** (a) This gene is transcribed at a very low rate or not at all, even though the general transcriptional machinery, including RNA polymerase, is bound to the promoter. (b) A regulatory protein that functions as a transcriptional activator becomes bound to an enhancer. The intervening DNA forms a loop, allowing the activator to contact one or more target proteins in the general transcriptional machinery, thereby increasing the rate of transcription.

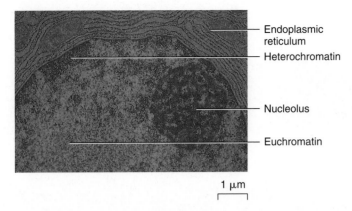

— Endoplasmic reticulum
— Heterochromatin

— Nucleolus

— Euchromatin

1 μm

Figure 13–10 Heterochromatin. The heterochromatin in this TEM of a human pancreas cell is dense and darkly staining and tends to be associated with the nuclear envelope. The euchromatin consists of a much looser fibrillar structure. *(D. Fawcett)*

becomes heterochromatic and is seen as the Barr body (see Fig. 10–16). Active genes are associated with a more loosely packed chromatin structure called **euchromatin** (Fig. 13–11).

GENE INACTIVATION BY DNA METHYLATION Inactive genes of vertebrates and some other organisms typically exhibit a pattern of **DNA methylation** in which the DNA has been chemically altered by enzymes that add methyl groups to certain cytosines. (The resulting 5-methylcytosine is still able to base pair

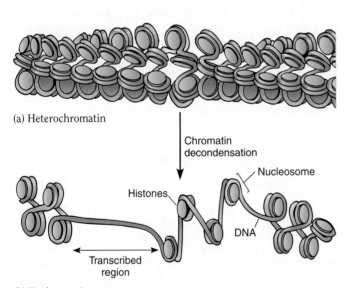

(a) Heterochromatin

Chromatin decondensation

— Nucleosome

Histones

DNA

Transcribed region

(b) Euchromatin

Figure 13–11 Effect of chromatin structure on transcription. **(a)** An inactive region of DNA (heterochromatin) is organized into tightly associated nucleosomes. **(b)** Active genes are found in decondensed chromatin (euchromatin). Chromatin decondensation is often a response to specific inducing signals. The loosely packed chromatin increases the accessibility to RNA polymerase required for transcription of the region. The histones are physically removed from the DNA in the region where transcription occurs.

with guanine in the usual way.) There is evidence that certain proteins selectively bind to methylated DNA and make it inaccessible to the transcription machinery.

DNA methylation is thought to reinforce gene inactivation rather than to serve as the initial mechanism. It appears that once a gene has been turned off by some other means, DNA methylation ensures that it will remain inactive. For example, the DNA of the inactive X of a female mammal becomes methylated after the chromosome has become a condensed Barr body. Each time the DNA replicates, methylation enzymes perpetuate the preexisting methylation pattern; hence, the DNA continues to be transcriptionally inactive in both daughter cells.

The long-lived, highly processed mRNAs of eukaryotes provide many opportunities for posttranscriptional control

The half-life of prokaryotic mRNA is usually measured in minutes; eukaryotic mRNA, even when it turns over rapidly, is far more stable. Prokaryotic mRNA is transcribed in a form that can be translated immediately. In contrast, eukaryotic mRNA molecules require further modification and processing before they can be used in protein synthesis. The message is capped, polyadenylated, spliced, and then transported from the nucleus to the cytoplasm to initiate translation (see Chapter 12). These events represent potential control points at which translation of the message and production of its encoded protein can be regulated.

Some pre-mRNAs can be processed in more than one way

Several forms of regulation involving mRNA processing have been discovered. In some instances, the same gene is used to produce one type of protein in one tissue and a related but somewhat different type of protein in another tissue. This is possible because some genes produce pre-mRNA molecules that have multiple splicing patterns; that is, they can be spliced in more than one way depending on the tissue. Typically, such a gene includes at least one segment that can be either an intron or an exon. As an intron, the sequence would be removed, but as an exon it would be retained. Through **differential mRNA processing,** the cells in each tissue can produce their own version of mRNA corresponding to the particular gene (Fig. 13–12). For example, this mechanism allows different forms of troponin, a protein that regulates muscle contraction, to be produced in different muscle tissues.

The stability of mRNA molecules can vary

Controlling the lifetime of a particular kind of mRNA molecule makes it possible to control the number of protein molecules translated from it. In some cases messenger RNA stability is under hormonal control. This is true for mRNA that codes for vitellogenin, a protein synthesized in the livers of certain female animals such as frogs and chickens. Vitellogenin is transported to the oviduct, where it is used in the formation of egg yolk proteins.

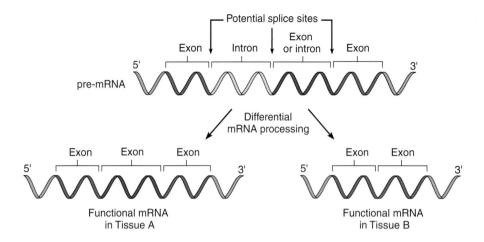

Potential splice sites

Exon | Intron | Exon or intron | Exon

pre-mRNA
5'   3'

Differential
mRNA processing

Exon Exon Exon
5'   3'

Exon Exon
5'   3'

Functional mRNA
in Tissue A

Functional mRNA
in Tissue B

Figure 13–12 Differential mRNA processing. In some cases a complex transcriptional unit can be processed in more than one way to yield two or more mRNAs, each of which encodes a related, but different, protein. In this generalized example the gene contains a segment that can be an exon in tissue A *(left)*, but an intron in tissue B *(right)*.

Vitellogenin synthesis is regulated by the hormone estradiol. When estradiol levels are high, the half-life of vitellogenin mRNA in frog liver is about 500 hours. When cells are deprived of estradiol, the half-life of the mRNA drops rapidly to less than 165 hours. This leads to a rapid decrease in cellular vitellogenin mRNA levels and a decreased synthesis of the vitellogenin protein. In addition to affecting the stability of the mRNA, the hormone seems to control the rate at which the mRNA is synthesized.

The activity of eukaryotic proteins may be altered by posttranslational chemical modifications

The ultimate phenotypic expression of a gene may also be controlled by regulation of the activity of the gene product. As in bacteria, many metabolic pathways in eukaryotes contain allosteric enzymes that are regulated through feedback inhibition. In addition, many eukaryotic proteins are extensively modified after they are synthesized.

In *proteolytic processing* proteins are synthesized as inactive precursors, which are converted to an active form by removal of a portion of the polypeptide chain. For example, proinsulin contains 86 amino acids. The removal of 35 amino acids yields the hormone insulin, which consists of two polypeptide chains containing 30 and 21 amino acids respectively, linked by disulfide bridges. Other proteins may be regulated in part by a process of *selective degradation,* which keeps their numbers constant within the cell.

Chemical modification, through the addition or removal of functional groups, can reversibly alter the activity of an enzyme. One common way of modifying the activity of an enzyme or other protein is the addition or removal of phosphate groups. Enzymes that add phosphate groups are called **kinases;** those that remove them are **phosphatases.** For example, the cyclin-dependent protein kinases discussed in Chapter 9 help control the cell cycle by adding phosphate groups to certain key proteins, causing them to become activated or inactivated. Chemical modifications such as protein phosphorylation also allow the cell to respond rapidly to certain hormones (see Chapter 47), or to fast-changing environmental or nutritional conditions.

SUMMARY WITH KEY TERMS

I. Most regulated genes in bacteria are organized into **operons,** each of which may encode several proteins.
 A. Each operon has a single **promoter** region upstream from the protein-coding regions.
 B. The **operator** is a sequence of bases that overlaps the promoter and serves as the regulatory switch responsible for **transcriptional level control** of the operon.
  1. A **repressor protein** binds specifically to the operator sequence and blocks transcription by preventing RNA polymerase from binding to the promoter.
  2. When the repressor is not bound to the operator, RNA polymerase can bind to the promoter and transcription can proceed.
 C. An **inducible** operon such as the lactose operon is normally turned off.
  1. The repressor protein is synthesized in an active form that binds to the operator.
  2. If lactose is present, it is converted to allolactose (the **inducer**), which binds an allosteric site on the repressor protein, causing it to change shape.
  3. The altered repressor cannot bind to the operator, and the operon is transcribed.

 D. A **repressible** operon such as the tryptophan operon is normally turned on.
  1. The repressor protein is synthesized in an inactive form that cannot bind to the operator.
  2. A metabolite (usually the end product of a metabolic pathway) acts as a **corepressor.**
  3. When intracellular corepressor levels are high, one of the molecules binds to an allosteric site on the repressor, changing its shape so that it can bind to the operator and thereby turn off transcription of the operon.
 E. Repressible and inducible operons are under **negative control.** When the repressor protein binds to the operator, transcription of the operon is turned off.
 F. Some inducible operons are also under **positive control.** A separate protein can bind to the DNA and stimulate transcription of the gene.
  1. The lactose operon is activated by **CAP (catabolite gene activator protein),** which binds to the promoter region, stimulating transcription by binding RNA polymerase tightly.
  2. To bind to the lactose operon, CAP requires **cAMP (cyclic AMP).** Levels of cAMP increase as levels of glucose decrease.

G. A group of operons can be organized into a multigene system, known as a **regulon,** which is controlled by a single regulatory protein. CAP activates a regulon associated with the metabolism of carbohydrates.

II. **Constitutive genes** are neither inducible nor repressible; they are active at all times. Regulatory proteins such as CAP and the repressor proteins are produced constitutively. These proteins work by recognizing and binding to specific base sequences in the DNA. The activity of constitutive genes is controlled by how efficiently RNA polymerase binds to their promoter regions.

III. Some **posttranscriptional controls** operate in prokaryotes.
   A. A **translational control** regulates the rate of translation of a particular mRNA.
   B. **Posttranslational controls** include **feedback inhibition** of key enzymes in some metabolic pathways.

IV. Eukaryotic genes are generally not organized into operons. Regulation of eukaryotic genes can occur at the levels of transcription, mRNA processing, translation, and the protein product.
   A. The promoter of a regulated eukaryotic gene consists of an RNA polymerase-binding site and short DNA sequences known as **upstream promoter elements (UPEs).** The efficiency of the promoter is determined by the number and types of UPEs within the promoter region.
   B. Inducible eukaryotic genes are controlled by **enhancer** elements, which can operate thousands of bases away from the promoter. Proteins that bind to enhancers appear to facilitate the binding of RNA polymerase to the promoter.

C. Eukaryotic genes are controlled by DNA-binding protein regulators known as **transcription factors.** Many of these are transcriptional activators; others are transcriptional repressors.
D. The activity of eukaryotic genes is affected by chromosome structure.
   1. Some genes whose products are required in large amounts exist as multiple copies in the chromosome. Other genes may be selectively amplified (i.e., **gene amplification**) by DNA replication in some cells.
   2. Genes can be inactivated by changes in chromosome structure. Densely packed regions of chromosomes called **heterochromatin** contain inactive genes. Active genes are associated with a loosely packed chromatin structure called **euchromatin.**
   3. **DNA methylation** is a mechanism that perpetuates gene inactivation.
E. Many eukaryotic genes are regulated after the RNA transcript is made.
   1. As a consequence of **differential mRNA processing,** a single gene can produce different forms of a protein in different tissues, depending on how the pre-mRNA is spliced.
   2. Certain regulatory mechanisms increase the stability of mRNA, allowing more protein molecules to be formed per mRNA molecule prior to degradation.
   3. Posttranslational control of eukaryotic genes can occur by feedback inhibition or by modification of the protein structure. The function of a protein can be changed by the addition of phosphate groups by **kinases,** or their removal by **phosphatases.**

POST-TEST

1. Regulation of most prokaryotic genes occurs at the level of (a) transcription (b) translation (c) replication (d) posttranslation (e) postreplication

2. The operator of an operon (a) encodes information for the repressor protein (b) is the binding site for the inducer (c) is the binding site for the repressor protein (d) is the binding site for RNA polymerase (e) encodes the information for the catabolite gene activator protein

3. A mutation that renders the regulatory gene of the lactose operon inactive would result in (a) the continuous transcription of the structural genes (b) no transcription of the structural genes (c) the binding of the repressor to the operator (d) no production of RNA polymerase (e) no difference in the rate of transcription

4. At a time when the lactose operon is actively transcribed (a) the operator is bound to the inducer (b) the lactose repressor is bound to the promoter (c) the operator is not bound to the promoter (d) the gene coding for the repressor is not expressed constitutively (e) the lactose repressor is bound to the inducer

5. A repressible operon codes for the enzymes of the following pathway. Which component of the pathway is most likely to be the corepressor for that operon?

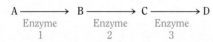

(a) substance A (b) substance B or C (c) substance D (d) enzyme 1 (e) enzyme 3

6. An mRNA molecule transcribed from the lactose operon contains nucleotide sequences complementary to (a) structural genes coding for enzymes (b) the operator region (c) the promoter region (d) the repressor gene (e) introns

7. Feedback inhibition is an example of control at the _____ level. (a) transcriptional (b) translational (c) posttranslational (d) replicational (e) all of the above

8. Which of the following control mechanisms is generally the most economical in terms of conserving energy and resources? (a) control by means of operons and regulons (b) feedback inhibition (c) selective degradation of mRNA (d) selective degradation of enzymes (e) gene amplification

9. A repressible operon, such as the tryptophan operon, is "off" when (a) the gene that codes for the repressor is expressed constitutively (b) the repressor-corepressor complex binds to the operator (c) the repressor binds to the structural genes (d) the corepressor binds to RNA polymerase (e) CAP binds to the promoter

10. Which of the following is an example of positive control? (a) transcription can occur when a repressor binds to an inducer (b) transcription cannot occur when a repressor binds to a corepressor (c) transcription is stimulated when a transcription activator binds to DNA (d) a and b (e) a and c

11. Which of the following are typically absent in prokaryotes? (a) enhancers (b) proteins that regulate transcription (c) repressors (d) promoters (e) operators

12. The "zipper" of a leucine zipper protein attaches (a) specific amino acids to specific DNA base pairs (b) two polypeptide chains to each other (c) one DNA region to another DNA region (d) amino acids to zinc atoms (e) RNA polymerase to the operator

13. Inactive genes tend to be found in (a) highly condensed chromatin, known as euchromatin (b) decondensed chromatin, known as euchromatin (c) highly condensed chromatin, known as heterochromatin (d) decondensed chromatin, known as heterochromatin (e) chromatin that is not organized as nucleosomes

REVIEW QUESTIONS

1. Make a sketch of the lactose operon and briefly describe its function. Be sure to include the following elements: (a) structural genes, (b) promoter, (c) operator, (d) CAP-binding site.
2. What structural features does the tryptophan operon have in common with the lactose operon? What features are different?
3. Why do we define the tryptophan operon as repressible and the lactose operon as inducible?
4. How is glucose involved in the positive control of the lactose operon? How is CAP similar to the lactose repressor protein? How is it different?
5. Compare the structure of a prokaryotic promoter region with known eukaryotic promoter regions. How does the regulation of inducible eukaryotic genes differ from the regulation of inducible prokaryotic genes?
6. Explain why it is necessary for certain genes in eukaryotic cells to be present in multiple copies.
7. How can the activity of some eukaryotic genes be affected by the structure of the chromosome?
8. Make a sketch illustrating how differential mRNA processing can give rise to different forms of a eukaryotic protein.

YOU MAKE THE CONNECTION

1. Develop a simple hypothesis that would explain the behavior of each of the following types of mutants in *E. coli*:
   (a) *Mutant a:* The map position of this mutation is in the tryptophan operon. The mutant cells are constitutive; that is, they produce all of the enzymes coded for by the tryptophan operon, even if large amounts of tryptophan are present in the growth medium.
   (b) *Mutant b:* The map position of this mutation is in the tryptophan operon. The mutant cells do not produce any of the enzymes coded for by the tryptophan operon under any conditions.
   (c) *Mutant c:* The map position of this mutation is some distance from the tryptophan operon. The mutant cells are constitutive; that is, they produce all of the enzymes coded for by the tryptophan operon, even if the growth medium contains large amounts of tryptophan.

   (d) *Mutant d:* The map position of this mutation is some distance from the tryptophan operon. The mutant cells do not produce any of the enzymes coded for by the tryptophan operon under any conditions.
2. Compare the types of bacterial genes associated with inducible operons, those associated with repressible operons, and those that are constitutive. Predict the category into which each of the following would most likely fit: (a) a gene that codes for RNA polymerase; (b) a gene that codes for an enzyme required to break down maltose; (c) a gene that codes for an enzyme used in the synthesis of adenine.
3. The regulatory gene that codes for the tryptophan repressor is not tightly linked to the tryptophan operon. Would it be advantageous if it were? Explain your answer.

RECOMMENDED READINGS

Hagman, M. "How Chromatin Changes Its Shape." *Science,* Vol. 285, 20 Aug. 1999. This review examines how posttranslational alterations of histone proteins, including phosphorylation and methylation, can affect the structure of chromatin.

Hardison, R. "The Evolution of Hemoglobin" *American Scientist,* Vol. 87, Mar.-Apr. 1999. Various forms of hemoglobin differ little in their amino acid sequences but are regulated quite differently.

Pennisi, E. "Chemical Shackles for Genes?" *Science,* Vol. 273, 2 Aug. 1996. DNA methylation is involved in the regulation of gene activity in plants as well as vertebrates.

Stein, G.S., J.L. Stein, A.J. van Wijnen, and J.B. Lian. "The Maturation of a Cell." *American Scientist,* Vol. 84, Jan.-Feb. 1996. The authors describe the activation of genes in the maturation of a bone cell.

● Visit our Web site at **http://www.info.brookscole.com/solomonbergmartin** for links to chapter-related resources on the World Wide Web. Additional on-line materials relating to this chapter can also be found on our Web site.

See chapter activity on BioActive Learner CD for additional help in mastering the chapter's material. Icon location in the chapter's margins shows which topics have tutorials or simulations in the CD.

14

Genetic Engineering

Bioreactor. This complex apparatus is an automated bioreactor that creates an optimal environment for genetically engineered bacteria to produce useful proteins. *(Rosenfeld Images Ltd/Science Photo Library/Photo Researchers, Inc.)*

LEARNING OBJECTIVES

After you have studied this chapter you should be able to

1. Draw a sketch that demonstrates how a typical restriction enzyme cuts DNA molecules and give examples of the ways in which these enzymes are used in recombinant DNA technology.
2. Summarize the properties of plasmids that allow them to be used as DNA cloning vectors.
3. Distinguish between a genomic DNA library and a complementary DNA (cDNA) library.
4. Explain why one would clone the same eukaryotic gene from both a genomic library and a cDNA library.
5. Identify some of the uses of DNA hybridization probes.
6. Describe how specific primers can be used to amplify specific genes from a mixture of genomic DNA or cDNA.
7. Draw a diagram that illustrates the most widely used DNA sequencing technique.
8. List some important proteins and other products that can be produced by genetic engineering techniques.
9. List some of the difficulties encountered in using *Escherichia coli* to produce proteins coded by eukaryotic genes and explain the rationale behind using transgenic plants and animals to solve some of those problems.

Beginning in the mid-1970s, a revolution in the field of biology occurred as the development of new ways of studying deoxyribonucleic acid (DNA) led to radically new research approaches. These techniques have had a major impact not only on genetic studies but also in areas ranging from cell biology to evolution, as well as on society.

This chapter begins with a consideration of **recombinant DNA technology,** in which DNA from different organisms is spliced together in the laboratory. The primary goal of this technology is to allow scientists to obtain a great many copies of any specific DNA segment to study it biochemically. Recombinant DNA technology allows scientists to introduce foreign DNA into the cells of microorganisms. Under the right conditions, this DNA is replicated and transmitted to the daughter cells when a cell divides. In this way a particular DNA sequence can be amplified, or **cloned,** to provide millions of identical copies that can be isolated in pure form. Today these methods have been supplemented by extremely valuable techniques that permit the cloning of DNA **in vitro** (outside of a living organism). Because new recombinant DNA methods are continually emerging, we will not attempt to explore them all. (Several Internet sites, such as "Access Excellence" and the "National Center for Biotechnology Information," are good sources of updated information.) Instead, we will discuss some of the major approaches that have provided a foundation for the technology.

We also consider the ways in which studies of cloned **DNA sequences** have been of immense value in allowing scientists to understand the organization of genes and the relationship between genes and their products. In fact, most of our knowledge of the complex structure and control of eukaryotic genes (see Chapters 12 and 13) and of the roles of genes in development (see Chapter 16) is derived from the application of these methods.

This chapter also explores the many practical applications of recombinant DNA technology. One of the rapidly advancing areas of study is **genetic engineering**—the modification of the DNA of an organism to produce new genes with new characteristics. Genetic engineering can take many forms, ranging from basic research, to the production of strains of bacteria that manufacture useful protein products, to the development of plants and animals that express foreign genes. This wide range of applications of ongoing discoveries in molecular genetics is causing a transformation of our view of **biotechnology,** the use of organisms to benefit humanity. Traditional forms of biotechnology include such familiar examples as the selective breeding of plants and the use of yeast to make alcoholic beverages or cause bread to rise. However, the examples of biotechnology most frequently cited today are applications of genetic engineering in such diverse areas as medicine and the pharmaceutical industries, foods and agriculture, and others. Biotechnology does not stand alone; its advances are greatly facilitated by other kinds of technology, including powerful computer programs and automated systems *(see photograph).*

■ RECOMBINANT DNA METHODS GREW OUT OF RESEARCH IN MICROBIAL GENETICS

Recombinant DNA technology was not developed quickly. It actually had its roots in the 1940s with genetic studies of bacteria and **bacteriophages** (literally "bacteria eaters"), the viruses that infect them (see Chapters 11 and 23). In the mid-1970s, after decades of basic research and the accumulation of extensive knowledge, the technology became feasible and available to the many scientists who now use these methods.

In recombinant DNA technology, special enzymes from bacteria, known as **restriction enzymes,** are used to cut DNA molecules only in specific places. Restriction enzymes allow researchers to reproducibly cut DNA into manageable segments.

Each fragment is then incorporated into a suitable **vector** molecule, a carrier capable of transporting it into a cell. Either bacteriophages or special DNA molecules called plasmids are commonly used as vectors. Recall from Chapter 11 that bacterial DNA is in the form of a circle; a **plasmid** is a separate, much smaller, circular DNA molecule that may be present and able to replicate inside a bacterial cell, typically *E. coli.* Plasmids can be introduced into bacterial cells by a method called transformation (see Chapter 11). For **transformation,** the uptake of foreign DNA by cells, to be efficient, researchers must alter the bacterial cell walls to make them permeable to the plasmid DNA molecules. Once a plasmid enters a cell, it is replicated and distributed to the daughter cells during cell division. When a recombinant plasmid (one that has foreign DNA spliced into it) replicates in this way, many copies of the foreign DNA are made (i.e., the foreign DNA is cloned).

Restriction enzymes are "molecular scissors"

The discovery of restriction enzymes was a major breakthrough in the development of recombinant DNA technology. Today large numbers of different types of restriction enzymes, each with its own characteristics, are readily available to researchers. For example, a restriction enzyme known as Hind III recognizes and cuts a DNA molecule at the restriction site 5'—AAGCTT—3', whereas the sequence 5'—GAATTC—3' is cut by another, known as EcoRI.[1] Why do bacteria produce such enzymes? Recall from Chapter 11 that during infection a bacteriophage injects its DNA into a bacterial cell. Such a cell can defend itself if it possesses restriction enzymes capable of attacking the bacteriophage DNA. The bacteria protect their own DNA from breakdown by modifying it after replication. An enzyme adds a methyl group to one or more bases in each restriction site so that the restriction enzyme is unable to recognize and cut the bacterial DNA.

Restriction enzymes enable scientists to cut DNA from chromosomes into shorter fragments in a controlled way. Many of the restriction enzymes used for recombinant DNA studies cut **palindromic** sequences, which means that the base sequence of one strand reads the same as its complement, but in the opposite direction. (Thus, the complement of our example, 5'—AAGCTT—3', reads 3'—TTCGAA—5'.) By cutting both strands of the DNA, but in a staggered fashion, these enzymes produce fragments with identical, complementary, single-stranded ends.

[1] The names of restriction enzymes are generally derived from the names of the bacteria from which they were originally isolated. Hence Hind III and EcoRI are derived from *Hemophilus influenzae* and *Escherichia coli,* respectively.

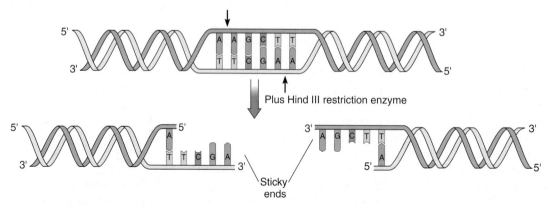

■ **Figure 14–1 Cutting DNA with a restriction enzyme.** Many restriction enzymes, like Hind III, cut DNA at sequences that are palindromic, thereby producing complementary sticky ends.

These ends are called "sticky ends" because they can pair (by hydrogen bonding) with the complementary, single-stranded ends of other DNA molecules that have been cut with the same enzyme (Fig. 14–1). Once two molecules have been joined together in this way, they can be treated with **DNA ligase** (see Chapter 11), an enzyme that covalently links the two DNA fragments to form a stable recombinant DNA molecule.

Restriction enzymes vary widely in the number of DNA bases that they recognize, ranging from as few as 4 to as many as 23 bases. If the restriction sites are randomly distributed in the DNA, we expect the restriction sequence of a "four-base cutter" to occur on the average of every 4^4, or 256, bases. A four-base cutter would therefore produce fragments with an average length of 256 bases, whereas a six-base cutter would produce fragments averaging 4^6, or 4096, bases.

Recombinant DNA is formed when DNA is spliced into a vector

In recombinant DNA technology, foreign DNA and plasmid DNA are both cut with the same restriction enzyme. The two types of DNA are then mixed together under conditions that facilitate hydrogen bonding between the complementary bases of the sticky ends, and the resulting recombinant DNA is stabilized by DNA ligase (Fig. 14–2).

The plasmids now used in recombinant DNA work have been extensively "engineered" in the laboratory to include features helpful in the isolation and analysis of cloned DNA (Fig. 14–3). Among these are (1) an origin of replication (see Chapter 11), (2) one or more restriction sites, and (3) genes that allow researchers to select cells that have been transformed by recombinant plasmids. These are genes that permit transformed cells to grow under specified conditions that do not allow growth of untransformed cells. In this way the researchers are making use of features that are also commonly found in naturally occurring plasmids. Typically, plasmids do not contain genes that are essential to the *E. coli* cells under normal conditions but often carry genes that are useful under specific environmental conditions, such as those that confer resistance to particular antibiotics or allow the cells to use a particular nutrient. For example, cells transformed with a plasmid that includes a gene for resistance to the antibiotic tetracycline can grow in a medium that contains tetracycline, but untransformed cells cannot.

A limiting property of any vector, however, is the size of the DNA fragment that it can effectively carry. The size of a DNA segment is often given in kilobases, with **1 kilobase (kb)** being equal to 1000 base pairs. Fragments smaller than 10 kb can usually be inserted into plasmids for use in *E. coli*. However, larger fragments require the use of bacteriophage vectors, which can handle up to 15 kb of DNA.

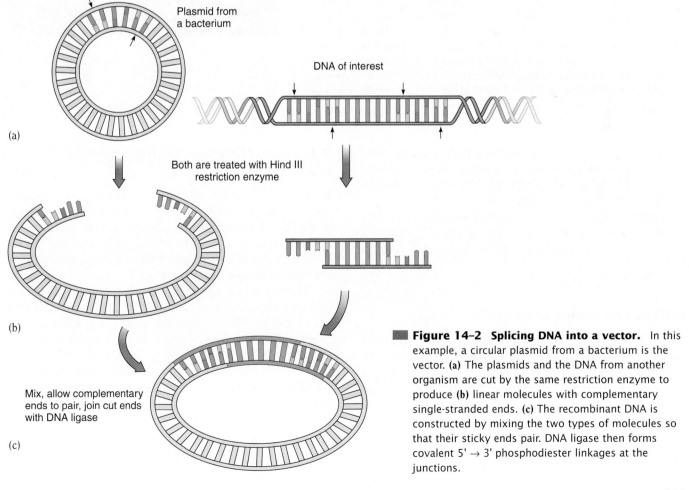

Plasmid from a bacterium

DNA of interest

(a)

Both are treated with Hind III restriction enzyme

(b)

Mix, allow complementary ends to pair, join cut ends with DNA ligase

(c)

Figure 14–2 Splicing DNA into a vector. In this example, a circular plasmid from a bacterium is the vector. **(a)** The plasmids and the DNA from another organism are cut by the same restriction enzyme to produce **(b)** linear molecules with complementary single-stranded ends. **(c)** The recombinant DNA is constructed by mixing the two types of molecules so that their sticky ends pair. DNA ligase then forms covalent 5' → 3' phosphodiester linkages at the junctions.

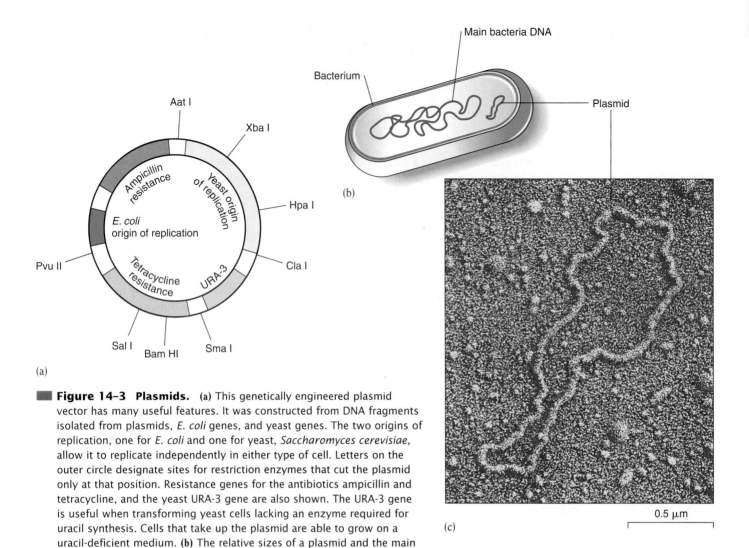

(a)

(b)

Main bacteria DNA

Bacterium

Plasmid

0.5 μm

(c)

Figure 14-3 Plasmids. **(a)** This genetically engineered plasmid vector has many useful features. It was constructed from DNA fragments isolated from plasmids, *E. coli* genes, and yeast genes. The two origins of replication, one for *E. coli* and one for yeast, *Saccharomyces cerevisiae*, allow it to replicate independently in either type of cell. Letters on the outer circle designate sites for restriction enzymes that cut the plasmid only at that position. Resistance genes for the antibiotics ampicillin and tetracycline, and the yeast URA-3 gene are also shown. The URA-3 gene is useful when transforming yeast cells lacking an enzyme required for uracil synthesis. Cells that take up the plasmid are able to grow on a uracil-deficient medium. **(b)** The relative sizes of a plasmid and the main DNA of a bacterium. **(c)** TEM of a plasmid from *E. coli.* *(c, Dr. Stanley Cohen/Science Photo Library/Photo Researchers, Inc.)*

Recombinant DNA can also be introduced into cells of more complex organisms. For example, engineered viruses are used as vectors in mammalian cells. These viruses have been disabled in such a way that they do not kill the cells they infect; instead their DNA, and any foreign DNA they carry, becomes incorporated into the chromosomes of the cell following infection. As discussed later, other methods have been developed that do not require a biological vector.

DNA can be cloned inside cells

Because a single gene is only a small part of the total DNA in an organism, isolating the piece of DNA containing that particular gene is like finding a needle in a haystack. A powerful detector is needed. Today there are many methods that permit the isolation of a specific nucleotide sequence from an organism. We start with methods in which DNA is cloned inside bacterial cells. We use the cloning of human DNA as an example, although the procedure can be applied to any organism.

A genomic library contains fragments of all DNA in the genome

The total DNA per cell is referred to as a **genome.** For example, if DNA is extracted from human cells, we refer to it as human genomic DNA. A **genomic library** is a collection of DNA fragments that are more or less representative of all the DNA in the genome. Each fragment is spliced into a plasmid, which is usually inserted inside a bacterial cell.

The first step in producing a genomic library is to cut the DNA with a restriction enzyme, generating a population of DNA fragments (Fig. 14–4*a*) . These fragments vary in size and in the genetic information they carry, but they all have identical sticky ends. Plasmid DNA to be used as a vector is treated with the same restriction enzyme, which converts the circular plasmids into linear molecules with sticky ends complementary to those of the human DNA fragments. Recombinant plasmids are produced by first mixing the two kinds of DNA (human and plasmid) together under conditions that promote hydrogen bonding of complementary bases. Then DNA ligase is used to covalently bond the paired ends

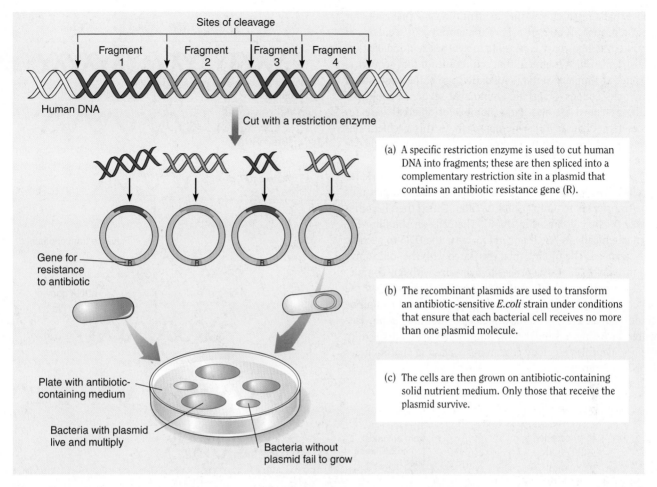

Sites of cleavage

Fragment 1 Fragment 2 Fragment 3 Fragment 4

Human DNA

Cut with a restriction enzyme

Gene for resistance to antibiotic

Plate with antibiotic-containing medium

Bacteria with plasmid live and multiply

Bacteria without plasmid fail to grow

(a) A specific restriction enzyme is used to cut human DNA into fragments; these are then spliced into a complementary restriction site in a plasmid that contains an antibiotic resistance gene (R).

(b) The recombinant plasmids are used to transform an antibiotic-sensitive *E.coli* strain under conditions that ensure that each bacterial cell receives no more than one plasmid molecule.

(c) The cells are then grown on antibiotic-containing solid nutrient medium. Only those that receive the plasmid survive.

Figure 14–4 Cloning genomic DNA. Only a small part of one chromosome is shown. A great many more DNA fragments would be produced from an entire genome.

of the plasmid and human DNA. Unavoidably, nonrecombinant plasmids are also formed because some plasmids revert to their original circular form without incorporating foreign DNA.

The plasmids are inserted into antibiotic-sensitive *E. coli* cells by transformation (Fig. 14–4b). Because the ratio of plasmids to cells is kept very low, it is rare for a cell to receive more than one plasmid molecule, and not all cells receive a plasmid. The normally antibiotic-sensitive cells are incubated on a nutrient medium that includes antibiotics, so only cells that have incorporated a plasmid (which contains a gene for antibiotic resistance) are able to grow (Fig. 14–4c). In addition, the plasmid has usually been engineered in ways that permit researchers to select only those cells containing *recombinant* plasmids.

A genomic library contains redundancies; that is, certain human DNA sequences have been inserted into plasmids more than once, purely by chance. However, each individual recombinant plasmid (analogous to a book in the library) contains only a single fragment of the total human genome. Each of these fragments is usually smaller than a gene; therefore, several fragments must be isolated to study the complete gene.

To allow identification of a plasmid containing a sequence of interest, each plasmid must be amplified, or cloned, until there are millions of copies to work with. This process occurs as the *E. coli* cells grow and divide. A dilute sample of the bacterial culture is spread on solid growth medium, so that the cells will be widely separated. Each cell divides many times, giving rise to a visible **colony,** which is a clone of genetically identical cells. All the cells of a particular colony contain the same recombinant plasmid, so during this process a specific sequence of human DNA is also cloned . The major task is to determine which colony (out of thousands) contains a cloned fragment of interest. There are many ways in which specific DNA sequences can be identified.

A specific DNA sequence can be detected by a complementary genetic probe

A common approach to the problem of detecting the DNA of interest involves the use of a **genetic probe,** which is usually a radioactively labeled segment of ribonucleic acid (RNA) or single-stranded DNA that can **hybridize** (become attached by base pairing) to complementary base sequences in the target gene.

Suppose that a researcher wishes to identify a gene that codes for a specific protein. If at least part of the amino acid sequence of that protein is known, it is possible to synthesize a radioactive, single-stranded DNA fragment that could code for that sequence. This is not as simple as it may sound: Because of the existence of synonymous codons, a specific amino acid sequence could potentially be coded for by a large number of different base sequences (see Chapter 12). One approach to this problem has been to synthesize a mixture of probes, each of which could code for the desired amino acid sequence.

Genetic probes can be used in a variety of ways. For example, cells from *E. coli* colonies containing recombinant plasmids can be transferred to a nitrocellulose filter, which then becomes a *replica* of the colonies (Fig. 14–5). The cells on the filter are treated chemically to lyse them and to cause the DNA to become single-stranded. The filter is then incubated with the radioactive probe mixture to allow the probes to hybridize with any complementary strands of DNA that may be present. Each spot on the filter containing DNA complementary to that particular probe becomes radioactive and can be detected by autoradiography (see Chapter 2), using a special x-ray film. Each spot on the film therefore identifies a colony containing a plasmid that includes the DNA of interest.

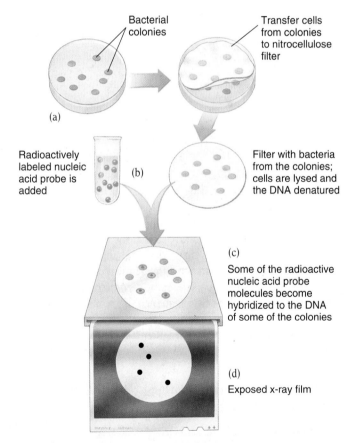

Figure 14–5 Use of a genetic probe. A radioactive nucleic acid probe (which can be either RNA or single-stranded DNA) reveals the presence of complementary sequences of DNA.

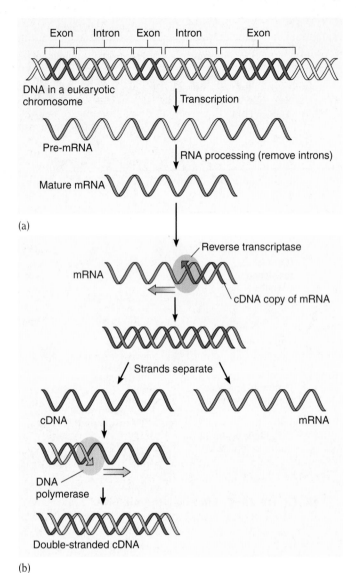

Figure 14–6 Formation of cDNA. (a) RNA processing occurs in the nucleus to form mature mRNA. **(b)** Researchers isolate mature mRNA and use the reverse transcriptase enzyme to produce single-stranded cDNA complementary to it. DNA polymerase is used to synthesize double-stranded DNA.

A cDNA library is complementary to mRNA and does not contain introns

For reasons that are discussed later, researchers frequently wish to avoid cloning introns and other parts of eukaryotic genes that do not directly code for proteins. They also may wish to clone only genes that are expressed in a particular cell type. In such cases they construct libraries consisting of DNA copies of mature messenger RNA (mRNA) from which introns have been removed. The copies, known as **complementary DNA (cDNA)** because they are complementary to RNA, also lack introns. **Reverse transcriptase** (see Chapter 12) is used to synthesize single-stranded cDNA, which is then separated from the mRNA and made double-stranded by DNA polymerase (Fig. 14–6).

A **cDNA library** is formed using mRNA from a single cell type as the starting material. The double-stranded cDNA molecules are inserted into plasmid or virus vectors, which then multiply in *E. coli* cells.

Cloning a gene from both a cDNA library and a genomic library has several advantages. Analysis of the genomic DNA clones gives useful information about the structure of the gene in the chromosome and the structure of the pre-mRNA transcript, as well as nontranscribed regulatory regions.

Analysis of cDNA clones allows investigators to determine certain characteristics of the protein encoded by the gene, including its exact amino acid sequence. The structure of the mature mRNA can also be studied. Furthermore, because the cDNA copy of the mRNA does not contain intron sequences, comparison of the cDNA and genomic DNA base sequences reveals the locations of intron and exon coding sequences in the gene.

Cloned cDNA sequences are also useful when it is desirable to produce a eukaryotic protein in *E. coli*. When an intron-containing human gene such as the gene for human growth hormone is introduced into *E. coli*, the bacterium is unable to remove the introns from the transcribed RNA to make a functional mRNA for the production of its protein product. If a cDNA clone of the gene is inserted into the bacterium, however, its transcript contains an uninterrupted coding region. A functional protein can be synthesized if the gene is inserted downstream of an appropriate bacterial promoter.

The polymerase chain reaction is a technique for amplifying DNA in vitro

The methods to amplify a specific DNA sequence described above all involve cloning DNA in cells, usually those of bacteria. These processes are time-consuming and require an adequate DNA sample as starting material. The **polymerase chain reaction (PCR)** technique allows researchers to amplify a tiny sample of DNA millions of times in a few hours (Fig. 14–7).

In PCR, DNA polymerase uses nucleotides and primers to replicate a DNA sequence in vitro, thereby producing two DNA molecules. The two strands of each molecule are then denatured (separated by heating) and replicated again, so then there are four double-stranded molecules. After the next cycle of heating and replication there are eight molecules, and so on, with the number of DNA molecules doubling in each cycle. After only 20 heating and cooling cycles (which are carried out using automated equipment) this exponential process yields 2^{20}, or more than 1 million, copies of the target sequence!

Because the reaction can only be carried out efficiently if the DNA polymerase can remain stable through many heating cycles, a special heat-resistant DNA polymerase, known as *Taq* polymerase, is used. The name of this enzyme reflects its source, *Thermus aquaticus,* a bacterium that lives in hot springs in Yellowstone Park. (Similar enzymes can be found in bacteria living in deep-sea thermal vents; see *Focus On: Life Without the Sun,* Chapter 53.)

The PCR technique is particularly valuable because only specific *target sequences* are replicated. Recall from Chapter 11 that DNA polymerase can add nucleotides only to a preexisting polynucleotide strand. In the cell, DNA synthesis begins with the formation of a short RNA primer, which is then extended by DNA polymerase. In the PCR technique, chemically synthesized short DNA single-stranded molecules with a specified nucleotide sequence are included in the reaction mixture. These attach to complementary target sequences of the single-stranded DNA and act as primers, thereby designating the starting point for replication by DNA polymerase. In this way, a specific sequence can be cloned from an unpurified mixture of DNA sequences.

The PCR technique has virtually limitless applications. It allows the amplification and analysis of tiny DNA samples from seemingly unlikely sources, ranging from crime scenes to archaeological remains. For example, in 1997 the first analysis of mitochondrial DNA obtained from the bones of Neandertals was reported (see Chapter 21).

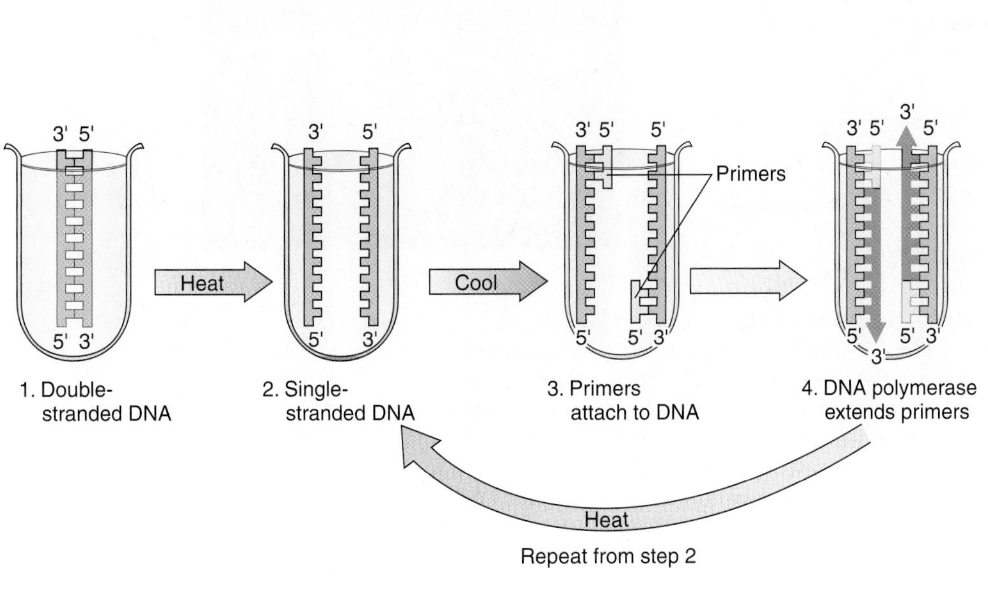

Figure 14–7 The polymerase chain reaction.
(1) The initial reaction mixture includes a very small amount of double-stranded DNA *(shown)*, DNA precursors (deoxyribonucleotides), specific nucleic acid primers, and heat-resistant *Taq* DNA polymerase. (2) The DNA is denatured (separated into single strands) by heat. (3) Each DNA strand acts as a template for DNA synthesis catalyzed by the *Taq* DNA polymerase. (4) The number of double-stranded DNA molecules doubles each time the cycle of heating and cooling is repeated.

If the PCR technique has a flaw, it is the fact that it is almost too sensitive. Even a tiny amount of contaminant DNA in a sample could become amplified if it includes a DNA sequence complementary to the primer, potentially leading to an erroneous conclusion. Researchers are constantly improving their methods to avoid this and other technical pitfalls.

Gel electrophoresis is the most widely used technique to separate macromolecules

Mixtures of certain macromolecules such as polypeptides, DNA fragments, or RNA can be separated by **gel electrophoresis,** a method that exploits the fact that these molecules carry charged groups that cause them to migrate in an electrical field. Figure 14–8 illustrates gel electrophoresis of DNA molecules. Both DNA and RNA migrate through the gel toward the positive pole of the electrical field because they are negatively charged due to their phosphate groups (see Chapters 11 and 12). Because the gel retards the movement of the large molecules more than the small molecules, the rate at which they travel is inversely proportional to their length (molecular weight). Including DNA fragments of known size as standards allows accurate measurement of the molecular weights of the unknown fragments.

The DNA fragments can be identified if they hybridize with a complementary genetic probe. However, it can be very cumbersome to work with DNA fragments contained in a gel. For this reason the DNA is usually denatured and then transferred to a nitrocellulose filter, which picks up the DNA much as a blotter picks up ink. The resulting "blot," which is essentially a replica of the gel, is incubated with a radioactive genetic probe, which hybridizes with any complementary DNA fragments. It is then used for autoradiography (see Chapter 2). The resulting spots on the x-ray film correspond to the locations of the fragments in the gel that are complementary to the probe. This type of **blot hybridization** (called a **Southern blot** after its inventor, E.M. Southern) has widespread applications. It is often used to diagnose certain types of genetic disorders. For example, in some cases the DNA of a mutant gene can be detected because it migrates differently in the gel than the DNA of its normal counterpart.

Similar blotting techniques are used to study RNA and proteins. When RNA molecules separated by electrophoresis are transferred to a membrane, the result is, rather in jest, called a **Northern blot.** In the same spirit, the term **Western blot** is applied to a blot consisting of polypeptides previously separated by gel electrophoresis. (So far, no one has invented a type of blot that could be called an "Eastern blot.") In the case of Western blotting,

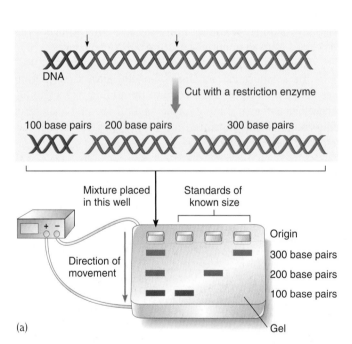

(a)

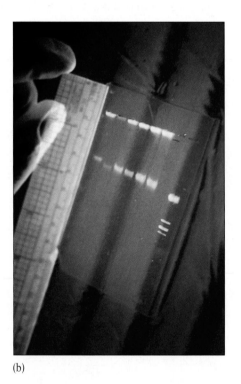

(b)

■ **Figure 14–8 Gel electrophoresis.** Charged molecules, such as DNA, RNA, or protein, can be separated based on the rate at which they migrate in an electrical field. **(a)** An electrical field is set up in a gel material, consisting of agarose or polyacrylamide, which is poured as a thin slab on a glass or Plexiglas holder. After the gel has solidified, samples containing a mixture of macromolecules of different sizes are loaded in wells formed at one end of the gel, and then an electrical current is applied. The smallest DNA fragments *(green)* travel the longest distance. **(b)** A gel containing separated DNA fragments. The gel is stained with ethidium bromide, a dye that binds to DNA and is fluorescent under UV light. *(b, Michael Gabridge/Visuals Unlimited)*

the polypeptides of interest are recognized by radioactive antibody molecules that bind to them specifically. For example, Western blotting is used diagnostically to detect the presence of proteins specific to human immunodeficiency virus-1 (HIV-1), the virus that causes acquired immunodeficiency syndrome (AIDS).

A great deal of information can be inferred from a DNA nucleotide sequence

A cloned piece of DNA can be used as a research tool for a wide variety of applications. Even if the purpose of cloning the gene is to obtain the encoded protein for some industrial or pharmaceutical process, a great deal must be known about the gene and how it functions before it can be engineered for a particular application. The usual first step is to determine the sequence of nucleotides.

The most commonly used method of DNA sequencing is based on the fact that a replicating DNA strand that has incorporated a modified synthetic nucleotide, known as a *dideoxynucleotide,* cannot elongate beyond that point. Unlike a "normal" deoxynucleotide (which lacks a hydroxyl group on its 2' carbon), a dideoxynucleotide also lacks a hydroxyl group on its 3' carbon (Fig. 14–9a). (Recall from Chapter 11 that a 3' hydroxyl group is needed to react each time a phosphodiester linkage is formed.) Thus, dideoxynucleotides terminate elongation during DNA replication.

Four different reaction mixtures are prepared. Each contains multiple single-stranded copies of the DNA to be sequenced, DNA polymerase, appropriate radioactively labeled primers, and all four deoxynucleotides needed to synthesize DNA: dATP, dCTP, dGTP, and dTTP. Each also includes a small amount of only one of the four dideoxynucleotides: ddATP, dd-CTP, ddGTP, or ddTTP[2] (Fig. 14–9b).

For example, consider how the reaction proceeds in the mixture that includes ddATP. At each site where adenine is specified, occasionally a growing strand will incorporate a ddATP and will be unable to elongate further. Consequently, a mixture of DNA fragments of varying lengths is formed in the reaction mixture. Each fragment that contains a ddATP marks a specific location where adenine would be normally found in the newly synthesized strand. Similarly, in the reaction mixture that includes ddCTP, each fragment that contains ddCTP marks the position of a cytosine in the newly synthesized strand, and so on (Fig. 14–9c).

The radioactive fragments from each reaction are denatured and then separated by gel electrophoresis, with each reaction mixture (corresponding to A, T, G, or C) occupying its own lane in the gel. The positions of the newly synthesized fragments in the gel can then be determined by autoradiography (Fig. 14–9d and e). Because the high resolution of the gel makes it possible to distinguish between fragments that differ in length by only a single nucleotide, one can read off the sequence in the newly synthesized DNA one base at a time, beginning with the shortest fragment. To follow the example in Figure 14–9d, if the shortest fragment is in the "G" lane, then the first base is G; similarly, if

the next shortest fragment is also in the G lane, then the next base is also G; if the third shortest fragment is in the "A" lane, then the third base is A, and so on. The entire sequence in the figure is 5'—GGAGCATAGCAT—3'. Of course, we are actually interested in the sequence of the original strand that served as the template, which is 3'—CCTCGTATCGTA—5'.

Knowing the DNA sequence of a cloned gene allows investigators to identify which parts of the DNA molecule contain the actual protein-coding sequences, as well as which parts may be regulatory regions involved in gene expression (see Chapter 13). Signals involved in mRNA processing and modification can be recognized, and the amino acid sequence of the encoded protein can be inferred directly from the base sequence. Prior to the development of DNA-sequencing methods, protein sequences were determined by laborious methods from highly purified protein samples. Although protein microsequencing technology has also advanced rapidly, in most cases cloning and sequencing a gene are easier than purifying and sequencing the encoded protein.

Advances in sequencing technology have made it possible for researchers to study the nucleotide sequences of a wide variety of organisms, both prokaryotic and eukaryotic. Much of this research received its initial impetus in conjunction with the Human Genome Project (see Chapter 15). The sequence of the 3 billion base pairs of the human genome was essentially completed in 2001. The genomes of many prokaryotes, both parasitic and free-living, have been completely sequenced. For example, the complete sequence of the 4.6 million base pairs (4288 genes) of *E. coli* was published in 1997. This was preceded by another major landmark, electronic publication of the complete sequence of the 12 million base pairs (6223 genes) of yeast, a unicellular eukaryote with an unusually small genome, in 1996. Sequencing projects encompass a variety of multicellular eukaryotes, with an emphasis on those that have been important research tools and/or are of agricultural and medical importance. For example, the genome of the fruit fly, *Drosophila melanogaster,* has been sequenced (more than 14,000 genes), as have those of two other widely used model organisms, *Caenorhabditis elegans* (a worm with almost 19,000 genes) and *Arabidopsis thaliana* (a plant with more than 26,000 genes) (see Chapter 16). We are in the middle of an extraordinary explosion of gene sequence data, largely because of the use of much more advanced automated sequencing methods.

DNA sequence information is now kept in large computer databases, many of which can be accessed through the Internet. Examples include databases maintained by the National Center for Biotechnology Information (a service of the U. S. National Library of Medicine and the National Institutes of Health) and by the Human Genome Organization (HUGO). These allow investigators to compare newly discovered sequences with those already known and to utilize many other kinds of information. By searching for DNA (and amino acid) sequences in a database, researchers can gain a great deal of insight into the function and structure of the gene product, as well as the evolutionary relationships among genes, and the variability among gene sequences in a population.

---

[2] The prefix "dd" is used for dideoxynucleotides, to distinguish them from deoxynucleotides, which are designated "d."

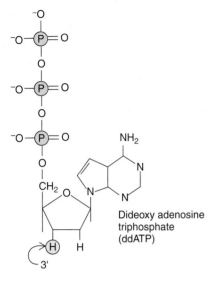

(a) Dideoxynucleotides are modified nucleotides that lack a 3' hydroxyl group and thus block further elongation of a new DNA chain.

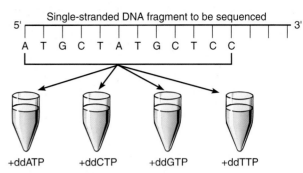

(b) Four different reaction mixtures are used to sequence a DNA fragment; each contains a small amount of a single dideoxynucleotide, such as ddATP. Larger amounts of the four normal deoxynucleotides (dATP, dCTP, dGTP, and dTTP) plus DNA polymerase and radioactively labeled primers are also included.

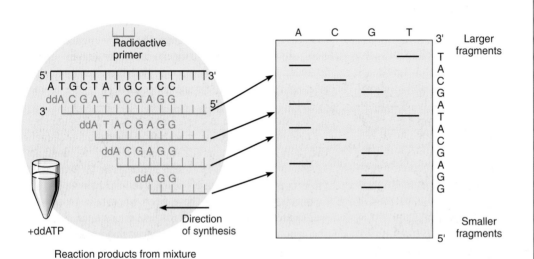

(c) The random incorporation of dideoxy ATP into the growing chain generates a series of smaller DNA fragments ending at all the possible positions where adenine is found in the newly synthesized fragments. These correspond to positions where thymine occurs in the original template strand.

(d) The radioactive products of each reaction mixture are separated by gel electrophoresis and located by exposing the gel to x-ray film. The nucleotide sequence of the newly synthesized DNA is read directly from the film (5' → 3'). The sequence in the original template strand is its complement (3' → 5').

(e) An exposed x-ray film of a DNA sequencing gel. The four lanes represent A, C, G, and T dideoxy reaction mixes, respectively.

■ Figure 14–9 DNA sequencing. *(e, Courtesy of B. Slatko, New England Biolabs)*

Restriction fragment length polymorphisms are a measure of genetic relationships

The variability of genes within a population can be studied in several different ways. As mentioned in the previous section, a direct approach is to determine DNA sequences. Advances in DNA sequencing technology will make this the most widely used method in the future.

A more traditional procedure uses restriction enzymes. It is based on the fact that random DNA mutations and recombination may result in individuals differing in the number and location of sites where a particular restriction enzyme cuts the DNA.

Therefore, each individual differs in the lengths of the fragments produced by that enzyme. Such **restriction fragment length polymorphisms** (commonly known as **RFLPs,** or "riflips") can be used to determine how closely related different members of the population are. (The term *polymorphism* literally means "many forms." A **genetic polymorphism** is said to exist if individuals of two or more discrete genetic types, or "morphs," are found in a population or species; see Chapter 18.)

Restriction enzymes are used to cut the DNA from two or more individuals, and the fragments are separated by gel electrophoresis (with the DNA from each individual in a separate lane). A Southern blot is made of the DNA on the gel, which is then denatured and allowed to hybridize with a genetic probe. Usually the probe is complementary to a sequence that is repeated and interspersed throughout the genome. The resulting patterns of bands, commonly referred to as DNA fingerprints, can then be compared (Fig. 14–10).

RFLP analysis is an especially powerful tool in the fields of population and evolutionary biology because it can measure the degree of genetic relatedness between individuals. It has also been very useful in settling cases of disputed parentage.

The most controversial use of DNA fingerprinting is in the field of forensics. Traditional RFLP analysis can be used if there is a large enough amount of blood, semen, or other DNA-containing tissue left at the scene of a crime. However, if even a tiny amount of such physical evidence is available, one or more target DNA sequences can be amplified by the PCR technique, and subjected to electrophoresis, yielding a DNA fingerprint that can be analyzed.

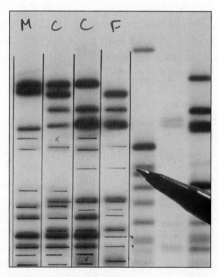

Figure 14–10 Gel electrophoresis showing a restriction fragment length polymorphism (RFLP). The lanes marked "M" and "F" contain DNA from a mother and father, respectively, and the two marked "C" contain DNA from their children. Note that every band present in one of the children is also found in at least one of the parents. *(David Parker/Science Photo Library/Photo Researchers, Inc.)*

If applied properly, DNA fingerprinting has the power to identify the guilty with a high degree of certainty. Conversely, it can exonerate the innocent. In fact, hundreds of convicted persons have won new trials and have been subsequently released from incarceration based on the application of DNA fingerprinting to physical evidence from the crime scene. Such evidence has been ruled admissible in many court cases, including certain trials that have received a great deal of attention in recent years. One limitation arises from the fact that the DNA samples are usually small and may have been degraded. Obviously, great care must be taken to prevent contamination of the samples. This is especially crucial if the PCR technique is to be used to amplify the DNA.

The development of DNA fingerprinting sparked a lively debate over how "unique" each individual pattern might be. For example, some scientists argued that a pattern that is quite rare in the general population might be more common in a particular ethnic group, and this might significantly affect the calculated probability of a match. As data on the frequency of particular patterns in various populations have accumulated, it has been learned that these concerns are of less practical importance than once thought. For example, the odds that two persons taken at random from the general population would have identical DNA fingerprints may be as low as one in several billion. If two persons are members of the same ethnic group, the odds of a match may increase but are usually still extremely low (perhaps one in several million).

■ GENETIC ENGINEERING HAS MANY APPLICATIONS

Recombinant DNA technology has provided not only a new and unique set of tools for examining fundamental questions about cells but also new approaches to problems of applied technology in many other fields. In some cases the production of genetically engineered proteins and organisms has begun to have considerable impact on our lives. The most striking of these have been in the fields of pharmacology and medicine.

In 1982 human insulin produced by *E. coli* became the first genetically engineered protein approved for use by humans. Prior to the use of recombinant DNA techniques to generate genetically altered bacteria capable of producing the human hormone, insulin was derived exclusively from other animals. Many diabetic persons become allergic to the insulin from animal sources because its amino acid sequence differs slightly from human insulin. The ability to produce the human hormone by recombinant DNA methods has resulted in significant medical benefits to diabetics.

Genetically engineered human growth hormone (see Chapter 47) is available to children who need it to overcome growth deficiencies. Human growth hormone could previously be obtained only from cadavers. Only small amounts were available, and evidence suggested that some of the preparations from cadavers were contaminated with infectious agents similar to those causing mad cow disease (see Chapter 23). The list of products that can be produced by genetic engineering is ever growing. These include treatments for multiple sclerosis, certain cancers, heart attacks, and certain forms of anemia. Recombinant DNA technology is also increasingly used to produce vaccines that provide safe and effective immunity against infectious diseases such as hepatitis B.

Additional engineering is required for a recombinant eukaryotic gene to be expressed in bacteria

Even if a gene has been isolated and successfully introduced into *E. coli,* the bacterium does not necessarily make the encoded protein in large quantities. Several obstacles stand in the way of producing gene products of eukaryotes in bacteria. One is that the gene has to be correctly associated with an appropriate set of regulatory and promoter sequences that the bacterial RNA polymerase can recognize. Recall from Chapters 12 and 13 that the regulatory regions of prokaryotic and eukaryotic genes are quite different. A usual approach to this problem is to combine the amino acid coding portion of a eukaryotic gene with a bacterial promoter sequence that can be strongly expressed. Some eukaryotic genes, for example, are fused to the lactose operon regulatory region (see Chapter 13); the protein product of the eukaryotic gene is synthesized when the bacterium is fed lactose in the growth medium.

We have already discussed the fact that bacterial cells cannot process RNA molecules containing eukaryotic intron sequences and that one solution to this problem is to introduce a cDNA copy of the gene. Other problems may arise in the expression of a recombinant protein in *E. coli* because of differences in the ways the proteins are expressed in prokaryotic and eukaryotic cells. Insulin, for example, is made in human cells from a large polypeptide that is folded in a specific way by the formation of three disulfide bonds, each joining two cysteines (sulfur-containing amino acids). After the polypeptide is folded, parts of the polypeptide are removed by proteolytic (protein-digesting) enzymes, leaving the insulin as two separate polypeptide chains held together by the disulfide bonds. *E. coli* lacks the specific enzymes necessary to cut the larger protein and is not able to fold the molecule properly. To overcome these problems, the gene was engineered to produce the two polypeptides separately. The recombinant proteins are then purified from the cells and allowed to associate in vitro. This procedure results in a relatively low yield of the active hormone, because the insulin can fold in several ways, only one of which results in a functional hormone.

It has been possible to circumvent some of these types of problems by introducing recombinant genes into eukaryotic cells such as yeast or other fungi, or cultured mammalian cells, that contain the protein-processing machinery required to produce fully functional proteins. Foreign proteins can also be produced by some types of genetically engineered plants or animals.

Transgenic organisms have incorporated foreign DNA into their cells

Plants and animals in which foreign genes have been incorporated are referred to as **transgenic** organisms. Varied approaches are used to insert foreign genes into plant or animal cells. Viruses are often used as vectors, although other methods, such as direct injection of DNA into cells, have also been applied.

Transgenic animals are valuable in research

Process of Science Transgenic animals are usually produced by microinjecting the DNA of a particular gene into the nucleus of a recipient fertilized egg cell or embryonic **stem cells** (see Chapter 1). The eggs are then implanted into the uterus of a female and allowed to develop. Alternatively, genetically modified embryonic stem cells are injected into isolated blastocysts (see Chapter 49) and then implanted into a foster mother.

Transgenic offspring have already been shown to have numerous valuable research applications over a wide range of investigations, including regulation of gene expression, immune system function, genetic diseases, viral diseases, and genes responsible for the development of cancer. The laboratory mouse *(Mus)* has become a particularly important model organism for these studies.

In a classic pioneering study of the control of gene expression, reported by the laboratory of R.L. Brinster in 1983, transgenic mice carrying a gene for rat growth hormone were produced (Fig. 14–11; also see Fig. 16–18a). Brinster and his colleagues wanted to understand the controls that allow certain genes to be expressed in some tissues and not in others. A mouse normally produces small amounts of growth hormone in its pituitary gland, but these researchers reasoned that other tissues might also be capable of producing growth hormone. First the gene for growth hormone was isolated from a library of genomic rat DNA. It was then combined with the promoter region of a mouse gene that normally produces metallothionein, a protein that is active in the liver and whose synthesis is stimulated by the presence of toxic amounts of heavy metals such as zinc. The metallothionein regulatory sequences were used as a switch to turn the production of rat growth hormone on and off at will. After the engineered gene was injected with a microinjection pipette into mouse embryo cells, the embryos were implanted into the uterus of a mouse and allowed to develop. Because of the difficulty in manipulating the embryos without damaging them, the gene transplant was successful in only a small fraction of the animals. When exposed to small amounts of zinc, these transgenic mice produced large amounts of growth hormone because the liver is a much larger organ than the pituitary gland. The mice grew rapidly, and one mouse, which developed from an embryo that had received two copies of the growth hormone gene, grew to more than double the normal size. As might be expected, such mice are often able to transmit their increased growth capability to their offspring.

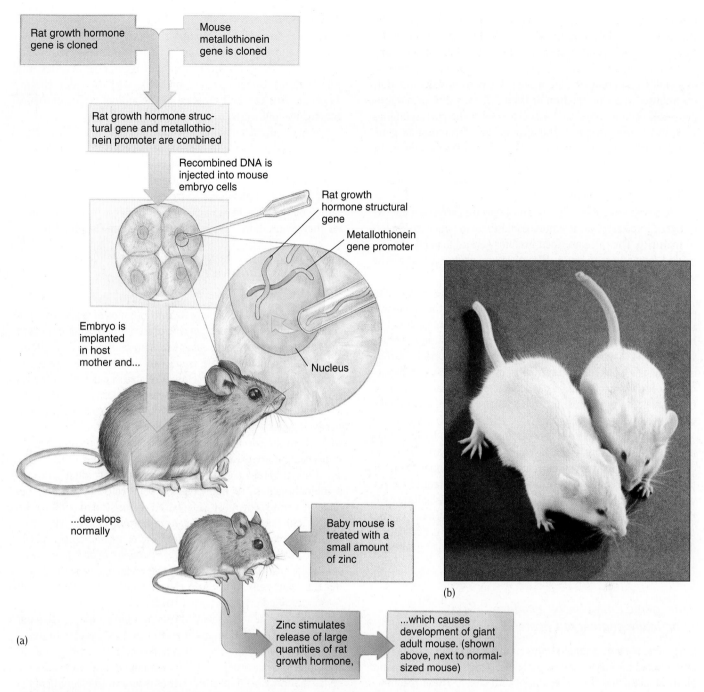

(a)

Rat growth hormone gene is cloned

Mouse metallothionein gene is cloned

Rat growth hormone structural gene and metallothionein promoter are combined

Recombined DNA is injected into mouse embryo cells

Rat growth hormone structural gene

Metallothionein gene promoter

Nucleus

Embryo is implanted in host mother and...

...develops normally

Baby mouse is treated with a small amount of zinc

(b)

Zinc stimulates release of large quantities of rat growth hormone,

...which causes development of giant adult mouse. (shown above, next to normal-sized mouse)

Figure 14–11 Transgenic mice. **(a)** How to make a giant mouse. **(b)** The mouse on the right is normal, while the mouse on the left is a transgenic animal that expresses rat growth hormone. *(Photo by R.L. Brinster, University of Pennsylvania Medical School)*

One extremely powerful research tool is **gene targeting,** a procedure in which a single gene is chosen and "knocked out" (inactivated) in a mouse. The roles of the inactivated gene can be determined by observing the phenotype of the mice bearing the knockout gene. For example, if the gene codes for a protein, the functions of that protein can be identified by studying individuals in which it is lacking. Because at least 99% of the loci of mice have human counterparts (although the specific alleles are usually different), information about *knockout genes* in mice provides details about human genes as well.

Gene targeting, pioneered by Mario Capecchi, a molecular geneticist at the University of Utah School of Medicine, is a rather complex and lengthy procedure; it takes about a year to develop a new strain of knockout mice. First, a nonfunctional (knockout) gene is introduced into mouse embryonic stem cells (ES cells). ES cells are particularly easy to handle because, like cancer cells, they can be grown in culture indefinitely. Most important, if they are placed into a mouse embryo, they are capable of dividing and producing all of the cell types normally found in the mouse. In a tiny fraction of these ES cells, the introduced gene will become physically associated with the corresponding gene in a chromosome. If this occurs, the chromosomal gene and the introduced gene will tend to exchange DNA segments in a poorly understood process known as *homologous recombination*. In this way, the normal allele in the mouse chromosome is replaced by the knockout allele.

Researchers inject ES cells they hope are carrying a knockout gene into early mouse embryos and allow the mice to develop to maturity. The mice are then bred for several generations, allowing researchers to eventually select any offspring that might be homozygous for the knockout gene.

If the gene is not lethal when inactivated, the researchers generally study homozygous animals that carry the knockout gene in every cell. However, because many genes are essential to life, researchers have modified the knockout technique to develop strains in which a specific gene is selectively inactivated in only one cell type. Today hundreds of different strains of knockout mice, each displaying its own characteristic phenotype, have been developed in various research laboratories, and the number continues to grow.

Gene targeting in mice is providing answers to basic biological questions relating to the development of embryos, the development of the nervous system, and the normal functioning of the immune system. This technique has great potential for revealing more about various human diseases, especially as we have learned that many thousands of diseases have a genetic component. Gene targeting is being used to study cancer, heart disease, respiratory diseases such as cystic fibrosis, sickle cell anemia, and other health problems.

Transgenic animals can produce genetically engineered proteins

Certain transgenic animal strains produce foreign proteins that are secreted into milk. For example, the gene for a human blood clotting factor has been introduced into sheep. These recombinant genes have been fused to the regulatory sequences of the milk protein genes and are therefore activated only in mammary tissues involved in milk production.

The advantage of obtaining the protein from milk is that potentially it can be produced in large quantities and can be harvested simply by milking the animal. The protein is then purified from the milk. The animals are not harmed by the introduction of the gene, and, because usually the progeny of the transgenic animal also produce the recombinant protein, transgenic strains can be established.

Transgenic animals are not only produced by microinjecting DNA into cells. Sometimes viruses are used as recombinant DNA vectors. RNA viruses called **retroviruses** make DNA copies of themselves by reverse transcription (see Chapter 12). Sometimes the DNA copies become integrated into the host chromosomes, where they are replicated along with host DNA. For example, genetically altered mouse leukemia viruses are retroviruses that can be used as vectors to incorporate recombinant genes into cultured cells. Under certain conditions genes carried by the engineered virus can be expressed in the animal cells to produce genetically engineered proteins.

A major disadvantage of introducing genes into cultured animal cells is that the yields of the proteins encoded by the foreign DNA carried by the viruses are generally low. However, these types of vectors show some promise as treatments for human genetic disorders. Procedures to treat human disorders by genetically modifying the cells of the patient are known as **gene transfer therapy** or, more simply, **gene therapy** (see Chapter 15).

Transgenic plants are increasingly important in agriculture

Plants have been selectively bred for thousands of years. The success of such efforts depends on the presence of desirable traits in the variety of plant being selected, or in closely related wild or domesticated plants whose traits can be transferred by crossbreeding. Local varieties or closely related species of cultivated plants often have traits, such as disease resistance, that could be advantageously introduced into varieties more suited to modern needs. If genes are introduced into plants from strains or species with which they do not ordinarily interbreed, the possibilities for improvement are greatly increased.

Unfortunately, a suitable vector for the introduction of recombinant genes into many types of plant cells has proved quite difficult to find. The most widely used vector system employs the crown gall bacterium, *Agrobacterium tumefaciens*. This bacterium normally produces plant tumors by introducing a special plasmid, called the *Ti* (for *tumor-inducing*) *plasmid,* into the cells of its host. The Ti plasmid induces abnormal growth by forcing the plant cells to produce elevated levels of a plant growth hormone called cytokinin (see Chapter 36).

It is possible to "disarm" the Ti plasmid so that it does not induce tumor formation and then to use it as a vector to insert genes into plant cells (Fig. 14–12). The cells into which the altered plasmid is introduced are essentially normal except for the genes that have been inserted. Genes placed in the plant genome in this fashion may be transmitted sexually, via seeds, to the next generation, but they can also be propagated asexually (e.g., by taking cuttings) if desired.

Unfortunately, not all plants take up DNA readily, and this is particularly true of the grain plants that are the major food source for humans. One useful approach has been the development of a genetic "shotgun." Microscopic gold fragments are coated with DNA and then shot into plant cells, penetrating the cell walls. Some of the cells retain the DNA and are transformed by it. Those cells can then be cultured and used to regenerate an entire plant (see Chapter 16). For example, such an approach has been successfully used to transfer a gene for resistance to a bacterial disease into cultivated rice from one of its wild relatives.

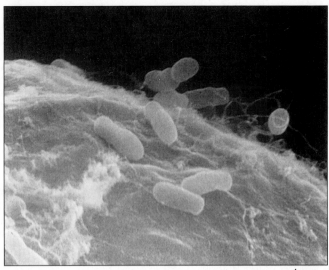

Figure 14–12 Transformation of plant cells. This SEM shows *Agrobacterium tumefaciens* infecting cultured plant cells. The close contact permits the transfer of plasmid DNA from the bacteria to the larger plant cells. *(Courtesy of Ann G. Matthysse)*

An additional complication of plant genetic engineering is that many important plant genes are located in the DNA of the chloroplasts (see Chapter 4). Chloroplasts are essential in photosynthesis, which is the basis for plant productivity. Obviously, it is useful to develop methods for changing the portion of the plant's DNA that resides within the chloroplast. Methods of chloroplast engineering are currently the focus of intense research.

The applications of transgenic plants are not limited to disease resistance and increased production of crops. Like some transgenic animals, certain transgenic plants can potentially be used to produce large quantities of medically important proteins, such as antibodies. The developers of this technology are conducting ongoing field trials to demonstrate the feasibility of these production methods.

Some people are concerned about the health effects of consuming foods derived from genetically modified plants, commonly known as GM foods (see Chapter 1). For this reason there is an ongoing controversy as to whether the use of such foods should be restricted or if they should be required to include special warning labels.

SAFETY GUIDELINES HAVE BEEN DEVELOPED FOR RECOMBINANT DNA TECHNOLOGY

When recombinant DNA technology was introduced in the early 1970s, many scientists considered the potential misuses to be at least as significant as the possible benefits. The possibility that an organism with undesirable environmental effects might be accidentally produced was a great concern, because it was anticipated that totally new strains of bacteria or other organisms, with which the world has no previous experience, might be difficult to control. This possibility was recognized by the scientists who developed the recombinant DNA methods and led them to insist on stringent guidelines for making the new technology safe.

Experiments in thousands of university and industrial laboratories over more than 25 years have seen recombinant DNA manipulations carried out safely. Laboratory strains of *E. coli* are poor competition for the wild strains in the outside world and quickly perish. Experiments thought to entail unusual risks are carried out in special facilities designed to contain disease-causing organisms and allow researchers to work with them safely. So far there is no evidence that hazardous genes have been accidentally cloned or that dangerous organisms have been released into the environment. However, malicious *intentional* manipulations of dangerous genes certainly remain a possibility.

Many of the restrictive guidelines for using recombinant DNA have been relaxed as the safety of the experiments has been established. Stringent restrictions still exist, however, in certain areas of recombinant DNA research where there are known dangers, or where questions about possible effects on the environment are still unanswered.

These restrictions are most evident in research that proposes to introduce recombinant organisms into the wild, such as agricultural strains of plants whose seeds or pollen might spread in an uncontrolled manner. A great deal of research activity is now concentrated on determining the effects of introducing transgenic organisms into a natural environment. Carefully conducted tests have shown that transgenic organisms are not dangerous to the environment simply because they are transgenic. However, it is important to assess the biology of each new recombinant organism. In this way scientists will be able to determine if it has characteristics that might cause it to present an environmental hazard under certain conditions. For example, if a transgenic crop plant has been engineered to resist an herbicide, might that gene be transferred, via pollen or by some other route, to that plant's weedy relatives, generating herbicide-resistant "superweeds?"

Other concerns relate to plants that have been engineered to produce pesticides, such as insecticides. For example, a transgenic plant may produce a relatively small amount of an insecticide, which may be sufficient to provide protection if the targeted insect population is not very numerous. However, the presence of low levels of the insecticide could potentially provide ideal conditions for selection for resistant individuals in the insect population. Another concern is that non-pest species could be harmed. For example, a great deal of attention has been paid to the finding that monarch butterfly larvae raised in the laboratory are harmed if they are fed pollen from corn plants genetically engineered to produce Bt toxin, a natural insecticide. Although more recent studies have suggested that monarch larvae living in a natural environment do not consume enough pollen to cause damage, such concerns persist and will have to be addressed on a case-by-case basis.

SUMMARY WITH KEY TERMS

I. **Recombinant DNA** technology is concerned with isolating and amplifying specific sequences of DNA by incorporating them into **vector** DNA molecules. The resulting recombinant DNA can then be propagated and amplified in organisms such as *E. coli.*

   A. **Restriction enzymes** are used to cut DNA into specific fragments.

      1. Each type of restriction enzyme recognizes and cuts DNA at a highly specific base sequence.

      2. Many restriction enzymes cleave DNA sequences to produce complementary, single-stranded cut ends (sticky ends).

   B. The most common recombinant DNA vectors are constructed from naturally occurring circular DNA molecules called **plasmids,** or from bacterial viruses called **bacteriophages;** both of these are found in some bacteria.

   C. Recombinant DNA molecules are often constructed by allowing the ends of a DNA fragment and a plasmid (which have both been cut with the same restriction enzyme) to associate by complementary base pairing. The DNA strands are then covalently linked by **DNA ligase** to form a stable recombinant molecule.

   D. Parts of genes are isolated from recombinant DNA libraries, which are mixtures of DNA fragments inserted into appropriate vectors.

      1. **Genomic libraries** are DNA fragments from the total DNA of an organism. Genes present in recombinant DNA genomic libraries from eukaryotes contain introns. Those genes can be amplified in *E. coli,* but the protein is not properly expressed.

      2. When a **cDNA library** is produced, **reverse transcriptase** is used to make DNA copies of mRNA isolated from eukaryotic cells; these copies, known as **complementary DNA (cDNA),** are then incorporated into recombinant DNA vectors. Because the introns have been removed from mRNA molecules, eukaryotic genes in cDNA libraries can sometimes be expressed in *E. coli* to make their protein products.

   E. The **polymerase chain reaction (PCR)** is a widely used, usually automated, **in vitro** technique in which a particular DNA sequence can be targeted by specific primers and then **cloned** by a special heat-resistant DNA polymerase.

   F. Analysis of a cloned sequence can yield useful information about the gene and its encoded protein and can enable investigators to identify and subclone DNA fragments for use as molecular probes.

      1. A **DNA sequence** gives information about the structure of the gene and the probable amino acid sequence of the encoded proteins. It can be compared with other sequences stored in massive databases.

      2. A radioactive DNA or RNA sequence can be used as a **genetic probe** to identify complementary nucleic acid sequences. In the **Southern blot technique,** DNA fragments are separated by gel electrophoresis, denatured, and then blotted onto a nitrocellulose filter. The radioactive probe is then hybridized by complementary base pairing to the DNA bound to the filter, and the radioactive band or bands of DNA can be identified by autoradiography.

   G. The degree of genetic relationship among the individuals in a population can be determined by comparing nucleotide sequences, or it can be estimated in other ways, including the study of **restriction fragment length polymorphisms (RFLPs).**

II. **Genetic engineering** is a technology that uses genetic and recombinant DNA methods to devise new combinations of genes to produce improved pharmaceutical and agricultural products.

   A. Genes isolated from one organism can be modified and expressed in other organisms ranging from *E. coli* to **transgenic** plants and animals.

      1. Expression of eukaryotic proteins in bacteria such as *E. coli* requires that the gene be linked to regulatory elements that the bacterium can recognize. In addition, bacterial cells do not contain many of the enzymes needed for the posttranslational processing of eukaryotic proteins.

      2. Expression of eukaryotic genes in eukaryotic host organisms shows great promise, because the processing and modification machinery for eukaryotic proteins is already present in these cells.

         a. Production of important pharmaceutical products can be engineered in transgenic animals and possibly in plants.

         b. Genetic engineering of plants and domestic animals holds the promise of increasing the availability of food, although some consumers are concerned about the safety of such foods.

   B. Recombinant DNA technology is carried out under certain safety guidelines.

POST-TEST

1. A plasmid (a) can be used as a DNA vector (b) is a type of bacteriophage (c) is a type of cDNA (d) is a retrovirus (e) b and c

2. DNA molecules with complementary "sticky ends" associate by (a) covalent bonds (b) hydrogen bonds (c) ionic bonds (d) disulfide bonds (e) phosphodiester linkages

3. Human DNA and a particular plasmid both have sites that can be cut by the restriction enzymes Hind III and EcoRI. To make recombinant DNA, one should (a) cut the plasmid with EcoRI and the human DNA with Hind III (b) use EcoRI to cut both the plasmid and the human DNA (c) use Hind III to cut both the plasmid and the human DNA (d) a or b (e) b or c

4. Which of the following sequences is *not* palindromic?

   (a) 5'—AAGCTT—3'   (b) 5'—GATC—3'
       3'—TTCGAA—5'   3'—CTAG—5'

   (c) 5'—GAATTC—3'   (d) 5'—CTAA—3'
       3'—CTTAAG—5'   3'—GATT—5'

   (e) b and d

5. The PCR technique uses (a) heat-resistant DNA polymerase (b) reverse transcriptase (c) DNA ligase (d) restriction enzymes (e) b and c

6. A cDNA clone contains (a) introns (b) exons (c) anticodons (d) a and b (e) b and c

7. The dideoxynucleotides ddATP, ddTTP, ddGTP, and ddCTP are important in DNA sequencing because they (a) cause premature termination of a growing DNA strand (b) are used as primers (c) cause the DNA fragments that contain them to migrate more slowly through a sequencing gel (d) are not affected by high temperatures (e) have more energy than deoxynucleotides

8. In restriction fragment length polymorphism (RFLP) analysis to determine parentage, (a) every band present in a child would be expected to be present in both of the true parents (b) every band present in a child would be expected to be present in at least one of the true parents (c) every band present in a true parent would be expected to be present in all of the children (d) a and b (e) b and c

9. In the Southern blot technique, _____ is/are transferred from a gel to a special nitrocellulose filter. (a) protein (b) RNA (c) DNA (d) bacterial colonies (e) reverse transcriptase

10. Gel electrophoresis separates nucleic acids on the basis of differences in (a) length (molecular weight) (b) charge (c) nucleotide sequence (d) relative proportions of adenine and guanine (e) relative proportions of thymine and cytosine

11. The Ti plasmid, carried by *Agrobacterium tumefaciens,* is especially useful for introducing genes into (a) *E. coli* (b) plants (c) animals (d) yeast (e) all eukaryotes

REVIEW QUESTIONS

1. What is meant by the term *genetic engineering?*
2. What are restriction enzymes? How are they used in recombinant DNA research?
3. What characteristics should be engineered into a plasmid to make it a useful cloning vector?
4. Diagram the process by which recombinant DNA molecules are usually constructed.
5. How is a gene library constructed? What are the relative merits of genomic libraries and cDNA libraries?
6. Sketch an example illustrating how a restriction map of a gene is made.
7. Why is the PCR technique valuable?

YOU MAKE THE CONNECTION

1. What are some of the problems that might arise if you were trying to produce a eukaryotic protein in a bacterium? How might some of these problems be solved by using transgenic plants or animals?
2. Would genetic engineering be possible if we did not know a great deal about the genetics of bacteria? Explain.
3. What are some of the ecological concerns regarding transgenic organisms? What kinds of information are needed to determine if these concerns are valid?

RECOMMENDED READINGS

Brown, K. "Seeds of Concern." *Scientific American,* Vol. 284, No. 4, Apr. 2001. An explanation of the potential environmental risks and benefits of genetically modified crops.

Butler, D., T. Reichardt, et al. "Long-term Effect of GM Crops Serves Up Food for Thought." *Nature,* Vol. 398, 22 Apr. 1999. A thoughtful, balanced consideration of the use of genetically modified crops.

Hopkin, K. "Risks on the Table." *Scientific American,* Vol. 284, No. 4, Apr. 2001. A discussion of the safety of the genetically modified foods contained in about 60% of the processed foods sold in the United States, as well as those that might be produced in the future.

Langridge, W.H. "Edible Vaccines." *Scientific American,* Vol 282, No. 3, Sep. 2000. The feasibility of producing oral vaccines in plants is being actively studied. Such vaccines hold the promise of providing easily administered immunizations to the world population.

Marvier, M. "Ecology of Transgenic Crops." *American Scientist,* Vol. 89. Mar.–Apr. 2001. A consideration of the difficulties in assessing the significance of potential environmental risks posed by transgenic plants.

Miller, R.V. "Bacterial Gene Swapping in Nature." *Scientific American,* Vol. 278, No. 1, Jan. 1998. This article assesses the potential mechanisms and extent of transfer of genes to other microbes by genetically engineered bacteria released into natural environments.

Mullis, K.B. "The Unusual Origin of the Polymerase Chain Reaction." *Scientific American,* Vol. 262, No. 4, Apr. 1990. A highly personal, first-hand account of the development of the PCR technique and an excellent illustration of the nature of scientific insight.

Nemeck, S. "Does the World Need GM Foods?" *Scientific American,* Vol. 284, No. 4, Apr. 2001. The author interviews both an advocate for the development of GM foods, and an opponent.

Ronald, P.C. "Making Rice Disease-Resistant." *Scientific American,* Vol. 277, No. 5, Nov. 1997. The applications of genetic engineering to rice breeding are expected to increase the food supply for the 2 billion people worldwide for whom rice is the mainstay of the diet.

Somerville, C., and J. Dangl. "Plant Biology in 2010." *Science,* Vol. 290, 15 Dec. 2000. The completion of the sequencing of the genome of the model plant *Arabidopsis* will enable researchers to attain far-reaching goals.

Weiner, D.B., and R.C. Kennedy. "Genetic Vaccines." *Scientific American,* Vol. 281, No. 1, Jul. 1999. Genetic engineering techniques can be used to produce vaccines that are composed of DNA.

Wolfenbarger, L.L., and P.R. Phifer. "The Ecological Risks and Benefits of Genetically Engineered Plants." *Science,* Vol. 290, 15 Dec. 2000. The authors argue that the ecological effects of genetically modified plants are inherently difficult to assess because of the complexity of ecological systems.

- Visit our Web site at **http://www.info.brookscole.com/solomonbergmartin** for links to chapter-related resources on the World Wide Web. Additional on-line materials relating to this chapter can also be found on our Web site.

See chapter activity on BioActive Learner CD for additional help in mastering the chapter's material. Icon location in the chapter's margins shows which topics have tutorials or simulations in the CD.

15

The Human Genome

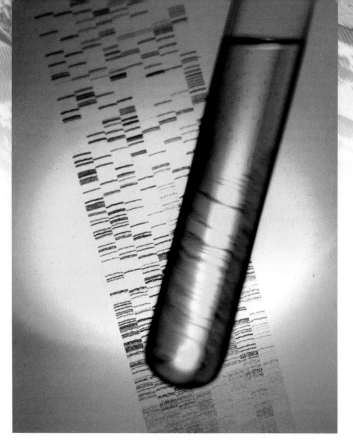

DNA autoradiogram. The autoradiogram shows the sequence of base pairs for a section of human DNA. *(TEK Image/Science Photo Library/Photo Researchers, Inc.)*

LEARNING OBJECTIVES

After you have studied this chapter you should be able to

1. Define human genetics, the human genome, bioinformatics, and pharmacogenomics.
2. Given a simple pedigree for a particular trait, determine the probable genotypes for all individuals in the pedigree.
3. Discuss the implications of the Human Genome Project, including the benefits and difficult ethical concerns.
4. Distinguish between chromosome abnormalities and single-gene defects.
5. Make a sketch illustrating how nondisjunction can occur in meiosis. Show how nondisjunction can be responsible for specific chromosome abnormalities such as Down syndrome, Klinefelter syndrome, and Turner syndrome.
6. State whether each of the following genetic defects is inherited as an autosomal recessive, autosomal dominant, or X-linked recessive: phenylketonuria (PKU), sickle cell anemia, cystic fibrosis, Tay-Sachs disease, Huntington disease, and hemophilia A.
7. Describe how amniocentesis is used in the prenatal diagnosis of human genetic abnormalities; state the relative advantages and disadvantages of amniocentesis and chorionic villus sampling.
8. Distinguish between genetic screening programs for newborns and adults.
9. Discuss the scope and implications of genetic counseling.

The principles of genetics apply to all organisms, including humans. There are, however, some important differences between genetic research on humans and genetic research on other organisms. To study aspects of inheritance in other species, geneticists ideally (1) have standard stocks of genetically identical individuals, that is, **isogenic strains**, that are homozygous at virtually all of their loci; (2) conduct **controlled matings** between members of different isogenic strains; and (3) raise the offspring under carefully controlled conditions.

Of course, experimental matings under controlled conditions are not feasible in the human population. In addition, human families are small, and 20 to 30 years or more elapse between generations. It is therefore virtually impossible to conduct genetic research in humans in the same way we do with other species.

Despite the inherent difficulties of studying inheritance in humans, knowledge in **human genetics**, the science of inherited variation in humans, is progressing very rapidly. Traditionally, human genetics was examined using such approaches as population studies of large extended families. More recently, the field of human genetics has been greatly facilitated by the medical attention given to genetic diseases in humans. The extensive medical records of diseases serve as a very useful data pool on which hypotheses may be based and against which they may be tested. Genetic studies of other organisms also have provided invaluable insights. Indeed, many phenomena in human inheritance that were initially puzzling have been explained by solving analogous problems in the inheritance of bacteria, yeasts, worms, fruit flies, or mice.

The **human genome**, the totality of genetic information in human cells, has been mapped and **sequenced** (the order of nucleotides in DNA has been identified) to determine how we are all alike—that is, what makes us human *(see figure)*. The human genome includes the DNA content of both the nucleus (which accounts for almost all genetic information in the human genome) and the mitochondria. Like genomes of other eukaryotic organisms, some of the human genome specifies the synthesis of polypeptides or RNA. However, much of the human genome consists of noncoding DNA, repetitive (multiple copies of) DNA, and gene segments for which there are currently no known functions. Relating specific genes to the proteins they code for and determining what these proteins do in the body are some of the avenues of human genetic research that will be pursued during the 21st century.

Recent advances in human genetics have enormous implications for the future. Already, the new knowledge has created several scientific fields, such as bioinformatics and pharmacogenomics. **Bioinformatics,** also called **biological computing,** includes the storage, retrieval, and comparison of DNA sequences within human DNA and between genomes of different species. The tools of bioinformatics are powerful computers and sophisticated software used to manage and analyze the data. For example, as new DNA sequences are determined, automated computer programs scan the sequences for patterns typically found in genes. Bioinformatics has already provided important insights into gene identification, gene function, and evolutionary relationships (by comparing databases of DNA sequences from different organisms).

Knowledge of the human genome promises a revolution in human health care, and some experts predict that in highly developed countries the average human life expectancy at birth will be 90 to 95 years by 2050. (As a comparison, the current average life expectancy in the United States is 77 years.) New health-related information about the human genome, from identifying genes associated with hypertension to identifying genes associated with specific cancers, is announced nearly every week.

Pharmacogenomics is a new field of gene-based medicine in which drugs are personalized to match a patient's genetic makeup. The subtle genetic differences among individuals are taken into account in pharmacogenomics. In as few as five to ten years, patients may take routine genetic screening tests before a doctor prescribes medicine for them. Many of these diagnostic tests will involve **DNA microarrays,** in which thousands of DNA molecules are placed on a glass slide or chip (see Fig. 16–5). DNA microarrays allow researchers to compare the activities of thousands of genes in normal and diseased cells. Since cancer and other diseases exhibit altered patterns of gene expression, the use of DNA microarrays has the potential to identify genes or the proteins they code for that can then be targeted by therapeutic drugs. Pharmacogenomics, like other fields in human genetics, poses difficult ethical questions. The genetic testing that will be an everyday part of pharmacogenomics raises issues of privacy, genetic bias, and potential discrimination.

In this chapter, we first examine how the human genome is studied, including the Human Genome Project. Then we discuss a variety of human genetic disorders and examine genetic testing, screening, and counseling, and how genetic diseases are treated. The chapter concludes with a consideration of ethical concerns that relate to our expanding knowledge of the human genome.

■ THE STUDY OF HUMAN GENETICS REQUIRES A VARIETY OF METHODS

Human geneticists use a variety of methods that allow them to make inferences about a trait's mode of inheritance. We consider three of these methods—the identification of chromosomes by karyotyping, the summary of family inheritance studies by pedigree construction, and DNA sequencing and mapping of genes by genome projects. Human inheritance is often studied most effectively by using a combination of these and other approaches.

Human chromosomes are studied by karyotyping

Cytogenetics is the study of chromosomes and their role in inheritance. Many of the basic principles of genetics were discovered by researchers working with simpler organisms, in which it was possible to relate genetic data to the number and structure of specific chromosomes. Some of the organisms used in genetics, such as the fruit fly *Drosophila,* have very few chromosomes (only four pairs in *Drosophila*). In *Drosophila* larval salivary glands and most other larval tissues, the chromosomes are large enough that their structural details are readily evident. This organism, therefore, has provided unique opportunities for correlating certain phenotypic changes with certain alterations in chromosome structure.

Process of Science Recall from Chapter 10 that the normal number of chromosomes for the human species is 46:44 **autosomes** (22 pairs) and 2 sex chromosomes (one pair). Until the mid-1950s, when modern methods of karyotyping began to be adopted, the accepted number of chromosomes for the human species was 48, based on a study of human chromosomes published in 1923. The reason researchers counted 48 human chromosomes was the difficulty in separating the chromosomes so they could be accurately counted. In 1951 T.C. Hsu treated cells with a hypotonic salt solution by mistake, which caused the chromosomes to spread apart beautifully. Other less serendipitous techniques were also developed, and in 1956, researchers Jo Hin Tjio and Albert Levan reported that humans have 46 chromosomes, not 48. Other researchers subsequently verified this report. The story of the human chromosome number is a valuable example of the self-correcting nature of science (although science sometimes takes a while to correct itself). The reevaluation of established facts and ideas, often by using improved techniques or new methods, is an essential part of the scientific process.

Human chromosomes are only visible in dividing cells (see Chapter 9), and it is difficult to obtain dividing cells directly from the human body. Blood is typically used because the white blood cells can be induced to divide in a culture medium by treating them with **lectins,** sugar-binding proteins extracted from plant seeds. Other sources of dividing cells include skin and, for prenatal chromosome studies, chorionic villi or fetal cells shed into the amniotic fluid (both discussed later in the chapter).

The term **karyotype** (from the Greek *kary,* meaning nucleus) refers both to the chromosome composition of an individual and to a photomicrograph showing that composition. In karyotyping, dividing human cells are cultured and then treated with the drug **colchicine,** which arrests the cells at mitotic metaphase or late prophase, when the chromosomes are most highly condensed. Next the cells are placed into a hypotonic solution that causes them to swell; this process spreads out the chromosomes so they can be readily observed. The cells are then flattened on microscope slides, and the chromosomes are stained to reveal the patterns of bands that are unique for each homologous pair. After the microscopic image has been scanned into a computer, the homologous pairs are electronically matched and placed together (Fig. 15–1*a;* also see Fig. 9–7 for a normal human karyotype).

Chromosomes are identified by length; position of the centromere; banding patterns, which are produced by staining chromosomes with dyes that produce dark and light cross-bands of varying widths; and other features such as *satellites,* which are tiny knobs of chromosome material at the tips of certain chromosomes (Fig. 15–1*b*). The largest human chromosome (chromosome 1) is about five times as long as the smallest one (chromosome 21), but there are only slight size differences among some of the intermediate-sized chromosomes. Differences from the normal karyotype—that is, deviations in chromosome number or structure—are associated with certain disorders.

Family pedigrees can help identify some inherited conditions

Early studies of human genetics usually dealt with readily identified pairs of contrasting traits and their distribution among members of a family. A chart that is constructed to show the transmission of genetic traits within a family over several generations is known as a **pedigree.** Pedigree analysis remains a useful technique, even in today's world of powerful molecular genetic techniques, because it helps molecular geneticists determine the exact interrelationships among the DNA molecules they analyze from related individuals. Pedigree analysis is also an important tool of genetic counselors and clinicians. However, because human families tend to be small and information on certain family members, particularly deceased relatives, may be lacking, pedigree analysis has certain limitations.

Pedigrees are produced using more or less standardized symbols. Examine Figure 15–2, which shows a hypothetical pedigree for **albinism,** a lack of pigmentation in the skin, hair, and eyes. Each horizontal row represents a separate generation, with the oldest generation (Roman numeral I) at the top and the most recent generation at the bottom. Within a given generation, the individuals are usually numbered consecutively, from left to right, using Arabic numerals. A horizontal line connects two parents, and a vertical line drops from the parents to their children.

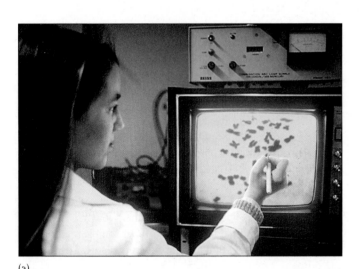

(a)

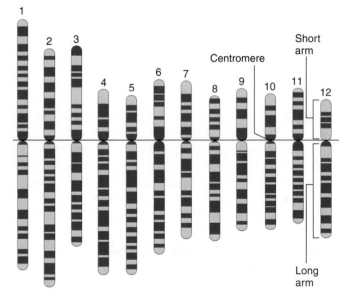

(b)

■ **Figure 15–1 Karyotyping.** **(a)** Using an image analysis computer to prepare a karyotype. The biologist is matching up homologous chromosomes and organizing them by size. Before computer use was widespread, researchers laboriously prepared karyotypes by cutting and pasting chromosomes from photographs. **(b)** Diagram of a human karyotype. The chromosomes are numbered in order of size, except that chromosome 21 is smaller than chromosome 22. Centromeres, satellites, and a compilation of banding patterns are shown. (a, *SIU Peter Arnold, Inc.;* b, *Adapted from Tobin, A.J., and R.E. Morel. Asking About Cells.* Harcourt College Publishers, *Philadelphia, 1997*)

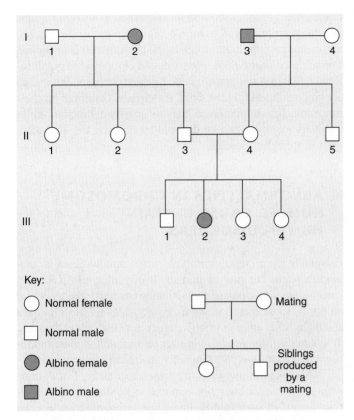

Key:

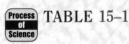

○ Normal female

□ Normal male

● Albino female

■ Albino male

□—○ Mating

Siblings produced by a mating

Figure 15–2 Pedigree analysis of albinism. By studying family histories, it is often possible to determine the genetic mechanism of the trait being studied. Consider III-2, an albino girl with two phenotypically normal parents, II-3 and II-4. The allele for albinism cannot be dominant because if it were, at least one of III-2's parents would have to be an albino. Also, albinism cannot be an X-linked recessive allele because if it were, her father would have to be an albino (and her mother would have to be a heterozygous carrier). This pedigree is easily explained if albinism is inherited as an autosomal (not carried on a sex chromosome) recessive allele. With an autosomal recessive allele, two phenotypically normal parents could produce an albino offspring (because they are heterozygotes and could each transmit a recessive allele).

For example, individuals II-3 and II-4 are parents of four offspring (III-1, III-2, III-3, and III-4). Note that it is possible for individuals in a given generation to be genetically unrelated. For example, II-1, II-2, and II-3 are unrelated to II-4 and II-5. Within a group of siblings, the oldest is on the left, and the youngest is on the right.

Studying pedigrees has enabled human geneticists to predict how phenotypic traits that are governed by the genotype at a single locus are inherited. Such traits are said to be *Mendelian*. About 10,000 Mendelian traits have been described in humans (see McKusick's on-line catalog, listed in the *Recommended Readings*). Pedigree analysis most often identifies three types of single-gene inheritance—autosomal dominant, autosomal recessive, and X-linked recessive; we define and discuss examples of these traits later in this chapter.

Traits that do not show a simple Mendelian inheritance pattern cannot be characterized as well using pedigree analysis. Such traits may be the result of interactions among genes at two,

three, or more loci. In other cases, **imprinting**—the expression of a gene based on its parental origin—occurs. In some genes the paternally inherited allele is always repressed (not expressed), whereas in other genes the maternally inherited allele is always repressed. Environmental factors may also play a major role in non-Mendelian inheritance patterns. Common birth defects, such as cleft palate and congenital heart disease, are examples of traits that do not show a simple Mendelian inheritance pattern.

The Human Genome Project is mapping the genes on all human chromosomes

In 1999 a significant milestone was reached: Human chromosome 22 was the first human chromosome to have virtually all of its DNA sequence determined (Table 15–1). One of the smallest chromosomes, human chromosome 22 contains at least 545 genes encoded in its more than 33 million bases of adenine, guanine, cytosine, and thymine.

Sequencing human chromosome 22 is part of the **Human Genome Project,** which is mapping and sequencing all of the DNA in the nuclear human genome—about 2.9 billion base pairs (Fig. 15–3). (The human mitochondrial genome was sequenced in 1981.) This international undertaking, which is based on the DNA from six to ten anonymous individuals, was essentially completed and published in 2001 by two independent teams, the International Human Genome Sequencing Consortium and Celera Genomics. The project includes not only sequencing the entire human genome but also eventually identifying where all of the perhaps 35,000 to 45,000 genes[1] are located in the sequenced DNA.

[1] Biologists do not yet know how many genes are in the human genome. Estimates range from 30,000 to more than 150,000, but as more data have accumulated from the Human Genome Project, many researchers have revised their estimates downward. Our estimate of 35,000 to 45,000 is from *Science,* Vol. 291, 16 Feb. 2001. A more accurate estimate should be available in the next few years.

Process of Science

TABLE 15–1   Some Important Milestones in Genetics

Year	Scientific Advance
1866	Mendel proposed the existence of hereditary factors now known as genes
1871	Nucleic acids discovered
1953	Structure of DNA determined
1960s	Genetic code explained (how proteins are made from DNA)
1977	DNA sequencing began
1986	DNA sequencing automated
1999	Sequencing of first human chromosome completed
2001	Draft sequence of entire human genome published

Figure 15–3 Display of DNA sequencing on a computer monitor attached to a DNA sequencing machine. The machine determines the base sequence of a strand of DNA and tags each of the four bases a different color. *(Bob Boston, Washington University School of Medicine)*

Gene identification represents a formidable challenge. How do you identify a gene if you know nothing about it? Only a fraction of human DNA is known to code for protein or RNA. The rest (95% or more) is either noncoding or has some function that has not yet been identified (see Chapter 12). In human chromosome 22, for example, the 545 genes that have been identified so far were determined because they code for proteins similar to those previously identified in humans or other organisms. There may be several hundred genes on human chromosome 22 that have yet to be identified. Despite the difficulties, progress is being made, and mapping studies will allow us to understand the physical and functional relationships among genes and groups of genes as revealed by their order on the chromosomes.

Now that the sequencing portion of the Human Genome Project is virtually completed, biologists will be busy for many decades analyzing the molecular data that characterize a human being. In addition to identifying genes, biologists want to study what each gene does, how it interacts with other genes, and how its expression is regulated in different tissues. All of the thousands of proteins produced in human cells will be identified, their three-dimensional structures determined, and their properties and functions evaluated.

Biologists also want to study the sequence variation within the human genome, including differences that might be related to illness or disease. The potential medical applications of the Human Genome Project are extremely promising. Mutations in genes on human chromosome 22, for example, are linked to at least 27 diseases known to have a genetic component. The causative genes of many of these disorders are not yet identified. For example, a gene involved in schizophrenia is strongly linked to human chromosome 22, but its location has not yet been discovered.

Sequencing and mapping studies are being carried out simultaneously on the mouse and rat genomes, to aid in analyzing the human genome. Sequencing the genomes of other model vertebrate organisms (the chicken, pig, pufferfish, and zebrafish) and one or more primates (such as the chimpanzee) is underway. Comparisons of the DNA sequences and chromosome organization of related genes and clusters of genes from different species are powerful tools for identifying the elements essential for their functions. If a human gene has an unknown function, clues about its role can often be deduced by studying the equivalent gene in a different species.

■ ABNORMALITIES IN CHROMOSOME NUMBER CAUSE CERTAIN HUMAN DISORDERS

Polyploidy, the presence of multiple sets of chromosomes, is common in plants but rare in animals. It may arise from failure of chromosomes to separate during meiosis or from fertilization of an egg by more than one sperm. Polyploidy is lethal in humans and many other animals when it occurs in all the cells of the body. Triploidy (3*n*), for example, is sometimes found in human embryos that have been spontaneously aborted in early pregnancy.

Abnormalities involving the presence or absence of a single extra chromosome are more common in humans. These conditions are called **aneuploidies.** Recall that ordinarily there are two of each kind of chromosome **(disomy).** An individual with an extra chromosome, that is, with three of one kind, is said to be **trisomic** for that kind of chromosome. An individual lacking one member of a pair of chromosomes is said to be **monosomic.** Table 15–2 summarizes some disorders produced by aneuploidies.

Aneuploidies generally arise as a result of an abnormal meiotic (or, rarely, mitotic) division in which chromosomes fail to separate at anaphase. This phenomenon, called **nondisjunction,** can occur with the autosomes or with the sex chromosomes. In meiosis, chromosome nondisjunction may occur during the first or second meiotic division (or both). For example, two X chromosomes that fail to separate at either the first or the second meiotic division might both enter the egg nucleus. Alternatively, the two joined X chromosomes might go into a polar body, leaving the egg with no X chromosome. (Recall from Chapter 9 that a polar body is a nonfunctional haploid cell produced during oogenesis; see Fig. 48–13.)

Nondisjunction of the XY pair during the first mitotic division in the male might lead to the formation of a sperm with both X and Y chromosomes or a sperm with neither an X nor a Y chromosome (Fig. 15–4). Similarly, nondisjunction at the second meiotic division can produce sperm with two Xs or two Ys. When an abnormal gamete unites with a normal one, the resulting zygote has a chromosome abnormality that will be present in every cell of the body.

Meiotic nondisjunction results in an abnormal chromosome number at the zygote stage of development, so that all cells in the individual have an abnormal chromosome number. In contrast, nondisjunction during a mitotic division occurs sometime later in development and leads to the establishment of a clone of abnormal cells in an otherwise normal individual. Such a mix-

TABLE 15–2 Chromosome Abnormalities: Some Disorders Produced by Aneuploidies

Karyotype	Common Name	Clinical Description
Trisomy 13	Patau syndrome	Multiple defects, with death typically by age 3 months.
Trisomy 18	Edwards syndrome	Ear deformities, heart defects, spasticity, and other damage; death typically by age 1 year, but some survive much longer.
Trisomy 21	Down syndrome	Overall frequency is about 1 in 800 live births. True trisomy is most often found among children of older (age 35+) mothers, but translocation resulting in the equivalent of trisomy is not age-related. Trisomy 21 is characterized by a fold of skin above the eye, varying degrees of mental retardation, short stature, protruding furrowed tongue, transverse palmar crease, cardiac deformities, and increased risk of leukemia and Alzheimer's disease.
XO	Turner syndrome	Short stature, webbed neck, sometimes slight mental retardation; ovaries degenerate in late embryonic life, leading to rudimentary sexual characteristics; gender is female; no Barr bodies.
XXY	Klinefelter syndrome	Male with slowly degenerating testes, enlarged breasts; one Barr body per cell.
XYY	XYY karotype	Unusually tall male with heavy acne, some tendency to mild mental retardation.
XXX	Triplo-X	Despite three X chromosomes, usually fertile females with normal intelligence; two Barr bodies per cell.

ture of cells with different chromosome numbers may or may not affect somatic (body) or germ-line (reproductive) tissues.

Individuals with Down syndrome are usually trisomic for chromosome 21

Down syndrome is one of the most common chromosome abnormalities in humans. (The term *syndrome* refers to a set of symptoms that usually occur together in a particular disorder.) It was named after John Down, the British physician who first described the condition in 1866. Affected individuals have abnormalities of the face, eyelids, tongue, hands, and other parts of the body and are often mentally and physically retarded (Fig. 15–5a). They are also unusually susceptible to certain diseases, such as leukemia and Alzheimer's disease.

Cytogenetic studies have revealed that most people with Down syndrome have 47 chromosomes because they are trisomic for chromosome 21, the smallest chromosome (Fig. 15–5b). Nondisjunction during meiosis is thought to be responsible for the presence of the extra chromosome. Although no genetic information is missing in these individuals, the extra copies of chromosome 21 genes bring about some type of genetic imbalance that is responsible for abnormal physical and mental development. Down syndrome is quite variable in expression, with some individuals far more severely affected than others. Researchers are using genetic engineering methods to attempt to pinpoint genes on chromosome 21 that affect mental development, as well as possible **oncogenes** (cancer-causing genes) and genes that may be involved in Alzheimer's disease.

Down syndrome occurs in all ethnic groups in about one out of 800 live births. Its incidence increases markedly with increasing maternal age (Fig. 15–6). (The occurrence of Down syn-

drome is not affected by the age of the father.) Down syndrome is 68 times more likely in the offspring of mothers who are 45 years of age than it is in the offspring of mothers who are 20 years of age. However, most babies with Down syndrome are born to mothers younger than 35 years of age, in part because these women greatly outnumber older mothers and in part because about 90% of older women who undergo prenatal testing decide to terminate the pregnancy if Down syndrome is diagnosed.

The relationship between increased incidence in Down syndrome and maternal age has been studied for decades, but an explanation for it is not known. Several hypotheses have been proposed to explain the maternal age effect, but none are supported unequivocally. For example, one hypothesis is that an aging womb is less likely to reject an abnormal fetus.

In general, chromosome aneuploidies involving the autosomes are devastating in their consequences. Other than Down syndrome, very few autosomal trisomies are known in live births (see Table 15–2), although many autosomal trisomies have been diagnosed in spontaneously aborted fetuses. The condition known as autosomal **monosomy,** in which only one member of a pair is present, does not occur in live births, perhaps because any deleterious allele inherited on the single chromosome will not be covered by a normal allele on a homologous chromosome.

Most sex chromosome aneuploidies are less severe than autosome aneuploidies

Sex chromosome aneuploidies appear to be relatively well tolerated (see Table 15–2), apparently at least in part because of the phenomenon of dosage compensation discussed in Chapter 10.

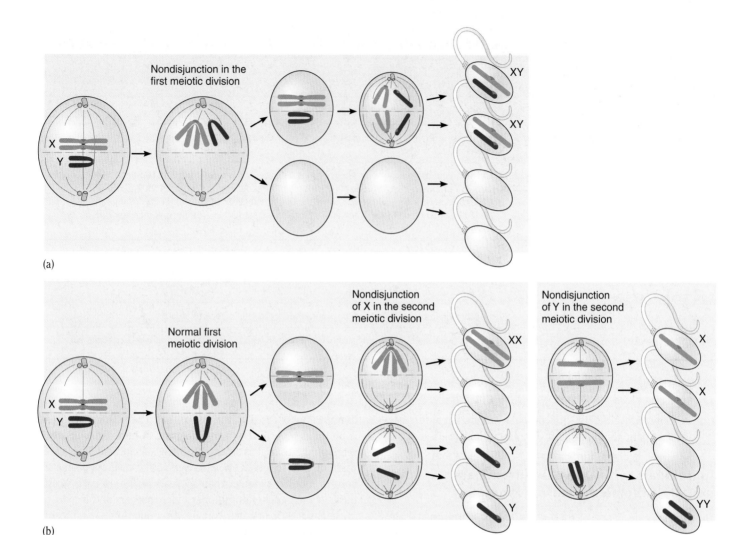

Figure 15–4 Meiotic nondisjunction. In these examples of nondisjunction of the sex chromosomes in the human male, only the X *(purple)* and Y *(blue)* chromosomes are shown. **(a)** Nondisjunction in the first meiotic division results in two XY sperm and two sperm with neither an X nor a Y. **(b)** Second-division nondisjunction of the X chromosome results in one sperm with two X chromosomes, two with one Y each, and one with no sex chromosomes. Nondisjunction of the Y results in one sperm with two Y chromosomes, two with one X each, and one with no sex chromosome.

According to the *single active X hypothesis,* mammals compensate for extra X chromosome material by rendering all but one X chromosome inactive. The inactive X is seen as a Barr body, a region of darkly staining, condensed chromatin next to the nuclear envelope of an interphase nucleus (see Fig. 10–16). The presence of the Barr body in the cells of normal females (but not of normal males) has been used as an initial screen to determine whether an individual is genetically female or male. As we will see in our discussion of sex chromosome aneuploidies, however, the Barr body test has serious limitations.

Individuals with **Klinefelter syndrome** have 47 chromosomes, including two Xs and one Y. They have small testes, produce few or no sperm and are therefore sterile. Evidence that the Y chromosome is the major determinant of the male phenotype has been substantiated by the fact that there is at least one gene on the Y chromosome that appears to act as a genetic switch, di-

recting male development. Males with Klinefelter syndrome tend to be unusually tall and to have female-like breasts. About half show some degree of mental retardation, but many live relatively normal lives. However, when their cells are examined they are found to have one Barr body per cell. On the basis of such a test, they would be erroneously classified as females. About 1 in 600 to 1000 live-born males has Klinefelter syndrome.

We designate the sex chromosome constitution for **Turner syndrome,** in which an individual has only one sex chromosome, an X chromosome, as XO. The O refers to the absence of a second sex chromosome. Because of the absence of the male-determining effect of the Y chromosome, these individuals develop as females. However, both their internal and external genital structures are underdeveloped, and they are sterile. Apparently a second X chromosome is necessary for the normal development of the ovaries in a female embryo. Examination of

(a)

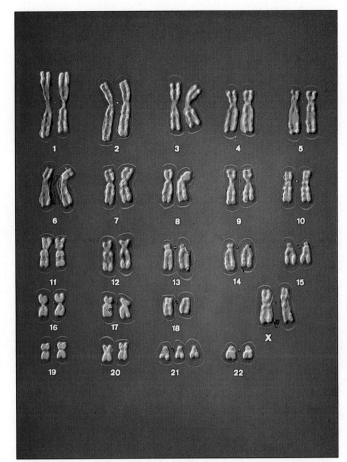

(b)

Figure 15–5 Down syndrome. **(a)** This male child with Down syndrome is working on a science experiment in his kindergarten class. Some individuals with Down syndrome learn to read and write. **(b)** Note the presence of an extra chromosome 21 in this color-enhanced karyotype of a female with Down syndrome. *(a, Richard Hutchings/Photo Researchers, Inc.; b, CNRI/Science Photo Library/Photo Researchers, Inc.)*

their cells reveals no Barr bodies because there is no extra X chromosome to be inactivated. Using the standards of the Barr body test, such an individual would be classified erroneously as a male. About 1 in 2500 live-born females has Turner syndrome.

People with an X chromosome plus two Y chromosomes are phenotypically males, and they are fertile. Other characteristics of these individuals (tall, with severe acne) hardly merit the term syndrome; hence the designation **XYY karyotype.** Some years ago there were several widely publicized studies that suggested that individuals with this condition are more likely to display criminal tendencies and to be imprisoned. However, these studies were flawed because they were based on small numbers of XYY men without adequate or well-matched control studies of XY males. The prevailing opinion in medical genetics today is that there are many undiagnosed XYY males in the general population who do not have overly aggressive or criminal behaviors and who are not incarcerated.

Aneuploidies usually result in prenatal death

Recognizable chromosome abnormalities are seen in less than one percent of all live births, but substantial evidence suggests that the rate at conception is much higher. At least 17% of pregnancies recognized at 8 weeks will end in spontaneous abortion (miscarriage). Approximately half of these spontaneously

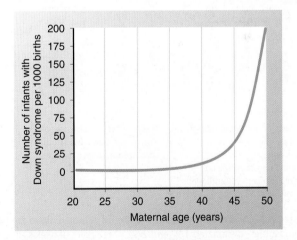

Figure 15–6 Down syndrome and maternal age. The estimated risk of a live birth of an infant with Down syndrome increases with maternal age. *(Adapted from Gardner, R.J.M. and G.R. Sutherland. Chromosome Abnormalities and Genetic Counseling. Oxford University Press, New York, 1996; and from Hecht, C.A. and E.B. Hook. "The Imprecision in Rates of Down Syndrome by One-Year Maternal Age Intervals: A Critical Analysis of Rates Used in Biochemical Screening." Prenatal Diagnosis, Vol. 14, 1994)*

aborted embryos have major chromosome abnormalities, including autosomal trisomies (e.g., trisomy 21), triploidy, tetraploidy, and Turner syndrome (XO). Autosomal monosomies are exceedingly rare, possibly because they induce a spontaneous abortion very early in the pregnancy, before a woman is even aware that she is pregnant. Some investigators place surprisingly high estimates (50% or more) on the rate of loss of very early embryos. It is widely assumed that chromosome abnormalities are responsible for a substantial fraction of these.

ABNORMALITIES IN CHROMOSOME STRUCTURE CAUSE CERTAIN DISORDERS

Chromosome abnormalities are not only caused by changes in chromosome *number* but also by distinct changes in the *structure* of one or more chromosomes. Here we consider three simple examples of structural abnormalities: translocations, deletions, and fragile sites.

Translocation is the attachment of part of a chromosome to a nonhomologous chromosome

In some cases part of one chromosome may break off and attach to a nonhomologous chromosome (a **translocation**), or two nonhomologous chromosomes may exchange parts (a **reciprocal** translocation). The consequences of translocations vary considerably but include situations in which some genes are missing **(deletions)**, and extra copies of other genes are present **(duplications)** (Fig. 15–7).

In about 4% of individuals with Down syndrome, only 46 chromosomes are present, but one is abnormal. Extra genetic material from chromosome 21 has been translocated onto one of the larger chromosomes, such as chromosome 14. We refer to this kind of abnormal translocation chromosome as a *14/21 chromosome*. Affected individuals have one chromosome 14, one 14/21 chromosome, and two normal copies of chromosome 21. All or part of the genetic material from chromosome 21 is thus present in triplicate. When the karyotypes of such an individual's parents are studied, either the mother or the father is usually found to have only 45 chromosomes, although she or he is generally phenotypically normal. The parent with 45 chromosomes has one chromosome 14, one 14/21 chromosome, and one chromosome 21; although the karyotype is abnormal, there is no extra genetic material. In contrast to trisomy 21, this translocation form of Down syndrome can run in families, and its incidence is not related to maternal age.

A deletion is loss of part of a chromosome

Sometimes chromosomes break but fail to rejoin. Such breaks result in deletions of as little as a few base pairs to as much as an entire chromosome arm. As you might expect, large deletions are lethal, whereas small deletions cause several recognizable human disorders.

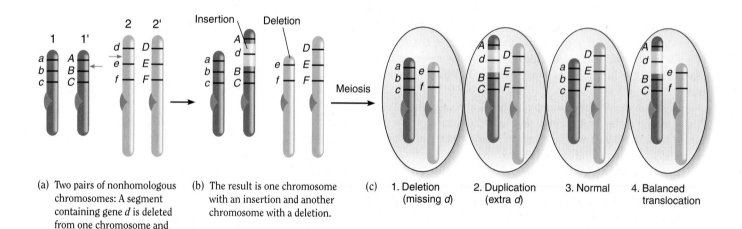

(a) Two pairs of nonhomologous chromosomes: A segment containing gene *d* is deleted from one chromosome and inserted into a nonhomologous chromosome.

(b) The result is one chromosome with an insertion and another chromosome with a deletion.

(c) 1. Deletion (missing *d*) 2. Duplication (extra *d*) 3. Normal 4. Balanced translocation

Figure 15–7 Translocation. (a) In this example, there are two pair of nonhomologous chromosomes, designated 1/1' and 2/2'. Three pairs of alleles, designated *A/a, B/b,* and *C/c* are on chromosomes 1/1', and three allelic pairs (*D/d, E/e,* and *F/f*) are on chromosomes 2/2'. Red arrows designate the breakage points in the chromosomes. (b) Allele *d* is deleted from chromosome 2 and inserted into chromosome 1'. (c) Following meiosis, four different combinations of chromosomes (and the genes on those chromosomes) are possible. (1) In one of the gametes, allele *d* is missing altogether. (2) In one gamete, there is an extra copy of *d*. (3) In one gamete, there is a complete set (one allele for each locus). (4) In one gamete, there is one allele for each locus, but allele *d* is not in its normal location on chromosome 2—that is, the gamete contains a balanced translocation.

One relatively common deletion disorder (1 in 50,000 live births) is **cri du chat syndrome,** in which part of the short arm of chromosome 5 is deleted. As in most deletions, the exact point of breakage in chromosome 5 varies from one individual to another; some cases of cri du chat involve a small loss, whereas others involve a more substantial deletion. Infants born with cri du chat syndrome typically have a small head with altered features described as a "moon face" and a distinctive cry that sounds like a kitten mewing. (The name *cri du chat* literally means "cry of the cat" in French.) Affected individuals usually survive beyond childhood but exhibit severe mental retardation.

Fragile sites are weak points at specific sites in chromatids

A **fragile site** occurs where part of a chromatid appears to be attached to the rest of the chromosome by a thin thread of DNA. Fragile sites may occur at a specific location on both chromatids of a particular chromosome. Such sites have been identified on the X chromosome as well as on certain autosomes. The location of a fragile site is exactly the same in all of an individual's cells, as well as in cells of other family members. Scientists report growing evidence that cancer cells may have breaks at these fragile sites. Whether cancer destabilizes the fragile sites, leading to breakage, or the fragile sites themselves contain genes that contribute to cancer is unknown at this time.

In **fragile X syndrome** the fragile site occurs near the tip of the X chromosome (Fig. 15–8). At the tip of an X chromosome, a nucleotide triplet (cytosine, guanine, guanine, or CGG) is normally repeated up to 50 times. The fragile X chromosome, however, repeats CGG from 200 to more than 1000 times. The effects of fragile X syndrome, which are more pronounced in males than in females, range from mild learning and attention disabilities to severe mental retardation and hyperactivity. According to the National Fragile X Foundation, about 80% of boys and 35% of girls with fragile X syndrome are at least mildly mentally retarded. Females with fragile X syndrome are usually heterozygous (because their other X chromosome is normal) and are therefore more likely to have normal intelligence. The discovery of the fragile X gene in 1991 and the development of the first fragile X mouse model in 1994 have provided researchers with ways to test potential treatments, including gene therapy.

MOST GENETIC DISEASES ARE INHERITED AS AUTOSOMAL RECESSIVE TRAITS

We have seen that several human disorders involve chromosome abnormalities. Hundreds of human disorders, however, involve enzyme defects caused by mutations of single genes. Phenylketonuria (PKU) and alkaptonuria (see Chapter 12) are examples of these disorders, which are sometimes referred to as an **inborn er-**

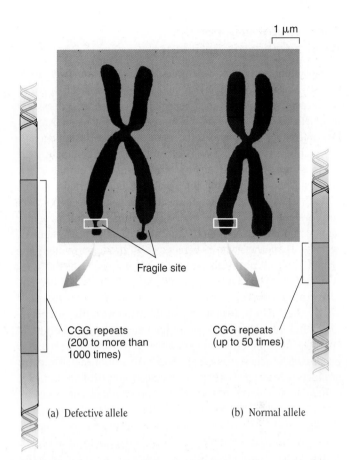

1 μm

Fragile site

CGG repeats (200 to more than 1000 times)

CGG repeats (up to 50 times)

(a) Defective allele

(b) Normal allele

Figure 15–8 Fragile X syndrome. Color-enhanced SEM of *(left)* an X chromosome with a fragile site and *(right)* a normal X chromosome. **(a)** The defective allele at the tip of the X chromosome repeats the nucleotide triplet CGG from 200 to more than 1000 times. **(b)** The normal allele repeats CGG up to 50 times. *(Science VU)*

ror of metabolism, a metabolic disorder caused by the mutation of a gene that codes for an enzyme needed in a biochemical pathway. Both PKU and alkaptonuria involve blocks in the metabolism of the amino acid phenylalanine. Only a small percentage of human genetic diseases have a simple inheritance pattern, but most of those that do are transmitted as autosomal recessive traits and so are expressed only in the homozygous state.

Why are these traits usually recessive? Most single-gene mutations that have an observable effect result in a gene that no longer works (it either does not produce enough gene product, or it produces a defective gene product). In most cases, the diploid cells are heterozygous and contain one normal copy of the gene and one mutated, nonfunctional copy. Since protein production is generally regulated by need, the cell will usually compensate by having the normal copy of the gene meet the demand. Thus, most genetic diseases are seen in homozygous recessive individuals—that is, they only exhibit the disorder when *both* copies of the gene are nonfunctional. In these relatively rare cases, in which both gene copies in the diploid cell contain mutations that make them nonfunctional, the cell's needs are not met, and the individual exhibits symptoms of the disorder.

Phenylketonuria results from an enzyme deficiency

Phenylketonuria (PKU), which is most common in individuals of western European descent, is an autosomal recessive disease that is a defect of amino acid metabolism. It affects about 1 in 10,000 live births in North America. Homozygous recessive individuals lack an enzyme that converts the amino acid phenylalanine to another amino acid, tyrosine. These individuals accumulate high levels of phenylalanine, phenylpyruvic acid, and similar compounds. The accumulating phenylalanine is converted to compounds known as phenylketones, which damage the central nervous system, including the brain. The ultimate result is severe mental retardation. An infant with PKU is usually healthy at birth because its mother, who is heterozygous, produces enough enzyme to prevent phenylalanine accumulation before birth. However, during infancy and early childhood, the toxic products eventually cause irreversible damage to the central nervous system.

In the 1950s it was found that if infants with PKU are identified and placed on a special low-phenylalanine diet early enough, the symptoms can be dramatically alleviated. (The diet is difficult to adhere to because it contains no meat, fish, dairy products, breads, or nuts. Also, the sugar substitute aspartame, found in many diet drinks and foods, should not be consumed by individuals with PKU because it contains phenylalanine.) Biochemical tests for PKU have been developed, and screening of newborns through a simple blood test is required in the United States. Because of these screening programs and the availability of effective treatment, thousands of PKU-diagnosed children have not developed severe mental retardation. Most such children must continue the diet through at least adolescence. Doctors recommend that the diet be continued throughout life because some adults who have discontinued the special diet show a decline in certain mental faculties, such as some loss of the ability to concentrate and some short-term memory loss.

Ironically, the success of PKU treatment in childhood presents a new problem today. If a homozygous female who has discontinued the special diet becomes pregnant, the high phenylalanine levels in her blood can result in damage to the brain of the fetus she is carrying, even though that fetus is heterozygous. Therefore, she must resume the diet, preferably before becoming pregnant. This procedure is usually (although not always) successful in preventing the effects of **maternal PKU.** Therefore it is especially important that females with PKU be aware of their condition so that they may obtain appropriate counseling and medical treatment during pregnancy.

Sickle cell anemia results from a hemoglobin defect

Sickle cell anemia is inherited as an autosomal recessive trait. The disease is most common in individuals of African descent (approximately 1 in 500 African-Americans), and about 1 in 12 African-Americans is heterozygous. The blood cells of an individual with sickle cell anemia are shaped like sickles, or half-moons, whereas normal red blood cells are biconcave discs.

The mutation that causes sickle cell anemia was first identified more than 50 years ago. The sickle cell contains abnormal hemoglobin molecules, which have the amino acid valine instead of glutamic acid at position 6 (the sixth amino acid from the amino terminal end) in the beta chain (see Chapter 3). The substitution of valine for glutamic acid makes the hemoglobin less soluble. As a result, it tends to form crystal-like structures that change the shape of the red blood cells (Fig. 15–9a). This sickling occurs in the veins after the oxygen has been released from the hemoglobin. The blood cells' abnormal sickled shape slows blood flow and blocks small blood vessels (Fig. 15–9b), with resulting tissue damage from lack of oxygen and essential nutrients, and painful episodes. Sickled red blood cells also have shorter life spans than normal red blood cells, leading to severe anemia in many affected individuals.

Available treatments for sickle cell anemia include pain relief measures, transfusions, and, more recently, medicines such as hydroxyurea, which activates the gene for the production of normal fetal hemoglobin (this gene is generally not expressed after birth). The presence of normal fetal hemoglobin in the blood dilutes the sickle cell hemoglobin so there are fewer painful episodes and less need for blood transfusions. The long-term effects of hydroxyurea are not known at this time, but there are concerns that it may induce tumor formation.

Ongoing research is directed toward eventually providing gene therapy for sickle cell anemia. Bone marrow transplants are also a promising future treatment for seriously ill individuals. The development of a mouse model of sickle cell anemia, which was reported in 1997, will allow researchers to test potential drug and genetic therapies.

The reason that the sickle cell allele occurs at a higher frequency in parts of Africa is well known. Individuals who are heterozygous *(Ss)* and carry alleles for both normal hemoglobin *(S)* and sickle cell hemoglobin *(s)* are more resistant to falciparum malaria, a severe form of malaria that is often fatal. The malarial parasite, which spends part of its life cycle inside red blood cells, does not thrive when sickle cell hemoglobin is present. (An individual heterozygous for sickle cell anemia produces both normal and sickle cell hemoglobin.) Areas in Africa where falciparum malaria occurs correlate well with areas in which the frequency of the sickle cell allele is more common in the human population. Thus, *Ss* individuals, who possess one copy of the mutant sickle cell allele, have a selective advantage over homozygous individuals, both *SS* (who may die of malaria) and *ss* (who may die of sickle cell anemia). This phenomenon, known as **heterozygote advantage,** is discussed further in Chapter 18 (see Fig. 18–7).

Cystic fibrosis results from defective ion transport

Cystic fibrosis is the most common autosomal recessive disorder in children of European descent (1 in 2500 births). About 1 in 25 individuals in the United States is a heterozygous carrier of the cystic fibrosis allele. Abnormal secretions in the body characterize this disorder. Its most severe effect is on the respiratory sys-

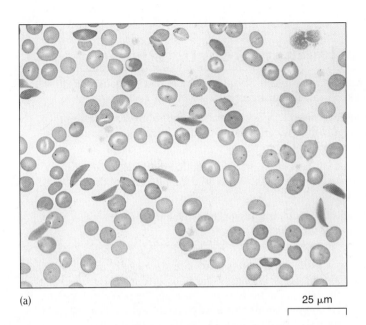

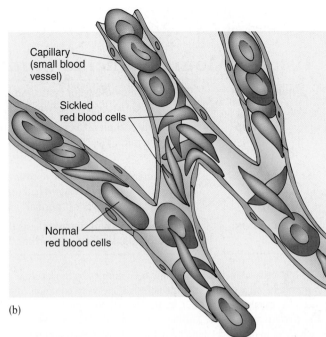

(a)

25 μm

(b)

■ Figure 15–9 Sickle cell anemia. **(a)** LM of sickled red blood cells. Some of the red blood cells from this individual with sickle cell anemia show an abnormal sickle shape. **(b)** Sickled red blood cells do not pass through small blood vessels as easily as normal red blood cells. The sickled blood cells can cause blockages that prevent oxygen from being delivered to tissues. *(a, G.W. Willis/Biological Photo Service)*

tem, which produces abnormally viscous mucus. The cilia that line the bronchi (see Chapter 44) cannot easily remove the mucus, and it thus becomes a culture medium for dangerous bacteria. These bacteria or their toxins attack the surrounding tissues, leading to recurring pneumonia and other complications. The heavy mucus also occurs elsewhere in the body (e.g., in the ducts of the pancreas, liver, intestines, and sweat glands), causing digestive difficulties and other effects.

The gene responsible for cystic fibrosis codes for a protein that controls the transport of chloride and certain other ions across cell membranes. The mutant protein, found in plasma membranes of epithelial cells lining the ducts of the lungs, intestines, pancreas, liver, sweat glands, and reproductive organs, results in the production of an unusually thick mucus that eventually leads to tissue damage. Although many mutant forms exist and these vary somewhat in severity of symptoms, the disease is usually very serious.

Antibiotics are used to control bacterial infections, and daily physical therapy is required to clear mucus from the respiratory system (Fig. 15–10). Treatment with an enzyme (produced by recombinant DNA technology) that breaks down the mucus is also helpful. Without treatment, death would occur in infancy. With treatment, the average life expectancy for individuals with cystic fibrosis is now about 30 years. Because of the serious limitations of available treatments, gene therapy for cystic fibrosis is under development.

The most severe mutant allele for cystic fibrosis predominates in northern Europe, and another, somewhat less serious, mutant

■ Figure 15–10 Treatment of cystic fibrosis. The traditional treatment for cystic fibrosis has been chest percussion, or gentle pounding on the chest, to clear mucus from clogged airways in the lungs. *(Abraham Menashe)*

Using a Mouse Model to Study a Human Genetic Disease

HYPOTHESIS: The alleles responsible for cystic fibrosis confer a heterozygote advantage because heterozygous individuals are less likely to die from certain types of life-threatening diarrhea.

METHOD: The effects of cholera toxin, which is produced by a bacterial infection and causes severe diarrhea, were studied in mice. The responses of three groups of mice were evaluated: (1) mice homozygous for an allele that causes cystic fibrosis, (2) heterozygous mice, and (3) normal mice.

RESULTS: Mice homozygous for a cystic fibrosis allele did not respond to cholera toxin; that is, the toxin did not cause diarrhea. Cholera toxin caused heterozygotes to lose only half as much fluid from the cells of the intestinal lining as did homozygous "normal" animals.

CONCLUSION: These results support the hypothesis that individuals heterozygous for the cystic fibrosis allele are less likely to die from certain kinds of diarrhea than normal individuals.

Human geneticists have long been puzzled by the fact that heterozygosity for cystic fibrosis alleles is so common among whites (1/20), particularly among Northern Europeans and those of Northern European descent. Recent advances in our understanding of the molecular biology of this genetic disease have led to a new explanation of why these alleles have persisted in the population. This new hypothesis is that heterozygous individuals are less likely to die from certain types of potentially fatal diarrhea, such as cholera.

In severe diarrhea, large amounts of water and electrolytes are lost from the intestine. If unchecked, particularly in infants and young children, this condition can result in death. It has been found that the allele that causes cystic fibrosis is a mutant form of a gene involved in controlling the body's water and electrolyte balance. This gene has been cloned and found to code for a protein, the *CFTR protein,* that serves as a chloride ion channel in the plasma membrane. (CFTR stands for *cystic fibrosis transmembrane conductance regulator.*) This ion channel is responsible for transporting chloride ions out of the cells lining the digestive tract and the respiratory system. When the chloride ions leave the cells, water follows by osmosis. Thus the normal secretions of these cells are relatively watery.

Because the cells of individuals with cystic fibrosis lack normal chloride ion channels, their secretions have a very low water content, and their sweat is very salty. Cells of heterozygous individuals have only half the usual number of functional CFTR ion channels, but these are sufficient to maintain normal fluidity of their secretions. However, this ion channel deficiency might be an advantage if an individual is infected by a pathogen that produces a toxin that causes the ion channels to remain constantly open, precipitating diarrhea. With only half as many normal ion channels, a heterozygote might lose only half as much chloride and water.

allele is more prevalent in southern Europe. Presumably these mutant alleles are independent mutations that have been maintained by natural selection. Some experimental evidence supports the hypothesis that heterozygous individuals are less likely to die from infectious diseases that produce severe diarrhea. (See *On the Cutting Edge: Using a Mouse Model to Study a Human Genetic Disease.*)

Tay-Sachs disease results from abnormal lipid metabolism in the brain

Tay-Sachs disease is an autosomal recessive disease that affects the central nervous system and results in blindness and severe mental retardation. The symptoms begin within the first year of life and result in death before the age of five years. Because of the absence of an enzyme, a normal membrane lipid in the brain cells fails to break down properly and accumulates in the lysosomes. Although research is ongoing, no effective treatment for Tay-Sachs disease is available at this time. However, an effective strategy for the treatment of Tay-Sachs in a mouse model was reported in 1997. This treatment, which involves oral administration of an inhibitor that reduces the synthesis of the lipid that accumulates in the lysosomes, offers the hope of an effective way to deal with Tay-Sachs disease in humans in the future.

The abnormal allele is especially common in the United States among Jews whose ancestors came from Eastern and Central Europe (Ashkenazi Jews). About 1 in 4000 live births in the North American Jewish population has the disease. By contrast, Jews whose ancestors came from the Mediterranean region (Sephardic Jews) have a very low frequency of the allele. Why the high frequency of such a harmful allele has been maintained in the Ashkenazi Jewish population is not known. It has been suggested that carriers of the Tay-Sachs allele may have some, as yet unknown, heterozygote advantage.

■ SOME GENETIC DISEASES ARE INHERITED AS AUTOSOMAL DOMINANT TRAITS

Huntington disease (HD), named after George Huntington, the American physician who first described it in 1872, is due to a rare autosomal dominant allele that affects the nervous system. The disease causes severe mental and physical deterioration, uncontrollable muscle spasms, personality changes, and ultimately death. No effective treatment has been found. Every child of an affected individual has a 50% chance of also being

Research on any disease is greatly facilitated if an animal model can be used for experimentation. Such a model became available when strains of mice homozygous for cystic fibrosis, as well as those that were heterozygous, were produced by gene targeting (see Chapter 14).

Sherif E. Gabriel and colleagues at the University of North Carolina used the cystic fibrosis mouse model to test the heterozygote advantage hypothesis (see Chapter 18).* They treated mice with cholera toxin produced by *Vibrio cholerae,* the bacterium that causes cholera. Cholera toxin is known to affect the functioning of the CFTR ion channels, causing the uncontrolled loss of chloride ions and water.

Their results neatly fit the predictions of the heterozygote advantage hypothesis. Animals homozygous for cystic fibrosis, that is, those with no functional CFTR channels, did not lose any fluid through their intestinal cells when exposed to cholera toxin. The toxin caused heterozygotes (with only half the number of normal CFTR channels) to lose only half as much fluid as mice with the normal number of channels.

Despite the success of this demonstration, it is not thought that cholera itself is the selective force responsible for the high incidence of cystic fibrosis alleles today. Cystic fibrosis is thought to have arisen more than 50,000 years ago, whereas European cholera epidemics were first recognized in the early 1800s. Rather, some other diarrhea-causing infection is probably the culprit.

Researchers have continued to test candidates likely to be responsible for a possible heterozygote advantage of cystic fibrosis alleles. In 1998 Gerald Pier and colleagues at the Harvard Medical School, University of Bristol, and University of Cambridge announced that the cystic fibrosis allele protects against typhoid fever, a diarrheal disease caused by the bacterium *Salmonella typhi.*[†] This bacterium enters human gastrointestinal cells with the CFTR channel protein but does not easily enter cells expressing a cystic fibrosis allele. These data are supported by studies in which no *S. typhi* entered cells of mice homozygous for the cystic fibrosis allele, and 86% fewer *S. typhi* entered heterozygous mouse cells compared with homozygous normal mouse cells.

Some researchers are now focusing their efforts on understanding the complex way in which the CFTR channel is activated or inactivated.[‡] It is hoped that this information will allow researchers to design drugs that enhance or inhibit chloride transport through the CFTR channel. Such drugs have the potential to treat cystic fibrosis (by activating the mutant channel) and diarrhea (by inhibiting the normal channel).

* Gabriel, S.E., K.N. Brigman, B.H. Koller, R.C. Boucher, and M.J. Stutts. "Cystic Fibrosis Heterozygote Resistance to Cholera Toxin in the Cystic Fibrosis Mouse Model." *Science,* Vol. 266, 7 Oct. 1994.

† Pier, G.B., M. Grout, T. Zaidi, G. Meluleni, S.S. Mueschenborn, G. Banting, R. Ratcliff, M.J. Evans, and W.H. Colledge. *"Salmonella typhi* Uses CFTR to Enter Intestinal Epithelial Cells." *Nature,* Vol. 393, 7 May 1998.

‡ Naren, A.P., E. Cormet-Boyaka, J. Fu, M. Villain, J.E. Blalock, M.W. Quick, and K.L. Kirk. "CFTR Chloride Channel Regulation by an Interdomain Interaction." *Science,* Vol. 286, 15 Oct. 1999.

affected (and, if affected, of passing the abnormal allele to his or her offspring). Ordinarily we would expect a dominant allele with such devastating effects to occur only as a new mutation and not to be transmitted to future generations. This disease is characterized by onset of symptoms relatively late in life (most do not develop the disease until their 30s or 40s), so an individual may have children before the disease develops (Fig. 15–11). In North America HD occurs at a frequency of 1 in 20,000 live births.

The gene responsible for HD was cloned in 1993. The mutation is a nucleotide triplet (cytosine, adenine, guanine, or CAG) that is repeated many times; the normal allele repeats CAG from 6 to 35 times, whereas the mutant allele repeats CAG from 40 to more than 150 times. Because the triplet CAG codes for the amino acid glutamine, the resulting proteins have long strands of glutamine. Interestingly, the number of nucleotide triplet repeats seems to be important in determining the age of onset and the severity of the disease; larger numbers of repeats correlate with an earlier age of onset and greater severity.

Much research is now directed at studying how the mutation is linked to neurodegeneration in the brain. A mouse model of HD has been produced that is providing valuable clues about the development of the disease. Once HD's mechanism of

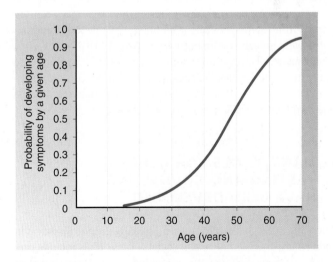

Figure 15–11 Age of onset of Huntington disease. The graph shows the probability that an individual affected with Huntington disease will have developed symptoms at a given age. The onset of Huntington disease occurs relatively late in life. (*Adapted from Harper, P.S.* Genetic Counseling, *5th edition. Butterworth-Heinemann, Oxford, 1998*)

action on nerve cells is better understood, it may be possible to develop effective treatments to slow the progression of the disease.

Cloning of the HD allele became the basis for tests that allowed those at risk to learn presymptomatically if they carry the allele. The decision to be tested for any genetic disease is understandably a highly personal one. Certainly, the information can be very useful for those who must make decisions such as whether or not to have children. However, someone who tests positive for the HD allele must then live with the virtual certainty of eventually developing this devastating and incurable disease. It is hoped that affected individuals who choose to be identified before the onset of symptoms may ultimately contribute to the development of effective treatments.

■ SOME GENETIC DISEASES ARE INHERITED AS X-LINKED RECESSIVE TRAITS

Hemophilia A was once referred to as a disease of royalty because of its high incidence among male descendants of Queen Victoria, but it is also found in many nonroyal pedigrees. Characterized by the lack of a blood clotting factor, Factor VIII, it causes severe internal bleeding in the head, joints, and other areas from even a slight wound. The mode of inheritance is X-linked recessive. Thus, affected individuals are almost exclusively male, having inherited the abnormal allele on the X chromosome from their heterozygous carrier mothers. (For a female to be affected by an X-linked trait, she would have to inherit the defective allele from both parents, whereas an affected male only needs to inherit one defective allele, from his mother.)

Treatments for hemophilia A consist of blood transfusions and administration of clotting factor VIII (the missing gene product) by injection. Unfortunately, these treatments are costly (as much as $40,000 a year for one individual). During the 1980s, many clotting factor VIII preparations made from human plasma were contaminated with human immunodeficiency virus-1 (HIV-1), the virus that causes AIDS, acquired immunodeficiency syndrome, and many men with hemophilia subsequently died. Since 1992, virus-free clotting factor VIII has been available from both human plasma and recombinant DNA technology (see Chapter 14).

■ MANY TOOLS FOR GENETIC TESTING AND COUNSELING HAVE BEEN DEVELOPED

There have been many advances in detecting genetic disorders in individuals, their families, and society. These tools include prenatal diagnosis and genetic screening. With these advances comes increased information for couples at risk of having children with genetic diseases. Helping couples understand and deal with genetic information now available has been the realm of the rapidly expanding field of genetic counseling.

Prenatal diagnosis can detect abnormalities in chromosome number and structure as well as many gene defects

Genetic abnormalities may become apparent during early prenatal development or not until late in adult life. Given that early detection increases the possibilities for prevention or alleviation of the effects of genetic abnormalities, efforts have been made over the years to detect such abnormalities before birth. In the past 20 years health care providers have become increasingly successful at prenatal diagnosis of many genetic diseases.

In one diagnostic technique known as **amniocentesis,** a sample of the fluid surrounding the fetus (the *amniotic fluid*) is obtained. A needle is inserted through the walls of the pregnant woman's abdomen, into the uterus, and then into the amniotic sac surrounding the fetus. Some of the amniotic fluid is withdrawn from the amniotic cavity into a syringe (Fig. 15–12). This procedure is normally safe from needle injuries because the positions of the fetus, placenta, and the needle can be determined through **ultrasound imaging** (see Fig. 49–21). There is a slight (about 0.5%, or 1 in 200) chance that amniocentesis will induce a miscarriage.

The amniotic fluid contains living cells sloughed off the body of the fetus and hence genetically identical to the cells of the fetus. These amniotic fluid cells can be cultured in the laboratory. After 10 to 14 days, dividing cells from the culture can be karyotyped to detect chromosome abnormalities. Amniocentesis, which has been performed since the 1960s, is routinely offered for pregnant women older than 35 years of age because their fetuses have a higher than normal risk of Down syndrome.

Other prenatal tests have been developed to detect many simply inherited genetic disorders, but these disorders are rare enough that the tests are usually done only if a particular problem is suspected. Enzyme deficiencies can often be detected through incubation of cells recovered from amniotic fluid with the appropriate substrate and measurement of the product; this technique has been useful in the prenatal diagnosis of disorders such as Tay-Sachs disease. The tests for several other diseases, including sickle cell anemia, HD, and cystic fibrosis, are carried out by directly testing the individual's DNA for the defective gene.

Amniocentesis is also useful in detecting a condition known as *spina bifida,* in which the spinal cord does not close properly during development. A relatively common (about 1 in 300 births) malformation, this birth defect is associated with abnormally high levels of a normally occurring protein, α-fetoprotein, in the amniotic fluid. Some of this protein crosses the placenta into the mother's blood, which can be tested for maternal serum α-fetoprotein (MSAFP) as a screen for spinal cord defects. If an elevated level of MSAFP is detected, diagnostic tests, such as ultrasound imaging and amniocentesis, are performed. (Interestingly, abnormally *low* levels of MSAFP are associated with Down syndrome and other trisomies.)

One problem with amniocentesis is that most of the conditions it detects are incurable, and the results are generally not obtained until well into the second trimester when terminating the pregnancy is both psychologically and medically more diffi-

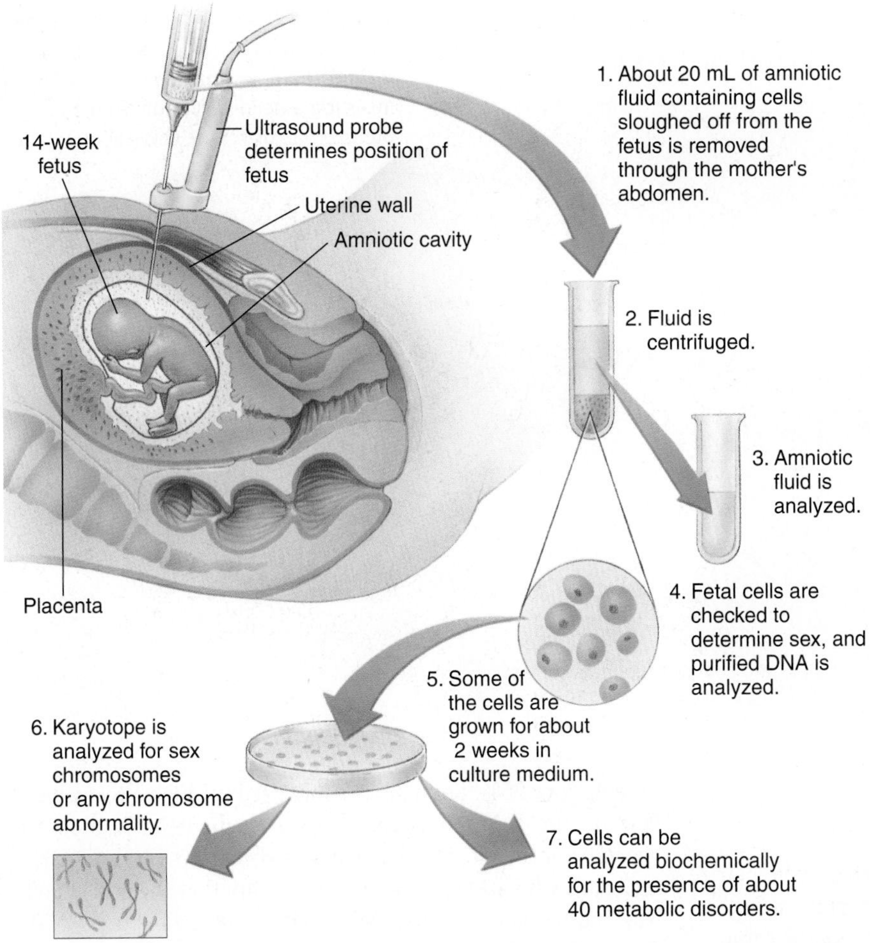

Figure 15–12 Amniocentesis.
Certain genetic diseases and other abnormal conditions can be diagnosed prenatally by amniocentesis.

14-week fetus

Ultrasound probe determines position of fetus

Uterine wall

Amniotic cavity

Placenta

1. About 20 mL of amniotic fluid containing cells sloughed off from the fetus is removed through the mother's abdomen.

2. Fluid is centrifuged.

3. Amniotic fluid is analyzed.

4. Fetal cells are checked to determine sex, and purified DNA is analyzed.

5. Some of the cells are grown for about 2 weeks in culture medium.

6. Karyotope is analyzed for sex chromosomes or any chromosome abnormality.

7. Cells can be analyzed biochemically for the presence of about 40 metabolic disorders.

cult than earlier. Therefore, efforts have been made to develop tests that yield results earlier in the pregnancy. One such test, **chorionic villus sampling (CVS),** involves removing and studying cells that will form the fetal contribution to the placenta (Fig. 15–13). CVS, which has been performed in the United States since about 1983, is associated with a slightly greater risk of infection or miscarriage than amniocentesis, but its advantage is that results can be obtained earlier than in amniocentesis, usually within the first trimester.

Although both amniocentesis and CVS can diagnose certain genetic disorders with a high degree of accuracy, they are not foolproof, and many disorders cannot be diagnosed. Therefore, the lack of an abnormal finding is no guarantee of a normal pregnancy.

Genetic screening searches for a particular genotype or karyotype in infants or adults

Genetic screening is a systematic search through a population for individuals with a genotype or karyotype that might cause a serious genetic disease in them or their offspring. There are two main types of genetic screening, for newborns and for adults, and each serves a different purpose. Screening of newborns is done primarily as the first step in preventive medicine, and screening of adults is done to help them make informed reproductive decisions.

Newborns are screened to detect and treat one or more genetic diseases before the onset of serious symptoms. The routine screening of infants for PKU, discussed earlier in the chapter, began in 1962 in Massachusetts. Laws in all 50 states of the United States, as well as in several other countries, currently require PKU screening. Sickle cell anemia is another genetic disease that is more effectively treated if the diagnosis is made early. Screening newborns for sickle cell anemia enables doctors to reduce infant mortality about 15% because they can administer daily doses of antibiotics, thereby preventing deadly bacterial infections to which infants with sickle cell anemia are susceptible.

Genetic screening of adults is done to identify carriers (heterozygotes) of recessive genetic disorders. The carriers are then counseled about the risks involved in having children if both prospective parents are heterozygous. Since the 1970s, about 1 million young Jewish adults in the United States, Israel, and other countries have been screened voluntarily for Tay-Sachs disease, and about 1 in 30 has been identified as a carrier. Tay-Sachs screening programs have resulted in a reduction in the incidence of Tay-Sachs disease by more than 90%.

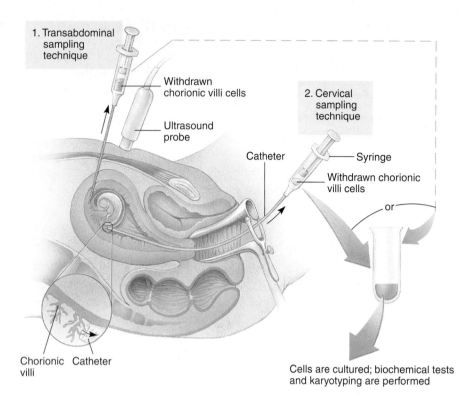

1. Transabdominal sampling technique

Withdrawn chorionic villi cells

Ultrasound probe

2. Cervical sampling technique

Catheter

Syringe

Withdrawn chorionic villi cells

or

Chorionic villi

Catheter

Cells are cultured; biochemical tests and karyotyping are performed

Figure 15–13 Chorionic villus sampling (CVS). This test allows the early diagnosis of some genetic abnormalities. Samples may be obtained by inserting a needle through (1) the uterine wall or (2) the cervical opening.

Genetic counselors educate people about genetic diseases

Couples who are concerned about the risk of abnormality in their children, either because they have had an abnormal child or have a relative affected by a hereditary disease, may seek **genetic counseling.** Genetic counselors provide medical and genetic information as well as support and guidance. Genetic clinics are available in most major metropolitan centers; these clinics are usually affiliated with medical schools.

Genetic counselors, who have received specialized training in counseling, medicine, and human genetics,[2] give people information needed to make reproductive decisions. Advice, tempered with respect and sensitivity, is given in terms of risk estimates—that is, the *probability* that any given offspring will inherit a particular condition. The counselor needs complete family histories of both the man and the woman and may screen for the detection of heterozygous carriers of certain conditions.

When a disease involves only a single gene locus, probabilities can usually be easily calculated. For example, if one prospective parent is affected with a trait that is inherited as an autosomal dominant disorder, such as Huntington disease, the probability that any given child will have the disease is 0.5, or 50%. The birth to phenotypically normal parents of a child affected with an autosomal recessive trait, such as albinism or PKU, establishes that both parents are heterozygous carriers, and the probability that any subsequent child will be affected is there-

fore 0.25, or 25%. For a disease inherited through a recessive allele on the X chromosome, such as hemophilia A, a normal woman and an affected man will have daughters who are carriers and sons who are normal. The probability that the son of a carrier mother and a normal father will be affected is 0.5, or 50%; the probability that their daughter will be a carrier is also 0.5.

It is important that identified carriers receive appropriate genetic counseling. A genetic counselor is trained not only to give information needed for reproductive decisions but also to help individuals understand their situation and avoid feeling stigmatized.

Genetic counselors often receive inquiries about mental retardation, epilepsy, deafness, congenital heart disease, and other conditions. It is possible that some environmental factor may have played a role in producing the abnormality in the affected child. Did the mother have an infectious disease such as rubella (German measles) during pregnancy? Was she receiving some kind of drug therapy, or was she subjected to ionizing radiation? Had the father been exposed to any potentially hazardous agents? By dissecting the environmental contributions, the geneticist can more accurately estimate the probability of the trait's recurrence in subsequent offspring.

■ GENE THERAPY IS BEING EXPLORED FOR SEVERAL GENETIC DISEASES

Because many difficulties are inherent in treating most serious genetic diseases, scientists have dreamed of developing actual cures. Today, genetic engineering may be bringing these dreams closer to reality. One strategy is to introduce the normal gene

[2] For information about obtaining a master's degree in genetic counseling, contact the National Society of Genetic Counselors, 233 Canterbury Drive, Wallingford, PA 19086; e-mail: nsgc@aol.com.

into certain body cells *(somatic cell gene therapy)*. The rationale is that, although a particular gene may be present in all cells, it is expressed only in some (see Chapter 16). Expression of the normal allele in only the cells that require it may be sufficient to give a normal phenotype.

This approach presents a number of technical obstacles. The solutions to these problems must be tailored to the nature of the gene itself, as well as to its product and the types of cells in which it must be expressed. First the gene must be cloned and the DNA introduced into the appropriate cells. One of the most successful techniques is to package the genetic material in a virus, creating a viral **vector.** Ideally the virus should infect a high percentage of the cells. Most important, the virus should do no harm, especially over the long term. For example, if the virus inserts the introduced gene into a part of the chromosome that codes for a **proto-oncogene,** a normal gene involved in growth and development, the proto-oncogene may change into an oncogene (see *Focus On: Oncogenes and Cancer* in Chapter 16).

Although many obstacles must be overcome, gene therapies for several genetic diseases are under development or are being tested on individuals in clinical trials. Scientists are currently addressing some of the unique problems presented by each disease.

Gene therapy programs are under increasing scrutiny

Until recently, major technical advances caused the number of clinical studies involving gene therapy to grow dramatically. However, in September 1999, a death in a gene therapy trial led to a shutdown of many trials, pending the outcome of investigations about health risks. The main safety concern in these investigations is the potential toxicity of viral vectors, the viruses that move the normal gene into target cells that currently have a defective gene. The vector that was used in the young patient who died was an adenovirus (see Fig. 23–1*b*), a virus required in large doses if enough genes are to be transferred to make the therapy effective. Unfortunately, the high viral doses triggered a fatally strong immune response in the patient's body.

Performing clinical studies on humans always has inherent risks. Patients must be carefully selected, and the potential benefits and risks, as far as they are known, must be explained thoroughly so the patient or, in the case of children, the parents can give an informed consent to the procedure.

■ BOTH HUMAN GENETICS AND BELIEFS ABOUT GENETICS AFFECT SOCIETY

Many misconceptions exist about genetic diseases and their effects on society. Some people erroneously think of certain individuals or populations as genetically unfit and responsible for many of society's ills. They argue, for example, that medical treatment of individuals affected with genetic diseases, especially those who are able to reproduce, increases the frequency of ab-

normal alleles in the population. This is true for autosomal dominant and X-linked diseases, but most genetic diseases that are simply inherited show an autosomal recessive inheritance pattern. Only homozygous individuals actually have the disease; heterozygous carriers, present in far greater numbers in the population, are phenotypically normal.

For example, if 1 in 25 individuals in the United States is heterozygous for cystic fibrosis, the chance that two parents will both be heterozygous is $1/25 \times 1/25 = 1/625$. On average, one-fourth of the children of such a couple would have cystic fibrosis, so the frequency of affected individuals in the population is about $1/625 \times 1/4 = 1/2500$. Because their numbers are usually very small compared with heterozygotes, reproduction by homozygotes does not greatly increase overall frequencies of abnormal alleles.

Abnormal alleles are present in *all* individuals and *all* ethnic groups; no one is exempt. According to one estimate, each of us is heterozygous for several (3 to 15) very harmful alleles, any of which could cause debilitating illness or death in the homozygous state. Why, then, are genetic diseases not more common? Each of us has many thousands of essential genes, any of which can be mutated. It is very unlikely that the abnormal alleles that one individual carries are also carried by that individual's mate. Of course, this possibility is more likely if the harmful allele is a relatively common one, such as the one responsible for cystic fibrosis.

Relatives are more likely than nonrelatives to carry the same harmful alleles, having inherited them from a common ancestor. In fact, a greater than normal frequency of a particular genetic disease among offspring of **consanguineous matings** (matings of close relatives) is often the first clue that the mode of inheritance is autosomal recessive. The offspring of consanguineous matings have a small but significantly increased risk of genetic disease. In fact, they can account for a disproportionately high percentage of those individuals in the population with autosomal recessive disorders. Because of this perceived social cost, first-cousin marriages are prohibited by most states in the United States. However, consanguineous marriages are still relatively common in many countries, particularly in developing countries, where other factors may mask the significance of genetic disease. A high incidence of infectious disease, for example, may result in so many deaths that the health effects of relatively uncommon genetic diseases are largely ignored in developing countries. The ability of a society to concern itself with genetic diseases is a luxury that comes with affluence.

Genetic discrimination has provoked heated debate

One of the fastest growing areas of medical diagnostics is genetic screening and testing, and the number of new genetic tests that screen for diseases such as cystic fibrosis, sickle cell anemia, HD, colon cancer, and breast cancer increases each year. However, genetic testing raises many social, ethical, and legal issues that society must address.

One of the most difficult issues is whether genetic information should be made available to health and life insurance companies. Many people think genetic information should not be given to insurance companies, but others, including employers, insurers, and many organizations representing people affected by genetic disorders, say such a view is unrealistic. If people use genetic tests to help them decide when to buy insurance and how much to buy, then insurers insist they should also have access to this information. Insurers say they need access to genetic data to help calculate equitable premiums (the whole idea of insurance is to average risk over a large population). However, there are concerns that insurers might use the results of genetic tests to discriminate against people with genetic diseases or to deny them coverage.

Doctors are concerned that people at risk for a particular genetic disease might delay being tested because they fear genetic discrimination from insurers and employers. The perception of genetic discrimination already exists in society. In a 1996 study, 25% of 332 people with family histories of one or more genetic disorders thought they had been refused life insurance, 22% thought they had been refused health insurance, and 13% thought they had been denied employment because of genetic discrimination. In a 1998 survey by the National Center for Genetic Resources, 63% of respondents said they probably or definitely would not take a genetic test if the results could be disclosed to either their employers or insurers.

Making the issue even more complicated is the fact that genetic tests are sometimes difficult to interpret, in part because there are many complex interactions between genes and the environment. If a woman tests positive for a gene that has been linked to breast cancer, for example, she is at significant risk, but testing positive does not necessarily mean that she will get breast cancer. Moreover, if she gets breast cancer, the age of onset and severity of the disease are not predicted by genetic tests. These uncertainties also make it difficult to decide what form of medical intervention, from frequent mammograms to surgical removal of healthy breasts, is appropriate.

The Ethical, Legal, and Social Implications (ELSI) Research Program of the National Human Genome Research Institute has developed principles designed to protect people against genetic discrimination. The Health Insurance Portability and Accountability Act of 1996 provides some safeguards against genetic discrimination, but ELSI has additional recommendations that have not yet been put into law. As this book goes to press, many bills that extend protection against workplace discrimination, health discrimination, and invasion of privacy based on genetic information are up for consideration by both federal and state legislatures. These issues will be debated for years to come.

SUMMARY WITH KEY TERMS

I. **Human genetics** is the science of inherited variation in humans. The **human genome** is the total genetic information in human cells.
   A. **Bioinformatics** includes the storage, retrieval, and comparison of DNA sequences within human DNA and between genomes of different species.
   B. **Pharmacogenomics** is a new field of gene-based medicine in which drugs are personalized to match a patient's genetic makeup.

II. Karyotyping, pedigree construction, and DNA sequencing and mapping of genes are some of the tools used in the study of human genetics.
   A. Studies of an individual's **karyotype** (the number and kinds of chromosomes present in the nucleus) permit detection of various chromosome abnormalities.
   B. A **pedigree** is a chart that shows the transmission of genetic traits within a family over several generations.
   C. The first phase of the Human Genome Project, an international effort to map and sequence all of the DNA in the human genome, was essentially completed in 2001.

III. **Aneuploidy,** in which there are either missing or extra copies of certain chromosomes, causes certain human disorders. Aneuploidies include **trisomy,** in which an individual possesses an extra chromosome, and **monosomy,** in which one member of a pair of chromosomes is lacking.
   A. **Trisomy 21,** the most common form of **Down syndrome,** and **Klinefelter syndrome** (XXY) are examples of trisomy.
   B. **Turner syndrome** (XO) is an example of monosomy.
   C. Trisomy and monosomy are caused by **nondisjunction,** in which sister chromatids or homologous chromosomes fail to disjoin (move apart) properly during meiosis or mitosis.

IV. Structural abnormalities in chromosomes cause certain human disorders.
   A. In a **translocation,** part of one chromosome becomes attached to another. About 4% of individuals with Down syndrome have a translocation in which part of chromosome 21 is attached onto one of the larger chromosomes, such as chromosome 14.
   B. A **deletion** can result in chromosome breaks that fail to rejoin. The deletion may range in size from a few base pairs to an entire chromosome arm. The most common deletion disorder in humans is **cri du chat syndrome,** in which part of the short arm of chromosome 5 is deleted.
   C. **Fragile sites** may occur at specific locations on both chromatids of a particular chromosome. In **fragile X syndrome** the fragile site occurs near the tip on the X chromosome; at that site the nucleotide triplet CGG is repeated many more times than is normal.

V. Most human genetic diseases that show a simple inheritance pattern are transmitted as autosomal recessive traits. An **inborn error of metabolism** is a metabolic disorder caused by the mutation of a gene that codes for an enzyme needed for a biochemical pathway.
   A. **Phenylketonuria (PKU)** is an autosomal recessive disorder in which toxic phenylketones damage the developing nervous system.
   B. **Sickle cell anemia** is an autosomal recessive disorder in which abnormal hemoglobin (the protein needed to carry oxygen in the blood) is produced.
   C. **Cystic fibrosis** is an autosomal recessive disorder in which abnormal secretions are produced in organs primarily of the respiratory and digestive systems.
   D. **Tay-Sachs disease** is an autosomal recessive disorder caused by abnormal lipid metabolism in the brain.

VI. **Huntington disease** has an autosomal dominant inheritance pattern. It results in mental and physical deterioration, usually beginning in middle age.

VII. **Hemophilia A** is an X-linked recessive disorder. It results in a defect in one of the components of blood required for clotting.

VIII. Prenatal diagnosis, genetic screening, and genetic counseling assist individuals and families in detecting and coping with genetic disorders.

A. Prenatal diagnosis increases the possibilities for prevention or alleviation of the effects of genetic abnormalities.

1. In **amniocentesis,** the amniotic fluid surrounding the fetus is sampled and the fetal cells suspended in the fluid are cultured and screened for genetic defects. Amniocentesis provides results in the second trimester of pregnancy.

2. In **chorionic villus sampling (CVS),** some chorion cells are removed and studied. CVS provides results in the first trimester of pregnancy.

B. **Genetic screening** is a systematic search through a population for individuals with a genotype or karyotype that might cause a serious genetic disease in them or their offspring. Screening of newborns is done primarily as the first step in preventive medicine, and screening of adults is done to help them make informed reproductive decisions.

C. Couples who are concerned about the risk of abnormality in their children may seek **genetic counseling.** Genetic counselors provide medical and genetic information.

D. Gene therapies for several genetic diseases are undergoing development or are being tested on individuals in clinical trials. Scientists are currently addressing some of the unique problems presented by each disease.

IX. The effect of human genetics on society is complex.

A. The fact that a particular abnormal allele is especially common in a certain population does not mean that group has a higher frequency of abnormal alleles in general.

B. Most abnormal alleles are recessive; therefore, they are manifested phenotypically only in homozygotes, who constitute a tiny fraction of the individuals with the allele. Virtually every individual in the population is a heterozygous carrier of several abnormal alleles.

C. One of the most difficult issues is whether genetic information should be made available to employers and to health and life insurance companies. Doctors are concerned that people at risk for a particular genetic disease might delay being tested because they fear genetic discrimination from insurers and employers.

POST-TEST

1. The most important tool in bioinformatics is (a) controlled matings (b) karyotyping (c) pedigree analysis (d) a computer (e) chorionic villus sampling

2. A pedigree is a diagram showing (a) controlled matings between members of different isogenic strains (b) the total genetic information in human cells, currently being mapped and sequenced (c) a comparison of DNA sequences among genomes of humans and other species (d) the subtle genetic differences among people (e) the expression of genetic traits among the members of two or more generations of a family

3. The Human Genome Project is (a) mapping and sequencing all of the DNA in the nuclear human genome (b) exclusively concerned with the comparison of DNA sequences between human DNA and DNA of other species (c) personalizing drugs to match an individual's genetic makeup (d) a systematic search for individuals with a genotype that might cause a serious genetic disease in them or their offspring (e) providing risk estimates on human genetic diseases

4. An abnormality in which there is one more or one fewer than the normal number of chromosomes is called a(an) (a) karyotype (b) fragile site (c) aneuploidy (d) trisomy (e) translocation

5. An individual with one extra chromosome (three of one kind) is said to be (a) monosomic (b) triploid (c) trisomic (d) consanguineous (e) isogenic

6. An individual who is missing one chromosome, having only one member of a pair, is said to be (a) monosomic (b) haploid (c) trisomic (d) consanguineous (e) isogenic

7. The failure of chromosomes to separate normally during cell division is called (a) a fragile site (b) an inborn error of metabolism (c) a satellite knob (d) a translocation (e) nondisjunction

8. The transfer of a part of one chromosome to a nonhomologous chromosome is called (a) a karyotype (b) an inborn error of metabolism (c) a pedigree (d) a translocation (e) nondisjunction

9. A photomicrograph of the array of stained metaphase chromosomes present in a given cell is called a(an) (a) karyotype (b) nucleotide triplet repeat (c) pedigree (d) inborn error of metabolism (e) translocation

10. Individuals with trisomy 21, or _____, are mentally and physically retarded and have abnormalities of the face, tongue, and eyelids. (a) Down syndrome (b) Klinefelter syndrome (c) Turner syndrome (d) Huntington disease (e) Tay-Sachs disease

11. An inherited disorder caused by a defective or absent enzyme is called a(an) (a) karyotype (b) trisomy (c) reciprocal translocation (d) inborn error of metabolism (e) aneuploidy

12. In _____, a genetic mutation codes for an abnormal hemoglobin molecule that is less soluble than usual and more likely than normal to crystallize and deform the shape of the red blood cell. (a) Down syndrome (b) Tay-Sachs disease (c) sickle cell anemia (d) PKU (e) hemophilia A

13. In an individual with _____, the mucus is abnormally viscous and tends to plug the ducts of the pancreas and liver and to accumulate in the lungs. (a) Down syndrome (b) Tay-Sachs disease (c) sickle cell anemia (d) PKU (e) cystic fibrosis

14. During this procedure, a sample of the fluid that surrounds the fetus is obtained by insertion of a needle through the walls of the abdomen and uterus. (a) DNA marker (b) chorionic villus sampling (c) ultrasound imaging (d) consanguineous mating (e) amniocentesis

15. For which of the following situations would a genetic counselor *not* recommend prenatal diagnosis involving amniocentesis or chorionic villus sampling? (a) there is an increased risk of a chromosomal abnormality (b) there is an increased risk of a single-locus (Mendelian) disease (c) there is an increased risk of a spinal cord defect (d) there is a desire to know the sex of the fetus (e) a pregnant woman is older than 35 years of age

1. What means have been devised for overcoming some of the difficulties in studying human inheritance?
2. What is meant by nondisjunction? What are some human abnormalities that appear to be the result of nondisjunction?
3. What is meant by inborn errors of metabolism? Give an example.
4. To be expressed, an autosomal recessive genetic disease must be homozygous. What relationship does this fact have to consanguineous matings?
5. What are some of the ways that heterozygous carriers of certain genetic diseases can be identified?
6. What are the relative advantages and disadvantages of amniocentesis and chorionic villus sampling?
7. Examine the following pedigrees and decide whether each disorder is most likely inherited by an autosomal recessive, an autosomal dominant, or an X-linked recessive allele. Determine the probable genotypes for all individuals shown.

 (a)   (b)   (c)

8. Complete the table at right by checking the correct box for each genetic disorder.

Disease	Chromosome Abnormality	Autosomal Recessive	Autosomal Dominant	X-Linked Recessive
Down syndrome				
Tay-Sachs disease				
Phenylketonuria				
Hemophilia A				
Sickle cell anemia				
Turner syndrome				
Huntington disease				
Klinefelter syndrome				
Cri du chat syndrome				
Fragile X syndrome				

1. Imagine that you are a genetic counselor. What advice or suggestions might you give in the following situations?
   a. A couple has come for advice because the woman had a sister who died of Tay-Sachs disease.
   b. A young man and woman who are not related are engaged to be married. However, they have learned that the man's parents are first cousins. They are worried about the possibility of increased risk of genetic defects in their own children.
   c. A young woman's paternal uncle (her father's brother) has hemophilia A. Her father is free of the disease, and there has never been a case of hemophilia A in her mother's family. Should she be concerned about the possibility of hemophilia A in her own children?
   d. A 20-year-old man is seeking counseling because his father recently was diagnosed with Huntington disease.
2. A deletion of part of an X chromosome may be lethal in a male but causes few problems in a female. Explain.
3. A common misconception about human genetics is that an individual's genes alone determine his or her destiny. Explain why this myth is incorrect. How is the perpetuation of this myth harmful to society?

Brown, K. "The Human Genome Business Today." *Scientific American,* Vol. 283, No. 1, Jul. 2000. Considers the business potential of new fields such as bioinformatics and pharmacogenomics.

Ezzell, C. "Beyond the Human Genome." *Scientific American,* Vol. 283, No. 1, Jul. 2000. The push is on to understand the proteins that are encoded in the human genome.

Friedmann, T. "Principles for Human Gene Therapy Studies." *Science,* Vol. 287, 24 Mar. 2000. This paper examines principles of medical ethics that must be addressed for human clinical trials involving gene therapy.

Hesman, T. "The Meaning of Life." *Science News,* Vol. 157, 29 Apr. 2000. Computers and gene-hunting programs are important tools in the field of bioinformatics.

Howard, K. "The Bioinformatics Gold." *Scientific American,* Vol. 283, No. 1, Jul. 2000. The medical potential of bioinformatics is examined in detail in this article.

Mange, E.J., and A.P. Mange. *Basic Human Genetics,* 2nd ed. Sinauer Associates, Inc., Sunderland, Massachusetts, 1999. This text provides excellent coverage of all aspects of human genetics, from the diagnosis of diseases to ethical concerns.

Marshall, E. "Gene Therapy on Trial." *Science,* Vol. 288, 12 May 2000. This article provides a detailed analysis of the gene therapy trial at the University of Pennsylvania that led to the 1999 death of a young patient suffering from a defective gene that codes for an essential liver enzyme.

McKusick, V.A. *Mendelian Inheritance in Man: A Catalog of Human Genes and Genetic Disorders,* 12th ed. Johns Hopkins University Press, Baltimore, 1998. This is the print version of the on-line OMIM (Online Mendelian Inheritance in Man) database (http://www.ncbi.nlm.nih.gov/Omim/).

Nagel, R.L. "Molecule, Heal Thyself." *Natural History,* Sept. 2000. The genetic component of human illnesses and injuries (e.g., a broken leg) has been vastly underestimated.

Nature, Vol. 409, 15 Feb. 2001. This issue focuses on the landmark completion of sequencing the human genome.

Pennisi, E. "Finally, the Book of Life and Instructions for Navigating It." *Science,* Vol. 288, 30 Jun. 2000. Much of the human genome has been sequenced, a goal that has huge implications for both biology and medicine.

Science, Vol. 291, 16 Feb. 2001. This issue is devoted to the completion of the human genome sequence, which is a milestone in science.

Shreeve, J. "Secrets of the Gene." *National Geographic,* Vol. 196, No. 4, Oct. 1999. Discusses how medicine and other fields should benefit from recent advances in human genetics.

Strasser, B.J. "Sickle Cell Anemia, a Molecular Disease." *Science,* Vol. 286, 19 Nov. 1999. This article, published on the 50-year anniversary of a groundbreaking paper by Linus Pauling and colleagues on sickle cell anemia, considers both the advances and the lack of progress made in treating sickle cell anemia since that time.

Wheelwright, J. "Betting on Designer Genes." *Smithsonian,* Jan. 2001. Some of the challenges involved in using gene transfer to treat a disease.

● Visit our Web site at **http://www.info.brookscole.com/solomonbergmartin** for links to chapter-related resources on the World Wide Web. Additional on-line materials relating to this chapter can also be found on our Web site.

16

Genes and Development

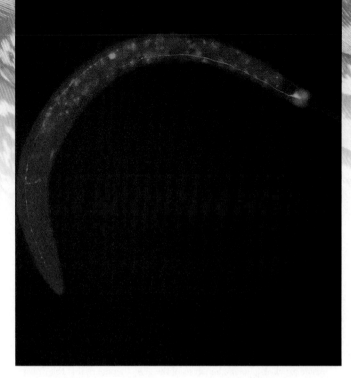

The model organism _Caenorhabditis elegans._ The small transparent body of this nematode worm allows researchers to locate cells in which a specific developmentally important gene is active. These cells show up as bright green spots in the photograph because they have been genetically engineered to produce a green fluorescent protein known as GFP. *(Courtesy of Dr. Martin Chalfie, Columbia University)*

LEARNING OBJECTIVES

After you have studied this chapter you should be able to

1. Distinguish between cell determination and cell differentiation.
2. Relate the process of pattern formation to morphogenesis.
3. Describe the kinds of experiments that indicate the totipotency of some differentiated plant cells and some animal nuclei. Discuss how these findings support the idea of nuclear equivalence.
4. Identify the attributes of an organism that would make it especially useful in studies on the genetic control of development. Discuss the value of transgenic organisms in research on the genetic control of development.
5. Indicate the features of the development and genetics of *Drosophila melanogaster, Caenorhabditis elegans,* the mouse *(Mus musculus),* and *Arabidopsis thaliana* that have made these organisms so valuable to researchers.
6. Distinguish among maternal effect genes, zygotic genes, and homeotic genes in *Drosophila.*
7. Explain the relationship between transcription factors and genes that control development. Provide some examples of genes that are known to function as genetic switches in development.
8. Define the phenomena of induction and programmed cell death, and give examples of the roles they play in development.
9. Describe the functions of some homeotic-like genes in plants.
10. Point out some of the known exceptions to the general phenomenon of nuclear equivalence.

The study of **development,** which is broadly defined as all the changes that occur in the life of an individual, encompasses some of the most fascinating and difficult problems in biology today. Of particular interest is the process by which cells specialize and organize into a complex organism. During the many cell divisions required for a single cell to develop into a multicellular organism, groups of cells become gradually committed to specific patterns of gene activity through a process called cell **determina-**

tion. The final step leading to cell specialization is cell **differentiation.** A differentiated cell can be recognized by its characteristic appearance and activities.

An even more intriguing part of the developmental puzzle is the building of the body, known as morphogenesis, or the development of form. In **morphogenesis,** cells in specific locations differentiate and become spatially organized into recognizable structures through a multistep process known as **pattern formation.**

Until the late 1970s, little was known about how certain genes interact with various signals from within the organism and from the environment to control development. Although certain genes affecting developmental pathways had been identified, their specific functions in the organism were not well understood. Because these networks are too complex to unravel using only traditional methods, it had been thought that it might be impossible to understand development. However, rapid progress in recombinant DNA technology led scientists to renew their search for developmental mutants and to apply the most sophisticated techniques to study them.

Today scientists interested in development study a variety of carefully chosen mutant organisms with altered developmental patterns. They use the tools of genetic engineering combined with more conventional descriptive and experimental approaches to derive fresh insights into the role of genetic information in the control of development. The organism in the photograph is *Caenorhabditis elegans,* a nematode worm with many attributes that make it unusually attractive for developmental studies. Work with such organisms has profound implications for our understanding of both normal human development and the kinds of malfunctions that can lead to birth defects and even "normal" aging. Although these worms may seem to have little in common with humans, scientists are learning that many of the genes important in development are quite similar in a wide range of organisms. These similarities have led to new ways to unravel evolutionary relationships, through the study of developmentally important genetic mechanisms that appear to be deeply rooted in the evolutionary history of multicellular organisms.

CELL DIFFERENTIATION USUALLY DOES NOT INVOLVE CHANGES IN DNA CONTENT

The human body, like those of other vertebrates, contains more than 200 recognizably different types of cells (Fig. 16–1). Combinations of these specialized cells, known as **differentiated cells,** are organized into remarkably diverse and complex structures such as the eye, the hand, and the brain, each capable of carrying out many sophisticated activities. Most remarkable of all, however, is the fact that all the structures of the body and the different cells within them are descended from a single fertilized egg.

All multicellular organisms undergo complex patterns of development. The root cells of plants, for example, have structures and functions very different from those of the various types of cells located in leaves. Remarkable diversity can also be found at the molecular level; most strikingly, each type of plant or animal cell makes a highly specific set of proteins (Fig. 16–2). In some cases, such as the protein hemoglobin in red blood cells, one cell-specific protein may make up more than 90% of the total mass of

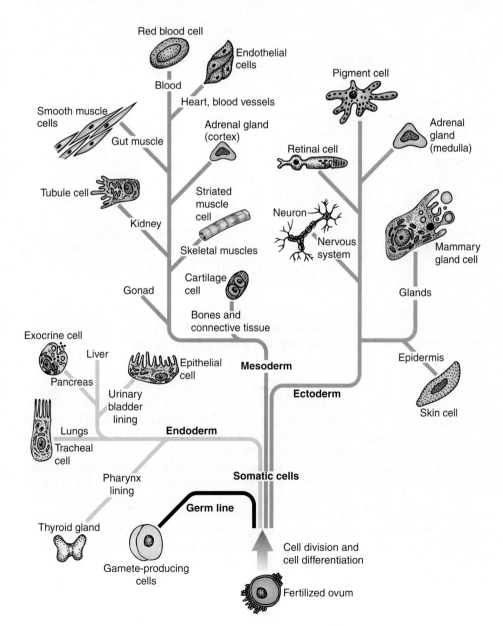

Figure 16–1 Vertebrate cell lineages. Repeated divisions of the fertilized egg *(bottom of the figure)* result in the establishment of tissues containing groups of specialized cells (see Chapter 49 for a discussion of how these are formed). Germ-line cells (cells that produce the gametes) are set aside early in development. Somatic cells progress along the developmental pathways, undergoing a series of commitments that progressively determine their fates.

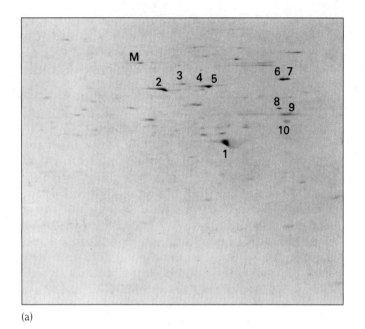

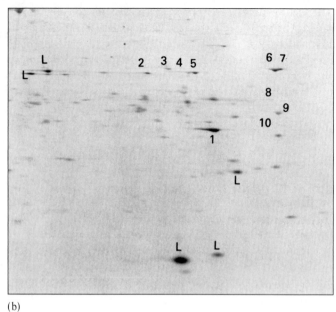

(a)

(b)

Figure 16–2 Cell-specific proteins. The spots in the photographs are proteins from **(a)** muscle and **(b)** liver cells of a mouse. The proteins were separated by two-dimensional gel electrophoresis, a method that separates the proteins in the horizontal direction by their electric charge, followed by a second separation in the vertical direction by molecular weight. Several hundred proteins can be distinguished in each panel. The spots that are labeled with numbers are present in all tissues, but notice that many of them are present in different amounts from one tissue to another. The proteins that are labeled with letters are found only in that specific tissue. *(Patrick O'Farrell, from Fig. 12–1 in Darnell, J., H. Lodish, and D. Baltimore,* Molecular Cell Biology. *Scientific American Books, New York, 1986)*

protein in the cell. Other cells may have a complement of cell-specific proteins that are each present in small amounts but still play essential roles. However, because certain proteins are required in every type of cell (all cells, for example, require certain enzymes for glycolysis), cell-specific proteins usually make up only a fraction of the total number of different kinds of proteins.

One explanation for the fact that each type of differentiated cell makes a unique set of proteins might be that during development each group of cells loses the genes it does not need and retains only those that are required. With just a few exceptions, however, this does not seem to be true. According to the concept of **nuclear equivalence,** the nuclei of essentially all differentiated adult cells of an individual are genetically (though not necessarily metabolically) identical to each other and to the nucleus of the fertilized egg cell from which they descended. This means that virtually all **somatic**[1] cells in an adult have the same genes, but different cells express different subsets of these genes.

[1] Somatic cells are cells of the body and are distinguished from *germ-line cells,* which ultimately give rise to a new generation. In animals, germ-line cells, whose descendants ultimately undergo meiosis and differentiate as gametes, are generally set aside early in development. In plants, the distinction between somatic cells and germ-line cells is not clear-cut, and the determination that certain cells will undergo meiosis is made much later in development.

The evidence for nuclear equivalence comes from cases in which differentiated cells or their nuclei have been found to be capable of supporting normal development. Such cells or nuclei are said to be **totipotent.**

A totipotent nucleus contains all the information required to direct normal development

In plants it is possible to demonstrate that at least some differentiated cells can be induced to become the equivalent of embryonic cells (Fig. 16–3). **Tissue culture** techniques are used to isolate individual cells from certain plants and to allow them to grow in a nutrient medium.

Some of the first experiments investigating cell totipotency in plants were conducted at Cornell University in the 1950s by F.C. Steward and others. Root cells from a carrot were induced to divide in a liquid nutrient medium and to form groups of cells called "embryoid" (embryo-like) bodies. These clumps of dividing cells could then be transferred to an agar medium, which provides nutrients plus a solid supporting structure for the developing plant cells. After transfer to the agar, some of the cells of the embryoid bodies gave rise to roots, stems, and leaves. The re-

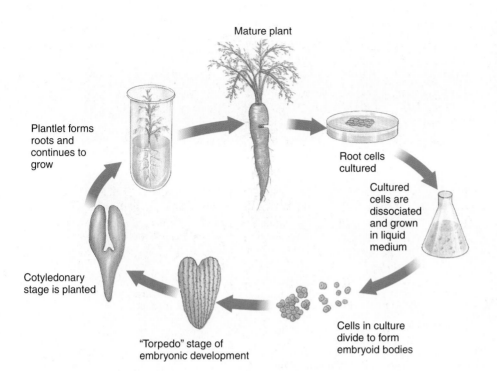

Mature plant

Plantlet forms
roots and
continues to
grow

Root cells
cultured

Cultured
cells are
dissociated
and grown
in liquid
medium

Cotyledonary
stage is planted

"Torpedo" stage of
embryonic development

Cells in culture
divide to form
embryoid bodies

Figure 16–3 Cell totipotency.
A complete carrot plant can develop from differentiated somatic cells. Carrot root tissues were cut into discs made up of phloem cells, which are specialized for nutrient transport. When these differentiated cells were cultured in a liquid nutrient medium, individual cells divided to form clumps of undifferentiated cells, known as embryoid bodies. The embryoid bodies, which closely resembled plant embryos in their early stages of development, then progressed to form embryonic shoots and roots. Transferring the embryonic tissue to a solid nutrient medium stimulated the tissues to form small plants, called plantlets, which then developed into mature plants.

sulting small plants, called *plantlets* to distinguish them from true seedlings, were then transplanted to soil, where they ultimately developed into adult plants capable of producing flowers and viable seeds. If these plants are all derived from the same parent plant, they are genetically alike and therefore constitute a **clone.** The methods of plant tissue culture are now extensively used to produce genetically engineered plants, for they allow the regeneration of whole plants from individual cells that have incorporated recombinant DNA molecules (see Chapter 36, *Focus On: Cell and Tissue Culture*).

Similar experiments have been attempted with animal cells, but so far it has not been possible to induce a fully differentiated somatic cell to behave like a zygote. Instead, it has been possible to test whether steps in the process of determination are reversible by transplanting the *nucleus* of a cell in a relatively late stage of development into an egg cell that has been enucleated (i.e., its own nucleus has been destroyed).

In the 1950s R. Briggs and T.J. King conducted experiments in which nuclei from amphibian cells at different stages of development were transplanted into egg cells. Some of the transplants proceeded normally through several developmental stages, and a few even developed into normal tadpoles. As a rule, the nuclei transplanted from cells at earlier stages were most likely to support development to the tadpole stage. As the fate of the cells became more and more determined, the probability that a transplanted nucleus could control normal development diminished rapidly (Fig. 16–4).

In experiments carried out in England in the 1960s by J. Gurdon, in a few cases nuclei isolated from the specialized intestinal cells of a tadpole were able to direct development up to the tadpole stage. This occurred infrequently, but in such experiments success counts more than failure, and we can safely conclude that at least some nuclei of differentiated animal cells are in fact totipotent.

For many years these successes with amphibians could not be repeated with mammalian embryos, leading many developmental biologists to conclude that some fundamental feature of mammalian reproductive biology might be an impenetrable barrier to mammalian cloning. This perception changed markedly in 1996 and 1997 with the first reports of the birth of cloned mammals. Since that time, successful cloning of several additional mammalian species has been accomplished (see *Focus On: Mammalian Cloning*).

It may not be particularly surprising that nuclei do not usually lose genetic material during development; after all, there should be no loss of chromosomes in the course of normal mitotic cell divisions. These demonstrations of nuclear totipotency also imply that apparently inactive genes are capable of being reactivated when cells or nuclei are placed in a suitable environment. Nevertheless, it is important to recognize that the nuclei of embryonic cells progressively undergo changes that make it more difficult to remain in a totipotent state. This is especially true of animal nuclei, although various kinds of animals may differ considerably in this regard.

Stem cells, undifferentiated cells that are not truly totipotent but nevertheless able to differentiate into more than one cell type, are of great scientific interest today. Studies on these cells not only help scientists understand the changes that occur when cells differentiate but also have far-reaching medical significance (see *Focus On: Stem Cells* on page 346).

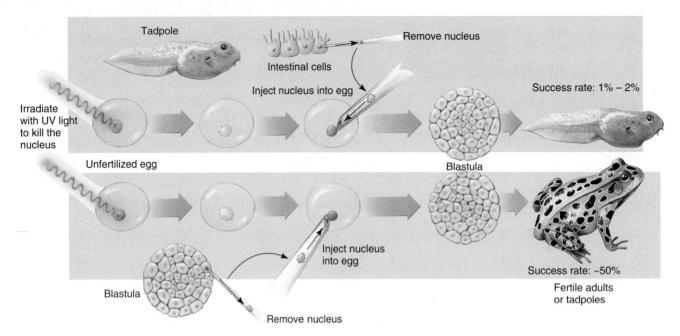

Figure 16–4 Nuclear totipotency. In nuclear transplantation experiments in amphibians, nuclei of differentiated cells at different stages of development were injected into eggs whose own nuclei had been destroyed by ultraviolet radiation. As seen in the upper panel, most trials using nuclei from tadpole intestinal cells (a relatively late developmental stage) resulted in no growth. In a small number of trials (about 1%–2% of the total) normal development did proceed to the tadpole stage, indicating that the genes necessary to program development up to that point were still present and able to be appropriately activated. However, the success rate improved dramatically if nuclei from earlier developmental stages were used. As shown in the lower panel, if a nucleus was taken from a cell at the blastula stage of development (when cell division has produced about 1000 cells formed in the shape of a ball), in about half the cases the transplanted nucleus could successfully program normal development resulting in a tadpole or fertile adult.

Most differences among cells are due to differential gene expression

Because genes do not appear to be lost regularly during development, the differences in the molecular composition of cells must occur by regulating the activities of different genes. This process of developmental gene regulation is often referred to as **differential gene expression.** As discussed in Chapter 13, the expression of eukaryotic genes can be regulated in many different ways and at many levels. For example, a particular enzyme may be produced in an inactive form and then be activated later. However, much of the regulation that is important in development occurs at the transcriptional level. The transcription of certain sets of genes is repressed, whereas other sets are activated. Even expression of genes that are **constitutive** (i.e., constantly transcribed) and active in all cells can be regulated during development so that the *quantity* of each product varies from one tissue type to another.

We can think of differentiation as a series of pathways leading from a single cell to cells in each of the different specialized tissues, arranged in an appropriate pattern. There are times when a cell makes genetic "commitments" to the developmental path its descendants will follow. These commitments gradually restrict the development of the descendants to a limited set of final tissue types. Determination, then, is a progressive fixation of the fate of a cell's descendants.

As the development of a cell becomes determined along a particular differentiation pathway, the physical appearance of the cell may not change significantly. Nevertheless, when a particular stage of determination is complete, the changes in the cell usually become self-perpetuating and are not easily reversed. Cell differentiation, then, is usually the last stage in the developmental process. At this stage, a precursor cell becomes structurally and functionally recognizable as a bone cell, for example, and its pattern of gene activity is different from that of a nerve cell, or any other cell type.

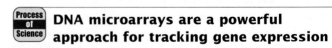 **DNA microarrays are a powerful approach for tracking gene expression**

Biotechnology (see Chapter 14) is now making it possible for researchers to study differential gene expression in increasingly sophisticated ways. The science of determining the roles of genes

Mammalian Cloning

In 1996 Ian Wilmut and coworkers at the Roslin Institute in Scotland reported that they had succeeded in cloning sheep, using nuclei from early sheep embryos (blastocyst stage; see Chapter 49). These scientists subsequently received worldwide attention in early 1997 when they announced the birth of a lamb, nicknamed "Dolly," derived from a cultured mammary gland cell (from an adult sheep) fused with an enucleated sheep's egg. The resulting cell divided and developed into an embryo that was then cultured in vitro until it reached a stage at which it could be transferred to a host mother. As might be expected, the overall success rate was low: Out of 277 fused cells, only 29 developed into embryos that could be transferred, and Dolly was the only live lamb produced. These researchers have also produced cloned transgenic lambs derived from fetal cells.

Why was Wilmut's team the first to succeed when so many other researchers had failed? Applying the basic principles of cell biology, they recognized that the cell cycles of the egg cytoplasm and the donor nucleus were incompatible; that is, the egg cell is a cell that is arrested at metaphase II of meiosis, whereas the actively growing donor cell is usually in the DNA synthesis phase (S), or in G_2. By withholding certain nutrients from the mammary gland cells used as donors, they were able to cause them to enter a nondividing state referred to as G_0 (see Chapter 9). This had the effect of synchronizing the donor nucleus to the cell cycle of the egg. They then used an electrical shock to cause the donor cell to fuse readily with the egg and initiate the development of the embryo.

Although an extremely high level of technical expertise is required, these and other researchers have been able to use modifications and extensions of these techniques to produce cloned calves, goats, pigs, and mice, and there is reason to think that the list of mammals that have been successfully cloned will continue to grow. However, the success rate for each set of trials continues to be extremely low, on the order of 1% to 2%, and the incidence of defects is high. The production of transgenic animals continues to be the main focus of this line of research (see Chapter 14). Researchers are very actively pursuing new techniques that they hope

will dramatically improve the efficiency of the cloning process, because only then will it be possible to produce large numbers of cloned transgenic animals that can be used for a variety of purposes.

Results such as these continue to fuel an ongoing debate regarding the

potential for human cloning and its ethical implications. In the United States, the National Bioethics Advisory Commission, whose recommendations are posted on the Internet, has been established to study this and other questions: http://www.nih.gov/nbac.htm.

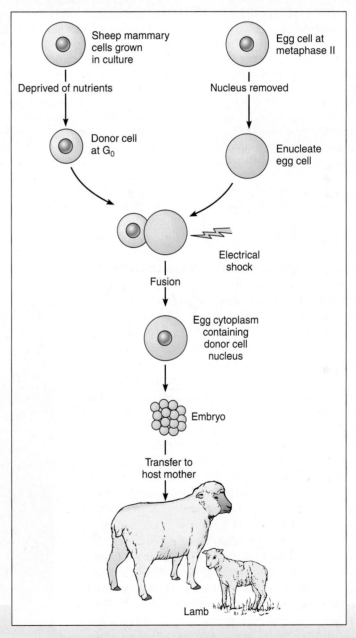

How to clone a sheep. An embryo produced by fusing a cultured adult sheep mammary cell with an enucleate sheep's egg is implanted into the uterus of a host mother and develops into a lamb.

Stem cells are undifferentiated cells that can divide to produce differentiated descendants, yet retain the ability to divide to reproduce themselves, thereby maintaining the stem cell population. The most versatile stem cells, those that have the ability to give rise to all tissues of the body, are known as **pluripotent** stem cells. Other stem cells appear to be more specialized; for example, neural stem cells can differentiate to form all types of brain cells, and stem cells in the bone marrow form various types of blood cells. However, recent studies have shown that even specialized stem cells may be more versatile than once thought. For example, neural stem cells have been shown to form blood cells when transplanted into bone marrow, and bone marrow stem cells can differentiate into muscle cells.

Stem cells are potential sources of cells to be transplanted into patients to treat serious conditions. For example, Parkinson's disease results from a progressive loss of cells that produce the neurotransmitter dopamine in a specific region of the brain. Transplantation of stem cells that have been induced to differentiate as dopamine-producing cells holds great promise as an effective long-term treatment. Similarly, stem cells may become a source of insulin-producing cells in the pancreas that are lacking in individuals with Type 1 diabetes (see Chapter 47) or of neurons in individuals who have suffered spinal cord injury or other types of neurological damage.

Researchers ultimately hope to establish lines of human pluripotent stem cells that can be grown indefinitely in culture, can be induced to differentiate under controlled conditions and stably maintain their differentiated state, and can be manipulated genetically. Although work on stem cells in mice and other mammals has been conducted for many years, similar studies in humans have progressed slowly despite the great promise of such research. Many of these studies have been funded by private companies. This is largely a consequence of governmental restrictions on research funding, due to ethical considerations that are related to the origins of stem cells. So far the only known sources of pluripotent stem cells are early embryos and specific types of cancer cells known as teratocarcinoma cells. Fetuses are also a source of some types of specialized stem cells. More recent findings that certain types of specialized stem cells also exist in tissues of adult mice, as well as human adults and children, may alleviate some ethical concerns. Unfortunately, these cells are rare and lack many of the advantages of embryonic cells.

---

in cells, known as **functional genomics,** includes the analysis of patterns of gene expression in different cell types. One approach is the use of DNA microarrays, which rely heavily on methods that originated in the computer industry (Fig. 16–5). Thousands of tiny spots of DNA, known as microdots, are "printed" on a "chip", which is usually a glass microscope slide. Each microdot contains many single-stranded copies of a fragment of DNA from a particular organism, and collectively all the microdots on a chip are a microarray that contains all or most of the DNA in that organism's genome.

RNA is then extracted from cells the researchers wish to study, and DNA complementary to it (cDNA) is synthesized using reverse transcriptase (see Chapter 14). The single-stranded cDNA molecules are tagged with a fluorescent dye and incubated with the DNA on the chip under conditions that promote complementary base pairing. If a particular segment of DNA on the chip corresponds to a gene that was very actively transcribed in the cells being studied, there will be many copies of the corresponding cDNA available to bind to that microdot, causing it to fluoresce very brightly. Conversely, a microdot that fluoresces dimly or not at all is one that contains DNA that was not actively transcribed in those cells. The chips are then scanned by instruments that detect the patterns of fluorescence, and the data are analyzed by powerful computers. These methods allow researchers to compare patterns of gene expression, as measured by RNA synthesis, in various cell types, or in the same cell type under different conditions.

Figure 16–5 Gene expression. Data from an experiment showing the expression of thousands of genes on a single GeneChip® probe array. *(Image courtesy of Affymetrix)*

MOLECULAR GENETICS HAS REVOLUTIONIZED THE STUDY OF DEVELOPMENT

Development has been an important area of research for many years, and considerable effort has been expended on studying the development of invertebrate and vertebrate animals. By identifying patterns of morphogenesis in different animals, researchers have been able to identify similarities, as well as differences, in the basic plan of development from a fertilized egg to an adult in organisms ranging from the sea urchin to mammals (see Chapter 49).

In addition to descriptive studies, many classic experiments have established important evidence concerning how groups of cells differentiate and undergo pattern formation. Researchers have developed elaborate screening programs to detect mutations that allow them to identify large numbers of developmental genes in both plants and animals. They then exploit a wide variety of molecular genetic techniques and other sophisticated methodologies to determine how those genes work and how they interact to coordinate developmental processes.

Certain organisms are well suited for studies of the genetic control of development

In studies of the genetic control of development, the choice of an organism to use as an experimental system has become increasingly important. One of the most powerful approaches involves the isolation of mutants with arrested or abnormal development at a particular stage. Not all organisms have useful characteristics that allow developmental mutants to be isolated and maintained for future study. The genetics of the fruit fly, *Drosophila melanogaster,* is so thoroughly understood that this organism has become one of the most important systems for such studies. Other organisms such as the nematode worm, *Caenorhabditis elegans;* the laboratory mouse, *Mus musculus;* certain plants, including *Arabidopsis thaliana,* a tiny weed with many convenient features; and some simple eukaryotes, such as the yeast *Saccharomyces cerevisiae,* have also become important models in developmental genetics. Each of these organisms has attributes that make it particularly useful for examining certain aspects of development.

DROSOPHILA MELANOGASTER PROVIDES RESEARCHERS WITH A WEALTH OF DEVELOPMENTAL MUTANTS

Undoubtedly the most extensive (and spectacular) examples of genes that control development have been identified in the fruit fly, *Drosophila melanogaster.* The *Drosophila* genome sequence became available in late 1999, and it has been determined that it includes about 13,600 protein-coding genes. One of the traditional advantages of using *Drosophila* as a research organism is the abundance of mutants (including developmental mutants) available for study and the relative ease with which a new mutation can be directly mapped on the chromosomes. The genetic analysis is greatly facilitated by special chromosomes found in certain tissues with large, metabolically active cells, including the salivary glands of the larvae. These **polytene** ("many-stranded") chromosomes are unusual interphase chromosomes formed when the DNA replicates many times but without mitosis and cytokinesis.

A typical polytene chromosome may consist of more than 1000 DNA double helices (along with associated histones and other proteins) aligned side by side (Fig. 16–6). Polytene chromosomes are therefore quite large and show a pattern of bands that is very useful in assigning a particular gene to a particular location on the chromosome. When a gene is active, the chromosome band in which it resides uncoils and forms a **puff,** which is a site of intense RNA synthesis. This evidence of gene activity is similar to that observed in lampbrush chromosomes of certain female meiotic cells (see Fig. 9–13).

Studies of *Drosophila* are also facilitated by the fact that foreign DNA can be injected into eggs and become incorporated into the fly's DNA in a process called **transformation** (by analogy with transformation in prokaryotes).

The *Drosophila* life cycle includes egg, larval, pupal, and adult stages

The life cycle of *Drosophila* consists of several distinct stages (Fig. 16–7). After the egg is fertilized, a period of embryogenesis occurs during which the zygote develops into a sexually immature form known as a **larva** (pl., *larvae*). After hatching from the egg, each larva undergoes several molts (shedding of the external covering or cuticle). Each molt allows an increase in size until the larva is ready to pupate. **Pupation** involves a molt and the hardening of the new external cuticle, so that the pupa is completely encased. The insect then undergoes a complete **metamorphosis** (change in form). During that time, most of the larval tissues degenerate and other tissues differentiate to form the body parts of the sexually mature adult fly.

The larvae are wormlike in appearance and look nothing like the adult flies. However, very early in embryogenesis of the developing larvae, precursor cells of many of the adult structures are organized as relatively undifferentiated paired structures called **imaginal discs.** This term comes from **imago,** the name given to the adult form of the insect. Each imaginal disc occupies a definite position in the larva and will form a specific structure, such as a wing or a leg, in the adult body (Fig. 16–8). The discs are formed by the time embryogenesis is complete and the larva is ready to begin feeding. In some respects the larva can be thought of as a complex developmental stage that is simply used to feed and nurture the precursor cells that give rise to the adult fly (which is the only form that can reproduce).

The organization of the precursors of the adult structures, including the imaginal discs, is under complex genetic control. So far more than 50 genes have been identified that specify the

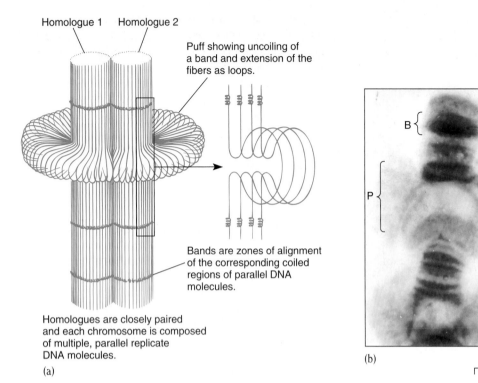

Homologue 1   Homologue 2

Puff showing uncoiling of a band and extension of the fibers as loops.

Bands are zones of alignment of the corresponding coiled regions of parallel DNA molecules.

Homologues are closely paired and each chromosome is composed of multiple, parallel replicate DNA molecules.

(a)

(b)   10 μm

Figure 16–6 *Drosophila* polytene chromosomes. These large chromosomes, found in cells of the salivary gland and some other tissues, aid in locating genes. **(a)** In contrast with the chromosomes of most somatic cells, homologous polytene chromosomes are paired, and each consists of more than 1000 parallel longitudinal DNA fibers, produced by repeated DNA synthesis without mitosis. **(b)** LM of a region of a polytene chromosome showing the pattern of stained bands of condensed chromatin (B) and decondensed puffed bands (P), which are the sites of intense RNA synthesis. Although the chromosome banding patterns vary from tissue to tissue, those in a particular tissue are constant and can be associated with the locations of mutant genes by genetic mapping and DNA hybridization methods.   *(b, Courtesy of U. Clever)*

formation of the discs, their positions within the larva, and their ultimate functions within the adult fly. Those genes have been identified through mutations that either prevent certain discs from forming or alter their structure or ultimate fate.

Many *Drosophila* developmental mutants affect the body plan

Many developmental mutants of *Drosophila* have been identified. Their effects on development in various combinations have been examined and studied extensively at the molecular level. In our discussion we pay particular attention to those that affect the segmented body plan of the organism, both in the larva and in the adult.

Early *Drosophila* development occurs in the following way. The structure of the egg becomes organized as it develops in the ovary of the female, as stores of messenger RNA (mRNA), along with yolk proteins and other cytoplasmic molecules, are passed into it from the surrounding maternal cells. Immediately after fertilization, the zygote nucleus in the egg divides, beginning a

remarkable series of 13 mitotic divisions. Each of these divisions takes only 5 or 10 minutes, which means that the DNA in the nuclei is replicated constantly at a very rapid rate. During that time the nuclei do not synthesize RNA. Cytokinesis does not take place, and the nuclei produced by the first seven divisions remain at the center of the embryo until the eighth division occurs. At that time, most of the nuclei start to migrate out from the center and to become localized at the periphery of the embryo. This is known as the *syncytial blastoderm* stage because the nuclei are not surrounded by individual plasma membranes. (A *syncytium* is a structure containing many nuclei.) Subsequently, cell membranes do form, and the embryo becomes known as a *cellular blastoderm.*

Maternal effect genes organize the egg cytoplasm

The genes that act to organize the structure of the egg cell are referred to as **maternal effect genes.** These are genes in the surrounding maternal tissues that are transcribed to produce mRNA

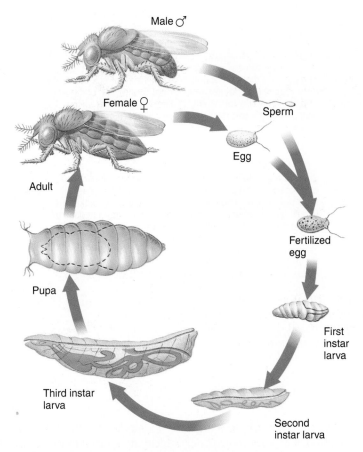

Figure 16–7 ***Drosophila* development.** A *Drosophila* passes through several stages as it develops from the egg to the sexually mature adult fly. About 12 days are required to complete the life cycle at 25° C. (The dotted lines within the pupa represent the animal undergoing metamorphosis.)

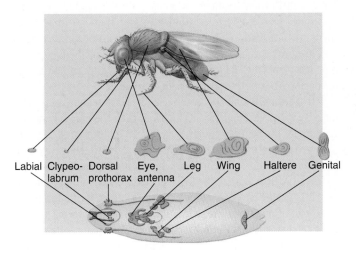

Figure 16–8 Imaginal discs. Each pair of discs in a *Drosophila* larva *(bottom)* develops into a specific pair of structures in the adult fly.

molecules to be transported into the developing egg. Analysis of mutants defective in these genes has revealed that many are involved in establishing the polarity of the embryo by designating which parts of the egg are dorsal or ventral and which are anterior or posterior (see Chapter 28); thus they are known as *egg polarity genes.*

Figure 16–9*a* illustrates concentration gradients for particular types of maternal mRNA in the very early embryo, at the beginning of nuclear migration. These mRNA transcripts of some of the maternal effect genes can be identified by their ability to hybridize with radioactive DNA probes derived from cloned genes. Alternatively, their protein products can be identified by antibodies that specifically bind to them. The protein produced by translation of the mRNA appears to be part of a system of determinants that organize the early pattern of development in the embryo. A combination of these protein gradients may provide positional information that specifies the fate of each nucleus or cell within the embryo. That information may then be interpreted by a cell as signals specifying the developmental path it should follow. For example, owing to the absence of specific signals in the egg, maternal effect mutations can produce an embryo with two heads or two posterior ends.

In many cases, the phenotype associated with a maternal effect mutation can be reversed by injecting normal maternal mRNA into the mutant embryo. When this is done, the fly develops normally, indicating that the gene product is needed only for a short time at the earliest stages of development.

Zygotic segmentation genes continue and extend the developmental program

As the nuclei start to migrate to the periphery of the embryo, **zygotic genes** begin to be expressed as production of some of the embryonic mRNA begins. (It is customary to refer to the genes of the embryo itself as zygotic genes, even though the embryo is no longer a zygote.) Zygotic genes that extend the developmental program beyond the pattern established by the maternal genome include the zygotic segmentation genes and the homeotic genes.

So far geneticists have identified at least 24 **zygotic segmentation genes** that are responsible for generating a repeating pattern of body segments within the embryo. The zygotic segmentation genes fall into three classes—gap genes, pair-rule genes, and segment polarity genes—representing a rough hierarchy of gene action.

The **gap genes** are apparently the first set of zygotic segmentation genes to act. These genes seem to interpret the maternal anterior-posterior information in the egg and begin organization of the body segments. A mutation in one of the gap genes usually causes the absence of one or more body segments in an embryo (Figs. 16–9*b* and 16–10*a*).

The other two classes of zygotic segmentation genes do not act on small groups of body segments but rather affect all segments. For example, mutations in the **pair-rule genes** delete every other segment (Fig. 16–10*b*), whereas mutations in **segment polarity genes** produce segments in which one part is

Morphology   **Gene activity**

Anterior   Posterior Anterior   Posterior

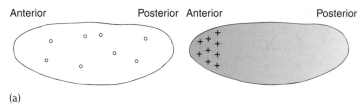 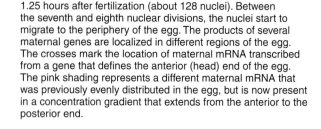

(a)

1.25 hours after fertilization (about 128 nuclei). Between the seventh and eighth nuclear divisions, the nuclei start to migrate to the periphery of the egg. The products of several maternal genes are localized in different regions of the egg. The crosses mark the location of maternal mRNA transcribed from a gene that defines the anterior (head) end of the egg. The pink shading represents a different maternal mRNA that was previously evenly distributed in the egg, but is now present in a concentration gradient that extends from the anterior to the posterior end.

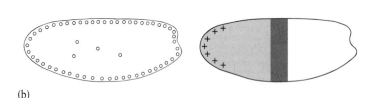

(b)

2 hours after fertilization (about 1500 nuclei). Most of the nuclei have reached the perimeter of the egg and have started to make their own mRNA. The maternal mRNA shown in pink in part *(a)* is now being transcribed from the corresponding zygotic gene by the nuclei in the anterior part of the embryo *(crosses)*. The mRNA from a certain zygotic gap gene is transcribed from cells in only one segment in the middle of the embryo shown in black. If that gap gene is mutated, part of the embryo will be missing because that particular segment will fail to develop.

Figure 16–9 Early development of *Drosophila*. Longitudinal sections illustrating the morphology of the embryo at different times after fertilization *(left)* are matched with greatly simplified representations of the patterns of gene activity at each stage *(right)*. *(After Akam, M.E., "The Molecular Basis for Metameric Pattern in the* Drosophila *Embryo." Development, Vol. 101, 1987)*

missing and the remaining part is duplicated as a mirror image (Fig. 16–10c). The effects of the different classes of mutants are summarized in Table 16–1.

Each zygotic segmentation gene can be shown to have distinctive times and places in the embryo in which it is most active

Mutant	Mutant	Mutant
Wild-type	Wild-type	Wild-type
(a) Gap genes	(b) Pair-rule genes	(c) Segment-polarity genes

Figure 16–10 Zygotic segmentation genes in *Drosophila*. Gap genes **(a)**, pair-rule genes **(b)**, and segment polarity genes **(c)** control the pattern of body segments in a *Drosophila* embryo. The blue bands mark the regions in which the protein products of these genes are normally expressed in wild-type embryos. These same regions are absent in embryos in which the gene is mutated; the resulting phenotype is characteristic of the class to which the gene belongs. *(After Nüsslein-Volhard, C., and E. Wieschaus, "Mutations Affecting Segment Number and Polarity in* Drosophila.*" Nature, Vol. 287, 1980)*

(Fig. 16–11). The observed pattern of expression of the maternal and zygotic genes controlling segmentation indicates that cells destined to form adult structures are determined by a progressive series of developmental decisions. First, the anterior-posterior (head-to-tail) axis and the dorsal and ventral regions of the embryo are determined by maternal segmentation genes thought to form gradients of **morphogens** in the egg. A morphogen is a chemical agent that affects the differentiation of cells and the development of form.

Zygotic segmentation genes then respond to the amounts of various morphogens at each location to control the production of a series of segments from the head to the posterior region. Then, within each segment, other genes are activated that read the position of the segment and interpret that information to specify which body part that segment should become. Within every segment, each cell's position is further specified so that it now has a specific "address" that is designated by combinations of the activities of the various regulatory genes.

It is thought that the zygotic segmentation genes act in sequence, with the gap genes acting first, then the pair-rule genes, and finally the segment polarity genes. In addition, members of each group can interact with each other. Each time a new group of genes acts, cells of a particular group become more finely restricted in the way that they will develop. As the embryo develops, it is progressively subdivided into smaller specified regions.

Most, if not all, of the segmentation genes (maternal and zygotic) code for **transcription factors,** proteins that regulate transcription in eukaryotic cells (see Chapter 13). For example, some of the segmentation genes code for a "zinc-finger" type of DNA-binding regulatory protein (see Fig. 13–8b). Others code for other types of transcription factors; these are discussed in the

TABLE 16–1 Classes of Genes Involved in Pattern Formation of Embryonic Segments in *Drosophila*

Type of Gene	Site of Gene Activity	Effects of Mutant Alleles and Proposed Function(s) of Genes
Maternal effect genes	Maternal tissues (ovary)	Many maternal effect mutations alter the polarity of the embryo; initiate pattern formation by activating zygotic regulatory genes in nuclei in certain locations in embryo
Zygotic segmentation genes		
Gap genes	Embryo	Mutant alleles cause one or more segments to be missing; some may influence activity of pair-rule genes, segment polarity genes, and homeotic genes
Pair-rule genes	Embryo	When mutated, cause alternate segments to be missing; some may influence activity of segment polarity genes and homeotic genes
Segment polarity genes	Embryo	Mutant alleles delete part of every segment and replace it with mirror image of remaining structure; may influence activity of homeotic genes
Homeotic genes	Embryo	Homeotic mutations cause parts of fly to form structures normally formed in other segments; control the identities of the segments

next section. The fact that many of the genes involved in the control of development code for transcription factors indicates that those proteins indeed act as genetic "switches" regulating the expression of other genes. Once proteins that function as transcription factors have been identified, it is possible to use the purified proteins to identify the DNA target sequences to which they bind. This approach has been increasingly useful in identifying additional parts of the regulatory pathway involved in different stages of development. Transcription factors also play a role in cancer (see *Focus On: Oncogenes and Cancer*).

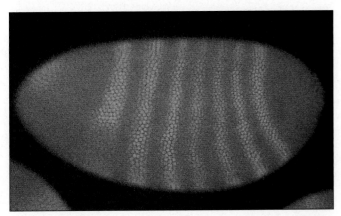

50 μm

Figure 16–11 Activity of a zygotic segmentation gene. The bright bands in this fluorescence LM reveal the presence of mRNA transcribed from one of the zygotic pair-rule loci known as *fushi tarazu* (Japanese for "not enough segments"). The segments of the larva that are normally derived from these bands are absent when this locus is mutated. *(Courtesy of Steve Paddock, Jim Langeland, Sean Carroll, Howard Hughes Medical Institute, University of Wisconsin)*

Homeotic genes specify the identity of each body segment

One function of the zygotic segmentation genes is to regulate the expression of a separate set of genes that actually designates the final adult structure formed by each of the imaginal discs. These genes are called **homeotic genes.** Because of their involvement in segment identity, mutations in homeotic genes cause one body part to be substituted for another and therefore produce some peculiar changes in the adult. Among the most striking examples are the *Antennapedia* mutants, which have legs that grow from the head at a position where the antennae would normally be found (Fig. 16–12 on page 354).

Homeotic genes in *Drosophila* were originally identified by the altered phenotypes produced by mutant alleles. When geneticists analyzed the DNA sequences of several homeotic genes, they discovered a short DNA sequence of approximately 180 base pairs that is characteristic of many homeotic genes as well as some other genes that play a role in development. This DNA sequence has been termed the **homeobox.** Each homeobox codes for a protein functional region called a **homeodomain,** consisting of 60 amino acids that form four α-helices. One of these serves as a recognition helix, which can bind to specific DNA sequences and affect transcription. Thus the products of the homeotic genes, like those of the earlier acting zygotic segmentation genes, are transcription factors. In fact, some of the segmentation genes also contain homeoboxes.

MAKING THE CONNECTION

How does the study of homeobox-containing genes provide insights into evolutionary relationships? Consider studies on *Hox* genes, clusters of homeobox-containing genes that specify the anterior-posterior axis during development. *Hox* genes were initially discovered in *Drosophila*, where they are arranged in two adjacent groups on

Oncogenes and Cancer

A cancer cell lacks normal biological inhibitions. Normal cells are tightly regulated by control mechanisms that cause them to divide when necessary and prevent them from growing and dividing at inappropriate times. Cells of many tissues in the adult are normally prevented from dividing; they reproduce only to replace a neighboring cell that has died or become damaged. Cancer cells have escaped such controls and can divide continuously.

As a consequence of their abnormal growth pattern, some cancer cells eventually form a mass of tissue called a **tumor.** If the tumor remains at the spot where it originated, it can usually be removed by surgery. One of the major problems with certain forms of cancer is that the cells can escape from the controls that maintain them in their proper location. These cells can **metastasize,** or spread, to different parts of the body, invading other tissues and forming multiple tumors. Lung cancer, for example, is particularly deadly because its cells are highly metastatic and can enter the blood and spread to form tumors in other parts of the lungs, or in other organs such as the liver and the brain. Tumors with cells that can metastasize are referred to as **malignant tumors.**

We now know that cancer is a disease caused by altered gene expression. Using recombinant DNA methods, researchers identified many of the genes that, when they function abnormally, transform normal cells into cancer cells. Each kind of cancer cell apparently owes its traits to at least one, and possibly several, of a relatively small set of genes known as **oncogenes** (cancer-causing genes). Oncogenes arise from changes in the

expression of certain genes called **proto-oncogenes,** which are *normal* genes found in all cells and involved in the control of growth and development.

Oncogenes were first discovered in viruses that can infect mammalian cells and transform them into cancer cells *(malignant transformation).* Such viruses

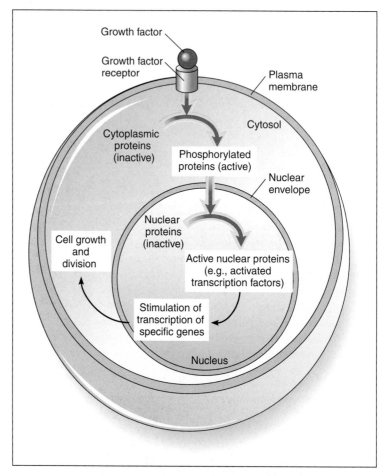

Simplified view of part of a growth control cascade. In this example, a growth factor stimulates cell growth. The growth factor receptor, as well as some of the other components of the system, are coded for by proto-oncogenes. When a proto-oncogene mutates, becoming an oncogene, the cell grows and divides even in the absence of the growth factor.

the chromosome: the *Antennapedia* complex and the *bithorax* complex. As homeobox-containing genes have been identified in other animals, including other arthropods, annelids (segmented worms), roundworms, and mammals, it has been found that these genes are also clustered and that their organization is remarkably similar to that seen in *Drosophila.* Figure 16–13 compares the organization of the *Hox* gene clusters of *Drosophila,* the roundworm *C. elegans* (to be discussed in the next section), and the laboratory

mouse. These images are matched with the regions where they are expressed in the animals. Remarkably, the *Drosophila* and mouse *Hox* genes are located in the same order along the chromosome, although the correlation is less exact for *C. elegans.* Furthermore, the linear order of the genes on the chromosome reflects the order of the corresponding regions they control (from anterior to posterior) in the animal. This organization apparently reflects the need for these genes to be transcribed in a specific temporal sequence.

can incorporate DNA sequences of the proto-oncogenes into their own nucleic acid. In some cases, the viruses alter the expression of the proto-oncogenes, converting them into oncogenes. This may happen if the DNA sequences come under the control of viral regulatory elements, which cause the gene to be transcribed at much higher than normal levels, or if the captured gene mutates so that its protein product is more active than the product of the normal proto-oncogene.

A proto-oncogene in a cell that has not been infected by a virus can also mutate and become an oncogene. One of the first oncogenes identified was isolated from a bladder tumor. In the cell that gave rise to the tumor, a proto-oncogene had undergone a single base-pair mutation; the result was that the amino acid glycine was replaced by a valine in the protein product of the gene. This subtle change was apparently a critical factor in the conversion of the normal cell into a cancer cell.

By means of recombinant DNA technology and other techniques of molecular biology, it has been possible for researchers to identify more than 60 oncogenes and their corresponding proto-oncogenes. Because the fundamental controls of normal cell division and differentiation probably evolved very early in the evolutionary history of eukaryotes, it is not surprising that very similar proto-oncogenes have been found in a diverse array of organisms, ranging from yeasts to humans. For example, the proto-oncogene counterpart of the oncogene found in some human bladder tumors has also been found in yeast cells.

Some of these controls are illustrated in greatly simplified form in the accompanying figure. The growth and division of cells can be triggered by one or more external signal molecules (see Chapter 5). Some of these substances are **growth factors** that bind to specific **growth factor receptors** associated with the cell surface, initiating a cascade of events inside the cell. Often the growth factor receptor complex acts as a **protein kinase** (an enzyme that phosphorylates proteins), which then phosphorylates specific amino acids of several cytoplasmic proteins. This posttranslational modification usually results in the activation of previously inactive enzymes. These activated enzymes are then able to catalyze the activation of certain nuclear proteins, many of which are transcription factors. Activated transcription factors bind to their DNA targets and stimulate transcription of specific sets of genes that initiate growth and cell division.

Even in the simplified scenario presented in the figure, it is evident that multiple steps are required to control cell proliferation. Remarkably, the proto-oncogenes that encode the products responsible for many of these steps have been identified. The current list of known proto-oncogenes includes genes that code for various growth factors or growth factor receptors and genes that respond to stimulation by growth factors (including many transcription factors). When one of these proto-oncogenes is expressed inappropriately (i.e., becomes an oncogene), the cell may misinterpret the signal and respond by growing and

dividing. For example, in some cases a proto-oncogene encoding a growth factor receptor becomes mutated in a way that causes the growth factor receptor to no longer be regulated. It is always switched "on," even in the absence of the growth factor that normally controls it.

Not all genes that cause cancer when mutated are proto-oncogenes. About one-half of all cancers are caused by a mutation in a **tumor suppressor gene.** These genes, also known as **anti-oncogenes,** normally interact with growth inhibiting factors to block cell division. When mutated they lose their ability to "put on the brakes," and uncontrolled growth ensues.

Certain oncogenes appear to be particularly common and are found in a variety of tumors. However, a change in a single proto-oncogene is usually insufficient to cause a cell to become malignant. The development of cancer is usually a multistep process involving both oncogenes and mutated tumor suppressor genes. Additional factors, such as the inappropriate activation of the enzyme responsible for the maintenance of telomeres, may also play a role (see Chapter 11, *On the Cutting Edge: Telomerase, Cellular Aging, and Cancer*). As more of these genes are discovered and their complex interactions are unraveled, we will gain a fuller understanding of the control of growth and development. This understanding is leading to improved diagnosis and treatment of various cancers.

Drosophila has only one *Antennapedia-bithorax* complex. However, humans and other vertebrates have four similar *Hox* gene clusters, each located in a different chromosome. These complexes probably arose through gene duplication. The fact that extra copies of these genes are present helps explain why mutations causing homeotic-like transformations are seldom seen in vertebrate animals. However, one particular type of *Hox* mutation that has been described in both mice and humans causes abnormalities in the limbs and genitalia. The involvement of the genitalia provides a further explanation for the rarity of these mutant alleles, because affected individuals are unlikely to reproduce.

The fact that very similar developmental controls are seen in organisms as diverse as insects, unsegmented roundworms, and vertebrates (including humans) indicates that the basic mechanism evolved early and has been highly conserved in all animals

Eye   Homeotic leg

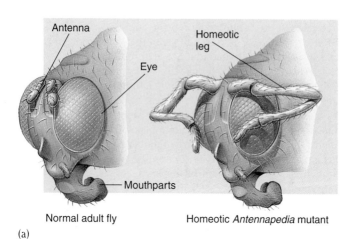

Antenna

Eye

Mouthparts

Normal adult fly

Homeotic leg

Homeotic *Antennapedia* mutant

(a)

(b)

250 µm

Figure 16–12 The *Antennapedia* locus. *Antennapedia* mutations of *Drosophila* cause homeotic transformations in which the antennae are replaced by legs or parts of legs. **(a)** Head of a normal fly and a fly with an *Antennapedia* mutation. **(b)** SEM of the head of a fly with a mutant allele of the *Antennapedia* locus that produces an extreme phenotype. Most of the mutant alleles of this locus produce only incomplete legs in place of the structures of the antennae. *(b, Dr. Thomas Kaufman)*

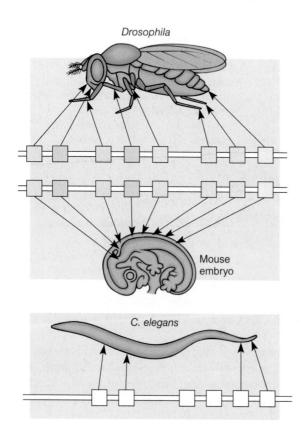

Drosophila

Mouse embryo

C. elegans

Figure 16–13 *Hox* gene clusters. The *Hox* gene clusters of *Drosophila* and the laboratory mouse are correlated with the parts of the body in which each gene is expressed. (Only one of the four mouse *Hox* gene clusters is shown.) Note that in each organism the order of the genes on the chromosome reflects their spatial order of expression in the embryo. Although not evident in the figure, some of these regions of expression overlap. The most anteriorly expressed genes are shown to the left, while those expressed most posteriorly are at the right. *C. elegans* also has similar clustered genes, although the gene order is not identical and there is evidence that not all are required for embryonic development. *(After Kenyon, C., and B. Wang. "A Cluster of* Antennapedia—*Class Homeobox Genes in a Nonsegmented Animal." Science, Vol. 253, 2 Aug, 1991; and Van Auken, K., et al. "Caenorhabditis elegans Embryonic Axial Patterning Requires Two Recently Discovered Posterior-Group* Hox *Genes." Proceedings of the National Academy of Sciences, Vol. 97, 25 Apr. 2000)*

that have an anterior-posterior axis, even those that are not segmented. It is becoming clear that once a successful way of controlling groups of genes and integrating their activities evolved, it was retained, although it has apparently been modified in various ways that provided for alterations of the body plan.

The finding of homeobox-like genes in plants suggests that these genes may be of ancient origin and may in fact be the genes that made multicellularity possible. Further investigations may allow researchers to develop an overall model of how the rudiments of morphogenesis are controlled in both plants and animals. These systems of master genes that control development are proving to be a rich source of "molecular fossils" that are illuminating evolutionary history in new and exciting ways.

■ *CAENORHABDITIS ELEGANS* HAS A VERY RIGID EARLY DEVELOPMENTAL PATTERN

C. elegans, a roundworm or nematode (see Chapter 29), has one of the simplest systems of genetic control of development. The study of this animal was begun in the 1960s by Sydney Brenner, a molecular biologist. Its genome of almost 19,000 genes was the first animal genome to be sequenced, and today it is an important tool for answering basic questions about the development of individual cells within a multicellular organism.

Even as an adult, *C. elegans* is only 1.5 mm long and contains only about 1000 somatic cells (the exact number depends on the sex) and about 2000 germ-line cells. Individuals can be either **hermaphrodites** (organisms with both sexes in the same individual) or males. Hermaphroditic individuals are self-fertilizing, which makes it easy to obtain offspring homozygous for newly induced recessive mutations. The availability of males that can mate with the hermaphrodites makes it possible to do genetic crosses as well.

Because the worm's body is transparent, researchers can follow the development of literally every one of its somatic cells (Fig. 16–14) using a Nomarski differential interference microscope (see Chapter 4). As a result of efforts by several laboratories, the lineage of each somatic cell in the adult has now been determined. Those studies have shown that the nematode has a very rigid developmental pattern. After fertilization, the egg undergoes repeated divisions to produce about 550 cells that make up the small, sexually immature larva. After the larva hatches from the egg case, further cell divisions give rise to the adult worm.

The lineage of each somatic cell in the adult can be traced to a single cell in a small group of **founder cells,** which are formed early in development (Fig. 16–15). If a particular founder cell is destroyed or removed, the structures that would normally develop from that cell are missing. A rigid developmental pattern, in which the fates of the cells are largely predetermined, is referred to as **mosaic development.** Each cell has a specific fate in the embryo, just as in art a specific tile forms a particular part of the pattern of a mosaic picture.

It was originally thought that each organ system in *C. elegans* might be derived from only one founder cell. Detailed analysis of cell lineages, however, reveals that many of the structures found in the adult, such as the nervous system and the musculature, are in fact derived from more than one founder cell (Fig. 16–15*h*). Conversely, a few lineages have been identified in

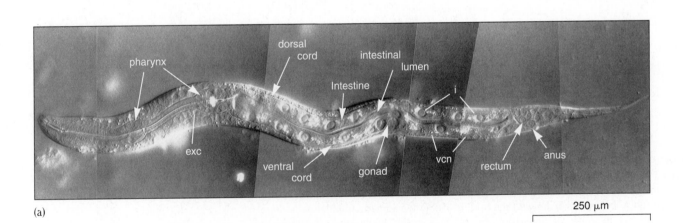

(a)

250 μm

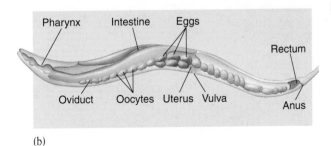

(b)

■ **Figure 16–14** *Caenorhabditis elegans.* This transparent organism has a fixed number of somatic cells. **(a)** Nomarski interference LM of the adult hermaphrodite nematode. (The abbreviated labels "exc," "i," and "vcn" refer to certain cells of the excretory, digestive and nervous system, respectively.) **(b)** Diagram illustrating structures in the adult hermaphrodite. The sperm-producing structures are not shown. *(a, Courtesy of Dr. John Sulston, Medical Research Council; b, from Fig. 22–6a in Walbot, V., and N. Holder,* Developmental Biology. *Random House, New York, 1987)*

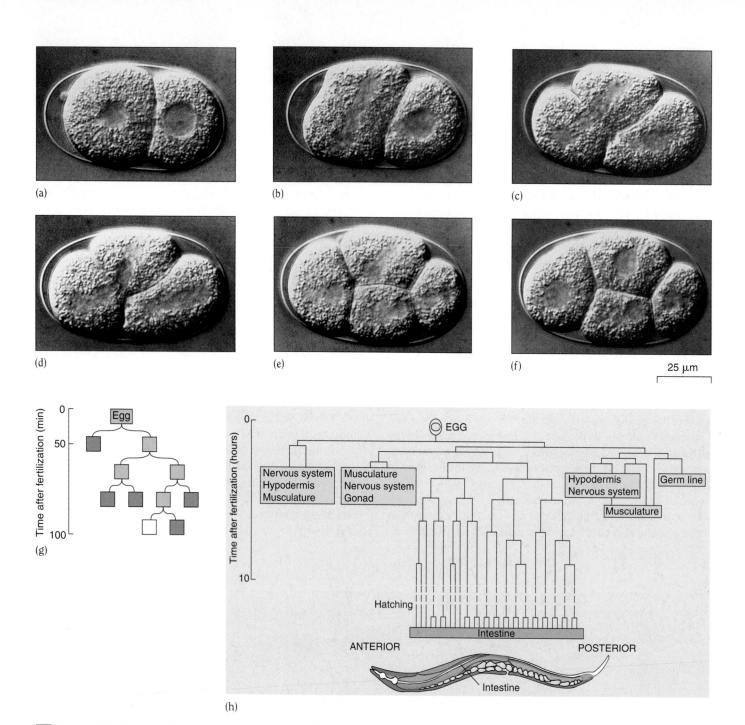

Figure 16–15 Cell lineages of *C. elegans*. All somatic cells of *C. elegans* are derived from five somatic founder cells produced during the early cell divisions of the embryo. **(a–f)** Nomarski interference LMs showing the early cell divisions of the embryo. **(g)** A lineage map showing the origins of the five somatic founder cells *(blue)*. The cell shown in white will give rise to the germ cells. **(h)** This lineage map traces the development of the cells that form the intestine. The dashed lines represent many cell divisions of a particular lineage. *(a–f, E. Schierenberg, from G. von Ehrenstein and E. Schierenberg, in* Nematodes as Biological Models, *Vol. 1, B. Zuckerman, ed. Academic Press, New York, 1980)*

which a nerve cell and a muscle cell are derived from the division of a single cell. Mutations affecting cell lineages have been isolated, and many of these appear to have properties that would be expected of genes involved in control of developmental decisions.

By using microscopic laser beams small enough to destroy individual cells, it is possible to determine what influence one cell may have on the development of a neighbor. Consistent with the rigid pattern of cell lineages, destruction of an individual cell in *C. elegans* results, in most cases, in the absence of all of the structures derived from that cell but with the normal differentiation of all of the neighboring somatic cells. This suggests that development in each cell is regulated through its own internal program.

However, the developmental pattern of *C. elegans* is not entirely mosaic. There are cases in which differentiation of a cell can be influenced by interactions with particular neighboring cells, a phenomenon known as **induction.** One example is the formation of the vulva (pl., *vulvae*), the structure through which the eggs are laid. A single nondividing cell, called the *anchor cell,* is a part of the ovary (the structure in which the germ-line cells undergo meiosis to produce the eggs). The anchor cell attaches to the ovary and to a point on the outer surface of the animal, triggering the formation of a passage through which the eggs pass to the outside. When the anchor cell is present, cells on the surface organize to form the vulva and its opening. If the anchor cell is destroyed by a laser beam, however, the vulva does not form and the cells that would normally form the vulva remain as surface cells (Fig. 16–16). The anchor cell therefore induces the surface cells to form a vulva.

Analysis of certain cell lineage mutations has been useful in understanding such inductive interactions. For example, several types of mutations cause more than one vulva to form. In such mutant animals, multiple vulvae form even if the anchor cell is destroyed. Thus, the mutant cells do not require an inductive signal from an anchor cell to form a vulva. Evidently in these mutants the gene or genes responsible for vulva formation are constitutive. Conversely, mutants lacking a vulva are also known. In some of these, the cells that would normally form the vulva appear unable to respond to the inducing signal from the anchor cell.

During development in *C. elegans,* there are instances in which cells die shortly after they are produced. This phenomenon, known as **apoptosis** or **programmed cell death** (see Chapter 4) has been observed in a wide variety of organisms, both plant and animal. For example, the human hand is formed as a webbed structure, but the fingers become individualized when the cells between them die. In *C. elegans,* these programmed cell deaths are under genetic control, and several mutants have been isolated that alter the pattern of these deaths. The loci identified by these mutations, in addition to mutations with similar effects in other organisms, are being analyzed at the molecular level and should shed considerable light on the general phenomena of cellular aging and programmed cell death.

Mutations are also known that appear to identify genes involved in developmental timing, known as **chronogenes.** One such locus has recessive alleles that cause certain cells to adopt fates that would ordinarily be seen later in development. Dominant al-

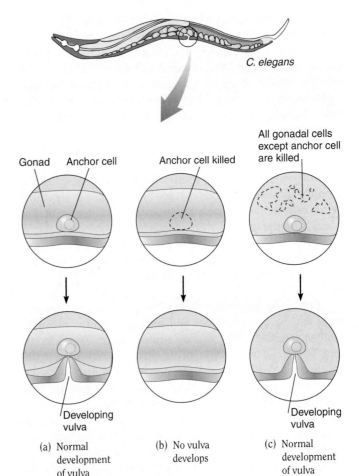

Figure 16–16 Induction. A single anchor cell induces neighboring cells to form the vulva in *C. elegans*. This schematic diagram shows how laser destruction of single cells or a group of cells can be used to demonstrate the influence of a cell on its neighbors.

leles of the same locus cause certain cells to adopt fates that would usually be expressed earlier. Such genes appear to be good candidates for "switches" that control developmental timing.

THE MOUSE IS A MODEL FOR MAMMALIAN DEVELOPMENT

Mammalian embryos develop in markedly different ways from the embryos of *Drosophila* and *C. elegans*. The laboratory mouse, *Mus musculus,* is the best studied example of early mammalian development. Numerous genes affecting development have been identified in the mouse, and the mouse genome sequence was virtually completed in 2001.

Cells of very early mouse embryos are totipotent

The early development of the mouse and other mammals is similar in many ways to human development, which is described in detail in Chapter 49. During the early developmental period, the embryo lives free in the reproductive tract of the female. It then implants in the wall of the uterus, after which its nutritional and respiratory needs are met by the mother. Consequently, mammalian eggs are very small and contain little in the way of food reserves. Almost all research on mouse development has concentrated on the stages leading to implantation because during those stages the embryo is free-living and can be experimentally manipulated. During that period, critical developmental commitments take place that have a significant effect on the future organization of the embryo.

Following fertilization, a series of cell divisions gives rise to a loosely packed group of cells. It has been possible to show that all the cells in the very early mouse embryo are equivalent. For example, at the two-cell stage of mouse embryogenesis, one of the two cells can be destroyed by pricking it with a fine needle. Implanting the remaining cell into the uterus of a surrogate mother in most cases leads to the development of a normal mouse.

Conversely, two embryos at the eight-cell stage of development can be fused together and implanted into a surrogate mother, resulting in the development of a normal-sized mouse (Fig. 16–17). By using two embryos with different genetic markers (such as coat color), it can be demonstrated that the resulting mouse has four genetic parents. These mice have fur with patches of different colors derived from clusters of genetically different cells. Animals formed in this way are called **chimeras.** (The term *chimera*, derived from the name of a mythical beast that had the head of a lion, the body of a goat, and the tail of a snake, is used today to refer to any organism that contains two or more kinds of genetically dissimilar cells arising from differ-

ent zygotes.) Chimeras have been important in allowing the use of genetically marked cells to trace the fates of certain cells during development.

The responses of mouse embryos to these kinds of manipulations are in marked contrast with the mosaic or predetermined nature of early C. *elegans* development, in which the destruction of one of the founder cells results in loss of a significant portion of the embryo. For this reason, we say that the mouse (and presumably other mammals) has highly **regulative development.** This means that the early embryo acts as a self-regulating whole that can accommodate missing or extra parts. On the other hand, it has not been possible so far to demonstrate totipotency of cells from slightly later stages of mouse development. However, as discussed in *Focus On: Mammalian Cloning* earlier in the chapter, successful nuclear transplantation experiments on mice leading to live births demonstrate that at least some nuclei of differentiated mouse cells are totipotent.

Transgenic mice are used in studies of developmental regulation

In transformation experiments similar to those done with *Drosophila,* foreign DNA injected into fertilized mouse eggs can be incorporated into the chromosomes and expressed (Fig. 16–18). The resulting **transgenic** mice have given researchers insights into how genes are activated during development. In addition, mouse genes can be inactivated ("knocked out") by the technique of **gene targeting** (see Chapter 14). For example, when a locus known as *Engrailed-1* is knocked out in mice, the resulting embryos exhibit lethal abnormalities in brain development.

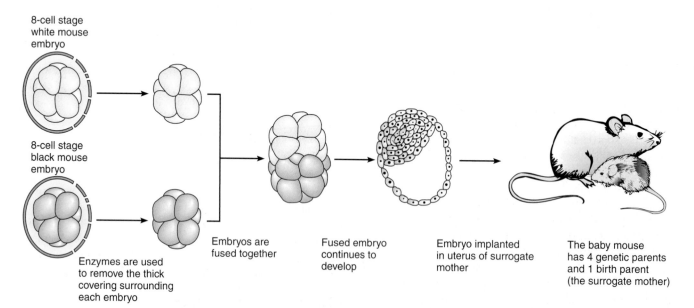

8-cell stage white mouse embryo

8-cell stage black mouse embryo

Enzymes are used to remove the thick covering surrounding each embryo

Embryos are fused together

Fused embryo continues to develop

Embryo implanted in uterus of surrogate mother

The baby mouse has 4 genetic parents and 1 birth parent (the surrogate mother)

Figure 16–17 Chimeric mice. Embryos can be removed from females of two different strains, and the cells combined in vitro. The resulting aggregate embryo continues to develop and is implanted in the uterus of a surrogate mother. The offspring has four different genetic parents. Although the surrogate mother is the birth mother, she is not genetically related.

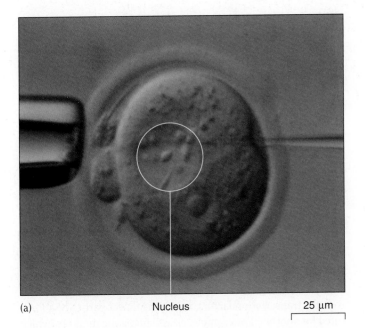

(a)   Nucleus   25 μm

Figure 16–18 Producing a transgenic mouse.
(a) Cloned DNA fragments are injected into the nucleus of a fertilized mouse egg by a glass needle, shown entering from the right, which is about 1 μm in diameter at the tip. The egg is held in place by suction on a holding pipet *(left)*. **(b)** The injected eggs are then surgically transferred to a surrogate mother. The presence of the foreign gene can be examined in the transgenic animal, or the animal can be bred to establish a transgenic line of mice. *(a, R.L. Brinster, University of Pennsylvania School of Veterinary Medicine)*

Scientists can identify a transgene (foreign gene) that has been introduced into a mouse and determine whether it is active by marking the gene in several ways. Sometimes a similar gene from a different species is used; its protein can be distinguished from the mouse protein by specific antibodies. It is also possible to construct a hybrid gene that contains the regulatory elements of a mouse gene of interest together with part of another gene that codes for a "reporter" protein, such as an enzyme not normally found in the mouse. Such studies have been important in showing which DNA sequences of a mouse homeobox gene determine where the gene is expressed in the embryo.

Many developmentally controlled genes have been introduced into mice and have yielded important information about gene regulation. When developmentally controlled genes from other species such as humans or rats have been introduced into mice, they are regulated in the same way that they normally are in the donor animal. For example, when introduced into the mouse, human genes encoding insulin, globin, and crystallin—which are normally expressed in cells of the pancreas, blood, and eye lens, respectively—are expressed only in those same tissues in the mouse. The fact that these genes are correctly expressed in their appropriate tissues indicates that the signals for tissue-specific gene expression are highly conserved through evolution. This is an exciting finding because it means that information on the

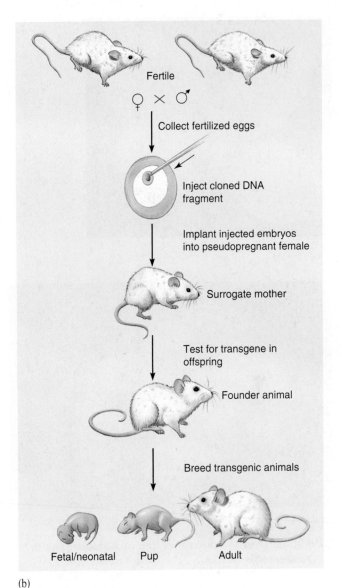

(b)

regulation of genes controlling development in one organism can have valuable applications to other organisms, including humans.

■ *ARABIDOPSIS THALIANA* IS A MODEL FOR PLANT DEVELOPMENT

Certain well-characterized plants are used in the study of the genetic control of development. Many of these are economically important crop plants such as corn, *Zea mays*. Genes with developmental effects are known in corn, including some that can be thought of as analogous to the homeotic genes of *Drosophila*.

Arabidopsis thaliana, the organism that is most widely used to study genetics and development in plants, is a member of the mustard family. Although *Arabidopsis* itself is a weed of no economic importance, it has several advantages for research. The plant completes its life cycle in just a few weeks and is small enough to be grown in a petri dish, permitting thousands of

(a)

(b)

■ Figure 16–19 Transformation of floral organs in *Arabidopsis* flowers. **(a)** A normal flower of *A. thaliana* has four outer leafy green sepals (hidden by the petals), four white petals, six stamens (the male reproductive structures), and a central pistil (the female reproductive structure). **(b)** This mutant has only sepals and petals because the C gene, which is responsible for the development of both the stamens and pistil, is nonfunctional and, therefore, not expressed. *(Dr. E. Meyerowitz, California Institute of Technology)*

individuals to be grown in limited space. Chemical mutagens can be used to produce mutant strains, and many developmental mutants have been isolated. Cloned foreign genes can be inserted into *Arabidopsis* cells, and these can be integrated into the chromosomes and expressed. These transformed cells can be induced to differentiate into transgenic plants.

In 2000 the *Arabidopsis* genome became the first plant genome to be sequenced. Although its genome is relatively small (the rice genome, for example, is about four times larger than that of *Arabidopsis*), it includes more than 25,000 protein-coding genes. In comparison, *Drosophila* has about 13,600 genes and *C. elegans* about 18,400. Many genes in *Arabidopsis* are function-

ally equivalent to genes in *Drosophila, C. elegans,* and other animal species.

Of particular importance to development are the more than 1500 genes that code for transcription factors (compared to 635 at last count for *Drosophila*). Not surprisingly, many of the genes that are known to specify the identities of the parts of the *Arabidopsis* flower code for transcription factors. During the development of *Arabidopsis* flowers, four distinct flower parts differentiate: sepals, petals, stamens, and carpels (Fig. 16–19*a*). Sepals cover and protect the flower when it is a bud, petals help attract animal pollinators to the flower, stamens produce pollen grains, and the pistil produces ovules, which develop into seeds following fertilization (see Chapter 27). The **ABC model** explains the molecular biology behind how these four organs develop. The A gene is needed to specify sepals, both A and B genes are needed to specify petals, both B and C genes are needed to specify stamens, and the C gene is needed to specify the pistil. Mutations in the A, B, or C organ-identity genes, all of which are homeotic and code for transcription factors, cause one flower part to be substituted for another. For example, class C homeotic mutants (which have an inactive C gene) have petals in place of stamens and sepals in place of the pistil. Therefore, the entire flower consists of only sepals and petals (Fig. 16–19*b*).

These findings in *Arabidopsis* vastly increase the number of molecular probes available from plants, which will allow many more genes that control development to be identified in various plant species and compared with genes from a wide range of organisms. The ongoing success of the *Arabidopsis* sequencing project has led to a bold new initiative, the 2010 Project, which has as its goal the understanding of the functions of all plant genes. This functional genomic information will lead to a far deeper understanding of plant development and evolutionary history.

■ SOME EXCEPTIONS TO THE PRINCIPLE OF NUCLEAR EQUIVALENCE HAVE BEEN FOUND

Although the concept of nuclear equivalence appears to apply to most cells in higher organisms, certain types of developmental regulation can involve physical changes in DNA. Such changes in the structure of the genome are not common.

Genomic rearrangements involve structural changes in DNA

The activity of some genes may be modified during development by different types of **genomic rearrangements** that lead to actual physical changes in the structure of the gene. In some cases, parts of genes are rearranged to make new coding sequences. This is an important mechanism for the development of the immune system (see Chapter 43).

One type of gene rearrangement is gene replacement. This takes place in the eukaryotic unicellular parasite *Trypanosoma,* which is a protozoon (see Fig. 24–5*b*). Trypanosomes carried by the tsetse fly in Africa cause sleeping sickness in humans and related diseases in other animals (Fig. 16–20). When the parasite infects humans, it is able to defeat the immune system by repeatedly changing the glycoprotein molecules that are exposed on the surface of its cell.

The trypanosome cell contains as many as 1000 different genes for cell surface molecules. The differences among their amino acid sequences are so great that an antibody that recognizes one of them would not recognize another. Only one or a few of those copies are expressed at any one time, depending on which copy is present at an **expression site,** which is usually located near the end of a chromosome. The genes in the expression site are exchanged in about one out of every 10^4 to 10^6 cells,

causing trypanosomes with novel antigens to appear every 7 to 10 days. Thus the infection is maintained by a constant supply of new cells with antigens that are not being targeted by the immune system. Although gene replacement clearly offers a mechanism that could serve as a regulatory "genetic switch," it is not known at present whether these mechanisms are relevant to development in multicellular eukaryotes.

Gene amplification increases the number of copies of specific genes

Some gene products are required in such large quantities during certain stages of development that a single copy of a gene cannot

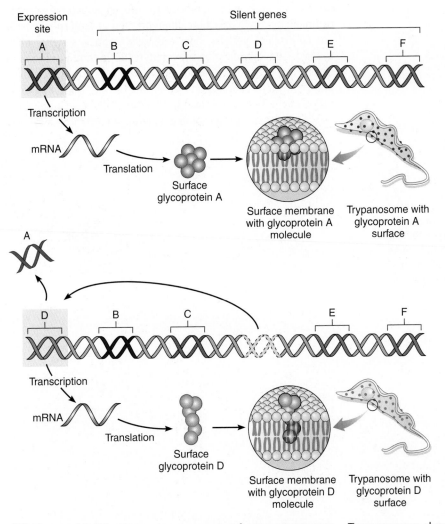

Figure 16–20 Gene rearrangement in trypanosomes. Trypanosomes change the molecules coating their surfaces frequently and are thus able to "outrun" the immune system of their human host. Each cell contains as many as a thousand silent genes, each coding for a different surface coat glycoprotein. Only one of those genes, which is located at a position near the end of a chromosome called the expression site, is active at any one time. As the trypanosomes multiply in the blood, occasionally a copy of one of the silent genes replaces the gene currently in the expression site, leading to the production of organisms with a new surface glycoprotein that is not recognized by the host's immune system.

be transcribed, nor can its mRNA be translated, rapidly enough to fill the needs of the developing cells. In certain cases, the number of gene copies may be increased, through a process known as **gene amplification,** to meet the demand. For example, the *Drosophila* chorion (eggshell) gene product is a protein made specifically in cells of the insect oviduct. These cells make massive amounts of the particular protein that envelops and protects the fertilized egg. The demand for chorion mRNA in those cells is met by specifically amplifying the chorion protein gene by DNA replication so that the DNA in that small region of the chromosome is copied many times (Fig. 16–21). In other cells of the insect body, however, the gene appears to exist as a single copy in the chromosome.

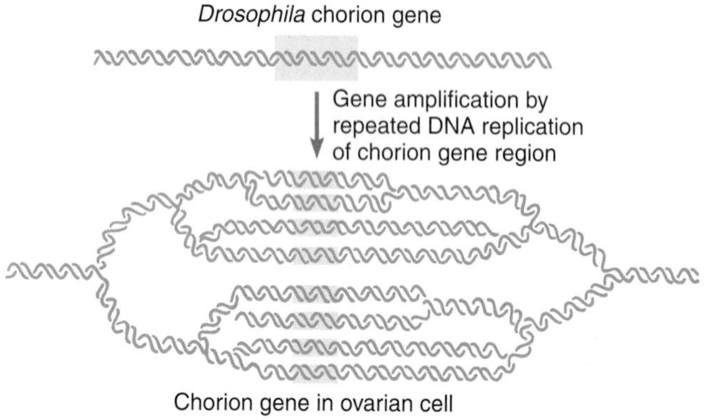

Drosophila chorion gene

Gene amplification by repeated DNA replication of chorion gene region

Chorion gene in ovarian cell

Figure 16–21 Gene amplification. In *Drosophila*, multiple replications of a small region of the chromosome result in the amplification of the chorion (eggshell) protein genes. Replication is initiated at a discrete chromosome origin of replication *(pink box)* for each copy of the gene that is produced; replication is randomly terminated, resulting in a series of forked structures in the chromosome.

■ THE STUDY OF DEVELOPMENTAL BIOLOGY PRESENTS MANY FUTURE CHALLENGES

New model organisms, each with characteristics that uniquely suit it for developmental studies, are now being added to the list of well-characterized experimental systems. In a herculean effort spearheaded by Christiane Nüsslein-Volhard of the University of Tübingen, Germany, researchers have identified more than 2000 developmental mutants of the zebrafish *(Danio rerio),* and the sequencing of its genome is underway. Previously best known to tropical fish enthusiasts, the zebrafish was chosen as a research subject mainly for its transparent embryos.

Scientists are now learning how genes are activated, inactivated, and modified and how batteries of master regulatory genes interact to control development. Eventually researchers expect to understand not only how differentiation and morphogenesis are controlled but also how the basic control systems have evolved. The identification of certain features common to many organisms, such as homeobox genes, will make the task easier, but the work has just begun (see On the Cutting Edge: The Evolution of the Vertebrate Head in Chapter 49). Many complex interactions remain to be explored, and many revelations await us.

I. **Development,** all the changes that occur in the life of an individual, includes the processes by which the descendants of a single cell specialize and organize into a complex organism.

   A. An organism contains many types of cells that are specialized both structurally and chemically to carry out specific functions. These cells are the product of a process of gradual commitment, called cell **determination,** which ultimately leads to the final step in cell specialization, called cell **differentiation.**

   B. **Morphogenesis,** the development of form, occurs through stages, referred to as **pattern formation,** in which cells become organized into structures.

   C. There is no evidence that genes are normally lost during most developmental processes.

      1. At least some nuclei from differentiated plant and animal cells are **totipotent** and contain all the genetic material that would be present in the nucleus of a zygote.

      2. **Nuclear equivalence** is the concept that, with a few exceptions, all of the nuclei of the differentiated **somatic** cells of an organism are identical to each other and to the nucleus of the single cell from which they descended.

      3. **Stem cells** can divide to produce differentiated descendants, yet retain the ability to divide to maintain the stem cell population. **Pluripotent** stem cells can give rise to all cell types.

      4. Differences among various cell types are apparently due to **differential gene expression. Functional genomics,** the study of the roles of specific genes, includes the analysis of patterns of RNA synthesis in cells.

II. Several organisms have characteristics that make them especially useful in studies of the genetic control of development.

   A. Many types of developmental mutants have been identified in the fruit fly, *Drosophila melanogaster.* Many of these mutations affect the segmented body plan of the organism.

      1. The earliest developmental program to operate in the egg is established by **maternal effect genes;** these are active prior to fertilization, and some produce gradients of **morphogens,** thereby affecting the segmentation pattern that is progressively established in the embryo.

      2. **Zygotic segmentation genes** do not become active until much later, when the embryo is no longer a zygote. They continue and extend the developmental program initiated by the maternal effect genes.

      3. The zygotic segmentation genes and their products interact with each other and with the products of the maternal effect genes according to a hierarchical pattern, with certain earlier acting genes controlling particular later acting genes.

      4. The later acting **homeotic genes** are responsible for specifying the identity of each segment.

      5. Many of the segmentation genes are known to code for **transcription factors.** Some of these contain a DNA sequence called a **homeobox,** which codes for a protein with a DNA-binding region called a **homeodomain.**

   B. *Caenorhabditis elegans* is a roundworm with **mosaic development,** a relatively rigid developmental pattern in which the fates of cells are largely predetermined.

      1. The lineage of every somatic cell in the adult is known, and each can be traced to a single **founder cell** in the early embryo.

      2. Mutations affecting cell lineages have been identified, and many of these appear to identify genes that control developmental processes such as **induction** (developmental interactions with neighboring cells), **programmed cell death (apoptosis),** and developmental timing (i.e., **chronogenes**).

   C. The laboratory mouse, *Mus musculus,* is extensively used in studies of mammalian development.

      1. In contrast to *C. elegans,* the mouse shows **regulative development,** which means that the very early embryo is a self-regulating whole and can develop normally even if it has extra or missing cells.

      2. **Transgenic** mice have been extremely useful in determining how genes are activated and regulated during development.

   D. Genes affecting the developmental pattern have also been identified in certain plants, including *Arabidopsis* and *Zea mays* (corn). Many of these code for transcription factors.

      1. The **ABC model** of interactions among three kinds of genes, designated the A gene, B gene, and C gene, explains how floral organs develop in *Arabidopsis.*

      2. All three genes are homeotic and code for **transcription factors.**

      3. Mutations in one or more of these genes cause one flower part to be substituted for another.

   E. Some homeobox genes are organized into complexes that appear to be systems of master genes specifying an organism's body plan. Remarkable parallels exist between the homeobox complex of *Drosophila* and those of other animals, including the laboratory mouse and *C. elegans.*

III. A few exceptions to the general rule of nuclear equivalence are known. Among these are **genomic rearrangement** (physical rearrangements of the DNA) and **gene amplification,** which provides more copies of certain genes for transcription.

1. Morphogenesis occurs through a series of stages known as (a) differentiation (b) determination (c) pattern formation (d) totipotency (e) selection

2. The "cloning" experiments carried out on amphibians demonstrated that (a) all differentiated amphibian cells are totipotent (b) some differentiated amphibian cells are totipotent (c) all nuclei from differentiated amphibian cells are totipotent (d) some nuclei from differentiated amphibian cells are totipotent (e) the mechanism of cellular differentiation always requires the loss of certain genes

3. *Drosophila* is a particularly good model for developmental studies because (a) a large number of developmental mutants are available (b) it has a fixed number of somatic cells in the adult (c) its embryos are transparent (d) it is a vertebrate (e) all of the above

4. The anterior-posterior axis of a *Drosophila* embryo is first established by certain (a) homeotic genes (b) maternal effect genes (c) zygotic segmentation genes (d) chronogenes (e) pair-rule genes

5. You discover a new *Drosophila* mutant in which mouthparts appear where the antennae are normally found. You would predict that the mutated gene is most likely a (a) homeotic gene (b) gap gene (c) pair-rule gene (d) maternal effect gene (e) segment polarity gene

6. Most zygotic segmentation genes code for (a) special transfer RNAs (b) enzymes (c) transcription factors (d) histones (e) transport proteins

7. The developmental pattern of *C. elegans* is said to be relatively mosaic because (a) development is controlled by gradients of morphogens (b) part of the embryo fails to develop if a founder cell is destroyed (c) some individuals are self-fertilizing hermaphrodites (d) all development is controlled by maternal effect genes (e) programmed cell deaths never occur

8. The formation of the vulva, the structure through which eggs are laid, in *C. elegans* involves (a) maternal effect genes that organize the egg cytoplasm (b) gradients of morphogens in the eggs (c) groups of *Hox* genes that form the *Antennapedia* complex and *bithorax* complex (d) induction of surface cells by the anchor cell (e) mutations in chronogenes, which control developmental timing

9. Which of the following illustrates the regulative nature of early mouse development? (a) the mouse embryo is free-living prior to implantation in the uterus (b) it is possible to produce a transgenic mouse (c) it is possible to produce a mouse in which a specific gene has been "knocked out" (d) genes related to *Drosophila* homeotic genes have been identified in mice (e) a chimeric mouse can be produced by fusing two mouse embryos

10. When the human gene that codes for insulin is introduced into fertilized mouse eggs that are subsequently allowed to develop, the insulin gene is correctly expressed in the mouse's pancreatic cells. This indicates that (a) the gene that codes for insulin is analogous to the homeotic genes of *Drosophila* (b) the signals for tissue-specific gene expression are highly conserved through evolution (c) like humans, the mouse has polytene chromosomes (d) unlike the rigid developmental pattern of *C. elegans*, the development of mice and humans is highly regulative (e) genomic rearrangements have occurred in the mouse embryo

11. *Arabidopsis* is useful as a model organism for the study of plant development because (a) it is of great economic importance (b) it has large polytene chromosomes (c) many developmental mutants have been isolated (d) it contains a large amount of DNA per cell (e) it has a rigid developmental pattern

12. According to the ABC model of floral organ development in *Arabidopsis*, the A gene is needed to specify sepals, the A and B genes to specify petals, the B and C genes to specify stamens, and the C gene to specify the pistil. If a mutation occurs in one of the B genes, rendering it inactive, the resulting flowers will consist of (a) sepals, petals, stamens, and pistils, (b) sepals, stamens, and pistils (c) petals, stamens, and pistils (d) sepals and pistils (e) petals and stamens

REVIEW QUESTIONS

1. Development consists of four main processes: cell determination, cell differentiation, pattern formation, and morphogenesis. Define each process and describe how they relate to one another.
2. What lines of evidence support the concept of nuclear equivalence?
3. What are the relative merits of *Drosophila*, *C. elegans*, the mouse, and *Arabidopsis* as model organisms for the study of development?
4. What is the value of homeotic genes in developmental studies?
5. Describe how transgenic organisms are useful in the study of gene regulation in development.
6. Give some examples of genomic rearrangements that are known to occur as a part of some developmental processes.
7. Under what conditions are examples of gene amplification seen?
8. What are oncogenes, and what is their relationship to cellular genes involved in the control of normal growth and development?

YOU MAKE THE CONNECTION

1. Why is an understanding of gene regulation in eukaryotes crucial to an understanding of developmental processes?
2. Why do developmental biologists need to understand biological diversity? Why is it necessary for scientists to study development in more than one type of organism?

RECOMMENDED READINGS

Hamadel, H., and C.A. Afshari. "Gene Chips and Functional Genomics." *American Scientist,* Vol. 88, Nov.–Dec. 2000. A discussion of the current and potential uses of gene chip technology, with an emphasis on the ability to detect alterations in gene expression caused by environmental toxins.

Hines, P.J., B.A. Purnell, and J. Marx. "Stem Cells Branch Out." *Science,* Vol. 287, 25 Feb. 2000. The introduction to a special multiarticle section entitled "Stem Cell Research and Ethics."

Hodgkin, J., H.R. Horvitz, B.R. Jasny, and J. Kimble. "*C. elegans:* Sequence to Biology." *Science,* Vol. 282, 11 Dec. 1998. The introduction to multiple papers in a special section on the *C. elegans* genome, the first animal genome to be sequenced.

Jasny, B.R. "The Universe of *Drosophila* Genes." *Science,* Vol. 287, 24 Mar. 2000. The introduction to a special section including multiple papers on the *Drosophila* genome sequence.

Malakoff, D. "The Rise of the Mouse, Biomedicine's Model Mammal." *Science,* Vol. 288, 14 Apr. 2000. A history of the use of the laboratory mouse in research and a perspective on future developments.

McKinnell, R.G., and M.A. DiBernardino. "The Biology of Cloning: History and Rationale." *Bioscience,* Vol. 49, No. 11, Nov. 1999. This review emphasizes the insights into the fundamental controls of developmental processes that have been provided by cloning.

McLaren, A. "Cloning: Pathways to a Pluripotent Future." *Science,* Vol. 288, 9 Jun. 2000. Perspectives on both the history and future of cloning.

Nüsslein-Volhard, C. "Gradients that Organize Embryo Development." *Scientific American,* Vol. 275, No. 2, Aug. 1996. The author, who shared the 1995 Nobel Prize for Physiology or Medicine with Eric Wieschaus and Edward B. Lewis, describes gene interactions that control *Drosophila* development.

Riechmann, J.L., et al. "*Arabidopsis* Transcription Factors: Genome-Wide Comparative Analysis Among Eukaryotes." *Science,* Vol. 290, 15 Dec. 2000. A comparison of transcription factors in *Arabidopsis, Drosophila, C. elegans,* and *Saccharomyces cerevisiae* (yeast, a unicellular fungus).

Somerville, C., and J. Dangl. "Plant Biology in 2010." *Science,* Vol. 290, 15 Dec. 2000. This article lays out the goals of an ambitious project in plant functional genomics.

- Visit our Web site at **http://www.info.brookscole.com/solomonbergmartin** for links to chapter-related resources on the World Wide Web. Additional on-line materials relating to this chapter can also be found on our Web site.

See chapter activity on BioActive Learner CD for additional help in mastering the chapter's material. Icon location in the chapter's margins shows which topics have tutorials or simulations in the CD.

CAREER VISIONS

Database Administrator

MARTIN SORICH

Martin Sorich is a database administrator at Genitope, a biotech "start-up" company that specializes in developing individualized therapies to boost the immune systems of cancer patients. A trained molecular biologist with seven years of experience in academic and industry labs, Martin has been at Genitope for two years. A Californian from the San Jose area, Martin started his higher education at De Anza College, a community college, where he earned an associate's degree in 1992. In 1994, he received a Bachelor of Science degree in Molecular Biology, with a Chemistry minor, at San Jose State University.

You have been involved with researching patient-specific immunotherapy at Genitope. Can you describe the goal of this research?

Basically, the goal of this study was to reproduce the clinical research that Dr. Ron Levy at Stanford has done for the past 10 years, to provide cancer patients—specifically those with lymphoma—with a better chance of fighting their disease. Dr. Levy was the first to do this type of active-immunotherapy research. Dr. Levy's process for producing patient-specific immunotherapies is labor-intensive, but it has a success rate of 85%. The founder of Genitope, Dr. Dan Denny, developed our company's molecular approach, which allows Genitope to process many samples at a time, and our success rate has been 100% in producing the immunotherapies. We're still in clinical trials, and we have really good results.

Genitope uses a molecular approach to develop patient-specific therapies that are directed against an individual lymphoma patient's own cancerous lymphocytes (lymphocytes are white blood cells that function as part of the immune system). Each lymphoma patient has a unique population of cancerous lymphocytes, all comprised of the same genetic makeup, because, in theory, they originated from a single cell. These lymphocytes can be recognized by the presence of a lymphoma-specific protein on their surfaces. The goal is to create a vaccine that will induce the patient's immune system to attack cancerous lymphocytes but not affect normal ones.

To develop this vaccine, the messenger RNA (mRNA) that codes for the lymphoma-specific protein is extracted from the patient's lymphoma cells. This mRNA is used to synthesize complementary DNA (cDNA) copies, which are then put into an expression vector. The expression vector is used to generate a mammalian cell line that produces large amounts of the lymphoma-specific protein, which is purified and used as a vaccine to immunize the patient. The patient's immune system mounts an immune response that causes the death of the cancerous lymphocytes.

. . . after meeting him I couldn't stop smiling for the rest of the day, because I knew my work helped save this man's life.

What was your particular role in developing patient-specific immunotherapies?

I was primarily involved in the early stages of the process—characterizing the tumor-specific genes, subcloning them into expression vectors, and preparing them for introduction into a mammalian cell line system.

Have you met any of the patients you were helping, the ones involved in clinical trials?

Yes. The first patient sample I received belonged to the first person who was immunized in our first clinical trial, and he mounted an immune response, which was great—the first one worked just like it was supposed to. I had the privilege of meeting the patient when his family visited Genitope. His wife was thanking everybody and was very grateful. I remember after meeting him I couldn't stop smiling for the rest of the day, because I knew my work helped save this man's life.

Was it your work at community college that made you decide to go on for your bachelor's degree?

Yes. As a child I enjoyed watching nature programs, and I'm the type of person who likes to figure out how things work; studying biology is figuring out how living things work. There were some influential instructors at De Anza, my community college, who guided me in making my career choice in biology. One of the instructors, Doug Cheeseman, taught an introductory biology course. In the first part of that course, he discussed genetics and molecular biology, such as what DNA is and how genes work. It was fairly basic, but it really intrigued me, and I think that's where my interest in molecular biology began.

Do you have any suggestions for undergraduates interested in careers in molecular biology, genetics, or biochemistry?

If they are interested in pursuing a research career, I would encourage them to get involved early on in laboratory work, volunteering either for a biotech company or for a professor who is involved in research that they find intriguing. This experience will help them achieve the goal of becoming a research scientist or of going on to graduate school.

These fossilized remains of a prehistoric fish *(Priscacara serata)* were discovered in Wyoming. *(Alfred Pasieka/Science Photo Library/Photo Researchers, Inc.)*

The Continuity of Life: Evolution

CHAPTERS

17

Introduction to Darwinian Evolution

Charles Darwin. This portrait was made shortly after Darwin returned to England from his voyage around the world. *(The Granger Collection, New York)*

The biological diversity represented by the millions of species currently living on our planet is thought to have evolved from a single ancestor during Earth's long history. Thus, organisms that are radically different, such as slime molds and crocodiles, are in fact distantly related to one another and are linked through numerous intermediate ancestors to a single, common ancestor. The British naturalist Charles Darwin (1809–1882), shown here at age 31, developed a remarkably simple, scientifically testable mechanism to explain this. He argued persuasively that all the species that exist today, as well as the countless extinct species that existed in the past, arose from ear-

lier ones by a process of *gradual divergence* (separation into separate evolutionary pathways), or evolution.

Evolution can be defined as the accumulation of inherited changes within populations over time. A **population** is a group of individuals of one species that live in the same geographical area at the same time. Evolution does not refer to changes that occur in an individual within its lifetime. Instead, evolution refers to changes in the characteristics of populations over the course of generations. These changes may be so small that they are difficult to detect or so great that the population differs markedly from its ancestral population. Eventually, two populations may diverge to such a degree that we refer to them as different species. (The concept of **species** is developed extensively in Chapter 19. For now, a simple working definition is that a species comprises a group of organisms with similar structure, function, and behavior that are capable of interbreeding with one another.) Thus, evolution has two main perspectives—the short-term adaptations of populations to changes in the environment (*microevolution,* see Chapter 18), and the long-term formation of different species from common ancestors (*macroevolution,* see Chapter 19).

The concept of evolution is the cornerstone of biology because it links all fields of the life sciences into a unified body of knowledge. As evolutionary geneticist Theodosius Dobzhansky put it, "Nothing in biology makes sense except in the light of evolution."[1] Biologists attempt to understand both the remarkable

[1] *American Biology Teacher,* Vol. 35, No. 125 (1973).

variety as well as the fundamental similarities of organisms within the context of evolution. Evolution allows biologists to compare common threads among organisms as seemingly different as bacteria, whales, lilies, and tapeworms. Behavioral evolution, evolutionary developmental biology, evolutionary genetics, evolutionary ecology, evolutionary systematics, and molecular evolution are examples of some of the biological disciplines that focus on evolution.

Evolution also has important practical applications. Agriculture must deal with the evolution of pesticide resistance in insects and other pests. Likewise, medicine must respond to the rapid evolutionary potential of disease-causing organisms such as bacteria. (Significant evolutionary change occurs in a very short time period in insects, bacteria, and other organisms with short lifespans.) The conservation management of rare and endangered species makes use of the evolutionary principles of population genetics (see Chapter 18). The rapid evolution of bacteria and fungi in polluted soils is used in the field of **bioremediation,** in which microorganisms are employed to clean up hazardous waste sites. Evolution even has applications beyond biology. For example, certain computer applications make use of algorithms that mimic natural selection in biological systems.

This chapter discusses Darwin and the scientific development of the theory of evolution by natural selection. It also presents several kinds of evidence that support evolution, including fossils, comparative anatomy, biogeography, developmental biology, molecular biology, and experimental studies of ongoing evolutionary change, both in the laboratory and in nature.

■ IDEAS ABOUT EVOLUTION ORIGINATED BEFORE DARWIN

Although Darwin is universally associated with evolution, ideas of evolution predate Darwin by centuries. Aristotle (384–322 B.C.) saw much evidence of natural affinities among organisms. This led him to arrange all of the organisms he knew in a "Scale of Nature" that extended from the exceedingly simple to the most complex. He visualized organisms as being imperfect but "moving toward a more perfect state." This idea has been interpreted by some scientific historians as the forerunner of evolutionary theory, but Aristotle was vague on the nature of this "movement toward perfection" and certainly did not propose that the process of evolution was driven by natural processes. Furthermore, modern evolutionary theory now recognizes that evolution does not move toward more "perfect" states, nor even necessarily toward greater complexity.

Long before Darwin, fossils had been discovered embedded in rocks. Some of these corresponded to parts of familiar species, but others were strangely unlike any known species. Fossils were often found in unexpected contexts. Marine invertebrates (sea animals without backbones), for example, were sometimes discovered in rocks high on mountains. Leonardo da Vinci (1452–1519) was among the first to correctly interpret these unusual finds as the remains of animals that had existed in previous ages but had become extinct.

The French naturalist Jean Baptiste de Lamarck (1744–1829) was the first scientist to propose that organisms undergo change over time as a result of some natural phenomenon rather than divine intervention. In his *Philosophie Zoologique*, published in 1809, Lamarck presented a possible explanation for how organisms evolved. Lamarck thought that all organisms were endowed with a vital force that drove them to change toward greater complexity over time. He also thought that organisms could pass traits acquired during their lifetimes to their offspring. For example, Lamarck suggested that the long neck of the giraffe developed when a short-necked ancestor stretched its neck to browse on the leaves of trees. Its offspring inherited the longer neck, which stretched still further as they ate. This process, repeated over many generations, supposedly resulted in the long necks of modern giraffes.

The proposed mechanism for Lamarckian evolution was discredited when the basis of heredity was later discovered. It remained for Darwin to discover the mechanism of evolution by natural selection.

 ## ■ DARWIN'S VOYAGE WAS THE BASIS FOR HIS THEORY OF EVOLUTION

Darwin, the son of a prominent physician, was sent at the age of 15 to study medicine at the University of Edinburgh. Finding himself unsuited for medicine, he transferred to Cambridge University to study theology. During that time, he became the protégé of the Reverend John Henslow, who was a professor of botany. Henslow encouraged Darwin's interest in the natural world. Shortly after receiving his degree, Darwin embarked as a naturalist on the H.M.S. *Beagle,* which was taking a five-year exploratory cruise around the world to prepare navigation charts for the British Navy.

The *Beagle* left Plymouth, England, in 1831 and cruised along the east and west coasts of South America (Fig. 17–1). While other members of the crew mapped the coasts and harbors, Darwin spent many weeks ashore studying the animals, plants, fossils, and geological formations of both coastal and inland regions, areas that had not been extensively explored. He collected and catalogued thousands of plant and animal specimens and kept notes of his observations—information that would become essential in the development of his theory.

The *Beagle* spent almost two months at the Galapagos Islands, 965 km (600 mi) west of Ecuador, where Darwin continued his observations and collections. He compared the animals and plants of the Galapagos with those of the South American mainland. He was particularly impressed by their similarities and wondered why the organisms of the Galapagos should resemble those from South America more than those from other islands in different parts of the world. Moreover, although there were similarities between Galapagos and South American species, there were also distinct differences. There were even recognizable differences in the reptiles and birds from one island to the next (Fig. 17–2). After he returned home, Darwin pondered these

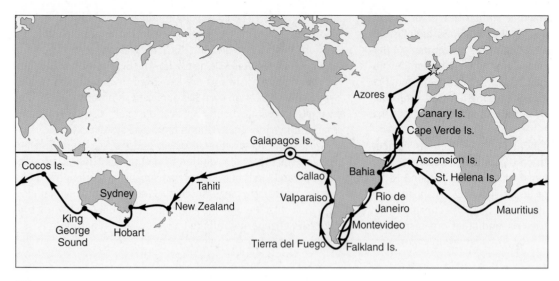

Figure 17–1 The voyage of H.M.S. *Beagle*. The five-year voyage began in Plymouth, England *(star)*, in 1831. Observations made in the Galapagos Islands *(bull's eye)* off the western coast of South America helped Darwin discover a satisfactory mechanism to explain how a population of organisms could change over time.

observations and attempted to develop a satisfactory explanation for the distribution of species among the islands.

Darwin drew on several lines of evidence when considering how species might have originated. Despite the work of Lamarck, the general notion in the mid-1800s was that the Earth was too young for organisms to have changed significantly since they had first appeared. During the early 19th century, however, geologists advanced the idea that mountains, valleys, and other physical features of Earth's surface did not originate in their present forms but developed slowly over long periods by the geological

(a)

(b)

(c)

Figure 17–2 Galapagos finches. Darwin inferred that these birds were derived from a common ancestral population of seed-eating birds from South America. Although they are largely similar in body size and coloration (males are often darker than females), the Galapagos finches differ markedly in beak size and shape. Variation in their beaks is the result of adaptations to different kinds of food. **(a)** The cactus ground finch *(Geospiza scandens)* feeds on the fleshy parts of cacti. **(b)** The large ground finch *(Geospiza magnirostris)* has an extremely heavy, nutcracker-type bill adapted for eating thick, hard-walled seeds. **(c)** The woodpecker finch *(Camarhyncus pallidus)* has insectivorous habits similar to those of woodpeckers but lacks the complex beak and tongue adaptations that permit woodpeckers to reach their prey. The adaptations of the woodpecker finch to this lifestyle are almost entirely behavioral—it digs insects out of bark and crevices using cactus spines, twigs, or even dead leaves. *(a and b, Frans Lanting/Minden Pictures; c, Miguel Castro/Photo Researchers, Inc.)*

processes of volcanic activity, uplift, erosion, and glaciation. Darwin took *Principles of Geology,* published by geologist Charles Lyell in 1830, with him on his voyage and studied it carefully. Lyell provided an important concept for Darwin—that the slow pace of geological processes, which still occur today, indicated that Earth was extremely old.

Other important evidence that influenced Darwin was the fact that breeders and farmers could develop many varieties of domesticated animals in just a few generations (Fig. 17–3). This was accomplished by choosing certain traits and breeding only individuals that exhibited the desired traits, a procedure known as **artificial selection.** Breeders, for example, had produced numerous dog varieties—bloodhounds, Dalmatians, Airedales, border collies, and Pekinese, to name a few—by artificial selection.

Many plant varieties were also produced by artificial selection. For example, cabbage, broccoli, Brussels sprouts, cauliflower, collard greens, kale, and kohlrabi are distinct vegetable crops that are all members of the same species, *Brassica oleracea* (Fig. 17–4). All seven were produced by selective breeding of the

Figure 17–4   Artificial selection in *Brassica oleracea.* An enlarged terminal bud (the "head") was selected in cabbage *(lower left),* flower clusters in broccoli *(upper left)* and cauliflower *(middle right),* axillary buds in Brussels sprouts *(bottom middle),* leaves in collards *(upper right)* and kale *(lower right),* and stems in kohlrabi *(middle). (John Arnaldi)*

Figure 17–3   Artificial selection in chickens. Shown is a chicken that was deliberately bred to resemble Big Bird on *Sesame Street.* Many show breeds of chickens exist that exhibit a great deal of variation. Domestic chickens are not a recognizable breed but are hybrids bred for their meat or egg production. *(Eric Sander)*

colewort, or wild cabbage, a leafy plant native to Europe and Asia. Beginning more than 4000 years ago, some farmers artificially selected wild cabbage plants that formed overlapping leaves. Over time, these leaves became so prominent that the plants, which resembled modern-day cabbages, became recognized as separate and distinct from their wild cabbage ancestor. Other farmers selected different features of the wild cabbage, giving rise to the other modifications. For example, kohlrabi was produced by selection for an enlarged storage stem, and Brussels sprouts by selection for enlarged axillary buds. Thus, humans are responsible for the evolution of *B. oleracea* into seven distinct vegetable crops. Darwin was impressed by the changes induced by artificial selection and thought that a similar selective process occurred in nature. Darwin therefore used artificial selection as a model when he developed the concept of natural selection.

The ideas of Thomas Malthus (1766–1834), a British clergyman and economist, were another important influence on Darwin. In *An Essay on the Principle of Population as It Affects the Future Improvement of Society,* published in 1798, Malthus noted that population growth is not always desirable—a view contrary to the beliefs of his day. He observed that populations have the capacity to increase geometrically ($1 \rightarrow 2 \rightarrow 4 \rightarrow 8 \rightarrow 16$) and thus outstrip the food supply, which has the capacity to increase only arithmetically ($1 \rightarrow 2 \rightarrow 3 \rightarrow 4 \rightarrow 5$). In the case of humans, Malthus suggested that the conflict between population and food supply generates famine, disease, and war, which serve as inevitable brakes on population growth.

■ DARWIN PROPOSED THAT EVOLUTION OCCURS BY NATURAL SELECTION

Malthus's idea that there is a strong and constant check on human population growth strongly influenced Darwin's explanation of evolution. Darwin's years of observing the habits of animals and plants had introduced him to the struggle for existence described by Malthus. It occurred to Darwin that in this struggle inherited variations favorable to survival would tend to be preserved, while unfavorable ones would be eliminated. The result would be **adaptation,** an evolutionary modification that improves the chances of survival and reproductive success in a given environment. Eventually, the accumulation of modifications might result in a new species. Time was the only thing required for new species to originate, and the geologists of the era, including Lyell, had supplied evidence that Earth was indeed old enough to provide an adequate period.

Darwin had at last developed a workable explanation of evolution, that of **natural selection,** in which better adapted organisms are more likely to survive and become the parents of the next generation. As a result of natural selection, the population changes over time; the frequency of favorable traits increases in successive generations while less favorable traits become scarce or disappear. Darwin spent the next 20 years formulating his arguments for natural selection, accumulating an immense body of evidence to support his theory, and corresponding with other scientists.

As Darwin was pondering his ideas, Alfred Russell Wallace (1823–1913), a British naturalist who studied the plants and animals of the Malay Archipelago for eight years, was similarly struck by the diversity of species and the peculiarities of their distribution. He wrote a brief essay on this subject and sent it to Darwin, by then a world-renowned biologist, asking his opinion. Darwin recognized his own theory and realized that Wallace had independently arrived at the same conclusion—that evolution occurs by natural selection. Darwin's colleagues persuaded him to present Wallace's manuscript along with an abstract of his own work, which he had prepared and circulated to a few friends several years earlier. Both papers were presented in July 1858 at a London meeting of the Linnaean Society. Darwin's monumental book, *The Origin of Species by Natural Selection; or, The Preservation of Favored Races in the Struggle for Life,* was published in 1859. Wallace's book, *Contributions to the Theory of Natural Selection,* was published in 1870, eight years after he returned from the Malay Archipelago.

Darwin's mechanism of evolution by natural selection consists of four observations about the natural world: variation, overproduction, limits on population growth, and differential reproductive success.

1. **Variation.** The individuals in a population exhibit variation. Each individual has a unique combination of traits, such as size, color, and ability to tolerate harsh environmental conditions. Some traits improve an individual's chances of survival and reproductive success, whereas others do not. It is important to remember that the variation necessary for evolution by natural selection must be inherited (Fig. 17–5). (Although

■ **Figure 17–5   Genetic variation in emerald tree boas.** These snakes, all of the same species (*Corallus caninus*), were caught in a small section of forest in French Guiana. Many snake species exhibit considerable variation in their coloration and patterns.   *(BIOS/Peter Arnold, Inc.)*

Darwin recognized the importance to evolution of inherited variation, he did not know the mechanism of inheritance.)

2. **Overproduction.** The reproductive ability of each species causes its populations to geometrically increase in number over time. That is, in every generation, each species has the capacity to produce more offspring than can survive.

3. **Limits on population growth,** or a struggle for existence. There is only so much food, water, light, growing space, and other resources available to a population, and, consequently, organisms compete with one another for these limited resources. Because there are more individuals than the environment can support, not all will survive to reproduce. Other limits on population growth include predators, disease organisms, and unfavorable weather conditions.

4. **Differential reproductive success.** Those individuals that possess the most favorable combination of characteristics (those that make individuals better adapted to their environment) are more likely to survive and reproduce. Because offspring tend to resemble their parents, the next generation inherits the parents' genetically based traits. Successful reproduction is the key to natural selection: The best-adapted individuals are those that reproduce most successfully, whereas less fit individuals die prematurely or produce fewer or inferior offspring.

Over time, enough changes may accumulate in geographically separated populations (often with slightly different environments) to produce new species. Darwin noted that the Galapagos finches appeared to have evolved in this way. The 13 species are all descended from a single species that found its way from the South American mainland. (The blue-black grassquit, a bird that lives in western South America, may be a close relative of the Galapagos finches.) The different islands of the Galapagos kept the finches isolated from one another, thereby allowing them to diverge into 13 separate species. Six of the 13 species are seed eaters, six are insect eaters, and one is a woodpecker-type insect eater. The evolution of new species is considered in greater detail in Chapter 19.

■ THE SYNTHETIC THEORY OF EVOLUTION COMBINES DARWIN'S THEORY WITH GENETICS

One of the premises on which Darwin based his theory of evolution by natural selection is that individuals transmit traits to the next generation. However, Darwin was unable to explain *how* this occurs or *why* individuals vary within a population. Although he was a contemporary of Gregor Mendel (see Chapter 10), who elucidated the basic patterns of inheritance, Darwin was apparently not acquainted with Mendel's work, which was not recognized by the scientific community until the early part of the 20th century.

During the 1930s and 1940s, biologists combined the principles of genetics with Darwin's theory of natural selection to develop a unified explanation of evolution known as neo-Darwinism or, more commonly, the **synthetic theory of evolution.**[2] (*Synthesis* in this context refers to combining parts of several previous theories to form a unified whole.)

The synthetic theory of evolution is a conceptual breakthrough that explains Darwin's observation of variation among offspring in terms of **mutation,** or changes in DNA, such as nucleotide substitutions. That is, mutation provides the genetic variability on which natural selection acts during evolution. The synthetic theory of evolution, which emphasizes the genetics of populations as the central focus of evolution, has held up well since it was developed (see Chapter 18). It has dominated the thinking and research of biologists working in many areas and has resulted in an enormous accumulation of new discoveries that validate evolution by natural selection.

Most biologists not only accept the basic principles of the synthetic theory of evolution but also try to better understand the causal processes of evolution. For example, what is the role of chance in evolution? How rapidly do new species evolve? These and other questions have arisen in part from a reevaluation of the fossil record and in part from new discoveries in molecular aspects of inheritance. Such critical analyses are an integral part of the scientific process because they stimulate additional observation and experimentation, along with reexamination of previous evidence. Science is an ongoing process, and information obtained in the future may require modifications to certain parts of the synthetic theory of evolution.

We now consider one of the many evolutionary questions currently being addressed by biologists: the relative effects of chance and natural selection on evolution.

[2] Some of the founders of the synthetic theory of evolution were biologists Theodosius Dobzhansky, Ronald Fisher, J.B.S. Haldane, Julian Huxley, Ernst Mayr, George Gaylord Simpson, G. Ledyard Stebbins, Jr., and Sewell Wright.

Biologists debate the effect of chance on evolution

Biologists have wondered, if we were able to repeat evolution by starting with similar organisms exposed to similar environmental conditions, would we get the same results? That is, would the same kinds of changes evolve, as a result of natural selection? Or would the organisms be quite different, as a result of random chance? Several recently reported examples of evolution in action suggest that chance may not be as important as natural selection.

A fruit fly species *(Drosophila subobscura)* native to Europe inhabits areas from Denmark to Spain. Biologists had noted that the northern flies have larger wings than southern flies (Fig. 17–6). The same fly species was accidentally introduced to North and South America in the late 1970s in two separate introductions. Ten years after its introduction to the Americas, biologists determined that no statistically significant changes in wing size had occurred in the different regions of North America. However, 20 years after its introduction, the fruit flies in North America exhibited the same type of north-south wing changes as in Europe. (It is not known why larger wings evolve in northern areas and smaller wings in southern climates.)

A study of the evolution of fish known as sticklebacks in three coastal lakes of west Canada yielded intriguingly similar results to the fruit fly study. When the lakes first formed several thousand years ago, molecular evidence indicates they were populated with the same ancestral species. (Analysis of the mitochondrial DNA of sticklebacks in the three lakes supports the hypothesis of a common ancestor.) In each lake, the same two species have evolved from the common ancestral fish: One species is large and consumes invertebrates along the bottom of

■ **Figure 17–6 Wing size in female fruit flies.** In Europe, female fruit flies *(Drosophila subobscura)* in northern countries have larger wings than flies in southern countries. Shown are two flies: one from Denmark *(right)* and the other from Spain *(left)*. The same evolutionary pattern rapidly emerged in North America after the accidental introduction of *D. subobscura* to the Americas. *(George Gilchrist)*

the lake, whereas the other species is smaller and consumes plankton at the lake's surface. Members of the two species within a single lake do not interbreed with one another, but individuals of the larger species from one lake will interbreed in captivity with individuals of the larger species from the other lakes. Similarly, smaller individuals from one lake will interbreed with smaller individuals from the other lakes.

Thus, natural selection appears to be a more important agent of evolutionary change than chance. If chance were the most important factor influencing the direction of evolution, then fruit fly evolution would not have proceeded the same way on two different continents, and stickleback evolution would not have proceeded the same way in three different lakes. (For more information on stickleback evolution, see Chapter 52.)

MANY TYPES OF SCIENTIFIC EVIDENCE SUPPORT EVOLUTION

A vast body of scientific evidence supports evolution, including observations from the fossil record, comparative anatomy, biogeography, developmental biology, and molecular biology. In addition, evolutionary hypotheses are increasingly being tested experimentally.

The fossil record provides strong evidence for evolution

Perhaps the most direct evidence for evolution comes from the discovery, identification, and interpretation of **fossils,** which are the remains or traces typically left in sedimentary rock by previously existing organisms. (The term *fossil* comes from the Latin word *fossilis,* meaning "something dug up.") Sedimentary rock forms by the accumulation and solidification of particles produced by the weathering of older rocks, such as volcanic rocks. In an undisturbed rock sequence, the oldest layer is at the bottom, and upper layers are successively younger. The study of sedimentary rock layers, including their composition, arrangement, and correlation (similarity) from one location to another, enables geologists to place events recorded in rocks in their correct sequence.

The fossil record shows a progression from the earliest unicellular organisms to the many unicellular and multicellular organisms living today. The fossil record therefore demonstrates that life has evolved through time. To date, paleontologists (scientists who study extinct species) have described and named about 300,000 fossil species, and more are being discovered all the time.

Although most fossils are preserved in sedimentary rock, some more recent remains have been exceptionally well preserved in bogs, tar, amber (ancient tree resin), or ice (Fig. 17–7). For example, the remains of a woolly mammoth deep-frozen in Siberian ice for more than 25,000 years were so well preserved that part of its DNA could be analyzed.

The formation and preservation of a fossil require that an organism be buried under conditions that slow or prevent the de-

cay process. This is most likely to occur if an organism's remains are covered quickly by a sediment of fine soil particles suspended in water. In this way remains of aquatic organisms may be trapped in bogs, mud flats, sandbars, or deltas. Remains of terrestrial organisms that lived on a flood plain may also be covered by water-borne sediments or, if the organism lived in an arid region, by wind-blown sand. Over time, the sediments harden to form sedimentary rock, and minerals usually replace the organism's remains so that many details of its structure, even cellular details, remain.

The fossil record is not a random sample of past life but instead is biased toward aquatic organisms and those living in the few terrestrial habitats conducive to fossil formation. Relatively few fossils of tropical rainforest organisms have been found, for example, because their remains decay extremely rapidly on the forest floor, before fossils can develop. Another reason for bias in the fossil record is that organisms with hard body parts such as bones and shells are more likely to form fossils than those with soft body parts.

Process of Science Because of the nature of the scientific process, each fossil discovery represents a separate "test" of the theory of evolution. If any of the tests fail, the theory would have to be modified to fit the existing evidence. The verifiable discovery, for example, of fossil remains of modern humans *(Homo sapiens)* in Precambrian rocks, which are more than 570 million years old, would falsify the theory of evolution as currently proposed. However, Precambrian rocks examined to date contain only fossils of simple organisms, such as algae and small, soft-bodied animals, that are thought to have evolved early in the history of life. The earliest fossils of *H. sapiens* with anatomically modern features do not appear in the fossil record until approximately 100,000 years ago (see Chapter 21).

Fossils provide a record of ancient organisms and some understanding of where and when they lived. Using fossils of organisms from different geological ages, the lines of descent (evolutionary relationships) that gave rise to modern-day organisms can sometimes be inferred. In many instances, fossils provide direct evidence of the origin of new species from preexisting species, including many transitional forms.

Transitions found in the fossil record document whale evolution

One question that has excited biologists for about a century is how whales and other cetaceans (marine mammals) evolved from land-dwelling mammals. During the 1980s and 1990s, paleontologists discovered several fossil intermediates in whale evolution that document the whales' transition from land to water. Based on fossil evidence, one candidate for the ancestor of whales is a now-extinct group of four-legged, land-dwelling mammals called mesonychians (Fig. 17–8a). These animals had unusually large heads and teeth that were remarkably similar to those of the earliest whales. About 50 million to 60 million years ago (mya), some descendants of mesonychians had adapted to swimming in shallow seas.

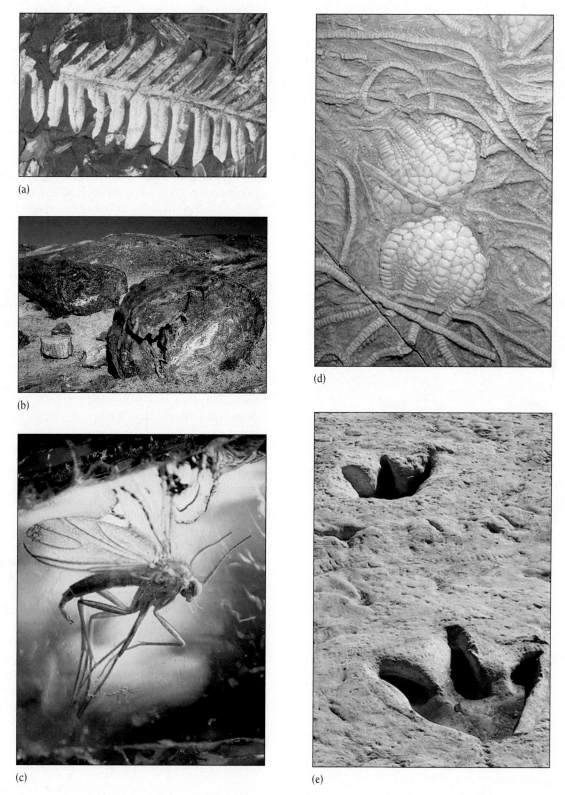

Figure 17–7 Fossils develop in different ways. (a) Although some fossils contain traces of organic matter, all that remains in this fossil of a seed fern leaf is an impression, or imprint, in the rock. (b) Petrified wood from the Petrified Forest National Park in Arizona consists of trees that were buried and infiltrated with minerals. (c) A 2-million-year-old insect fossil (a midge) was embedded in amber. (d) A cast fossil of ancient echinoderms called crinoids formed when the crinoids decomposed, leaving a mold that later filled with dissolved minerals that hardened. (e) Dinosaur footprints, each 75 to 90 cm (2.5 to 3 ft) in length, provide clues about the posture, gait, and behavior of these extinct animals. *(a, Carolina Biological Supply Company/Phototake, New York City; b, Kenneth Murray/Photo Researchers, Inc.; c, Alfred Pasieka/Science Photo Library/Photo Researchers, Inc.; d, A.J. Copley/Visuals Unlimited; e, Scott Berner/Visuals Unlimited)*

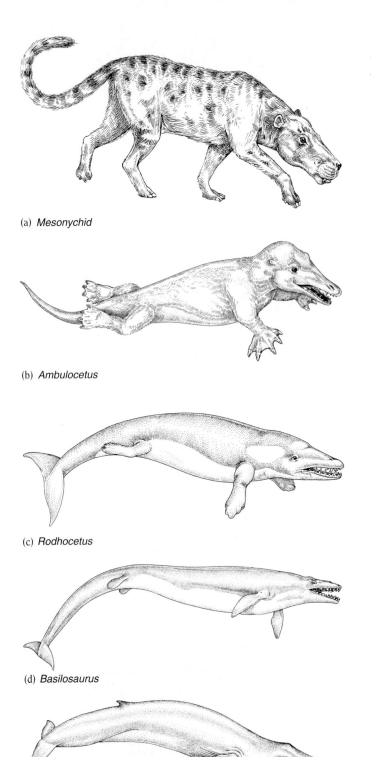

(a) *Mesonychid*

(b) *Ambulocetus*

(c) *Rodhocetus*

(d) *Basilosaurus*

(e) *Balaenoptera* (blue whale)

Fossils of *Ambulocetus natans,* a 50-million-year-old whale discovered in Pakistan, have many features of modern whales but also possess hind limbs and feet (Fig. 17–8*b*). (Modern whales do not have hind limbs, although vestigial pelvic and hind limb bones persist. Vestigial structures are discussed later in the chapter.) The vertebrae of *Ambulocetus'* lower back were very flexible, allowing its back to move dorsoventrally (up and down) during swimming and diving, like modern whales. In addition to swimming, this ancient whale moved about on land, perhaps as sea lions do today.

Rodhocetus is a fossil whale found in slightly younger rocks in Pakistan (Fig. 17–8*c*). The vertebrae of *Rodhocetus* were even more flexible than those of *Ambulocetus,* allowing a more powerful dorsoventral movement during swimming. *Rodhocetus* may have been totally aquatic.

By 40 mya, the whale transition from land to ocean was almost complete. Egyptian fossils of *Basilosaurus,* a whale that lived at that time, indicate a streamlined body and front flippers for steering, like modern-day whales (Fig. 17–8*d*). *Basilosaurus* retained vestiges of its land-dwelling ancestors—a pair of reduced hind limbs that were disjointed from the backbone and probably not used in locomotion. Reduction in the hind limbs continued to the present. The modern blue whale has vestigial pelvis and femur bones embedded in its body (Fig. 17–8*e*). (The closest living relatives of whales and porpoises are hoofed mammals such as antelopes, deer, giraffes, and hippos, discussed later in the chapter.)

Various methods can be used to determine the age of fossils

Because layers of sedimentary rock occur naturally in the sequence of their deposition, with the more recent layers on top of the older, earlier ones (Fig. 17–9), most fossils are dated by their relative position in sedimentary rock. However, geological events occurring after the rocks were initially formed have occasionally changed the relationships of some rock layers. Geologists identify specific sedimentary rocks not only by their positions in layers but also by features such as mineral content and by the fossilized remains of certain organisms, known as **index fossils,** that characterize a specific layer over large geographical areas. Index fossils are fossils of organisms that existed for a relatively short geological time but were preserved as fossils in large numbers. With this information, geologists can arrange rock layers and the fossils they contain in chronological order and identify comparable layers in widely separated locations.

■ **Figure 17–8 Fossil intermediates in whale evolution.** **(a)** *Mesonychid,* an extinct terrestrial mammal, may have been the ancestor of whales. **(b)** *Ambulocetus natans,* a transitional form between modern whale descendants and their terrestrial ancestors, possessed a number of recognizable whale features yet retained the hind limbs of its four-legged ancestors. **(c)** The more recent *Rodhocetus* had flexible vertebrae that permitted a powerful dorsoventral movement during swimming. **(d)** *Basilosaurus* was more streamlined and possessed tiny nonfunctional hindlimbs. **(e)** *Balaenoptera,* the modern blue whale, contains vestiges of pelvis and leg bones. *(a–d, adapted from Fig. 2 on pages 260–261 in Futuyma, D.J. Science on Trial: The Case for Evolution. Sinauer Associates, Inc., Sunderland, MA, 1995)*

Figure 17–9   Exposed layers of sedimentary rock.
Shown are weathered rock layers near the Paria River in the Grand Staircase–Escalante National Monument, Utah. The younger layers overlie the older layers. Many layers date to the Mesozoic era, from 248 to 65 mya. Characteristic fossils are associated with each layer. *(Tom Till)*

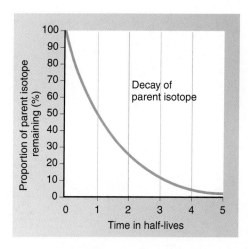

Figure 17–10   Radioisotope decay.   At time zero, the sample is composed entirely of the radioisotope, and the radioactive clock begins ticking. After one half-life, only 50% of the original radioisotope remains. During each succeeding half-life, one-half of the remaining radioisotope is converted to decay product(s).

Radioactive isotopes, also called **radioisotopes,** present in a rock provide a means to accurately measure its age (see Chapter 2). Radioisotopes emit invisible radiations. As a radioisotope emits radiation, its nucleus changes into the nucleus of a different element in a process known as **radioactive decay.** For example, the radioactive nucleus of uranium-235 decays over time into lead-207.

Each radioisotope has its own characteristic rate of decay. The period of time required for one half of the atoms of a radioisotope to change into a different atom is known as its **half-life** (Fig. 17–10). Radioisotopes differ significantly in their half-lives. For example, the half-life of iodine-132 is only 2.4 hours, whereas the half-life of uranium-235 is 704 million years. The half-life of a particular radioisotope is constant and does not vary with temperature, pressure, or any other environmental factor.

The age of a fossil in sedimentary rock is usually estimated by measuring the relative proportions of the original radioisotope and its decay product in volcanic rock intrusions that penetrate the sediments. For example, the half-life of potassium-40 is 1.3 billion years, meaning that in 1.3 billion years half of the radioactive potassium will have decayed into its decay product, argon-40. The radioactive clock begins ticking when the magma solidifies into volcanic rock. The rock initially contains some

potassium but no argon. Because argon is a gas, it escapes from hot rock as soon as it forms, but when potassium decays in rock that has cooled and solidified, the argon accumulates in the crystalline structure of the rock. If the ratio of potassium-40 to argon-40 in the rock being tested is 1:1, the rock is 1.3 billion years old.

Several radioisotopes are commonly used to date fossils. These include potassium-40 (half-life 1.3 billion years), uranium-235 (half-life 704 million years), and carbon-14 (half-life 5730 years). Potassium-40, with its long half-life, can be used to date fossils that are many hundreds of millions of years old. Radioisotopes other than carbon-14 are used to date the *rock* in which fossils are found, whereas carbon-14 is used to date the *carbon remains* of anything that was once living, such as wood, bones, and shells. Whenever possible, the age of a fossil is independently verified using two or more different radioisotopes.

Carbon-14, which is continuously produced in the atmosphere from nitrogen-14 (by cosmic radiation), subsequently decays back to nitrogen-14. Because the formation and the decay of carbon-14 occur at constant rates, the ratio of carbon-14 to carbon-12 (the more abundant, stable isotope of carbon) is constant in the atmosphere. Since each organism absorbs carbon from the atmosphere, its ratio of carbon-14 to carbon-12 is the same as the atmosphere.[3] When an organism dies, however, it no longer absorbs carbon, and the proportion of carbon-14 in its remains declines as carbon-14 decays to nitrogen-14. Because of its relatively short half-life, carbon-14 is useful for dating fossils that are 50,000 years old or less. It is particularly useful for dating archaeological sites.

---

[3]Organisms absorb carbon from the atmosphere either directly (by photosynthesis) or indirectly (by consuming photosynthetic organisms).

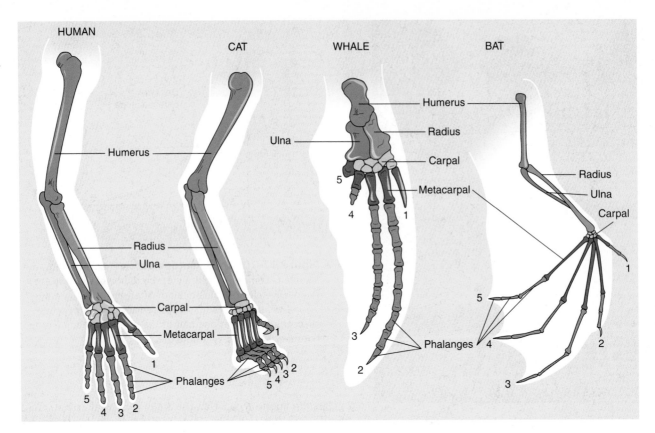

Figure 17–11 Homology in animals. The human arm, cat forelimb, whale flipper, and bat wing have a basic underlying similarity of structure because they are derived from a common ancestor. The five digits are numbered in each drawing.

Comparative anatomy of related species demonstrates similarities in their structures

Comparing the structural details of features found in different but related organisms reveals a basic similarity. Such features that are derived from the same structure in a common ancestor are termed **homologous features;** the condition is known as **homology.** For example, consider the limb bones of mammals. A human arm, a cat forelimb, a whale front flipper, and a bat wing, although quite different in appearance, have strikingly similar arrangements of bones, muscles, and nerves. Figure 17–11 shows a comparison of their skeletal structures. Each has a single bone (the humerus) in the part of the limb nearest the trunk of the body, followed by the two bones (radius and ulna) of the forearm, a group of bones (carpals) in the wrist, and a variable number of digits (metacarpals and phalanges). This similarity is particularly striking because arms, forelimbs, flippers, and wings are used for different types of locomotion, and there is no overriding mechanical reason for them to be so similar structurally. Similar arrangements of parts of the forelimb are evident in ancestral reptiles and amphibians and even in the first fishes that came out of water onto land hundreds of millions of years ago.

Leaves are an example of homology in plants. In many plant species, leaves have been modified for functions other than photosynthesis. A cactus spine and a pea tendril, although quite dif-

ferent in appearance, are homologous because both are modified leaves (Fig. 17–12). The spine protects the succulent stem tissue of the cactus, whereas the tendril, which winds around a small object once it makes contact, helps support the climbing stem of the pea plant. Such modifications in organs used in different ways are the expected outcome of a common evolutionary origin. The basic structure present in a common ancestor was modified in different ways for different functions as various descendants subsequently evolved.

Not all species with "similar" features have descended from a recent common ancestor, however. Structurally similar features that are not homologous but simply have similar functions in distantly related organisms are said to be **homoplastic features;** such a condition is called **homoplasy.**[4] For example, the wings of various distantly related flying animals, such as insects and birds, resemble each other superficially; they are homoplastic features that evolved over time to meet the common function of flight, though they are different in more fundamental aspects. Bird wings are modified forelimbs supported by bones, whereas insect wings may have evolved from gill-like appendages present in the aquatic ancestors of insects. Spines, which are modified

[4]An older, less precise term that some biologists still use for nonhomologous features with similar functions is *analogy*.

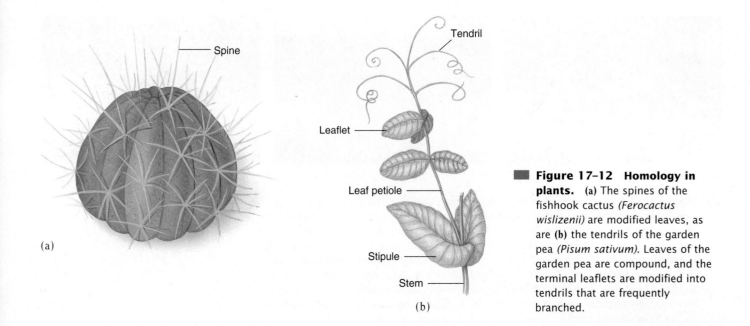

Figure 17–12 Homology in plants. (a) The spines of the fishhook cactus *(Ferocactus wislizenii)* are modified leaves, as are (b) the tendrils of the garden pea *(Pisum sativum)*. Leaves of the garden pea are compound, and the terminal leaflets are modified into tendrils that are frequently branched.

leaves, and thorns, which are modified stems, are an example of homoplasy in plants. Spines and thorns resemble one another superficially but are homoplastic features that evolved independently to solve the common need for protection from herbivores (Fig. 17–13).

Like homology, homoplasy offers crucial evidence of evolution. Homoplastic features are of evolutionary interest because they demonstrate that organisms with separate ancestries may adapt in similar ways to similar environmental demands. Such independent evolution of similar structures in distantly related organisms is known as **convergent evolution.** Aardvarks, anteaters, and pangolins are an excellent example of convergent

evolution (Fig. 17–14). They resemble one another in lifestyle and certain structural features. All have strong, sharp claws to dig open ant and termite mounds and elongated snouts with long, sticky tongues to catch these insects. Yet aardvarks, anteaters, and pangolins evolved from three distantly related orders of mammals. (See Chapter 22 for further discussion of homology and homoplasy. Also, see Figure 30–27, which shows several examples of convergent evolution in placental and marsupial mammals.)

Comparative anatomy reveals the existence of **vestigial structures.** Many organisms contain organs or parts of organs that are seemingly nonfunctional and degenerate, often

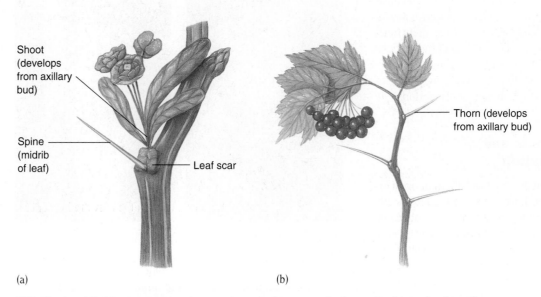

Figure 17–13 Homoplasy. (a) A spine of Japanese barberry *(Berberis thunbergii)* is a modified leaf. (In this example, the spine is actually the midrib of the original leaf, which has been shed.) (b) Thorns of downy hawthorn *(Crataegus mollis)* are modified stems that develop from axillary buds.

(a)

(b)

(c)

■ **Figure 17–14 Convergent evolution.** Three distantly related mammals exhibit similarities in lifestyle and certain structural features as a result of convergent evolution. These species adapted independently to eat ants and termites in similar grassland/forest environments in different parts of the world. **(a)** The aardvark (*Orycteropus afer*) is native to central, southern, and eastern Africa. **(b)** A giant anteater (*Myrmecophaga tridactyla*) at a termite mound. The anteater is native to Latin America, from southern Mexico to northern Argentina. **(c)** The pangolin (*Manis crassicaudata*) is native to Africa and southern and southeastern Asia. *(a, Kjell B. Sandved/Visuals Unlimited; b, Gunter Ziesler/Peter Arnold, Inc.; c, Mandal Ranjit/Photo Researchers, Inc.)*

undersized or lacking some essential part. Vestigial structures are remnants of more developed structures that were present and functional in ancestral organisms. In the human body, more than 100 structures are considered vestigial, including the appendix, coccyx (fused tailbones), third molars (wisdom teeth), and the muscles that move our ears. Whales and pythons have vestigial hindlimb bones (Fig. 17–15); pigs have vestigial toes that do not touch the ground; wingless birds such as the kiwi have vestigial wing bones; and many blind, burrowing or cave-dwelling animals have nonfunctioning, vestigial eyes.

The occasional presence of a vestigial structure is to be expected as a species adapts to a changing mode of life. Some structures become much less important for survival and may end up as vestiges. When a structure no longer confers a selective advantage, it usually becomes smaller and loses much or all of its function with the passage of time. Since the presence of the vestigial structure is usually not harmful to the organism, however, selective pressure for completely eliminating it is weak, and the vestigial structure can be found in many subsequent generations.

The distribution of plants and animals supports evolution

The study of the past and present geographical distribution of organisms is called **biogeography.** Darwin was interested in biogeography and considered why the species found on ocean islands tend to resemble species of the nearest mainland, even if the environment is different, but not to resemble species on islands with similar environments in other parts of the world. Darwin studied the plants and animals of two sets of arid islands—the Cape Verde Islands, some 650 km (about 400 mi) west of Dakar, Africa, and the Galapagos Islands, a comparable distance west of Ecuador, South America. On each group of islands, the plants and terrestrial animals were indigenous (native), but

those of the Cape Verde Islands resembled African species and those of the Galapagos resembled South American species. The similarities of Galapagos species to South American species were particularly striking considering that the Galapagos Islands are dry and rocky and the nearest part of South America is humid

(a)

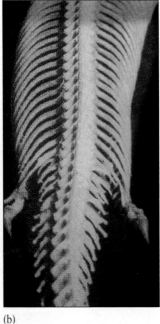
(b)

■ **Figure 17–15 Vestigial structures. (a)** An African rock python (*Python sebae*). There are several dozen species of pythons distributed throughout Asia and Africa. **(b)** Close-up view of a python skeleton showing the hindlimb bones. All pythons have remnants of hindlimb bones embedded in their bodies. *(a, E.R. Degginger/Animals Animals; b, J.D. Cunningham/Visuals Unlimited)*

and has a lush tropical rain forest. Darwin concluded that species from the neighboring continent migrated or were carried to the islands, where they subsequently adapted to the new environment and, in the process, evolved into new species.

If evolution were not a factor in the distribution of species, we would expect to find a given species everywhere that it could survive. However, the geographical distribution of organisms that actually exists makes sense in the context of evolution. For example, Australia, which has been a separate land mass for millions of years, has distinctive organisms. Australia has populations of egg-laying mammals (monotremes) and pouched mammals (marsupials) not found anywhere else. Two hundred million years ago, Australia and the other continents were joined together in a major land mass. Over the course of millions of years, the Australian continent gradually separated from the others. The monotremes and marsupials in Australia continued to thrive and diversify. The isolation of Australia also prevented placental mammals, which arose elsewhere at a later time, from competing with its monotremes and marsupials. In other areas of the world where placental mammals occurred, most monotremes and marsupials became extinct.

We now consider how Earth's dynamic geology has affected biogeography and evolution.

Earth's geological history is related to biogeography and evolution

In 1915 the German scientist Alfred Wegener, who had noted a correspondence between the geographical shapes of South America and Africa, proposed that all the land masses had at one time been joined into one huge supercontinent, which he called Pangaea (Fig. 17–16a). He further suggested that Pangaea had subsequently broken apart and that the various land masses had separated in a process known as **continental drift.** Wegener did not know of any mechanism that could have caused continental drift, and so his idea, although debated initially, was largely ignored.

In the 1960s, scientific evidence accumulated that provided the explanation for continental drift. Earth's crust is composed of seven large plates (plus a few smaller ones) that float on the mantle, which is the mostly solid[5] layer of Earth lying beneath the crust and above the core. The land masses are situated on some

[5]Most of the rock in the upper portion of the mantle is solid, although 1% or 2% is melted. Because of its higher temperature, the solid rock of the mantle is more plastic than the solid rock of the lithosphere above it.

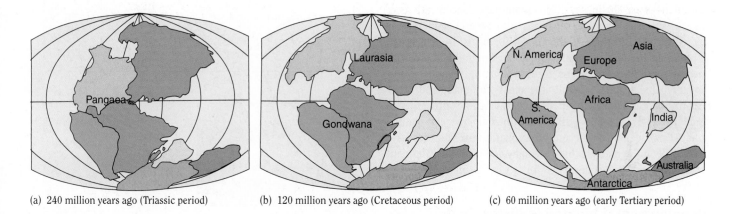

(a) 240 million years ago (Triassic period) (b) 120 million years ago (Cretaceous period) (c) 60 million years ago (early Tertiary period)

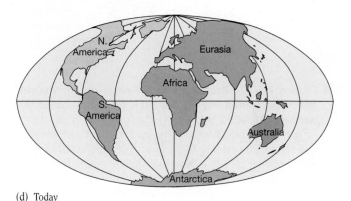

(d) Today

Figure 17–16 Continental drift. **(a)** The supercontinent Pangaea, about 240 mya. **(b)** Breakup of Pangaea into Laurasia (Northern Hemisphere) and Gondwana (Southern Hemisphere), 120 mya. **(c)** Further separation of land masses, 60 mya. Note that Europe and North America were still joined and that India was a separate land mass. **(d)** The continents today.

of these plates. As the plates move, the continents change their relative positions (Fig. 17–16b, c, and d). The movement of the crustal plates is termed **plate tectonics.**

Any area where two plates meet is a site of intense geological activity. Earthquakes and volcanoes are common in such a region. Both San Francisco, noted for its earthquakes, and the Mount Saint Helens volcano are situated where two plates meet. If land masses lie on the edges of two adjacent plates, mountains may form. The Himalayas formed when the plate carrying India rammed into the plate carrying Asia. When two plates grind together, one of them is sometimes buried under the other in a process known as subduction. When two plates move apart, a ridge of lava forms between them. The Atlantic Ocean is getting larger because of the expanding zone of lava along the Mid-Atlantic Ridge, where two plates are separating.

Knowledge that the continents were at one time connected and have since drifted apart is useful in explaining certain aspects of biogeography (Fig. 17–17). Likewise, continental drift has played a major role in the evolution of different organisms. When Pangaea originally formed during the late Permian period, it brought together terrestrial species that had evolved separately from one another, leading to competition and some extinctions. Marine life was adversely affected, in part because, with the continents joined as one large mass, less coastline existed. (Because coastal areas are shallower, they contain high concentrations of marine species.) Pangaea separated into several land masses approximately 180 mya. As the continents began to drift apart, populations became geographically isolated in different environmental conditions and began to diverge along separate evolutionary pathways. As a result, the plants, animals, and other organisms of previously connected continents—South America and Africa, for example—differ. Continental drift also caused gradual changes in ocean and atmospheric currents that have profoundly influenced the biogeography and evolution of organisms. (Biogeography is discussed further in Chapter 54.)

Developmental biology is increasingly being used to explain evolution

How snakes became elongated and lost their limbs has long intrigued evolutionary biologists. Comparative anatomy indicates, for example, that pythons have vestigial hind limb bones embedded in their bodies (see Fig. 17–15). Other snakes have lost their hind limbs entirely.

Increasingly, developmental biology, particularly at the molecular level, is providing answers to such questions. In many cases, evolutionary changes such as limblessness in snakes, occur as a result of changes in genes that affect the orderly sequence of events that occur during development. In pythons, for example, the loss of forelimbs and elongation of the body are linked to mutations in several *Hox* genes that affect the expression of body patterns and limb formation in a wide variety of animals (see Chapter 16 discussion of *Hox* gene complexes). Apparently the hind limbs do not develop because python embryonic tissue does not respond to internal signals that trigger leg elongation. Developmental biologists speculate that mu-

tations in the *Hox* genes probably occurred first, resulting in an ancient snake with hind limbs but no forelimbs. The fossil record supports this hypothesis: A fossil of a primitive snake with such features has been identified *(Pachyrhachis problematicus)*.

Scientific evidence overwhelmingly demonstrates that development in different animals is controlled by the same kinds of genes; these genetic similarities in a wide variety of organisms

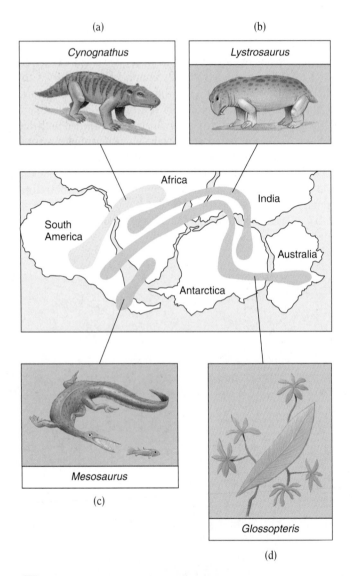

Figure 17–17 Distribution of fossils on continents that were joined during the Permian and Triassic periods (286–213 mya). (a) *Cynognathus* was a carnivorous reptile found in Triassic rocks in South America and Africa. (b) *Lystrosaurus* was a large herbivorous reptile with beaklike jaws that lived during the Triassic period. Fossils of *Lystrosaurus* have been found in Africa, India, and Antarctica. (c) *Mesosaurus* was a small freshwater reptile found in Permian rocks in South America and Africa. (d) *Glossopteris* was a seed-bearing tree dating from the Permian period. *Glossopteris* fossils have been found in South America, Africa, India, Antarctica, and Australia. *(Adapted from Colbert, E.H. Wandering Lands and Animals. Hutchinson, London, 1973)*

reflect a shared evolutionary history. For example, all vertebrates have similar patterns of embryological development that indicate they share a common ancestor. Segmented muscles, pharyngeal (gill) pouches, a tubular heart without left and right sides, a system of arteries known as aortic arches in the gill region, and many other features are found in all vertebrate embryos. All these structures are necessary and functional in the developing fish. The small, segmented muscles of the fish embryo give rise to the segmented muscles used by the adult fish in swimming. The gill pouches break through to the surface as gill slits. The adult fish heart remains undivided and pumps blood forward to the gills that develop in association with the aortic arches.

Since none of these embryonic features persists in the adults of reptiles, birds, or mammals, why are these fishlike structures present in their embryos? Evolution is a conservative process, and natural selection builds on what has come before rather than starting from scratch. The evolution of new features often does not require the evolution of new developmental genes but instead depends on a modification in developmental genes that already exist (see Chapter 19 discussion of preadaptations). Terrestrial vertebrates are thought to have evolved from fishlike ancestors; therefore, they share some of the early stages of development still found in fish today. The accumulation of genetic changes over time in these vertebrates has modified the basic body plan laid out in fish development.

Molecular comparisons among organisms provide evidence for evolution

Similarities and differences in the biochemistry and molecular biology of various organisms provide evidence for evolutionary relationships. Lines of descent based solely on biochemical and molecular characters often resemble lines of descent based on structural and fossil evidence. Molecular evidence for evolution includes the universal genetic code and the conserved sequences of amino acids in proteins and of nucleotides in DNA.

The genetic code is virtually universal

Organisms owe their characteristics to the types of proteins that they possess, which in turn are determined by the sequence of nucleotides in their messenger ribonucleic acid (mRNA), as specified by the order of nucleotides in their DNA. Evidence that all life is related comes from the fact that all organisms use a genetic code that is virtually identical.[6] Recall from Chapter 12 that the genetic code specifies a triplet (a sequence of three nucleotides in DNA) that codes for a particular codon (a sequence of three nucleotides in mRNA) that codes for a particular amino acid in a polypeptide chain. For example, "AAA" in DNA codes for "UUU" in mRNA, which codes for the amino acid phenylalanine in organisms as diverse as shrimp, humans, bacteria, and tulips. In fact, "AAA" codes for phenylalanine in all organisms examined to date.

The universality of the genetic code—no other code has been found in any organism—is compelling evidence that all organisms arose from a common ancestor. The genetic code has been maintained and transmitted through all branches of the evolutionary tree since its origin in some extremely early (and successful) organism.

Proteins and DNA contain a record of evolutionary change

Thousands of comparisons of protein and DNA sequences from various species have been done during the past 25 years or so. In many cases, sequence-based relationships agree with earlier studies that based evolutionary relationships on similarities in structure among living organisms and in fossil data of extinct organisms.

Investigations of the sequence of amino acids in proteins that play the same roles in many species have revealed both great similarities and certain specific differences. Even organisms that are remotely related, such as humans, fruit flies, sunflowers, and yeasts, share some proteins, such as cytochrome c, which is part of the electron transport chain in aerobic respiration. To survive, all aerobic organisms need a respiratory protein with the same basic structure and function as the cytochrome c of their common ancestor. Consequently, not all amino acids that confer the structural and functional features of cytochrome c are free to change. Any mutations that changed the amino acid sequence at structurally important sites of the cytochrome c molecule would have been harmful, and natural selection would have prevented such mutations from being passed to future generations. However, in the course of the long, independent evolution of different organisms, mutations have resulted in the substitution of many amino acids at less important locations in the cytochrome c molecule. The greater the differences in the amino acid sequences of their cytochrome c molecules, the longer it is thought to have been since two species diverged.

Because a protein's amino acid sequences are coded in DNA,[7] the differences in amino acid sequences indirectly reflect the nature and number of underlying DNA base-pair changes that must have occurred during evolution. Such molecular information is determined directly by **DNA sequencing,** in which the order of nucleotide bases in DNA is determined. Generally, the more closely species are considered related on the basis of other scientific evidence, the greater the percentage of nucleotide sequences that their DNA molecules have in common. By using the DNA sequence data in Table 17–1, for example, you can conclude that the closest living relative of humans is the chimpanzee (because its DNA has the lowest percentage differences in the sequence examined). Which of the primates in Table 17–1 is the most distantly related to humans? (Primate evolution is discussed in Chapter 21.)

---

[6] There is some minor variation in the genetic code. For example, mitochondria have some deviations from the standard code.

[7] Of course, not all DNA codes for proteins (witness introns and transfer RNA genes). DNA sequencing of non–protein-coding DNA is also useful in determining evolutionary relationships.

TABLE 17–1 Differences in Nucleotide Sequences in DNA as Evidence of Phylogenetic Relationships*

Species Pairs	Percent Divergence in a Selected DNA Sequence[†]
Human–chimpanzee	1.7
Human–gorilla	1.8
Human–orangutan	3.3
Human–gibbon	4.3
Human–rhesus monkey (Old World monkey)	7.0
Human–spider monkey (New World monkey)	10.8
Human–tarsier	24.6

*From Goodman, M., et al. "Primate Evolution at the DNA Level and a Classification of Hominoids." *Journal of Molecular Evolution*, Vol. 30, 1990.

[†]Noncoding sequences of β-globin genes.

Process of Science In some cases, molecular evidence challenges traditional evolutionary ideas that were based on structural comparisons among living species and/or on studies of fossil skeletons. Consider artiodactyls, an order of even-toed hoofed mammals such as pigs, camels, deer, antelope, cattle, and hippopotamuses. Traditionally, whales, which do not possess toes, are not classified as artiodactyls (although early fossil whales possessed an even number of toes on their appendages). Figure 17–18 depicts a hypothetical phylogenetic tree for whales and selected artiodactyls based on molecular data. Such **phylogenetic trees**—diagrams showing lines of descent—can be derived from differences in a given DNA nucleotide sequence. This diagram suggests whales should be classified as artiodactyls and shows that hippopotamuses are more closely related to whales than any other artiodactyl. The branches representing whales and hippopotamuses are thought to have diverged relatively recently because of the close similarity of DNA sequences in these species. In contrast, camels, which have DNA sequences that are less similar to whales, diverged much earlier. The molecular evidence indicates that whales and hippopotamuses share a recent common ancestor, a hippo-like artiodactyl that split from the rest of the artiodactyl line some 55 mya. However, available fossil evidence does not currently provide support for the molecular hypothesis; a fossil ancestor common to both whales and hippos has not yet been discovered. (Recall from earlier in the chapter that most paleontologists currently suggest that the mesonychians, which are not ancient artiodactyls, may have been the ancestor of whales.) Paleontologists hope that future fossil discoveries will help clarify this discrepancy between molecular and fossil data.

DNA sequencing is used to estimate the time of divergence between two closely related species or taxonomic groups

Within a given taxonomic group, mutations are assumed to have occurred at a fairly steady rate over millions of years. Thus, if more differences occur in the same sequences of DNA of one species compared with another, more time must have elapsed since the two diverged from a common ancestor. (The *same* DNA sequence refers to the nucleotide sequence in homologous segments of DNA in the species being compared.)

From the number of alterations in homologous DNA sequences taken from different species, we can develop a **molecular clock** to estimate the time of divergence between two closely related species or higher taxonomic groups. A molecular clock makes use of the average rate at which a particular gene evolves. The clock is calibrated by comparing the number of nucleotide differences between two organisms with the dates of evolutionary branch points that are known from the fossil record. Once a molecular clock is calibrated, past evolutionary events whose

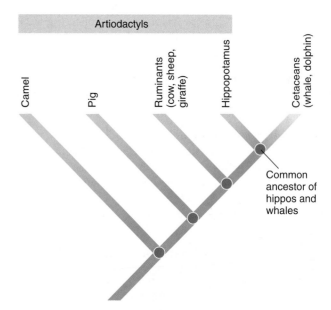

■ **Figure 17–18 Phylogenetic tree of whales and their closest living relatives.** This diagram, which is based on DNA sequence differences among selected mammals, shows hypothetical evolutionary relationships. It suggests that artiodactyls are the close relatives of whales, that the hippopotamus is the closest living relative of whales, and that artiodactyls and whales share a common ancestor in the distant past. However, this common ancestor has yet to be identified in the fossil record. (Ruminants are artiodactyls that have a multichambered stomach and that chew regurgitated plant material to improve its digestibility.) (*Adapted from Nikaido, M., et al. "Phylogenetic Relationships among Cetartiodactyls Based on Insertions of Short and Long Interspersed Elements: Hippopotamuses Are the Closest Extant Relatives of Whales." Proceedings of the National Academy of Sciences, Vol. 96, 31 Aug. 1999*)

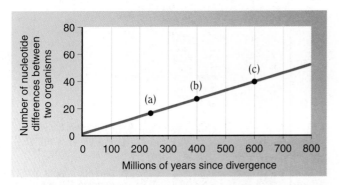

Figure 17-19 Calibration and use of a molecular clock. In this hypothetical example, the DNA of a specific gene is sequenced for birds, reptiles, fish, and insects. The number of nucleotide differences between birds and reptiles (a) is placed on a graph at the time at which birds and reptiles are thought to have diverged (based on fossil evidence). Likewise, the number of nucleotide differences between reptiles and fish (b) is placed on the graph at the time of branching indicated by the fossil record. A line is drawn through points (a) and (b) and extended, enabling scientists to estimate a much earlier time (c) at which the insect line diverged from the vertebrate line. Because a single gene may have large statistical errors when used as a molecular clock, molecular biologists typically obtain more reliable estimates of divergence times by constructing multiple molecular clocks from many different genes.

timing is not known with certainty can be estimated (Fig. 17–19).

Molecular clocks can be used to complement geological estimates of the divergence of species or to assign tentative dates to evolutionary events that lack fossil evidence. Where there is no fossil record of an evolutionary event, molecular clocks are the only way to estimate the timing of that event. Molecular clocks are also used, along with fossil evidence and structural data, to help reconstruct **phylogeny,** which is the evolutionary history of a group of related species (see Chapter 22). By assigning tentative dates to the divergence of species, molecular clocks show the relative order of branch points in phylogeny.

Molecular clocks must be developed and interpreted with care. Mutation rates vary among different genes and among distantly related taxonomic groups, causing molecular clocks to tick at different rates. Some genes, such as the gene for the respiratory protein cytochrome *c,* code for proteins that lose their function if the amino acid sequence changes slightly; these genes evolve slowly. Other genes, such as genes for blood-clotting proteins, code for proteins that are less constrained by changes in amino acid sequence; these genes evolve rapidly.

Although many dates estimated by molecular clocks are in agreement with fossil evidence, some discrepancies between molecular clocks and fossils exist. In most of these cases, the molecular clock's estimates of divergence times of particular organisms are much older than the dates at which the groups are first observed in the fossil record. Resolving these differences will require additional research in both molecular biology and paleontology.

Bacteria and other organisms that cause infectious disease are evolving resistance to drugs

Beginning in the late 1980s, an alarming increase in the incidence of tuberculosis (TB) has been documented worldwide. TB currently kills more than 2 million people each year. In the 30 or so years before the 1980s, the number of cases of TB had declined, at least in the developed world, largely as a result of treating TB with antibiotics, which are drugs intended to harm or kill bacteria and other microorganisms.

The evolution of drug-resistant strains in the bacterium that causes TB *(Mycobacterium tuberculosis)* is a disturbing trend. These strains are resistant to one or more antibiotics that traditionally were used to treat TB. Drug-resistant TB is deadly: As many as 80% of the people infected with multidrug-resistant TB (MDR-TB) die within two months of diagnosis—even with medical care. The problem with MDR-TB is particularly serious in five countries—Estonia, China, Latvia, Russia, and Iran—where 5% to 14% of all patients first diagnosed with TB are infected with multidrug-resistant strains.

Bacteria are continually evolving, even inside the bodies of human and animal hosts. Bacteria develop genetic resistance through mutations (see Chapters 11 and 12) and through acquiring new genes from plasmids (see Chapters 11 and 14, discussion of transformation) or viruses (see Chapter 23, discussion of transduction). When an antibiotic is used to treat a bacterial infection, a few bacteria may survive because they are genetically resistant to the antibiotic, and they pass these genes to future generations. As a result of selection, the bacterial population contains a larger percentage of antibiotic-resistant bacteria than before.

Poor prescribing practices by doctors and poor patient compliance with treatment are factors in the development of drug-resistant strains of the TB bacterium. A person infected with TB must take three to ten pills of antibiotics each day for at least six months. After the first month of treatment, the person usually feels better; many patients decide to quit taking their medication at this point. When this happens, the TB bacteria still lurking in their bodies—those with a resistance to the prescribed antibiotic—rally. The evolution of a strain of bacteria resistant to several drugs is a worst-case scenario.

Process of Science — Evolutionary hypotheses can be tested experimentally

Increasingly, biologists are designing imaginative experiments, often in natural settings, to test evolutionary hypotheses. David Reznick from the University of California at Santa Barbara and John Endler from James Cook University in Australia have studied evolution in guppy populations in Venezuela and Trinidad, a small island in the southern Caribbean.

Reznick and Endler observed that different streams have different kinds and numbers of fishes that prey on guppies. Predatory fish that prey on larger guppies are present at lower elevations in all streams; these areas of intense predation pressure are known as *high predation habitats*. Predators are often excluded from tributaries or upstream areas by rapids and waterfalls. The areas above such barriers are known as *low predation habitats* because they contain only one species of small predatory fish that occasionally eat smaller guppies.

Differences in predation are correlated with many differences in the guppies, such as male coloration, behavior, and attributes known as *life history traits,* including age and size at sexual maturity, the number of offspring per litter, the size of the offspring, and the frequency of reproduction. For example, guppy adults are larger in streams at higher elevations and smaller in streams at lower elevations. Reznick and colleagues have studied these life history traits and considered the role that predators in the two habitats might have played in the evolution of differences in life histories.

Reznick and his colleagues paid particular attention to the differences in guppy size, hypothesizing that these differences are related to predator preferences. However, they first had to rule out the possibility that some unknown environmental factor was responsible for the size differences. To determine this, they captured adult female guppies from high and low predation habitats in Trinidad and sent them to their laboratory. They exploited a convenient property of guppy reproductive biology—adult females are virtually always pregnant. Because these females store sperm, each female was able to produce a series of litters when she was isolated in the laboratory. The offspring of each female were then mated to produce a second generation. All the guppies were reared in identical predator free laboratory environments.

The second generation of guppies descended from females from low predation habitats grew into larger, later maturing adults. Conversely, the second generation from high predation habitats grew into smaller adults that matured at an earlier age. It is assumed that any differences among guppy populations that persist after two generations in identical laboratory environments have a genetic basis. This experiment therefore demonstrated that differences in size between the two populations were inherited; that is, they were not caused by some nongenetic factor, such as the availability of food.

Genetic differences between the two guppy populations are of particular interest because ecologists had predicted before this study that higher mortality rates found in high predation habitats would select for earlier maturity and smaller size at maturity. These predicted life history differences are consistent with the genetic differences observed among these populations of guppies.

Do predators actually cause these differences to evolve? Reznick and colleagues tested this evolutionary hypothesis by conducting field experiments in Trinidad. Taking advantage of waterfalls that prevent upstream movement of guppies, guppy predators, or both, they moved either guppies or guppy predators over such barriers. For example, guppies from a high predation habitat were introduced into a low predation habitat by moving them over a barrier waterfall into a section of stream that was free of guppies and large predators. The only fish species that lived in this section of stream prior to the introduction was the predator that occasionally preyed on small guppies.

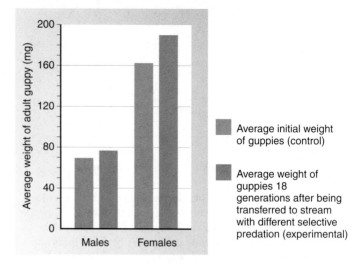

Figure 17–20 Experimental evidence of natural selection in guppies. Male and female guppies from a stream in which the predators preferred large adult guppies as prey *(brown bars)* were transferred to a stream in which the predators preferred juveniles and small adults. After 11 years, the descendants of these guppies *(pink bars)* were measurably larger in size, compared with their ancestors. *(Data from Reznick, D.N., et al. "Evaluation of the Rate of Evolution in Natural Populations of Guppies (Poecilia reticulata)." Science, Vol. 275, 28 Mar. 1997)*

Eleven years later, they captured adult females from the introduction site (low predation habitat) and the control site below the barrier waterfall (high predation habitat). They bred these females in their laboratory and compared the life history traits of succeeding generations, as in the earlier study. The descendants of guppies introduced into the low predation habitat matured at an older age and larger size than the descendants of guppies collected from the control site below the waterfall (Fig. 17–20). They also produced fewer, but larger, offspring. The life histories of the introduced fish had therefore evolved to be similar to those of fish that are typically found in such low predation habitats. These and other studies have also demonstrated that the predators have played an active role in the evolution of other traits, such as average number of offspring produced during the lifetime of an individual female (fecundity), male coloration, and behavior.

These and other experiments demonstrate that evolution is not only real but that it is occurring now, driven by selective environmental forces, such as predation, that can be experimentally manipulated. Darwin incorrectly assumed evolution is so gradual that humans cannot observe it. As Jonathan Weiner, author of *The Beak of the Finch: A Story of Evolution in Our Time,* puts it, "Darwin did not know the strength of his own theory. He vastly underestimated the power of natural selection. Its action is neither rare nor slow. It leads to evolution daily and hourly, all around us, and we can watch."

I. **Evolution,** genetic change in a **population** of organisms over time, is the unifying concept of biology.
   A. The concept of evolution is the cornerstone of biology because it links all fields of the life sciences into a unified body of knowledge.
   B. Evolution has important practical applications in fields such as agriculture, medicine, conservation biology, **bioremediation,** and computers.
II. Charles Darwin's voyage on the H.M.S. *Beagle* was the basis for his theory of evolution.
   A. Darwin tried to explain his observations of the similarities between animals and plants of the arid Galapagos Islands and the humid South American mainland.
   B. Darwin was influenced by **artificial selection,** in which breeders develop many varieties of domesticated plants and animals in just a few generations.
   C. Darwin applied Thomas Malthus's ideas on the natural increase in human populations to natural populations.
   D. The idea that Earth was extremely old, which was promoted by Charles Lyell and other geologists, influenced Darwin.
III. Charles Darwin and Alfred Wallace independently proposed the theory of evolution by **natural selection,** which is based on four observations.
   A. *Variation:* Genetic variation exists among the individuals in a population.
   B. *Overproduction:* The reproductive ability of each species causes its populations to geometrically increase in number over time.
   C. *Limits on population growth:* Organisms compete with one another for the resources needed for life, such as food, living space, water, and light.
   D. *Differential reproductive success:* The offspring with the most favorable combination of characteristics are most likely to survive and reproduce, passing those genetic characteristics to the next generation. Thus, natural selection results in **adaptations,** which are evolutionary modifications that improve the chances of survival and reproductive success in a particular environment.
   E. Over time, enough changes may accumulate in geographically separated populations (often with slightly different environments) to produce new species.
IV. The **synthetic theory of evolution,** or **neo-Darwinism,** combines Darwin's theory of evolution by natural selection with modern genetics to explain how species adapt to their environment.
   A. **Mutation** provides the genetic variability that natural selection acts on during evolution.
   B. The synthetic theory of evolution emphasizes the genetics of populations rather than of individuals.
V. The concept that evolution has occurred and is occurring is now well documented.
   A. Direct evidence of evolution comes from **fossils,** the remains or traces of ancient organisms.
      1. Layers of sedimentary rock normally occur in their sequence of deposition, with the more recent layers on top of the older, earlier ones.
      2. **Index fossils** characterize a specific layer over large geographical areas.
      3. **Radioisotopes** present in a rock provide a way to accurately measure the rock's age.

B. Evidence supporting evolution is derived from comparative anatomy.
   1. **Homologous features** have basic structural similarities, even though the structures may be used in different ways, because homologous features derive from the same structure in a common ancestor. Homologous features indicate evolutionary affinities among the organisms possessing them.
   2. **Homoplastic features** have similar functions in quite different, distantly related organisms. Homoplastic features demonstrate **convergent evolution,** in which organisms with separate ancestries adapt in similar ways to comparable environmental demands.
   3. **Vestigial structures** are nonfunctional or degenerate remnants of structures that were present and functional in ancestral organisms. Structures occasionally become vestigial as species adapt to different modes of life.
C. **Biogeography,** the distribution of plants and animals, supports evolution.
   1. Areas that have been separated from the rest of the world for a long time have organisms that are unique to those areas.
   2. At one time the continents were joined to form a supercontinent. **Continental drift,** which caused the various land masses to break apart and separate, has played a major role in evolution.
D. Developmental biology provides evidence of evolution.
   1. Evolutionary changes are often the result of mutations in genes that affect the orderly sequence of events during development.
   2. Scientific evidence demonstrates that development in different animals is controlled by the same kinds of genes, which indicates that these animals have a shared evolutionary history.
   3. The accumulation of genetic changes since organisms diverged, or took separate evolutionary pathways, has modified the pattern of development in more complex vertebrate embryos.
E. Molecular biology provides evidence of evolution.
   1. The universality of the genetic code is compelling evidence that all life is related.
   2. The sequence of amino acids in common proteins reveals greater similarities in closely related species.
   3. **DNA sequencing** determines the order of nucleotide bases in DNA. A greater proportion of the nucleotide sequence in DNA is identical in closely related organisms.
   4. A **phylogenetic tree,** a diagram showing lines of descent, can be derived from differences in a given DNA nucleotide sequence in various organisms.
   5. A **molecular clock** estimates the time of divergence between two closely related species or higher taxonomic groups.
F. Bacteria that cause infectious diseases such as tuberculosis are evolving resistance to antibiotics.
G. Experimental data provide evidence of evolution.
   1. Reznick has studied the effects of predation intensity on the evolution of guppy populations in both the laboratory and nature.
   2. Such experiments are a powerful way for investigators to test the underlying processes of natural selection.

1. Evolution is based on which of the following concepts? (a) organisms share a common origin (b) over time, organisms have diverged from a common ancestor (c) an animal's body parts can change over its lifetime, and these acquired changes can be passed to the next generation (d) a and b are correct (e) a, b, and c are correct

2. Evolution is the accumulation of genetic changes within _____ over time. (a) individuals (b) populations (c) communities (d) a and b (e) a and c

3. Charles Darwin proposed that evolution could be explained by the differential reproductive success of organisms that resulted from their naturally occurring variation. Darwin called this process (a) coevolution (b) convergent evolution (c) natural selection (d) artificial selection (e) homoplasy

4. Which of the following statements is *false?* (a) Darwin was the first to supply convincing evidence for biological evolution (b) Darwin was the first to propose that organisms change over time (c) Wallace independently developed the same theory as Darwin (d) Darwin's theory is based on four observations about the natural world (e) Darwin's studies in the Galapagos strongly influenced his ideas about evolution

5. Which of the following is *not* part of Darwin's mechanism of evolution? (a) differential reproductive success (b) variation in a population (c) inheritance of acquired (nongenetic) traits (d) overproduction of offspring (e) struggle for existence

6. The synthetic theory of evolution (a) is based on the sequence of fossils in rock layers (b) uses genetics to explain the source of hereditary variation that is essential to natural selection (c) was first proposed by ancient Greek scholars (d) considers the influence of the geographical distribution of organisms on their evolution (e) is reinforced by homologies that are explained by common descent

7. Jewish and Muslim men have been circumcised for many generations, yet this practice has had no effect on the penile foreskin of their offspring. This observation disproves evolution as envisioned by (a) Lamarck (b) Darwin (c) Wallace (d) Lyell (e) Malthus

8. Which of the following is *least* likely to have occurred after a small population of finches reached the Galapagos Islands from the South American mainland? (a) after many generations, the finches became increasingly different from the original population (b) over time, the finches adapted to their new environment (c) after many generations, the finches were unchanged and unmodified in any way (d) the finches were unable to survive in their new home and died out

9. The fossil record (a) usually occurs in sedimentary rock (b) sometimes appears fragmentary (c) is relatively complete for tropical rainforest organisms but incomplete for aquatic organisms (d) a and b are correct (e) a, b, and c are correct

10. The molecular record found inside cells suggests that evolutionary changes are caused by an accumulation of (a) traits acquired through need (b) alterations in the order of nucleotides in DNA (c) characters acquired during an individual's lifetime (d) hormones (e) environmental changes

11. In _____, the selecting agent is the environment, whereas in _____, the selecting agent is humans. (a) natural selection; convergent evolution (b) mutation; artificial selection (c) homoplasy; homology (d) artificial selection; natural selection (e) natural selection; artificial selection

12. Structures that are similar in underlying form in different species due to a common evolutionary origin are called (a) homoplastic (b) homologous (c) vestigial (d) convergent (e) synthetic

13. Aardvarks, anteaters, and pangolins are only distantly related but are similar in structure and form as a result of (a) homology (b) convergent evolution (c) biogeography (d) vestigial structures (e) artificial selection

14. The species of the Galapagos Islands (a) are similar to those on the Cape Verde Islands (b) are similar to those on the South American mainland (c) are identical to those on the Cape Verde Islands (d) are identical to those on the South American mainland (e) are similar to those on both the African and South American mainlands

15. In the guppy experiments, Reznick determined that (a) different streams have the same kinds of fishes that prey on guppies (b) guppy adults are larger in streams at lower elevations (c) differences in guppy size are related to availability of food (d) guppies living in an environment with large predators tend to be smaller in size (e) fish that prey on guppies exert no influence on guppy evolution

R E V I E W   Q U E S T I O N S

1. Explain briefly the concept of evolution by natural selection.

2. Why are only inherited variations important in the evolutionary process?

3. What part of Darwin's theory was he unable to explain? How does the synthetic theory of evolution fill this gap?

4. How do scientists date fossils? How do fossils provide evidence of evolution?

5. Distinguish among homologous features, homoplastic features, and vestigial structures. How does each provide evidence of evolution?

6. How does continental drift occur?

7. Explain why fossils of *Mesosaurus,* an extinct reptile that could not swim across open water, are found in the southern parts of both Africa and South America.

8. How does developmental biology provide evidence of a common ancestry for vertebrates as diverse as reptiles, birds, pigs, and humans?

9. Explain why there are many species of marsupials in Australia and only a few marsupials elsewhere.

10. What is indicated if the DNA from two species is found to be almost identical?

11. Explain how predator preference drives the evolution of size in guppies.

1. The use of model organisms, such as the laboratory mouse, for biomedical testing and research is based on the assumption that all organisms share a common ancestor. On what evidence is this assumption based?

2. What adaptations must an animal possess to swim in the ocean? Why are such genetically different organisms as porpoises, which are mammals, and sharks, which are fish, so similar in form?

3. The human fetus grows a coat of fine hair, the lanugo, that is shed before or shortly after birth. Fetuses of chimpanzee and other primates also grow coats of hair, but they are not shed. Explain these observations based on what you have learned in this chapter.

4. Write short paragraphs explaining each of the following statements:
   a. Natural selection chooses from among the individuals in a population those most suited to *current* environmental conditions. It does not guarantee survival under future conditions.
   b. Individuals do not evolve, but populations do.
   c. The organisms that exist today do so because their ancestors possessed traits that allowed them and their offspring to thrive.
   d. At the molecular level, evolution can take place by the replacement of one nucleotide by another.
   e. Evolution is said to have occurred within a population when measurable genetic changes are detected.

5. Although most salamanders have four legs, a few species that live in shallow water lack hind limbs and have extremely tiny forelimbs *(see photograph)*. Develop a hypothesis to explain how limbless salamanders came about according to Darwin's mechanism of evolution by natural selection. How could you test your hypothesis?

The narrow-striped dwarf siren (*Pseudobranchus striatus axanthus*). This aquatic salamander, which is native to Florida, resembles an eel. *(Suzanne L. Collins and Joseph T. Collins/Photo Researchers, Inc.)*

Diamond, J. "Evolving Backward." *Discover,* Sep. 1998. An examination of vestigial structures that have been lost or reduced in the course of evolution.

Gould, S.J. "A Division of Worms." *Natural History,* Feb. 1999. This eminent paleontologist examines Jean-Baptiste Lamarck's considerable contributions to anatomy and taxonomy.

Grenard, S. "Is Rattlesnake Venom Evolving?" *Natural History,* Jul./Aug. 2000. Evidence suggests that the venom of North America's rattlesnakes is becoming more potent, possibly in response to prey that are evolving resistance to rattlesnake venom.

Huey, R.B., G.W. Gilchrist, M.L. Carlson, D. Berrigan, and L. Serra. "Rapid Evolution of a Geographic Cline in Size in an Introduced Fly." *Science,* Vol. 287, 14 Jan. 2000. This paper describes the study of rapid fruit fly evolution that was discussed in the chapter.

Mayr, E. "Darwin's Influence on Modern Thought." *Scientific American,* Vol. 283, No. 1, Jul. 2000. The author, one of the 20th century's most influential evolutionary biologists, considers the wide reach of Darwin's ideas, which permeate modern thinking on many subjects.

McComas, W.F. "The Discovery and Nature of Evolution by Natural Selection: Misconceptions and Lessons from the History of Science." *The American Biology Teacher,* Vol. 59, No. 8, Oct. 1997. The author provides some fascinating insights into Darwin's development of his theory of evolution by natural selection.

Monastersky, R. "The Whale's Tale." *Science News,* Vol. 156, 6 Nov. 1999. Although much is known about how whales evolved from life on land to life in the water, a few important questions remain to be answered.

Nesse, R.M., and G.C. Williams. "Evolution and the Origins of Disease." *Scientific American,* Vol. 279, No. 5, Nov. 1998. Increasingly, physicians are considering health, disease, and modern medical practices in an evolutionary context.

Pennisi, E., and W. Roush. "Developing a New View of Evolution." *Science,* Vol. 277, 4 Jul. 1997. How developmental biologists are illuminating some of the mysteries of evolution by studying the genes that control embryonic development.

Porter, D.M., and P.W. Graham. *The Portable Darwin.* Penguin Books, New York, 1993. This collection of Darwin's writings reveals the diverse interests of the man who profoundly changed the intellectual climate of the 19th and 20th centuries.

Science and Creationism: A View from the National Academy of Sciences, 2nd ed. National Academy Press, Washington, D.C., 1999. A great introduction to the evidence for evolution.

Weiner, J. *The Beak of the Finch: A Story of Evolution in Our Time.* Knopf, New York, 1994. This Pulitzer Prize-winning book focuses on the research of Peter and Rosemary Grant on evolution in the Galapagos finches.

Zimmer, C. "Hidden Unity." *Discover,* Jan. 1998. Discusses the similarities of developmental genes in a wide variety of organisms. Several very similar genes, for example, control the development of eyes in animals as diverse as humans and insects.

- Visit our Web site at **http://www.info.brookscole.com/solomonbergmartin** for links to chapter-related resources on the World Wide Web. Additional on-line materials relating to this chapter can also be found on our Web site.

See chapter activity on BioActive Learner CD for additional help in mastering the chapter's material. Icon location in the chapter's margins shows which topics have tutorials or simulations in the CD.

18

Evolutionary Change in Populations

Genetic variation in snail shells. Shown are the shell patterns and colors in a single snail species (*Cepaea nemoralis*), native to Scotland. Variation in shell color may have adaptive value in these snails because some colors predominate in cooler environments, whereas other colors are more common in warmer habitats. *(G.I. Bernard/Animals Animals)*

LEARNING OBJECTIVES

After you have studied this chapter you should be able to

1. Define population, population genetics, genetic equilibrium, and microevolution.
2. Distinguish among genotype, phenotype, and allele frequencies.
3. Discuss the significance of the Hardy-Weinberg principle as it relates to evolution, and list the five conditions required for genetic equilibrium.
4. Use the Hardy-Weinberg principle to solve problems involving populations.
5. Discuss how each of the following alters allele frequencies in populations: nonrandom mating, mutation, genetic drift, gene flow, and natural selection.
6. Distinguish among stabilizing selection, directional selection, and disruptive selection, and give an example of each.
7. Describe the nature and extent of genetic variation, including genetic polymorphism, balanced polymorphism, neutral variation, and geographical variation.
8. Explain how the sickle cell allele illustrates heterozygote advantage.
9. Relate how frequency-dependent selection affects genetic variation.

As we saw in Chapter 17, evolution occurs in populations, not individuals. Although natural selection results from differential survival and reproduction of individuals, individuals do not evolve during their lifetimes. Evolutionary change, which includes modifications in structure, physiology, ecology, and behavior, is inherited from one generation to the next. Although Darwin recognized that evolution occurs in populations, he did not understand how traits are passed to successive generations. One of the most significant advances in biology since Darwin's time has been the demonstration of the genetic basis of evolution. As you will see in this chapter, Gregor Mendel's principles of inheritance (see Chapter 10) underlie Darwinian evolution.

Recall from Chapter 17 that a **population** consists of all the individuals of the same species that live in a particular place at the same time. Individuals within a population vary in many recog-

nizable traits. A population of snails, for example, may vary in shell size, weight, or color *(see photograph)*. Some of this variation is due to the environment, and some is due to heredity.

Biologists study variation in a particular trait by taking measurements of that trait in a population. By comparing the trait in parents and offspring, it is possible to estimate the amount of observed variation that is genetic, as represented by the number, frequency, and kinds of alleles in a population. (Recall from Chapter 10 that an **allele** is one of two or more alternate forms of a gene. Alleles occupy corresponding positions, or **loci,** on homologous chromosomes.)

In this chapter we present some basic concepts of **population genetics,** the study of genetic variability within a population and of the forces that act on it. Population genetics represents an extension of Mendelian inheritance. We contrast genetic equilibrium with evolutionary change and discuss the five factors responsible for evolutionary change: nonrandom mating, mutation, genetic drift, gene flow, and natural selection. We then consider genetic variation as the raw material for evolution.

GENOTYPE, PHENOTYPE, AND ALLELE FREQUENCIES CAN BE CALCULATED

Each population possesses a **gene pool,** which includes all the alleles for all the genes present in the population. Because diploid organisms possess a maximum of two different alleles at each genetic locus, a single individual typically has only a small fraction of the alleles present in a population's gene pool. The genetic variation that is evident among individuals in a given population indicates that each individual has a different combination of the alleles in the gene pool.

The evolution of populations is best understood in terms of genotype, phenotype, and allele frequencies. Suppose, for example, that all 1000 individuals of a hypothetical population have their genotypes tested, with the following results:

Genotype	Number	Genotype Frequency
AA	490	0.49
Aa	420	0.42
aa	90	0.09
Total	1000	1.00

Each **genotype frequency** is the proportion of a particular genotype in the population. Genotype frequency is usually expressed as a decimal fraction, and the sum of all genotype frequencies is 1.0 (somewhat like probabilities, which were discussed in Chapter 10). For example, the genotype frequency for the *Aa* genotype is $420 \div 1000 = 0.42$.

A **phenotype frequency** is the proportion of a particular phenotype in the population. If each genotype corresponds to a specific phenotype, then the phenotype and genotype frequencies are the same. If allele *A* is dominant over allele *a,* however, the phenotype frequencies in our hypothetical population would be the following:

Phenotype	Number	Phenotype Frequency
Dominant	910	0.91
Recessive	90	0.09
Total	1000	1.00

(In this example, the dominant phenotype is the sum of two genotypes, *AA* and *Aa,* and so the number 910 is obtained by adding 490 + 420.)

An **allele frequency** is the proportion of a specific allele (that is, of *A* or *a*) in a particular population. As mentioned earlier, each individual, being diploid, has two alleles at each genetic locus. Since we started with a population of 1000 individuals, we must account for a total of 2000 alleles. The 490 *AA* individuals have 980 *A* alleles, whereas the 420 *Aa* individuals have 420 *A* alleles, making a total of 1400 *A* alleles in the population. The total number of *a* alleles in the population is $420 + 90 + 90 = 600$. Now it is easy to calculate allele frequencies:

Allele	Number	Allele Frequency
A	1400	0.7
a	600	0.3
Total	2000	1.0

THE HARDY-WEINBERG PRINCIPLE DESCRIBES GENETIC EQUILIBRIUM

In the example just discussed, we observe that only 90 of the 1000 individuals in the population exhibit the recessive phenotype characteristic of the genotype *aa.* The remaining 910 individuals exhibit the dominant phenotype and are either *AA* or *Aa.* You might assume that, after many generations, genetic recombination during sexual reproduction would cause the dominant allele to become more common in the population. You might also assume that the recessive allele would eventually disappear altogether. These were common assumptions of many biologists early in the 20th century. However, these assumptions were incorrect because the frequencies of alleles and genotypes do not change from generation to generation unless influenced by outside factors (discussed later).

A population whose allele and genotype frequencies do not change from generation to generation is said to be at **genetic equilibrium.** Such a population, with no net change in allele or genotype frequencies over time, is not undergoing evolutionary change. However, evolution is occurring in a population in which there are changes in allele frequencies over successive generations.

The explanation for the stability of successive generations in populations at genetic equilibrium was provided independently by Godfrey Hardy, an English mathematician, and Wilhelm Weinberg, a German physician, in 1908. They pointed out that the expected frequencies of various genotypes in a population can be described mathematically. The resulting **Hardy-Weinberg principle** shows that in large populations the process of inheritance does not by itself cause changes in allele frequencies. It also explains why dominant alleles are not necessarily more common than recessive ones. The Hardy-Weinberg principle represents an ideal situation that seldom occurs in the natural world. However, it is useful because it provides a model to help us understand the real world. Knowledge of the Hardy-Weinberg principle is essential to understanding the mechanisms of evolutionary change in sexually reproducing populations.

We now expand our original example to illustrate the Hardy-Weinberg principle. Keep in mind as we go through these calculations, that in most cases, we only know the phenotype frequencies. (When alleles are dominant and recessive, it is usually impossible to visually distinguish heterozygous individuals from homozygous dominant individuals.) The Hardy-Weinberg principle allows us to use phenotype frequencies to calculate the expected genotype frequencies and allele frequencies, assuming we have a clear understanding of the genetic basis for the trait under study.

As mentioned earlier, the frequency of either allele, *A* or *a*, is represented by a number that ranges from zero to one. An allele that is totally absent from the population has a frequency of zero. If all the alleles of a given locus are the same in the population, then the frequency of that allele is one.

Because only two alleles, *A* and *a,* exist at the locus in our example, the sum of their frequencies must equal one. If we let *p* represent the frequency of the dominant *(A)* allele in the population, and *q* the frequency of the recessive *(a)* allele, then we can summarize their relationship with a simple binomial equation, $p + q = 1$. When we know the value of either *p* or *q*, we can calculate the value of the other: $p = 1 - q$ and $q = 1 - p$.

Squaring both sides of $p + q = 1$ results in $(p + q)^2 = 1$. This equation can be expanded to describe the relationship of the allele frequencies to the genotypes in the population. When it is expanded, we obtain the frequency of the offspring genotypes:

$$p^2 \quad + \quad 2pq \quad + \quad q^2 \quad = \quad 1$$

Frequency of *AA* Frequency of *Aa* Frequency of *aa* All the individuals in a population

We always begin Hardy-Weinberg calculations by determining the frequency of the homozygous recessive genotype. From the fact that we had 90 homozygous recessive individuals in our population of 1000, we infer that the frequency of the *aa* genotype, q^2, is 90/1000, or 0.09. Since q^2 equals 0.09, *q* (the frequency of the recessive *a* allele)is equal to the square root of 0.09, or 0.3. From the relationship between *p* and *q*, we conclude that the frequency of the dominant *A* allele, *p*, equals $1 - q = 1 - 0.3 = 0.7$.

Based on this information, we can calculate the frequency of homozygous dominant *(AA)* individuals: $p^2 = 0.7 \times 0.7 = 0.49$ (Fig. 18–1). The frequency of heterozygous individuals *(Aa)*, would be: $2pq = 2 \times 0.7 \times 0.3 = 0.42$. Thus, approximately 490 individuals are expected to be homozygous dominant, and 420 are expected to be heterozygous. Note that the sum of homozygous dominant and heterozygous individuals equals 910, the number of individuals with the dominant phenotype that we started with.

Any population in which the distribution of genotypes conforms to the relation $p^2 + 2pq + q^2 = 1$, whatever the absolute values for *p* and *q* may be, is at genetic equilibrium. The Hardy-Weinberg principle allows biologists to calculate allele frequencies in a given population if we know the genotype frequencies, and vice versa. These values can be used as a basis of comparison with a population's allele or genotype frequencies in succeeding generations. During that time, if the allele or genotype frequencies deviate from the values predicted by the Hardy-Weinberg principle, then the population is evolving. (You can test your understanding of the Hardy-Weinberg principle by solving the problems in the Review Questions at the end of this chapter.)

Genetic equilibrium occurs if certain conditions are met

The Hardy-Weinberg principle of genetic equilibrium tells us what to expect when a sexually reproducing population is not evolving. The relative proportions of alleles and genotypes in

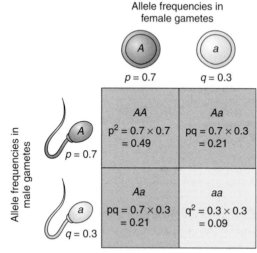

Genotypes	*AA*	*Aa*	*aa*
Frequency of genotypes in population	0.49	0.42 (0.21 + 0.21)	0.09
Frequency of alleles in gametes	*A* = 0.49 + 0.21 = 0.7	*a* = 0.21 + 0.09 = 0.3	

(a) Genotype and allele frequencies

(b) Segregation of alleles and random fertilization

■ **Figure 18–1 Hardy-Weinberg principle** (a) How to calculate frequencies of the alleles *A* and *a* in the gametes. (b) When eggs and sperm containing *A* or *a* alleles unite randomly, the frequency of each of the possible genotypes (*AA*, *Aa*, *aa*) among the offspring is calculated by multiplying the frequencies of the alleles *A* and *a* in eggs and sperm.

successive generations will always be the same, provided the following five conditions are met:

1. **Random mating.** In unrestricted random mating, each individual in a population has an equal chance of mating with any individual of the opposite sex. In our example, the individuals represented by the genotypes *AA*, *Aa*, and *aa* must mate with one another at random and must not select their mates on the basis of genotype or any other factors that result in nonrandom mating.

2. **No net mutations.** There must be no mutations that convert *A* into *a* or vice versa. That is, the frequencies of *A* and *a* in the population must not change due to mutations.

3. **Large population size.** Allele frequencies in a small population are more likely to be changed by random fluctuations (i.e., by genetic drift, which is discussed later) than are allele frequencies in a large population.

4. **No migration.** There can be no exchange of genes with other populations that might have different allele frequencies. In

other words, there can be no migration of individuals into or out of a population.

5. **No natural selection.** If natural selection is occurring, certain phenotypes (and their corresponding genotypes) are favored over others. Consequently, the allele frequencies will change, and the population will evolve.

Human MN blood groups are a valuable illustration of the Hardy-Weinberg principle

Humans possess dozens of antigens on the surfaces of their blood cells. (An *antigen* is a molecule, usually a protein or carbohydrate, that can be recognized as foreign by cells of another organism's immune system.) One group of antigens, designated the MN blood group, stimulates the production of antibodies when injected into rabbits or guinea pigs. However, humans do not produce antibodies for M and N, so the MN blood group is not medically important, for example, when giving blood transfusions. (Recall the discussion of the medically important ABO alleles in Chapter 10.) The MN blood group is of interest to population geneticists, however, because the genotype frequencies can be observed directly (the alleles for the MN blood group, usually designated *M* and *N,* are codominant) and compared with calculated frequencies.

Genotype	Phenotype (Antigen on RBC)
MM	Antigen M only
MN	Antigens M and N
NN	Antigen N only

The following data are typical of the MN blood group in people in the United States:

Genotype	Observed
MM	320
MN	480
NN	200
Total	1000

Because there are 1000 diploid individuals in the sample, there are a total of 2000 alleles. The frequency of *M* alleles in the population = $p = (2 \times 320 + 480) \div 2000 = 0.56$. The frequency of *N* alleles in the population = $q = (2 \times 200 + 480) \div 2000 = 0.44$. As a quick check, the sum of the frequencies should equal one. Does it?

If this population is in genetic equilibrium, then the expected *MM* genotype frequency = $p^2 = (0.56)^2 = 0.31$. The expected *MN* genotype frequency = $2pq = 2 \times 0.56 \times 0.44 = 0.49$. The expected *NN* genotype frequency = $q^2 = (0.44)^2 = 0.19$. As a quick check, the sum of the three genotype frequencies should equal 1. Does it?

You can use the calculated genotype frequencies to determine how many individuals in a population of 1000 should have the expected genotype frequencies. By comparing the expected numbers with the actual results observed, you can see how closely the population is to genetic equilibrium. Simply multiply each genotype frequency by 1000:

Genotype	Observed	Expected
MM	320	313.6
MN	480	492.8
NN	200	193.6
Total	1000	1000

The expected numbers closely match the observed numbers, indicating that the *MN* blood groups in the human population are almost at genetic equilibrium. This is not surprising, given that the *MN* characteristic has no medical significance and does not produce a visible trait that might affect random mating.

■ MICROEVOLUTION OCCURS WHEN A POPULATION'S ALLELE OR GENOTYPE FREQUENCIES CHANGE

Evolution represents a departure from the Hardy-Weinberg principle of genetic equilibrium. The degree of departure between the observed allele or genotype frequencies and those expected by the Hardy-Weinberg principle indicates the amount of evolutionary change. This type of evolution—generation-to-generation changes in allele or genotype frequencies *within* a population—is sometimes referred to as **microevolution** because it often involves relatively small or minor changes, usually over a few generations. Changes in the allele frequencies of a population result from five microevolutionary processes: nonrandom mating, mutation, genetic drift, gene flow, and natural selection. When one or more of these processes is acting on a population, allele or genotype frequencies will change from one generation to the next.

■ NONRANDOM MATING CHANGES GENOTYPE FREQUENCIES

When individuals select mates on the basis of phenotype (thereby selecting the corresponding genotype), they can bring about evolutionary change in the population. Two examples of nonrandom mating are inbreeding and assortative mating.

In many populations, individuals mate more often with close neighbors than with more distant members of the population. As a result, neighbors tend to be more closely related—that is, genetically similar—to one another. The mating of genetically similar individuals that are more closely related than if they had been chosen at random from the entire population is known as **inbreeding.** Although inbreeding does not change the overall allele frequency, the frequency of homozygous genotypes increases with each successive generation of inbreeding. The most extreme example of inbreeding is self-fertilization, which is particularly common in plants.

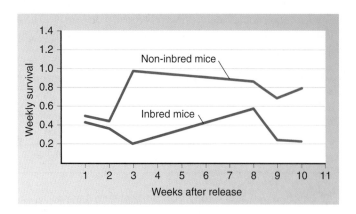

Figure 18–2 Survival of inbred and non-inbred mice. The mouse population was sampled six times (each for a three-day span) during a 10-week period. Non-inbred mice *(red)* had a higher survival rate than inbred mice *(blue)*. Values on the Y-axis are the estimated proportion of mice that survived from one week to the next. Hence, a value of 0.6 means that 60% of the mice alive at the beginning of the week survived through that week. *(Adapted from Jiménez, J.A., et al. "An Experimental Study of Inbreeding Depression in a Natural Habitat." Science, Vol. 266, 14 Oct. 1994)*

Inbreeding does not appear to be detrimental in some populations, but in others it causes **inbreeding depression,** in which inbred individuals have lower fitness than non-inbred individuals. **Fitness** is the relative ability of a given genotype to make a genetic contribution to subsequent generations; fitness is usually measured as the average number of surviving offspring of one genotype compared to the average number of surviving offspring of competing genotypes. Inbreeding depression, as evidenced by fertility declines and high juvenile mortality, is thought to be caused by the expression of harmful recessive alleles as homozygosity increases with inbreeding.

Several studies in the 1990s provided direct evidence of the deleterious consequences of inbreeding in nature. For example, white-footed mice *(Peromyscus leucopus)* were taken from a field and used to develop both inbred and non-inbred populations in the laboratory. When these laboratory-bred populations were returned to nature, their survivorship was estimated from release-recapture data. The non-inbred mice had a statistically significant higher rate of survival (Fig. 18–2). It is not known why the inbred mice had a lower survival rate. Some possibilities include higher disease susceptibility, poorer ability to evade predators, lesser ability to find food, and lesser ability to win fights with other white-footed mice.

Assortative mating, in which individuals select mates by their phenotypes, is another example of nonrandom mating. For example, biologists selected two phenotypes—high bristle number and low bristle number—in a fruit fly *(Drosophila melanogaster)* population. Although they made no effort to control mating, they observed that the flies preferentially mated with those of similar phenotypes. Females with high bristle number tended to mate with males with high bristle number, and females with low bristle number tended to mate with males with low bristle number. Such selection of mates with the same phenotype is known as *positive assortative mating* (as opposed to the less common phenomenon, *negative assortative mating,* in which mates with opposite phenotypes are selected). Positive assortative mating is practiced in many human societies, in which men and women tend to marry individuals like themselves in such characteristics as height or intelligence. Like inbreeding, assortative mating usually increases homozygosity at the expense of heterozygosity in the population and does not change the overall allele frequencies in the population. However, assortative mating changes genotype frequencies only at the loci involved in mate choice, whereas inbreeding affects genotype frequencies in the entire genome.

■ MUTATION INCREASES VARIATION WITHIN A POPULATION

Variation is introduced into a population through **mutation,** which is an unpredictable change in deoxyribonucleic acid (DNA) (Fig. 18–3). Mutations, which are the source of all new alleles, can result from (1) a change in the nucleotide base pairs of a gene, (2) a rearrangement of genes within chromosomes so that their interactions produce different effects, or (3) a change in chromosome structure. Mutations occur unpredictably and spontaneously. The rate of mutation appears to be relatively con-

(a)   (b)

Figure 18–3 Fruit fly *(Drosophila melanogaster)* mutation. (a) A normal fly. (b) A mutant with vestigial wings. Because mutations are random changes in genetic material, most mutations are neutral or harmful to the organism. Yet for island-dwelling insects, fully developed wings might be more of a disadvantage than an advantage, permitting the insect to be too easily blown away from land. Perhaps for this reason, flies and other insects that live on small islands frequently have reduced wings or are entirely wingless. *(a, b, Peter J. Bryant/Biological Photo Service)*

stant for a particular gene but may vary by several orders of magnitude among genes within a single species and among different species.

Not all mutations pass from one generation to the next. Those occurring in somatic (body) cells are not inherited. When an individual with such a mutation dies, the mutation is lost. Some mutations, however, occur in reproductive cells. These mutations may or may not overtly affect the offspring, because most of the DNA in a cell is "silent" and does not code for specific polypeptides or proteins that are responsible for physical characteristics. Even if a mutation occurs in the DNA that codes for a polypeptide, it may still have little effect on the structure or function of that polypeptide (we discuss such *neutral variation* later in the chapter). However, when a polypeptide is sufficiently altered to change its function, the mutation is usually harmful. By acting against seriously abnormal phenotypes, natural selection eliminates or reduces to low frequencies the most harmful mutations. Mutations with small phenotypic effects, even if slightly harmful, have a better chance of being incorporated into the population, where at some later time, under different environmental conditions, they may produce traits that are useful or adaptive for the population.

Mutations do not determine the *direction* of evolutionary change. Consider a population living in an increasingly dry environment. A mutation producing a new allele that helps an individual adapt to dry conditions is no more likely to occur than one for adapting to wet conditions or one with no relationship to the changing environment. The production of new mutations simply increases the genetic variability that can be acted on by natural selection and, therefore, the potential for new adaptations.

Mutation by itself causes small deviations in allele frequencies from those predicted by the Hardy-Weinberg principle. Although allele frequencies may be changed by mutation, these changes are typically several orders of magnitude smaller than changes caused by other evolutionary forces, such as genetic drift. As an evolutionary force, mutation is usually negligible, but it is important as the ultimate source of variation for evolution.

■ IN GENETIC DRIFT, RANDOM EVENTS CHANGE ALLELE FREQUENCIES

The size of a population has important effects on allele frequencies because random events, or chance, will tend to cause changes of relatively greater magnitude in a small population. If a population consists of only a few individuals, an allele present at a low frequency in the population could be completely lost purely by chance. Such an event would be most unlikely in a large population. For example, consider two populations, one with 10,000 individuals and one with 10 individuals. If an uncommon allele occurs at a frequency of 10%, or 0.1, in both populations, then 1900 individuals in the large population possess the allele.[1] That same frequency, 0.1, in the smaller population

means that only about two individuals possess the allele.[2] From this exercise, it is easy to see that there is a greater likelihood of losing the rare allele from the smaller population than from the larger one. Predators, for example, might happen to kill one or two individuals possessing the uncommon allele in the smaller population purely by chance, so that these individuals would leave no offspring.

The production of random evolutionary changes in small breeding populations is known as **genetic drift.** Genetic drift results in changes in allele frequencies in a population from one generation to another. One allele may be eliminated from the population purely by chance, regardless of whether that allele is beneficial, harmful, or of no particular advantage or disadvantage. Thus, genetic drift can decrease genetic variation *within* a population, although it tends to increase the genetic differences *among* different populations.

When bottlenecks occur, genetic drift becomes a major evolutionary force

Because of fluctuations in the environment, such as depletion in food supply or an outbreak of disease, a population may periodically experience a rapid and marked decrease in the number of individuals. The population is said to go through a **bottleneck** during which genetic drift can occur in the small population of survivors. As the population again increases in size, many allele frequencies may be quite different from those in the population preceding the decline.

Scientists hypothesize that genetic variation in the cheetah (see Figs. 50–9 and 50–19c) was considerably reduced by a bottleneck that occurred at the end of the last Ice Age, some 10,000 years ago. At that time, cheetahs nearly became extinct, perhaps due to overhunting by humans. The few surviving cheetahs possessed greatly reduced genetic variability, and as a result, the cheetah population today is nearly genetically uniform or homogeneous.

 Are cheetahs endangered because of their extreme genetic uniformity or because of loss of habitat? The outlook for the cheetah's long-term survival is far from certain. There are currently about 12,000 cheetahs in sub-Saharan Africa and northern Iran.

For many years, lack of genetic diversity and inbreeding depression were considered the primary factors responsible for the cheetah's plight. Evidence of the extreme genetic uniformity in cheetahs was demonstrated in the 1980s when biologists discovered that unrelated cheetahs accepted skin grafts from one another. (Normally, only identical twins accept skin grafts so readily.) Geneticists hypothesized that inbreeding depression was responsible for problems with cheetahs in captive breeding programs. Compared with other large cats, cheetah males exhibit low sperm counts, many of their sperm have abnormalities, and

[1] $2pq + q^2 = 2(0.9)(0.1) + (0.1)^2 = 0.18 + 0.01 = 0.19; 0.19 \times 10,000 = 1900$

[2] $0.19 \times 10 = 1.9$

cheetah females do not bear as many offspring. Also, many cheetah offspring have health problems and are more susceptible to disease.

Notwithstanding the cheetah's genetic uniformity, ecologists who study cheetahs say that inbreeding depression is not impairing the cheetah's chance of breeding success. They have observed that the main cause of juvenile mortality is predation—lions and hyenas kill most young cheetahs—rather than the consequences of defective genes. Moreover, ecologists say that male cheetahs have no difficulty siring offspring in nature, despite their low sperm counts and high rates of sperm abnormalities.

Ecologists would like the focus on saving the cheetah to switch from genetic to environmental factors, that is, from captive breeding in zoos to what ecologists perceive as the real threat to the cheetah's survival—loss of habitat. Although geneticists agree that protection of habitat should be the main focus in attempts to save the cheetah (and all other endangered species) from extinction, they also emphasize that lack of genetic diversity should remain an important consideration in conservation strategies to save the cheetah.

Several studies reported in the late 1990s support the geneticists' view. For example, inbreeding and loss of genetic diversity were correlated with the extinction of local populations of butterflies (Glanville fritillaries) on Finnish islands. In addition, genetically uniform, declining populations of two different species—adders in Sweden and greater prairie chickens in Illinois (Fig. 18–4)—recovered when genetically diverse individuals from large populations were introduced into the genetically impoverished populations. Such experiments demonstrate that preserving genetic variability is an important way to increase the viability of wild populations.

Figure 18–4 Male greater prairie chicken (Tympanuchus cupido) in a courtship display. The greater prairie chicken's population plummeted in Illinois, from an estimated 100 million in 1900 to fewer than 50 in the mid-1990s. Studies comparing Illinois greater prairie chickens to greater prairie chickens living in nearby states showed the Illinois greater prairie chickens had lost much of their genetic diversity. This loss was substantiated by a comparison of DNA in Illinois greater prairie chickens with DNA in museum specimens collected in Illinois during the 1930s to 1960s. Fortunately, the Illinois population has recovered somewhat, after more than 500 greater prairie chickens from Minnesota, Kansas, and Nebraska (where greater prairie chicken populations are still thriving) were introduced during the 1990s and subsequently interbred with the Illinois birds. Photographed in Nebraska. *(Bob and Clara Calhoun/Bruce Coleman, Inc.)*

The founder effect occurs when a few "founders" establish a new colony

When one or a few individuals from a large population establish, or found, a colony (as when a few birds separate from the rest of the flock and fly to a new area), they bring with them only a small fraction of the genetic variation present in the original population. As a result, the only alleles represented among their descendants will be those few that the colonizers happened to possess. Typically, the allele frequencies in the newly founded population are quite different from those of the parent population. The genetic drift that results when a small number of individuals from a large population colonize a new area is called the **founder effect.**

The founder effect has been observed in populations of wild plants on islands off the Pacific coast of Canada. The Canadian mainland has several wild species of small, weedy annuals in the daisy family. These plants produce wind-dispersed seeds with fluffy parachutes similar to dandelion fruits. The seeds of mainland populations range in size from small to large, as do the fluffy parachutes. Sampling of these plants on 240 islands off the Canadian coast over a ten-year period revealed that the youngest island populations produced significantly smaller seeds than mainland populations. (Ages of island populations were easy to estimate be-

cause new colonizations occurred frequently.) This observation illustrates both the founder effect (only small seeds with large parachutes remain aloft to be blown by the wind to the nearby islands) and rapid evolutionary change by natural selection.

The Finnish people may also illustrate the founder effect. Geneticists who sampled DNA from Finns and from the European population at large found that Finns exhibit considerably less genetic variation than other Europeans. This evidence supports the hypothesis that Finns are descended from a small group of people who settled in that area that is now Finland about 4000 years ago and, because of the geography, remained separate from other European societies for centuries.

■ GENE FLOW GENERALLY INCREASES VARIATION WITHIN A POPULATION

Members of a species tend to be distributed in local populations that are genetically isolated to some degree from other populations. For example, the bullfrogs of one pond form a population separated from those in an adjacent pond. Some exchanges occur by migration between ponds, but the frogs in one pond are much more likely to mate with those in the same pond. Members of most species tend to be distributed in such local populations. Because each population is isolated to some extent from other populations of the species, they can have distinct genetic traits and gene pools.

The migration of breeding individuals between populations causes a corresponding movement of alleles, or **gene flow,** that can have significant evolutionary consequences. As alleles flow from one population to another, they usually increase the amount of genetic variability within the recipient population. If sufficient gene flow occurs between two populations, they become more similar genetically. Because gene flow has a tendency to reduce the amount of variation between two populations, it tends to counteract the effects of natural selection and genetic drift, both of which often cause populations to become increasingly distinct.

If migration by members of a population is considerable, and if populations differ in their allele frequencies, then significant genetic changes can result in local populations. For example, by 10,000 years ago modern humans occupied almost all of Earth's major land areas except a few islands. Because the population density was low in most locations, the small, isolated human populations underwent random genetic drift and natural selection. More recently (during the past 300 years or so), major migrations have caused an increase in gene flow, significantly altering allele frequencies within previously isolated human populations.

■ NATURAL SELECTION CHANGES ALLELE FREQUENCIES IN A WAY THAT INCREASES ADAPTATION

Natural selection is the mechanism of evolution first proposed by Darwin in which members of a population that possess more successful adaptations to the environment are more likely to survive and reproduce (see Chapter 17). Over successive generations, the proportion of favorable alleles increases in the population. In contrast with other microevolutionary processes (nonrandom mating, mutation, genetic drift, and gene flow), natural selection leads to adaptive evolutionary change. Natural selection not only explains why organisms are well adapted to the environments in which they live but also helps to account for the remarkable diversity of life. Natural selection enables populations to change, thereby adapting to different environments and different ways of life.

Natural selection is the differential reproduction of individuals with different traits, or phenotypes (and therefore different genotypes), in response to the environment. Natural selection results in the preservation of individuals with favorable phenotypes and elimination of those with unfavorable phenotypes. Individuals that are able to survive and produce fertile offspring have a selective advantage.

The mechanism of natural selection does not cause the development of a "perfect" organism. Rather, it weeds out those individuals whose phenotypes are less adapted to environmental challenges, while allowing better adapted individuals to survive and pass their alleles to their offspring. By reducing the frequency of alleles that result in the expression of less favorable traits, the probability is increased that favorable alleles responsible for an adaptation will come together in the offspring.

Natural selection operates on an organism's phenotype

Natural selection does not act directly on an organism's genotype. Instead, it acts on the phenotype, which is, at least in part, an expression of the genotype. The phenotype represents an interaction of all the alleles in the organism's genotype with the environment. It is rare that a single gene has complete control over a single phenotypic trait, such as Mendel originally observed in garden peas. Much more common is the interaction of alleles of several loci for the expression of a single trait (see Chapter 10). Many plant and animal characteristics are under this type of polygenic control.

When traits (e.g., human height) are under polygenic control, a range of phenotypes occurs, with most of the population located in the median range and fewer at either extreme. This is a normal distribution or standard bell curve (Fig. 18–5a; see also Fig. 10–22). Three kinds of selection occur that cause changes in the normal distribution of phenotypes in a population: stabilizing, directional, and disruptive selection. Although we consider each process separately, their influences generally overlap in nature.

Stabilizing selection favors intermediate phenotypes

The process of natural selection associated with a population that is well adapted to its environment is known as **stabilizing selection.** Most populations are probably under the influence of stabilizing forces most of the time. Stabilizing selection selects against phenotypic extremes. In other words, individuals with an average, or intermediate, phenotype are favored.

Because stabilizing selection tends to decrease variation by favoring individuals near the mean of the normal distribution at the expense of those at either extreme, the bell curve narrows (Fig. 18–5b). Although stabilizing selection decreases the amount of variation in a population, variation is rarely eliminated by this process because other microevolutionary processes act against a decrease in variation. For example, mutation is slowly but continually adding to the genetic variation within a population.

One of the most widely studied cases of stabilizing selection involves human birth weight, which is under polygenic control and is also influenced by environmental factors. Extensive data from hospitals have shown that infants born with intermediate weights are most likely to survive (Fig. 18–6). Infants at either extreme (too small or too large) have higher rates of mortality. When newborn infants are too small, their body systems are immature, and when they are too large, they have difficult deliveries because they cannot pass as easily through the cervix and vagina. Stabilizing selection operates to reduce the variability in birth weight so that it is close to the weight with the minimum mortality rate.

Directional selection favors one phenotype over another

If an environment changes over time, **directional selection** may favor phenotypes at one of the extremes of the normal distribution (Fig. 18–5c). Over successive generations, one phenotype gradually replaces another. So, for example, if greater size is

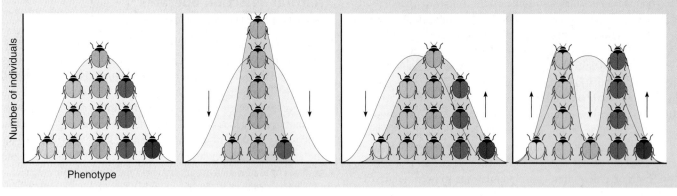

(a) No selection   (b) Stabilizing selection   (c) Directional selection   (d) Disruptive selection

Figure 18–5 Modes of selection. The blue screen represents the distribution of individuals by phenotype (in this example, color variation) in the original population. The purple screen represents the distribution by phenotype in the evolved population. The arrows represent the pressure of natural selection on the phenotypes. **(a)** A trait that is under polygenic control (in this example, wing colors in a hypothetical population of beetles) exhibits a normal distribution of phenotypes in the absence of selection. **(b)** As a result of stabilizing selection, which trims off extreme phenotypes, variation about the mean is reduced. **(c)** Directional selection shifts the curve in one direction, changing the average value of the trait. **(d)** Disruptive selection, which trims off intermediate phenotypes, results in two or more peaks.

advantageous in a new environment, larger individuals will become increasingly common in the population. Directional selection can only occur, however, if alleles favored under the new circumstances are already present in the population.

Darwin's Galapagos finches provide an excellent example of directional selection. Since 1973, Peter and Rosemary Grant of Princeton University have studied the Galapagos finches. The Grants did a meticulous analysis of finch eating habits and beak sizes on Isla Daphne Major during three extended droughts (1977–1978, 1980, and 1982), one of which was followed by an extremely wet El Niño event (1983). During the droughts, the number of insects and small seeds declined, and large, heavy seeds became the finches' primary food source. Many finches died during this time, and most of the survivors were larger birds whose beaks were larger and deeper. In a few generations, these larger birds became more common in the population (Table 18–1). Following the wet season, however, smaller seeds became the primary food source, and smaller finches with average-sized beaks were favored. In this example, natural selection is directional: During the drought, natural selection operated in favor of the larger phenotype, whereas following the wet period, selection occurred in the opposite direction, favoring the smaller phenotype. The guppy populations studied in Venezuela and Trinidad (see Chapter 17) are another example of directional selection.

Disruptive selection favors phenotypic extremes

Sometimes extreme changes in the environment may favor two or more different phenotypes at the expense of the mean. That is, more than one phenotype may be favored in the new environment. **Disruptive selection** is a special type of directional selection in which there is a trend in several directions rather than

just one (Fig. 18–5d). It results in a divergence, or splitting apart, of distinct groups of individuals within a population. Disruptive selection, which is relatively rare, selects against the average, or intermediate, phenotype.

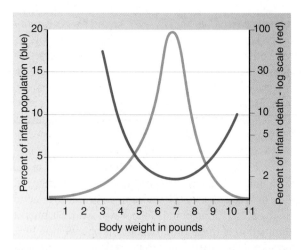

Figure 18–6 Stabilizing selection. The blue curve shows the distribution of birth weights in a sample of 13,730 infants. The red curve shows mortality (death) at each birth weight. This figure shows that infants with very low or very high birth weights have higher death rates than infants of average weight. The optimum birth weight, that is, the one with the lowest mortality, is close to the average birth weight (about 7 pounds). *(Adapted from Cavalli-Sforza, L.L., and W.F. Bodmer. The Genetics of Human Populations. W.H. Freeman and Company, San Francisco, 1971)*

TABLE 18–1 Population Changes in *Geospiza fortis* Before and After the 1976–1977 Drought

Trait	Average Before Drought (634)*	Average After Drought (135)*	Difference
Weight (g)	16.06	17.13	+1.07
Wing length (mm)	67.88	68.87	+0.99
Tarsus (leg, just above the foot) length (mm)	19.08	19.29	+0.21
Bill length (mm)	10.63	10.95	+0.32
Bill depth (mm)	9.21	9.70	+0.49
Bill width (mm)	8.58	8.83	+0.25

*Number of birds in sample.

From Grant, P.R. and B.R. Grant. "Predicting Microevolutionary Responses to Directional Selection on Heritable Variation." *Evolution,* Vol. 49, 1995.

Limited food supply during a severe drought caused a population of finches on another island in the Galapagos to experience disruptive selection. The finch population initially exhibited a variety of beak sizes and shapes. Because the only foods available on this island during the drought were wood-boring insects and seeds from cactus fruits, natural selection favored birds with beaks suitable for obtaining these types of food. Finches with longer beaks survived because they could open cactus fruits, and those with wider beaks survived because they could strip off tree bark to expose insects. However, finches with intermediate beaks were unable to use either food source efficiently and consequently had a lower survival rate.

Natural selection can induce change in the types and frequencies of alleles in populations only if there is preexisting inherited variation. Genetic variation is the raw material for evolutionary change, as it provides the diversity on which natural selection can act. Without genetic variation, evolution cannot occur. We now examine the genetic basis for variation that is acted on by natural selection.

■ GENETIC VARIATION IS NECESSARY FOR NATURAL SELECTION

Populations contain abundant genetic variation that was originally introduced by mutation. Sexual reproduction, with its associated crossing-over, independent assortment of chromosomes during meiosis, and random union of gametes, also contributes to genetic variation. The sexual process allows the variability introduced by mutation to be combined in new ways, which may be expressed as new phenotypes.

Genetic polymorphism exists among genes and the proteins for which they code

One way of evaluating genetic variation in a population is to examine **genetic polymorphism,** which is the presence in a population of two or more alleles for a given locus. Genetic polymorphism is extensive in populations, although many of the alleles are present at low frequencies. Much of genetic polymorphism is not evident because it does not produce distinct phenotypes.

One way that biologists estimate the total amount of genetic polymorphism in populations is by comparing the different forms of a particular protein. Each form consists of a slightly different amino acid sequence that is coded for by a different allele. For example, tissue extracts containing a particular enzyme may be analyzed by gel electrophoresis for different individuals. In gel electrophoresis, the enzymes are placed in slots on an agarose gel, and an electric current is applied that causes each enzyme to migrate across the gel (see Fig. 14–8). Slight variations in amino acid sequences in the different forms of a particular enzyme cause each to migrate at a different rate, which can be detected using special stains or radioactive labels. Table 18–2 shows the degree of polymorphism in selected plant and animal groups based on gel electrophoresis of several enzymes. Note that genetic polymorphism tends to be greater in plants than in animals.

Determining the sequence of nucleotides in DNA from individuals in a population provides a *direct* estimate of genetic polymorphism. One method of DNA sequencing is described in Figure 14–9. DNA sequencing of specific genes in an increasing number of organisms, including humans, indicates that genetic polymorphism is extensive in most populations.

Balanced polymorphism can exist for long periods of time

Balanced polymorphism is a special type of genetic polymorphism in which two or more alleles persist in a population over many generations as a result of natural selection. Heterozygote advantage and frequency-dependent selection are mechanisms that preserve balanced polymorphism.

TABLE 18-2 Genetic Polymorphism of Selected Enzymes Within Plant and Animal Species

Organism	Number of Species Examined	Percentage of Enzymes Studied That Are Polymorphic
Plants		
Gymnosperms	55	70.9
Flowering plants (monocots)	111	59.2
Flowering plants (dicots)	329	44.8
Invertebrates		
Marine snails	5	17.5
Land snails	5	43.7
Insects	23	32.9
Vertebrates		
Fishes	51	15.2
Amphibians	13	26.9
Reptiles	17	21.9
Birds	7	15.0
Mammals	46	14.7

*Plant data adapted from Hamrick, J.L., and M.J. Godt. "Allozyme Diversity in Plant Species." In Brown, A.H.D., M.T. Clegg, A.L. Kahler, and B.J. Weir (eds.). *Plant Population Genetics, Breeding, and Genetic Resources,* Sunderland, MA, Sinauer Associates, 1990. Animal data adapted from Hartl, D. *Principles of Population Genetics,* Sunderland, MA, Sinauer Associates, 1980, and Hedrick, P.W. *Genetics of Populations,* Boston, Science Books International, 1983.

Genetic variation may be maintained by heterozygote advantage

We have seen that natural selection often causes unfavorable alleles to be eliminated from a population while favorable alleles are retained. However, natural selection sometimes helps to maintain genetic diversity, including alleles that are unfavorable in the homozygous state, in a population. This happens, for example, when the heterozygote, *Aa,* has a higher degree of fitness than either homozygote, *AA* or *aa.* This phenomenon, known as **heterozygote advantage,** is demonstrated in humans by the selective advantage of heterozygous carriers of the sickle cell allele.

The mutant allele *(s)* for sickle cell anemia produces an altered hemoglobin that deforms or sickles the red blood cells, making them more likely to form dangerous blockages in capillaries and to be destroyed in the liver, spleen, or bone marrow (see Chapter 15). Individuals who are homozygous for the sickle cell allele *(ss)* usually die at an early age if medical treatment is not available.

Heterozygous individuals carry alleles for both normal *(S)* and sickle cell hemoglobin. The heterozygous condition *(Ss)* causes an individual to be more resistant to a type of severe malaria (caused by the parasite *Plasmodium falciparum*) than

those individuals who are homozygous for the normal hemoglobin allele *(SS).* In a heterozygous individual, each allele produces its own specific kind of hemoglobin, and the red blood cells contain the two kinds in roughly equivalent amounts. Such cells do not ordinarily sickle as readily as cells containing only the *s* allele. In addition, the red blood cells containing the abnormal hemoglobin are more resistant to infection by the malaria-causing parasite, which lives in red blood cells, than are the red blood cells containing only normal hemoglobin.

Where malaria is a problem, each of the two types of homozygous individuals is at a disadvantage. Those homozygous for the sickle cell allele are likely to die of sickle cell anemia, whereas those homozygous for the normal allele may die of malaria. The heterozygote is therefore more fit than either homozygote. In parts of Africa, the Middle East, and southern Asia where *P. falciparum* malaria is prevalent, heterozygous individuals survive in greater numbers than either homozygote (Fig. 18–7). The *s* allele is maintained at a high frequency in the population even though the homozygous recessive condition is almost always lethal.

What happens to the frequency of *s* alleles in Africans and others who possess it when they migrate to the United States and other nonmalarial countries? As might be expected, the frequency of the *s* allele gradually declines in such populations, possibly because it confers a selective disadvantage by causing sickle cell anemia in homozygous individuals but no longer confers a selective advantage by preventing malaria in heterozygous individuals. The *s* allele never disappears from the population, however, because it is "hidden" from selection in heterozygous individuals and because it is reintroduced into the American population by gene flow from the African population.

Genetic variation may be maintained by frequency-dependent selection

Thus far in our discussion of natural selection, we have assumed that the fitness of particular phenotypes (and their corresponding genotypes) is independent of their frequency in the population. There are, however, cases of **frequency-dependent selection,** in which the fitness of a particular phenotype depends on how frequently it appears in the population. Often, a phenotype has a greater selective value when it is rare than when it is common in the population. Such phenotypes lose their selective advantage as they become more common.

Frequency-dependent selection often acts to maintain genetic variation in populations of prey species. In this case, the predator catches and consumes the more common phenotype but may ignore the rarer phenotypes. Consequently, the less common phenotype produces more offspring and therefore makes a greater relative contribution to the next generation. Frequency-dependent selection has been demonstrated with aquatic insects called water boatmen (Fig. 18–8a), which have three distinct color phenotypes. When all three phenotypes are present at equal frequencies, fish are more likely to consume the most obvious (i.e., least camouflaged) form. However, in popula-

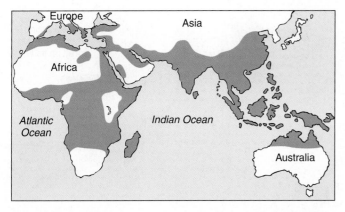

(a) *P. falciparum* malaria

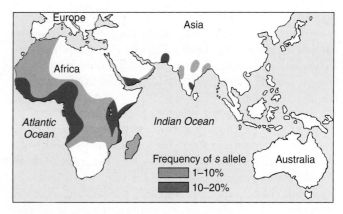

(b) Sickle cell anemia

■ **Figure 18-7 Heterozygote advantage.** The geographical distribution of **(a)** *P. falciparum* malaria *(green)* is compared with that of **(b)** sickle cell anemia *(red and orange)*. The greater fitness of heterozygous individuals in malarial regions supports the hypothesis of heterozygote advantage, which can be seen by the large area of codistribution. *(Adapted from Allison, A.C. "Protection Afforded by Sickle-Cell Traits Against Subtertian Malarial Infection." Brit. Med. J., Vol. 1, 1954)*

(a)

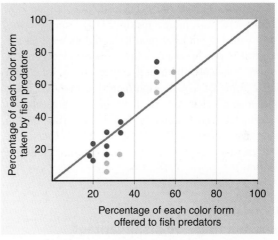

(b)

KEY
- ● Least camouflaged color phenotype
- ● Somewhat camouflaged color phenotype
- ● Most camouflaged color phenotype

■ **Figure 18-8 Frequency-dependent selection in water boatmen.** **(a)** Water boatmen are aquatic insects that swim in ponds and streams by using their middle and hind legs as oars. These insects, which are the preferred food of many fishes, occur in three color forms that range from light to dark brown (only one color is shown). **(b)** In this experiment, different proportions of the three color phenotypes of water boatmen *(Sigara distincta)* were offered to predatory fish in aquaria. The solid line represents the situation that would occur if the percentage of each color phenotype eaten by predators were the same as the percentage offered to the predators. The results indicate that the predators preferentially ate the more common form, regardless of color. (For each of the color phenotypes, the data points at higher percentages offered are above the solid line, whereas the data points at lower percentages offered tend to be below the solid line.) Thus, frequency-dependent selection operates to maintain all three phenotypes within a given population. *(a, Stephen Dalton/ Photo Researchers, Inc.; b, Adapted from Clark, B. "Balanced Polymorphism and the Diversity of Sympatric Species." Syst. Assoc. Publ., Vol. 4, 1962)*

tions where one phenotype is present in greater numbers than the other two, fish preferentially eat the most abundant form, regardless of its color (Fig. 18–8b). Thus, frequency-dependent selection acts to decrease the frequency of the more common phenotypes (and their genotypes) and increase the frequency of the less common types.

Frequency-dependent selection is also demonstrated in scale-eating fish (cichlids of the species *Perissodus microlepsis*) from Lake Tanganyika in Africa. The scale-eating fish, which obtain food by biting scales off other fish, have either left-pointing or right-pointing mouths. A single locus with two alleles determines this characteristic; the allele for right-pointing mouth is dominant over the allele for left-pointing mouth. These fish attack their prey from behind, and from a single direction, depending on mouth morphology. Those with left-pointing mouths always attack the right flanks of their prey, whereas those with right-pointing mouths always attack the left flanks (Fig. 18–9a).

The prey species are more successful at evading attacks from the more common form of scale-eating fish. For example, if the cichlids with right-pointing mouths are more common than those with left-pointing mouths, the prey are attacked more often on their left flanks. They therefore become more wary against such attacks, conferring a selective advantage to the less common cichlids with left-pointing mouths. The cichlids with left-pointing mouths would be more successful at obtaining food and would therefore have more offspring. Over time, the frequency of fish with left-pointing mouths would increase in the population, until their abundance causes frequency-dependent selection to work against them and confer an advantage on the now less-common fish with right-pointing mouths. Thus, frequency-dependent selection maintains both populations of fish at approximately equal numbers (Fig. 18–9b). (See *On the Cutting Edge: Explaining the Rapid Loss of Cichlid Diversity in Lake Victoria* in Chapter 19 for another fascinating example of cichlid evolution.)

Neutral variation may give no selective advantage or disadvantage

Some of the genetic variation observed in a population may confer no apparent selective advantage or disadvantage in a particular environment. For example, random changes in DNA that do not alter protein structure usually do not affect the phenotype. Variation that does not alter the ability of an individual to survive and reproduce and is, therefore, not adaptive is called **neutral variation.**

The extent of neutral variation in organisms is difficult to determine. It is relatively easy to demonstrate that an allele is beneficial or harmful, provided that its effect is observable. But the variation in alleles that involves only slight differences in the proteins they code for may or may not be neutral. These alleles may be influencing the organism in subtle ways that are difficult to measure or assess. Also, an allele that is neutral in one environment may be beneficial or harmful in another.

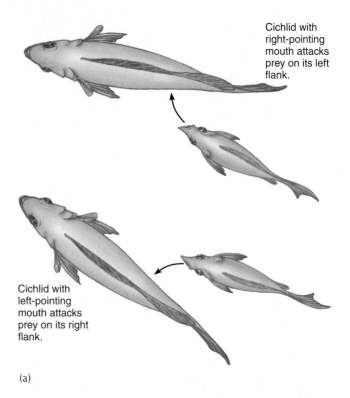

Cichlid with right-pointing mouth attacks prey on its left flank.

Cichlid with left-pointing mouth attacks prey on its right flank.

(a)

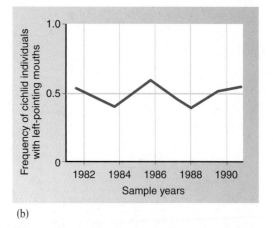

(b)

■ **Figure 18–9 Frequency-dependent selection in scale-eating cichlids.** (a) Scale-eating cichlids have two forms, right-pointing mouths and left-pointing mouths. Individuals with right-pointing mouths attack prey on the left flank, whereas individuals with left-pointing mouths attack prey on the right flank. (b) The frequency of fish with left-pointing mouths over a ten-year period. Frequency-dependent selection maintains the frequencies of left-pointing and right-pointing fish in approximately equal numbers, that is, at about 0.5. *(b, Adapted from Hori, M. "Frequency-Dependent Natural Selection in the Handedness of Scale-Eating Cichlid Fish." Science, Vol. 260, 9 Apr. 1993)*

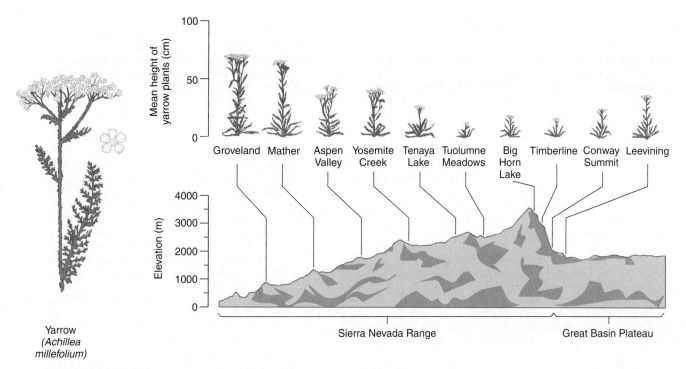

Figure 18-10 Clinal variation in yarrow (Achillea millefolium). Seeds from widely dispersed populations in the Sierra Nevada of California and Nevada were collected and grown for several generations under identical conditions in the same test garden at Stanford, California. The plants retained their distinctive heights, revealing genetic differences that were related to the elevation where the plants were collected. Plants descended from individuals adapted to higher elevations were shorter than those from lower elevations. *(After Clausen, J., D.D. Keck, and W.M. Hiesey. "Experimental Studies on the Nature of Species: III. Environmental Responses of Climatic Races of Achillea." Carnegie Institute Washington Publication, Vol. 58, 1948)*

Populations in different geographical areas often exhibit genetic adaptations to local environments

In addition to the genetic variation among individuals within a population, genetic differences often exist among different populations within the same species, a phenomenon known as *geographical variation*. One type of geographical variation is a **cline,** which is a gradual change in a species' phenotype and genotype frequencies through a series of geographically separate populations as a result of an environmental gradient. A cline exhibits variation in the expression of such traits as color, size, shape, physiology, or behavior. Clines are common among species with continuous ranges over large geographical areas. For example, the body sizes of many widely distributed birds and mammals increase gradually as the latitude increases, presumably because

larger animals are better able to withstand the colder temperatures of winter.

The common yarrow *(Achillea millefolium),* a wildflower that grows in a variety of North American habitats from lowlands to mountain highlands, exhibits clinal variation in height in response to different climates at different altitudes. Although substantial variation exists among individuals within each population, individuals in populations at higher altitudes are, on average, shorter than those at lower altitudes. The genetic basis of these clinal differences can be experimentally demonstrated by growing a series of populations from different geographical areas in the same environment (Fig. 18–10). Despite being exposed to identical environmental conditions, each experimental population exhibits the traits characteristic of the altitude from which it was collected.

I. **Population genetics** is the study of genetic variability within a population and of the forces that act on it.
   A. A **population** consists of all the individuals of the same species that live in a particular place at the same time.
   B. Each population possesses a **gene pool,** which includes all the **alleles** for all the genes present in the population.
II. The evolution of populations is best understood in terms of phenotype, genotype, and allele frequencies, which are usually expressed as decimal fractions.
   A. A **genotype frequency** is the proportion of a particular genotype in the population.
   B. A **phenotype frequency** is the proportion of a particular phenotype in the population.
   C. An **allele frequency** is the proportion of a specific allele of a given gene locus in the population.
      1. If the allele frequencies remain constant from generation to generation, the population is not undergoing evolutionary change and is said to be at **genetic equilibrium.**
      2. If the allele frequencies change over successive generations, the population is undergoing **microevolution.**
III. The **Hardy-Weinberg principle** states that in a population at genetic equilibrium, allele and genotype frequencies do not change from generation to generation.
IV. Allele and/or genotype frequencies may be changed by nonrandom mating, mutation, genetic drift, gene flow, and natural selection.
   A. In nonrandom mating, individuals select mates on the basis of phenotype and indirectly on its corresponding genotype(s).
      1. **Inbreeding** is the mating of genetically similar individuals that are more closely related than if they had been chosen at random from the entire population. Inbreeding in some populations causes **inbreeding depression,** in which inbred individuals have lower **fitness** than non-inbred individuals.
      2. In **assortative mating** individuals select mates by their phenotypes.
      3. Both inbreeding and assortative mating increase the frequency of homozygous genotypes.
   B. New alleles originate as **mutations,** unpredictable changes in DNA. Mutations increase the genetic variability that can be acted on by natural selection.

C. **Genetic drift** is a random change in the allele frequencies of a small population. Genetic drift can decrease genetic variation within a population, and the changes caused by genetic drift are usually not adaptive.
   1. A sudden decrease in population size due to adverse environmental factors is known as a **bottleneck.**
   2. The **founder effect** is genetic drift that occurs when a small population colonizes a new area.
D. The migration of individuals between populations causes a corresponding movement of alleles, or **gene flow,** that can cause changes in allele frequencies.
E. Changes in allele frequencies that lead to adaptation are caused by **natural selection.**
   1. Natural selection operates on an organism's phenotype.
   2. Natural selection can change the genetic composition of a population in a favorable direction for a particular environment.
      a. **Stabilizing selection** favors the mean at the expense of phenotypic extremes.
      b. **Directional selection** favors one phenotypic extreme over another, causing a shift in the phenotypic mean.
      c. **Disruptive selection** favors two or more phenotypic extremes.
V. Most populations have abundant genetic variability.
   A. **Genetic polymorphism** is the presence in a population of two or more alleles for a given locus.
   B. **Balanced polymorphism** is a special type of genetic polymorphism in which two or more alleles persist in a population over many generations as a result of natural selection.
      1. **Heterozygote advantage** occurs when the heterozygote exhibits greater fitness than either homozygote. Genetic variation is maintained in the population.
      2. In **frequency-dependent selection,** a genotype's selective value varies with its frequency of occurrence.
   C. Genetic variation that confers no detectable selective advantage is called **neutral variation.**
   D. Geographical variation is genetic variation that exists among different populations within the same species. A **cline** is a gradual change in a species' phenotype and genotype frequencies through a series of geographically separate populations.

1. The genetic description of an individual is its genotype, whereas the genetic description of a population is its (a) phenotype (b) gene pool (c) genetic drift (d) founder effect (e) changes in allele frequencies

2. In a diploid species, each individual possesses (a) one allele for each locus (b) two alleles for each locus (c) three or more alleles for each locus (d) all the alleles found in the gene pool (e) half of the alleles found in the gene pool

3. The MN blood group is of interest to population geneticists because (a) people with genotype *MN* cannot receive blood transfusions from either *MM* or *NN* people (b) the *MM, MN, and NN* genotype frequencies can be observed directly and compared with calculated expected frequencies (c) the *M* allele is dominant to the N allele (d) people with the *MN* genotype exhibit frequency-dependent selection (e) people with the *MN* genotype exhibit heterozygote advantage

4. If all copies of a given locus have the same allele, then the allele frequency is (a) 0 (b) 0.1 (c) 0.5 (d) 1.0 (e) 10.0

5. If a population's allele and genotype frequencies remain constant from generation to generation (a) the population is undergoing evolutionary change (b) the population is said to be at genetic equilibrium (c) microevolution has taken place (d) directional selection is occurring, but only for a few generations (e) genetic drift is a significant evolutionary force

6. Comparing the different forms of a particular protein in a population provides biologists with an estimate of (a) genetic drift (b) genetic polymorphism (c) gene flow (d) heterozygote advantage (e) frequency-dependent selection

7. The continued presence of the allele that causes sickle cell anemia in areas where *P. falciparum* malaria is prevalent demonstrates which of the following phenomena? (a) inbreeding depression (b) frequency-dependent selection (c) heterozygote advantage (d) genetic drift (e) bottleneck

8. Frequency-dependent selection often acts to maintain _____ in a population. (a) assortative mating (b) genetic drift (c) gene flow (d) genetic variation (e) stabilizing selection

9. According to the Hardy-Weinberg principle (a) allele frequencies are not dependent on dominance or recessiveness but remain essentially un-

changed from generation to generation (b) the sum of allele frequencies for a given locus is always greater than 1 (c) if a locus has a single allele, its frequency must be zero (d) allele frequencies change from generation to generation (e) the process of inheritance, by itself, causes changes in allele frequencies

10. What is the correct equation for the Hardy-Weinberg principle?

(a) $p^2 + pq + 2q^2 = 1$ (b) $p^2 + 2pq + 2q^2 = 1$
(c) $2p^2 + 2pq + 2q^2 + 1$ (d) $p^2 + pq + q^2 = 1$
(e) $p^2 + 2pq + q^2 = 1$

11. The Hardy-Weinberg principle is applicable provided (a) population size is small (b) migration only occurs at the beginning of the breeding season (c) mutations occur at a constant rate (d) matings occur exclusively between individuals of the same genotype (e) natural selection does not occur

12. Which of the following is *not* an evolutionary agent that causes change in allele frequencies? (a) mutation (b) natural selection (c) genetic drift (d) random mating (e) gene flow from migration

13. Mutation (a) leads to adaptive evolutionary change (b) adds to the genetic variation of a population (c) is the result of genetic drift (d) almost always benefits the organism (e) a and b are correct

14. Which of the following is *not* true of natural selection? (a) Natural selection acts to preserve favorable traits and eliminate unfavorable traits. (b) The offspring of individuals that are better adapted to the environment will make up a larger proportion of the next generation. (c) Natural selection directs the course of evolution by preserving the traits acquired during an individual's lifetime. (d) Natural selection acts on a population's genetic variability, which arises through mutation. (e) Natural selection may result in changes in allele frequencies in a population.

15. In _____ individuals with a phenotype near the phenotypic mean of the population are favored over those with phenotypic extremes. (a) microevolution (b) stabilizing selection (c) directional selection (d) disruptive selection (e) genetic equilibrium

REVIEW QUESTIONS

1. In a human population of 1000, 840 are tongue rollers (*TT* or *Tt*), and 160 are non–tongue rollers (*tt*). What is the frequency of the dominant allele (*T*) in the population?

2. In a population at genetic equilibrium, the frequency of allele *A* is 0.5. What is the frequency of the homozygous dominant genotype (*AA*)? What is the frequency of the heterozygous genotype (*Aa*)?

3. If 96% of the garden peas in a population at genetic equilibrium are tall (*TT* or *Tt*), what is the frequency of the dominant allele (*T*)?

4. If 16% of the individuals in a population at genetic equilibrium are homozygous recessive (*aa*), what is the frequency of the recessive allele in the population? What is the frequency of the dominant allele?

5. The genotype frequencies of a population are determined to be 0.6 *AA*, 0.0 *Aa* (there are no heterozygotes), and 0.4 *aa*. Is this population at genetic equilibrium? Why or why not?

6. The chemical phenylthiocarbamide (PTC) tastes bitter to most people but is tasteless to others. About 30% of Americans are PTC nontasters

(*tt*), and 70% are PTC tasters (*TT* or *Tt*). Assuming the population is at genetic equilibrium, estimate the frequency of the nontaster (*t*) and taster (*T*) alleles.

7. If a population of 2000 is at genetic equilibrium but contains only 180 individuals with the recessive phenotype (*rr*), what is the expected frequency of the recessive allele (*r*) nine generations later if equilibrium is maintained?

8. If the genotype frequencies in a population at genetic equilibrium are 0.36 *TT*, 0.48 *Tt*, and 0.16 *tt*, what are the allele frequencies of *T* and *t*?

9. If the genotype frequencies in a population at genetic equilibrium are 0.64*TT*, 0.32*Tt*, and 0.04*tt*, what are the allele frequencies of *T* and *t*?

10. The frequency of the allele *A* in a population at genetic equilibrium is 0.7. What is the expected frequency of the *Aa* genotype?

Answers to these Review Questions are included in the Appendix with the Post-Test answers.

YOU MAKE THE CONNECTION

1. Why are mutations almost always neutral or harmful?

2. Explain this apparent paradox: We discuss evolution in terms of *genotype* fitness (the selective advantage that a particular genotype confers on an individual), yet natural selection acts on an organism's *phenotype*.

3. How are the cichlids with right-pointing and left-pointing mouths an example of balanced polymorphism?

RECOMMENDED READINGS

Case, T.J. "Natural Selection Out on a Limb." *Nature,* Vol. 387, 1 May 1997. This "News and Views" article discusses the significance of a long-term experiment (also in this issue) that documents microevolution in lizards introduced on several small Caribbean islands.

Christensen, D. "Weight Matters, Even in the Womb." *Science News,* Vol. 158, 9 Dec. 2000. An interesting extension of research on the possible relationship between birth weight and chronic diseases later in life.

Grant, P.R. "Natural Selection and Darwin's Finches." *Scientific American,* Vol. 265, No. 4, Oct. 1991. A study of the finches of the Galapagos Islands reveals natural selection in action during a drought.

King, R.B., and R. Lawson. "Microevolution in Island Water Snakes." *Bio-Science,* Vol. 47, No. 5, May 1997. The authors demonstrated the interaction between natural selection and gene flow in determining color pattern differences in populations of Lake Erie water snakes.

Madsen, T., R. Shine, M. Olsson, and H. Wittzell. "Restoration of an Inbred Adder Population." *Nature,* Vol. 402, 4 Nov. 1999. A genetically uniform population of adders was declining in number and in danger of extinction until biologists added genetically diverse adders from other populations. The introduced adders bred with local adders, resulting in greater genetic diversity, as demonstrated by gel electrophoresis, and allowing the adder population to make a dramatic recovery.

Mange, E.J., and A.P. Mange. *Basic Human Genetics,* 2nd ed. Sinauer Associates, Inc., Sunderland, MA, 1999. This text has an excellent chapter on population genetics that includes the *MN* blood groups as well as many other human examples. Much of our chapter's section on calculating frequencies was modeled after the presentation in this text.

Mayr, E. *Population, Species, and Evolution.* Harvard University Press, Cambridge, MA, 1970. A classic discussion of evolution.

Milius, S. "Dull Birds and Bright Ones Beat So-So Guys." *Science News,* Vol. 158, 28 Oct. 2000. An example of disruptive selection in male lazuli buntings.

Milius, S. "Wild Inbred Butterflies Risk Extinction." *Science News,* Vol. 153, 4 Apr. 1999. The study summarized here provides convincing evidence that inbreeding figures in extinction.

Pennisi, E. "Tracking a Sparrow's Fall." *Science,* Vol. 285, 9 Jul. 1999. This "New Focus" reports on a documented example in nature of the effects of inbreeding in a population of song sparrows.

Soulé, M.E., and L.S. Mills. "No Need to Isolate Genetics." *Science,* Vol. 282, 27 Nov. 1998. This perspective introduces a study (page 1695 of the same issue) of the decline and subsequent recovery of the greater prairie chicken population in Illinois.

Weiner, J. *The Beak of the Finch: A Story of Evolution in Our Time.* Alfred A. Knopf, New York, 1994. This Pulitzer Prize–winning book focuses on the research of Peter and Rosemary Grant on evolution in the Galapagos finches.

● Visit our Web site at **http://www.info.brookscole.com/solomonbergmartin** for links to chapter-related resources on the World Wide Web. Additional on-line materials relating to this chapter can also be found on our Web site.

See chapter activity on BioActive Learner CD for additional help in mastering the chapter's material. Icon location in the chapter's margins shows which topics have tutorials or simulations in the CD.

19

Speciation and Macroevolution

Interbreeding between different species. Shown is a "zebrass," a sterile hybrid formed by a cross between a zebra and a donkey that retains features of both parental species. Although such matings may occur under artificial conditions, such as the wildlife ranch in Texas where this cross took place, zebras and donkeys do not interbreed in the wild. *(Gary Retherford/Photo Researchers, Inc.)*

LEARNING OBJECTIVES

After you have studied this chapter you should be able to

1. Define a species and explain the limitations of the biological species concept.
2. Explain the significance of reproductive isolating mechanisms and distinguish among the different prezygotic and postzygotic barriers.
3. Explain the mechanism of allopatric specification and give an example.
4. Explain the mechanisms of sympatric specification and give both plant and animal examples.
5. Take either side in a debate on the pace of evolution by representing the opposing views of gradualism and punctuated equilibrium.
6. Define macroevolution and distinguish among microevolution, speciation, and macroevolution.
7. Discuss macroevolution in the context of novel features, including preadaptations, allometric growth, and paedomorphosis.
8. Discuss the macroevolutionary significance of adaptive radiation and extinction.
9. Explain how the course of evolution was affected by continental drift.

I n Chapters 17 and 18, we examined natural selection and how populations evolve. We now focus our attention on how species and higher taxa (for example, new classes)[1] evolve. We do not know exactly how many species exist, but biologists estimate there may be something on the order of 10 million to 100 million different species.[2] About 1.75 million species have been scientifi-

cally named and described. These include 250,000 plant species, 42,000 vertebrate animals, and some 750,000 insects.

The concept of distinct kinds of organisms, known as **species** (from Latin, meaning "kind") is not new. However, every definition of species has some sort of limitation. Linnaeus, the 18th century biologist who is considered the founder of modern taxonomy, classified plants and other organisms into separate species based on structural differences (see Chapter 22). This method, known as the *morphological species concept,* is still used to help characterize species, but structure alone is not adequate to explain what constitutes a species.

Population genetics did much to clarify the concept of species. According to the **biological species concept,** first expressed by Ernst Mayr in 1940, a species consists of one or more populations whose members are capable of interbreeding in nature to produce fertile offspring and do not interbreed with—that is, are reproductively isolated from—members of different species. In other words, each species has a gene pool that is separate from that of other species, and reproductive barriers restrict each species from interbreeding with other species.

One of the problems with the biological species concept is that it applies only to sexually reproducing organisms. Organisms that reproduce asexually do not interbreed, so we cannot think of them in terms of reproductive isolation. These organisms and extinct organisms are classified on the basis of structural and biochemical characteristics. Another potential problem with the biological species concept is that organisms assigned to different

---

[1] The taxonomic categories (taxa) above the level of species are artificial constructs used by humans to indicate degrees of relatedness among organisms. As described in Chapter 1, closely related species are grouped into the same genus (pl., *genera*), similar genera into the same family, similar families into the same order, similar orders into the same class, and similar classes into the same phylum.

[2] Reaka-Kudla, M.L., D.E. Wilson, and E.O. Wilson, eds. *Biodiversity II.* Joseph Henry Press, Washington, D.C., 1997.

species may successfully interbreed if brought into the artificial environment and caging of a wildlife ranch *(see photograph)*, circus, zoo, greenhouse, aquarium, or laboratory. For that reason, natural matings alone can be used to test biological species identity; captive matings are not valid.

This chapter discusses reproductive barriers that isolate species from one another, the possible evolutionary mechanisms that explain how the millions of species that live today or lived in the past originated from ancestral species, and the rates of evolutionary change. We then examine *macroevolution,* which is large-scale phenotypic changes (such as the appearance of wings with feathers during the evolution of birds from reptiles) that permit the evolution of taxonomic groups at the species level and higher—new genera, families, orders, classes, and even phyla.

SPECIES ARE REPRODUCTIVELY ISOLATED IN VARIOUS WAYS

A number of **reproductive isolating mechanisms** prevent interbreeding between two different species whose ranges overlap. These mechanisms preserve the genetic integrity of each species because gene flow between the two species is prevented. Most species have two or more mechanisms that block a chance occurrence of individuals from two closely related species overcoming a single reproductive isolating mechanism. Most occur before mating or fertilization occurs *(prezygotic),* whereas others work after fertilization has taken place *(postzygotic).*

Prezygotic barriers interfere with fertilization

Prezygotic barriers are reproductive isolating mechanisms that prevent fertilization from taking place. Because male and female gametes never come into contact, an interspecific zygote (fertilized egg formed by the union of an egg from one species and a sperm from another species) is never produced. Prezygotic barriers include temporal isolation, habitat isolation, behavioral isolation, mechanical isolation, and gametic isolation.

Sometimes genetic exchange between two groups is prevented because they reproduce at different times of the day, season, or year. Such examples demonstrate **temporal isolation.** For example, two very similar species of fruit flies, *Drosophila pseudoobscura* and *Drosophila persimilis,* have ranges that overlap to a great extent, but they do not interbreed. *D. pseudoobscura* is sexually active only in the afternoon and *D. persimilis* only in the morning. Similarly, two frog species have overlapping ranges in eastern Canada and the United States. The wood frog *(Rana sylvatica)* usually mates in late March or early April, when the water temperature is about 7.2° C (45° F), whereas the northern leopard frog *(Rana pipiens)* usually mates in mid-April, when the water temperature is 12.8° C (55° F) (Fig. 19–1).

Although two closely related species may be found in the same geographical area, they usually live and breed in different habitats in that area. This causes **habitat isolation** between the two species. For example, the five species of small *Empidonax* flycatchers in the eastern part of North America are nearly identical in appearance and have overlapping ranges (Fig. 19–2). They exhibit habitat isolation because, during the breeding season, each species is found in a particular habitat within its range, so potential mates from different species do not meet. The least flycatcher *(Empidonax minimus)* frequents open woods, farms, and orchards; the acadian flycatcher *(Empidonax virescens)* is found in deciduous forests, particularly in beech trees, and swampy woods; the alder flycatcher *(Empidonax alnorum)* prefers wet thickets of alders; the yellow-bellied flycatcher *(Empidonax flaviventris)*

(a)

(b)

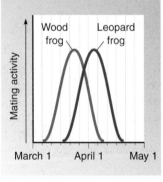
(c)

Figure 19–1 Temporal isolation in wood and leopard frogs. (a) The wood frog *(Rana sylvatica)* mates in early spring, often before the ice has completely melted in the ponds. **(b)** The leopard frog *(R. pipiens)* typically mates a few weeks later. **(c)** Graph of peak mating activity in wood and leopard frogs. In nature, wood and leopard frogs do not interbreed, although they have done so in the laboratory. *(a, L. & D. Klein/Photo Researchers, Inc.; b, Rod Planck/Photo Researchers, Inc.)*

Figure 19–2 Habitat isolation in flycatchers. Each flycatcher species is found in a particular habitat during mating. The acadian flycatcher *(Empidonax virescens)* frequents deciduous forests and swampy woods during its breeding season. Shown is a male at his nest in West Virginia. *(Bill Beatty/Visuals Unlimited, Inc.)*

Sometimes members of different species court and even attempt copulation, but the incompatible structures of their genital organs prevent successful mating. Structural differences that inhibit mating between species produce **mechanical isolation.** For example, many flowering plant species have physical differences in their flower parts that help them maintain their reproductive isolation from one another. In such plants, the flower parts are adapted for specific insect pollinators. Two species of sage, for example, have overlapping ranges in southern California. Black sage *(Salvia mellifera),* which is pollinated by small bees, has a floral structure different from that of white sage *(Salvia apiana),* which is pollinated by large carpenter bees (Fig. 19–4). Interestingly, black sage and white sage are also prevented from mating by a temporal barrier: black sage flowers in early spring, and white sage flowers in late spring and early summer. Presumably, mechanical isolation prevents insects from cross-pollinating the two species should they happen to flower at the same time.

If mating has taken place between two species, their gametes may still not combine. Molecular and chemical differences between species cause **gametic isolation,** in which the egg and sperm of different species are incompatible. In aquatic animals that release their eggs and sperm into the surrounding water simultaneously, interspecific fertilization is extremely rare (Fig. 19–5). The surface of the egg contains specific proteins that bind only to complementary molecules on the surface of sperm cells of the same species (see Chapter 49). A similar type of molecular recognition often occurs between pollen grains and the stigma (receptive surface of the female part of the flower) so that pollen does not germinate on the stigma of a different plant species.

nests in conifer woods; and the willow flycatcher *(Empidonax traillii)* frequents brushy pastures and willow thickets.

Many animal species exchange a distinctive series of signals before mating. Such courtship behaviors illustrate **behavioral isolation** (also known as **sexual isolation**). Bowerbirds, for example, exhibit species-specific courtship patterns. The male satin bowerbird of Australia constructs an elaborate bower of twigs, adding decorative blue parrot feathers and white flowers at the entrance (Fig. 19–3). When a female approaches the bower, the male dances about her, holding a particularly eye-catching decoration in his beak. While dancing, he sings a courtship song that consists of a variety of sounds, including buzzes and laughlike hoots. These specific courtship behaviors keep similar bird species reproductively isolated from the satin bowerbird. If a male and female of two different species begin courtship, it stops when one member does not recognize or respond to the signals of the other. Another example of behavioral isolation involves the wood frogs and northern leopard frogs (just discussed as an example of temporal isolation). Males of these two species have very specific vocalizations to attract females of their species for breeding. These vocalizations reinforce the reproductive isolation of these species.

Figure 19–3 Behavioral isolation in bowerbirds. Each bowerbird species has highly specialized courtship patterns that prevent its mating with another species. The male satin bowerbird *(Ptilonorhynchus violacens)* constructs an enclosed place, or bower, of twigs to attract a female. (The bower is the dark "tunnel" on the left.) Note the flowers and blue decorations, including human-made objects such as bottle caps, that he has arranged at the entrance to his bower. *(R. Brown/VIREO)*

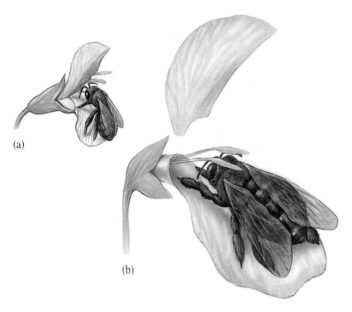

(a)

(b)

■ **Figure 19–4 Mechanical isolation in black sage and white sage.** Differences in floral structures between black sage and white sage allow them to be pollinated by different insects. Because the two species exploit different pollinators, they cannot interbreed. **(a)** The petal of the black sage functions as a landing platform for small bees. Larger bees cannot fit on this platform. **(b)** The larger landing platform and longer stamens of white sage allow pollination by larger California carpenter bees (a different species). If smaller bees land on white sage, their bodies do not brush against the stamens. (The upper part of the white sage flower has been removed.)

Postzygotic barriers prevent gene flow when fertilization occurs

Fertilization sometimes occurs between gametes of two closely related species despite the existence of **prezygotic barriers.** When this happens, postzygotic barriers that increase the likelihood of reproductive failure come into play. Generally, the embryo of an interspecific hybrid spontaneously aborts. Embryonic development is a complex process requiring the precise interaction and coordination of many genes. Apparently, the genes from parents belonging to different species do not interact properly in regulating the mechanisms for normal development. In this case, reproductive isolation occurs by **hybrid inviability.** For example, nearly all the hybrids die in the embryonic stage when the eggs of a bullfrog are fertilized artificially with sperm from a leopard frog. Similarly, in crosses between different species of irises, the embryos die before reaching maturity.

If an interspecific hybrid does live, it may not be able to reproduce. There are several reasons for this. Hybrid animals may exhibit courtship behaviors incompatible with those of either parental species and, as a result, they will not mate. More often, **hybrid sterility** occurs when problems during meiosis cause the gametes of an interspecific hybrid to be abnormal. Hybrid sterility is particularly common if the two parental species have dif-

ferent chromosome numbers. For example, a mule is the offspring of a female horse ($2n = 64$) and a male donkey ($2n = 62$) (Fig. 19–6). This type of union almost always results in sterile offspring ($2n = 63$) because chromosomal synapsis (the pairing of homologous chromosomes during meiosis) and segregation cannot occur properly. The zebrass shown in the chapter introduction also exhibits hybrid sterility due to different chromosome numbers. Donkeys have 62 chromosomes, and zebras, depending on the species, have 32, 44, or 46 chromosomes.

Occasionally, a mating between two F_1 hybrids produces a second hybrid generation (F_2). The F_2 hybrid may exhibit **hybrid breakdown,** the inability of a hybrid to reproduce due to some defect. For example, hybrid breakdown in the F_2 generation of a

■ **Figure 19–6 Hybrid sterility in mules.** Mules are interspecific hybrids formed by mating a female horse with a male donkey. Although the mule *(center)* exhibits valuable characteristics of each of its parents, it is sterile. *(John Eastcott/Yva Momatiuk/Animals Animals)*

TABLE 19–1 Reproductive Isolating Mechanisms

Mechanism	How It Works
Prezygotic Barriers	Prevent fertilization
Temporal isolation	Similar species reproduce at different times
Habitat isolation	Similar species reproduce in different habitats
Behavioral isolation	Similar species have distinctive courtship behaviors
Mechanical isolation	Similar species have structural differences in their reproductive organs
Gametic isolation	Gametes of similar species are chemically incompatible
Postzygotic Barriers	Reduce viability or fertility of hybrid
Hybrid inviability	Interspecific hybrid dies at early stage of embryonic development
Hybrid sterility	Interspecific hybrid survives to adulthood but is unable to reproduce successfully
Hybrid breakdown	Offspring of interspecific hybrid are unable to reproduce successfully

cross between two sunflower species was 80%. In other words, 80% of the F_2 generation were defective in some way and could not reproduce successfully. Hybrid breakdown can also occur in the F_3 and later generations.

Table 19–1 summarizes the various prezygotic and postzygotic barriers that prevent interbreeding between two species.

The genetic basis of isolating mechanisms are being elucidated

Recent progress has been made in identifying some of the genes involved in reproductive isolation. For example, scientists have determined the genetic basis for prezygotic isolation in species of abalone, large mollusks found along the Pacific coast of North America. In abalone, the fertilization of eggs by sperm requires lysin, a sperm protein that attaches to a lysin receptor protein located on the egg envelope. After attachment, the lysin produces a hole in the egg envelope that permits the sperm to penetrate the egg. Scientists cloned the lysin receptor gene and demonstrated that this gene varies among abalone species. Differences in the lysin receptor protein in various abalone species determine sperm compatibility with the egg. Sperm of one abalone species will not attach to a lysin receptor protein of an egg of a different abalone species.

A gene involved in postzygotic isolating mechanisms has been identified and cloned in fruit flies (*Drosophila* sp.). The gene causes sterility in male hybrids formed by a cross between *Drosophila mauritiana* and *Drosophila simulans*. The actual

function of the gene is currently unknown, but scientists hypothesize it may control the transcription of a different gene that is involved in spermatogenesis, the production of sperm.

■ REPRODUCTIVE ISOLATION IS THE KEY TO SPECIATION

We are now ready to consider how entirely new species may arise from previously existing ones. The evolution of a new species is called **speciation**. The fossil record suggests that there are two patterns of speciation: Some speciation events are anagenic, whereas others are cladogenic. **Anagenesis**, or **phyletic evolution**, refers to the relatively small, progressive evolutionary changes in a single lineage over long periods. Given enough time, anagenesis results in the conversion of one species into a different species. Thus, a *sequence* of species occurs over time without an increase in the *number* of species. Beginning with Charles Darwin, many evolutionary biologists have focused on anagenesis and tried to determine how a single species changes over time, by means of natural selection.

Other evolutionary biologists concentrate on species multiplication. In **cladogenesis**, or **branching evolution**, two or more populations of an ancestral species split and diverge, eventually forming two or more new species. Such a cluster of species (or other taxa) that are all derived from a single common ancestor is known as a **clade** (see Chapter 22). Over time, the process of cladogenesis increases *species richness*, which is the number of species (see Chapter 52).

The formation of two species from a single species occurs when a population becomes reproductively isolated from other members of the species, and the gene pools of the two separated populations begin to diverge in genetic composition. When a population is sufficiently different from its ancestral species that no genetic exchange can occur between them, we say that speciation has occurred. Speciation is thought to occur in two ways: allopatric speciation and sympatric speciation.

Long physical isolation and different selective pressures result in allopatric speciation

Speciation that occurs when one population becomes geographically separated from the rest of the species and subsequently evolves by natural selection and/or genetic drift is known as **allopatric speciation** (from the Greek *allo*, "different," and *patri*, "native land"). Allopatric speciation is thought to be the most common method of speciation, and the evolution of new animal species has been almost exclusively by allopatric speciation.

The geographical isolation required for allopatric speciation may occur in several ways. Earth's surface is in a constant state of change. Such change includes rivers shifting their courses; glaciers migrating; mountain ranges forming; land bridges developing that separate previously united aquatic populations; and large lakes diminishing into several smaller, geographically separated pools.

What might be an imposing geographical barrier to one species may be of no consequence to another. Birds and cattails, for example, do not become isolated when a lake subsides into smaller pools; birds can easily fly from one pool to another, and cattails disperse their pollen and fruits by air currents. Fish, on the other hand, are usually unable to cross the land barriers between the pools and so become reproductively isolated. In the Death Valley region of California and Nevada, large interconnected lakes formed during wetter climates of the last Ice Age. These lakes were populated by one or several species of pupfish. Over time, the climate became drier, and the large lakes dried up, leaving isolated pools. Presumably, each pool contained a small population of pupfish that gradually diverged from the common ancestral species by genetic drift and natural selection in response to the high temperatures, high salt concentrations, and low oxygen levels characteristic of desert springs. Today, there are more than 20 species of pupfish, and many, such as the Devil's Hole pupfish *(Cyprinodon diabolis)* and the Owens pupfish *(Cyprinodon radiosus),* are restricted to one or two isolated springs (Fig. 19–7).

Allopatric speciation also occurs when a small population migrates or is dispersed (e.g., by a chance storm) and colonizes a new area away from the range of the original species. This colony is geographically isolated from its parental species, and the small microevolutionary changes that accumulate in the isolated gene pool over many generations may eventually be sufficient to form a new species. Because islands provide the geographical isolation required for allopatric speciation, they offer excellent opportunities to study this evolutionary mechanism. A few individuals of a few species probably colonized the Galapagos Islands and the Hawaiian Islands, for example. The hundreds of unique species

Figure 19–8 Allopatric speciation of the Hawaiian goose (the nene). Nene (pronounced "nay–nay"; *Branta sandvicensis*) are geese originally found only on volcanic mountains on the geographically isolated islands of Hawaii and Maui, which are some 4200 km (2600 mi) from the nearest continent. Compared with other geese, the feet of Hawaiian geese are not completely webbed, their toenails are longer and stronger, and their foot pads are thicker; these adaptations enable Hawaiian geese to walk easily on lava flows. Nene are thought to have evolved from a small population of geese that originated in North America. Photographed in Hawaii Volcanoes National Park, Hawaii. *(Victoria McCormick/Animals Animals)*

presently found on each island presumably descended from these original colonizers (Fig. 19–8; also see Chapter 17).

Speciation is more likely to occur if the original isolated population is small. Recall that genetic drift, including the founder effect, is more consequential in small populations (see Chapter 18). Genetic drift tends to result in rapid changes in allele frequencies in the small, isolated population. The divergence caused by genetic drift is further accentuated by the different selective pressures of the new environment to which the population is exposed.

The Kaibab squirrel is an example of allopatric speciation in progress

About 10,000 years ago, when the American Southwest was less arid, the forests in the area supported a tree squirrel with conspicuous tufts of hair sprouting from its ears. A small tree squirrel population living on the Kaibab Plateau of the Grand Canyon became geographically isolated when the climate changed, causing areas to the north, west, and east to become desert. Just a few miles to the south lived the rest of the squirrels, known as Abert squirrels, but the two groups were separated by the Grand Canyon. With changes over time in both its appearance and its ecology, the Kaibab squirrel is on its way to becoming a new species.

During its many years of geographical isolation, the small population of Kaibab squirrels has diverged from the widely dis-

Figure 19–7 Allopatric speciation of pupfish *(Cyprinodon).* Shown is one of the more than 20 pupfish species that apparently evolved when larger lakes in southern Nevada dried up about 10,000 years ago, leaving behind small, isolated desert pools fed by springs. The pupfish's short, stubby body is characteristic of fish that live in springs; fish that live in larger bodies of water are more streamlined. *(Steinhart Aquarium, Tom McHugh/Photo Researchers, Inc.)*

tributed Abert squirrels in several ways. Perhaps most evident are changes in fur color. The Kaibab squirrel now has a white tail and a black belly, in contrast to the gray tail and white belly of the Abert squirrel (Fig. 19–9). It is not clear why these striking changes arose in Kaibab squirrels.

Some scientists consider the Kaibab squirrel and the Abert squirrel as distinct populations of the same species *(Sciurus aberti)*. Because the Kaibab and Abert squirrels are reproductively isolated from each other, however, some scientists have classified the Kaibab squirrel as a different species *(Sciurus kaibabensis)*.

Porto Santo rabbits may be an example of extremely rapid allopatric speciation

Allopatric speciation has the potential to occur quite rapidly. Early in the 15th century, a small population of rabbits was released on Porto Santo, a small island off the coast of Portugal. Because there were no other rabbits or competitors and no predators on the island, the rabbits thrived. By the 19th century, these rabbits were markedly different from their European ancestors. They were only half as large (weighing slightly more than 500 g, or 1.1 lb), with a different color pattern and a more nocturnal lifestyle. Most significantly, attempts to mate Porto Santo rabbits with mainland European rabbits failed. Many biologists concluded that, within 400 years, an extremely brief period in evolutionary history, a new species of rabbit had evolved.

Not all biologists agree that the Porto Santo rabbit is a new species. The objection stems from a more recent breeding experiment and is based on biologists' lack of a consensus about the definition of a species. In the experiment, foster mothers of the wild Mediterranean rabbit raised newborn Porto Santo rabbits. When they reached adulthood, these Porto Santo rabbits mated successfully with Mediterranean rabbits to produce healthy, fertile offspring. To some biologists, this experiment clearly demonstrated that Porto Santo rabbits are not a separate species but instead are an example of speciation in progress, much like the Kaibab squirrels just discussed. Other biologists think the Porto

Santo rabbit is a separate species because it does not interbreed with other rabbits under natural conditions. They point out that the breeding experiment was successful only after the baby Porto Santo rabbits were raised under artificial conditions that probably modified their natural behavior.

Two populations diverge in the same physical location by sympatric speciation

Although geographical isolation is an important factor in many cases of evolution, it is not an absolute requirement. In **sympatric speciation** (from the Greek *sym*, "together," and *patri*, "native land"), a new species evolves within the same geographical region as the parental species. The divergence of two gene pools in the same geographical range occurs when reproductive isolating mechanisms evolve at the start of the speciation process. Sympatric speciation is especially common in plants. The role of sympatric speciation in animal evolution is probably much less important than allopatric speciation; until recently, sympatric speciation in animals has been difficult to demonstrate in nature.

There are at least two ways in which sympatric speciation can occur: a change in **ploidy** (the number of chromosome sets making up an organism's genome) and a change in ecology. We now examine each of these mechanisms.

Allopolyploidy is an important mechanism of sympatric speciation in plants

As discussed earlier, the union of two gametes from different species rarely forms viable offspring; if offspring are produced, they are usually sterile. Before gametes form, meiosis occurs to reduce the chromosome number (see Chapter 9). For the chromosomes to be parceled correctly into the gametes, homologous chromosome pairs must come together (a process called *synapsis*) during prophase I. This cannot usually occur in interspecific hybrid offspring because not all the chromosomes are homologous. However, if the chromosome number doubles *before*

(a)

(b)

■ **Figure 19–9 Allopatric speciation in progress.** **(a)** The Kaibab squirrel, with its white tail, is found north of the Grand Canyon. **(b)** The Abert squirrel, with its gray tail and white belly, is found south of the Grand Canyon. *(a, Tom and Pat Leeson; b, Kent and Donna Dannen)*

meiosis, then pairing of homologous chromosomes can take place. Although not a common occurrence, this spontaneous doubling of chromosomes has been documented in a variety of plants and a few animals. It produces nuclei with multiple sets of chromosomes.

Polyploidy, the possession of more than two sets of chromosomes, is a major factor in plant evolution. Reproductive isolation occurs in a single generation when a polyploid species with multiple sets of chromosomes arises from diploid parents. There are two kinds of polyploidy: autopolyploidy and allopolyploidy. An **autopolyploid** contains multiple sets of chromosomes from a single species, and an **allopolyploid** contains multiple sets of chromosomes from two or more species. We restrict our discussion to allopolyploidy because its occurrence in nature is much more common.

Allopolyploidy occurs in conjunction with **hybridization,** which is sexual reproduction between individuals from closely related species. Allopolyploidy can produce a fertile interspecific hybrid because the polyploid condition provides the homologous chromosome pairs necessary for synapsis during meiosis. As a result, gametes may be viable (Fig. 19–10). An allopolyploid, that is, an interspecific hybrid produced by allopolyploidy, can reproduce with itself (self-fertilize) or with a similar individual. However, allopolyploids are reproductively isolated from both parents because their gametes have a different number of chromosomes than those of either parent.

If a population of allopolyploids (i.e., a new species) becomes established, selective pressures cause one of three outcomes. First, the new species may be unable to compete successfully against species that are already established, and so it becomes extinct. Second, the allopolyploid individuals may assume a new role in the environment and so coexist with both parental species. Third, the new species may successfully compete with either or both of its parental species. If it has a combination of traits that confers greater fitness than one or both parental species for all or part of the original range of the parent(s), the hybrid species may replace the parent(s).

Although allopolyploidy is extremely rare in animals, it is considered a significant factor in the evolution of flowering plant species. As many as 80% of all flowering plant species are thought to be polyploids, and most of these are allopolyploids. Moreover, allopolyploidy provides a mechanism for extremely rapid speciation. A single generation is all that is needed to form a new, reproductively isolated species. Allopolyploidy may explain the rapid appearance of many flowering plant species in the fossil record and their remarkable diversity (about 235,000 species) today.

The kew primrose *(Primula kewensis)* is an example of sympatric speciation that was documented at the Royal Botanic Gardens at Kew, England, in 1898 (Fig. 19–11). The interspecific hybrid of two primrose species, *Primula floribunda* $(2n = 18)$ and *Primula verticillata* $(2n = 18)$, *P. kewensis* had a chromosome number of 18 but was sterile. Then, at three different times, it was reported to have spontaneously formed a fertile branch, which was an allopolyploid $(2n = 36)$ that produced viable seeds of *P. kewensis.*

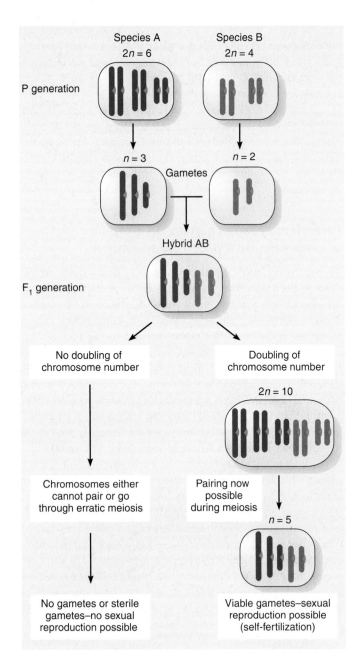

Figure 19–10 Sympatric speciation by allopolyploidy in plants. When two species (designated the P generation) successfully interbreed, the interspecific hybrid offspring (the F_1 generation) are almost always sterile *(bottom left).* If the chromosomes double, proper synapsis and segregation of the chromosomes can occur, and viable gametes can be produced *(bottom right).* (Unduplicated chromosomes are shown for clarity.)

The mechanism of sympatric speciation has been experimentally verified for many plant species. One example is a group of species, collectively called hemp nettles, that occurs in temperate parts of Europe and Asia. One hemp nettle, *Galeopsis tetrahit* $(2n = 32)$, is a naturally occurring allopolyploid thought to have formed by the hybridization of two species, *Galeopsis pu-*

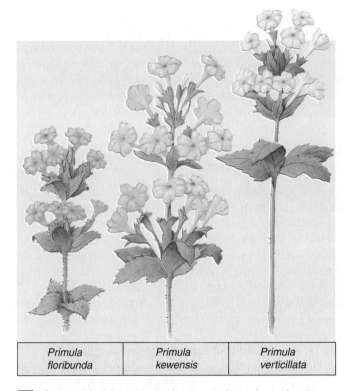

| Primula floribunda | Primula kewensis | Primula verticillata |

■ Figure 19–11 Sympatric speciation of a primrose. An allopolyploid primrose, *Primula kewensis,* arose in 1898 as an allopolyploid derived from the interspecific hybridization of *P. floribunda* and *P. verticillata.* Today *P. kewensis* is a popular houseplant.

bescens ($2n = 16$) and *Galeopsis speciosa* ($2n = 16$). This process occurred in nature but was experimentally reproduced. *Galeopsis pubescens* and *G. speciosa* were crossed to produce F_1 hybrids, most of which were sterile. Nevertheless, both F_2 and F_3 generations were produced. The F_3 generation included a polyploid plant with $2n = 32$ that self-fertilized to yield fertile F_4 offspring that could not mate with either of the parental species. These allopolyploid plants had the same appearance and chromosome number as the naturally occurring *G. tetrahit.* When the experimentally produced plants were crossed with the naturally occurring *G. tetrahit,* a fertile F_1 generation was formed. Thus, the experiment duplicated the speciation process that occurred in nature.

Changing ecology can cause sympatric speciation in animals

Biologists have observed the occurrence of sympatric speciation in animals, but its significance—how often it occurs and under what conditions—is still actively debated. Many examples involve parasitic insects and rely on genetic mechanisms other than polyploidy. For example, in the 1860s in the Hudson River Valley of New York, a population of fruit maggot flies *(Rhagoletis pomonella)* parasitic on the small red fruits of native hawthorn trees was documented to have switched to a new host, domestic apples, which had been introduced from Europe. Although the

sister populations (hawthorn maggot flies and apple maggot flies) continue to occupy the same geographical area, no gene flow occurs between them because they eat, mate, and lay their eggs on different hosts (Fig. 19–12). In other words, because the hawthorn and apple maggot flies have diverged and are reproductively isolated from each other, they have effectively become separate species. Most entomologists, however, still recognize hawthorn and apple maggot flies as a single species because their appearance is virtually identical.

In situations like the fruit maggot flies, it is thought that a mutation arises in an individual and spreads through a small group of insects by sexual reproduction. The mutation causes disruptive selection (see Chapter 18), which favors a distinct phenotype by allowing the mutants to have a different ecological opportunity—in this case, to parasitize a different host species—than the original phenotype. Additional mutations may occur that cause the sister populations to diverge even further.

In 1988 biologists reported that hawthorn and apple maggot flies have genetic differences in three chromosomal regions and identified genetic markers associated with changes in the timing of fly development. Both hawthorn and apple larvae (maggots) tunnel out of the fruit before winter, drop to the ground, and burrow into the soil. However, hawthorn maggot flies emerge from the ground as adults later in the summer than apple

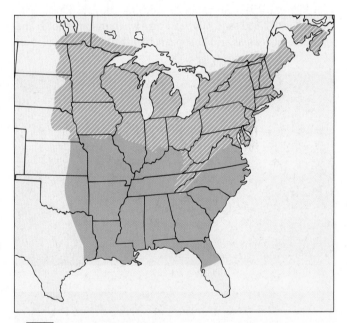

■ Hawthorn maggot fly range

▨ Apple maggot fly and hawthorn maggot fly range

■ Figure 19–12 Ranges of apple and hawthorn maggot flies. Apple and hawthorn maggot flies are sympatric throughout the northern half of the hawthorn maggot fly's range. *(Adapted from Bush, G.L. "Sympatric Host Race Formation and Speciation in Frugivorous Flies of the Genus Rhagoletis [Diptera, Tephritidae]."* Evolution, *Vol. 23, No. 2, Jun. 1969)*

maggot flies, a difference that further contributes to their reproductive isolation.

Biologists have studied the speciation of colorful fishes known as cichlids (pronounced "sik-lids") in several East African lakes (Fig. 19–13). The different species of cichlids in a given lake have remarkably different eating habits. Some graze on algae; some consume dead organic material at the bottom of the lake; and others are predatory and eat plankton (microscopic aquatic organisms), insect larvae, the scales off fish, or even other cichlid species. In some cichlids food preferences are related to size (e.g., smaller cichlids consume plankton), which in turn is related to mating preference (small, plankton-eating cichlids mate only with other small, plankton-eating cichlids). In other cichlids related species do not differ in size but only in color, and females mate with males of specific colors. Recent DNA sequence data indicate that the cichlid species within a single lake are more closely related to one another than they are to fishes in nearby lakes or rivers. These molecular data suggest that cichlid species evolved sympatrically, or at least within the confines of a lake, rather than by repeated colonizations by fish populations in nearby rivers.

How rapidly did sympatric speciation occur in cichlids? In 1996 scientists published seismic and drill core data that suggest that the more than 500 endemic (i.e., found nowhere else) cichlid species in Lake Victoria evolved in a remarkably short time—less than 12,400 years. This inference is based on evidence that Lake Victoria dried up completely during the late Pleistocene (from about 17,000 to 12,400 years ago) when much of north and equatorial Africa was arid. It appears that the cichlids evolved af-ter the climate became wetter and Lake Victoria refilled. If future data substantiate this conclusion, it means that the evolution of Lake Victoria's cichlids is the fastest known for such a large number of vertebrate species. (See *On the Cutting Edge: Explaining the Rapid Loss of Cichlid Diversity in Lake Victoria* for a discussion of how human activities have altered the evolutionary mechanism that maintains cichlid diversity.)

Reproductive isolation breaks down in hybrid zones

When two populations have significantly diverged as a result of geographical separation, there is no easy way to determine if the speciation process is complete (recall the disagreement about whether Porto Santo rabbits are a separate species or a *subspecies,* which is a taxonomic subdivision of a species). If such populations, subspecies, or species come into contact, they may hybridize where they meet, forming a **hybrid zone,** or area of overlap in which interbreeding occurs. Hybrid zones are typically narrow, presumably because the hybrids are not well adapted for either parental environment, and the hybrid population is typically very small compared with the parental populations.

On the Great Plains of North America, red-shafted and yellow-shafted flickers (types of woodpeckers) meet and interbreed. The red-shafted flicker, named for the male's red underwings and tail, is found in the western part of North America, from the Great Plains to the Pacific Ocean. Yellow-shafted flicker males, which have yellow underwings and tails, range east of the Rock-

(a)

(c)

(b)

Figure 19–13 Color variation in Lake Victoria cichlids. **(a)** *Pundamilia pundamilia* males have bluish-silver bodies. **(b)** *Pundamilia nyererei* males have red backs. **(c)** *Pundamilia* "red head" males have a red chest. (The "red head" species has not yet been scientifically named.) Some evidence suggests that changes in male coloration may be the first step in speciation of Lake Victoria cichlids. Later, other traits, including ecological characteristics, diverge. (Female cichlids generally have cryptic coloration; their drab colors help them blend into their surroundings.) *(Courtesy of Ole Seehausen/Leiden University, The Netherlands, and Hull University, United Kingdom)*

ies. Hybrid flickers, which form a stable hybrid zone from Texas to southern Alaska, are varied in appearance, although many have orange-colored underwings and tails.

Process of Science Biologists are not in agreement about whether the red-shafted and yellow-shafted flickers are separate species or geographical subspecies. According to the biological species concept, if red-shafted and yellow-shafted flickers are two species, they should maintain their reproductive isolation. On the other hand, the flicker hybrid zone has not expanded, that is, the two types of flickers have maintained their distinctiveness and have not rejoined into a single, freely interbreeding population.

The study of hybrid zones has made important contributions to what is known about speciation. As in other fields of science, disagreements and differences of opinion are an important part of the scientific process because they stimulate new ideas, hypotheses, and experimental tests that expand our base of scientific knowledge.

■ EVOLUTIONARY CHANGE CAN OCCUR RAPIDLY OR GRADUALLY

We have seen that speciation is hard for us to directly observe as it occurs. Does the fossil record provide clues about how rapidly new species arise? Biologists have long recognized that the fossil record lacks many transitional forms; the starting points (ancestral species) and the end points (new species) are present, but the intermediate stages in the evolution from one species to another are often lacking. This observation has traditionally been explained by the incompleteness of the fossil record. Biologists have attempted to fill in the missing parts with new fossil discoveries, much as a writer might fill in the middle of a novel when the beginning and end are already there.

Two different models—punctuated equilibrium and gradualism—have been developed to explain evolution as observed in the fossil record (Fig. 19–14). The **punctuated equilibrium** model was proposed by paleontologists who question whether the fossil record really is as incomplete as it initially appeared. First advanced by Stephen Jay Gould and Niles Eldredge in 1972, the punctuated equilibrium model suggests that the fossil record accurately reflects evolution as it actually occurs. That is, in the history of a species, long periods of **stasis** (little or no evolutionary change) are punctuated, or interrupted, by short periods of rapid speciation that are perhaps triggered by changes in the environment, that is, periods of great evolutionary stress. Thus, speciation normally proceeds in "spurts." These relatively short periods of active evolution (e.g., 100,000 years) are followed by long periods (e.g., 2 million years) of stability.

With punctuated equilibrium, speciation can occur in a relatively short period. Keep in mind, however, that a "short" amount of time for speciation may be thousands of years. Such a span is short when compared with the several million years of a species'

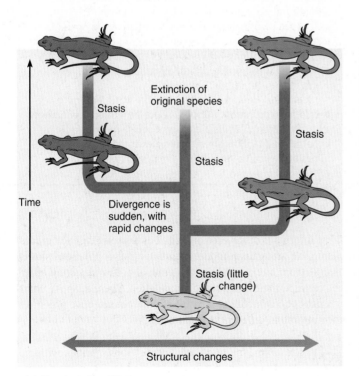

(a) Punctuated equilibrium

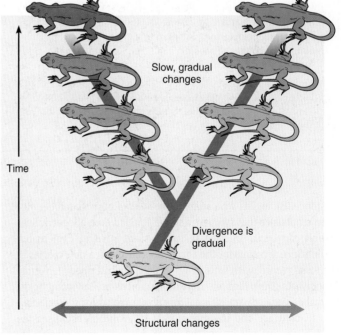

(b) Gradualism

■ **Figure 19–14 Punctuated equilibrium and gradualism.** In this figure, structural changes in the lizards are represented by changes in skin color. **(a)** In punctuated equilibrium, long periods of stasis are interrupted by short periods of rapid speciation. **(b)** In gradualism, a slow, steady change in species occurs over time.

Explaining the Rapid Loss of Cichlid Diversity in Lake Victoria

HYPOTHESIS: The number of cichlid species in Lake Victoria is declining because of changes in their habitat that affect sexual isolation between species.

METHOD: Take field measurements in 22 different locations in Lake Victoria. Verify these field observations with laboratory experiments.

RESULTS: Increasing turbidity of Lake Victoria's water is preventing females of cichlid species from choosing mates of their own species, which they do based on color variations among the males of different species. As a result, females are interbreeding with males of other species, and the number of cichlid species declines as the distinctive gene pools of different species are merging.

CONCLUSION: Cichlid diversity has declined and will continue to decline unless effective measures are taken to reduce pollution in Lake Victoria immediately.

The hundreds of small, colorful cichlid species that diversified in Lake Victoria have always intrigued evolutionary biologists. However, many of these species are rapidly disappearing, and about half of the 500 species that biologists estimate lived in Lake Victoria in 1978 are now extinct. The Nile perch, a voracious predator that was deliberately introduced into the lake in 1960 to stimulate the local fishing economy and whose population exploded during the 1980s, has been blamed for the extinction of most of the cichlid species that have disappeared.

Biologists from Leiden University in the Netherlands observed, however, that species were also disappearing in lake habitats where the Nile perch is known to have little or no impact. Ole Seehausen and colleagues measured environmental features at 22 localities with such habitats and found strong correlations between bright and diverse male colors, the number of species, and clear, well-lit water.*

* Seehausen, O., J.J.M. Van Alphen, and F. Witte, "Cichlid Fish Diversity Threatened by Eutrophication that Curbs Sexual Selection." *Science*, Vol. 277, 19 Sept. 1997.

The better the light in a given part of the lake, the more colorful the males and the greater the number of species present at a specific site. Each species has its own distinct male coloration, which matches the preferences of females of that species in choosing mates, and has evolved under sexual selection. **Sexual selection,** which is choosing a mate based on its color or some other characteristic, is discussed in Chapter 50. In clear water, members of each species do not interbreed with members of other species.

As nearby forests have been cut, soil erosion has made the water of Lake Victoria more turbid (cloudy). Increased agricultural activity in the area has also contributed fertilizer as well as sediment pollution. Water transparency in open (deep) lake water has decreased from an average of 6.8 m in the 1920s to 2.2 m in the 1990s, whereas water transparency in shallow areas along the shoreline has decreased from 3 m to 1.5 m in the past decade.

Seehausen demonstrated that as the water became more turbid from pollution, light could not penetrate as effectively, and the spectrum of visible colors became narrower. He hypothesized that, as a result, females could not distinguish males of their own species from males of closely related

existence. Biologists who support the idea of punctuated equilibrium emphasize that sympatric speciation and even allopatric speciation can occur in such relatively short periods. Punctuated equilibrium accounts for the abrupt appearance of a new species in the fossil record, with little or no evidence of intermediate forms. Proponents think that few transitional forms appear in the fossil record because few transitional forms occurred during speciation.

In contrast, the traditional view of evolution espouses the **gradualism** model, in which evolution proceeds continuously over long periods. Gradualism is rarely observed in the fossil record because the record is incomplete. (Recall from Chapter 17 that the conditions required for fossil formation are quite precise. Most organisms decompose when they die, leaving no trace of their existence.) Occasionally, a complete fossil record of tran-

sitional forms is discovered and cited as a strong case for gradualism. The gradualism model maintains that populations slowly diverge from one another by the gradual accumulation of adaptive characteristics within each population. These adaptive characteristics accumulate as a result of different selective pressures encountered in different environments.

Process of Science The abundant fossil evidence of long periods with no change in a species has been used to argue against the gradualism model of evolution. Gradualists, however, maintain that any periods of stasis evident in the fossil record are the result of stabilizing selection (see Chapter 18). They also emphasize that stasis in fossils is deceptive because fossils do not reveal all aspects of evolution. While fossils display changes in external

species. As discussed in the chapter, the cichlids of Lake Victoria are young species, having evolved during the past 12,000 years. Their relative youth means that these species may not have yet evolved reproductive isolating mechanisms other than mate preference based on color. It also means that closely related species are able to interbreed without loss of fertility. With increasing turbidity, males lost their bright colors because producing them was no longer rewarded, and females have mated with males of other species, producing fertile, healthy offspring. Thus, males are losing their bright colors, and many original species are being replaced by fewer hybrids.

Further support for this hypothesis comes from laboratory experiments. When aquaria were well lit, females of two closely related cichlid species (one with blue males, the other one with red) consistently chose mates of their own species over those of the other species. When biologists blocked the light to simulate the turbid conditions in parts of Lake Victoria, however, females often chose males of the other species.

More recently, Seehausen has evaluated possible explanations for the extraordinary diversity in cichlids. Based on his observations and the observations of others, Seehausen hypothesized that cichlids speciate by disruptive sexual selection on polymorphic coloration.[†] **Polymorphic coloration** is the presence in a population of two or more colors in either males or females. If cichlid mating preferences are based on color, and if color preferences vary between individuals (and it appears they often do), this mating behavior tends to cause disruptive sexual selection. Recall from Chapter 18 that disruptive selection results in a divergence, or splitting apart, of distinct groups of individuals within a population. **Disruptive sexual selection** is a special type of disruptive selection that is based on mate preference.

Seehausen tested predictions of his hypothesis by studying the geographical distribution, coloring, and relatedness of 41 rock-dwelling cichlid species endemic to Lake Victoria. In some cases, he found that speciation was "in progress," with members of the same species in the process of diverging into two or more groups based solely on differences in male or female coloration. These groups (known as *color morphs*) were not completely reproductively isolated and so were considered incipient species (species just beginning to form).[‡] Seehausen also observed that closely related species that were completely reproductively isolated exhibited the same color variations he had found associated with disruptive sexual selection in incipient species, and these closely related species usually had sympatric distributions.

Seehausen's research, like all good science, seeks to reduce the apparent complexity of the world—in this case, the extraordinary number of cichlid species—to general principles that can provide new insights—in this case, into evolutionary processes. Although Seehausen's hypothesis on disruptive sexual selection is well supported for rock-dwelling Lake Victoria cichlids, it must be further tested with cichlid species that inhabit other environments and other lakes before it can be widely accepted.

[†] Seehausen, O. and J.J.M. Van Alphen. "Can Sympatric Speciation by Disruptive Sexual Selection Explain Rapid Evolution of Cichlid Diversity in Lake Victoria?" *Ecology Letters*, Vol. 2, 1999.

[‡] Seehausen, O., J.J.M. Van Alphen, and R. Lande. "Color Polymorphism and Sex Ratio Distortion in a Cichlid Fish as an Incipient Stage in Sympatric Speciation by Sexual Selection." *Ecology Letters*, Vol. 2, 1999.

---

structure and skeletal structure, genetic changes in physiology, internal structure, and behavior—all of which also represent evolution—are not evident. Gradualists recognize rapid evolution only when strong directional selection occurs.

Punctuated equilibrium and gradualism are related to cladogenesis and anagenesis, the two patterns of evolution discussed earlier in this chapter. The key prediction of punctuated equilibrium is that structural changes should be concentrated at the point of speciation through cladogenesis, as shown in Figure 19–14a. Gradualism predicts that structural changes need not be associated with cladogenesis and may take place at any point in a species' history. Note that anagenic change is shown in the right-hand and left-hand branches of Figure 19–14b. This difference between punctuated equilibrium and gradualism is important to the process of science since what each model predicts can be tested against future discoveries in the fossil record.

Many biologists embrace both models to explain the fossil record; they also contend that the pace of evolution may be abrupt in certain instances and gradual in others and that neither punctuated equilibrium nor gradualism exclusively characterizes the complex changes associated with evolution. Other biologists do not view the distinction between punctuated equilibrium and gradualism as real. They suggest that genetic changes occur gradually and at a roughly constant pace and that the majority of these mutations do not cause speciation. When the mutations that do cause speciation occur, they are dramatic and produce a pattern consistent with the punctuated equilibrium model.

■ MACROEVOLUTION INVOLVES MAJOR EVOLUTIONARY EVENTS

Macroevolution includes dramatic changes that occur over long time spans in evolution. One concern of macroevolution is to explain evolutionary novelties, which are large phenotypic changes such as the appearance of wings with feathers during the evolution of birds from reptiles. These phenotypic changes are so great that the new species possessing them are assigned to different genera or higher taxonomic categories. Studies of macroevolution also attempt to discover and explain major changes in species diversity through time, such as occur during adaptive radiation, when many species appear, and mass extinction, when many species disappear. Thus, evolutionary novelties, adaptive radiation, and mass extinction are important aspects of macroevolution.

Evolutionary novelties originate through modifications of preexisting structures

New designs arise from structures already in existence. A change in the basic pattern of an organism can produce something unique, such as wings on insects, flowers on plants, and feathers on birds. Usually these evolutionary novelties are variations of some preexisting structures, called **preadaptations,** that originally fulfilled one role but were subsequently modified in a way that was adaptive for a different role. Feathers, which evolved from reptilian scales and may have originally provided thermal insulation in primitive birds and some dinosaurs (see Chapter 20), represent a preadaptation for flight. That is, with gradual modification, feathers evolved to function in flight as well as to fulfill their original thermoregulatory role. (Interestingly, a few feather-footed birds exist; this phenotype is the result of a change in gene regulation that alters scales, normally found on bird feet, into feathers.)

Similarly, the mammalian middle ear bones originated from modified jawbones of reptiles. Consider the malleus, a hammer-shaped bone that is in contact with the eardrum in the mammalian middle ear (see Chapter 41). During the evolution of mammals, it is hypothesized that the articular bone of the reptile lower jaw became smaller and lighter and was gradually transformed into the malleus bone. Supporting evidence includes embryological studies, which indicate that the early stages of articular bone development in reptiles are the same as developmental stages in the malleus bone in mammals. In addition, fossils of mammal-like reptiles show some of the intermediate steps between articular and malleus bones.

How do such evolutionary novelties originate? Many are probably due to changes during **development,** which is the orderly sequence of events that occur as an organism grows and matures. Regulatory genes may exert control over hundreds of other genes during development, and very slight genetic changes in regulatory genes could ultimately cause major structural changes in the organism (see section on developmental biology in Chapter 17).

For example, during development, most organisms exhibit varied rates of growth for different parts of the body, known as **allometric growth** (from the Greek *allo,* "different," and *metr,* "measure"). The size of the head in human newborns is large in proportion to the rest of the body. As a human grows and matures, its torso, hands, and legs grow more rapidly than the head. Allometric growth is found in many organisms, including the male fiddler crab with its single, oversized claw, and the ocean sunfish with its enlarged tail (Fig. 19–15). If growth rates are al-

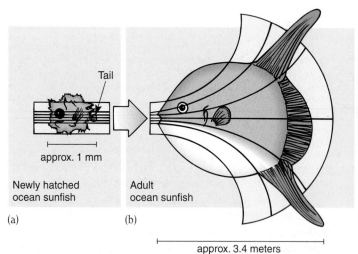

Tail

approx. 1 mm

Newly hatched ocean sunfish

(a)

Adult ocean sunfish

(b)

approx. 3.4 meters

(c)

■ **Figure 19–15 Allometric growth in the ocean sunfish.** The tail end of an ocean sunfish *(Mola mola)* grows faster than the head end, resulting in the unique shape of the adult. **(a)** A newly hatched ocean sunfish, only 1 mm long, has an extremely small tail. **(b)** This allometric transformation can be visualized by drawing rectangular coordinate lines through a picture of the juvenile fish and then changing the coordinate lines mathematically. **(c)** An ocean sunfish swims off the coast of southern California. The adult ocean sunfish may reach 4 m (13 ft) and weigh about 1500 kg (3300 lb). *(Richard Herrmann)*

tered even slightly, drastic changes in the shape of an organism may result, changes that may or may not be adaptive. For example, allometric growth may help explain the extremely small and relatively useless forelegs of the dinosaur *Tyrannosaurus rex,* as compared with its ancestors.

Sometimes novel evolutionary changes occur when a species undergoes changes in the *timing* of development in comparison with its ancestor. Consider, for example, the changes that would occur if juvenile characteristics were retained in the adult stage, a phenomenon known as **paedomorphosis** (from the Greek *paed,* "child," and *morph,* "form"). Adults of some salamander species have external gills and tail fins, features found only in the larval (immature) stages of other salamanders. Retention of external gills and tail fins throughout life obviously alters the salamander's behavioral and ecological characteristics (Fig. 19–16). Perhaps such salamanders succeeded because they had a selective advantage over "normal" adult salamanders, that is, by remaining aquatic, they did not have to compete for food with the terrestrial adult forms of related species. The paedomorphic forms also escaped the typical predators of terrestrial salamanders (although they had other predators in their aquatic environment). The biological basis of paedomorphosis in salamanders has been studied and is probably the result of mutations in genes that block the production of hormones that stimulate metamorphic changes. When paedomorphic salamanders receive hormone injections, they develop into normal adults.

Adaptive radiation is the diversification of an ancestral species into many species

Adaptive radiation is the evolutionary diversification of many related species from one or a few ancestral species in a relatively short period. The concept of adaptive zones was developed to help explain why adaptive radiations take place. **Adaptive zones** are new ecological opportunities that were not exploited by an ancestral organism. At the species level, an adaptive zone is essentially identical to one or more similar *ecological niches* (the functional roles of species within a community; see Chapter 52). Examples of adaptive zones include nocturnal flying to catch small insects; grazing on grass while migrating across a savanna; and swimming at the ocean's surface to filter out plankton. When many adaptive zones are empty, as was the case of Lake Victoria when it refilled some 12,000 years ago (discussed earlier in the chapter), colonizing species such as the cichlids are able to rapidly diversify and exploit them.

Because islands have fewer species than do mainland areas of similar size, latitude, and topography, vacant adaptive zones are more common on islands than on continents. Consider the Hawaiian honeycreepers, a group of related birds found on the Hawaiian Islands. When the honeycreeper ancestors reached Hawaii, few other birds were present. The succeeding generations of honeycreepers quickly diversified into many new species and, in the process, occupied the many available adaptive zones that are normally occupied by finches, honeyeaters, treecreepers, and woodpeckers on the mainland. The diversity of their bills, like those of Galapagos finches (see Chapter 17), is a particularly

Figure 19–16 Paedomorphosis in a salamander. An adult axolotl salamander (*Ambystoma mexicanum*) retains the juvenile characteristics of external gills (feathery structures protruding from the neck) and a tail fin *(not visible)*. Paedomorphosis allows the axolotl to remain permanently aquatic and to reproduce without developing typical adult characteristics. *(Jane Burton/Bruce Coleman, Inc.)*

good illustration of adaptive radiation (Fig. 19–17). Some honeycreeper bills are curved to extract nectar out of tubular flowers, for example, whereas others are short and thickened for ripping away bark in search of insects.

Another example of vacant adaptive zones involves the Hawaiian silverswords, 28 species of closely related plants found only on the Hawaiian Islands. When the silversword ancestor, a California plant related to daisies, reached the Hawaiian Islands, many diverse environments, such as exposed lava flows, dry woodlands, moist forests, and bogs, were present and more or less unoccupied. The succeeding generations of silverswords quickly diversified, occupying the many adaptive zones available to them. The diversity in their leaves, which changed during the course of natural selection to enable different populations to adapt to various levels of light and moisture, is a particularly good illustration of adaptive radiation (Fig. 19–18). Leaves of silverswords that are adapted to shady moist forests are large, for example, whereas those of silverswords living in exposed dry areas are small. The leaves of silverswords living on exposed volcanic slopes are covered with dense silvery hairs that may reflect some of the intense ultraviolet radiation off the plant.

Adaptive radiation appears to be more common during periods of major environmental change, but it is difficult to determine if these changes actually induce adaptive radiation. It is possible that major environmental change indirectly affects

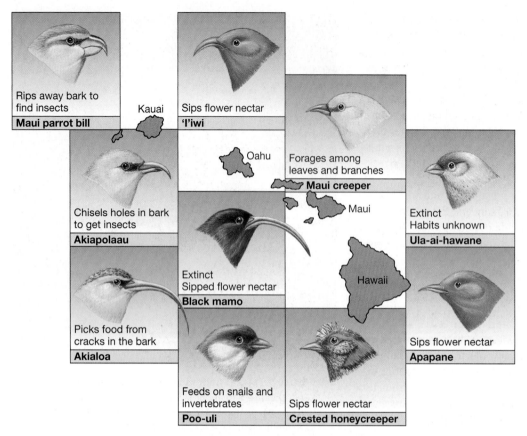

Figure 19–17 Adaptive radiation in Hawaiian honeycreepers. Compare the various beak shapes and methods of obtaining food. Many honeycreeper species are now extinct or nearing extinction as a result of human activities, including the destruction of habitat and the introduction of predators such as rats, dogs, and pigs. By late 2000, for example, the poo-uli population consisted of three known individuals.

adaptive radiation by increasing the rate of extinction. Extinction produces empty adaptive zones, which provide new opportunities for those species that remain. Mammals, for example, had existed as small nocturnal insectivores (insect eaters) for millions of years before undergoing adaptive radiation leading to the modern mammalian orders. This radiation was presumably triggered by the extinction of the dinosaurs. Mammals diversified and exploited a variety of adaptive zones relatively soon after the dinosaurs' demise. Flying bats, running gazelles, burrowing moles, and swimming whales all originated from the small, insect-eating, ancestral mammals.

The appearance of novel features is usually associated with major periods of adaptive radiation. For example, shells and skeletons may have been the evolutionary novelties responsible for a period of adaptive radiation at the beginning of the Paleozoic era (see Chapter 20), in which most animal phyla, living and extinct, appeared. Care must be taken in interpreting a cause-and-effect relationship between the appearance of a novel feature and adaptive radiation, however. It is tempting to take a simplistic approach and assume, for example, that the evolution of the flower facilitated the adaptive radiation of thousands of species of flowering plants. It is true that the flowering plants diversified after the evolution of the flower, which may have presented a more competitive method of sexual reproduction because it permitted

pollination by insects and other animals. However, adaptive radiation in the flowering plants may instead be a consequence of other adaptations that also evolved. (Chapter 27 discusses other flowering plant adaptations as well as their highly successful mode of reproduction.)

Extinction is an important aspect of evolution

Extinction, the end of a lineage, occurs when the last individual of a species dies. The loss is permanent, for once a species is extinct it can never reappear. Extinctions have occurred continually since the origin of life; by one estimate, only 1 species is alive today for every 2000 that have become extinct. Extinction is the eventual fate of all species, in the same way that death is the eventual fate of all individual organisms.

Although extinction has a negative short-term impact on species richness, it can facilitate evolution over a period of thousands to millions of years. As mentioned previously, when species become extinct, their adaptive zones become vacant. Consequently, those organisms still living are presented with new opportunities for speciation and may diverge, filling in some of the unoccupied zones. In other words, the extinct species may eventually be replaced by new species.

(a)   (b)   (c)

Figure 19–18 Adaptive radiation in Hawaiian silverswords. The ancestor of the Hawaiian silverswords was a California plant similar to the daisy. The 28 silversword species are found in three closely related genera. They live in a variety of habitats, from rain forests to exposed mountain slopes. **(a)** The Haleakala silversword (*Argyroxyphium sandwicense* ssp. *macrocephalum*) is found only in the cinders on the upper slope of Haleakala Crater on the island of Maui. This plant is adapted to low precipitation and high levels of ultraviolet radiation. **(b)** This silversword species (*Wilkesia gymnoxiphium*), which superficially resembles a yucca, is found only along the slopes of Waimea Canyon on the island of Kauai. **(c)** *Daubautia scabra* is a small, herbaceous silversword found in moist to wet environments on several Hawaiian islands. (The fern fronds in the background give an idea of the small size of *D. scabra.*) *(a–c, Jack Jeffrey Photography)*

During the long history of life, extinction appears to have occurred at two different rates. The continuous, low-level extinction of species is sometimes called **background extinction.** In contrast, five or possibly six times during Earth's history, **mass extinctions** of numerous species and higher taxa have taken place in both terrestrial and marine environments. The most recent mass extinction, which occurred about 65 million years ago (mya), killed off many marine organisms, terrestrial plants, and vertebrates, including the last of the dinosaurs (Fig. 19–19). The time span over which a mass extinction occurred may have been several million years, but that is relatively short compared with the 3.5 billion years or so of Earth's history of life. Each period of mass extinction has been followed by a period of adaptive radiation of some of the surviving groups.

The causes of past episodes of mass extinction are not well understood. Both environmental and biological factors seem to have been involved. Major changes in climate could have adversely affected those plants and animals that lacked the genetic flexibility to adapt. Marine organisms, in particular, are adapted to a steady, unchanging climate. If Earth's temperature were to increase or decrease by just a few degrees overall, many marine species would probably perish.

It is also possible that past mass extinctions were due to changes in the environment induced by catastrophes. If a large comet or small asteroid collided with Earth, for example, the dust ejected into the atmosphere on impact could have blocked much of the sunlight. In addition to disrupting the food chain by killing many plants (and therefore terrestrial animals), this event would have lowered Earth's temperature, leading to the death of many marine organisms. Evidence that the extinction of dinosaurs was caused by an extraterrestrial object's collision with Earth continues to accumulate (see Chapter 20).

Biological factors also trigger extinction. Competition among species may lead to the extinction of those species that cannot compete effectively. The human species, in particular, has had a profound impact on the rate of extinction. The habitats of many animal and plant species have been altered or destroyed by humans, and habitat destruction can result in a species' extinction. Some biologists think that we have entered the greatest mass extinction episode in Earth's history. (Extinction is discussed further in Chapter 55.)

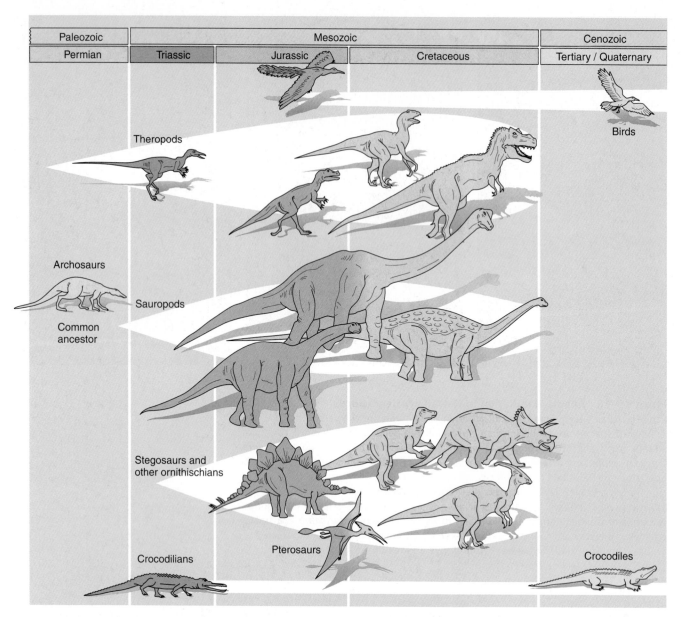

Paleozoic	Mesozoic			Cenozoic
Permian	Triassic	Jurassic	Cretaceous	Tertiary / Quaternary

Theropods

Birds

Archosaurs

Common ancestor

Sauropods

Stegosaurs and other ornithischians

Pterosaurs

Crocodilians

Crocodiles

■ **Figure 19–19 Mass extinction of the archosaurs.** At the end of the Cretaceous period, approximately 65 mya, a mass extinction of many organisms, including the remaining dinosaurs, occurred. (Dinosaurs had already been declining in diversity throughout the latter part of the Cretaceous period.) Most of the archosaurs (one of five main groups of reptiles) became extinct. The only lines to survive were crocodiles and birds, both of which are archosauran descendants.

■ IS MICROEVOLUTION RELATED TO SPECIATION AND MACROEVOLUTION?

The concepts presented in Chapters 17 and 18 represent the **synthetic theory of evolution,** in which mutation provides the genetic variation on which natural selection acts. The synthetic theory of evolution combines Darwin's theory with important aspects of genetics. Many aspects of the synthetic theory of evolution have been tested and verified at the population and subspecies levels. Many biologists contend that microevolutionary processes (natural selection, mutation, genetic drift, and gene

flow) account for the genetic variation within species and for the origin of new species. These biologists also think that macroevolution can be explained by microevolutionary processes.

A considerable body of data from many fields supports the synthetic theory of evolution as it relates to speciation and macroevolution. Consider, for example, the evolution of amphibians from fish, which was a major macroevolutionary event in the history of vertebrates. Study of the few known fossil intermediates has demonstrated that the transition from aquatic fish to terrestrial amphibian occurred as evolutionary novelties, such as changes in the limbs and skull roof, were added. These novelties accumulated as a succession of small changes over a period of 9 million to 14 million years. This time scale is sufficient to have allowed natural selection and other microevolutionary processes to have produced the novel characters.

Although few biologists doubt the role of natural selection and microevolution in generating specific adaptations, some question the *extent* of microevolution's role in the overall pattern of life's history. These biologists ask whether speciation and macroevolution have been dominated by microevolutionary processes or by external, chance events (e.g., an impact by an as-teroid). Chance events do not "care" about adaptive superiority but instead lead to the random extinction or survival of species. In the case of an asteroid impact, for example, those species that survive may do so because they were "lucky" enough to be in a protected environment at the time of impact. If chance events have been the overriding factor during life's history, then microevolution cannot be the exclusive explanation for the biological diversity we have today (see additional discussion of the role of chance in evolution in Chapter 17).

SUMMARY WITH KEY TERMS

I. According to the **biological species concept,** a **species** consists of one or more populations whose members freely interbreed in nature to produce fertile offspring and do not freely interbreed with members of different species.

II. **Reproductive isolating mechanisms** restrict gene flow between species.
   A. **Prezygotic barriers** are reproductive isolating mechanisms that prevent fertilization from taking place.
      1. **Temporal isolation** occurs when two species reproduce at different times of the day, season, or year.
      2. In **habitat isolation,** two closely related species live and breed in different habitats in the same geographical area.
      3. In **behavioral isolation,** distinctive courtship behaviors prevent mating between species.
      4. **Mechanical isolation** is due to incompatible structural differences in the reproductive organs of similar species.
      5. In **gametic isolation,** gametes from different species are incompatible owing to molecular and chemical differences.
   B. **Postzygotic barriers** are reproductive isolating mechanisms that prevent gene flow after fertilization has taken place.
      1. **Hybrid inviability** is the death of interspecific embryos during development.
      2. **Hybrid sterility** prevents interspecific hybrids that survive to adulthood from reproducing successfully.
      3. **Hybrid breakdown** prevents the offspring of hybrids that survive to adulthood and successfully reproduce from reproducing beyond one or a few generations.
   C. Some of the genes involved in reproductive isolation in certain species have been identified.

III. **Speciation** is the evolution of a new species from an ancestral population. **Anagenesis** refers to relatively small, progressive evolutionary changes in a single lineage over long periods. **Cladogenesis** occurs when two or more populations of an ancestral species split and diverge, eventually forming two or more new species.
   A. **Allopatric speciation** occurs when one population becomes geographically isolated from the rest of the species and subsequently diverges.
      1. Speciation is more likely to occur if the original isolated population is small, because genetic drift is more significant in small populations.
      2. Examples of allopatric speciation include Death Valley pupfish, Kaibab squirrels, and Porto Santo rabbits.
   B. **Sympatric speciation** does not require geographical isolation.
      1. Sympatric speciation in plants results almost exclusively from **allopolyploidy,** in which a **polyploid** individual (one with more than two sets of chromosomes) is a hybrid derived from two species. Two examples of sympatric speciation by allopolyploidy are the kew primroses and hemp nettles.
      2. Sympatric speciation occurs in animals, such as fruit maggot flies and cichlids, but how often it occurs and under what conditions remain to be determined.

   C. A **hybrid zone** is an area in which two related populations, subspecies, or species meet and interbreed. Hybrid zones are typically narrow, presumably because the hybrids are not well adapted for either parental environment. Red-shafted and yellow-shafted flickers have a hybrid zone in the western part of North America.

IV. The interpretation of evolution, as observed in the fossil record, is currently being debated.
   A. According to the **punctuated equilibrium** model, evolution of species proceeds in spurts. Short periods of active speciation intersperse long periods of **stasis.**
   B. According to the **gradualism** model, populations slowly diverge from one another by the accumulation of adaptive characteristics within a population.

V. **Macroevolution** refers to dramatic evolutionary changes that occur over long time spans.
   A. Macroevolution includes the appearance of evolutionary novelties, which are phenotypic changes so great that the new species possessing them are assigned to different genera or higher taxonomic categories.
      1. Evolutionary novelties may be due to changes during **development.** Slight genetic changes in regulatory genes, for example, could ultimately cause major structural changes in the organism.
      2. Evolutionary novelties may originate from **preadaptations,** structures that originally fulfilled one role but changed in a way that was adaptive for a different role. Feathers and mammalian middle ear bones are examples of preadaptations.
      3. Changes in **allometric growth,** varied rates of growth for different parts of the body, result in overall changes in the shape of an organism. Examples include the ocean sunfish and the male fiddler crab.
      4. **Paedomorphosis,** the retention of juvenile characteristics in the adult, can occur owing to changes in the timing of development. Adult axolotl salamanders, with external gills and tail fins, are an example of paedomorphosis.
   B. **Adaptive radiation** is the process of diversification of an ancestral species into many new species.
      1. **Adaptive zones** are new ecological opportunities that were not exploited by an ancestral organism. When many adaptive zones are empty, colonizing species are able to rapidly diversify and exploit them.
      2. Hawaiian honeycreepers and silverswords both underwent adaptive radiation after their ancestors colonized the Hawaiian Islands.
   C. **Extinction** is the death of a species. When species become extinct, the adaptive zones that they occupied become vacant, allowing other species to evolve and fill them.
      1. **Background extinction** is the continuous, low-level extinction of species.
      2. **Mass extinction** is the extinction of numerous species and higher taxa in both terrestrial and marine environments.

1. Two populations belong to the same species if (a) their members freely interbreed in nature (b) individuals from the two populations produce fertile offspring (c) their members do not interbreed with individuals of different species (d) a and c are correct (e) a, b, and c are correct

2. The zebrass is an example of (a) a fertile hybrid (b) a sterile hybrid (c) prezygotic barriers (d) a biological species (e) allopolyploidy

3. A prezygotic barrier prevents (a) the union of egg and sperm (b) reproductive success by an interspecific hybrid (c) the development of the zygote into an embryo (d) allopolyploidy from occurring (e) changes in allometric growth

4. The reproductive isolating mechanism in which two closely related species live in the same geographical area but reproduce at different times is (a) temporal isolation (b) behavioral isolation (c) mechanical isolation (d) gametic isolation (e) hybrid inviability

5. Interspecific hybrids, if they survive, are (a) always sterile (b) always fertile (c) usually sterile (d) usually fertile (e) never sterile

6. Which of the following evolutionary patterns is/are responsible for an increase in species diversity? (a) anagenesis (b) cladogenesis (c) prezygotic barriers (d) postzygotic barriers (e) hybrid zones

7. The first step leading to allopatric speciation is (a) hybrid inviability (b) hybrid breakdown (c) adaptive radiation (d) geographical isolation (e) paedomorphosis

8. The pupfish in the Death Valley region are an example of which evolutionary process? (a) background extinction (b) allopatric speciation (c) sympatric speciation (d) allopolyploidy (e) paedomorphosis

9. Sympatric speciation (a) is most common in animals (b) does not require geographical isolation (c) accounts for the evolution of the Hawaiian nene (d) involves the accumulation of gradual genetic changes (e) usually takes millions of years

10. Which of the following evolutionary processes is associated with allopolyploidy? (a) gradualism (b) allometric growth (c) sympatric speciation (d) mass extinction (e) preadaptation

11. According to the punctuated equilibrium model (a) populations slowly diverge from one another (b) the evolution of species occurs in spurts interspersed with long periods of stasis (c) evolutionary novelties originate from preadaptations (d) reproductive isolating mechanisms restrict gene flow between species (e) the fossil record, being incomplete, does not accurately reflect evolution as it actually occurred

12. The evolutionary conversion of reptilian scales into a bird's feathers is an example of (a) allometric growth (b) paedomorphosis (c) gradualism (d) hybrid breakdown (e) preadaptation

13. Adaptive radiation is common following a period of mass extinction, probably because (a) the survivors of a mass extinction are remarkably well adapted to their environment (b) the unchanging environment following a mass extinction drives the evolutionary process (c) many adaptive zones are empty (d) many ecological niches are filled (e) the environment induces changes in the timing of development for many species

14. Adaptive radiations do not appear to have ever occurred (a) on isolated islands (b) in birds such as honeycreepers (c) in environments colonized by few species (d) in plants such as silverswords (e) in environments with many existing species

15. The Hawaiian silverswords are an excellent example of which evolutionary process? (a) allometry (b) anagenesis (c) microevolution (d) adaptive radiation (e) extinction

1. Compare the biological species concept with the morphological species concept.

2. Give an example of each of the following: (a) temporal isolation; (b) habitat isolation; (c) behavioral isolation; (d) mechanical isolation; (e) gametic isolation.

3. Describe the three types of postzygotic barriers and give an example of each.

4. Identify at least five geographical barriers that might lead to allopatric speciation.

5. Explain how hybridization and polyploidy can cause a new plant species to form in as little as one generation.

6. If you were in a debate and had to support the gradualism model, what would you say? How would you support the punctuated equilibrium model? Are these two ideas mutually exclusive?

7. Why are evolutionary novelties a concern of scientists studying macroevolution?

8. Give an example of each of the following: (a) preadaptation; (b) allometric growth; (c) paedomorphosis.

9. What roles do extinction and adaptive radiation play in macroevolution?

1. Why is allopatric speciation more likely to occur if the original isolated population is small?

2. Using the definition of the biological species concept given in the chapter introduction, is the Porto Santo rabbit an example of a speciation event that occurred in historical times, or is it an example of speciation in progress? Explain your answer.

3. Based on what you have learned about prezygotic and postzygotic isolating mechanisms, which reproductive isolating mechanism(s) would you say is/are probably at work between the Porto Santo rabbit and its mainland relative?

4. Based on what you have learned in the chapter, hypothesize what the common ancestor of the more than 20 species of desert pupfish may have looked like. (*Hint:* The ancestral species lived in one or more large lakes.) How could you test your hypothesis?

5. Could hawthorn and apple maggot flies be considered an example of assortative mating (discussed in Chapter 18)? Explain your answer.

6. Since mass extinction is a natural process that may facilitate evolution during the period of thousands to millions of years that follow it, should humans be concerned about the current mass extinctions that we are causing? Why or why not?

RECOMMENDED READINGS

Barlow, G.W. *The Cichlid Fishes: Nature's Grand Experiment in Evolution.* Perseus Publishing, Cambridge, MA, 2000. Examines the numerous specialized adaptations of cichlids and the many unanswered questions about cichlid behavior and evolution.

Boake, C.R.B. "Flying Apart: Mating Behavior and Speciation." *BioScience,* Vol. 50, No. 6, Jun. 2000. Discusses research on speciation as it relates to behavioral isolation in Hawaiian fruit flies. The author focuses on four fruit fly species, each endemic to a single island, although all four species live and mate in comparable habitats on their respective islands.

Eldredge, N. *Reinventing Darwin: The Great Debate at the High Table of Evolutionary Theory.* Wiley, New York, 1995. A lively, if partisan, survey of the intense debate in evolutionary theory stimulated by punctuated equilibrium and other ideas. (Recall that Niles Eldredge was one of the first to advance the punctuated equilibrium model.)

Hoffman, A.A., and M.J. Hercus. "Environmental Stress as an Evolutionary Force." *BioScience,* Vol. 50, No. 3, Mar. 2000. Examines what is known about how stressful environmental conditions affect evolutionary change.

Mayr, E. *Animal Species and Evolution.* Harvard University Press, Cambridge, 1963. This classic on animal evolution was written by the biologist who introduced the biological species concept and is a strong proponent of the allopatric speciation model.

Milius, S. "Superstud Grass Menaces San Francisco Bay." *Science News,* Vol. 154, 14 Nov. 1998. An introduced species of cordgrass threatens a native species with hybridization.

Milner, R. "Ernst Mayr at 93." *Natural History,* May 1997. An interview with one of the 20th century's greatest biologists.

Morell, V. "Earth's Unbounded Beetlemania Explained." *Science,* Vol. 281, 24 Jul. 1998. Describes research that seeks to explain why beetles had such an explosive adaptive radiation. (There are about 330,000 species of beetles.)

Stiassny, M.L.J., and A. Meyer. "Cichlids of the Rift Lakes." *Scientific American,* Vol. 280, No. 2, Feb. 1999. Beautiful illustrations accompany this fascinating account of the diversity in cichlids.

Turner, G. "Small Fry Go Big Time." *New Scientist,* 2 Aug. 1997. An overview of the evolution of cichlid species in Lake Victoria and other African great lakes.

Wright, K. "Pupfish in Peril." *Discover,* Jul. 1999. Pupfish species, a wonderful example of allopatric speciation, are increasingly threatened by human activities such as agriculture and mining. These activities pump groundwater from the aquifer that supplies the desert pools in which pupfish live.

- Visit our Web site at **http://www.info.brookscole.com/solomonbergmartin** for links to chapter-related resources on the World Wide Web. Additional on-line materials relating to this chapter can also be found on our Web site.

See chapter activity on BioActive Learner CD for additional help in mastering the chapter's material. Icon location in the chapter's margins shows which topics have tutorials or simulations in the CD.

20

The Origin and Evolutionary History of Life

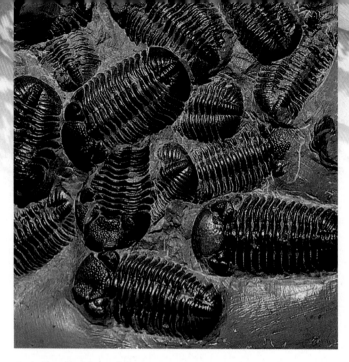

Fossil trilobites (*Phacops rana*). These extinct arthropods, which were about 3 cm (1.2 in) long, flourished in the ocean during the Paleozoic era. They ranged from 1 mm to 1 m in length, depending on the species. Note the large, well-developed eyes (visible on either side of the head region). *(William E. Ferguson)*

LEARNING OBJECTIVES

After you have studied this chapter you should be able to

1. Describe the conditions thought to have existed on early Earth.
2. Contrast the prebiotic broth hypothesis and the iron-sulfur world hypothesis.
3. Outline the major steps hypothesized to have occurred in the origin of cells.
4. Explain how the evolution of photosynthetic autotrophs affected both the atmosphere and other organisms.
5. Describe the endosymbiont theory and summarize the evidence supporting it.
6. List the geological eras in chronological order and give approximate dates for each.
7. Briefly describe the distinguishing organisms and major biological events of Precambrian time and of the Paleozoic, Mesozoic, and Cenozoic eras.

The preceding three chapters were concerned with the evolution of organisms, but we have not yet dealt with what many regard as a fundamental question of biological evolution: How did life begin? Although biologists generally accept the hypothesis that life developed from nonliving matter, exactly how this process, called **chemical evolution,** occurred is not certain. Chemical evolution probably involved several stages. Current models suggest that small organic molecules first formed spontaneously and accumulated over time. These molecules may have been able to accumulate rather than being broken down (as occurs today) because conditions were different. The two factors presently responsible for breaking down organic molecules—free oxygen and living organisms—were absent from early Earth.

Large organic macromolecules such as proteins and nucleic acids could have then assembled from the smaller molecules. The macromolecules interacted with one another, combining into more complicated structures that could eventually metabolize and replicate. Natural selection favored macromolecular assemblages with cell-like structures. Their descendants eventually became the first true cells. After the first cells originated, they diverged over several billion years into the rich biological diversity that characterizes our planet today. Photosynthesis, aerobic respiration, and eukaryotic cell structure represent several major advances that evolved during the history of life.

Geological evidence, in particular the fossil record, provides us with much of what is known about the history of life, such as what kinds of organisms existed and where and when they lived. Certain organisms appear in the fossil record, then disappear and are replaced by others. Initially, unicellular prokaryotes predominated, followed by unicellular eukaryotes. The first multicellular eukaryotes—soft-bodied animals that did not leave many fossils—appeared in the ocean approximately 630 million years ago (mya). Shelled animals and many other marine invertebrates (animals without backbones) appeared next, as exemplified by trilobites *(see photograph),* members of a large group of primitive aquatic arthropods. Marine invertebrates were followed by the first vertebrates. The first fishes with jaws appeared and diversified; some of these gave rise to amphibians, which also spread and diversified. About 300 mya, amphibians gave rise to reptiles, which diversified and populated the land. Reptiles in turn gave rise independently to birds and to mammals. Plants underwent a comparable evolutionary history and diversification.

In this chapter we survey life over a vast span of time, starting some 3.8 billion years ago (bya) when our planet was relatively young. We examine proposed models about how life began and trace life's long evolutionary history from its beginnings to the present.

EARLY EARTH PROVIDED THE CONDITIONS FOR CHEMICAL EVOLUTION

Many biologists speculate that life originated only once and that life's beginnings occurred under environmental conditions quite different from those of today. We must therefore examine the conditions of early Earth to understand the origin of life. Although we will never be certain about the exact conditions that existed when life arose, scientific evidence from a number of sources provides us with valuable clues that help us formulate plausible scenarios. Study of the origin of life is an active area of scientific research today, and many important contributions are adding to our understanding of how life began.

Astrophysicists and geologists have determined that Earth is approximately 4.6 billion years old. The atmosphere of early Earth apparently included carbon dioxide (CO_2), water vapor (H_2O), carbon monoxide (CO), hydrogen (H_2), and nitrogen (N_2). It may also have contained some ammonia (NH_3), hydrogen sulfide (H_2S), and methane (CH_4), although these reduced molecules may have been rapidly broken down by ultraviolet radiation from the sun. The early atmosphere probably contained little or no free oxygen (O_2).

Four requirements must have existed for the chemical evolution of life: little or no free oxygen, a source of energy, the availability of chemical building blocks, and time. First, life could have begun only in the absence of free oxygen. Oxygen is quite reactive and would have oxidized the organic molecules that are necessary building blocks in the origin of life. Earth's early atmosphere was probably strongly reducing, which means that any free oxygen would have reacted with other elements to form oxides. Thus, oxygen would have been tied up in compounds.

The origin of life would also have required energy to do the work of building biological molecules from simple inorganic chemicals. Early Earth was a place of high energy with violent thunderstorms; widespread volcanic activity; bombardment from meteorites and other extraterrestrial objects; and intense radiation, including ultraviolet radiation from the sun (Fig. 20–1). The young sun probably produced more ultraviolet radiation than it does today, and ancient Earth had no protective ozone layer to filter it.

A third requirement would have been the presence of the chemical building blocks needed for chemical evolution. These included water, dissolved inorganic minerals (present as ions), and the gases present in the early atmosphere. A final requirement for the origin of life was time for molecules to accumulate and react with one another. Earth is approximately 4.6 billion years old, and the earliest traces of life are approximately 3.8 billion years old; therefore, life had a maximum of 800 million years to get started.

Process of Science | Organic molecules formed on primitive Earth

Because organic molecules are the building materials for organisms, it is reasonable to first consider how they might have originated. There are two main models that try to explain how the organic precursors of life originated: The **prebiotic broth hypothesis** proposes that these molecules formed near Earth's surface, whereas the **iron-sulfur world hypothesis** proposes that organic precursors formed at cracks in the ocean's floor.

■ **Figure 20–1 An artist's interpretation of conditions on early Earth.** The strongly reducing atmosphere lacked oxygen; volcanoes erupted, spewing gases that contributed to the atmosphere; and violent thunderstorms produced torrential rainfall that eroded the land. Meteorites and other extraterrestrial objects continually bombarded Earth, causing cataclysmic changes in the crust, ocean, and atmosphere. *(Courtesy of Reader's Digest Books. Drawing by H.K. Wimmer)*

The prebiotic broth hypothesis suggests that organic molecules were produced at Earth's surface

The concept that simple organic molecules such as sugars, nucleotide bases, and amino acids could form spontaneously from simpler raw materials was first advanced in the 1920s by two scientists working independently: A.I. Oparin, a Russian biochemist, and J.B.S. Haldane, a Scottish physiologist and geneticist.

Their hypothesis was tested in the 1950s by American biochemists Stanley Miller and Harold Urey, who designed a closed apparatus that simulated conditions that presumably existed on early Earth (Fig. 20–2). They exposed an atmosphere rich in H_2, CH_4, H_2O, and NH_3 to an electrical discharge that simulated lightning. Their analysis of the chemicals produced in a week revealed that amino acids and other organic molecules had formed. Although more recent data suggest that Earth's early atmosphere was not rich in methane or ammonia, similar experiments using different combinations of gases have produced a wide variety of organic molecules that are important in contemporary organisms. These include all 20 amino acids, several sugars, lipids, the nucleotide bases of RNA and DNA, and ATP (when phosphate is present). Thus, before life began, its chemical building blocks may have been accumulating as a necessary step in chemical evolution.

Oparin envisioned that the organic molecules would, over vast spans of time, accumulate in the shallow seas to form a "sea of organic soup." Under such conditions, he envisioned smaller organic molecules (monomers) combining to form larger ones (polymers). Evidence gathered since Oparin's time indicates that organic polymers may have formed and accumulated on rock or clay surfaces rather than in the primordial seas. Clay, which consists of microscopic particles of weathered rock, is particularly intriguing as a possible site for early polymerizations because it binds organic monomers and contains zinc and iron ions that might have served as catalysts. Laboratory experiments have confirmed that organic polymers form spontaneously from monomers on hot rock or clay surfaces.

The iron-sulfur world hypothesis suggests that organic molecules were produced at hydrothermal vents

In a different scenario of chemical evolution, some biologists have hypothesized that early polymerizations leading to the origin of life may have occurred in cracks in the deep ocean floor where hot water, carbon monoxide, and minerals such as iron and nickel sulfides spew forth. Such **hydrothermal vents** would have been better protected than Earth's surface from the catastrophic effects of meteorite bombardment.

Today these hot springs produce precursors of biological molecules and of energy-rich "food," including hydrogen sulfide and methane. These chemicals support a diverse community of microorganisms, clams, crabs, tube worms, and other animals (see *Focus On: Life Without the Sun* in Chapter 53).

Testing the iron-sulfur world hypothesis at hydrothermal vents is difficult, but laboratory experiments simulating the high pressures and temperatures at the vents have yielded intriguing results. For example, experiments have demonstrated that ammonia, one of the precursors of proteins and nucleic acids, is produced in abundance, suggesting that vents may have been ammonia-rich environments in the prebiotic world.

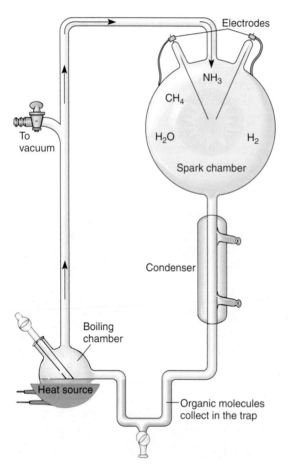

■ Figure 20–2 Testing the prebiotic broth hypothesis. Diagram of the apparatus that Miller and Urey used to simulate the reducing atmosphere of early Earth. An electrical spark was produced in the upper right flask to simulate lightning. The gases present in the flask reacted together, forming a variety of simple organic compounds that accumulated in the trap at the bottom.

■ THE FIRST CELLS PROBABLY ASSEMBLED FROM ORGANIC MOLECULES

After the first polymers formed, could they have assembled spontaneously into more complex structures? Scientists have synthesized several different **protobionts,** which are assemblages of abiotically produced (i.e., not produced by organisms) organic polymers. They have been able to recover protobionts that resemble living cells in several ways, thus providing clues as to how aggregations of complex nonliving molecules took that "giant leap" and became living cells. These protobionts exhibit many functional and structural attributes of living cells. They often divide in half (binary fission) after they have sufficiently "grown." Protobionts maintain an internal chemical environment that is different from the external environment (homeostasis), and some of them show the beginnings of metabolism (catalytic activity). They are highly organized, considering their relatively simple composition.

Microspheres are a type of protobiont formed by adding water to abiotically formed polypeptides (Fig. 20–3). Some microspheres demonstrate excitability: They produce an electrical potential across their surfaces, reminiscent of electrochemical gradients in cells. Microspheres can also absorb materials from their surroundings (selective permeability) and respond to changes in osmotic pressure as though they were enveloped by membranes, even though they contain no lipid.

The study of protobionts allows us to appreciate that relatively simple "pre-cells" can exhibit some of the properties of contemporary life. However, it is a major step (or several steps) to go from simple molecular aggregates such as protobionts to living cells. Although much has been learned about how organic molecules may have formed on primitive Earth, the problem of how pre-cells evolved into living cells remains to be solved.

It is not known exactly when life first appeared on Earth. **Microfossils** (ancient remains of microscopic life) indicate that cells were thriving 3.5 bya, and nonfossil evidence—isotopic "fingerprints" of carbon from living organisms—indicates that life existed even earlier, perhaps 3.8 bya.

The earliest cells were prokaryotic. Australian and South African rocks have yielded microscopic fossils of prokaryotic cells 3.1 to 3.5 billion years old. **Stromatolites,** another type of fossil evidence of the earliest cells, are rocklike columns composed of

(a)

(b)

■ **Figure 20–4 Stromatolites. (a)** Living stromatolites at Hamlin Pool in Western Australia, which are composed of mats of cyanobacteria and minerals such as calcium carbonate, are several thousand years old. **(b)** Cutaway view of a fossil stromatolite showing the layers of cyanobacteria and sediments that accumulated over time. This stromatolite, also from Western Australia, is about 3.5 billion years old. Such ancient stromatolites were much more common than living stromatolites today. *(a, Fred Bavendam/Peter Arnold, Inc.; b, Biological Photo Service)*

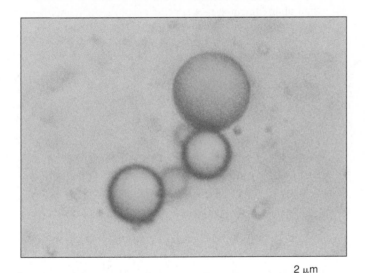

2 µm

■ **Figure 20–3 Microspheres.** These tiny protobionts exhibit some of the properties of life. *(Steven Brooke and Richard LeDuc)*

many minute layers of prokaryotic cells, usually cyanobacteria (Fig. 20–4). Over time, sediment collects around the cells and mineralizes. Meanwhile, a new layer of living cells grows over the older, dead cells. Fossil stromatolite reefs are found in a number of places in the world, including Great Slave Lake in Canada and the Gunflint Iron Formations along Lake Superior in the United States. Some fossil stromatolites are extremely ancient. One group in Western Australia, for example, is several billion years old. Living stromatolite reefs are still found in hot springs and in warm, shallow pools of fresh and salt water.

We have said that the origin of cells from macromolecular assemblages was a major step in the origin of life. Actually, the evolution of cells probably occurred in a series of small steps. One of the most significant parts of that process would have been the evolution of molecular reproduction.

Molecular reproduction was a crucial step in the origin of cells

In living cells, genetic information is stored in the nucleic acid DNA, which is transcribed into messenger RNA (mRNA), which in turn is translated into the proper amino acid sequence in proteins. All three macromolecules in the DNA → RNA → protein sequence contain precise information, but only DNA and RNA are capable of self-replication, although only in the presence of the proper enzymes. Because both RNA and DNA can form spontaneously on clay in much the same way that other organic polymers do, the question becomes which molecule, DNA or RNA, first appeared in the prebiotic world.

Some scientists have suggested that RNA was the first informational molecule to evolve in the progression toward a self-sustaining, self-reproducing cell and that proteins and DNA came along later. According to a model known as the **RNA world,** the chemistry of prebiotic Earth gave rise to self-replicating RNA molecules that functioned as both enzymes and substrates for their own replication. We represent the replication of RNA in the RNA world scenario as a circular arrow:

 RNA

One of the features of RNA is that it often has catalytic properties; such enzymatic RNAs are called **ribozymes.** In contemporary cells, ribozymes help catalyze the synthesis of RNA and process precursors into rRNA, tRNA, and mRNA (see Chapter 12). Before the evolution of true cells, ribozymes may have catalyzed their own replication in the clays, shallow rock pools, or hydrothermal vents where life originated. When RNA strands are added to a test tube containing RNA nucleotides but no enzymes, the nucleotides combine to form short RNA molecules. The rate of this reaction is increased if zinc is added as a catalyst. (Recall that zinc is bound to clay.)

The occurrence of an RNA world early in the history of life can never be proven, but experiments with **in vitro evolution,** also called **directed evolution,** have shown that it is feasible. These experiments address an important question about the RNA world, namely, could RNA molecules have catalyzed the many different chemical reactions needed for life? In directed evolution, a large pool of RNA molecules with different sequences are mixed together and selected for their ability to catalyze a single biologically important reaction (Fig. 20–5). Those molecules that have at least some catalytic ability are then amplified and mutated before being exposed to another round of selection. After this cycle is repeated several times, the RNA molecules at the end of the selection process are able to function efficiently as catalysts for the reaction. In vitro evolution studies have shown that RNA has a large functional repertoire—that is, RNA can catalyze a variety of biologically important reactions.

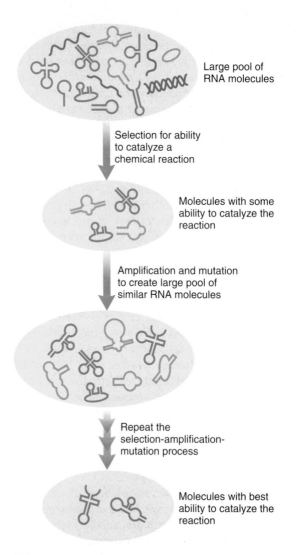

Large pool of RNA molecules

Selection for ability to catalyze a chemical reaction

Molecules with some ability to catalyze the reaction

Amplification and mutation to create large pool of similar RNA molecules

Repeat the selection-amplification-mutation process

Molecules with best ability to catalyze the reaction

Figure 20–5 In vitro evolution of RNA molecules. RNA molecules are selected from a large pool based on their ability to catalyze a specific reaction, then amplified and mutated before undergoing 7 to 20 additional repetitions of the same process. The final group of RNA molecules is the most efficient at catalyzing the chemical reaction that was selected for. More than two dozen synthetic RNA catalysts have been developed by in vitro evolution.

In the RNA world, ribozymes (catalytic RNAs) initially catalyzed protein synthesis and other important biological reactions; only later did protein enzymes catalyze these reactions.

RNA → protein

Interestingly, RNA can direct protein synthesis by catalyzing peptide bond formation. Some single-stranded RNA molecules fold back on themselves as a result of interactions among the nucleotides composing the RNA strand. Sometimes the conformation (shape) of the folded RNA molecule is such that it weakly binds to an amino acid. If amino acids are held close together by RNA molecules, they may bond together, forming a polypeptide.

We have considered how the evolution of informational molecules may have given rise to RNA and later to proteins. If a self-replicating RNA capable of coding for proteins appeared before DNA, how did DNA, the universal molecule of heredity in cells, become involved? Perhaps RNA made double-stranded copies of itself that eventually evolved into DNA.

$$DNA \leftarrow RNA \rightarrow protein$$

The incorporation of DNA into the information transfer system would have been advantageous because the double-helix conformation of DNA is more stable (i.e., less reactive) than the single-stranded conformation of RNA. Such stability in a molecule that stores genetic information would have provided a decided advantage in the prebiotic world (as it does today).

In the DNA/RNA/protein world, then, DNA became the information storage molecule, RNA remained involved in protein synthesis, and protein enzymes catalyzed most cellular reactions, including DNA replication, RNA synthesis, and protein synthesis.

$$DNA \rightarrow RNA \rightarrow protein$$

RNA is still a necessary component of the information transfer system because DNA is not catalytic. Thus natural selection at the molecular level favored the DNA → RNA → protein information sequence. Once DNA was incorporated into this sequence, RNA molecules assumed their present role as an intermediary in the transfer of genetic information.

Several additional steps had to occur before a true living cell could evolve from macromolecular aggregations. For example, the genetic code must have arisen extremely early in the prebiotic world because all organisms possess it, but how did it originate? Also, how did a plasma membrane of lipid and protein come to envelop the pre-cell assemblages, thereby permitting the accumulation of some molecules and the exclusion of others?

The first cells were probably heterotrophs, not autotrophs

The earliest cells probably obtained the organic molecules they needed from the environment, rather than synthesizing them. These primitive **heterotrophs** probably consumed many types of organic molecules that had spontaneously formed—sugars, nucleotides, and amino acids, to name a few. By fermenting these organic compounds, they obtained the energy needed to support life. Fermentation is, of course, an anaerobic process (i.e., performed in the absence of oxygen), and the first cells were almost certainly **anaerobes.**

When the supply of spontaneously generated organic molecules was gradually depleted, only certain organisms could survive. Mutations had probably already occurred that permitted some cells to obtain energy directly from sunlight, perhaps by using sunlight to make ATP. These cells, which did not require the energy-rich organic compounds that were now in short supply in the environment, had a distinct selective advantage.

Photosynthesis requires not only light energy but also a source of electrons, which are used to reduce CO_2 when organic molecules such as glucose are synthesized (see Chapter 8). Most likely, the first photosynthetic **autotrophs** (organisms that produce their own food from simple raw materials) used the energy of sunlight to split hydrogen-rich molecules such as H_2S, releasing elemental sulfur (not oxygen) in the process. Indeed, the green sulfur bacteria and the purple sulfur bacteria still use H_2S as a hydrogen source for photosynthesis.[1]

The first photosynthetic autotrophs to obtain hydrogen by splitting water were the cyanobacteria. Water was quite abundant on early Earth, as it is today, and the selective advantage that splitting water bestowed on them allowed cyanobacteria to thrive. In the process of splitting water, oxygen was released as a gas (O_2). Initially, the oxygen released from photosynthesis oxidized minerals in the ocean and in Earth's crust, and oxygen did not begin to accumulate in the atmosphere for a long time. Eventually, however, oxygen levels increased in the ocean and the atmosphere.

The timing of the events just described can be estimated on the basis of geological and fossil evidence. Fossils from that period, which include rocks that contain traces of chlorophyll, as well as the fossil stromatolites discussed previously, indicate that the first photosynthetic organisms appeared approximately 3.1 to 3.5 bya. This evidence suggests that heterotrophic forms existed even earlier.

Aerobes appeared after oxygen increased in the atmosphere

By 2 bya, cyanobacteria had produced sufficient oxygen to begin significantly changing the composition of the atmosphere. The increase in atmospheric oxygen had a profound effect on life. Obligate anaerobes (those organisms that cannot use oxygen for cellular respiration) were poisoned by the oxygen, and many species undoubtedly perished. Some anaerobes, however, survived in environments where oxygen does not penetrate; others evolved adaptations to neutralize the oxygen so that it could not harm them. Some organisms, called **aerobes,** evolved a respiratory pathway that used the oxygen to extract more energy from food and convert it to ATP energy. Aerobic respiration was joined to the existing anaerobic process of glycolysis.

The evolution of organisms that could use oxygen in their metabolism had several consequences. Organisms that respire aerobically gain much more energy from a single molecule of glucose than anaerobes gain by fermentation. As a result, the newly evolved aerobic organisms were more efficient and more competitive than anaerobes. Coupled with the poisonous nature of oxygen to anaerobes, the efficiency of aerobes forced anaerobes into relatively minor roles. Today the vast majority of organisms, including plants, animals, and most fungi, protists, and prokaryotes, use aerobic respiration, whereas only a few bacteria and even fewer protists and fungi are anaerobic.

The evolution of aerobic respiration had a stabilizing effect on both oxygen and carbon dioxide levels in the biosphere.

[1]Members of a third group of bacteria, the purple nonsulfur bacteria, use other organic molecules or hydrogen gas as a hydrogen source.

Photosynthetic organisms used carbon dioxide as a source of carbon for the synthesis of organic compounds. This raw material would have been depleted from the atmosphere in a relatively brief period without the advent of aerobic respiration, which releases carbon dioxide as a waste product from the complete breakdown of organic molecules. Carbon thus started cycling in the biosphere, moving from the nonliving physical environment, to photosynthetic organisms, to heterotrophs that ate the photosynthetic organisms (see Chapter 53). Carbon was released back into the physical environment as carbon dioxide by aerobic respiration, and the carbon cycle continued. In a similar manner, molecular oxygen was produced by photosynthesis and used during aerobic respiration.

Another significant consequence of photosynthesis occurred in the upper atmosphere, where molecular oxygen reacted to form **ozone,** O_3 (Fig. 20–6). A layer of ozone eventually blanketed Earth, preventing much of the sun's ultraviolet radiation from penetrating to the surface. With the ozone layer's protection from the mutagenic effect of ultraviolet radiation, organisms were able to live closer to the surface in aquatic environments and eventually to move onto land. Because the energy in ultraviolet radiation may have been necessary to form organic molecules, however, their abiotic synthesis decreased.

Eukaryotic cells descended from prokaryotic cells

Eukaryotes may have appeared in the fossil record as early as 1.5 to 1.6 bya, and geochemical evidence suggests that eukaryotes were present much earlier. In 1999 Australian geochemists reported steranes, molecules derived from steroids, in Australian rocks dated at 2.7 billion years. Because bacteria are not known to produce steroids, the steranes are thought to be biomarkers for eukaryotes. (These ancient rocks lack fossil traces of ancient organisms because they have since been exposed to heat and pressure that would have destroyed any fossilized cells. Steranes, however, are very stable in the presence of heat and pressure.)

Eukaryotes arose from prokaryotes. Recall from Chapter 4 that prokaryotic cells lack nuclear envelopes as well as other membranous organelles such as mitochondria and chloroplasts. The **endosymbiont theory,** advanced by Lynn Margulis, declares that organelles such as mitochondria and chloroplasts may each have originated from mutually advantageous symbiotic relationships between two prokaryotic organisms (Fig. 20–7). Chloroplasts apparently evolved from photosynthetic bacteria (cyanobacteria) that lived inside larger heterotrophic cells, while mitochondria presumably evolved from aerobic bacteria (perhaps purple bacteria) that lived inside larger anaerobic cells. Thus, early eukaryotic cells were composed of assemblages of formerly free-living prokaryotes.

How did these bacteria come to be **endosymbionts,** which are organisms that live symbiotically inside a host cell? They may have originally been ingested, but not digested, by a host cell. Once incorporated, they could have survived and reproduced along with the host cell so that future generations of the host also contained endosymbionts. The two organisms developed a mutualistic relationship in which each contributed something to the other. Eventually the endosymbiont lost the ability to exist outside its host, and the host cell lost the ability to survive without its endosymbionts. This theory stipulates that each of these partners brought to the relationship something the other lacked. For example, mitochondria provided the ability to carry out the aerobic respiration lacking in the original anaerobic host cell. Chloroplasts provided the ability to use a simple carbon source (carbon dioxide) to produce needed organic molecules. The host cell provided a safe habitat and raw materials or nutrients.

The principal evidence in favor of the endosymbiont theory is that mitochondria and chloroplasts possess some (although not all) of their own genetic material and translational components. They have their own DNA (as a circular molecule similar to that of prokaryotes; see Chapter 23) and their own ribosomes (which resemble prokaryotic rather than eukaryotic ribosomes). Mitochondria and chloroplasts also possess some of the machin-

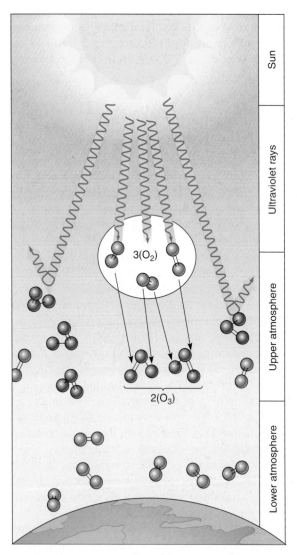

Sun

Ultraviolet rays

Upper atmosphere

Lower atmosphere

3(O_2)

2(O_3)

Figure 20–6 How ozone forms. Ozone (O_3) forms in the upper atmosphere when ultraviolet radiation from the sun breaks the double bonds of oxygen molecules.

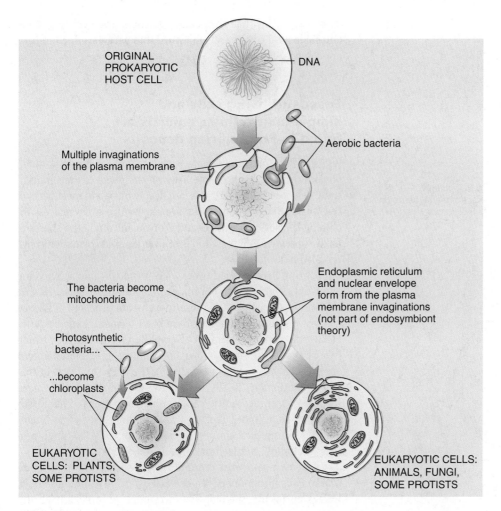

ORIGINAL PROKARYOTIC HOST CELL

DNA

Aerobic bacteria

Multiple invaginations of the plasma membrane

The bacteria become mitochondria

Endoplasmic reticulum and nuclear envelope form from the plasma membrane invaginations (not part of endosymbiont theory)

Photosynthetic bacteria...

...become chloroplasts

EUKARYOTIC CELLS: PLANTS, SOME PROTISTS

EUKARYOTIC CELLS: ANIMALS, FUNGI, SOME PROTISTS

■ **Figure 20–7 The endosymbiont theory.** Chloroplasts and mitochondria of eukaryotic cells are thought to have originated from various bacteria that lived as endosymbionts inside other cells.

ery for protein synthesis, including tRNA molecules, and are able to conduct protein synthesis on a limited scale independent of the nucleus. Furthermore, it is possible to poison mitochondria and chloroplasts with an antibiotic that affects prokaryotic but not eukaryotic cells. As discussed in Chapter 4, mitochondria and chloroplasts are enveloped by double membranes. The outer membrane apparently developed from the invagination of the host cell's plasma membrane, whereas the inner membrane is derived from the endosymbiont's plasma membrane. (The endosymbiont theory is discussed in greater detail in Chapter 24.)

Many endosymbiotic relationships exist today. For example, many corals have algae living as endosymbionts within their cells (see Fig. 52–12). In the gut of the termite lives a protozoon (*Myxotricha paradoxa*) that in turn has several different endosymbionts, including spirochete bacteria that are attached to the protozoon and function as whiplike flagella, allowing it to move.

The endosymbiont theory does not completely explain the evolution of eukaryotic cells from prokaryotes. It does not explain, for example, how the genetic material in the nucleus came to be surrounded by a double membranous envelope. A few biol-

ogists reject the endosymbiont theory and subscribe to the **autogenous model,** in which eukaryotes arose from prokaryotes by the proliferation of internal membranes to form cellular compartments; these internal membranes were derived from the prokaryotic plasma membrane. Regardless of how eukaryotic cells evolved, their advent set the stage for further evolutionary developments.

■ THE FOSSIL RECORD PROVIDES CLUES TO THE HISTORY OF LIFE

The sequence of biological, climate, and geological events that make up the history of life is recorded in rocks and fossils. The sediments of Earth's crust consist of five major rock strata (layers), each subdivided into minor strata, lying one on top of the other. Very few places on Earth are covered by all layers, but the strata that are present typically occur in the correct order, with younger rocks on top of older ones. These sheets of rock were formed by the accumulation of mud and sand at the bottoms of the ocean, seas, and lakes. Each layer contains certain

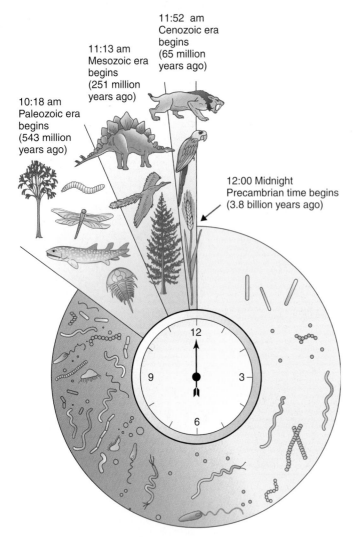

11:52 am
Cenozoic era
begins
(65 million
years ago)

11:13 am
Mesozoic era
begins
(251 million
years ago)

10:18 am
Paleozoic era
begins
(543 million
years ago)

12:00 Midnight
Precambrian time begins
(3.8 billion years ago)

Figure 20–8 An interpretive scale of biological time. Because it is difficult to interpret time in millions or billions of years, using a clock may help represent such vast spans of time. Life began 3.8 bya, at 12:00 midnight. More than 10 hours later, at 10:18 A.M., the Paleozoic era began. The beginning of the Mesozoic era, 251 mya, would be at 11:13 A.M. The Cenozoic era, which began 65 mya, would start at 11:52 A.M. The last epoch of the Cenozoic era, the Holocene epoch, began 10,000 years ago, which would be represented by the last 0.1 second before 12:00 noon. Representative life forms for each era are included.

characteristic fossils, known as **index fossils,** that serve to identify deposits made at approximately the same time in different parts of the world (see Chapter 17).

Geologists divide Earth's 4.6-billion-year history into units of time based on major geological, climate, and biological events. Relatively little is known about Earth from its beginnings approximately 4.6 bya up to 543 mya, a period known informally as **Precambrian time.** The fossil record of ancient organisms is abundant beginning about 543 mya. This most recent time, from 543 mya to the present, is divided into three **eras** based primar-

ily on organisms that were characteristic of each era (Fig. 20–8 and Table 20–1). Eras are subdivided into **periods,** which in turn are composed of **epochs.**

Fossils of living cells and simple multicellular animals are found in Precambrian deposits

Signs of Precambrian life date back to about 3.8 bya. Not much physical evidence is available because the rocks of Precambrian time, being extremely ancient, are deeply buried in most parts of the world. Precambrian rocks are exposed in a few places, including the bottom of the Grand Canyon and along the shores of Lake Superior. More than 400 Precambrian rock formations have revealed microfossils.

During Precambrian time, widespread volcanic activity and giant upheavals raised mountains, and the heat, pressure, and churning associated with these movements probably destroyed most of whatever fossils may have been formed. Some evidence of life still remains as traces of graphite or pure carbon, which may be the transformed remains of primitive life. These remains are especially abundant in what were the ocean and seas of that time. Additionally, fossils resembling cyanobacteria have been recovered from several Precambrian formations. The fossils found in later (more recent) Precambrian rocks show unambiguous examples of some major groups of bacteria, fungi, protists (including multicellular algae), and animals.

One rich source of Precambrian fossil deposits is the Ediacaran Hills (pronounced "ee-dee-ack'a-ran") in South Australia. **Ediacaran fossils,** the oldest known fossils of multicellular animals, are from very late in Precambrian time—from 600 to 543 mya. Biologists have not yet resolved the phylogenetic affinities of the simple, soft-bodied animals found there and at other late Precambrian sites around the world. The oldest, simplest Ediacaran fossils are from 600-million-year-old rocks in the Mackenzie Mountains of northwest Canada.

Some Ediacaran animals appear to be early examples of jellyfish, soft corals, segmented worms, mollusks, and soft-bodied arthropods, whereas others show no resemblance to any other known fossil or living organism (Fig. 20–9). If this interpretation is correct, then at least some of the Ediacaran animals were ancestral to animals that followed. Other biologists who have studied the fossils, however, think that the Ediacaran animals have a body plan that is different from all known animal phyla. If this interpretation is correct, then these animals probably went extinct by the end of the Precambrian and would not be directly related to modern animals.

A considerable diversity of organisms evolved during the Paleozoic era

The **Paleozoic era** began approximately 543 mya and lasted approximately 192 million years. It is divided into six periods: Cambrian, Ordovician, Silurian, Devonian, Carboniferous, and Permian.

TABLE 20-1   Some Important Biological Events in Geological Time

Time*	Era	Period	Epoch	Geological/Climatic Conditions	Plants and Microorganisms	Animals
0.01	Cenozoic	Quaternary	Holocene	End of last Ice Age; warmer climate; higher sea levels as glaciers melt	Decline of some woody plants; rise of herbaceous plants	Age of *Homo sapiens*
2			Pleistocene	Multiple ice ages; glaciers in Northern Hemisphere	Extinction of some plant species	Extinction of many large mammals at end
5		Tertiary	Pliocene	Uplift and mountain-building; volcanoes; climate much cooler; North and South America join at Isthmus of Panama	Expansion of extensive grasslands and deserts; decline of forests	Many grazing mammals; large carnivorous mammals; first known human-like primates
24			Miocene	Mountains form; climate drier and cooler	Flowering plants continue to diversify	Great diversity of grazing mammals and songbirds
33			Oligocene	Rise of Alps and Himalayas; most land low; volcanic activity in Rockies; climate cool and dry	Spread of forests; flowering plant communities expand	Apes appear; present mammalian families are represented
55			Eocene	Climate warmer	Flowering plants dominant	Modern mammalian orders appear and diversify; modern bird orders appear
65			Paleocene	Continental seas disappear; climate mild to cool and wet	Semitropical vegetation (flowering plants and conifers) widespread	Primitive mammals diversify rapidly
144	Mesozoic	Cretaceous		Continents separate; most continents low; large inland seas and swamps; climate warm	Rise of flowering plants	Dinosaurs reach peak, then become extinct at end; toothed birds become extinct; primitive mammals
206		Jurassic		Continents low; inland seas; mountains form; continental drift begins; climate mild	Gymnosperms common	Large, specialized dinosaurs; first toothed birds; primitive insectivorous mammals diversify
251		Triassic		Many mountains form; widespread deserts; climate warm and dry	Gymnosperms dominant; ferns common	First dinosaurs; first mammals
290	Paleozoic	Permian		Glaciers; continents rise and merge as Pangaea; climate variable	Conifers diversify; cycads appear	Modern insects appear; mammal-like reptiles; extinction of many Paleozoic invertebrates and vertebrates at end of Permian
354		Carboniferous		Lands low and swampy; climate warm and humid, becoming cooler later	Forests of ferns, club mosses, horsetails, and gymnosperms; mosses and liverworts	First reptiles; spread of ancient amphibians; many insect forms; ancient sharks abundant
408		Devonian		Glaciers; inland seas	Vascular plants diversify and become well established; first forests; gymnosperms appear; bryophytes appear	Many trilobites; fishes with jaws appear and diversify; amphibians appear; wingless insects appear
439		Silurian		Most continents remain covered by seas; climate warm	Algae dominant in aquatic environments; vascular plants appear	Jawless fishes diversify; coral reefs common; terrestrial arthropods
495		Ordovician		Sea covers most continents	Marine algae dominant; fossil spores of terrestrial plants (bryophytes?)	Invertebrates dominant; coral reefs appear; first fishes appear
543		Cambrian		Oldest rocks with abundant fossils; lands low; climate mild and wet	Algae; bacteria and cyanobacteria; fungi	Age of marine invertebrates; modern and extinct animal phyla represented; first chordates

*Time from beginning of period to present (millions of years).

Figure 20–9 A Precambrian fossil (*Dickinsonia costata*). The organism, from the Ediacaran Hills of South Australia, lived in shallow marine waters and is unlike any known modern organism. The fossil is about 5 cm (2 in) long. *(William E. Ferguson)*

Rocks rich in fossils represent the oldest subdivision of the Paleozoic era, the Cambrian period. From about 565 mya to 525 mya, evolution was in such high gear, with the sudden appearance of many new animal groups, that this period has been nicknamed the **Cambrian explosion.** Fossils of all contemporary animal phyla are present, along with many bizarre, extinct phyla, in marine sediments. The sea floor was covered with sponges, corals, sea lilies, sea stars, snails, clamlike bivalves, primitive squidlike cephalopods, lamp shells (brachiopods), trilobites (see chapter opening photograph; also see Fig. 29–16). In addition, small vertebrates—cartilaginous fishes, first reported in 1999—became established in the marine environment. Scientists have not determined the factor or factors responsible for the Cambrian explosion, which has been unmatched in the evolutionary

history of life. There is some evidence that oxygen concentrations, which had continued to gradually increase in the atmosphere, passed some critical environmental threshold (10% of present-day oxygen, or higher) late in Precambrian time. Scientists who advocate the *oxygen enrichment hypothesis* note that until late in Precambrian time, Earth possessed insufficient oxygen to support larger animals. The most important fossil sites that document the Cambrian explosion are the **Chenjiang site** in China (for early Cambrian fossils) and the **Burgess Shale** in British Columbia (for middle Cambrian fossils; Fig. 20–10).

The major animal body plans, which are discussed in Chapter 28, were established so early in the history of the eukaryotes that no major change in body plan or basic structure has occurred since. This probably indicates that, early in the Cambrian period, each animal phylum had reached a degree of adaptation that allowed it to exploit its environment and accommodate changes in its surroundings with relatively limited modifications in its body plan.

According to geologists, the continents were gradually flooded during the Cambrian period. In the Ordovician period, much land was covered by shallow seas, in which there was another burst of evolutionary diversification, although not as dramatic as the Cambrian explosion. The Ordovician seas were inhabited by giant cephalopods, squidlike animals with straight shells 5 to 7 m (16 to 23 ft) long and 30 cm (12 in) in diameter. Coral reefs first appeared during this period, as did small, jawless, bony-armored fishes called *ostracoderms* (Fig. 20–11). Lacking jaws, these fishes typically had round or slitlike mouth openings that may have sucked in small food particles from the water or scooped up bottom organic debris. Ordovician deposits also contain fossil spores of terrestrial (land-dwelling) plants, which suggests that the colonization of land had begun.

During the Silurian period, jawless fishes diversified considerably, and jawed fishes first appeared. Definitive evidence of two life forms of great biological significance appeared in the Silurian period: terrestrial plants and air-breathing animals. The first

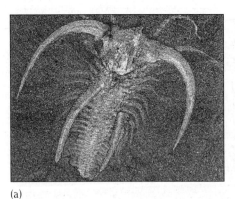

(a)

(b)

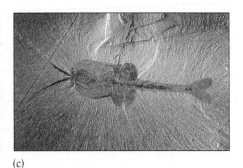

(c)

Figure 20–10 Fossils from the Cambrian explosion. **(a)** *Marrella splendens* was a small arthropod. **(b)** *Wiwaxia* was a bristle-covered marine worm that was distantly related to earthworms. It had scaly armor and needle-like spines for protection. **(c)** *Waptia fieldensis* was a crustacean that may have been an ancestor of modern crustaceans such as shrimp. All three of these fossils were discovered in the Burgess Shale in the Canadian Rockies of British Columbia. *(a–c, Chip Clark)*

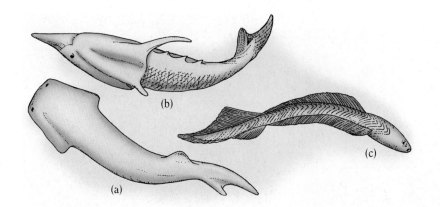

Figure 20–11 Representative ostracoderms. (a) *Thelodus*, (b) *Pterapsis*, and (c) *Jamoytius* are fossil ostracoderms, primitive jawless fishes that appeared in the Devonian period. Ostracoderms ranged from 10 to 50 cm (4 to 20 in) in length.

known plants resembled ferns in that they possessed vascular (conducting) tissue and reproduced by spores (see Chapter 26). The evolution of plants allowed animals to colonize the land because plants provided the first terrestrial animals with food and shelter. All air-breathing land animals discovered in Silurian rocks were arthropods—millipedes, spider-like arthropods, and possibly centipedes. From an ecological perspective, the energy flow from plants to animals probably occurred via detritus, which is organic debris from decomposing organisms, rather than directly from living plant material. Millipedes eat plant detritus today, and spiders and centipedes prey on millipedes and other animals.

A great variety of fishes appeared in the Devonian period. In fact, the Devonian period is frequently called the Age of Fishes. Jawless ostracoderms persisted into the Devonian, but this period also witnessed the explosive radiation of fishes with jaws, an adaptation that enables a vertebrate to chew and bite. Armored *placoderms,* an extinct group of jawed fishes, diversified to exploit varied lifestyles, from bottom-dwelling filter-feeders to the most voracious predators of the time (see Fig. 30–11*b*). Appearing in Devonian deposits are sharks and the two predominant types of bony fish: lobe-finned fishes (including the coelacanths and lungfishes) and ray-finned fishes, which gave rise to the major orders of modern fishes. Coelacanths, primitive bony fish with lobed fins, were originally thought to have become extinct; in 1938, however, the first living coelacanth was discovered in the deep waters off the coast of Madagascar (see Fig. 30–16). This discovery was of great scientific significance because it gave paleontologists an opportunity to test their hypotheses about fossil coelacanths by comparing them with the living species. Lungfishes, an ancient group of air-breathing fish, were most common during the Devonian period; only about six species persist today, in South America, Africa, and Australia.

Upper (more recent) Devonian sediments contain fossil remains of salamander-like amphibians (labyrinthodonts) that were often quite large, with short necks and heavy, muscular tails (see Fig. 30–17). These animals, whose skulls were encased in bony armor, were in many respects quite similar to the lobe-finned fishes, one of which may have been their immediate ancestor; for example, early amphibians possessed fishlike tail fins and scaly body coverings. Early amphibians probably spent most of their time in and around water. Wingless insects also originated in the late Devonian period.

The early vascular plants diversified during the Devonian period in a burst of evolution that rivaled that of animals during the Cambrian explosion. With the exception of flowering plants, all major plant groups appeared during the Devonian. Forests of ferns, club mosses, horsetails, and seed ferns (an extinct group of ancient plants that had fernlike foliage but reproduced by forming seeds) flourished.

The Carboniferous period is named for the great swamp forests whose remains persist today as major coal deposits. Much of the land during this time was covered with low swamps filled with horsetails, club mosses, ferns, seed ferns, and gymnosperms (seed-bearing plants such as conifers) (Fig. 20–12).

Amphibians, which underwent an **adaptive radiation** and exploited both aquatic and terrestrial ecosystems, were the dominant terrestrial carnivores of the Carboniferous period. Reptiles first appeared and diverged to form two major lines at this time. One line (sauropsids) consisted of mostly small and mid-sized, insectivorous (insect-eating) lizards; this line would later lead to lizards, snakes, crocodiles, dinosaurs, and birds. The other reptilian line (synapsids) led to a diverse group of Permian and early Mesozoic mammal-like reptiles. Two groups of winged insects, cockroaches and dragonflies, appeared in the Carboniferous period. The dragonflies ranged in size from those smaller than today's dragonflies to some with wingspans of 75 cm (2.5 ft).

Amphibians continued in importance during the Permian period, but they were no longer the dominant carnivores in terrestrial ecosystems. During the Permian period, the mammal-like reptiles diversified explosively and dominated both carnivorous and herbivorous terrestrial lifestyles. One important group of mammal-like reptiles, originating in the Permian and extending into the Mesozoic era, were the *therapsids,* a group that included the ancestor of mammals (discussed shortly; also see Fig. 30–23).

During the Permian period, seed plants diversified and dominated most plant communities. Cone-bearing conifers were widespread, and cycads (plants resembling palms, with crowns of fernlike leaves and large, seed-containing cones) and ginkgoes (trees with broad, fan-shaped leaves and exposed, fleshy seeds) appeared.

The greatest mass extinction of all time occurred at the end of the Paleozoic era, between the Permian and Triassic periods, 251 mya. More than 90% of all existing marine species became

KEY

1–13	club mosses
14–16	seed ferns
17–19	ferns
20–21	horsetails
22	early gymnosperm
23	primitive insect
24	early dragonfly
25, 26	early roaches

■ **Figure 20–12 Reconstruction of a Carboniferous forest.** Plants of this period included giant ferns, horsetails, and club mosses as well as seed ferns and early gymnosperms. *(No. GEO85638c, Field Museum of Natural History, Chicago)*

extinct at this time, as did more than 70% of the vertebrate genera living on land. There is also evidence of a major extinction of plants at this time. The Permian period was characterized by great changes in climate and topography. By the late Permian, the sea level had dropped, and the distribution of shallow seas on continental shelves shrank to less than one-third of their distribution during the early Permian. In the early Triassic, the sea level rose and shallow seas expanded again.

The cause of the late Permian mass extinction is controversial. Changes in sea level may account for the massive extinctions of marine invertebrates. The reduction of shallow seas also would have caused climate instability on land, perhaps triggering the extinction of terrestrial organisms observed at that time as well. Another hypothesis for the Permian-Triassic extinction episode is the occurrence of widespread oxygen depletion in the ocean, an event that is supported by geochemical evidence. Cataclysmic volcanic eruptions that occurred in Siberia over a period of 1 million years have also been linked to the late Permian mass extinction; these eruptions may have caused global cooling. Regardless of the cause of this mass extinction episode, evidence reported during the late 1990s and early 2000s suggests that the extinction occurred globally in a very compressed period, within a few hundred thousand years. This is extremely short in the geological time scale and suggests that some sort of catastrophic event caused the extinctions.

Dinosaurs and other reptiles dominated the Mesozoic era

The **Mesozoic era** began about 251 mya and lasted some 186 million years. It is divided into the Triassic, Jurassic, and Cretaceous periods. Fossil deposits from the Mesozoic era occur worldwide. Notable sites include the **Yixian formation** in northeast China, the Solnhofen Limestone in Germany, northwestern Patagonia in Argentina, the Sahara Desert in central Niger, the badlands in South Dakota, and other sites in western North America.

The outstanding feature of the Mesozoic era was the origin, differentiation, and ultimately the extinction of a large variety of reptiles. For this reason, the Mesozoic era is commonly called the Age of Reptiles. Most of the modern orders of insects appeared during the Mesozoic era. Snails and bivalves (clams and their relatives) increased in number and diversity, and sea urchins reached their peak diversity. From a botanical viewpoint, the Mesozoic era was dominated by gymnosperms until the mid-Cretaceous period, when the flowering plants first diversified.

During the Triassic period, reptiles underwent an adaptive radiation leading to many groups. On land, the dominant Triassic groups were the mammal-like therapsids, which ranged from small-sized insectivores to moderately large herbivores, and a diverse group of *thecodonts,* early "ruling reptiles," that were primarily carnivores (Fig. 20–13a). The thecodont group was ancestral to dinosaurs, flying reptiles, and birds.

In the ocean, several important marine reptile groups, the plesiosaurs and ichthyosaurs, appeared in the Triassic and persisted into the Cretaceous. *Plesiosaurs* were aquatic reptiles with bodies up to 15 m (about 49 ft) long and paddle-like fins (Fig. 20–13b). *Ichthyosaurs,* also aquatic reptiles, had body forms superficially resembling those of sharks or porpoises, with short necks, large dorsal fins, and shark-type tails (Fig. 20–13c). Ichthyosaurs had very large eyes, which may have enabled them to see when diving to depths of 500 m or more.

During the late Triassic period, many new reptiles and their descendants appeared. Turtles appeared more than 210 mya. Both marine and land turtles have survived to the present with few skeletal changes. The first mammals to appear in the Triassic period were small insectivores that evolved from the mammal-like therapsids of the Triassic. Mammals diversified into a variety of mostly small, nocturnal insectivores during the remainder of the Mesozoic, with marsupial and placental mammals appearing in the Cretaceous period. *Pterosaurs,* the first flying reptiles, appeared and underwent considerable diversification during the Mesozoic era (Fig. 20–13d). This group produced some quite spectacular forms, most notably the giant *Quetzalcoatlus,* known from fragmentary Cretaceous fossils in Texas to have a wingspan of 11 to 15 m (36 to 49 ft). In addition, the two main dinosaur lines (discussed later) were established by the end of the Triassic period.

During the Jurassic and Cretaceous periods, other important groups—such as crocodiles, lizards, snakes, and birds—appeared, and the dinosaurs diversified dramatically to "inherit the Earth." Crocodiles originated in the early Jurassic, probably from a thecodont ancestor. Lizards and snakes appeared in the late Jurassic and early Cretaceous periods, respectively. Most of the Mesozoic snakes and lizards were similar to their present-day descendants. One group of lizards, the *mosasaurs,* were large, voracious marine predators during the late Cretaceous period. The mosasaurs, which attained lengths of 10 m (33 ft) or more, did not survive to the present (Fig. 20–13e).

Dinosaurs underwent an impressive radiation throughout the Jurassic and Cretaceous periods. There were two main groups of dinosaurs: the *saurischians,* with pelvic bones similar to those of modern-day lizards, and the *ornithischians,* with pelvic bones similar to those of birds (Fig. 20–14). Some saurischians were fast, bipedal forms ranging from those the size of a dog to the ultimate representatives of this group, the gigantic carnivores of the Cretaceous period, *Tyrannosaurus, Giganotosaurus,* and *Carcharodontosaurus* (Figs. 20–13f and 20–15). Other saurischians were huge, quadrupedal dinosaurs that ate plants. Some of these were the largest terrestrial animals that have ever lived, including *Argentinosaurus,* with an estimated length of 30 m (98 ft) and an estimated weight of 72 to 90 metric tons (80 to 100 tons) (Fig. 20–13g). It is thought that *Argentinosaurus* and other plant-eating saurischians ate huge quantities of vegetation such as needles (leaves) from tall conifers.

The other group of dinosaurs, the ornithischians, was entirely herbivorous. Although some ornithischians were bipedal, most were quadrupedal. Some had no front teeth and possessed stout, horny, birdlike beaks. In some species these beaks were broad and ducklike, hence the common name, duck-billed dinosaurs (Fig. 20–13h). Other ornithischians had great armor plates, possibly as protection against carnivorous saurischians. *Ankylosaurus,* for example, had a broad, flat body covered with armor plates (actually bony scales embedded in the skin) and large, laterally projecting spikes (Fig. 20–13i).

Many traditional ideas about dinosaurs—that they were cold-blooded, slow-moving monsters living in swamps, for example—have been reconsidered over the last 30 years. Recent evidence suggests that at least some dinosaurs may have been warm-blooded, agile, and capable of moving extremely fast. Many dinosaurs appear to have had complex social behaviors, including courtship rituals and parental nurturing of their young. Some species lived in social groups and hunted in packs.

Birds appeared by the late Jurassic period, and most paleontologists think they evolved directly from theropod dinosaurs. A few paleontologists dispute this idea and think that birds evolved from more primitive reptiles. Excellent bird fossils, many showing the outlines of feathers, have been preserved from the Juras-

Figure 20–13 Representative animals of the Mesozoic era. Figures are not drawn to scale. **(a)** This Triassic thecodont, *Euparkia*, was about 150 cm (5 ft) long. Because its forelimbs are shorter than its hind limbs, *Euparkia* was probably bipedal. **(b)** *Elasmosaurus* was a long-necked plesiosaur. Other plesiosaurs had short necks and superficially resembled seals. Some plesiosaurs attained a length of 15 m (about 49 ft). **(c)** *Opthalmosaurus* was an ichthyosaur that superficially resembled a shark or porpoise. It was about 3.6 m (12 ft) long. Other ichthyosaurs were much larger; one ichthyosaur reported in 1996 may have been 45 m (146 ft) long.
(d) *Pteranodon* was a pterosaur from the Cretaceous period with a wingspan of 7 to 9.2 m (23–30 ft), depending on the species. Pterosaur wings were membranes of skin that were supported by an elongated fourth finger bone. Some pterosaurs had long tails, whereas others lacked tails. **(e)** *Tylosaurus* was a large (about 10 m [33 ft] long) marine lizard (a mosasaur).
(f) *Giganotosaurus*, whose fossil remains were discovered in Argentina, was the largest (more than 12 m [39 ft] in length) predatory saurischian. **(g)** *Argentinosaurus*, a herbivorous saurischian from Argentina, is the largest known animal to have ever walked on land. It was 35 to 40 m (115–130 ft) long. **(h)** *Hadrosaurus* was a duck-billed, plant-eating ornithischian. It was 7 to 10 m (23–33 ft) long and had hundreds of cheek teeth (its bill was toothless). **(i)** *Ankylosaurus* was a heavily armored ornithischian. Ankylosaurs ranged from 2 to 6 m (7–20 ft) in length.

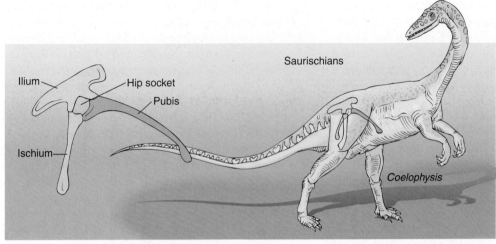

(a)

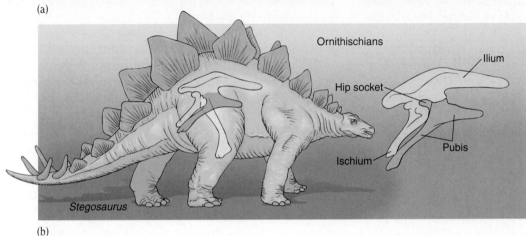

(b)

■ **Figure 20–14 Saurischian and ornithischian dinosaurs.** The two orders of dinosaurs are distinguished primarily by differences in their pelvic bones. (In each dinosaur figure, the pale yellow femur is shown relative to the pelvic bone.) **(a)** The saurischian pelvis. Note the opening (hip socket), a trait possessed by no quadrupedal vertebrates other than dinosaurs. **(b)** The ornithischian pelvis also has the hole in the hip socket but differs from the saurischian pelvis in that it has a backward-directed extension of the pubis.

sic period. *Archaeopteryx,* one of the oldest known birds, lived about 150 mya (see Fig. 30–21*b*). It was about the size of a pigeon and had rather feeble wings that it used to glide rather than actively fly. Although *Archaeopteryx* is considered a bird (witness the feathers), it had many reptilian features, including a mouthful of teeth and a long, bony tail.

Thousands of well-preserved bird fossils have been found in early Cretaceous deposits in China. These include *Sinornis,* a 135-million-year-old sparrow-sized bird capable of perching, and the magpie-sized *Confuciusornis,* the earliest known bird with a toothless beak. *Confuciusornis* may date back as far as 142 million years. The Chinese fossils from the Yixian formation document a variety of very primitive birds that possessed many reptilian features yet were clearly able to fly.

At the end of the Cretaceous period, 65 mya, dinosaurs, pterosaurs, and many other animals abruptly became extinct. Many gymnosperms, with the exception of conifers, also perished. Although several explanations for the mass extinction at

■ **Figure 20–15 Reconstruction of a skull of *Carcharodontosaurus.*** The fossil remains of this fearsome predator were discovered in North Africa. *(Paul Sereno. Reprinted with permission of* Discover*)*

the end of the Cretaceous period have been proposed, an increasing amount of evidence suggests that a catastrophic collision of a large extraterrestrial body with Earth resulted in dramatic climate changes. Part of the evidence is a small band of dark clay with a high concentration of iridium located between Mesozoic and Cenozoic sediments at more than 200 sites around the world. Iridium is rare on Earth but abundant in meteorites, leading many to conclude that Earth was hit by a large extraterrestrial object at that time. (The force of the impact would have driven the iridium into the atmosphere to be deposited later on the land by precipitation.) The Chicxulub crater, which is buried under the Yucatán Peninsula in Mexico, is the apparent site of the collision at the close of the Cretaceous period. The impact produced giant tsunamis (tidal waves) that deposited materials from the extraterrestrial body around the perimeter of the Gulf of Mexico, from Alabama to Guatemala. It may have caused worldwide forest fires and giant dust clouds that lowered temperatures for many years.

Although it is widely accepted that a collision with an extraterrestrial body occurred 65 mya, there is no consensus about the effects of such an impact on organisms. The extinction of many marine organisms at or immediately after the time of the impact was probably the result of the environmental upheaval produced by the collision. However, a number of clam species associated with the mass extinction at the end of the Cretaceous period appear to have become extinct *before* the impact, suggesting that some of the massive extinctions occurring then were caused by other factors.

The Cenozoic era is known as the Age of Mammals

With equal justice the **Cenozoic era** could be called the Age of Mammals, the Age of Birds, the Age of Insects, or the Age of Flowering Plants. This era is marked by the appearance of all these forms in great variety and numbers of species. The Cenozoic era extends from 65 mya to the present. It is subdivided into two periods: the Tertiary period, encompassing some 63 million years, and the Quaternary period, which covers the last 2 million years. The Tertiary period is subdivided into five epochs, named from earliest to latest: Paleocene, Eocene, Oligocene, Miocene, and Pliocene. The Quaternary period is subdivided into the Pleistocene and Holocene epochs.

Flowering plants, which arose during the Cretaceous period, continued to diversify during the Cenozoic era. During the Paleocene and Eocene epochs, fossils indicate that tropical to semitropical plant communities extended to relatively high latitudes. Palms, for example, are found in Eocene deposits in Wyoming. Later in the Cenozoic era, there is evidence of more open habitats. Grasslands and savannas occurred throughout much of North America during the Miocene epoch, with deserts developing later in the Pliocene and Pleistocene epochs. During the Pleistocene epoch, plant communities changed dynamically in response to fluctuating climates associated with the multiple advances and retreats of continental glaciers.

During the Eocene epoch, there was an explosive radiation of birds, which acquired specializations for many different habitats. The jaws and beak of the flightless giant bird *Diatryma,* for example, may have been adapted primarily for crushing and slicing vegetation in Eocene forests, marshes, and grasslands (Fig. 20–16). Other paleontologists argue that these giant birds were carnivores that killed or scavenged mammals and other vertebrates. The songbirds diversified extensively during the Miocene epoch to become the most diverse order of living birds.

During the Paleocene epoch, an explosive radiation of primitive mammals occurred. Most of these were small forest dwellers that are not closely related to modern mammals. During the Eocene epoch, mammals continued to diverge, and all the modern orders first appeared. Again, many of the mammals were small, but there were also some larger herbivores—the *titanotheres,* for example, which got progressively larger during the Eocene epoch (Fig. 20–17a).

During the Oligocene epoch, many modern families of mammals appeared, including the first fossil apes in Africa. A number of lineages showed specializations that suggest a more open type of habitat, such as grassland or savanna. For example, many mammals were larger and had longer legs for running, specialized teeth for chewing coarse vegetation or for preying on animals, and increases in their relative brain sizes. These specializations continued in the Miocene and Pliocene epochs. Es-

Figure 20–16 A representative bird from the Eocene epoch. *Diatryma,* a giant, flightless bird, stood 2.1 m (7 ft) tall and weighed about 175 kg (385 lb).

Figure 20–17 Representative North and South American mammals of the Cenozoic era. Figures are not drawn to scale. **(a)** *Brontotherium* was a titanothere from the late Eocene epoch. It was 2.5 m (8 ft) tall at the shoulder. **(b–f)** Mammals of the Pliocene and Pleistocene epochs. **(b)** The elephant-like mastodon *(Mammut)* was at home in forests, lakes, and rivers. *Mammut* was 2.5 m (8 ft) tall at the shoulder. **(c)** The saber-toothed cat *(Smilodon),* which had short, powerful legs and was about the size of the modern African lion, was found in both North and South America. Its enlarged canine teeth were approximately 18 cm (7 in) long and were curved like sabers. **(d)** This camel-like mammal *(Macrauchenia)* from South America probably browsed in forest clearings. *Macrauchenia,* which was about 3 m (10 ft) tall, is usually depicted with a short trunk because, like elephants, its nasal openings are on the skull roof rather than in the front of the skull. **(e)** *Megatherium* was a South American giant ground sloth. As long as 6 m (20 ft), *Megatherium* had 18-cm (7-in) claws that may have been used to strip bark from trees. Other paleontologists think *Megatherium* used its claws to stab prey. **(f)** The giant armadillo *(Glyptodon)* lived on the pampas of South America. Encased in bony armor, *Glyptodon* was about 2 m (6.5 ft) long. Later glyptodont species reached 4 m (13 ft).

pecially diverse during these epochs were hoofed mammals such as horses, which underwent an adaptive radiation to include both browsing and grazing lifestyles. Carnivores specialized for long-distance running after prey also appeared in the Pliocene epoch. (Before that, carnivores were primarily ambush predators.) Human ancestors are found during the Pliocene epoch, about 4.4 mya, in Africa; the genus *Homo* appeared approximately 2.3 mya. (Primate evolution, including human evolution, is discussed in Chapter 21.)

The Pliocene and Pleistocene epochs witnessed a spectacular North and South American large-mammal fauna, including mastodons, saber-toothed cats, camels, giant ground sloths, giant armadillos, and numerous other species (Fig. 20–17b–f). However, many of the large mammals became extinct at the end of the Pleistocene. This extinction may have been due to climate change—the Pleistocene epoch was marked by several ice ages—and/or the influence of humans, which had spread from Africa to Europe and Asia, and later to North and South America by crossing a land bridge between Siberia and Alaska. Strong archaeological evidence exists that this mass extinction event was concurrent with the appearance of human hunters that possessed Clovis spear-point technology.

SUMMARY WITH KEY TERMS

I. Biologists generally agree that life originated from nonliving matter by **chemical evolution.** Although chemical evolution is very difficult to test experimentally, hypotheses about the origin of life are testable.
  A. Four requirements for chemical evolution are
    1. The absence of oxygen, which would have reacted with and oxidized abiotically produced organic molecules.
    2. Energy to form organic molecules.
    3. Chemical building blocks, including water, minerals, and gases present in the atmosphere, to form organic molecules.
    4. Sufficient time for molecules to accumulate and react.
  B. Four steps are hypothesized in chemical evolution.
    1. Small organic molecules formed spontaneously and accumulated.
      a. The **prebiotic broth hypothesis** proposes that organic molecules formed near Earth's surface in a "sea of organic soup" or on rock or clay surfaces.
      b. The **iron-sulfur world hypothesis** suggests that organic molecules were produced at **hydrothermal vents,** cracks in the deep ocean floor.
    2. Macromolecules assembled from the small organic molecules.
    3. Macromolecular assemblages called **protobionts** formed from macromolecules.
      a. According to a model known as the **RNA world,** RNA was the first informational molecule to evolve in the progression toward a self-sustaining, self-reproducing cell.
      b. Natural selection at the molecular level resulted in the DNA → RNA → protein information sequence.
      c. Experiments with **in vitro evolution,** also called **directed evolution,** have demonstrated how RNA could have evolved to catalyze a variety of biologically important reactions.
    4. Cells arose from the macromolecular assemblages.
II. The oldest cells in the fossil record are 3.1 to 3.5 billion years old. Non-fossil evidence places earliest life at 3.8 billion years old.
  A. The first cells were prokaryotic **heterotrophs** that obtained organic molecules from the environment. They were almost certainly **anaerobes.**
  B. Later, **autotrophs,** organisms that produce their own organic molecules by photosynthesis, arose.
  C. The evolution of photosynthesis ultimately changed early life because it generated oxygen, which accumulated in the atmosphere, and permitted the evolution of **aerobes,** organisms that could use oxygen for a more efficient type of cellular respiration.
  D. Eukaryotic cells arose from prokaryotic cells. According to the **endosymbiont theory,** certain eukaryotic organelles (mitochondria and chloroplasts) evolved from prokaryotic **endosymbionts** within larger prokaryotic hosts.
III. Earth's history is divided into three **eras.** Each era is divided into **periods,** which are divided into **epochs.**
  A. During **Precambrian time,** which extended from approximately 4.6 bya up to 543 mya, life began and diverged into different groups of

bacteria, protists (including algae), fungi, and simple multicellular animals.
    1. Signs of Precambrian life date back to about 3.8 bya.
    2. **Microfossils,** ancient remains of microscopic life, and **stromatolites,** rocklike columns containing many minute layers of prokaryotic cells, date back about 3.5 billion years.
    3. One rich source of Precambrian fossil deposits is the Ediacaran Hills in South Australia. **Ediacaran fossils** of multicellular animals are from very late in Precambrian time—from 590 to 543 mya.
  B. During the **Paleozoic era,** which began approximately 543 mya and lasted approximately 192 million years, all major groups of plants, except for flowering plants, and all animal phyla appeared.
    1. During the Cambrian period, the pace of evolution was so rapid that this period has been nicknamed the **Cambrian explosion.** The most important fossil sites that document the Cambrian explosion are the **Chenjiang site** in China (for early Cambrian fossils) and the **Burgess Shale** in British Columbia (for middle Cambrian fossils).
    2. Fish and amphibians flourished, and reptiles appeared and diversified during the Paleozoic era.
    3. The greatest mass extinction of all time occurred at the end of the Paleozoic era, 251 mya. More than 90% of all existing marine species and more than 70% of land-dwelling vertebrate genera became extinct at this time, as well as many plant species.
  C. The **Mesozoic era** began about 251 mya and lasted some 186 million years.
    1. The Mesozoic era was characterized by the appearance of flowering plants and the evolutionary diversification of reptiles. Dinosaurs, which descended from early reptiles, dominated Earth during the Mesozoic era. Insects flourished, and birds and early mammals evolved.
    2. The two main groups of dinosaurs were the saurischians, with pelvic bones similar to modern-day lizards, and the ornithischians, with pelvic bones similar to those of birds.
    3. At the end of the Cretaceous period, 65 mya, a great many animals abruptly became extinct. A collision of Earth with a large extraterrestrial body may have resulted in dramatic climate changes that played a role in this mass extinction episode.
  D. In the **Cenozoic era,** which extends from 65 mya to the present, flowering plants, birds, insects, and mammals diversified greatly.
    1. All the modern orders of mammals appeared and diversified during the Eocene epoch. During the Oligocene epoch, many modern families of mammals appeared, including the first apes in Africa. A spectacular North and South American large-mammal fauna evolved during the Pliocene and Pleistocene epochs.
    2. Birds diversified during the Eocene epoch, adapting to various lifestyles and habitats. The songbirds diversified extensively during the Miocene epoch.

1. Energy, the absence of oxygen, chemical building blocks, and time were the requirements for (a) chemical evolution (b) biological evolution (c) the Cambrian explosion (d) the mass extinction episode at the end of the Cretaceous period (e) directed evolution

2. Protobionts (a) form spontaneously in hydrothermal vents in the ocean floor (b) are heterotrophs that obtain the organic molecules they need from the environment (c) are assemblages of abiotically produced organic polymers that resemble living cells in several ways (d) are autotrophs that use sunlight to split hydrogen sulfide (e) are fossilized mats of cyanobacteria

3. Many scientists think that _____ was the first information molecule to evolve. (a) DNA (b) RNA (c) a protein (d) an amino acid (e) a lipid

4. The first cells were probably (a) heterotrophs (b) autotrophs (c) anaerobes (d) both a and c (e) both b and c

5. According to the endosymbiont theory (a) life originated from nonliving matter (b) the pace of evolution quickened at the start of the Cambrian period (c) chloroplasts, mitochondria, and possibly other organelles originated from intimate relationships among prokaryotic organisms (d) banded iron formations reflect the buildup of sufficient oxygen in the atmosphere to oxidize iron at Earth's surface (e) the first photosynthetic organisms appeared 3.1 to 3.5 bya

6. All geological time prior to the beginning of the Paleozoic era some 543 mya is informally known as (a) the Cenozoic era (b) the Paleozoic era (c) the Mesozoic era (d) Precambrian time (e) the Cambrian period

7. Geologists divide Earth's history, from Precambrian time to the present, into (a) three periods (b) three epochs (c) three eras (d) five periods (e) five eras

8. Ediacaran fossils (a) are the oldest known fossils of multicellular animals (b) come from the Burgess Shale in British Columbia (c) contain remains of large salamander-like organisms (d) are the oldest fossils of early vascular plants (e) contain a high concentration of iridium

9. The correct chronological order of geological eras, starting with the oldest, is (a) Paleozoic, Cenozoic, and Mesozoic (b) Mesozoic, Cenozoic, and Paleozoic (c) Mesozoic, Paleozoic, and Cenozoic (d) Paleozoic, Mesozoic, and Cenozoic (e) Cenozoic, Paleozoic, and Mesozoic

10. The time of greatest evolutionary diversification in the history of life occurred during the (a) Cambrian period (b) Ordovician period (c) Silurian period (d) Carboniferous period (e) Permian period

11. The greatest mass extinction episode in the history of life occurred at what boundary? (a) Pliocene-Pleistocene (b) Permian-Triassic (c) Mesozoic-Cenozoic (d) Cambrian-Ordovician (e) Triassic-Jurassic

12. The Mesozoic era is divided into three periods, which are (a) Cambrian, Ordovician, and Silurian (b) Devonian, Carboniferous, and Permian (c) Triassic, Jurassic, and Cretaceous (d) Cretaceous, Tertiary, and Quaternary (e) Pliocene, Pleistocene, and Holocene

13. The Age of Reptiles corresponds to the (a) Paleozoic era (b) Mesozoic era (c) Cenozoic era (d) Pleistocene epoch (e) Permian period

14. Evidence exists that a catastrophic collision between Earth and a large extraterrestrial body occurred 65 mya, resulting in the extinction of (a) Precambrian worms, mollusks, and soft-bodied arthropods (b) jawless ostracoderms and jawed placoderms (c) dinosaurs, pterosaurs, and many gymnosperm species (d) mastodons, saber-toothed cats, and giant ground sloths

15. Flowering plants and mammals diversified and became dominant during the (a) Paleozoic era (b) Mesozoic era (c) Cenozoic era (d) Devonian period (e) Cambrian period

REVIEW QUESTIONS

1. What are the four requirements for chemical evolution, and why is each essential?

2. How did the presence of molecular oxygen in the atmosphere affect early life?

3. Give at least two types of evidence that support the endosymbiont theory.

4. Arrange the following sets of organisms in order of appearance in the fossil record, starting with the earliest: (a) eukaryotic cells, multicellular organisms, prokaryotic cells; (b) reptiles, mammals, amphibians, fish; (c) flowering plants, ferns, gymnosperms.

YOU MAKE THE CONNECTION

1. If you were experimenting on how protobionts evolved into cells and you developed a protobiont that was capable of self-replication, would you consider it a living cell? Why or why not?

2. If living cells were created in a test tube from nonbiological components by chemical processes, would this accomplishment prove that life evolved in a similar manner billions of years ago? Why or why not?

3. Why did the evolution of complex multicellular organisms such as plants and animals have to be preceded by the evolution of oxygen-producing photosynthesis?

4. How might studying outer space help us reconstruct the evolutionary history of life on Earth?

RECOMMENDED READINGS

Doebler, S.A. "The Dawn of the Protein Era." *BioScience,* Vol. 50, No. 1, Jan. 2000. Discusses various hypotheses about the origin of proteins or nucleic acids as the first molecules of life.

Doolittle, W.F. "Uprooting the Tree of Life." *Scientific American,* Vol. 282, No. 2, Feb. 2000. This article, which describes what is currently known about the origin of prokaryotes and eukaryotes, is an excellent example of how scientific knowledge progresses from general controversy to consensus.

Erickson, G.M. "Breathing Life into *Tyrannosaurus rex.*" *Scientific American,* Vol. 281, No. 3, Sep. 1999. Paleontologists are beginning to unravel secrets regarding the feeding behavior of the tyrannosaurs.

Fortey, R. "Crystal Eyes." *Natural History,* Oct. 2000. Examines the eyes of trilobites, marine animals that have been extinct for 250 million years.

Gould, S.J. "Tales of a Feathered Tail." *Natural History,* Nov. 2000. This article is one of a long series of essays written by the popular evolutionary biologist at Harvard University.

Hoffmann, H.J. "Messel: Window on an Ancient World." *National Geographic,* Vol. 197, No. 2, Feb. 2000. Some of the world's most remarkable fossils of the Eocene epoch in the Cenozoic era come from an abandoned mine pit in Messel, Germany.

Hoffmann, H.J. "When Life Nearly Came to an End: The Permian Extinction." *National Geographic,* Vol. 198, No. 3, Sep. 2000. The largest mass extinction episode in Earth's history occurred 250 mya, at the end of Earth's Permian period.

Landweber, L.F., P.J. Simon, and T.A. Wagner. "Ribozyme Engineering and Early Evolution." *BioScience,* Vol. 48, No. 2, Feb. 1998. This article explains in vitro evolution of RNA molecules and how it may mimic early RNA evolution.

Monastersky, R. "Life Grows Up." *National Geographic,* Vol. 193, No. 4, Apr. 1998. Highlights Ediacaran fossils of ancient, soft-bodied animals.

Motani, R. "Rulers of the Jurassic Seas." *Scientific American,* Vol. 283, No. 6, Dec. 2000. Presents some of the fascinating information known about the reptilian ichthyosaurs that lived in the ocean when dinosaurs roamed the land.

Nisbet, E.G., and N.H. Sleep. "The Habitat and Nature of Early Life." *Nature,* Vol. 409, 22 Feb. 2001. This insightful review article examines the environment of early Earth, when life was first evolving.

Simpson, S. "Life's First Scalding Steps." *Science News,* Vol. 155, 9 Jan. 1999. Reviews the hypothesis that chemicals produced at hydrothermal vents could have led to the evolution of living organisms.

Webster, D. "A Dinosaur Named Sue." *National Geographic,* Vol. 195, No. 6, Jun. 1999. Highlights what has been learned from studying the most complete *Tyrannosaurus rex* fossil ever discovered.

Westenberg, K. "From Fins to Feet." *National Geographic,* Vol. 195, No. 5, May 1999. Highlights the evolution of tetrapods—animals with backbones and four limbs—during the Devonian period.

- Visit our Web site at **http://www.info.brookscole.com/solomonbergmartin** for links to chapter-related resources on the World Wide Web. Additional on-line materials relating to this chapter can also be found on our Web site.

 See chapter activity on BioActive Learner CD for additional help in mastering the chapter's material. Icon location in the chapter's margins shows which topics have tutorials or simulations in the CD.

21

The Evolution of Primates

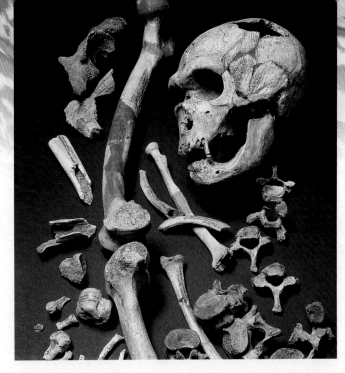

Fossilized remains of a Neandertal man. Each of these fossils, which were found in La Chapelle-aux-Saints, France, has been carefully catalogued and studied. Some of the bones are deformed due to osteoarthritis. *(John Reader/Science Photo Library/Photo Researchers, Inc.)*

LEARNING OBJECTIVES

After you have studied this chapter you should be able to

1. Describe the structural adaptations that primates possess for life in treetops and explain why even primates that live on the ground have these adaptations.
2. List the three suborders of primates and give representative examples of each.
3. Explain the significance of each of the following fossil primates: *Eosimias, Aegyptopithecus, Proconsul,* and the dryopithecines.
4. Distinguish among mammals, primates, anthropoids, hominoids, and hominids.
5. Describe skeletal and skull differences between apes and hominids.
6. Compare the following early hominids: *Ardipithecus ramidus, Australopithecus anamensis, Australopithecus afarensis,* and *Australopithecus africanus.*
7. Distinguish among the following members of genus *Homo: Homo habilis, Homo ergaster, Homo erectus, Homo heidelbergensis, Homo neanderthalensis,* and *Homo sapiens.*
8. Discuss the current debate over the origin of modern humans and briefly describe the opposing out of Africa and multiregional hypotheses.
9. Describe cultural evolution and its impact on the biosphere.

Twelve years after Darwin wrote *The Origin of Species by Natural Selection,* he published another controversial book, *The Descent of Man,* which addressed human evolution. In it, Darwin hypothesized that humans and apes share a common ancestry. For nearly a century after Darwin, fossil evidence of human ancestry remained fairly incomplete. However, research over the last few decades, especially in Africa, has yielded fossils that provide an increasingly clear answer to the question, "Where did we come from?"

Humans and other primates, such as lemurs, tarsiers, monkeys, and apes, are mammals. Mammals (class Mammalia) arose from mammal-like reptiles known as therapsids more than 200 million years ago (mya), during the Mesozoic era (see Chapter 20). These early mammals remained a minor component of life on Earth for almost 150 million years before rapidly diversifying during the Cenozoic era (the last 65 million years). Mammals are **endothermic** (they use metabolic energy to maintain a constant body temperature); produce body hair for such functions as insulation, protective coloration, and waterproofing; and feed their young with milk from mammary glands. Most mammals are **viviparous,** which means that their eggs develop into young offspring within the female body.

It is currently thought that the three groups of living mammals—the monotremes, marsupials, and placental mammals—all are descended from the same common ancestor. The **monotremes** are mammals, such as the duck-billed platypus, that lay eggs (see Chapter 30). The **marsupials,** such as kangaroos and opossums, carry their young in an abdominal pouch after giving birth to them in a very underdeveloped condition. **Placental mammals,** the largest and most successful group, possess a **placenta,** an organ that exchanges materials between the mother and the embryo/fetus developing in the uterus. Placental mammals give birth to their young in a more developed condition than marsupials.

The first primates appeared about 55 mya, apparently descendants of small shrewlike placental mammals that lived in trees and ate insects. Many traits of the 233 living primate species are related to their **arboreal** (tree-dwelling) past. Humans and their ancestors *(see photograph),* who differ from most other primates because they did not remain in the trees but instead adapted to a terrestrial way of life, are the main focus of this chapter.

Fossil evidence has allowed **paleoanthropologists,** scientists who study human evolution, to infer not only the structure but also the habits of early humans and other primates. Teeth and bones are the main fossil evidence studied by paleoanthropologists. Much information can be obtained, for example, by studying teeth, which have changed dramatically during the course of primate and human evolution. Because tooth enamel is more mineralized (harder) than bone, teeth are more likely to be fossilized. The teeth of each primate species, living or extinct, are distinctive enough to identify the species, approximate age, diet, and even sex of the individual. Consider *Australopithecus robustus,* which lived in southern Africa about 2 mya, at a time that the climate was becoming more arid and the forests were giving way to grasslands. Its large jaws and molars (broad-ridged teeth in the back of the mouths of adult mammals) indicate that its diet included tough foods such as roots, tubers, and seeds.

■ EARLY PRIMATE EVOLUTION REFLECTED AN ARBOREAL EXISTENCE

Fossil evidence indicates that the first true primates appeared by the early Eocene epoch about 55 mya. These early primates had digits with nails, and their eyes were directed more forward on the head. The climate was milder then, and early primates were widely distributed over much of North America, Europe, and Asia. (Recall from Chapter 17 that North America was still attached to Europe at that time.) As the climate became cooler and drier toward the end of the Eocene epoch, many of these early primates became extinct.

Several novel adaptations evolved in early primates that allowed them to live in trees. One of the most significant features of primates is that they have five grasping digits: four lateral digits (fingers) plus a partially or fully opposable thumb or big toe (Fig. 21–1). The opposable first digit enables primates to grasp objects such as branches. Nails (instead of claws) provide a protective covering for the tips of the digits, and the fleshy pads at the ends of the digits are sensitive to touch. Another arboreal feature is long, slender limbs that rotate freely at the hips and shoulders, giving primates full mobility to climb and search for food in the treetops. The location of eyes in front of the head provides stereoscopic, or three-dimensional, vision. Stereoscopic vision is vital in an arboreal environment, especially for species that leap from branch to branch, because an error in depth perception might cause a fatal fall. In addition to sharp sight, hearing is acute in primates.

Primates share several other characteristics, including a relatively large brain size. It has been suggested that increased sensory input associated with their sharp vision and greater agility favored the evolution of larger brains. Primates are generally very social and intelligent animals that reach sexual maturity relatively late in life. They typically have long life spans. Females usually bear one offspring at a time; the baby is helpless and requires a long period of nurturing and protection.

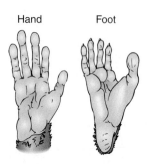

(a) Lemur *(Eulemur mongoz)*

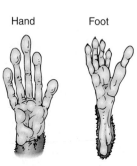

(b) Tarsier *(Tarsius spectrum)*

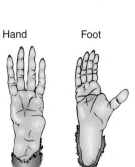

(c) Woolly spider monkey *(Brachyteles arachnoides)*

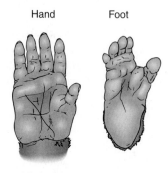

(d) Gorilla *(Gorilla gorilla)*

■ **Figure 21–1 Right hands and feet of selected primates.** Primates have five grasping digits, and the thumb or big toe is often partially or fully opposable. **(a)** Lemur. **(b)** Tarsier. **(c)** Wooly spider monkey. **(d)** Gorilla. *(Figures not drawn to scale.) (Adapted from Schultz, A.H.* The Life of Primates. *Weidenfeld & Nicholson, London, 1969)*

LIVING PRIMATES MAY BE CLASSIFIED INTO THREE SUBORDERS

Many biologists currently divide the order Primates into three suborders (Table 21–1 and Fig. 21–2). The suborder Prosimii includes lemurs, galagos, and lorises, the suborder Tarsiiformes includes tarsiers, and the suborder Anthropoidea includes **anthropoids** (monkeys, apes, and humans).

All lemurs are restricted to the island of Madagascar off the coast of Africa (Fig. 21–3). Because of extensive habitat destruction and hunting, they are highly endangered. Lorises, which are found in tropical areas of Southeast Asia and Africa, resemble lemurs in many respects, as do galagos, which live in sub-Saharan Africa. Lemurs, lorises, and galagos have retained several early mammalian features, such as elongated, pointed faces.

Tarsiers are found in rain forests of Indonesia and the Philippines (Fig. 21–4). They are small primates (about the size of a small rat) and are very adept leapers. These nocturnal primates resemble anthropoids in a number of ways, including their shortened snouts and forward-pointing eyes.

TABLE 21–1 A Classification of Living Groups in the Order Primates*

Suborder Prosimii
  Infraorder Lemuriformes (lemurs)
  Infraorder Lorisoformes (galagos, lorises)

Suborder Tarsiiformes (tarsiers)

Suborder Anthropoidea
  Infraorder Platyrrhini (New World primates)
  Infraorder Catarrhini (Old World primates)
    Superfamily Cercopithecoidea (Old World monkeys)
    Superfamily Hominoidea (Old World apes and humans)
      Family Hylobatidae (gibbons)
      Family Pongidae (orangutans, gorillas, chimpanzees)
      Family Hominidae (humans)

* There are many alternative classifications of primates. For example, classifications based on molecular data place humans and the great apes (orangutans, gorillas, and chimpanzees) in a single family.

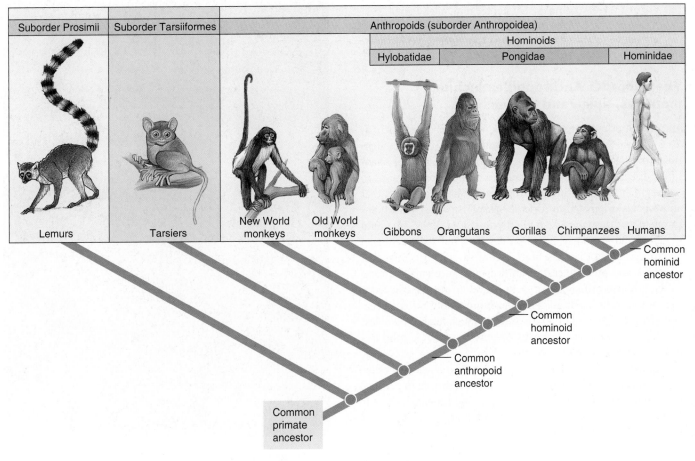

Figure 21–2 Primate evolution. This diagram shows hypothetical phylogenetic relationships among living primates, based on current scientific evidence. The three families of hominoids recognized by many biologists are shown. *(Figures not drawn to scale.)*

Figure 21–3 Lemurs. A mother ring-tailed lemur (*Lemus catta*) and her baby share a piece of fruit. Lemurs are native to Madagascar. *(Frans Lanting/Minden Pictures)*

The suborder Anthropoidea includes monkeys, apes, and humans

Anthropoid primates arose during the middle Eocene epoch, at least 45 mya. Several different fossil anthropoids have been identified from Asia and North Africa, and there is a growing scientific consensus about the relationships of these fossil groups to one another and to living anthropoids. Evidence indicates that anthropoids originated in Africa or Asia. The oldest known anthropoid fossils, such as 42-million-year-old *Eosimias,* are found in China and Myanmar. Based on details about their dentition and the few bones that have been discovered, scientists infer that *Eosimias* and other ancestral anthropoids were small, insect-eating arboreal primates that were active during the day. Once they arose, anthropoids quickly spread throughout Europe, Asia, and Africa and arrived in South America much later. (The oldest known South American primate, *Branisella,* which is from Bolivia, is dated at 26 million years.)

One significant difference between anthropoids and other primates is in the size of their brains. The cerebrum, in particular, is more developed in monkeys, apes, and humans, where it functions as the center for learning, voluntary movement, and interpretation of sensation.

Monkeys are generally diurnal (active during the day) tree dwellers. They tend to eat fruit and leaves, with nuts, seeds, buds, insects, spiders, birds' eggs, and even small vertebrates playing a smaller part in their diets. The two main groups of monkeys, New World monkeys and Old World monkeys, are named for the hemispheres where they diversified. Monkeys in South and Cen-

tral America are called New World monkeys, whereas monkeys in Africa, Asia, and Europe are called Old World monkeys. New and Old World monkeys have been evolving separately for tens of millions of years.

One of the most important unanswered questions in anthropoid evolution concerns *how* monkeys arrived in South America. Africa and South America had already drifted apart (see Chapter 17), so the ancestors of New World monkeys may have rafted from Africa to South America on floating masses of vegetation. (The South Atlantic Ocean would have been about half as wide as it is today, and any islands that may have been present could have provided "stepping stones.") Alternatively, the ancestors of New World monkeys may have dispersed from Asia to North America to South America. Once established in the New World, these monkeys rapidly diversified.

New World monkeys are restricted to Central and South America and include marmosets, capuchins, howler monkeys, squirrel monkeys, and spider monkeys. New World monkeys are arboreal, and some possess long, slender limbs that permit easy movement in the trees (Fig. 21–5*a*). A few have **prehensile** tails

Figure 21–4 Tarsiers. The huge eyes of the tarsier (*Tarsius bancanus*) help it find insects, lizards, and other prey when it hunts at night. When a tarsier sees an insect, it pounces on it and grasps the prey with its hands. Tarsiers live in the rain forests of Indonesia and the Philippines. *(Frans Lanting/Minden Pictures)*

(a)

(b)

capable of wrapping around branches and serving as fifth limbs. Some New World monkeys have shorter thumbs, and in certain cases the thumbs are totally absent. Their facial anatomy is different from that of the Old World monkeys; they have flattened noses with the nostrils opening to the side. They live in groups and exhibit complex social behaviors.

Old World monkeys are distributed in tropical parts of Africa and Asia. In addition to baboons and macaques (pronounced muh-kacks'), the Old World group includes guenons, mangabeys, langurs, and colobus monkeys. Most Old World monkeys are arboreal, although some, such as baboons and macaques, spend much of their time on the ground (Fig. 21–5b). The ground dwellers, which are **quadrupedal** ("four-footed"; they walk on all fours), arose from arboreal monkeys. None of the Old World monkeys has a prehensile tail, and some have extremely short tails. They have a fully opposable thumb, and unlike the New World monkeys, their nostrils are closer together and directed downward. Old World monkeys are intensely social animals.

Many classification schemes place apes and humans in three families

Old World monkeys shared a common ancestor with the **hominoids,** a group composed of apes and **hominids** (humans and their ancestors). A fairly primitive anthropoid was discovered in Egypt and named *Aegyptopithecus* (Fig. 21–6a). *Aegyptopithecus,* a cat-sized, forest-dwelling arboreal monkey with a few apelike characteristics, lived during the Oligocene epoch, approximately 34 mya.

During the Miocene epoch, approximately 20 mya, apes and Old World monkeys diverged. The oldest fossils with hominoid features were discovered in East Africa, mostly in Kenya. *Proconsul,* for example, appears early in the Miocene epoch, about 20 mya. It has a larger brain than monkeys, apelike teeth and diet (fruits), but a monkey-like body. At least 30 other early hominoid species lived during the Miocene epoch, but most of them became extinct and were not the common ancestor of modern apes and humans.

Miocene fossils of forest-dwelling, chimpanzee-sized apes called *dryopithecines,* which lived about 15 mya, are of special

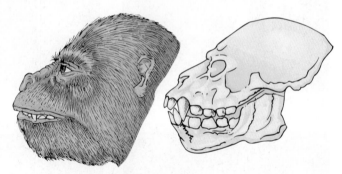

(a) Oligocene anthropoid, *Aegyptopithecus*

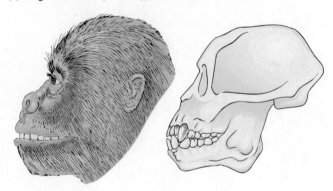

(b) Miocene ape, *Dryopithecus*

■ **Figure 21–6 *Aegyptopithecus* and *Dryopithecus*.** **(a)** Fossils of *Aegyptopithecus,* a fairly primitive anthropoid, were discovered in Egypt. **(b)** *Dryopithecus,* a more advanced ape, may have given rise to modern hominoids. *(Figures not drawn to scale.)*

interest because this hominoid lineage may have given rise to modern apes as well as to the human line (Fig. 21–6b). The dryopithecines, such as *Dryopithecus, Kenyapithecus,* and *Morotopithecus,* were distributed widely across Europe, Africa, and Asia. As the climate gradually cooled and became drier, their range became more limited. These apes had highly modified bodies for swinging through the branches of trees, although there is also evidence that some of them may have left the treetops for the ground as dense forest gradually changed into open woodland.

Many questions about the relationships among the various early apes have been generated by the discovery of these and other Miocene hominoids. As future fossil finds are evaluated, they may lead to a rearrangement of ancestors in the hominoid family tree.

Many biologists classify the five genera of hominoids alive today into three families: Gibbons *(Hylobates)* are known as lesser apes and are placed in the family Hylobatidae. The family Pongidae includes orangutans *(Pongo),* gorillas *(Gorilla),* and chimpanzees *(Pan),* and the family Hominidae includes humans *(Homo).* Re-

(a)

(b)

(c)

(d)

Figure 21–7 Apes. **(a)** White-handed gibbons *(Hylobates lar)* are extremely acrobatic and often move through the trees by brachiation. **(b)** An orangutan *(Pongo pygmaeus)* mother and baby. **(c)** A young lowland gorilla *(Gorilla gorilla)* in knuckle-walking stance. **(d)** A bonobo chimpanzee *(Pan paniscus)* grooms another member of the group. Bonobos are endemic to a single country, the Democratic Republic of Congo (formerly Zaire). *(a, Joe McDonald/Visuals Unlimited; b, BIOS/Peter Arnold, Inc.; c, Nancy Adams/Tom Stack & Associates; d, K. & K. Ammann/Bruce Coleman, Inc.)*

cent molecular evidence indicates a closer relationship between humans and the greater apes, particularly chimpanzees, and some scientists now classify them in the same family.

Gibbons are natural acrobats that can **brachiate,** or arm-swing, with their weight supported by one arm at a time (Fig. 21–7a). Orangutans are also tree dwellers, but chimpanzees and especially gorillas have adapted to life on the ground (Fig. 21–7b–d). Gorillas and chimpanzees have retained long arms typical of brachiating primates but use these to assist in quadrupedal walking, sometimes known as **knuckle-walking** because of the way they fold (flex) their digits when moving. Apes, like humans, lack tails. They are generally much larger than monkeys, although gibbons are a notable exception.

Evidence of the close relatedness of orangutans, gorillas, chimps, and humans is abundant at the molecular level. The amino acid sequence of the chimpanzee's hemoglobin is identical to that of the human; hemoglobin molecules of the gorilla and rhesus monkey differ from the human's by 2 and 15 amino acids, respectively. DNA sequence analyses indicate that chimpanzees are likely to be our nearest living relatives among the apes (see Table 17–1). Molecular evidence suggests that gorillas may have diverged from the chimpanzee and hominid lines some 8 to 10 mya, whereas chimpanzee and hominid lines probably separated about 6 mya.

THE FOSSIL RECORD PROVIDES CLUES TO HOMINID EVOLUTION

Scientists have a growing storehouse of hundreds of hominid fossils, which provide useful information about general trends in the body design, appearance, and behavior of ancestral humans. It is evident, for example, that early hominids adopted a **bipedal** (two-footed) posture before their brains enlarged. Despite the wealth of fossil evidence, interpretations of hominid characteristics, taxonomy, and phylogeny continue to be vigorously debated, and new discoveries raise new questions. Furthermore, hominid evolution, like other scientific fields, is influenced by the different perspectives of the various workers studying it. The lack of a scientific consensus regarding certain aspects of hominid evolution is, therefore, an expected part of the scientific process.

Evolutionary changes from the earliest hominids to modern humans are evident in some of the characteristics of the skeleton and skull. Compared with the ape skeleton, the human skeleton possesses distinct differences that reflect our ability to stand erect and walk on two feet (Fig. 21–8). These differences also reflect the habitat change for early hominids, from an arboreal existence in the forest to a life spent at least partly on the ground.

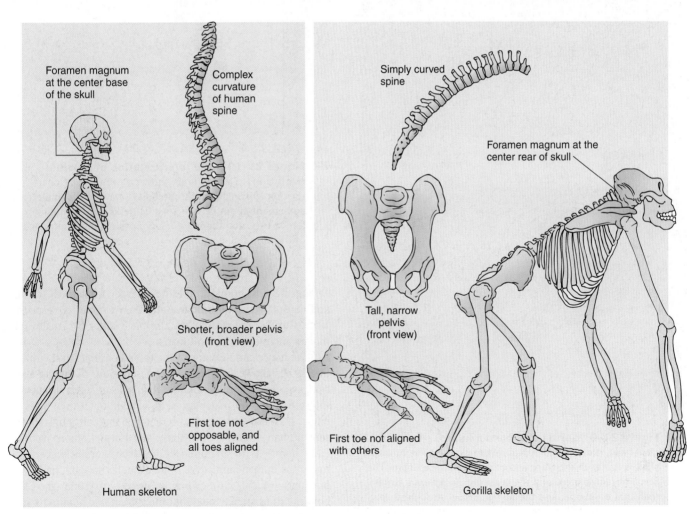

Figure 21–8 Gorilla and human skeletons. When gorilla and human skeletons are compared, the skeletal adaptations for bipedalism in humans become apparent.

The curvature of the human spine provides better balance and weight distribution for bipedal locomotion. The human pelvis is shorter and broader than the ape pelvis, providing a better attachment of muscles used for upright walking. The hole in the base of the skull for the spinal cord, called the **foramen magnum,** is located in the middle of the rear of the skull in apes. In contrast, the human foramen magnum is centered in the skull base, positioning the head for erect walking. An increase in the length of the legs relative to the arms, and alignment of the big toe with the rest of the toes, further adapted the early hominids for bipedalism.

Another major trend in hominid evolution was an increase in the size of the brain relative to the size of the body (Fig. 21–9). The ape skull possesses prominent bony ridges above the eye sockets, whereas these **supraorbital ridges** are lacking in modern human skulls. Human faces are flatter than those of apes, and the jaws are different. The arrangement of teeth in the ape jaw is somewhat rectangular, compared with a rounded, or U-shaped,

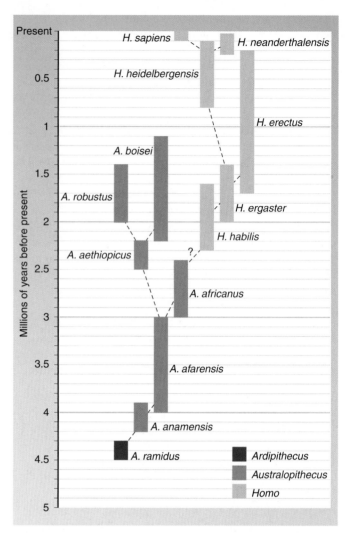

■ **Figure 21–10 One interpretation of hominid evolution.** Dashed lines show possible evolutionary relationships. Paleoanthropologists are not in complete agreement about certain specific details of the human family tree, and there are many possible interpretations of the human lineage.

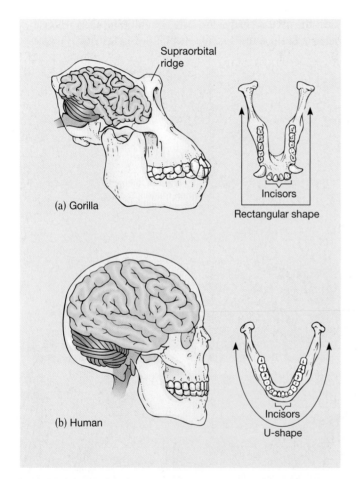

■ **Figure 21–9 Gorilla and human heads.** **(a)** The ape skull has a pronounced supraorbital ridge. **(b)** The human skull is flatter in the front and has a pronounced chin. The human brain, particularly the cerebrum *(purple),* is larger than that of an ape, and the human jaw is structured so that the teeth are arranged in a U shape. Human canines and incisors are also smaller than those of apes.

arrangement in humans. Apes have larger front teeth (canines and incisors) than do humans, and their canines are especially large. Gorillas and orangutans also have larger back teeth (premolars and molars) than humans.

We now examine some of the fossil hominids in the human lineage. As you read the following descriptions of human evolution, keep in mind that much of what is discussed is still open to interpretation and major revision as additional discoveries are made. It is also important to remember that, although we present human evolution in a somewhat linear fashion, from ancient hominids to anatomically and behaviorally modern humans, the human family tree is not a single trunk but has several branches (Fig. 21–10). *Homo sapiens* is the only species of hominid in existence today, but more than one hominid species coexisted at any given time for most of the past 4 million years.

The earliest hominid belongs to the genus *Ardipithecus*

Hominid evolution began in Africa. The earliest hominid, which belongs to the genus *Ardipithecus*, appeared at least 4.4 mya. *Ardipithecus* gave rise to *Australopithecus*, a genus that includes several species that lived between 4 and 1 mya. These two genera of early hominids, often referred to as **australopithecines,** or "southern man apes," had longer arms, shorter legs, and smaller brains relative to modern humans.[1] The actual number of australopithecine species for which fossil evidence has been found is under debate, because in some cases, differences in the relatively few skeletal fragments could indicate either variation among individuals within a species or evidence of separate species. Most paleoanthropologists recognize at least six species of australopithecines.

The first fossils of the earliest hominids were discovered by Tim White, Berhane Asfaw, and Gen Suwa in 1992 and assigned to ***Ardipithecus ramidus*** in 1995. The specific epithet *ramidus* is derived from a word meaning "root" in the Afar language, spoken in the region of Ethiopia where the fossils were found. This hominid, which is more primitive than any other known hominid, is quite close to the "root" of the human family tree, that is, to the last common ancestor of modern hominids and chimpanzees. Because no leg bones were found in the initial discovery, it has not yet been determined if *A. ramidus* was bipedal. Future discoveries may clarify this important point.

The genus *Australopithecus* contains the immediate ancestors of the genus *Homo*

Hominids that existed between 3.9 and 4.2 mya are assigned to the species ***Australopithecus anamensis,*** first named in 1995 by Meave Leakey and her coworkers from fossils discovered in East Africa. This hominid species, which has a mixture of apelike and human-like features, presumably arose from *Ardipithecus ramidus*. A comparison of male and female *A. anamensis* body sizes and canine teeth reveals **sexual dimorphism,** marked phenotypic differences between the two sexes of the same species. (The modern-day gorilla exhibits sexual dimorphism.) The back teeth and jaws of *A. anamensis* are larger than those of modern chimpanzees, whereas the front teeth are smaller and more like those of later hominids. A fossil leg bone, the tibia, indicates that *A. anamensis* had an upright posture and was bipedal, although it also may have foraged in the trees. Thus, bipedalism occurred early in human evolution and may have been the first human adaptation.

Australopithecus afarensis, another primitive hominid, appears to have arisen directly from *A. anamensis*. Many fossils of *A. afarensis* skeletal remains have been discovered in Africa, including a remarkably complete skeleton nicknamed Lucy found in Ethiopia in 1974 by a team led by Donald Johanson. Lucy, a small

hominid approximately 1.04 m (3 ft, 5 in) is thought to be about 3.2 million years old. In 1978, Mary Leakey and coworkers discovered beautifully preserved fossil footprints of three *A. afarensis* individuals who walked more than 3.6 mya. In 1994 the first adult skull of *A. afarensis* was found. The skull, characterized by a relatively small brain, pronounced supraorbital ridges, a jutting jaw, and large canine teeth, is an estimated 3 million years old. It is probable that *A. afarensis* did not construct tools or make fires, since no evidence of tools or fire has been found at fossil sites.

Many paleoanthropologists think *A. afarensis* gave rise to several australopithecine species, including **Australopithecus africanus,** which may have appeared as early as 3 mya. The first *A. africanus* fossil was discovered in South Africa in 1924, and since then hundreds have been found. This hominid walked erect and possessed hands and teeth that were distinctly human-like. Based on characteristics of the teeth, it is thought that *A. africanus* ate both plants and animals. Like *A. afarensis*, it had a small brain, more like that of its primate ancestors than of present-day humans.

Three australopithecine species (*A. robustus* from South Africa, and *A. aethiopicus* and *A. boisei,* both from East Africa) are larger than *A. africanus* and have extremely large molars, very powerful jaws, relatively small brains, and bony skull crests. Most females lacked the skull crests and had substantially smaller jaws, another example of sexual dimorphism in early hominids. The teeth and jaws suggest a diet, perhaps of tough roots and tubers, that would require powerful grinding. These so-called *robust australopithecines* may or may not be closely related but are generally thought to represent evolutionary offshoots, or side branches, of human evolution. The first robust australopithecine, *A. aethiopicus,* appeared about 2.5 mya. Some researchers classify robust australopithecines in a separate genus (*Paranthropus*).

Homo habilis is the oldest member of the genus *Homo*

The first hominid to have enough uniquely human features to be placed in the same genus as modern humans is ***Homo habilis.*** It was first discovered in the early 1960s at Olduvai Gorge in Tanzania. Since then other fossils of *H. habilis* have been discovered in East and South Africa. *Homo habilis* was a small hominid with a larger brain and smaller premolars and molars than the australopithecines. This hominid appeared approximately 2.3 mya and persisted for about 0.75 million years. Fossils of *H. habilis* have been found in numerous areas in Africa. These sites contain primitive tools, stones that had been chipped, cracked, or hammered to make sharp edges for cutting or scraping.[2] *Oldowan* pebble choppers and flakes, for example, were probably used to cut through animal hides to obtain meat and to break bones for their nutritious marrow.

---

[1] Do not make the mistake of thinking that our smaller-brained ancestors were inferior to ourselves. Ancestral hominids were evolutionarily successful in that they were well adapted to their environment and survived for millions of years.

[2] The oldest known stone tools, discovered in the mid-1990s by Sileshi Semaw and colleagues, were found in Gona, Ethiopia. These ancient tools were made some 2.6 mya, but because no hominid remains have been found at the site yet, it is not known who made them.

The relationship between the australopithecines and *H. habilis* is not clear. Using physical characteristics of their fossilized skeletons as evidence, many paleoanthropologists have inferred that the australopithecines were ancestors of *H. habilis*. Some researchers do not think *H. habilis* belongs in the genus *Homo,* and they suggest it should be reclassified as *Australopithecus habilis.* Discoveries of additional fossils may help clarify these relationships.

Homo erectus apparently evolved from *Homo habilis*

Numerous fossils of **Homo erectus** have been found throughout Africa and Asia. (The first fossil evidence of *H. erectus* was found in Indonesia in the 1890s.) *Homo erectus* is thought to have originated in Africa about 1.7 mya and then to have spread quickly to Europe and Asia. The oldest fossils of *H. erectus* that have been found in Southeast Asia, for example, may be as old as 1.8 million years, although the most widely accepted date is about 1 million years. Peking man and Java man, discovered in Asia, were later examples of *H. erectus,* which existed until at least 200,000 years ago; some populations of *H. erectus* may have persisted more recently.

Homo erectus was taller than *H. habilis.* Its brain, which was larger than that of *H. habilis,* got progressively larger during the course of its evolution. Its skull, although larger, did not possess totally modern features, retaining the heavy supraorbital ridge and projecting face that are more characteristic of its ape ancestors (Fig. 21–11). *Homo erectus* is the first hominid to have fewer differences between the sexes.

The increased mental faculties associated with an increased brain size enabled these early humans to make more advanced stone tools, known as *Acheulean* tools, including hand axes and other implements that have been interpreted as choppers, borers, and scrapers. Their intelligence also allowed them to survive in cold areas. *Homo erectus* obtained food by hunting or scavenging and may have worn clothing, built fires, and lived in caves or shelters. Evidence of weapons (spears) has been unearthed at *Homo erectus* sites in Europe.

Ideas regarding *Homo erectus,* like many other aspects of human evolution, are changing with each new fossil discovery. Many scientists now hypothesize that the fossils classified as *H. erectus* really represent two species, **Homo ergaster,** an earlier African species, and *H. erectus,* a later East Asian offshoot. The best known fossils of *H. ergaster* come from the Lake Turkana region in Kenya. Researchers who support this split speculate that *Homo ergaster* may be the direct ancestor of later humans, whereas *Homo erectus* may be an evolutionary dead end. It is hoped that future fossil discoveries will help clarify the status of *Homo erectus.*

Archaic *Homo sapiens* appeared about 800,000 years ago

Archaic *Homo sapiens* are regionally diverse descendants of *Homo erectus* or *Homo ergaster* that lived in Africa, Asia, and Europe from about 800,000 to 100,000 years ago. They thus

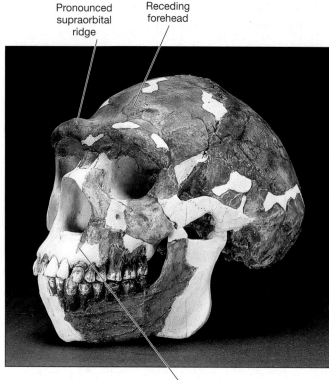

Figure 21–11 *Homo erectus* **skull from China.** The reconstructed portions are white. Note the receding forehead, pronounced supraorbital ridge, and projecting face and jaws. *(Ken Mowbray)*

overlapped both *H. erectus* populations and the later appearing Neandertals (discussed later). Some researchers classify archaic *Homo sapiens* as a separate species, **Homo heidelbergensis.**

Neandertals appeared approximately 230,000 years ago

Neandertals[3] were first discovered in the Neander Valley in Germany. They lived throughout Europe and western Asia from about 230,000 to 30,000 years ago. These early humans had short, sturdy builds. Their faces projected slightly, their chins and foreheads receded, they had heavy supraorbital ridges and jawbones, and their brains and front teeth were larger than those of modern humans. Their nasal cavities were large, and their cheekbones were receding. Scientists have suggested that the large noses provided larger surface areas in Neandertal sinuses, enabling them to better warm the cold air of Ice Age Eurasia as air traveled through the head to the lungs.

Scientists have not reached a consensus about whether the Neandertals are a separate species from modern humans. Many think the anatomical differences between Neandertals and mod-

[3] Neandertal was formerly spelled "Neanderthal." The silent "h" has been dropped in modern German but not in the scientific name.

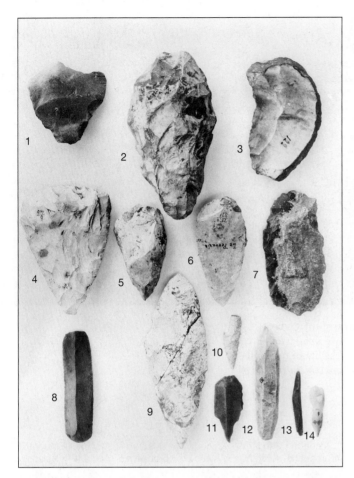

Figure 21–12 Mousterian tools. Mousterian tools are named after a Neandertal site in Le Moustier, France. Mousterian tools included a variety of skillfully made stone tools, such as hand axes, flakes, scrapers, borers, and spear points. (*1* to *4* are earlier tools, and *8* to *14* are later tools.) *(Photo Researchers, Inc.)*

ern humans mean that they were separate species, ***Homo neanderthalensis*** and ***Homo sapiens.*** Other scientists disagree and think that Neandertals were a group of *Homo sapiens.*

Neandertal tools, known as *Mousterian* tools, include the oldest known spear points (Fig. 21–12). Neandertal tools were more sophisticated than those of *H. erectus.* Studies of Neandertal sites indicate that they hunted large animals. The existence of skeletons of elderly Neandertals and of Neandertals with healed fractures may demonstrate that they cared for the aged and the sick, an indication of advanced social cooperation. They apparently had rituals, possibly of religious significance, and sometimes buried their dead.

Process of Science The disappearance of the Neandertals some 30,000 years ago is a mystery that has sparked debate among paleoanthropologists. Other groups of *H. sapiens* with more modern features coexisted for tens of thousands of years with the Neandertals. Perhaps the other humans out-competed or exterminated the Neandertals, leading to their extinction. It is also pos-

sible that the Neandertals interbred with these humans, diluting their features beyond recognition.

Analysis of **mitochondrial DNA (mtDNA)** contributes useful data to such controversies. Each of the several hundred mitochondria within a cell has about ten copies of a small loop of DNA that codes for transfer RNAs, ribosomal RNAs, and certain respiratory enzymes. Mitochondrial DNA mutates more rapidly than nuclear DNA, so mtDNA is a sensitive indicator of evolution. In 1997 Svante Pääbo and colleagues analyzed mtDNA extracted from a Neandertal bone and reported that it differs significantly from all modern human mtDNA sequences, although it is more similar to human than to chimpanzee mtDNA. This finding suggests that Neandertals are an evolutionary dead end that did not interbreed with more modern humans.

To be considered authentic, the results of scientific research must be independently reproducible. Hence, a molecular analysis of mtDNA from a different Neandertal bone, reported by Igor V. Ovchinnikov in 2000, is significant. Ovchinnikov's findings corroborate those of Pääbo, that is, that Neandertals did not contribute to the modern human mtDNA.

The question of the relationship between Neandertals and anatomically modern humans remains controversial, however. In 1999 researchers reported the discovery of a 4-year-old child's remains in Portugal. The skeleton, dated at 24,500 years of age, has traits of both modern humans and Neandertals (short lower limb bones). The child lived several thousand years after Neandertals are thought to have disappeared, and the researchers who discovered it view it as an example of mixed ancestry, meaning that Neandertals and anatomically modern humans are members of the same species who interbred freely. Other scientists disagree with their interpretation and think the so-called Neandertal features of the child may reflect normal variation inherent in the human species.

The origin of modern *Homo sapiens* is hotly debated

Homo sapiens with anatomically modern features existed in Africa and the Middle East at least 100,000 years ago. The *H. sapiens* skull lacked a heavy brow ridge and possessed a distinct chin. By about 30,000 years ago, anatomically modern humans were the only members of genus *Homo* remaining. European remains of these ancient people are referred to as **Cro-Magnons.** Their weapons and tools were complex and often made of materials other than stone, including bone, ivory, and wood. They made stone blades that were extremely sharp. Cro-Magnons developed art, including cave paintings, engravings, and sculpture, possibly for ritualistic purposes (Fig. 21–13). Their sophisticated tools and art indicate that they may have possessed language, which would have been used to transmit their culture to younger generations.

Process of Science Two opposing hypotheses currently exist about the origin of these modern humans: the *out of Africa* hypothesis and the *multiregional* hypothesis (Fig. 21–14). The out of Africa hypothesis holds that modern *H. sapiens* arose in Africa

CHAPTER 21 The Evolution of Primates **459**

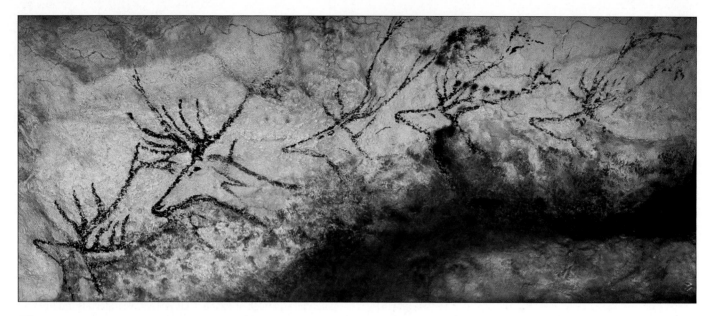

Figure 21–13 Cro-Magnon cave paintings. These are some of the earliest known examples of human art. Discovered in Lascaux, France, these images of reindeer have been interpreted as having religious significance, possibly to guarantee a successful hunt. *(Photo by J. Beckett/D. Stipkovich, courtesy Department of Library Services, American Museum of Natural History)*

between 200,000 and 100,000 years ago and then migrated to Europe and Asia, displacing the Neandertals and other more primitive humans living there. According to the multiregional hypothesis, modern humans evolved from *H. erectus*. They originated, beginning as early as 2 mya, as separately evolving populations living in several parts of Africa, Asia, and Europe. Each of these populations evolved in its own distinctive way but occasionally met and interbred with other populations, thereby preventing complete reproductive isolation. The variation found today in different geographical populations therefore represents a continuation of this multiregional process.

Data from *Homo* fossils, as well as molecular biology and population genetics studies of modern humans, have been cited in support of both hypotheses, and both have vigorous defenders and strong detractors. Such disagreement is an important part of the scientific process because it stimulates research that may ultimately resolve the issue.

Analysis of DNA provides evidence on the origin of modern humans

Molecular anthropology, the comparison of biological molecules from present-day individuals of regional human populations, provides clues that help scientists unravel the origin of modern humans and trace human migrations. The out of Africa hypothesis was originally supported by studies in the late 1980s of mtDNA from various human populations. In 1992 the statistical assumptions used in one analysis of mtDNA were found to be erroneous, leading to questions about the validity of this purported

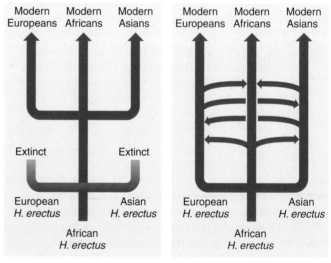

(a) Out of Africa hypothesis (b) Multiregional hypothesis

Figure 21–14 Competing hypotheses on the origin of modern humans. Scientists agree that *Homo erectus* arose in Africa and migrated to other continents. What happened then is the controversy. **(a)** According to the out of Africa hypothesis, all but the African line of *H. erectus* went extinct. In Africa, *H. erectus* evolved into modern humans, which migrated to other continents. **(b)** According to the multiregional hypothesis, modern humans evolved from *H. erectus* populations in different regions of the world. The smaller horizontal arrows in **(b)** represent gene flow (migration and interbreeding among the different populations).

test of the out of Africa hypothesis. Multiple subsequent molecular studies comparing DNA sequences from different human groups, however, all have produced essentially the same answer—that modern humans are descended from an early human population that lived in southern Africa.

For example, a 1996 study examined the genetic variation in two stretches of DNA on human chromosome 12 from 1600 people living in 42 different populations around the world (13 African, 2 Middle Eastern, 7 European, 9 Asian, 3 Pacific, and 8 Amerindian populations). The DNA segments varied depending on where the populations lived. Based on the results, scientists divided the present-day human population into three groups: sub-Saharan Africans, northeastern Africans, and non-Africans. (Sub-Saharan Africa refers to all countries located south of the Sahara Desert.) The sub-Saharan Africans exhibited the greatest genetic diversity, whereas the non-African populations were the least diverse. These findings are consistent with the predictions of the out of Africa hypothesis for two reasons. First, according to the hypothesis, the sub-Saharan populations are expected to be more diverse because they are older and have had a longer time to accumulate that diversity. Second, the small populations thought to have emigrated from Africa could not have been representative of the total diversity present in the larger African population (recall the discussion in Chapter 18 on the founder effect and genetic drift).

Such research has not disproved the multiregional hypothesis, but it indicates the direction for additional research on other segments of human DNA. A series of recent genetic studies of both mtDNA and nuclear DNA has strengthened the case for Africa as the birthplace of modern humans, and in 1999 scientists announced that the ancestors common to all humans were probably ancient Khoisans, an indigenous group in southern Africa. This conclusion was based on separate analyses of DNA from both mitochondria and the Y chromosome. Both studies indicated that the Khoisan people are the most ancient of all human groups.

Some molecular research has suggested that the out of Africa hypothesis may not be as simple as originally envisioned—that is, humans from Africa may not have completely replaced the archaic humans on other continents but may have interbred to some extent with them as they evolved into modern humans. Although many of the human genes that were analyzed have demonstrated an African ancestry, a few appear to have arisen in Asia and to have been introduced at a later time into African populations, probably by migration from Asia to Africa. Thus, certain ancestral human populations in both Africa and Asia may have contributed to the gene pool of modern humans.

■ HUMANS UNDERGO CULTURAL EVOLUTION

Genetically speaking, humans are not very different from other primates. At the level of our DNA sequences, we are roughly 98% identical to gorillas and 99% identical to chimpanzees. Our rela-

tively few genetic differences, however, give rise to several important distinguishing features, such as greater intelligence and the ability to capitalize on it through **cultural evolution,** which is the transmission of knowledge from one generation to the next. (It should be noted that researchers are increasingly in agreement that humans are not the only animals to possess culture. Chimpanzees have primitive cultures that include tool-using techniques, hunting methods, and social behaviors, all of which vary from one population to another. These cultural traditions are passed from one generation to the next by teaching and imitation; see *On the Cutting Edge: Cultural Variation among Chimpanzee Groups* in Chapter 50.)

Human culture is dynamic; it is modified as we obtain new knowledge. Human cultural evolution is generally divided into three stages: (1) the development of hunter-gatherer societies; (2) the development of agriculture; and (3) the Industrial Revolution.

Early humans were hunters and gatherers who relied on what was available in their immediate environment. They were nomadic, and as the resources in a given area were exhausted or as the population increased, they migrated to a different area. These societies required a division of labor and the ability to make tools and weapons, which were needed not only to kill game but also to scrape hides, dig up roots and tubers, and cook food. Although we are not certain when hunting was incorporated into human society, we do know that it declined in importance approximately 15,000 years ago. This may have been due to a decrease in the abundance of large animals, triggered in part by overhunting. A few isolated groups of hunter-gatherer societies, including the Inuit of northern polar regions and the Mbuti of Africa, have survived into the 21st century.

Development of agriculture resulted in a more dependable food supply

Evidence that humans had begun to cultivate crops approximately 10,000 years ago includes the presence of agricultural tools and plant material at archaeological sites. Agriculture, which involves keeping animals as well as cultivating plants, resulted in a more dependable food supply. Recent archaeological evidence suggests that agriculture arose in several steps. Although there is variation from one site to another, plant cultivation, in combination with hunting, usually occurred first. Animal domestication followed later. Agriculture, in turn, often led to more permanent dwellings because considerable time was invested in growing crops in one area. Villages and cities often grew up around the farmlands, but the connection between agriculture and the establishment of villages and towns is complicated by recent discoveries. For example, Abu Hureyra in Syria was a village founded *before* agriculture arose. The villagers subsisted on the rich plant life of the area and the migrating herds of gazelle. Once people turned to agriculture, however, they seldom went back to hunting and gathering to obtain food.

Archaeological evidence indicates that agriculture developed independently in several different regions. There were three main centers of agriculture and several minor ones. Each of the main centers was associated with cultivation of a cereal crop, although other foods were grown as well. Cereals are grasses, which are members of the monocot group of flowering plants (see Chapter 27). The cereals associated with the three main centers of agriculture are wheat, corn, and rice.

Wheat was cultivated in the semiarid regions along the eastern edge of the Mediterranean. Other crops that originated there include peas, lentils, grapes, and olives. Central and South America were the sites of the maize (corn) culture. Squash, chili peppers, beans, and potatoes were also cultivated there. In southern China, evidence exists of the early cultivation of rice and other crops such as soybeans.

Corn, wheat, and rice all are propagated by seed, which requires fairly sophisticated agricultural practices. Growing plants that could be propagated vegetatively may have occurred earlier. Plants raised in this manner, such as bananas, yams, potatoes, and manioc, do not preserve as well as grains because of their high water content. That may be the reason we have little archaeological evidence of their cultivation.

Other advances in agriculture include the domestication of animals, which were kept to supply food, milk, and hides. Archaeological evidence indicates that wild goats and sheep were probably the first animals to be domesticated in southwest Turkey, northern Iraq, and Iran. In the Old World, animals were also used to prepare fields for planting. Another major advance in agriculture was irrigation, which began more than 5000 years ago in Egypt.

Producing food agriculturally was more time-consuming than hunting and gathering, but it was also more productive. In hunter-gatherer societies, everyone shares the responsibility for obtaining food. In agricultural societies, fewer people are needed to provide food for everyone. Thus agriculture freed some people to pursue other endeavors, including religion, art, and various crafts.

Cultural evolution has had a profound impact on the biosphere

Cultural evolution has had far-reaching effects on both human society and on other organisms. The Industrial Revolution, which began in the 18th century, caused populations to concentrate in urban areas near centers of manufacturing. Advances in agriculture encouraged urbanization because fewer and fewer people were needed in rural areas to produce food for everyone. The spread of industrialization increased the demand for natural resources to supply the raw materials for industry.

Cultural evolution has permitted the human population, which reached 6.14 billion in 2001, to expand so dramatically that there are serious questions about Earth's ability to support so many people indefinitely (see Chapter 51). According to the U.N. Food and Agricultural Organization, about 828 million people lack access to the food needed to be healthy and lead productive lives. To further compound the problem, the United Nations projects that 3 billion *additional* people will be added to the world population by the year 2050.

Cultural evolution has resulted in large-scale disruption and degradation of the environment. Tropical rain forests and other natural environments are rapidly being eliminated. Soil, water, and air pollution occur in many places. Since World War II, soil degradation due to poor agricultural practices, overgrazing, and deforestation has occurred in an area equal to 17% of the Earth's total vegetated surface area. Many species cannot adapt to the rapid environmental changes caused by humans and thus are becoming extinct. The decrease in biological diversity due to extinction is alarming (see Chapter 55).

On a positive note, we are aware of the damage we are causing, and we have the intelligence to modify our behavior to improve these conditions. Education, including the study of biology, may help future generations develop environmental sensitivity, making cultural evolution our salvation rather than our destruction.

SUMMARY WITH KEY TERMS

I. Primates are **placental mammals** that arose from small, **arboreal** (tree dwelling), shrewlike mammals.
   A. Primates are adapted for an arboreal existence by the presence of five grasping digits, including an opposable thumb or toe; long, slender limbs that move freely at the hips and shoulders; and eyes located in front of the head.
   B. Primates are divided into three suborders.
      1. The suborder Prosimii includes lemurs, galagos, and lorises.
      2. The suborder Tarsiiformes includes tarsiers.
      3. The suborder Anthropoidea includes **anthropoids** (monkeys, apes, and humans).
II. Anthropoids arose from early primate ancestors.
   A. The early anthropoids branched into two groups: the New and Old World primates.
   B. **Hominoids** (apes and humans) arose from the Old World monkey lineage.

C. There are four modern genera of apes: gibbons, orangutans, gorillas, and chimpanzees.
III. The **hominid** line consists of humans and their ancestors.
   A. Hominid evolution began in Africa.
      1. The earliest known hominids belong to ***Ardipithecus ramidus,*** which appeared about 4.4 mya.
      2. *Ardipithecus ramidus* presumably gave rise to ***Australopithecus anamensis.*** The genus *Australopithecus,* which includes at least six species that lived between about 4 and 1.25 mya, contains the immediate ancestors of the genus *Homo.*
      3. *Ardipithecus* and *Australopithecus* species are often referred to as **australopithecines.** *Australopithecus* species were **bipedal** (walked on two feet), a hominid feature. It is not yet known if *Ardipithecus* was bipedal.

B. **Homo habilis** was the earliest known hominid with some of the human features lacking in the australopithecines, including a slightly larger brain. *H. habilis* fashioned crude tools from stone.

C. **Homo erectus** had a larger brain than *H. habilis;* made more sophisticated tools; and may have worn clothing, built fires, and lived in caves or shelters. Some scientists now think that fossils identified as *Homo erectus* represent two different species, **Homo ergaster,** an earlier African species that gave rise to archaic *Homo sapiens,* and *Homo erectus,* a later Asian offshoot that may be an evolutionary dead end.

D. **Archaic *Homo sapiens*** lived in Africa, Asia, and Europe from about 800,000 to 100,000 years ago. Some researchers classify archaic *Homo sapiens* as a separate species, **Homo heidelbergensis.**

E. **Neandertals** existed from about 230,000 to 30,000 years ago.
   1. Neandertals had short, sturdy builds; receding chins and foreheads; heavy supraorbital ridges and jawbones; larger front teeth; and nasal cavities with unusual triangular bony projections.
   2. Many scientists think that Neandertals were a separate species, **Homo neanderthalensis,** whereas some scientists think Neandertals were a type of modern human.
   3. The disappearance of Neandertals is a mystery.

F. Anatomically modern humans **(Homo sapiens)** existed 100,000 years ago.
   1. By about 30,000 years ago, anatomically modern humans were the only members of genus *Homo* remaining. European remains of these ancient people are referred to as **Cro-Magnons.**
   2. The origin of modern humans is controversial. Two hypotheses, the out of Africa and the multiregional hypotheses, purport to explain the origin of modern humans. **Molecular anthropology,** the comparison of biological molecules from individuals of regional human populations, generally favors the African origin of modern humans.

IV. **Cultural evolution** is the transmission of knowledge from one generation to the next.
   A. Large human brain size makes cultural evolution possible.
   B. Two significant advances in cultural evolution were the development of agriculture and the Industrial Revolution.

POST·TEST

1. The first primates evolved about 55 mya from (a) shrewlike monotremes (b) therapsids (c) shrewlike placental mammals (d) tarsiers (e) shrewlike marsupials

2. The anthropoids are more closely related to _____ than to _____. (a) tarsiers; lemurs (b) lemurs; monkeys (c) tree shrews; tarsiers (d) lemurs; tarsiers (e) tree shrews; monkeys

3. Unlike Old World monkeys, some New World monkeys possess (a) body hair (b) five grasping digits (c) a well-developed cerebrum (d) a bipedal walk (e) a prehensile tail

4. Apes and humans are collectively called (a) mammals (b) primates (c) anthropoids (d) hominoids (e) hominids

5. With what group do hominoids share the most recent common ancestor? (a) Old World monkeys (b) New World monkeys (c) tarsiers (d) lemurs (e) lorises and galigos

6. The _____ in humans is centered at the base of the skull, positioning the head for erect walking. (a) supraorbital ridge (b) foramen magnum (c) pelvis (d) bony skull crest (e) femur

7. The oldest evidence of bipedalism is found in the tibia of (a) *Australopithecus afarensis* (b) *Australopithecus anamensis* (c) *Australopithecus africanus* (d) *Homo erectus* (e) *Homo habilis*

8. Humans and their *immediate* ancestors are collectively called (a) mammals (b) primates (c) anthropoids (d) hominoids (e) hominids

9. The earliest hominid belongs to the genus (a) *Aegyptopithecus* (b) *Dryopithecus* (c) *Ardipithecus* (d) *Australopithecus* (e) *Homo*

10. The earliest hominid to be placed in the genus *Homo* is (a) *H. habilis* (b) *H. ergaster* (c) *H. erectus* (d) *H. heidelbergensis* (e) *H. neanderthalensis*

11. Some scientists now think that fossils identified as *Homo erectus* represent which two different species? (a) *H. habilis* and *H. erectus* (b) *H. ergaster* and *H. erectus* (c) *H. heidelbergensis* and *H. ergaster* (d) *H. neanderthalensis* and *H. erectus* (e) *H. neanderthalensis* and *H. sapiens*

12. Archaic *Homo sapiens* appeared about _____ years ago. (a) 5 million (b) 800,000 (c) 230,000 (d) 100,000 (e) 5000

13. _____ were an early group of humans with short, sturdy builds and heavy supraorbital ridges that lived throughout Europe and western Asia from about 230,000 to 30,000 years ago. (a) Australopithecines (b) Dryopithecines (c) Archaic *Homo sapiens* (d) Neandertals (e) Cro-Magnons

14. The modern human skull *lacks* (a) small canines (b) a foramen magnum centered in the skull (c) pronounced supraorbital ridges (d) a U-shaped arrangement of teeth on the jaw (e) a large cranium (brain case)

15. The comparison of genetic material from individuals of regional populations of humans, used to help unravel the origin and migration of modern humans, is known as (a) paleoarchaeology (b) cultural anthropology (c) molecular anthropology (d) cytogenetics (e) genetic dimorphism

REVIEW QUESTIONS

1. Distinguish between each of the following pairs: (a) mammals and primates (b) anthropoids and hominoids (c) hominoids and hominids (d) australopithecines and the genus Homo
2. Describe three different ways primates are adapted to an arboreal existence.
3. Identify at least three differences between the skulls of apes and humans.
4. Explain at least three ways in which an ape skeleton differs from a human skeleton.
5. Distinguish between each of the following pairs: (a) *Homo habilis* and *Homo erectus* (b) *Homo ergaster* and *Homo erectus* (c) *Homo erectus* and *Homo heidelbergensis* (d) *Homo neanderthalensis* and *Homo sapiens*

6. Describe the two currently proposed hypotheses that explain where modern humans originated.
7. What is cultural evolution, and how has it affected Earth?
8. Add the following labels to the diagram: suborder Anthropoidea, suborder Prosimii, suborder Tarsiformes, Hominids, Hominoids, Hylobatidae, and Pongidae. Use Figure 21–2 to check your answers.

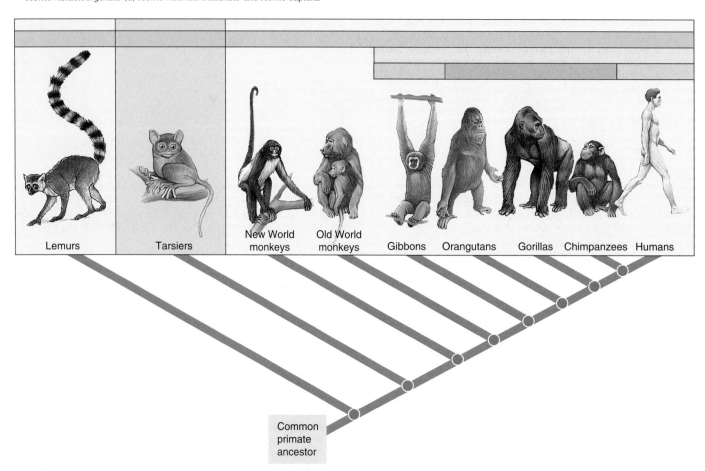

Lemurs | Tarsiers | New World monkeys | Old World monkeys | Gibbons | Orangutans | Gorillas | Chimpanzees | Humans

Common primate ancestor

YOU MAKE THE CONNECTION

1. What types of as-yet-undiscovered scientific evidence would help explain how monkeys got to South America from the Old World?
2. Why are classifying fossil hominid species and determining their evolutionary relationships to one another such controversial endeavors?
3. Which hypothesis of the origin of modern humans (out of Africa or multiregional) seems to more closely match our understanding of evolutionary processes in general? Explain your answer.

4. If you were evaluating whether other early humans exterminated the Neandertals, what kinds of archaeological evidence might you look for?
5. The remains of Cro-Magnons have been found in southern Europe alongside reindeer bones, but reindeer currently exist only in northern Europe and Asia. Can you explain the apparent discrepancy?

RECOMMENDED READINGS

Bower, B. "Out on a Limb." *Science News,* Vol. 158, 25 Nov. 2000. The fact that relatively minor alterations in certain developmental genes can lead to major changes in body form may affect the validity of cladistic analysis of human evolution.

Bower, B. "Salvaged DNA Adds to Neandertals' Mystique." *Science News,* Vol. 157, 1 Apr. 2000. A second retrieval of ancient DNA from a Neandertal supports the hypothesis that Neandertals did not interbreed with anatomically modern humans.

Brainard, J. "Giving Neandertals Their Due." *Science News,* Vol. 154, 1 Aug. 1998. Recent studies suggest that the Neandertals produced relatively sophisticated ornaments and tools.

Gore, R. "People Like Us." *National Geographic,* Vol. 198, No. 1, Jul. 2000. This article examines what is known about human culture and behavior from 100,000 years ago to 10,000 years ago.

Kahn, P., and A. Gibbons. "DNA from an Extinct Human." *Science,* Vol. 277, 11 Jul. 1997. This research news article highlights the first successful attempt to extract and analyze DNA from a fossil Neandertal bone.

Keyser, A.W. "The Dawn of Humans: Finds in South Africa." *National Geographic,* Vol. 197, No. 5, May 2000. Discusses recent fossil discoveries of *Australopithecus robustus,* an evolutionary side branch of the human tree.

Larick, R., R.L. Ciochon, and Y. Zaim. "Fossil Farming in Java." *Natural History,* Jul./Aug. 1999. Indonesian farmers have found many hominid fossils while they cultivate their crops.

Leakey, M., and A. Walker. "Early Hominid Fossils from Africa." *Scientific American,* Vol. 276, No. 6, Jun. 1997. An overview of exciting discoveries of early hominid fossils (*Ardipithecus* and *Australopithecus*) and their significance to human evolution.

Morell, V. "Forming the Robust Australopithecine Face." *Science,* Vol. 284, 9 Apr. 1999. This news article reports on a research paper in the same issue. It emphasizes that many of the unique facial characteristics of the robust australopithecines are the result of a change in dental proportions (i.e., the extremely large premolars and molars characteristic of robust australopithecines).

Tattersall, I. "A Hundred Years of Missing Links." *Natural History,* Dec. 2000/Jan. 2001. The author reviews the 20th century's significant discoveries in human evolution in this centennial issue of *Natural History.*

Tattersall, I. "Once We Were Not Alone." *Scientific American,* Vols. 282, No. 1, Jan. 2000. Although *Homo sapiens* are the only hominids that exist today, during the course of human evolution, many hominid species coexisted.

Vogel, G. "Chimps in the Wild Show Stirrings of Culture." *Science,* Vol. 284, 25 Jun. 1999. A growing number of researchers say that chimpanzees have a primitive form of culture, including variation in tool use and social customs from one population to another.

Wong, K. "Who Were the Neandertals?" *Scientific American,* Vol. 282, No. 4, Apr. 2000. New (and controversial) evidence suggests that Neandertals interbred with anatomically modern humans.

- Visit our Web site at **http://www.info.brookscole.com/solomonbergmartin** for links to chapter-related resources on the World Wide Web. Additional on-line materials relating to this chapter can also be found on our Web site.

 See chapter activity on BioActive Learner CD for additional help in mastering the chapter's material. Icon location in the chapter's margins shows which topics have tutorials or simulations in the CD.

Wildlife Forensic Specialist

COOKIE SIMS

Cookie Sims carries out wildlife forensics work at the National Fish and Wildlife Forensic Laboratory in Ashland, Oregon, which is part of the U.S. Fish and Wildlife Service Office of Law Enforcement. She earned a B.S. in biology at Southern Oregon University and is currently enrolled in the biology department's master's program. Cookie began her work in wildlife forensics as a college student, when she became intrigued by the lab's function and volunteered her time there.

What is the mission of the wildlife forensics lab?

The mission of the wildlife forensics lab is the same as that of the U.S. Fish and Wildlife Service, which is to work with others to conserve, protect, and enhance fish, wildlife, plants, and their habitats, for the continuing benefit of the American people. The specific duty of the forensics lab is to provide forensic identification services to wildlife law enforcement officers at field stations and ports of entry in the United States.

What are the responsibilities and duties of a "forensic specialist"? Specifically, what does your job involve?

My title is forensic specialist in mammals, birds, and reptiles. The responsibilities of a forensic specialist can vary. Specialty areas in the lab include morphology, genetics, pathology, photography and videography, firearms examination, computer technology, and criminalistics (such as trace evidence and fingerprint analysis). I work in the morphology section. In our section, we use visual and microscopic techniques to identify a wide range of wildlife parts and products that come to the lab as evidence in wildlife law enforcement cases. Another important duty is providing expert witness testimony in court cases.

Give examples of specific crimes against wildlife that the lab pursues.

Some involve poaching, such as illegally hunting deer out of season. There are also crimes that violate particular wildlife laws, such as the Migratory Bird Treaty Act or the Marine Mammal Protection Act.

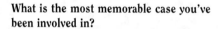

I feel like any advancement in your education is another open door down the road for you.

What is the most memorable case you've been involved in?

That's a hard question, because so many of the cases are memorable. Much of the evidence the lab receives results from violations of importation and exportation laws in the United States. Animal products are seized by wildlife inspectors at ports of entry. We get the weirdest items, such as zebra foot bookends, alligator purses, and feather crafts. One of the most memorable things we received was a smoked, dried animal nose. We had never gotten a nose before to identify. We found out that the nose originated in Southeast Asia, so we had an idea of the range of animals it could be from. We searched through our collection and through the literature available, and our mammalogist identified it as a serow nose. A serow is an animal in the same order as goats and antelopes that lives in Southeast Asia. We happened to have a taxidermied head of this animal, and the nose matched perfectly. It was amazing. That was definitely a memorable case.

You don't deal with the importation of live animals?

No, live animals are taken care of at the ports by wildlife inspectors. We only deal with parts or products. We sometimes receive whole dead animals to determine cause of death or answer some other question.

How is wildlife forensics similar or different to forensics pursued by a typical city's law enforcement agencies?

They are very similar. All crime labs do two things: identify evidence, and attempt to

link the suspect, victim, and crime scene. Our lab is much like a human crime lab, except the victims are animals. Also, typical city law enforcement agencies work with one species—humans. But in wildlife forensics we have to consider virtually all the animals in the world.

Do you specialize in the protection of any particular animal species?

We basically deal with endangered or threatened animals that are protected by certain laws. The Endangered Species Act, a federal law, and CITES, an international treaty, both protect certain animals.

You are currently working on your master's degree; why did you decide to enter a graduate program?

I feel like any advancement in your education is another open door down the road for you. In biology, and I would think in any science field, a higher degree will allow you to go more places and do more things.

How would you advise an undergraduate interested in a career in wildlife forensics?

I would really emphasize keeping your options open by taking general biology courses, so that you are well rounded and have more opportunities when job searching. For government job availability, the Web site www.usajobs.opm.gov is a great resource for summer jobs. One of the things I would really advise is to volunteer your time, either at your school or with a local agency.

Appendix A

Post-Test Answers

CHAPTER 1

1. a   2. a   3. e   4. c   5. a   6. b   7. a
8. c   9. c   10. b   11. a   12. b   13. b   14. d
15. c   16. b   17. b

CHAPTER 2

1. c   2. d   3. e   4. a   5. b   6. c   7. d   8. a
9. e   10. a   11. d   12. e

CHAPTER 3

1. a   2. d   3. b   4. e   5. e   6. d   7. c   8. c
9. a   10. d   11. a   12. e   13. c   14. b

CHAPTER 4

1. b   2. a   3. d   4. d   5. d   6. a   7. e   8. d
9. a   10. a   11. b   12. a   13. a   14. e   15. d

CHAPTER 5

1. d   2. c   3. c   4. c   5. a   6. b   7. a   8. c
9. b   10. b   11. b   12. e   13. c   14. e

CHAPTER 6

1. a   2. c   3. c   4. d   5. b   6. d   7. b   8. d
9. e   10. e   11. a   12. e   13. c   14. b   15. a

CHAPTER 7

1. c   2. a   3. d   4. e   5. a   6. a   7. b   8. c
9. c   10. a   11. c   12. d   13. e   14. b   15. c

CHAPTER 8

1. a   2. d   3. c   4. a   5. a   6. c   7. a   8. e
9. e   10. a   11. c   12. b   13. c   14. a   15. c

CHAPTER 9

1. d   2. a   3. d   4. e   5. c   6. a   7. e   8. d
9. b   10. d   11. c   12. b

CHAPTER 10

1. c   2. d   3. c   4. c   5. d   6. b   7. e   8. c
9. e   10. c   11. b   12. a

Chapter 10   Review Questions

1. a. all yellow   b. $\frac{1}{2}$ yellow: $\frac{1}{2}$ green   c. all yellow
   d. $\frac{3}{4}$ yellow: $\frac{1}{4}$ green
2. 150
3. The short-winged condition is recessive. Both parents are heterozygous.
4. The blue-eyed man is homozygous recessive; his brown-eyed wife is heterozygous.
5. Repeated matings of the roan bull and the white cow will yield an approximate 1:1 ratio of roan-to-white offspring. Repeated matings among roan offspring will yield red, roan, and white offspring in an approximate 1:2:1 ratio. The mating of two red individuals will yield only red offspring.
6. There are 36 possible outcomes when a pair of dice is rolled. There are six ways of obtaining a seven: 1,6; 6,1; 2,5; 5,2; 3,4; and 4,3. There are five ways of rolling a six: 1,5; 5,1; 2,4; 4,2; and 3,3. There are also five ways of rolling an eight: 2,6; 6,2; 3,5; 5,3; and 4,4.
7. The genotype of the brown spotted rabbit is *bbSS*. The genotype of the black, solid rabbit is *BBss*. An F_1 rabbit would be black, spotted *(BbSs)*. The F_2 is expected to be 9/16 black, spotted *(B_S_)*, 3/16 black, solid *(B_ss)*, 3/16 brown, spotted *(bbS_)*, and 1/16 brown, solid *(bbss)*.
8. The F_1 offspring are expected to be black, short-haired. There is a 1/16 chance of brown and tan, long-haired offspring in the F_2 generation.
9. Yes
10. Pleiotropic
11. The rooster is *PpRr;* hen A is *PpRR;* hen B is *Pprr;* and hen C is *PPRR.*
12. a. Both parents are heterozygous for a single locus. b. One parent is heterozygous and the other parent homozygous recessive (for a single locus). c. Both parents are heterozygous (for two loci) d. One parent is heterozygous and the other is homozygous recessive (for two loci).

13. The expected types of F$_2$ plants are: 1/16 of the plants produce 2 kg fruits; $\frac{1}{4}$ of the plants produce 1.75 kg fruits, $\frac{3}{8}$ of the plants produce 1.5 kg fruits, $\frac{1}{4}$ of the plants produce 1.25 kg fruits, and 1/16 of the plants produce 1 kg fruits.

14. All male offspring of this cross are barred, and all females are nonbarred, thus allowing the sex of the chicks to be determined by their phenotypes.

15. This is a two-point test cross involving linked loci. The parental class of offspring are *Aabb* and *aaBb;* the recombinant classes are *AaBb* and *aabb*. There is 4.6% recombination, which corresponds to 4.6 map units between the loci.

16. If genes B and C are 10 map units apart, gene A is in the middle. If genes B and C are 2 map units apart, gene C is in the middle.

CHAPTER 11

1. d   2. d   3. b   4. e   5. a   6. d   7. c   8. e
9. b   10. a   11. c

CHAPTER 12

1. e   2. d   3. c   4. b   5. a   6. e   7. c   8. a
9. b   10. d   11. e

CHAPTER 13

1. a   2. c   3. a   4. e   5. c   6. a   7. c   8. a
9. b   10. c   11. a   12. b   13. c

CHAPTER 14

1. a 2. b 3. e 4. d 5. a 6. b 7. a 8. b 9. c 10. a 11. b

CHAPTER 15

1. d 2. e 3. a 4. c 5. c 6. a 7. e 8. d 9. a 10. a 11. d
12. c 13. e 14. e 15. d

CHAPTER 16

1. c   2. d   3. a   4. b   5. a   6. c   7. b   8. d
9. e   10. b   11. c   12. d

CHAPTER 17

1. d   2. b   3. c   4. b   5. c   6. b   7. a   8. c
9. d   10. b   11. e   12. b   13. b   14. b   15. d

CHAPTER 18

1. b   2. b   3. b   4. d   5. b   6. b   7. c   8. d
9. a   10. e   11. e   12. d   13. b   14. c   15. b

Chapter 18 Review Questions

1. 0.6   2. 0.25; 0.5   3. 0.8   4. 0.4; 0.6   5. No. If it were at genetic equilibrium, the genotype frequency of *Aa* would be $2pq = 0.48$.   6. Frequency of $t = 0.55$; frequency of $T = 0.45$ 7. 0.3   8. $T = 0.6$; $t = 0.4$ 9. $T = 0.8$; $t = 0.2$ 10. 0.42

CHAPTER 19

1. e   2. b   3. a   4. a   5. c   6. b   7. d   8. b
9. b   10. c   11. b   12. e   13. c   14. e   15. d

CHAPTER 20

1. a   2. c   3. b   4. d   5. c   6. d   7. c   8. a
9. d   10. a   11. b   12. c   13. b   14. c   15. c

CHAPTER 21

1. c   2. a   3. e   4. d   5. a   6. b   7. b   8. e
9. c   10. a   11. b   12. b   13. d   14. c   15. c

CHAPTER 22

1. b   2. c   3. a   4. d   5. b   6. b   7. e   8. c
9. a   10. a   11. a   12. a   13. b   14. e   15. a

CHAPTER 23

1. a   2. e   3. a   4. b   5. c   6. a   7. d   8. b
9. b   10. a   11. b   12. a   13. d   14. c   15. e
16. c   17. b   18. e   19. d   20. a   21. b   22. d

CHAPTER 24

1. c   2. a   3. c   4. d   5. b   6. d   7. d   8. e
9. b   10. b   11. e   12. d   13. a   14. e   15. c

CHAPTER 25

1. a   2. b   3. e   4. d   5. d   6. a   7. b   8. c
9. a   10. c   11. c   12. c   13. e   14. b   15. a

CHAPTER 26

1. d   2. a   3. b   4. c   5. d   6. b   7. a   8. e
9. a   10. c   11. d   12. c   13. e   14. c   15. d
16. b   17. d   18. e   19. a   20. b   21. b   22. e
23. d   24. c   25. e

CHAPTER 27

1. e   2. b   3. c   4. d   5. a   6. e   7. d   8. d
9. c   10. b   11. d   12. a   13. c   14. a   15. c

CHAPTER 28

1. d   2. d   3. e   4. b   5. e   6. a   7. c   8. c
9. b   10. a   11. a   12. b   13. a   14. c   15. c

CHAPTER 29

1. b   2. c   3. a   4. b   5. e   6. b   7. d   8. e
9. c   10. b   11. c   12. d   13. a   14. d   15. b
16. b   17. a   18. e   19. e

CHAPTER 30

1. d   2. b   3. a   4. a   5. b   6. e   7. c   8. b
9. a   10. d   11. c   12. c   13. a   14. d   15. c

CHAPTER 31

1. c   2. a   3. d   4. e   5. b   6. c   7. c   8. b
9. e   10. c   11. b   12. a   13. c   14. b   15. d

CHAPTER 32

1. c   2. b   3. d   4. d   5. b   6. e   7. c   8. a
9. d   10. d   11. a   12. e   13. c   14. c   15. a

CHAPTER 33

1. e   2. b   3. d   4. c   5. d   6. e   7. b   8. a
9. c   10. d   11. e   12. c   13. b   14. a   15. b

CHAPTER 34

1. c   2. b   3. b   4. d   5. b   6. e   7. a   8. c
9. c   10. d   11. d   12. a   13. d   14. b   15. e

CHAPTER 35

1. e   2. c   3. d   4. e   5. c   6. a   7. c   8. b
9. c   10. b   11. d   12. c   13. a   14. d   15. a

CHAPTER 36

1. d   2. b   3. e   4. c   5. e   6. a   7. d   8. a
9. a   10. b   11. c   12. c   13. e   14. e   15. b

CHAPTER 37

1. b   2. b   3. a   4. c   5. b   6. c   7. a   8. e
9. c   10. e   11. a   12. d   13. b   14. d   15. a
16. a   17. e

CHAPTER 38

1. d   2. a   3. c   4. c   5. a   6. b   7. d   8. b
9. a   10. e   11. a   12. c   13. e   14. b   15. d

CHAPTER 39

1. c   2. e   3. a   4. b   5. e   6. d   7. e   8. e
9. a   10. c   11. c   12. c   13. c   14. b   15. d

CHAPTER 40

1. b   2. d   3. c   4. b   5. d   6. a   7. a   8. d
9. a   10. c   11. e   12. d   13. b   14. b   15. d
16. a

CHAPTER 41

1. e   2. c   3. a   4. d   5. e   6. c   7. b   8. a
9. e   10. d   11. b   12. a   13. c   14. b   15. c
16. b

CHAPTER 42

1. b   2. d   3. b   4. a   5. b   6. c   7. e   8. e
9. a   10. c   11. e   12. d   13. a   14. c   15. d

CHAPTER 43

1. b   2. a   3. d   4. c   5. e   6. c   7. a   8. b
9. c   10. a   11. d   12. a   13. c   14. e   15. d
16. b   17. a

CHAPTER 44

1. c   2. a   3. b   4. a   5. c   6. b   7. b   8. a
9. d   10. e   11. b   12. a   13. e   14. c   15. d

CHAPTER 45

1. a   2. a   3. c   4. d   5. d   6. e   7. e   8. b
9. b   10. d   11. a   12. b   13. c   14. c   15. a

CHAPTER 46

1. c   2. b   3. a   4. c   5. d   6. e   7. b
8. e   9. d   10. d   11. c   12. a   13. b   14. d
15. e

CHAPTER 47

1. b   2. c   3. a   4. d   5. c   6. e   7. b
8. a   9. d   10. e   11. b   12. d   13. a   14. e
15. c

CHAPTER 48

1. b   2. c   3. a   4. e   5. b   6. d   7. a
8. c   9. e   10. d   11. c   12. a   13. e   14. b
15. e

CHAPTER 49

1. d   2. a   3. a   4. d   5. b   6. e   7. b
8. b   9. c   10. b   11. c   12. c   13. d

CHAPTER 50

1. c   2. b   3. a   4. e   5. c   6. e   7. a
8. a   9. b   10. a   11. b   12. a   13. e   14. a
15. b   16. b   17. a   18. e

CHAPTER 51

1. b   2. b   3. a   4. e   5. a   6. c   7. b
8. a   9. d   10. e   11. a   12. b   13. b   14. e
15. c

Chapter 51 Review Questions 10 to 13

10. Netherlands. (The density of the Netherlands is 16 million ÷ 990 mi^2 = 16,161 people/mi^2. The density of the United States is 284.5 million ÷ 3,615,200 mi^2 = 78 people/mi^2.)

11. The 2002 population of India will be 1050.5 million.
12. The 2002 world death rate was 9 per 1000 people.

13.

TABLE 51–A   Life Table

Age Interval (Years)	Number Alive at Beginning of Age Interval	Proportion Alive at Beginning of Age Interval	Proportion Dying During Age Interval	Death Rate for Age Interval
0–1	1000	1.000	0.790	0.790
1–2	210	0.210	0.110	0.524
2–3	100	0.100	0.054	0.540
3–4	46	0.046	0.046	1.000
4–5	0	0.000	0.000	

CHAPTER 52

1. d   2. d   3. d   4. d   5. e   6. c   7. c   8. d
9. a   10. d   11. e   12. d   13. e   14. d   15. d

CHAPTER 53

1. c   2. d   3. e   4. d   5. a   6. d   7. e   8. e
9. d   10. b   11. c   12. d   13. e   14. d   15. b

CHAPTER 54

1. c   2. b   3. a   4. d   5. e   6. c   7. b   8. d
9. b   10. a   11. b   12. c   13. a   14. e   15. e

CHAPTER 55

1. d   2. e   3. c   4. c   5. b   6. e   7. c   8. e
9. c   10. d   11. b   12. d   13. c   14. a   15. b

Appendix B

Periodic Table of the Elements

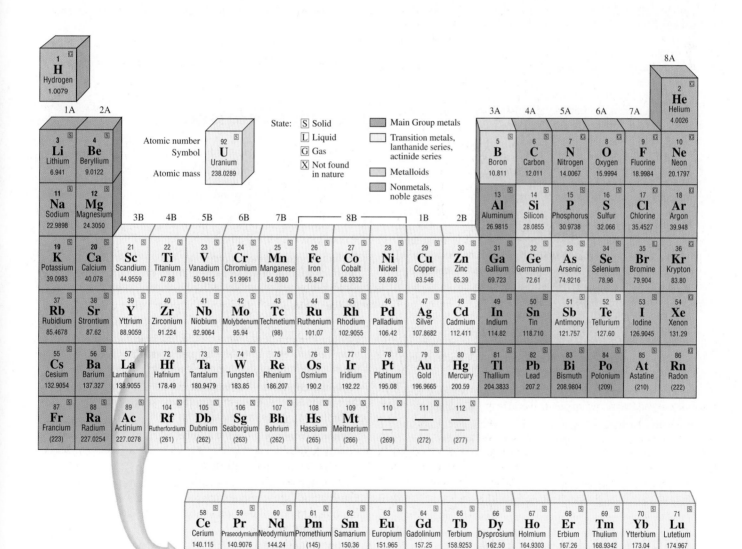

Appendix C

The Classification of Organisms

The system of cataloging organisms used in this book is described in Chapter 1 and in Part 5. In this edition of *Biology*, we use a six-kingdom classification: Eubacteria, Archaebacteria, Protista, Fungi, Plantae, and Animalia. Prokaryotic organisms, distinguished from eukaryotes by their smaller ribosomes and absence of a nuclear envelope and other membranous organelles, are classified in kingdoms Eubacteria and Archaebacteria. Because many biologists prefer the three-domain approach, we also discuss the domains: **Archaea** (which corresponds to kingdom Archaebacteria), **Eubacteria** (or simply **Bacteria**), and **Eukarya** (eukaryotes). We have omitted many groups, especially extinct ones, to simplify the vast number of diverse categories of living organisms and their relationships to one another. Note that we have omitted the viruses from this survey, because they do not fit into any of the six kingdoms.

■ KINGDOM EUBACTERIA

Very large, diverse group of prokaryotic organisms (lack nuclear envelopes, mitochondria, and other membranous organelles; ribosomes smaller than in eukaryotes). Typically unicellular, but some form colonies or filaments. Mainly heterotrophic, but some groups are photosynthetic or chemosynthetic. Reproduction is primarily asexual by fission. Bacteria are nonmotile or move by beating flagella. When present, flagella are solid (rather than the 9 + 2 type typical of eukaryotes). More than 10,000 species.

Bacterial nomenclature and taxonomic practices are controversial and changing. In one system, eubacteria are classified in three main groups: (1) bacteria with a gram-negative type of cell wall, (2) bacteria with a gram-positive type of cell wall, and (3) bacteria with no cell walls (mycoplasmas). See Chapter 23, Table 23–3.

Gram-negative bacteria. Thin cell wall containing peptidoglycan. Include *proteobacteria, chlamydias, spirochetes, cyanobacteria*.

Gram-positive bacteria. Thick cell wall of peptidoglycan. All are nonphotosynthetic, and many produce spores. Include *actinomycetes, lactic acid bacteria, mycobacteria, streptococci, staphylococci, clostridia*.

Bacteria that lack a rigid cell wall. Extremely small bacteria bounded by a plasma membrane. *Mycoplasmas*.

■ KINGDOM ARCHAEBACTERIA

Prokaryotes with cell walls lacking peptidoglycan. Distinguished by their ribosomal RNA, lipid structure, and specific enzymes. Archaebacteria are found in extreme environments—hot springs, sea vents, dry and salty seashores, boiling mud, and near ash-ejecting volcanoes. Three main groups (considered phyla by some microbiologists) are *methanogens, extreme halophiles,* and *extreme thermophiles*.

Methanogens. Anaerobes that produce methane gas from simple carbon compounds.

Extreme Halophiles. Inhabit saturated salt solutions.

Extreme Thermophiles. Grow at 70°C or higher, some thrive above the boiling point.

■ KINGDOM PROTISTA

Primarily unicellular or simple multicellular eukaryotic organisms that do not form tissues and that exhibit relatively little division of labor. Most modes of nutrition occur in this kingdom. Life cycles may include both sexually and asexually reproducing phases and may be extremely complex, especially in parasitic forms. Locomotion is by cilia, flagella, amoeboid movement, or by other means. Flagella and cilia have 9 + 2 structure.

Phylum Zoomastigina. *Flagellates*. Single cells that move by means of flagella. Some free-living; many symbiotic; some pathogenic. Reproduction usually asexual by binary fission.

Phylum Rhizopoda. *Amoebas*. Shelled or naked unicellular protists whose movement is associated with pseudopodia.

Phylum Foraminifera. *Foraminiferans*. Unicellular protists that produce calcareous tests (shells) with pores through which cytoplasmic projections extend, forming a sticky net to entangle prey.

Phylum Actinopoda. *Actinopods*. Unicellular protists that produce axopods (long, filamentous cytoplasmic projections) that protrude through pores in their siliceous shells.

Phylum Ciliophora. *Ciliates*. Unicellular protists that move by means of cilia. Reproduction is asexual by binary fission or sexual by conjugation. About 7200 species.

Phylum Apicomplexa. *Apicomplexans*. Parasitic unicellular protists that lack specific structures for locomotion. At some stage in life cycle, they develop spores (small infective agents). Some pathogenic. About 3900 species.

Phylum Dinoflagellata. *Dinoflagellates*. Unicellular (some colonial), photosynthetic, biflagellate. Cell walls, composed of overlapping cell plates, contain cellulose. Contain chlorophylls *a* and *c* and carotenoids, including fucoxanthin. About 2100 species.

Phylum Bacillariophyta. *Diatoms.* Unicellular (some colonial), photosynthetic. Most nonmotile, but some move by gliding. Cell walls composed of silica rather than cellulose. Contain chlorophylls *a* and *c* and carotenoids, including fucoxanthin. About 5600 species.

Phylum Chrysophyta. *Golden algae.* Unicellular (some colonial), photosynthetic, biflagellate (some lack flagella). Cells covered by tiny scales of either silica or calcium carbonate. Contain chlorophylls *a* and *c* and carotenoids, including fucoxanthin. About 500 species.

Phylum Euglenophyta. *Euglenoids.* Unicellular, photosynthetic, two flagella (one of them very short). Flexible outer covering. Contain chlorophylls *a* and *b* and carotenoids. About 1000 species.

Phylum Chlorophyta. *Green algae.* Unicellular, colonial, siphonous, and multicellular forms. Some motile and flagellated. Photosynthetic; contain chlorophylls *a* and *b* and carotenoids. About 7000 species.

Phylum Rhodophyta. *Red algae.* Most multicellular (some unicellular), mainly marine. Some (coralline algae) have bodies impregnated with calcium carbonate. No motile cells. Photosynthetic; contain chlorophyll *a,* carotenoids, phycocyanin, and phycoerythrin. About 4000 species.

Phylum Phaeophyta. *Brown algae.* Multicellular, often quite large (kelps). Photosynthetic; contain chlorophylls *a* and *c* and carotenoids, including fucoxanthin. Biflagellate reproductive cells. About 1500 species.

Phylum Myxomycota. *Plasmodial slime molds.* Spend part of life cycle as a thin, streaming, multinucleate plasmodium that creeps along on decaying leaves or wood. Flagellated or amoeboid reproductive cells; form spores in sporangia. About 500 species.

Phylum Acrasiomycota. *Cellular slime molds.* Vegetative (nonreproductive) form unicellular; move by pseudopods. Amoeba-like cells aggregate to form a multicellular pseudoplasmodium that eventually develops into a fruiting body that bears spores. About 70 species.

Phylum Oomycota. *Water molds.* Consist of branched, coenocytic mycelia. Cellulose and/or chitin in cell walls. Produce biflagellate asexual spores. Sexual stage involves production of oospores. Some parasitic. About 580 species.

■ KINGDOM FUNGI

All eukaryotic, mainly multicellular organisms that are heterotrophic with saprotrophic or parasitic nutrition. Body form often a mycelium, and cell walls consist of chitin. No flagellated stages except in chytrids. Reproduce by means of spores, which may be produced sexually or asexually. Cells usually haploid or dikaryotic, with brief diploid period following fertilization.

Phylum Chytridiomycota. *Chytridiomycetes* or *chytrids.* Parasites and decomposers found principally in fresh water. Motile cells (gametes and zoospores) contain a single, posterior flagellum. Reproduce both sexually and asexually. About 1000 species.

Phylum Zygomycota. *Zygomycetes.* Produce sexual resting spores called zygospores, and asexual spores in a sporangium. Hyphae are coenocytic. Many are heterothallic (two mating types). About 800 species.

Phylum Ascomycota. *Ascomycetes* or *sac fungi.* Sexual reproduction involves formation of ascospores in little sacs called asci. Asexual reproduction involves production of spores called conidia, which pinch off from conidiophores. Hyphae usually have perforated septa. About 30,000 species.

Phylum Basidiomycota. *Basidiomycetes* or *club fungi.* Sexual reproduction involves formation of basidiospores on a basidium. Asexual reproduction uncommon. Heterothallic. Hyphae usually have perforated septa. About 25,000 species.

Phylum Deuteromycota. *Deuteromycetes* or *imperfect fungi.* Sexual stage has not been observed. Most reproduce only by conidia. About 25,000 species.

■ KINGDOM PLANTAE

Multicellular eukaryotic organisms with differentiated tissues and organs. Cell walls contain cellulose. Cells frequently contain large vacuoles; photosynthetic pigments in plastids. Photosynthetic pigments are chlorophylls *a* and *b,* and carotenoids. Nonmotile. Reproduce both asexually and sexually, with alternation of gametophyte (*n*) and sporophyte (*2n*) generations.

Phylum Bryophyta. *Mosses.* Nonvascular plants that lack xylem and phloem. Marked alternation of generations with dominant gametophyte generation. Motile sperm. The gametophytes generally form a dense green mat consisting of individual plants. About 9000 species.

Phylum Hepatophyta. *Liverworts.* Nonvascular plants that lack xylem and phloem. Marked alternation of generations with dominant gametophyte generation. Motile sperm. The gametophytes of certain species have a flat, liver-like thallus; other species are more mosslike in appearance. About 6000 species.

Phylum Anthocerotophyta. *Hornworts.* Nonvascular plants that lack xylem and phloem. Marked alternation of generations with dominant gametophyte generation. Motile sperm. The gametophyte is a small, flat green thallus with scalloped edges. Spores are produced on an erect, hornlike stalk. About 100 species.

Phylum Pterophyta. *Ferns.* Vascular plants with a dominant sporophyte generation. Generally homosporous. Gametophyte is free-living and photosynthetic. Reproduce by spores. Motile sperm. About 11,000 species.

Phylum Psilotophyta. *Whisk ferns.* Vascular plants with a dominant sporophyte generation. Homosporous. Stem is distinctive because it branches dichotomously; plant lacks true roots and leaves. The gametophyte is subterranean and nonphotosynthetic and forms a mycorrhizal relationship with a fungus. Motile sperm. About 12 species.

Phylum Sphenophyta. *Horsetails.* Vascular plants with hollow, jointed stems and reduced, scalelike leaves. Although modern representatives are small, some extinct species were treelike. Homosporous. Gametophyte a tiny photosynthetic plant. Motile sperm. About 15 species.

Phylum Lycophyta. *Club mosses.* Sporophyte plants are vascular with branching rhizomes and upright stems that bear microphylls. Although modern representatives are small, some extinct species were treelike. Some homosporous, others heterosporous. Motile sperm. About 1000 species.

Phylum Coniferophyta. *Conifers.* Heterosporous vascular plants with woody tissues (trees and shrubs) and needle-shaped or scale-like leaves. Most are evergreen. Seeds are usually borne naked on the surface of cone scales. Nutritive tissue in the seed is haploid female gametophyte tissue. Nonmotile sperm. About 550 species.

Phylum Cycadophyta. *Cycads.* Heterosporous, vascular, dioecious plants that are small and shrubby or larger and palmlike. Produce naked seeds in conspicuous cones. Flagellated sperm. About 140 species.

Phylum Ginkgophyta. *Ginkgo.* Broad-leaved deciduous trees that bear naked seeds directly on branches. Dioecious. Contain vascular tissues. Flagellated sperm. The ginkgo tree is the only living representative. One species.

Phylum Gnetophyta. *Gnetophytes.* Woody shrubs, vines, or small trees that bear naked seeds in cones. Contain vascular tissues. Possess many features similar to flowering plants. About 70 species.

Phylum Anthophyta. *Flowering plants* or *angiosperms.* Largest, most successful group of plants. Heterosporous; dominant sporophytes with extremely reduced gametophytes. Contain vascular tissues. Bear flowers, fruits, and seeds (enclosed in a fruit; seeds contain endosperm as nutritive tissue). Double fertilization. More than 235,000 species.

■ KINGDOM ANIMALIA

Multicellular eukaryotic heterotrophs with differentiated cells. In most animals, cells are organized to form tissues; tissues are organized to form organs; and tissues and organs form specialized body systems that carry on specific functions. Most animals have a well-developed nervous system and can respond rapidly to changes in their environment. Most are capable of locomotion during some time in their life cycle. Most animals are diploid and reproduce sexually with eggs and sperm. A flagellated haploid sperm unites with a large, nonmotile haploid egg to form a zygote that undergoes cleavage.

Phylum Porifera. *Sponges.* Mainly marine. Body bears many pores through which water circulates. Food is filtered from the water by collar cells (choanocytes). Solitary or colonial. Asexual reproduction by budding; external sexual reproduction in which sperm are released and swim to internal egg. Larva is motile. About 10,000 species.

Phylum Cnidaria. *Hydras, jellyfish, sea anemones, corals.* Radial symmetry. Tentacles surrounding mouth. Stinging cells (cnidocytes) contain stinging structures called nematocysts. Polyp and medusa forms. Planula larva. Solitary or colonial. Marine, with a few freshwater forms. About 10,000 species.

Phylum Ctenophora. *Comb jellies.* Biradial symmetry. Free-swimming; marine. Two tentacles and eight longitudinal rows of cilia resembling combs; animal moves by means of these bands of cilia. About 100 species.

Phylum Platyhelminthes. *Flatworms.* Acoelomate (no body cavity); region between body wall and internal organs filled with tissue. Planarians are free-living; flukes and tapeworms are parasitic. Body dorsoventrally flattened; cephalization; three tissue layers. Simple nervous system with ganglia in head region. Excretory organs are protonephridia with flame cells. About 20,000 species.

Coelomates

These animals have a true coelom, a body cavity completely lined with mesoderm. Two evolutionary branches of coelomates are protostomes and deuterostomes.

Protostomes

Coelomates with spiral, determinate cleavage; mouth typically develops from blastopore. Two branches of protostomes are Lophotrochozoa and Ecdysozoa.

Lophotrochozoa

Phylum Nemertea. *Proboscis worms* (also called ribbon worms). Long, dorsoventrally flattened body with complex proboscis used for defense and for capturing prey. Definite organ systems. Complete digestive tract. Circulatory system with blood. Functionally acoelomate, but do have a small true coelom in the proboscis. About 900 species.

Phylum Mollusca. *Snails, clams, squids, octopods.* Unsegmented, soft-bodied animals usually covered by a dorsal shell. Have a ventral, muscular foot. Most organs located above foot in visceral mass. A shell-secreting mantle covers the visceral mass and forms a mantle cavity, which contains gills. Trochophore and/or veliger larva. About 50,000 species.

Phylum Annelida. *Segmented worms.* Polychaetes, earthworms, leeches. Both body wall and internal organs are segmented. Body segments separated by septa. Some have nonjointed appendages. Setae used in locomotion. Closed circulatory system; metanephridia; specialized regions of digestive tract. Trochophore larva. About 15,000 species.

Phylum Brachiopoda. *Lamp shells.* One of the lophophorate phyla. Marine; body enclosed between two shells. About 350 species.

Phylum Phoronida. One of the lophophorate phyla. Tube-dwelling marine worms. About 12 species.

Phylum Bryozoa. One of the lophophorate phyla. Mainly marine; sessile colonies produced by asexual budding. About 5000 species.

Ecdysozoa

Phylum Rotifera. *Wheel animals.* Microscopic, wormlike animals. Anterior end has ciliated crown that looks like a wheel when the cilia beat. Posterior end tapers to a foot. Characterized by pseudocoelom (body cavity not completely lined with mesoderm). Constant number of cells. About 1800 species.

Phylum Nematoda. *Roundworms. Ascaris,* hookworms, pinworms. Slender, elongated, cylindrical worms; covered with cuticle. Characterized by pseudocoelom. Free-living and parasitic forms. About 15,000 species.

Phylum Arthropoda. *Arachnids (spiders, mites, ticks), crustaceans (lobsters, crabs, shrimp), insects, centipedes, millipedes.* Segmented animals with paired, jointed appendages and a hard exoskeleton made of chitin. Open circulatory system with dorsal heart. Hemocoel occupies most of body cavity, and coelom is reduced. More than 1 million species.

Deuterostomes

Coelomates with radial, indeterminate cleavage. Blastopore develops into anus, and mouth forms from a second opening.

Phylum Echinodermata. *Sea stars, sea urchins, sand dollars, sea cucumbers.* Marine animals that have pentaradial symmetry as adults but bilateral symmetry as larvae. Endoskeleton of small, calcareous plates. Water vascular system; tube feet for locomotion. About 7000 species.

Phylum Hemichordata. *Acorn worms.* Marine animals with an anterior muscular proboscis, connected by a collar region to a long wormlike body. The larval form resembles an echinoderm larva. About 85 species.

Phylum Chordata. *Subphylum Urochordata (tunicates), subphylum Cephalochordata (lancelets), subphylum Vertebrata (fishes, amphibians, reptiles, birds, mammals).* Notochord; pharyngeal gill slits; dorsal, tubular nerve cord, and postanal tail present at some time in life cycle. About 48,000 species.

Appendix D

Careers in Biology

The following organizations, professional associations, and World Wide Web sites provide career information upon request.

■ GENERAL

American Association for the Advancement of Science

1200 New York Avenue, NW
Washington, DC 20005
202-326-6400
Web Site: http://www.aaas.org
E-mail: info@aaas.org

American Institute of Biological Sciences

Communications Office
1444 Eye Street NW, Suite 200
Washington, DC 20005
202-628-1500 (ext. 261)
Web Site: http://www.aibs.org/careers/index.html
E-mail: cmoulton@aibs.org

Association for Tropical Biology

Executive Director, W. John Kress
Department of Botany MRC-166
National Museum of Natural History
Smithsonian Institute
Washington, DC 20560
202-357-3392
(Fax) 202-786-2563
Web Site: http://atb.botany.ufl.edu
E-mail: kressj@nmnh.si.edu

Association for Women in Science (AWIS)

1200 New York Avenue, NW
Suite 650
Washington, DC 20005
202-326-8940
(Fax) 202-326-8960
Web Site: http://www.awis.org
E-mail: awis@awis.org

Biology Careers Page

Web Site: http://furman.careerhighway.com

Bio Online

Web Site: http://www.bio.com
E-mail: jobs@bio.com

Bioscience Links

Web Site: http://mcb.harvard.edu/BioLinks.html

Federation of American Societies for Experimental Biology

9650 Rockville Pike
Bethesda, MD 20814-3998
301-530-7020
(Fax) 301-571-0699
Web Site: http://www.faseb.org
E-mail: careers@faseb.org

JobHunt: Science, Engineering, and Medicine

Web Site: http://www.job-hunt.org/science.html

National Academy of Science, National Academy of Engineering, Institute of Medicine, National Research Council: A Career Planning Center

Web Site: http://www.nas.edu/careers

Pursuit

Pursuing careers in science, engineering, and mathematics for persons with disabilities
Web Site: http://rehab.uiuc.edu/career/library.html

Women in Technology International (WITI)

6345 Balboa Boulevard, #257
Encino, CA 91316
818-334-WITI
(Fax) 818-342-9891
Web Site: http://www.witi.com

■ AGRICULTURE/AGRONOMY

Careers in Agriculture and Agri-Food
Web Site: http://www.cfa-fca.ca/careers/index1.html

American Society of Agronomy

667 South Segoe Road
Madison, WI 53711
608-273-8080 (ext. 314)
Web Site: http://www.agronomy.org
E-mail: Lmalison@agronomy.org (Leann Malison)

■ ART AND COMMUNICATIONS

Association of Medical Illustrators

2965 Flowers Road South, Suite 105
Atlanta, GA 30341
770-454-7933
(Fax) 770-458-3314
Web Site: http://www.medical-illustrators.org
E-mail: assnhq@mindspring.com

Bio Communications Association

115 Stoneridge Drive
Chapel Hill, NC 27514-9737
(Phone/Fax) 919-967-8246
Web Site: http://www.bca.org
E-mail: BCAoffice@aol.com

Medical Library Association

65 East Wacker Place, Suite 1900
Chicago, IL 60602-4805
312-419-9094
(Fax) 312-419-8950
Web Site: http://www.mlanet.org
E-mail: mlapd1@mlahq.org

National Association of Science Writers

P.O. Box 294
Greenlawn, NY 11740
516-757-5664
(Fax) 516-757-0069
Web Site: http://www.nasw.org
E-mail: diane@nasw.org

■ BIOCHEMISTRY

American Society for Biochemistry and Molecular Biology (ASBMB)

9650 Rockville Pike
Bethesda, MD 20814-3996
Web Site: http://www.faseb.org/asbmb
E-mail: aps@scisoc.org

■ BIOMEDICAL ENGINEERING

Biomedical Engineering Society

8401 Corporate Drive, Suite 110
Landover, MD 20785-2224
301-459-1999
(Fax) 301-459-2444
Web Site: http://mecca.org/BME/BMES/society/index.htm
E-mail: bmes@netcom.com

■ BIOMEDICAL SCIENCE

Employment Links for the Biomedical Scientist

Web Site: http://www.his.com/~graeme/employ.html

■ BIOPHYSICS

The Biophysical Society

9650 Rockville Pike
Bethesda, MD 20814
301-530-7114
(Fax) 301-530-7133
Web Site: http://www.biophysics.org/biophys/society/biohome.htm
E-mail: society@biophysics.faseb.org

■ BOTANY

American Phytopathological Society

3340 Pilot Knob Road
St. Paul, MN 55121-2097
612-454-7250
(Fax) 612-454-0766
Web Site: http://www.apsnet.org

American Society of Plant Physiologists

15501 Monona Drive
Rockville, MD 20855-2768
301-251-0560
(Fax) 301-279-2996
Web Site: http://www.aspp.org
E-mail: aspp@aspp.org

Botanical Society of America

Kim Hiser, Business Manager
1735 Neil Avenue
Columbus, OH 43210-1293
614-292-3519
Web Site: http://www.botany.org

Mycological Society of America

Attention: Linda Hartwick
Allen Marketing and Management
810 E. 10th Street
Lawrence, KS 66044
785-843-1235
(Fax) 785-843-1274
Web Site: http://www.erin.utoronto.ca/~w3msa
E-mail: lhardwick@allenpress.com

Phycological Society of America

Blackwell Science, Inc.
350 Main Street, Commerce Place
Malden, MA 02148
718-388-8250
(Fax) 781-388-8270
Web Site: http://www.psaalgae.org
E-mail: csjournal@blacksci.com

■ CELL BIOLOGY

American Society for Cell Biology (ASCB)

8120 Woodmont Avenue, Suite 750
301-347-9300 (ext. 2755)
(Fax) 301-347-9310
Web Site: http://www.ascb.org
E-mail: ascbinfo@ascb.org

Cell & Molecular Biology Online

Web Site: http://www.cellbio.com

■ DENTISTRY

American Association of Dental Schools

202-667-9433
(Fax) 202-667-0642
Web Site: http://www.aads.jhu.edu
E-mail: adea@adea.org

American Dental Association
211 E. Chicago Avenue
Chicago, IL 60611
312-440-2500
(Fax) 312-440-2800
Web Site: http://www.ada.org
E-mail: publicinfo@ada.org

■ EDUCATION

National Association of Biology Teachers (NABT)

12030 Sunrise Valley Drive, Suite 110
Reston, VA 20191
703-264-9696
(Fax) 703-264-7778
Web Site: http://www.nabt.org
E-mail: office@nabt.org

■ ENTOMOLOGY

Entomological Society of America

9301 Annapolis Road
Lanham, MD 20706-3115
301-731-4535
(Fax) 301-731-4538
Web Site: http://www.entsoc.org
E-mail: esa@entsoc.org

■ ENVIRONMENT/ECOLOGY

Ecological Society of America

1707 H Street NW, Suite 400
Washington, DC 20006
202-833-8773
(Fax) 202-833-8775
Web Site: http://www.sdsc.edu/projects/ESA/esa.htm
E-mail: esahq@esa.org

Environmental Careers Organization (ECO)

179 South Street
Boston, MA 02111
617-426-4375
(Fax) 617-423-0998
Web Site: http://www.eco.org

Midcontinent Ecological Science Center: Explore Science Careers

Midcontinent Ecological Science Center
4512 McMurry Avenue
Fort Collins, CO 80525-3400
970-226-9100
(Fax) 970-226-9230
Web Site: http://www.mesc.nbs.gov/science-careers.html

National Wildlife Federation

11100 Wildlife Center Drive
Reston, VA 20190-5362
703-438-600
Web Site: http://www.nwf.org
E-mail: jobopp@nwf.org

Nature Conservancy

4245 N. Fairfax Drive, Suite 100
Arlington, VA 22203
1-800-628-6860
Web Site: http://nature.org

■ ENVIRONMENTAL LAW

Environmental Defense Fund

257 Park Avenue South
New York, NY 10010
1-800-684-3322
Web Site: http://www.edf.org

Environmental Law Institute

1616 P Street, NW, Suite 200
Washington, DC 20036
202-939-3800
(Fax) 202-939-3868
Web Site: http://www.eli.org

■ FORENSICS

American Academy of Forensic Sciences

The Forensic Sciences Foundation, Inc.
410 North 21st Street, Suite 203
Colorado Springs, CO 80904-2798
719-636-1100
(Fax) 719-636-1993
Web Site: http://www.aafs.org
E-mail: Membship@aafs.org

■ GENETICS

Genetics Society of America

9650 Rockville Pike
Bethesda, MD 20814-3889
301-571-1825
Web Site: http://www.nsgc.org
E-mail: estrass@genetics.faseb.org

National Society of Genetic Counselors

NSGC Executive Office
233 Canterbury Drive
Wallingford, PA 19086-6617
610-872-7608
Web Site: http://members.aol.com/nsgcweb/nsgchome.htm
E-mail: nsgc@aol.com

Careers in Biotechnology

Web Site: http://www.accessexcellence.org

■ MARINE BIOLOGY

American Society of Limnology and Oceanography

Web Site: http://www.aslo.org

Careers & Jobs in Marine Biology & Oceanography

Web Site: http://www-marine.stanford.edu/HMS web/careers.html

Scripps Research Institute

10550 North Torrey Pines Road
La Jolla, CA 92037
858-784-1000
Web Site: http://www.scripps.edu

Virginia Institute of Marine Science

Sea Grant Advisory Board Program
Gloucester Point, VA 23062-1346
804-684-7164
Web Site: http://www.vims.edu/adv/ed/careers

Woods Hole Oceanographic Institution

Information Office
Co-op Building, MS #16
Woods Hole, MA 02543
508-548-1400
(Fax) 508-457-2034
Web Site: http://www.whoi.edu
E-mail: information@whoi.edu

■ MATHEMATICAL BIOLOGY (BIOINFORMATICS)

The Society for Mathematical Biology

Web Site: http://www.smb.org

■ MEDICINE

American Academy of Family Physicians

11400 Tomahawk Creek Parkway
Leawood, KS 66211-2672
913-906-6000
Web Site: http://www.aafp.org
E-mail: fp@aafp.org

American Academy of Pediatrics

141 Northwest Point Boulevard
Elk Grove Village, IL 60007-1098
847-434-4000
(Fax) 847-434-8000
Web Site: http://www.aap.org
E-mail: pedscareer@aap.org

American Association of Immunologists

9650 Rockville Pike
Bethesda, MD 20814-3994
301-530-7178
(Fax) 301-571-1816
Web Site: http://www.aai.org
E-mail: infoaai@aai.faseb.org

American Medical Association

515 North State Street
Chicago, IL 60610
312-464-5000
Web Site: http://www.ama-assn.org

Clinical Immunology Society

611 E. Wells Street
Milwaukee, WI 53202
414-224-8095
(Fax) 414-272-6070
Web Site: http://www.clinimmsoc.org

Research! America (Medical Research)

908 King Street, Suite 400E
Alexandria, VA 22314
703-739-2577
Web Site: http://www.researchamerica.org
E-mail: researcham@aol.com

■ MICROBIOLOGY

American Society for Microbiology

1752 N Street
Washington, DC 20036
202-737-3600
Web Site: http://www.asmusa.org
E-mail: FellowshipsCareerInformation@asmusa.org

■ MICROSCOPY

Microscopy Society of America

Bostrom Corp.
230 East Ohio, Suite 400
Chicago, IL 60611
312-644-1527
(Fax) 312-644-8557
Web Site: http://www.msa.microscopy.com
E-mail: BusinessOffice@MSA.Microscopy.Com

■ NURSING

American Nurses Association

600 Maryland Avenue, SW
Suite 100W
Washington, DC 20024-2571
1-800-274-4ANA
Web Site: http://www.ana.org

National Association for Practical Nurse Education and Service

1400 Spring Street
Suite 300
Silver Spring, MD 20910
301-588-2491
Web Site: http://www.aoa.dhhs.gov/aoa/die/bo.html
E-mail: napnes@bellatlantic.net

■ NUTRITION

American Dietetic Association

216 West Jackson Boulevard
Chicago, IL 60606-6995
312-899-0040
(Fax) 312-899-1979
Web Site: http://www.eatright.org/careers.html
E-mail: network@eatright.org

Institute of Food Technologists

Professional Development Department
221 North LaSalle Street, Suite 300
Chicago, IL 60601-1291
312-782-8424
(Fax) 312-782-8348
Web Site: http://www.ift.org

■ PHARMACEUTICALS

American Association of Colleges of Pharmacy

1426 Prince Street
Alexandria, VA 22314-2841
703-729-2330
(Fax) 703-836-8982
Web Site: http://www.aacp.org
E-mail: angieaacp@aol.com

American Pharmaceutical Association

2215 Constitution Avenue, NW
Washington, DC 20037-2985
202-628-4410
(Fax) 202-783-2351
Web Site: http://www.aoa.dhhs.gov/aoa/dir/49.html

■ PHYSICAL THERAPY

American Physical Therapy Association

1111 North Fairfax Street
Alexandria, VA 22314
703-684-2782
(Fax) 703-684-7343
Web Site: http://www.apta.org

■ PHYSIOLOGY

American Physiological Society

9650 Rockville Pike
Bethesda, MD 20814
301-530-7160
Web Site: http://www.biophysics.org
E-mail: mfrank@aps.faseb.org

■ PSYCHIATRY/PSYCHOLOGY

American Psychiatric Association

Division of Public Affairs
1400 K Street, NW
Washington, DC 20005
1-888-357-7924
(Fax) 202-682-6850
Web Site: http://www.psych.org
E-mail: apa@psych.org

American Psychological Association

750 First Street, NE
Washington, DC 20002
202-336-5500
Web Site: http://www.apa.org
E-mail: education@apa.org

■ PUBLIC HEALTH

American Public Health Association

1015 15th Street, NW
Washington, DC 20005-2605
202-789-5600
(Fax) 202-789-5661
Web Site: http://www.apha.org

■ TAXONOMY

American Society of Plant Taxonomists

Web Site: http://www.sysbof.org

Association of Systematic Collections

1725 K Street, NW, Suite 601
Washington, DC 20006-1401
202-835-9050
(Fax) 202-835-7334
Web Site: http://www.ascoll.org
E-mail: asc@ascoll.org

■ ZOOLOGY

American Association of Zoo Keepers

Topeka Zoological Park
635 S.W. Gage Boulevard
Topeka, KS 66606
913-272-5821 or 913-273-1980
Web Site: http://www.aazk.org

American Society of Mammalogists

Monte L. Bean Life Science Museum
Brigham Young University
Provo, UT 84602-0200
Web Site: http://wkuwebl.wku.edu/~asm

American Zoo and Aquarium Association

8403 Colesville Road
Suite 710
Silver Spring, MD 20910-3314
301-562-0777
(Fax) 562-0888
Web Site: http://www.aza.org

Society for Integrative and Comparative Biology (SICB) (formerly: American Society of Zoologists)

1313 Dolley Madison Boulevard
Suite 402
McLean, VA 22101
703-790-1745
(Fax) 703-790-2672
Web Site: http://www.sicb.org
E-mail: sicb@burkinc.com

Appendix E

Understanding Biological Terms

Your task of mastering new terms will be greatly simplified if you learn to dissect each new word. Many terms can be divided into a prefix, the part of the word that precedes the main root, the word root itself, and often a suffix, a word ending that may add to or modify the meaning of the root. As you progress in your study of biology, you will learn to recognize the more common prefixes, word roots, and suffixes. Such recognition will help you analyze new terms so that you can more readily determine their meaning and will also help you remember them.

■ PREFIXES

a-, ab- from, away, apart (abduct, move away from the midline of the body)

a-, an-, un- less, lack, not (asymmetrical, not symmetrical)

ad- (also **af-, ag-, an-, ap-**) to, toward (adduct, move toward the midline of the body)

allo- different (allometric growth, different rates of growth for different parts of the body during development)

ambi- both sides (ambidextrous, able to use either hand)

andro- a man (androecium, the male portion of a flower)

anis- unequal (anisogamy, sexual reproduction in which the gametes are of unequal sizes)

ante- forward, before (anteflexion, bending forward)

anti- against (antibody, proteins that have the capacity to react against foreign substances in the body)

auto- self (autotroph, organism that manufactures its own food)

bi- two (biennial, a plant that takes two years to complete its life cycle)

bio- life (biology, the study of life)

circum-, circ- around (circumcision, a cutting around)

co-, con- with, together (congenital, existing with or before birth)

contra- against (contraception, against conception)

cyt- cell (cytology, the study of cells)

di- two (disaccharide, a compound made of two sugar molecules chemically combined)

dis- apart (dissect, cut apart)

ecto- outside (ectoplasm, outer layer of cytoplasm)

end-, endo- within, inner (endoplasmic reticulum, a network of membranes found within the cytoplasm)

epi- on, upon (epidermis, upon the dermis)

ex-, e-, ef- out from, out of (extension, a straightening out)

extra- outside, beyond (extraembryonic membrane, a membrane that encircles and protects the embryo)

gravi- heavy (gravitropism, growth of a plant in response to gravity)

hemi- half (cerebral hemisphere, lateral half of the cerebrum)

hetero- other, different (heterozygous, having unlike members of a gene pair)

homeo- unchanging, steady (homeostasis, reaching a steady state)

homo-, hom- same (homologous, corresponding in structure; homozygous, having identical members of a gene pair)

hyper- excessive, above normal (hypersecretion, excessive secretion)

hypo- under, below, deficient (hypotonic, a solution whose osmotic pressure is less than that of a solution with which it is compared)

in-, im- not (incomplete flower, a flower that does not have one or more of the four main parts)

inter- between, among (interstitial, situated between parts)

intra- within (intracellular, within the cell)

iso- equal, like (isotonic, equal osmotic concentration)

macro- large (macronucleus, a large, polyploid nucleus found in ciliates)

mal- bad, abnormal (malnutrition, poor nutrition)

mega- large, great (megakaryocyte, giant cell of bone marrow)

meso- middle (mesoderm, middle tissue layer of the animal embryo)

meta- after, beyond (metaphase, the stage of mitosis after prophase)

micro- small (microscope, instrument for viewing small objects)

mono- one (monocot, a group of flowering plants with one cotyledon, or seed leaf, in the seed)

oligo- small, few, scant (oligotrophic lake, a lake deficient in nutrients and organisms)

oo- egg (oocyte, cell that gives rise to an egg cell)

paedo- a child (paedomorphosis, the preservation of a juvenile characteristic in an adult)

para- near, beside, beyond (paracentral, near the center)

peri- around (pericardial membrane, membrane that surrounds the heart)

photo- light (phototropism, growth of a plant in response to the direction of light)

poly- many, much, multiple, complex (polysaccharide, a carbohydrate composed of many simple sugars)

post- after, behind (postnatal, after birth)

pre- before (prenatal, before birth)

pseudo- false (pseudopod, a temporary protrusion of a cell, i.e., "false foot")

retro- backward (retroperitoneal, located behind the peritoneum)

semi- half (semilunar, half-moon)

sub- under (subcutaneous tissue, tissue immediately under the skin)

super, supra- above (suprarenal, above the kidney)

sym- with, together (sympatric speciation, evolution of a new species within the same geographical region as the parent species)

syn- with, together (syndrome, a group of symptoms that occur together and characterize a disease)

trans- across, beyond (transport, carry across)

■ SUFFIXES

-able, -ible able (viable, able to live)

-ad used in anatomy to form adverbs of direction (cephalad, toward the head)

-asis, -asia, -esis condition or state of (euthanasia, state of "good death")

-cide kill, destroy (biocide, substance that kills living things)

-emia condition of blood (anemia, a blood condition in which there is a lack of red blood cells)

-gen something produced or generated or something that produces or generates (pathogen, an organism that produces disease)

-gram record, write (electrocardiogram, a record of the electrical activity of the heart)

-graph record, write (electrocardiograph, an instrument for recording the electrical activity of the heart)

-ic adjective-forming suffix that means *of* or *pertaining to* (ophthalmic, of or pertaining to the eye)

-itis inflammation of (appendicitis, inflammation of the appendix)

-logy study or science of (cytology, study of cells)

-oid like, in the form of (thyroid, in the form of a shield, referring to the shape of the thyroid gland)

-oma tumor (carcinoma, a malignant tumor)

-osis indicates disease (psychosis, a mental disease)

-pathy disease (dermopathy, disease of the skin)

-phyll leaf (mesophyll, the middle tissue of the leaf)

-scope instrument for viewing or observing (microscope, instrument for viewing small objects)

■ SOME COMMON WORD ROOTS

abscis cut off (abscission, the falling off of leaves or other plant parts)

angi, angio vessel (angiosperm, a plant that produces seeds enclosed within a fruit or "vessel")

apic tip, apex (apical meristem, area of cell division located at the tips of plant stems and roots)

arthr joint (arthropods, invertebrate animals with jointed legs and segmented bodies)

aux grow, enlarge (auxin, a plant hormone involved in growth and development)

blast a formative cell, germ layer (osteoblast, cell that gives rise to bone cells)

brachi arm (brachial artery, blood vessel that supplies the arm)

bry grow, swell (embryo, an organism in the early stages of development)

cardi heart (cardiac, pertaining to the heart)

carot carrot (carotene, a yellow, orange, or red pigment in plants)

cephal head (cephalad, toward the head)

cerebr brain (cerebral, pertaining to the brain)

cervic, cervix neck (cervical, pertaining to the neck)

chlor green (chlorophyll, a green pigment found in plants)

chondr cartilage (chondrocyte, a cartilage cell)

chrom color (chromosome, deeply staining body in nucleus)

cili small hair (cilium, a short, fine cytoplasmic hair projecting from the surface of a cell)

coleo a sheath (coleoptile, a protective sheath that encircles the stem in grass seedlings)

conjug joined together (conjugation, a sexual phenomenon in certain protists)

cran skull (cranial, pertaining to the skull)

decid falling off (deciduous, a plant that sheds its leaves at the end of the growing season)

dehis split (dehiscent fruit, a fruit that splits open at maturity)

derm skin (dermatology, study of the skin)

ecol dwelling, house (ecology, the study of organisms in relation to their environment, i.e., "their house")

enter intestine (enterobacteria, a group of bacteria that include species that inhabit the intestines of humans and other animals)

evol to unroll (evolution, descent with modification, or gradual directional change)

fil a thread (filament, the thin stalk of the stamen in flowers)

gamet a wife or husband (gametangium, the part of a plant, protist, or fungus that produces reproductive cells)

gastr stomach (gastrointestinal tract, the digestive tract)

glyc, glyco sweet, sugar (glycogen, storage form of glucose)

gon seed (gonad, an organ that produces gametes)

gutt a drop (guttation, loss of water as liquid "drops" from plants)

gymn naked (gymnosperm, a plant that produces seeds that are not enclosed with a fruit, i.e., "naked")

hem blood (hemoglobin, the pigment of red blood cells)

hepat liver (hepatic, of or pertaining to the liver)

hist tissue (histology, study of tissues)

hydr water (hydrolysis, a breakdown reaction involving water)

leuk white (leukocyte, white blood cell)

menin membrane (meninges, the three membranes that envelop the brain and spinal cord)

morph form (morphogenesis, development of body form)

my, myo muscle (myocardium, muscle layer of the heart)

myc a fungus (mycelium, the vegetative body of a fungus)

nephr kidney (nephron, microscopic unit of the kidney)

neur, nerv nerve (neuromuscular, involving both the nerves and muscles)

occiput back part of the head (occipital, back region of the head)

ost bone (osteology, study of bones)

path disease (pathologist, one who studies disease processes)

ped, pod foot (bipedal, walking on two feet)

pell skin (pellicle, a flexible covering over the body of certain protists)

phag eat (phagocytosis, process by which certain cells ingest particles and foreign matter)

phil love (hydrophilic, a substance that attracts, i.e., "loves," water)

phloe bark of a tree (phloem, food-conducting tissue in plants that corresponds to bark in woody plants)

phyt plant (xerophyte, a plant adapted to xeric, or dry, conditions)

plankt wandering (plankton, microscopic aquatic protists that float or drift passively)

rhiz root (rhizome, a horizontal, underground stem that superficially resembles a root)

scler hard (sclerenchyma, cells that provide strength and support in the plant body)

sipho a tube (siphonous, a type of tubular body form found in certain algae)

som body (chromosome, deeply staining body in the nucleus)

sor heap (sorus, a cluster or "heap" of sporangia in a fern)

spor seed (spore, a reproductive cell that gives rise to individual offspring in plants, protists, and fungi)

stom a mouth (stoma, a small pore, i.e., "mouth," in the epidermis of plants)

thigm a touch (thigmotropism, plant growth in response to touch)

thromb clot (thrombus, a clot within a blood vessel)

tropi turn (thigmotropism, growth of a plant in response to contact with a solid object, as when a tendril "turns" or wraps around a wire fence)

visc pertaining to an internal organ or body cavity (viscera, internal organs)

xanth yellow (xanthophyll, a yellowish pigment found in plants)

xyl wood (xylem, water-conducting tissue in plant, the "wood" of woody plants)

zoo an animal (zoology, the science of animals)

The biological sciences use a great many abbreviations and with good reason. Many technical terms in biology and biological chemistry are both long and difficult to pronounce. Yet it can be difficult for beginners, when confronted with something like NADPH or EPSP, to understand the reference. Here are some of the common abbreviations used in biology for your ready reference.

A Adenine
ABA Abscisic acid
ACTH Adrenocorticotropic hormone
AD Alzheimer's disease
ADA Adenosine deaminase
ADH Antidiuretic hormone
ADP Adenosine diphosphate
AIDS Acquired immunodeficiency syndrome
AMP Adenosine monophosphate
amu Atomic mass unit (dalton)
APC Anaphase-promoting complex *or* antigen presenting cell
ATP Adenosine triphosphate
AV node or valve Atrioventricular node or valve (of heart)
B lymphocyte or B cell Lymphocyte responsible for antibody-mediated immunity
BH Brain hormone (of insects)
BMR Basal metabolic rate
bya Billion years ago
C Cytosine
C$_3$ Three-carbon pathway for carbon fixation (Calvin cycle)
C$_4$ Four-carbon pathway for carbon fixation (Hatch-Slack pathway)
CAM Crassulacean acid metabolism
cAMP Cyclic adenosine monophosphate
CAP Catabolite gene activator protein
CD4 T cell Helper T cell (T$_h$); has a surface marker designated CD4
CD8 T cell T cell with a surface marker designated CD8; includes cytotoxic T cells
Cdk cyclin-dependent protein kinase
cDNA Complementary deoxyribonucleic acid
CFCs Chlorofluorocarbons
CFTR Cystic fibrosis transmembrane conductance regulator
CITES The Convention on International Trade in Endangered Species of Wild Flora and Fauna
CNS Central nervous system
CoA Coenzyme A
COPD Chronic obstructive pulmonary disease
CP Creatine phosphate
CPR Cardiopulmonary resuscitation
CR Conditioned response
CS Conditioned stimulus
CSF Cerebrospinal fluid

CVS Cardiovascular system
DAG Diacylglycerol
DNA Deoxyribonucleic acid
DOC Dissolved organic carbon
E$_A$ Activation energy (of an enzyme)
ECG Electrocardiogram
ECM Extracellular matrix
EEG Electroencephalogram
EKG Electrocardiogram
EM Electron microscope or micrograph
ENSO El Niño—Southern Oscillation
EPSP Excitatory postsynaptic potential (of a neuron)
ER Endoplasmic reticulum
ES cells Embryonic stem cells
F$_1$ First filial generation
F$_2$ Second filial generation
Fab portion The part of an antibody that binds to an antigen
Factor VIII Blood clotting factor (absent in hemophiliacs)
FAD/FADH$_2$ Flavin adenine dinucleotide (oxidized and reduced forms, respectively)
FAP Fixed action pattern
Fc portion The part of an antibody that interacts with cells of the immune system
FSH Follicle-stimulating hormone
G Guanine
G$_1$ phase First gap phase (of the cell cycle)
G$_2$ phase Second gap phase (of the cell cycle)
G3P Glyceraldehyde-3-phosphate
G protein Cell signaling molecule that requires GTP
GA$_3$ Gibberellin
GABA Gamma-aminobutyric acid
GH Growth hormone (somatotropin)
GnRH Gonadotropin-releasing hormone
GTP Guanosine triphosphate
HBEF Hubbard Brook Experimental Forest
HCFCs Hydrochlorofluorocarbons
hCG Human chorionic gonadotropin
HD Huntington disease
HDL High-density lipoprotein
HFCs Hydrofluorocarbons
hGH Human growth hormone
HIV Human immunodeficiency virus
HLA Human leukocyte antigen
IAA Indole acetic acid (natural auxin)
Ig Immunoglobulin, as in IgA, IgG, etc.
IGF Insulin-like growth factor
IP$_3$ Inositol triphosphate

IPCC United Nations Intergovernmental Panel on Climate Change

IPSP Inhibitory postsynaptic potential (of a neuron)

IUCN World Conservation Union

IUD Intrauterine device

JH Juvenile hormone (of insects)

kb Kilobase

LDH Lactic dehydrogenase enzyme

LDL Low-density lipoprotein

LH Luteinizing hormone

LM Light microscope or micrograph

LSD Lysergic acid diethylamide

LTP Long-term potentiation

MAO Monoamine oxidase

MAPs Microtubule-associated proteins

MHC Major histocompatibility complex

MI Myocardial infarction

MPF Mitosis-promoting factor

MRI Magnetic resonance imaging

mRNA Messenger RNA

MSAFP Maternal serum α-fetoprotein

mtDNA Mitochondrial DNA

MTOC Microtubule organizing center

mya Million years ago

9 + 2 structure Cilium or flagellum (of a eukaryote)

9 × 3 structure Centriole or basal body (of a eukaryote)

n, $2n$ The chromosome number of a gamete and of a zygote, respectively

NAD^+/NADH Nicotinamide adenine dinucleotide (oxidized and reduced forms, respectively)

$NADP^+$/NADPH Nicotinamide adenine dinucleotide phosphate (oxidized and reduced forms, respectively)

NAG *N*-acetyl glucosamine

NK cell Natural killer cell

NMDA *N*-methyl-D aspartate (an artificial ligand)

NSF National Science Foundation

P generation Parental generation

P53 A tumor suppressor gene

P680 Reaction center of photosystem II

P700 Reaction center of photosystem I

PABA Para-aminobenzoic acid

PCR Polymerase chain reaction

PEP Phosphoenolpyruvate

Pfr Phytochrome (form that absorbs far red light)

PGA Phosphoglycerate

PID Pelvic inflammatory disease

PKU Phenylketonuria

PNS Peripheral nervous system

pre-mRNA Precursor messenger RNA (in eukaryotes)

Pr Phytochrome (form that absorbs red light)

PTH Parathyroid hormone

RAS Reticular activating system

RBC Red blood cell (erythrocyte)

REM sleep Rapid eye movement sleep

RFLP Restriction fragment length polymorphism

RNA Ribonucleic acid

rRNA Ribosomal RNA

Rubisco Ribulose bisphosphate carboxylase/oxygenase

RuBP Ribulose bisphosphate

S phase DNA synthetic phase (of the cell cycle)

SA node Sinoatrial node (of heart)

SCID Severe combined immunodeficiency

SEM Scanning electron microscope or micrograph

snRNP Small nuclear ribonucleoprotein complex

ssp Subspecies

STD Sexually transmitted disease

T Thymine

T lymphocyte or T cell Lymphocyte responsible for cell-mediated immunity

T_c lymphocyte Cytotoxic T cell

T_h lymphocyte Helper T cell (CD4 T cell)

TATA box Base sequence in eukaryotic promoter

TCA cycle Tricarboxylic acid cycle (synonym for citric acid cycle)

TCR T-cell antigen receptor

TEM Transmission electron microscope or micrograph

Tm Tubular transport maximum

TNF Tumor necrosis factor

tRNA Transfer RNA

U Uracil

UPE Upstream promoter element

UR Unconditioned response

US Unconditioned stimulus

UV light Ultraviolet light

WBC White blood cell (leukocyte)

Glossary

abiotic factors   Elements of the nonliving, physical environment that affect a particular organism. Compare with *biotic factors*.

abscisic acid (ab-sis′ik)   A plant hormone involved in dormancy and responses to stress.

abscission (ab-sizh′en)   The normal (usually seasonal) fall of leaves or other plant parts, such as fruits or flowers.

abscission layer   The area at the base of the petiole where the leaf will break away from the stem. Also known as abscission zone.

absorption (ab-sorp′shun)   The movement of nutrients and other substances through the wall of the digestive tract and into the blood or lymph.

absorption spectrum   A graph of the amount of light at specific wavelengths that has been absorbed as light passes through a substance. Each type of molecule has a characteristic absorption spectrum. Compare with *action spectrum*.

accessory fruit   A fruit composed primarily of tissue other than ovary tissue, e.g., apple, pear. Compare with *aggregate, simple,* and *multiple fruits*.

acetyl coenzyme A (acetyl CoA) (as′uh-teel)   A key intermediate compound in metabolism; consists of a two-carbon acetyl group covalently bonded to coenzyme A.

acetyl group   A two-carbon group derived from acetic acid (acetate).

acetylcholine (ah′′see-til-koh′leen)   A common neurotransmitter released by cholinergic neurons, including motor neurons.

achene (a-keen′)   A simple, dry fruit with one seed in which the fruit wall is separate from the seed coat, e.g., sunflower fruit.

acid   A substance that is a hydrogen ion (proton) donor; acids unite with bases to form salts. Compare with *base*.

acidic solution   A solution in which the concentration of hydrogen ions (H^+) exceeds the concentration of hydroxide ions (OH^-). An acidic solution has a pH less than 7. Compare with *basic solution* and *neutral solution*.

acid precipitation   Precipitation that is acidic as a result of both sulfur and nitrogen oxides forming acids when they react with water in the atmosphere.

acclimitization   Adjustment to seasonal changes.

acoelomate (a-seel′oh-mate)   An animal lacking a body cavity (coelom). Compare with *coelomate* and *pseudocoelomate*.

acquired immunodeficiency syndrome (AIDS)   A serious, potentially fatal disease caused by the human immunodeficiency virus (HIV).

acromegaly (ak′′roh-meg′ah-lee)   A condition characterized by overgrowth of the extremities of the skeleton, fingers, toes, jaws, and nose. It may be produced by excessive secretion of growth hormone by the anterior pituitary gland.

acrosome reaction (ak′roh-sohm)   A series of events in which the acrosome, a caplike structure covering the head of a sperm cell, releases proteolytic (protein-digesting) enzymes and undergoes other changes that permit the sperm to penetrate the outer coverings of the egg.

actin (ak′tin)   The protein of which microfilaments are composed. Actin, together with the protein myosin, is responsible for muscle contraction.

actin filaments   Thin filaments composed mainly of the protein actin; actin and myosin filaments make up the myofibrils of muscle fibers.

actinopods (ak-tin′o-podz)   Protozoa characterized by axopods that protrude through pores in their shells. See *radiolarians*.

action potential   An electric signal resulting from depolarization of the plasma membrane in a neuron or muscle cell. Compare with *resting potential*.

action spectrum   A graph of the effectiveness of light at specific wavelengths in promoting a light-requiring reaction. Compare with *absorption spectrum*.

activation energy (E_A)   The kinetic energy required to initiate a chemical reaction.

activator protein   A positive regulatory protein that stimulates transcription when bound to DNA. Compare with *repressor protein*.

active immunity   Immunity that develops as a result of exposure to antigens; it may occur naturally after recovery from a disease or be artificially induced by immunization with a vaccine. Compare with *passive immunity*.

active site   A specific region of an enzyme (generally near the surface) that accepts one or more substrates and catalyzes a chemical reaction. Compare with *allosteric site*.

active transport   All forms of transport of a substance across a membrane that do not rely on the potential energy of a concentration gradient for the substance being transported and therefore require an additional energy source (often ATP); includes carrier-mediated active transport, endocytosis, and exocytosis. Compare with *diffusion* and *facilitated diffusion*.

adaptation   (1) An evolutionary modification that improves an organism's chances of survival and reproductive success; (2) A decline in the response of a receptor subjected to repeated or prolonged stimulation.

adaptive immune responses   See *specific immune responses*.

adaptive radiation   The evolution of a large number of related species from an unspecialized ancestral organism.

adaptive zone   A new ecological opportunity that was not exploited by an ancestral organism; used by evolutionary biologists to explain the ecological paths along which different taxa evolve.

addiction Physical dependence on a drug, generally based on physiological changes that take place in response to the drug; when the drug is withheld, the addict may suffer characteristic withdrawal symptoms.

adenine (ad'eh-neen) A nitrogenous purine base that is a component of nucleic acids and ATP.

adenosine triphosphate (ATP) (a-den'oh-seen) An organic compound containing adenine, ribose, and three phosphate groups; of prime importance for energy transfers in cells.

adhering junction A type of anchoring junction between cells; connects epithelial cells.

adipose tissue (ad'i-pohs) Tissue in which fat is stored.

adrenal cortex (ah-dree'nul kor'teks) The outer region of each adrenal gland; secretes steroid hormones, including mineralocorticoids and glucocorticoids.

adrenal glands (ah-dree'nul) Paired endocrine glands, one located just superior to each kidney; secrete hormones that help regulate metabolism and help the body cope with stress.

adrenal medulla (ah-dree'nul meh-dull'uh) The inner region of each adrenal gland; secretes epinephrine and norepinephrine.

adrenergic neuron (ad-ren-er'jik) A neuron that releases norepinephrine or epinephrine as a neurotransmitter. Compare with *cholinergic neuron*.

adventitious (ad''ven-tish'us) Of plant organs, such as roots or buds, that arise in an unusual position on a plant.

aerobe Organism that grows or metabolizes only in the presence of molecular oxygen. Compare with *anaerobe*.

aerobic (air-oh'bik) Growing or metabolizing only in the presence of molecular oxygen. Compare with *anaerobic*.

aerobic respiration See *respiration*.

afferent (af'fer-ent) Leading toward some point of reference. Compare with *efferent*.

afferent neurons Neurons that transmit action potentials from sensory receptors to the brain or spinal cord. Compare with *efferent neurons*.

age structure The number and proportion of people at each age in a population. Age structure diagrams represent the number of males and females at each age, from birth to death, in the population.

aggregate fruit A fruit that develops from a single flower with many separate carpels, e.g., raspberry. Compare with *simple, accessory,* and *multiple fruits*.

aggregated distribution See *clumped dispersion*.

agnathans (ag-na'thanz) Jawless fishes; historical class of vertebrates, including lampreys, hagfishes, and many extinct forms.

albinism (al'bih-niz-em) A hereditary inability to form melanin pigment, resulting in light coloration.

AIDS See *acquired immunodeficiency syndrome*.

albumin (al-bew'min) A class of protein found in most animal tissues; a fraction of plasma proteins.

aldehyde An organic molecule containing a carbonyl group bonded to at least one hydrogen atom. Compare with *ketone*.

aldosterone (al-dos'tur-ohn) A steroid hormone produced by the vertebrate adrenal cortex; stimulates sodium reabsorption. See *mineralocorticoids*.

algae (al'gee) (sing. *alga*) An informal group of unicellular, or simple multicellular, photosynthetic protists that are important producers in aquatic ecosystems; includes dinoflagellates, diatoms, euglenoids, golden algae, green algae, red algae, and brown algae.

allantois (a-lan'toe-iss) An extraembryonic membrane of reptiles, birds, and mammals that stores the embryo's nitrogenous wastes; most of the allantois is detached at hatching or birth.

allele frequency The proportion of a specific allele in the population.

alleles (al-leels') Genes governing variation of the same character that occupy corresponding positions (loci) on homologous chromosomes; alternative forms of a gene.

allelopathy (uh-leel'uh-path''ee) An adaptation in which toxic substances secreted by roots or shed leaves inhibit the establishment of competing plants nearby.

allergen A substance that stimulates an allergic reaction.

allergy A hypersensitivity to some substance in the environment, manifested as hay fever, skin rash, asthma, food allergies, etc.

all-or-none law The principle that neurons transmit an impulse in a similar way no matter how weak or strong the stimulus; the neuron either transmits an action potential (all) or does not (none).

allopatric speciation (al-oh-pa'trik) Speciation that occurs when one population becomes geographically separated from the rest of the species and subsequently evolves. Compare with *sympatric speciation*.

allopolyploid (al''oh-pol'ee-ploid) A polyploid whose chromosomes are derived from two species. Compare with *autopolyploid*.

allosteric regulators Substances that affect protein function by binding to allosteric sites.

allosteric site (al-oh-steer'ik) (1) A regulatory site located on a protein that is separate from the functional site. The binding of a specific regulator to the allosteric site alters the conformation and function of the protein; (2) A site on an enzyme other than the active site, to which a specific substance (other than the normal substrate) can bind, thereby changing the shape and activity of the enzyme. Compare with *active site*.

alpha (α) helix A regular, coiled type of secondary structure of a polypeptide chain, maintained by hydrogen bonds. Compare with *beta (β)-pleated sheet*.

alpine tundra An ecosystem located in the higher elevations of mountains, above the tree line and below the snow line. Compare with *tundra*.

alternation of generations A type of life cycle characteristic of plants and a few algae and fungi in which they spend part of their life in a multicellular *n* gametophyte stage and part in a multicellular *2n* sporophyte stage. The gametophyte develops from a spore and produces gametes; the sporophyte develops from a zygote and produces spores.

altruistic behavior Behavior in which one individual helps another, seemingly at its own risk or expense.

alveolus (al-vee'o-lus) (pl. *alveoli*) (1) An air sac of the lung through which gas exchange with the blood takes place; (2) A saclike unit of some glands, e.g., mammary glands.

Alzheimer's disease (AD) A progressive, degenerative brain disorder characterized by amyloid plaques and neurofibrillary tangles.

amino acid (uh-mee'no) An organic compound containing an amino group (—NH₂) and a carboxyl group (—COOH); may be joined by peptide bonds to form the polypeptide chains of protein molecules.

amino group A weakly basic functional group; abbreviated —NH₂.

aminoacyl-tRNA (uh-mee''no-ace'seel) Molecule consisting of an amino acid covalently linked to a transfer RNA.

aminoacyl-tRNA synthetase   One of a family of enzymes, each responsible for covalently linking an amino acid to its specific transfer RNA.

ammonification (uh-moe''nuh-fah-kay'shun)   The conversion of nitrogen-containing organic compounds to ammonia (NH_3) by certain soil bacteria (ammonifying bacteria); part of the nitrogen cycle.

amniocentesis (am''nee-oh-sen-tee'sis)   Sampling of the amniotic fluid surrounding a fetus to obtain information about its development and genetic makeup. Compare with *chorionic villus sampling*.

amnion (am'nee-on)   In terrestrial vertebrates, an extraembryonic membrane that forms a fluid-filled sac for the protection of the developing embryo.

amniotes   Terrestrial vertebrates: reptiles, birds, and mammals; animals whose embryos are enclosed by an amnion.

amoeba (a-mee'ba) (pl. *amoebas*)   A unicellular protozoon that moves by means of pseudopodia.

amphibians   Members of vertebrate class that includes salamanders, frogs, and caecilians.

amphipathic molecule (am''fih-pa'thik)   A molecule containing both hydrophobic and hydrophilic regions.

ampulla   Any small saclike extension, e.g., the expanded structure at the end of each semicircular canal of the ear.

amylase (am'-uh-laze)   Starch-digesting enzyme, e.g., human salivary amylase or pancreatic amylase.

amyloplasts   See *leukoplasts*.

anabolic steroids   Synthetic androgens that increase muscle mass, physical strength, endurance, and aggressiveness, but cause serious side effects; these drugs are often abused.

anabolism (an-ab'oh-lizm)   The aspect of metabolism in which simpler substances are combined to form more complex substances, resulting in the storage of energy, the production of new cellular materials, and growth. Compare with *catabolism*.

anaerobe   Organism that grows or metabolizes only in the absence of molecular oxygen. See *facultative anaerobe* and *obligate anaerobe*. Compare with *aerobe*.

anaerobic (an''air-oh'bik)   Growing or metabolizing only in the absence of molecular oxygen. Compare with *aerobic*.

anaerobic respiration   See *respiration*.

anagenesis   Progressive evolutionary changes in a single lineage over long periods. Also called phyletic evolution. Compare with *cladogenesis*.

anaphase (an'uh-faze)   The stage of mitosis, and of meiosis I and II, in which the chromosomes move to opposite poles of the cell; anaphase occurs after metaphase and before telophase.

anaphylaxis (an''uh-fih-lak'sis)   An acute allergic reaction following sensitization to a foreign substance or other substance.

ancestral characters   See *shared ancestral characters*.

androgen (an'dro-jen)   Any substance that possesses masculinizing properties, such as a sex hormone. See *testosterone*.

androgen-binding protein (ABP)   A protein produced by Sertoli cells in the testes; binds and concentrates testosterone.

anemia (uh-nee'mee-uh)   A deficiency of hemoglobin or red blood cells.

aneuploidy (an'you-ploy-dee)   Any chromosomal aberration in which there are either extra or missing copies of certain chromosomes.

angiosperms (an'jee-oh-spermz'')   The traditional name for flowering plants, a very large (about 235,000 species), diverse phylum of plants that form flowers for sexual reproduction and produce seeds enclosed in fruits; include monocots and dicots.

angiotensin I (an-jee-o-ten'sin)   A polypeptide produced by the action of renin on a plasma protein (angiotensinogen).

angiotensin II   A peptide hormone formed by the action of angiotensin-converting enzyme on angiotensin I; stimulates aldosterone secretion by the adrenal cortex.

animal pole   The non-yolky, metabolically active pole of a vertebrate or echinoderm egg. Compare with *vegetal pole*.

anion (an'eye-on)   A particle with one or more units of negative charge, such as a chloride ion (Cl^-) or hydroxide ion (OH^-). Compare with *cation*.

anisogamy (an''eye-sog'uh-me)   Sexual reproduction involving motile gametes of similar form but dissimilar size. Compare with *isogamy* and *oogamy*.

annelid (an'eh-lid)   A member of phylum Annelida; segmented worm such as earthworm.

annual plant   A plant that completes its entire life cycle in one year or less. Compare with *perennial* and *biennial*.

antenna complex   The currently accepted arrangement of chlorophyll, accessory pigment molecules, and pigment-binding proteins into light-gathering units in the thylakoid membranes of photoautotrophic eukaryotes. See *reaction center* and *photosystem*.

antennae (sing. *antenna*)   Sensory structures characteristic of some arthropod groups.

anterior   Toward the head end of a bilaterally symmetrical animal. Compare with *posterior*.

anther (an'thur)   The part of the stamen in flowers that produces microspores and, ultimately, pollen grains.

antheridium (an''thur-id'ee-im) (pl. *antheridia*)   In plants, the multicellular male gametangium (sex organ) that produces sperm cells. Compare with *archegonium*.

anthropoid (an'thra-poid)   A member of a suborder of primates that includes monkeys, apes, and humans.

antibody (an'tee-bod''ee)   A specific protein (immunoglobulin) that recognizes and binds to specific antigens; produced by plasma cells.

antibody-mediated immunity   A type of specific immune response in which B cells differentiate into plasma cells and produce antibodies that bind with foreign antigens, leading to the destruction of pathogens.

anticodon (an''tee-koh'don)   A sequence of three nucleotides in transfer RNA that is complementary to, and combines with, the three nucleotide codon on messenger RNA, thus helping to specify the addition of a particular amino acid to the end of a growing polypeptide.

antidiuretic hormone (ADH) (an''ty-dy-uh-ret'ik)   A hormone secreted by the posterior lobe of the pituitary that controls the rate of water reabsorption by the kidney.

antigen (an'tih-jen)   Any molecule, usually a protein or large carbohydrate, that can be specifically recognized as foreign by cells of the immune system.

antigen-antibody complex   The combination of antigen and antibody molecules.

antimicrobial peptides   Soluble molecules that destroy pathogens.

anti-oncogene   A gene (also known as a tumor suppressor gene) whose normal role is to block cell division in response to certain growth inhibiting factors; when mutated, may contribute to the formation of a cancer cell. Compare with *oncogene*.

antioxidants Certain enzymes (e.g., catalase and peroxidase), vitamins, and other substances that destroy free radicals and other reactive molecules.

anus (ay′nus) The distal end and outlet of the digestive tract.

aorta (ay-or′tah) The largest and main systemic artery of the vertebrate body; arises from the left ventricle and branches to distribute blood to all parts of the body except the lungs.

aphotic region (ay-fote′ik) The lower layer of the ocean (deeper than 100 m or so) where light does not penetrate.

apical dominance (ape′ih-kl) The inhibition of lateral buds by a shoot tip.

apical meristem (mehr′ih-stem) An area of dividing tissue, located at the tip of a shoot or root, that gives rise to primary tissues; apical meristems cause an increase in the length of the plant body. Compare with *lateral meristems*.

apicomplexans A group of parasitic protozoa that lack structures for locomotion and that produce sporozoites as infective agents; malaria is caused by an apicomplexan. Also called *sporozoa*.

apoenzyme (ap′′oh-en′zime) Protein portion of an enzyme; requires the presence of a specific coenzyme to become a complete functional enzyme.

apomixis (ap′′uh-mix′us) A type of reproduction in which fruits and seeds are formed asexually.

apoplast A continuum consisting of the interconnected, porous plant cell walls, along which water moves freely. Compare with *symplast*.

apoptosis (ap-uh-toe′sis) Programmed cell death; apoptosis is a normal part of an organism's development and maintenance. Compare with *necrosis*.

aposematic coloration The conspicuous coloring of a poisonous or distasteful organisms that enables potential predators to easily see and recognize it. Also called warning coloration. Compare with *cryptic coloration*.

arachnids (ah-rack′nids) Eight-legged arthropods such as spiders, scorpions, ticks, and mites.

arachnoid The middle of the three meningeal layers that cover and protect the brain and spinal cord; see *pia mater* and *dura mater*.

archaebacteria (ar′′kuh-bak-teer′ee-uh) Prokaryotic organisms with a number of features, such as the absence of peptidoglycan in their cell walls, that set them apart from the rest of the bacteria. Compare with *eubacteria*.

archaic *Homo sapiens* Regionally diverse descendants of *Homo erectus* that lived in Africa, Asia, and Europe from about 800,000 to 100,000 years ago; considered by some paleoanthropologists to be a separate species, *Homo heidelbergensis*.

archegonium (ar′′ke-go′nee-um) (pl. *archegonia*) In plants, the multicellular female gametangium (sex organ) that contains an egg. Compare with *antheridium*.

archenteron (ark-en′ter-on) The central cavity of the gastrula stage of embryonic development that is lined with endoderm; primitive digestive system.

arctic tundra See tundra.

Ardipithecus ramidus The earliest known hominid; an australopithecine that lived about 4.4 million years ago. See *australopithecines*.

arterial pulse See *pulse, arterial*.

arteriole (ar-teer′ee-ole) A very small artery. Vasoconstriction and vasodilation of arterioles help regulate blood pressure.

artery A thick-walled blood vessel that carries blood away from a heart chamber and toward the body organs. Compare with *vein*.

arthropod (ar′throh-pod) An invertebrate that belongs to phylum Arthropoda; characterized by a hard exoskeleton, a segmented body, and paired, jointed appendages.

artificial insemination The impregnation of a female by artificially introducing sperm from a male.

artificial selection The selection by humans of traits that are desirable in plants or animals, and breeding only those individuals that possess the desired traits.

ascocarp (ass′koh-karp) The fruiting body of an ascomycete.

ascomycete (ass′′koh-my′seat) Member of a phylum of fungi characterized by the production of nonmotile asexual conidia and sexual ascospores.

ascospore (ass′koh-spor) One of a set of sexual spores, usually eight, contained in a special spore case (an ascus) of an ascomycete.

ascus (ass′kus) A saclike spore case in ascomycetes that contains sexual spores called ascospores.

asexual reproduction Reproduction in which there is no fusion of gametes and in which the genetic makeup of parent and of offspring is usually identical. Compare with *sexual reproduction*.

assimilation (of nitrogen) The conversion of inorganic nitrogen (nitrate, NO_3^-, or ammonia, NH_3) to the organic molecules of living things; part of the nitrogen cycle.

association areas Areas of the brain that link sensory and motor areas; responsible for thought, learning, memory, language abilities, judgment, and personality.

association neuron See *interneuron*.

assortative mating Sexual reproduction in which individuals pair nonrandomly, i.e., select mates on the basis of phenotype.

asters Clusters of microtubules radiating out from the poles in dividing cells that have centrioles.

astrocyte A type of glial cell; some are phagocytic; others regulate the composition of the extracellular fluid in the central nervous system.

atherosclerosis (ath′′ur-oh-skle-row′sis) A progressive disease in which lipid deposits accumulate in the inner lining of arteries, leading eventually to impaired circulation and heart disease.

atom The smallest quantity of an element that can retain the chemical properties of that element.

atomic mass The total number of protons and neutrons in an atom; expressed in atomic mass units or daltons.

atomic mass unit (amu) The approximate mass of a proton or neutron; also called dalton.

atomic number The number of protons in the atomic nucleus of an atom, which uniquely identifies the element to which the atom corresponds.

ATP See *adenosine triphosphate*.

ATP synthase Large enzyme complex that catalyzes the formation of ATP from ADP and inorganic phosphate by chemiosmosis; contains a transmembrane channel through which protons diffuse down a concentration gradient; located in the inner mitochondrial membrane, the thylakoid membrane of chloroplasts, and the plasma membrane of bacteria.

atrial natriuretic peptide (ANP) A hormone released by the atrium of the heart; helps regulate sodium excretion and lowers blood pressure.

atrioventricular (AV) node (ay′′tree-oh-ven-trik′you-lur) Mass of specialized cardiac tissue that receives an impulse from the sinoatrial node (pacemaker) and conducts it to the ventricles.

atrioventricular (AV) valve (of the heart) A valve between each atrium and its ventricle that prevents backflow of blood. The right AV valve is the tricuspid valve, the left AV valve is the mitral valve.

atrium (of the heart) (ay′tree-um) A heart chamber that receives blood from the veins.

australopithecines Early hominids that lived between about 4.4 and 1.25 million years ago, based on fossil evidence. Includes several species in two genera, *Ardipithecus* and *Australopithecus*.

Australopithecus afarensis Hominids that lived between about 3.6 and 3.0 million years ago, e.g., Lucy, discovered at Hadar, Ethiopia, in 1974. *A. afarensis* may have arisen from *A. anamensis*.

Australopithecus africanus Hominids that lived between about 3.0 and 2.5 million years ago. *A. africanus* may have arisen from *A. afarensis*.

Australopithecus anamensis Hominids that lived between about 3.9 and 4.2 million years ago. May have arisen from *Ardipithecus ramidus*; had an upright posture and was bipedal.

autocrine regulation A type of regulation in which a signaling molecule (e.g., a hormone) is secreted into interstitial fluid and then acts on the cells that produce it. Compare with *paracrine regulation*.

autogenous model The idea that eukaryotes arose from prokaryotes by the proliferation of internal membranes, derived from the plasma membrane, to form cellular compartments. Compare with *endosymbiont theory*.

autoimmune disease (aw′′toh-ih-mune′) A disease in which the body produces antibodies against its own cells or tissues. Also called autoimmunity.

autonomic nervous system (aw-tuh-nom′ik) The portion of the peripheral nervous system that controls the visceral functions of the body, e.g., regulates smooth muscle, cardiac muscle, and glands, thereby helping to maintain homeostasis. Its divisions are the sympathetic and parasympathetic nervous systems. Compare with *somatic nervous system*.

autopolyploid A polyploid whose chromosomes are derived from a single species. Compare with *allopolyploid*.

autoradiography Method for detection of radioactive decay; radiation causes the appearance of dark silver grains in special x-ray film.

autosome (aw′toh-sohm) A chromosome other than the sex (X and Y) chromosomes.

autotroph (aw′toh-trof) An organism that synthesizes complex organic compounds from simple inorganic raw materials; also called producer or primary producer. Compare with *heterotroph*. See *chemoautotroph* and *photoautotroph*.

auxin (awk′sin) A plant hormone involved in various aspects of growth and development, such as stem elongation, apical dominance, and root formation on cuttings, e.g., indole acetic acid (IAA).

avirulent Unable to cause disease in a host. Compare with *virulent*.

Avogadro′s number The number of units (6.02×10^{23}) present in one mole of any substance.

axillary bud A bud in the axil of a leaf. Compare with *terminal bud*.

axon (aks′on) The long extension of the neuron that transmits nerve impulses away from the cell body. Compare with *dendrite*.

axopods (aks′o-podz) Long, filamentous cytoplasmic projections characteristic of actinopods.

B cell (B lymphocyte) A type of white blood cell responsible for antibody-mediated immunity. When stimulated, B cells differentiate to become plasma cells that produce antibodies. Compare with *T cell*.

bacillus (bah-sill′us) (pl. *bacilli*) A rod-shaped bacterium. Compare with *coccus, spirillum, vibrio,* and *spirochete*.

background extinction The continuous, low-level extinction of species that has occurred throughout much of the history of life. Compare with *mass extinction*.

bacteria (bak-teer′ee-uh) A general term for two groups of unicellular, prokaryotic microorganisms, the archaebacteria and eubacteria. Most bacteria are decomposers, but some are parasites and others are autotrophs.

bacteriophage (bak-teer′ee-oh-fayj) A virus that can infect a bacterium (literally, "bacteria eater"). Also called phage.

balanced polymorphism (pol′′ee-mor′fizm) The presence in a population of two or more genetic variants that are maintained in a stable frequency over several generations.

bark The outermost covering over woody stems and roots; consists of all plant tissues located outside the vascular cambium.

baroreceptors (bare′′oh-ree-sep′torz) Receptors within certain blood vessels that are stimulated by changes in blood pressure.

Barr body A condensed and inactivated X chromosome appearing as a distinctive dense spot in the nucleus of certain cells of female mammals.

basal body (bay′sl) Structure involved in the organization and anchorage of a cilium or flagellum. Structurally similar to a centriole; each is in the form of a cylinder composed of nine triplets of microtubules (9×3 structure).

basal metabolic rate (BMR) The amount of energy expended by the body at resting conditions, when no food is being digested and no voluntary muscular work is being performed.

base (1) A substance that is a hydrogen ion (proton) acceptor; bases unite with acids to form salts. Compare with *acid*. (2) A nitrogenous base in a nucleotide or nucleic acid. See *purines* and *pyrimidines*.

basement membrane The thin, noncellular layer of an epithelial membrane that attaches to the underlying tissues; composed of tiny fibers and polysaccharides produced by the epithelial cells.

base-substitution mutation A change in one base pair in DNA. See *missense mutation* and *nonsense mutation*.

basic solution A solution in which the concentration of hydroxide ions (OH^-) exceeds the concentration of hydrogen ions (H^+). A basic solution has pH greater than 7. Compare with *acidic solution* and *neutral solution*.

basidiocarp (ba-sid′ee-o-karp) The fruiting body of a basidiomycete, e.g., a mushroom.

basidiomycete (ba-sid′′ee-o-my′seat) Member of a phylum of fungi characterized by the production of sexual basidiospores.

basidiospore (ba-sid′ee-o-spor) One of a set of sexual spores, usually four, borne on a basidium of a basidiomycete.

basidium (ba-sid′ee-um) The clublike spore-producing organ of basidiomycetes that bears sexual spores called basidiospores.

basilar membrane The multicellular tissue in the inner ear that separates the cochlear duct from the tympanic canal; the sensory cells of the organ of Corti rest on this membrane.

Batesian mimicry (bate′see-un mim′ih-kree) The resemblance of a harmless or palatable species to one that is dangerous, unpalatable, or poisonous. Compare with *Müllerian mimicry*.

behavioral ecology The scientific study of behavior in natural environments from the evolutionary perspective.

behavioral isolation A prezygotic reproductive isolating mechanism in which reproduction between similar species is prevented because each group possesses its own characteristic courtship behavior; also called sexual isolation.

bellwether species An organism that provides an early warning of environmental damage. Examples include lichens, which are very sensitive to air pollution, and amphibians, which are sensitive to a wide variety of environmental stressors.

benthos (ben'thos) Bottom-dwelling sea organisms that fix themselves to one spot, burrow into the sediment, or simply walk about on the ocean floor.

berry A simple, fleshy fruit in which the fruit wall is soft throughout, e.g., tomato, banana, grape.

beta (β) oxidation Process by which fatty acids are converted to acetyl CoA before entry into the citric acid cycle.

beta (β)-pleated sheet A regular, folded, sheetlike type of protein secondary structure, resulting from hydrogen bonding between two different polypeptide chains or two regions of the same polypeptide chain. Compare with *alpha (α) helix*.

biennial plant (by-en ee-ul) A plant that takes two years to complete its life cycle. Compare with *annual* and *perennial*.

bilateral symmetry A body shape with right and left halves that are approximately mirror images of one another. Compare with *radial symmetry*.

bile The fluid secreted by the liver; emulsifies fats.

binary fission (by'nare-ee fish'un) Equal division of a cell or organism into two; a type of asexual reproduction.

binomial system of nomenclature (by-nome'ee-ul) System of naming a species by the combination of the genus name and a specific epithet.

bioaccumulation The buildup of a persistent toxic substance, such as certain pesticides, in an organism's body.

biodiversity See *biological diversity*.

biogenic amines A class of neurotransmitters that includes norepinephrine, serotonin, and dopamine.

biogeochemical cycle (bye''o-jee''o-kem'ee-kl) Process by which matter cycles from the living world to the nonliving, physical environment and back again, e.g., the carbon cycle, the nitrogen cycle, and the phosphorus cycle.

biogeography The study of the past and present geographical distributions of organisms.

bioinformatics A new scientific field that uses powerful computers to store, retrieve, and compare biological information. Much of bioinformatics is concerned with DNA sequences within human DNA and between genomes of different species. Also called biological computing.

biological clocks Mechanisms by which activities of organisms are adapted to regularly recurring changes in the environment. See *circadian rhythm*.

biological computing See *bioinformatics*.

biological diversity The variety of living organisms, from their genes to the ecosystems in which they live; includes species richness, genetic diversity, and ecosystem diversity. Also called biodiversity.

biological magnification The increased concentration of toxic chemicals, such as PCBs, heavy metals, and certain pesticides, in the tissues of organisms at higher trophic levels in food webs.

biological species concept See *species*.

biomass (bye'o-mas) A quantitative estimate of the total mass, or amount, of living material in a particular ecosystem.

biome (by'ohm) A large, relatively distinct terrestrial region characterized by a similar climate, soil, plants, and animals, regardless of where it occurs on Earth.

bioremediation A method to clean up a hazardous waste site that uses microorganisms to break down toxic pollutants, or plants to selectively accumulate toxins so they can be easily removed from the site.

biosphere All of Earth's living organisms.

biotic factors Elements of the living world that affect a particular organism, that is, its relationships with other organisms. Compare with *abiotic factors*.

biotic potential See *intrinsic rate of increase*.

bipedal Walking on two feet.

bipolar cell A type of neuron in the retina of the eye; receives input from the photoreceptors (rods and cones) and synapses on ganglion cells.

biramous appendages Appendages with two jointed branches at their ends; characteristic of crustaceans.

bivalent (by-vale'ent or biv'ah-lent) See *tetrad*.

blade (1) The thin, expanded part of a leaf; (2) The flat, leaflike structure of certain multicellular algae.

blastocoel (blas'toh-seel) The fluid-filled cavity of a blastula.

blastocyst The mammalian blastula. See *blastula*.

blastodisc A small disc of cytoplasm at the animal pole of a reptile or bird egg; cleavage is restricted to the blastodisc (meroblastic cleavage).

blastopore (blas'toh-pore) The primitive opening into the body cavity of an early embryo that may become the mouth (in protostomes) or anus (in deuterostomes) of the adult organism.

blastula (blas'tew-lah) In animal development, a hollow ball of cells produced by cleavage of a fertilized ovum. Known as a blastocyst in mammalian development.

blood A fluid, circulating connective tissue that transports nutrients and other materials through the bodies of many types of animals.

blood pressure The force exerted by blood against the inner walls of the blood vessels.

bloom The sporadic occurrence of huge numbers of algae in freshwater and marine ecosystems.

body mass index (BMI) An index of weight in relation to height; calculated by dividing the square of the weight (square kilograms) by height (meters).

Bohr effect Increased oxyhemoglobin dissociation due to lowered pH; occurs as carbon dioxide concentration increases.

bolting The production of a tall flower stalk by a plant that grows vegetatively as a rosette (growth habit with a short stem and a circular cluster of leaves).

bond energy The energy required to break a particular chemical bond.

bone tissue Principal vertebrate skeletal tissue; a type of connective tissue.

boreal forest (bor'ee-uhl) See *taiga*.

bottleneck A sudden decrease in a population size due to adverse environmental factors; may result in genetic drift; also called genetic bottleneck or population bottleneck.

Bowman's capsule A double-walled sac of cells that surrounds the glomerulus of each nephron.

brachiopods (bray'kee-oh-pods) The phylum of solitary marine invertebrates possessing a pair of shells, and internally, a pair of coiled arms with ciliated tentacles; one of the lophophorate phyla.

brain A concentration of nervous tissue that controls neural function; in vertebrates, the anterior, enlarged portion of the central nervous system.

brain stem   The part of the vertebrate brain that includes the medulla, pons, and midbrain.

branchial   Pertaining to the gills or gill region.

branching evolution   See *cladogenesis*.

bronchiole (bronk'ee-ole)   Air duct in the lung that branches from a bronchus; divides to form air sacs (alveoli).

bronchus (bronk'us) (pl. *bronchi*)   One of the branches of the trachea and its immediate branches within the lung.

brown alga   One of a phylum of predominantly marine algae that are multicellular and contain the pigments chlorophyll *a* and *c*, and carotenoids, including fucoxanthin.

bryophytes (bry'oh-fites)   Nonvascular plants including mosses, liverworts, and hornworts.

bryozoans   Animals belonging to phylum Bryozoa, one of the three lophophorate phyla; form sessile colonies by asexual budding.

bud   An undeveloped shoot that can develop into flowers, stems, or leaves. Buds are enclosed in bud scales.

bud scale   A modified leaf that covers and protects a dormant bud.

bud scale scar   Scar on a twig left when a bud scale abscises from the terminal bud.

budding   Asexual reproduction in which a small part of the parent's body separates from the rest and develops into a new individual; characteristic of yeasts and certain other organisms.

buffer   A substance in a solution that tends to lessen the change in hydrogen ion concentration (pH) that otherwise would be produced by adding an acid or base.

bulb   A globose, fleshy, underground bud that consists of a short stem with fleshy leaves, e.g., onion.

bundle scar   Marks on a leaf scar left when vascular bundles of the petiole break during leaf abscission.

bundle sheath cells   Tightly packed cells that form a sheath around the veins of a leaf.

bundle sheath extension   Support cells that extend from the bundle sheath of a leaf vein toward the upper and/or lower epidermis.

buttress root   A bracelike root at the base of certain trees that provides upright support.

C₃ plant   Plant that carries out carbon fixation solely by the Calvin cycle. Compare with *C₄ plant* and *CAM plant*.

C₄ plant   Plant that fixes carbon initially by the Hatch-Slack pathway, in which the reaction of CO_2 with phosphoenolpyruvate is catalyzed by PEP carboxylase in leaf mesophyll cells; the products are transferred to the bundle sheath cells, where the Calvin cycle takes place. Compare with *C₃ plant* and *CAM plant*.

calcitonin (kal-sih-toh'nin)   A hormone secreted by the thyroid gland that rapidly lowers the calcium content in the blood.

callus (kal'us)   Undifferentiated tissue formed on an explant (excised tissue or organ) in plant tissue culture.

calmodulin   A calcium-binding protein; when bound it alters the activity of certain enzymes or transport proteins.

calorie   The amount of heat energy required to raise the temperature of 1g of water 1°C; equivalent to 4.184 joules. Compare with *kilocalorie*.

Calvin cycle   Cyclic series of reactions in the chloroplast stroma in photosynthesis; fixes carbon dioxide and produces carbohydrate. See *C₃ plant*.

calyx (kay'liks)   The collective term for the sepals of a flower.

cambium   See *lateral meristems*.

Cambrian explosion   A span of 40 million years, from about 565 to 525 million years ago, during which many new animal groups appeared in the fossil record.

CAM plant   Plant that carries out crassulacean acid metabolism; carbon is initially fixed into organic acids at night in the reaction of CO_2 and phosphoenolpyruvate, catalyzed by PEP carboxylase; during the day the acids break down to yield CO_2, which enters the Calvin cycle. Compare with *C₃ plant* and *C₄ plant*.

cAMP   See *cyclic AMP*.

cancer cells   See *malignant*.

CAP   See *catabolite gene activator protein*.

capillaries (kap'i-lare-eez)   Microscopic blood vessels in the tissues that permit exchange of materials between cells and blood.

capillary action   The ability of water to move in small diameter tubes as a consequence of its cohesive and adhesive properties.

capping   See *mRNA cap*.

capsid   Protein coat surrounding the nucleic acid of a virus.

capsule   (1) The portion of the moss sporophyte that contains spores; (2) A simple, dry, dehiscent fruit that opens along many sutures or pores to release seeds; (3) A gelatinous coat that surrounds some bacteria.

carbohydrate   Compound containing carbon, hydrogen, and oxygen, in the approximate ratio of C:2H:O, e.g., sugars, starch, and cellulose.

carbon cycle   The worldwide circulation of carbon from the abiotic environment into living things and back into the abiotic environment.

carbon fixation reactions   Reduction reactions of photosynthesis in which carbon from carbon dioxide becomes incorporated into organic molecules, leading to the production of carbohydrate; requires ATP and NADPH.

carbonyl group   A polar functional group consisting of a carbon attached to an oxygen by a double bond; found in aldehydes and ketones.

carboxyl group   A weakly acidic functional group; abbreviated —COOH.

carcinogen (kar-sin'oh-jen)   An agent that causes cancer or accelerates its development.

cardiac cycle   One complete heart beat.

cardiac muscle   Involuntary, striated type of muscle found in the vertebrate heart. Compare with *smooth muscle* and *skeletal muscle*.

cardiac output   The volume of blood pumped by the left ventricle into the aorta in one minute.

cardiovascular disease   Disease of the heart or blood vessels; the leading cause of death in most industrial societies.

carnivore (kar'ni-vor)   An animal that feeds on other animals; flesh-eater; also called secondary or tertiary consumer. Secondary consumers eat primary consumers (herbivores), whereas tertiary consumers eat secondary consumers.

carotenoids (ka-rot'n-oidz)   A group of yellow to orange plant pigments synthesized from isoprene subunits; include carotenes and xanthophylls.

carpel (kar'pul)   The female reproductive unit of a flower; carpels bear ovules. Compare with *pistil*.

carrier-mediated active transport   Transport across a membrane of a substance from a region of low concentration to a region of high concentration; requires both a transport protein with a binding site for the specific substance and an energy source (often ATP).

carrier-mediated transport   Any form of transport across a membrane that uses a membrane-bound transport protein with a binding site for a specific substance; includes both facilitated diffusion and carrier-mediated active transport.

carrying capacity The largest population that a particular habitat can support and sustain for an indefinite period, assuming there are no changes in the environment.

cartilage A flexible skeletal tissue of vertebrates; a type of connective tissue.

Casparian strip (kas-pare′ee-un) A band of waterproof material around the radial and transverse walls of endodermal root cells.

catabolism The aspect of metabolism in which complex substances are broken down to form simpler substances; catabolic reactions are particularly important in releasing chemical energy stored by the cell. Compare with *anabolism*.

catabolite gene activator protein (CAP) A positively acting regulator that becomes active when bound to cAMP; active CAP stimulates transcription of the lactose operon and other operons that code for enzymes used in catabolic pathways. Also known as cyclic AMP receptor protein (CRP).

catalyst (kat′ah-list) A substance that increases the speed at which a chemical reaction occurs without being used up in the reaction. Enzymes are biological catalysts.

catecholamine (cat″eh-kole′-ah-meen) A class of compounds including dopamine, epinephrine, and norepinephrine; these compounds serve as neurotransmitters and hormones.

cation A particle with one or more units of positive charge, such as a hydrogen ion (H^+) or calcium ion (Ca^{2+}). Compare with *anion*.

cDNA library A collection of recombinant plasmids that contain complementary DNA (cDNA) copies of mRNA templates. The cDNA, which lacks introns, is synthesized by reverse transcriptase. Compare with *genomic DNA library*.

cell The basic structural and functional unit of life, which consists of living material bounded by a membrane.

cell cycle Cyclic series of events in the life of a dividing eukaryotic cell; consists of mitosis, cytokinesis, and the stages of interphase.

cell determination See *determination*.

cell differentiation See *differentiation*.

cell fractionation The technique used to separate the components of cells by subjecting them to centrifugal force. See *differential centrifugation* and *density gradient centrifugation*.

cell plate The structure that forms during cytokinesis in plants, separating the two daughter cells produced by mitosis.

cell signaling Mechanisms of communication between cells. Cells can signal one another with secreted signaling molecules, or a signaling molecule on one cell can combine with a receptor on another cell. Examples include the synaptic signaling of neurons and endocrine signaling. See *signal transduction*.

cell theory The theory that the cell is the basic unit of life, of which all living things are composed, and that all cells are derived from preexisting cells.

cell wall The structure outside the plasma membrane of certain cells; may contain cellulose (plant cells), chitin (most fungal cells), peptidoglycan and/or lipopolysaccharide (most bacterial cells), or other material.

cellular respiration See *respiration*.

cellular slime mold A phylum of fungus-like protists whose feeding stage consists of unicellular, amoeboid organisms that aggregate to form a pseudoplasmodium during reproduction.

cellulose (sel′yoo-lohs) A structural polysaccharide composed of beta glucose subunits; the main constituent of plant primary cell walls.

Cenozoic era A geological era that began about 65 million years ago and extends to the present time.

center of origin The geographical area where a given species originated.

central nervous system (CNS) In vertebrates, the brain and spinal cord. Compare with *peripheral nervous system (PNS)*.

centrifuge A device used to separate cells or their components by subjecting them to centrifugal force.

centriole (sen′tree-ohl) One of a pair of small, cylindrical organelles lying at right angles to each other near the nucleus in the cytoplasm of animal cells and certain protist and plant cells; each centriole is in the form of a cylinder composed of nine triplets of microtubules (9×3 structure).

centromere (sen′tro-meer) A specialized constricted region of a chromatid; contains the kinetochore. In cells at prophase and metaphase, sister chromatids are joined in the vicinity of their centromeres.

cephalization The evolution of a head; the concentration of nervous tissue and sense organs at the front end of the animal.

cephalochordates Members of the chordate subphylum that includes the lancelets.

cerebellum (ser-eh-bel′um) A convoluted subdivision of the vertebrate brain concerned with the coordination of muscular movements, muscle tone, and balance.

cerebral cortex (ser-ee′brul kor′tex) The outer layer of the cerebrum composed of gray matter and consisting mainly of nerve cell bodies.

cerebrospinal fluid (CSF) The fluid that bathes the central nervous system of vertebrates.

cerebrum (ser-ee′brum) A large, convoluted subdivision of the vertebrate brain; in humans, it functions as the center for learning, voluntary movement, and interpretation of sensation.

chaos The tendency of a simple system to exhibit complex, erratic dynamics; used by some ecologists to model the state of flux displayed by some populations.

chaparral (shap″uh-ral′) A biome with a Mediterranean climate (mild, moist winters and hot, dry summers). Chaparral vegetation is characterized by drought-resistant, small-leaved evergreen shrubs and small trees.

chaperones See *molecular chaperones*.

character displacement The tendency for two similar species to diverge (become more different) in areas where their ranges overlap; reduces interspecific competition.

chelicerae (keh-lis′er-ee) The first pair of appendages in certain arthropods; clawlike appendages located immediately anterior to the mouth and used to manipulate food into the mouth.

chemical bond A force of attraction between atoms in a compound. See *covalent bond, hydrogen bond,* and *ionic bond*.

chemical compound Two or more elements combined in a fixed ratio.

chemical evolution The origin of life from nonliving matter.

chemical formula A representation of the composition of a compound; the elements are indicated by chemical symbols with subscripts to indicate their ratios. See *molecular formula, structural formula,* and *simplest formula*.

chemical symbol The abbreviation for an element; usually the first letter (or first and second letters) of the English or Latin name.

chemiosmosis Process by which phosphorylation of ADP to form ATP is coupled to the transfer of electrons down an electron transport chain; the electron transport chain powers proton pumps that produce a proton gradient across the membrane; ATP is formed as protons diffuse through transmembrane channels in ATP synthase.

chemoautotroph (kee''moh-aw'toh-trof) Organism that obtains energy from inorganic compounds and synthesizes organic compounds from inorganic raw materials; includes some bacteria. Compare with *photoautotroph, photoheterotroph,* and *chemoheterotroph.*

chemoheterotroph (kee''moh-het'ur-oh-trof) Organism that uses organic compounds as a source of energy and carbon; includes animals, fungi, and many bacteria. Compare with *photoautotroph, photoheterotroph,* and *chemoautotroph.*

chemoreceptor (kee''moh-ree-sep'tor) A sensory receptor that responds to chemical stimuli.

chemotroph (kee'moh-trof) Organism that uses organic compounds or inorganic substances, such as iron, nitrate, ammonia, or sulfur, as sources of energy. Compare with *phototroph.* See *chemoautotroph* and *chemoheterotroph.*

chiasma (ky-az'muh) (pl. *chiasmata*) An X-shaped site in a tetrad (bivalent) usually marking the location where homologous (nonsister) chromatids previously underwent crossing-over.

chimera (ky meer'' uh) An organism composed of two or more kinds of genetically dissimilar cells.

chitin (ky'tin) A nitrogen-containing structural polysaccharide that forms the exoskeleton of insects and the cell walls of many fungi.

chlorophyll (klor'oh-fil) A group of light-trapping green pigments found in most photosynthetic organisms.

chlorophyll-binding proteins About 15 different proteins associated with chlorophyll molecules in the thylakoid membrane.

chloroplasts (klor'oh-plastz) Membranous organelles that are the sites of photosynthesis in eukaryotes; occur in some plant and algal cells.

cholinergic neuron (kohl''in-air'jik) A nerve cell that secretes acetylcholine as a neurotransmitter. Compare with *adrenergic neuron.*

chondrichthyes (kon-drik'-thees) The class of cartilaginous fishes that includes the sharks, rays, and skates.

chondrocytes Cartilage cells.

chordates (kor'dates) Deuterostome animals that, at some time in their lives, possess a cartilaginous, dorsal skeletal structure called a notochord; a dorsal, tubular nerve cord; pharyngeal gill grooves; and a postanal tail.

chorion (kor'ee-on) An extraembryonic membrane in reptiles, birds, and mammals that forms an outer cover around the embryo, and in mammals contributes to the formation of the placenta.

chorionic villus sampling (CVS) (kor''ee-on'ik) Study of extraembryonic cells that are genetically identical to the cells of an embryo, making it possible to assess its genetic makeup. Compare with *amniocentesis.*

choroid layer A layer of cells filled with black pigment that absorbs light and prevents reflected light from blurring the image that falls on the retina; the layer of the eyeball outside the retina.

chromatid (kroh'mah-tid) One of the two identical halves of a duplicated chromosome; the two chromatids that make up a chromosome are referred to as sister chromatids.

chromatin (kro'mah-tin) The complex of DNA and protein that makes up eukaryotic chromosomes.

chromoplasts Pigment-containing plastids; usually found in flowers and fruits.

chromosomes Structures in the cell nucleus that are composed of chromatin and contain the genes. The chromosomes become visible under the microscope as distinct structures during cell division.

chylomicrons (kie-low-my'kronz) Protein-covered fat droplets produced in the intestinal cells; they enter the lymphatic system and are transported to the blood.

chytrid See *chytridiomycete.*

chytridiomycete (ki-trid''ee-o-my'seat) A member of a phylum of fungi characterized by the production of flagellated cells at some stage in their life history. Also called chytrid.

ciliate (sil'e-ate) A unicellular protozoon covered by many short cilia.

cilium (sil'ee-um) (pl. *cilia*) One of many short, hairlike structures that project from the surface of some eukaryotic cells and are used for locomotion or movement of materials across the cell surface; composed of two single microtubules surrounded by nine double microtubules (9 + 2 structure), covered by a plasma membrane.

circadian rhythm (sir-kay'dee-un) An internal rhythm that approximates the 24-hour day. See *biological clocks.*

circulatory system The body system that functions in internal transport and protects the body from disease.

cisternae (sing. *cisterna*) Stacks of flattened membranous sacs that make up the Golgi complex.

citrate (citric acid) A six-carbon organic acid.

citric acid cycle Series of chemical reactions in aerobic respiration in which acetyl coenzyme A is completely degraded to carbon dioxide and water with the release of metabolic energy that is used to produce ATP; also known as the Krebs cycle and the tricarboxylic acid (TCA) cycle.

clade A taxon containing a common ancestor and all the taxa descended from it; a monophyletic group.

cladistics An approach to classification based on recency of common ancestry rather than degree of structural similarity. Also called phylogenetic systematics. Compare with *phenetics* and *evolutionary systematics.*

cladogenesis A branching type of evolution in which two or more populations of an ancestral species split and diverge; also called branching evolution. Compare with *anagenesis.*

cladogram A branching diagram that illustrates taxonomic relationships based on the principles of cladistics.

class A taxonomic category made up of related orders.

classical conditioning A type of learning in which an association is formed between some normal response to a stimulus and a new stimulus, after which the new stimulus elicits the response.

cleavage Series of mitotic cell divisions, without growth, that converts the zygote to a multicellular blastula.

cleavage furrow A constricted region of the cytoplasm that forms and progressively deepens during cytokinesis of animal cells, thereby separating the two daughter cells.

cline Gradual change in phenotype and genotype frequencies among contiguous populations that is the result of an environmental gradient.

clitoris (klit'o-ris) A small, erectile structure at the anterior part of the vulva in female mammals; homologous to the male penis.

cloaca (klow-a'ka) An exit chamber in some animals that receives digestive wastes and urine; may also serve as an exit for gametes.

clonal selection Lymphocyte activation in which a specific antigen causes activation, cell division, and differentiation only in cells that express receptors with which the antigen can bind.

clone (1) A population of cells descended by mitotic division from a single ancestral cell; (2) A population of genetically identical organisms asexually propagated from a single individual. Also see *DNA cloning*.

cloning The process of forming a clone.

closed circulatory system A type of circulatory system in which the blood flows through a continuous circuit of blood vessels; characteristic of annelids, cephalopods, and vertebrates. Compare with *open circulatory system*.

closed system An entity that does not exchange energy or matter with its surroundings. Compare with *open system*.

club mosses A phylum of seedless vascular plants with a life cycle similar to ferns.

clumped dispersion The spatial distribution pattern of a population in which individuals are more concentrated in specific parts of the habitat. Also called aggregated distribution and patchiness. Compare with *random dispersion and uniform dispersion*.

cnidarians (ni-dah′ree-anz) Phylum of animals that have stinging cells called cnidocytes, two tissue layers, and radial symmetry; include hydras and jellyfish.

cnidocytes Stinging cells characteristic of cnidarians.

coated pit A depression in the plasma membrane, the cytosolic side of which is coated with the protein clathrin; important in receptor-mediated endocytosis.

cochlea (koke′lee-ah) The structure of the inner ear of mammals that contains the auditory receptors (organ of Corti).

coccus (kok′us) (pl. *cocci*) A bacterium with a spherical shape. Compare with *bacillus, spirillum, vibrio,* and *spirochete*.

codominance (koh′′dom′in-ants) Condition in which two alleles of a locus are expressed in a heterozygote.

codon (koh′don) A triplet of mRNA nucleotides. The 64 possible codons collectively constitute a universal genetic code in which each codon specifies an amino acid in a polypeptide, or a signal to either start or terminate polypeptide synthesis.

coelacanths A genus of lobe-finned fish that have survived to the present day.

coelom (see′lum) The main body cavity of most animals; a true coelom is lined with mesoderm. Compare with *pseudocoelom*.

coelomate (seel′oh-mate) Animal possessing a true coelom. Compare with *acoelomate* and *pseudocoelomate*.

coenocyte (see′no-site) An organism consisting of a multinucleate cell, i.e., the nuclei are not separated from one another by septa.

coenzyme (koh-en′zime) An organic cofactor for an enzyme; generally participates in the reaction by transferring some component, such as electrons or part of a substrate molecule.

coenzyme A (CoA) Organic cofactor responsible for transferring groups derived from organic acids.

coevolution The reciprocal adaptation of two or more species that occurs as a result of their close interactions over a long period.

cofactor A nonprotein substance needed by an enzyme for normal activity; some cofactors are inorganic (usually metal ions); others are organic (coenzymes).

cohesive Having the property of sticking together.

cohort A group of individuals of the same age.

colchicine A drug that blocks the division of eukaryotic cells by binding to tubulin subunits, which make up the microtubules that comprise the major component of the mitotic spindle.

coleoptile (kol-ee-op′tile) A protective sheath that encloses the young stem in certain monocots.

collagens (kol′ah-gen) Proteins found in the collagen fibers of connective tissues.

collecting duct A tube in the kidney that receives filtrate from several nephrons and conducts it to the renal pelvis.

collenchyma (kol-en′kih-mah) Living cells with moderately but unevenly thickened primary cell walls; collenchyma cells help support the herbaceous plant body.

commensalism (kuh-men′sul-iz-m) A type of symbiosis in which one organism benefits and the other one is neither harmed nor helped. Compare with *mutualism* and *parasitism*.

commercial harvest The collection of commercially important organisms from the wild. Examples include the commercial harvest of parrots (for the pet trade) and cacti (for houseplants).

community An association of different species living together in a defined habitat with some degree of interdependence. Compare with *ecosystem*.

community ecology The description and analysis of patterns and processes within the community.

compact bone Dense, hard bone tissue found mainly near the surfaces of a bone.

companion cell A cell in the phloem of flowering plants that is responsible for loading and unloading sugar into the sieve tube member for translocation.

competition The interaction among two or more individuals that attempt to use the same essential resource, such as food, water, sunlight, or living space. See *interspecific* and *intraspecific competition*. See *interference* and *exploitation competition*.

competitive exclusion The concept that no two species with identical living requirements can occupy the same ecological niche indefinitely. Eventually, one species will be excluded by the other as a result of interspecific competition for a resource in limited supply.

competitive inhibitor A substance that binds to the active site of an enzyme, thus lowering the rate of the reaction catalyzed by the enzyme. Compare with *noncompetitive inhibitor*.

complement A group of proteins in blood and other body fluids that are activated by an antigen-antibody complex, and then destroy pathogens.

complementary DNA (cDNA) DNA synthesized by reverse transcriptase, using RNA as a template.

complete flower A flower that possesses all four parts: sepals, petals, stamens, and carpels. Compare with *incomplete flower*.

compound eye An eye, such as that of an insect, composed of many light-sensitive units called ommatidia.

concentration gradient A difference in the concentration of a substance from one point to another, as for example, across a cell membrane.

condensation synthesis A reaction in which two monomers are combined covalently through the removal of the equivalent of a water molecule. Compare with *hydrolysis*.

cone (1) In botany, a reproductive structure in many gymnosperms that produces either microspores or megaspores; (2) In zoology, one of the conical photoreceptive cells of the retina that is particularly sensitive to bright light and, by distinguishing light of various wavelengths, mediates color vision. Compare with *rod*.

conidiophore (kah-nid′e-o-for′′) A specialized hypha that bears conidia.

conidium (kah-nid′e-um) (pl. *conidia*) An asexual spore that is usually formed at the tip of a specialized hypha called a conidiophore.

conifer (kon′ih-fur) Any of a large phylum of gymnosperms that are woody trees and shrubs with needle-like, mostly evergreen, leaves and with seeds in cones.

conjugation (kon''jew-gay'shun) (1) A sexual process in certain protists that involves exchange or fusion of a cell with another cell; (2) A mechanism for DNA exchange in bacteria that involves cell-to-cell contact.

connective tissue Animal tissue consisting mostly of intercellular substance (fibers scattered through a matrix) in which the cells are embedded, e.g., bone.

consanguineous mating A mating between close relatives.

conservation biology A multidisciplinary science that focuses on the study of how humans impact organisms and on the development of ways to protect biological diversity.

constitutive gene A gene that is constantly transcribed.

consumer See *heterotroph*.

consumption overpopulation A situation in which each individual in a human population consumes too large a share of resources; results in pollution, environmental degradation, and resource depletion. Compare with *people overpopulation*.

contest competition See *interference competition*.

continental drift The theory that continents were once joined together and later split and drifted apart.

contraception Any method used to intentionally prevent pregnancy.

contractile root (kun-trak'til) A specialized type of root that contracts and pulls a bulb or corm deeper into the soil.

contractile vacuole A membrane-bounded organelle that is found in certain freshwater protists, such as *Paramecium,* and that appears to have an osmoregulatory function; it periodically fills with water, then contracts to expel the contents into the surroundings.

control group In a scientific experiment, a group in which the experimental variable is kept constant. The control provides a standard of comparison used to verify the results of the experiment.

controlled mating A mating in which the genotypes of the parents are known.

convergent circuit (kun-vur'jent) A neural pathway in which a postsynaptic neuron is controlled by signals coming from two or more presynaptic neurons. Compare with *divergent circuit*.

convergent evolution (kun-vur'jent) The independent evolution of structural or functional similarity in two or more distantly related species, usually as a result of adaptations to similar environments.

corepressor Substance that binds to a repressor protein, converting it to its active form, which is capable of preventing transcription.

Coriolis effect (kor''e-o'lis) The tendency of moving air or water to be deflected from its path to the right in the Northern Hemisphere and to the left in the Southern Hemisphere. Caused by the direction of Earth's rotation.

cork cambium (kam'bee-um) A lateral meristem that produces cork cells and cork parenchyma; cork cambium and the tissues it produces make up the outer bark of a woody plant. Compare with *vascular cambium*.

cork cell A cell in the bark that is produced outwardly by the cork cambium; cork cells are dead at maturity and function for protection and reduction of water loss.

cork parenchyma (par-en'kih-mah) One or more layers of parenchyma cells produced inwardly by the cork cambium.

corm A short, thickened underground stem specialized for food storage and asexual reproduction, e.g., crocus, gladiolus.

cornea (kor'nee-ah) The transparent covering of an eye.

corolla (kor-ohl'ah) A collective term for the petals of a flower.

corpus callosum (kah-loh'sum) In mammals, a large bundle of nerve fibers interconnecting the two cerebral hemispheres.

corpus luteum (loo'tee''um) The temporary endocrine tissue in the ovary that develops from the ruptured follicle after ovulation; secretes progesterone and estrogen.

cortex (kor'tex) (1) The outer part of an organ, such as the cortex of the kidney; compare with *medulla*. (2) The tissue between the epidermis and vascular tissue in the stems and roots of many herbaceous plants.

cortical reaction Process occurring after fertilization that prevents additional sperm from entering the egg; also known as the slow block to polyspermy.

cosmopolitan species Species that have a nearly worldwide distribution and occur on more than one continent or throughout much of the ocean. Compare with *endemic species*.

cotransport The active transport of a substance from a region of low concentration to a region of high concentration by coupling its transport to the transport of a substance down its concentration gradient.

cotyledon (kot''uh-lee'dun) The seed leaf of a plant embryo, which may contain food stored for germination.

cotylosaurs The first reptiles; also known as stem reptiles.

countercurrent exchange system A biological mechanism that enables maximum exchange between two fluids. The two fluids must be flowing in opposite directions and have a concentration gradient between them.

coupled reactions A set of reactions in which an exergonic reaction provides the free energy required to drive an endergonic reaction; energy coupling generally occurs through a common intermediate.

covalent bond The chemical bond involving shared pairs of electrons; may be single, double, or triple (with one, two, or three shared pairs of electrons, respectively). Compare with *ionic bond* and *hydrogen bond*.

covalent compound A compound in which atoms are held together by covalent bonds; covalent compounds consist of molecules. Compare with *ionic compound*.

cranial nerves The ten to twelve pairs of nerves in vertebrates that emerge directly from the brain.

cranium The bony framework that protects the brain in vertebrates.

crassulacean acid metabolism See *CAM plant*.

creatine phosphate An energy-storing compound found in muscle cells.

cretinism (kree'tin-izm) A chronic condition due to lack of thyroid secretion during fetal development and early childhood; results in retarded physical and mental development if untreated.

cri-du-chat A human genetic disease caused by loss of part of the short arm of chromosome 5 and characterized by mental retardation, a cry that sounds like a kitten mewing, and death in infancy or childhood.

cristae (kris'tee) (sing. *crista*) Shelflike or finger-like inward projections of the inner membrane of a mitochondrion.

Cro-Magnons Prehistoric humans (*Homo sapiens*) with modern features (tall, erect, lacking a heavy brow) who lived in Europe some 30,000 years ago.

cross bridges The connections between myosin and actin filaments in muscle fibers; formed by the binding of myosin heads to active sites on actin filaments.

crossing-over The breaking and rejoining of homologous (nonsister) chromatids during early meiotic prophase I that results in an exchange of genetic material.

CRP See *catabolite gene activator protein*.

cryptic coloration Colors or markings that help some organisms hide from predators by blending into their physical surroundings. Compare with *aposematic coloration*.

cryptochrome A proteinaceous pigment that strongly absorbs blue light: implicated in resetting the biological clock in plants, fruit flies, and mice.

ctenophores (ten'oh-forz) Phylum of marine animals (comb jellies) whose bodies consist of two layers of cells enclosing a gelatinous mass. The outer surface is covered with comblike rows of cilia, by which the animal moves.

cuticle (kew'tih-kl) (1) A noncellular, waxy covering over the epidermis of the aerial parts of plants that reduces water loss; (2) The outer covering of some animals, such as roundworms.

cyanobacteria (sy-an''oh-bak-teer'ee-uh) Prokaryotic photosynthetic microorganisms that possess chlorophyll and produce oxygen during photosynthesis. Formerly known as blue-green algae.

cycad (sih'kad) Any of a phylum of gymnosperms that live mainly in tropical and semitropical regions and have stout stems (to 20 m in height) and fernlike leaves.

cyclic AMP (cAMP) A form of adenosine monophosphate in which the phosphate is part of a ring-shaped structure; acts as a regulatory molecule and second messenger in organisms ranging from bacteria to humans.

cyclic AMP receptor protein See *catabolite gene activator protein*.

cyclic electron transport In photosynthesis, the cyclic flow of electrons through Photosystem I; ATP is formed by chemiosmosis, but O_2 and NADPH are not produced. Compare with *noncyclic electron transport*.

cyclins Regulatory proteins whose levels oscillate during the cell cycle; activate cyclin-dependent protein kinases.

cystic fibrosis A genetic disease with an autosomal recessive inheritance pattern; characterized by secretion of abnormally thick mucus, particularly in the respiratory and digestive systems.

cytochromes (sy'toh-kromz) Iron-containing heme proteins of an electron transport system.

cytokines Signaling proteins that regulate interactions between cells in the immune system. Important groups include interferons, interleukins, tumor necrosis factors, and chemokines.

cytokinesis (sy''toh-kih-nee'sis) Stage of cell division in which the cytoplasm divides to form two daughter cells.

cytokinin (sy''toh-ky'nin) A plant hormone involved in various aspects of plant growth and development, such as cell division and delay of senescence.

cytoplasm The plasma membrane and cell contents with the exception of the nucleus.

cytosine A nitrogenous pyrimidine base that is a component of nucleic acids.

cytoskeleton The dynamic internal network of protein fibers that includes microfilaments, intermediate filaments, and microtubules.

cytosol The fluid component of the cytoplasm in which the organelles are suspended.

cytotoxic T cell T lymphocyte that destroys cancer cells and other pathogenic cells on contact. Also known as CD8 T cell and killer T cell.

dalton See *atomic mass unit (amu)*.

day-neutral plant A plant whose flowering is not controlled by variations in day length that occur with changing seasons.

Compare with *long-day, short-day,* and *intermediate-day plants*.

deamination (dee-am-ih-nay'shun) The removal of an amino group ($—NH_2$) from an amino acid or other organic compound.

decarboxylation A reaction in which a molecule of CO_2 is removed from a carboxyl group of an organic acid.

deciduous A term describing a plant that sheds leaves or other structures at regular intervals; e.g., during autumn. Compare with *evergreen*.

decomposers Microbial heterotrophs that break down dead organic material and use the decomposition products as a source of energy. Also called saprotrophs or saprobes.

deductive reasoning The reasoning that operates from generalities to specifics and can make relationships among data more apparent. Compare with *inductive reasoning*. See *hypothetico-deductive approach*.

deforestation The temporary or permanent removal of forest for agriculture or other uses.

dehydrogenation (dee-hy''dro-jen-ay'shun) A form of oxidation in which hydrogen atoms are removed from a molecule.

deletion (1) A chromosome abnormality in which part of a chromosome is missing, e.g., cri-du-chat; (2) The loss of one or more base pairs from DNA, which can result in a frameshift mutation.

demographics The science that deals with human population statistics, such as size, density, and distribution.

denature (dee-nay'ture) To alter the physical properties and three-dimensional structure of a protein, nucleic acid, or other macromolecule by treating it with excess heat, strong acids, or strong bases.

dendrite (den'drite) A branch of a neuron that receives and conducts nerve impulses toward the cell body. Compare with *axon*.

dendritic cells A set of immune cells present in many tissues that capture antigens and present them to T cells.

dendrochronology (den''dro-kruh-naal'uh-gee) A method of dating using the annual rings of trees.

denitrification (dee-nie''tra-fuh-kay'shun) The conversion of nitrate (NO_3^-) to nitrogen gas (N_2) by certain bacteria (denitrifying bacteria) in the soil; part of the nitrogen cycle.

dense connective tissue A type of tissue that may be irregular, as in the dermis of the skin, or regular, as in tendons.

density-dependent factor An environmental factor whose effects on a population change as population density changes; density-dependent factors tend to retard population growth as population density increases and enhance population growth as population density decreases. Compare with *density-independent factor*.

density gradient centrifugation Procedure in which cellular components are placed in a layer on top of a density gradient, usually made up of a sucrose solution and water. Cell structures migrate during centrifugation, forming a band at the position in the gradient where their own density equals that of the sucrose solution.

density-independent factor An environmental factor that affects the size of a population but is not influenced by changes in population density. Compare with *density-dependent factor*.

deoxyribonucleic acid (DNA) Double-stranded nucleic acid; contains genetic information coded in specific sequences of its constituent nucleotides.

deoxyribose Pentose sugar lacking a hydroxyl ($—OH$) group on carbon-2'; a constituent of DNA.

depolarization (dee-pol''ar-ih-zay'shun)   A decrease in the charge difference across a plasma membrane; may result in an action potential in a neuron or muscle cell.

derived characters   See *shared derived characters*.

dermal tissue system   The tissue that forms the outer covering over a plant; the epidermis or periderm.

dermis (dur'mis)   The layer of dense connective tissue beneath the epidermis in the skin of vertebrates.

desert   A temperate or tropical biome in which lack of precipitation limits plant growth.

desertification   The degradation of once-fertile land into nonproductive desert; caused partly by soil erosion, deforestation, and overgrazing by domestic animals.

desmosomes (dez'moh-somz)   Button-like plaques, present on two opposing cell surfaces, that hold the cells together by means of protein filaments that span the intercellular space.

determinate growth   Growth of limited duration, as for example, in flowers and leaves. Compare with *indeterminate growth*.

determination   The developmental process by which one or more cells become progressively committed to a particular fate. Determination is a series of molecular events usually leading to differentiation. Also called cell determination.

detritivore (duh-try'tuh-vore)   An organism, such as an earthworm or crab, that consumes fragments of freshly dead or decomposing organisms; also called detritus feeder.

detritus (duh-try'tus)   Organic debris from decomposing organisms.

detritus feeder   See *detritivore*.

deuteromycetes (doo''ter-o-my'seats)   An artificial grouping of fungi characterized by the absence of sexual reproduction but usually having other traits similar to ascomycetes; also called imperfect fungi.

deuterostome (doo'ter-oh-stome)   Major division of the animal kingdom in which the anus develops from the blastopore; includes the echinoderms and chordates. Compare with *protostome*.

development   All the progressive changes that take place throughout the life of an organism.

diabetes mellitus (mel'i-tus)   The most common endocrine disorder; in Type I diabetes, there is a marked decrease in the number of beta cells in the pancreas resulting in insulin deficiency. In the more common Type II diabetes, insulin receptors on target cells do not bind with insulin (insulin resistance). Both types result in hyperglycemia and decreased use of glucose by cells.

diacylglycerol (DAG) (di''as-il-glis'er-ol)   A lipid consisting of glycerol combined chemically with two fatty acids; also called diglyceride. Can act as a second messenger that increases calcium concentration and activates enzymes. Compare with *monoacylglycerol* and *triacylglycerol*.

dialysis   The diffusion of certain solutes across a selectively permeable membrane.

diaphragm   In mammals, the muscular floor of the chest cavity; contracts during inhalation, expanding the chest cavity.

diastole (di-ass'toh-lee) Phase of the cardiac cycle in which the heart is relaxed. Compare with *systole*.

diatom (die'eh-tom'')   A usually unicellular alga that is covered by an ornate, siliceous shell consisting of two overlapping halves; an important component of plankton in both marine and fresh waters.

dichotomous branching (di-kaut'uh-mus)   In botany, a type of branching in which one part always divides into two more or less equal parts.

dicot (dy'kot)   One of the two classes of flowering plants; dicot seeds contain two cotyledons, or seed leaves. Compare with *monocot*.

differential centrifugation   Separation of cellular particles according to their mass, size, or density. In differential centrifugation the supernatant is spun at successively higher revolutions per minute.

differential gene expression   The expression of different subsets of genes at different times and in different cells during development.

differentiated cell   A specialized cell; carries out unique activities, expresses a specific set of proteins, and usually has a recognizable appearance.

differentiation (dif''ah-ren-she-ay'shun)   Development toward a more mature state; a process changing a young, relatively unspecialized cell to a more specialized cell. Also called cell differentiation.

diffusion   The net movement of particles (atoms, molecules, or ions) from a region of higher concentration to a region of lower concentration (i.e., down a concentration gradient), resulting from random motion. Compare with *facilitated diffusion* and *active transport*.

digestion   The breakdown of food to smaller molecules.

diglyceride   See *diacylglycerol*.

dihybrid cross (dy-hy'brid)   A genetic cross that takes into account the behavior of alleles of two loci. Compare with *monohybrid cross*.

dikaryotic (dy-kare-ee-ot'ik)   Condition of having two nuclei per cell (i.e., $n + n$), characteristic of certain fungal hyphae. Compare with *monokaryotic*.

dimer   An association of two monomers (e.g. a disaccharide or a dipeptide).

dinoflagellate (dy''noh-flaj'eh-late)   A unicellular, biflagellate, typically marine alga that is an important component of plankton; usually photosynthetic.

dioecious (dy-ee'shus)   Having male and female reproductive structures on separate plants; compare with *monoecious*.

dipeptide   See *peptide*.

diploid (dip'loyd)   The condition of having two sets of chromosomes per nucleus. Compare with *haploid* and *polyploid*.

diplomonads   Small, mostly parasitic zooflagellates with one or two nuclei, no mitochondria, and one to four flagella

direct fitness   An individual's reproductive success, measured by the number of viable offspring it produces. Compare with *inclusive fitness*.

directed evolution   See *in vitro evolution*.

directional selection   The gradual replacement of one phenotype with another due to environmental change that favors phenotypes at one of the extremes of the normal distribution. Compare with *stabilizing selection* and *disruptive selection*.

disaccharide (dy-sak'ah-ride)   A sugar produced by covalently linking two monosaccharides (e.g., maltose or sucrose).

disomy   The normal condition in which both members of a chromosome pair are present in a diploid cell or organism. Compare with *monosomy* and *trisomy*.

dispersal   The movement of individuals among populations. Compare with *migration*.

dispersion   The pattern of distribution in space of the individuals of a population relative to their neighbors; may be clumped, random, or uniform.

disruptive selection   A special type of directional selection in which changes in the environment favor two or more variant phenotypes at the expense of the mean. Compare with *stabilizing selection* and *directional selection*.

distal   Remote; farther from the point of reference. Compare with *proximal*.

distal convoluted tubule   The part of the renal tubule that extends from the loop of Henle to the collecting duct. Compare with *proximal convoluted tubule*.

disturbance   In ecology, any event that disrupts community or population structure.

divergent circuit   A neural pathway in which a presynaptic neuron stimulates many postsynaptic neurons. Compare with *convergent circuit*.

diving reflex   A group of physiological mechanisms, such as decrease in metabolic rate, that are activated when a mammal dives to its limit.

division   A taxonomic category below that of kingdom, comparable to a phylum; often used in classifying plants, fungi, and certain protists.

dizygotic twins   Twins that arise from the separate fertilization of two eggs; commonly known as fraternal twins. Compare with *monozygotic twins*.

DNA   See *deoxyribonucleic acid*.

DNA cloning   The process of selectively amplifying DNA sequences so their structure and function can be studied.

DNA-dependent RNA polymerase   See *RNA polymerase*.

DNA ligase   Enzyme that catalyzes the joining of the 5′ and 3′ ends of two DNA fragments; essential in DNA replication and used in recombinant DNA technology.

DNA methylation   A process in which gene inactivation is perpetuated by enzymes that add methyl groups to DNA.

DNA microarray   A diagnostic test involving thousands of DNA molecules placed on a glass slide or chip.

DNA polymerases   Family of enzymes that catalyze the synthesis of DNA from a DNA template, by adding nucleotides to a growing 3′ end.

DNA provirus   Double-stranded DNA molecule that is an intermediate in the life cycle of an RNA tumor virus (retrovirus).

DNA replication   The process by which DNA is duplicated; ordinarily a semiconservative process in which a double helix gives rise to two double helices, each with an "old" strand and a newly synthesized strand.

DNA sequencing   Procedure by which the sequence of nucleotides in DNA is determined.

domain   (1) A structural and functional region of a protein; (2) A taxonomic category that includes one or more kingdoms.

dominance hierarchy   A linear "pecking order" into which animals in a population may organize according to status; regulates aggressive behavior within the population.

dominant allele (al-leel′)   An allele that is always expressed when it is present, regardless of whether it is homozygous or heterozygous. Compare with *recessive allele*.

dopamine   A neurotransmitter of the biogenic amine group.

dormancy   A temporary period of arrested growth in plants or plant parts such as spores, seeds, bulbs, and buds.

dorsal (dor′sl)   Toward the uppermost surface or back of an animal. Compare with *ventral*.

dosage compensation   Genetic mechanism by which the expression of X-linked genes is made equivalent in XX females and XY males.

double fertilization   A process in the flowering plant life cycle in which there are two fertilizations; one fertilization results in the formation of a zygote, whereas the second results in the formation of endosperm.

doubling time   The amount of time it takes for a population to double in size, assuming that its current rate of increase does not change.

Down syndrome   An inherited condition in which individuals have abnormalities of the face, eyelids, tongue, and other parts of the body, and are physically and mentally retarded; usually results from trisomy of chromosome 21.

drupe (droop)   A simple, fleshy fruit in which the inner wall of the fruit is hard and stony, e.g., peach, cherry.

duodenum (doo′′o-dee′num)   The portion of the small intestine into which the contents of the stomach first enter.

duplication   An abnormality in which a set of chromosomes contains more than one copy of a particular chromosomal segment; the translocation form of Down syndrome is an example.

dura mater   The tough, outer meningeal layer that covers and protects the brain and spinal cord. Also see *arachnoid* and *pia mater*.

dynamic equilibrium   The condition of a chemical reaction when the rate of change in one direction is exactly the same as the rate of change in the opposite direction, i.e., the concentrations of the reactants and products are not changing, and the difference in free energy between reactants and products is zero.

ecdysone (ek′dih-sone)   See *molting hormone*.

Ecdysozoa   A branch of the protostomes that includes animals that molt, such as the rotifers, nematodes, and arthropods.

echinoderms (eh-kine′oh-derms)   Phylum of spiny-skinned marine deuterostome invertebrates characterized by a water vascular system and tube feet; include sea stars, sea urchins, and sea cucumbers.

echolocation   Determination of the position of objects by detecting echos of high-pitched sounds emitted by an animal; a type of sensory system used by bats and dolphins.

ecological niche   See *niche*.

ecological pyramid   A graphical representation of the relative energy value at each trophic level. See *pyramid of biomass, pyramid of energy,* and *pyramid of numbers*.

ecological succession   See *succession*.

ecology (ee-kol′uh-jee)   A discipline of biology that studies the interrelations among living things and their environments.

ecosystem (ee′koh-sis-tem)   The interacting system that encompasses a community and its nonliving, physical environment. Compare with *community*.

ecosystem management   A conservation focus that emphasizes restoring and maintaining ecosystem quality rather than the conservation of individual species.

ecosystem services   Important environmental services, such as clean air to breathe, clean water to drink, and fertile soil in which to grow crops, that ecosystems provide.

ecotone   The transition zone where two communities or biomes meet and intergrade.

ectoderm (ek′toh-derm)   The outer germ layer of the early embryo; gives rise to the skin and nervous system. Compare with *mesoderm* and *endoderm*.

ectotherm   An animal whose temperature fluctuates with that of the environment; may use behavioral adaptations to regulate temperature; sometimes referred to as cold-blooded. Compare with *endotherm*.

edge effect   The ecological phenomenon in which ecotones between adjacent communities often contain a greater number of species or greater population densities of certain species than either adjacent community.

effector A muscle or gland that contracts or secretes in direct response to nerve impulses.

efferent (ef'fur-ent) Leading away from some point of reference. Compare with *afferent*.

efferent neurons Neurons that transmit action potentials from the brain or spinal cord to muscles or glands. Compare with *afferent neurons*.

ejaculation (ee-jak''yoo-lay'shun) A sudden expulsion, as in the ejection of semen from the penis.

electrolyte A substance that dissociates into ions when dissolved in water; the resulting solution can conduct an electrical current.

electron A particle with one unit of negative charge and negligible mass, located outside the atomic nucleus. Compare with *neutron* and *proton*.

electron configuration The arrangement of the electrons around the atom. In a Bohr model the electron configuration is depicted as a series of concentric circles.

electron microscope A microscope capable of producing high-resolution, highly magnified images through the use of an electron beam (rather than light). Transmission electron microscopes (TEMs) produce images of thin sections; scanning electron microscopes (SEMs) produce images of surfaces.

electron shell Group of orbitals of electrons with similar energies.

electron transport system A series of chemical reactions during which hydrogens or their electrons are passed along an electron transport chain from one acceptor molecule to another, with the release of energy.

electronegativity A measure of an atom's attraction for electrons.

electrophoresis, gel See *gel electrophoresis*.

electroreceptor A receptor that responds to electrical stimuli.

element A substance that cannot be changed to a simpler substance by a normal chemical reaction.

elimination Ejection of undigested food from the body. Compare with *excretion*.

El Niño—Southern Oscillation (ENSO) (el nee'nyo) A recurring climatic phenomenon that involves a surge of warm water in the Pacific Ocean and unusual weather patterns elsewhere in the world.

elongation (in protein synthesis) Cyclic process by which amino acids are added one by one to a growing polypeptide chain. See *initiation* and *termination*.

embryo (em'bree-oh) (1) A young organism before it emerges from the egg, seed, or body of its mother; (2) Developing human until the end of the second month, after which it is referred to as a fetus; (3) In plants, the young sporophyte produced following fertilization and subsequent development of the zygote.

embryo sac The female gametophyte generation in flowering plants.

embryo transfer See *host mothering*.

emigration A type of migration in which individuals leave a population and thus decrease its size. Compare with *immigration*.

enantiomers (en-an'tee-oh-merz) Two isomeric chemical compounds that are mirror images.

endangered species A species whose numbers are so severely reduced that it is in imminent danger of extinction throughout all or part of its range. Compare with *threatened species*.

Endangered Species Act A U.S. law that authorizes the U.S. Fish and Wildlife Service to protect from extinction all endangered and threatened species in the United States and abroad.

endemic species Localized, native species that are not found anywhere else in the world. Compare with *cosmopolitan species*.

endergonic reaction (end'er-gon''ik) A nonspontaneous reaction; a reaction requiring a net input of free energy. Compare with *exergonic reaction*.

endocrine gland (en'doh-crin) A gland that secretes hormones directly into the blood or tissue fluid instead of into ducts. Compare with *exocrine gland*.

endocrine system The body system that helps regulate metabolic activities; consists of ductless glands and tissues that secrete hormones.

endocytosis (en''doh-sy-toh'sis) The active transport of substances into the cell by the formation of invaginated regions of the plasma membrane that pinch off and become cytoplasmic vesicles. Compare with *exocytosis*.

endoderm (en'doh-derm) The inner germ layer of the early embryo; becomes the lining of the digestive tract and the structures that develop from the digestive tract—liver, lungs, and pancreas. Compare with *ectoderm* and *mesoderm*.

endodermis (en''doh-der'mis) The innermost layer of the plant root cortex. Endodermal cells have a waterproof Casparian strip around their radial and transverse walls that ensures that water and minerals can enter the root xylem only by passing through the endoderm cells.

endolymph (en'doh-limf) The fluid of the membranous labyrinth and cochlear duct of the ear.

endomembrane system See *internal membrane system*.

endometrium (en''doh-mee'tree-um) The uterine lining.

endoplasmic reticulum (ER) (en'doh-plaz''mik reh-tik'yoo-lum) An interconnected network of internal membranes in eukaryotic cells enclosing a compartment, the ER lumen. Rough ER has ribosomes attached to the cytosolic surface; smooth ER, a site of lipid biosynthesis, lacks ribosomes.

endorphins (en-dor'finz) Neuropeptides released by certain brain neurons; block pain signals.

endoskeleton (en''doh-skel'eh-ton) Bony and/or cartilaginous structures within the body that provide support. Compare with *exoskeleton*.

endosperm (en'doh-sperm) The 3*n* nutritive tissue that is formed at some point in the development of all angiosperm seeds.

endospore A resting cell formed by certain bacteria; highly resistant to heat, radiation, and disinfectants.

endosymbiont (en''doe-sim'bee-ont) An organism that lives inside the body of another kind of organism. Endosymbionts may benefit their host (mutualism) or harm their host (parasitism).

endosymbiont theory The theory that certain organelles such as mitochondria and chloroplasts originated as symbiotic prokaryotes that lived inside other, free-living, prokaryotic cells. Compare with *autogenous model*.

endothelium (en-doh-theel'ee-um) The tissue that lines the cavities of the heart, blood vessels, and lymph vessels.

endotherm (en'doh-therm) An animal that uses metabolic energy to maintain a constant body temperature despite variations in environmental temperature; e.g., birds and mammals. Compare with *ectotherm*.

endotoxin A poisonous substance in the cell walls of gram-negative bacteria. Compare with *exotoxin*.

end product inhibition See *feedback inhibition*.

energy The capacity to do work; can be expressed in kilojoules or kilocalories.

energy of activation See *activation energy*.

enhanced greenhouse effect See *greenhouse effect*.

enhancers Regulatory DNA sequences that can be located long distances away from the actual coding regions of a gene.

enkephalins (en-kef′ah-linz) Neuropeptides released by certain brain neurons that block pain signals.

enterocoely (en′ter-oh-seely) The process by which the coelom forms as a cavity within mesoderm produced by outpocketings of the primitive gut (archenteron); characteristic of many deuterostomes. Compare with *schizocoely*.

enthalpy The total potential energy of a system; sometimes referred to as the heat content of the system.

entropy (en′trop-ee) Disorderliness; a quantitative measure of the amount of the random, disordered energy that is unavailable to do work.

environmental resistance Unfavorable environmental conditions, such as crowding, that prevent organisms from reproducing indefinitely at their intrinsic rate of increase.

enzyme (en′zime) An organic catalyst (usually a protein) that accelerates a specific chemical reaction by lowering the activation energy required for that reaction.

enzyme-substrate complex The temporary association between enzyme and substrate that forms during the course of a catalyzed reaction; also called ES complex.

eosinophil (ee-oh-sin′oh-fil) A type of white blood cell whose cytoplasmic granules absorb acidic stains; functions in parasitic infestations and allergic reactions.

epidermis (ep-ih-dur′mis) (1) An outer layer of cells that covers the body of plants and functions primarily for protection; (2) The outer layer of vertebrate skin.

epididymis (ep-ih-did′ih-mis) (pl. *epididymides*) A coiled tube that receives sperm from the testis and conveys it to the vas deferens.

epiglottis A thin, flexible structure that guards the entrance to the larynx, preventing food from entering the airway during swallowing.

epinephrine (ep-ih-nef′rin) Hormone produced by the adrenal medulla; stimulates the sympathetic nervous system.

epistasis (ep′ih-sta-sis) Condition in which certain alleles of one locus can alter the expression of alleles of a different locus.

epithelial tissue (ep-ih-theel′ee-al) The type of animal tissue that covers body surfaces, lines body cavities, and forms glands; also called epithelium.

epoch The smallest unit of geological time; a subdivision of a period.

equilibrium See *dynamic equilibrium, genetic equilibrium,* and *punctuated equilibrium*.

era One of the main divisions of geological time; eras are subdivided into periods.

erythroblastosis fetalis (eh-rith′row-blas-toe′′-sis fi-tal′is) Serious condition in which Rh$^+$ red blood cells (which bear antigen D) of a fetus are destroyed by maternal anti-D antibodies.

erythrocyte (eh-rith′row-site) A vertebrate red blood cell; contains hemoglobin, which transports oxygen.

erythropoietin (eh-rith′′row-poy′ih-tin) A peptide hormone secreted mainly by kidney cells; stimulates red blood cell production.

ES complex See *enzyme-substrate complex*.

essential nutrient A nutrient that must be provided in the diet because the body cannot make it or cannot make it in sufficient quantities to meet nutritional needs, e.g., essential amino acids and essential fatty acids.

ester linkage Covalent linkage formed by the reaction of a carboxyl group and a hydroxyl group, with the removal of the equivalent of a water molecule; the linkage includes an oxygen atom bonded to a carbonyl group.

estivation A state of torpor caused by lack of food or water during periods of high temperature. Compare with *hibernation*.

estrogens (es′troh-jens) Female sex hormones produced by the ovary; promote the development and maintenance of female reproductive structures and of secondary sex characteristics.

estuary (es′choo-wear-ee) A coastal body of water that connects to an ocean, in which fresh water from the land mixes with salt water.

ethology (ee-thol′oh-jee) The study of animal behavior under natural conditions from the point of view of adaptation.

ethyl alcohol A two-carbon alcohol.

ethylene (eth′ih-leen) A gaseous plant hormone involved in various aspects of plant growth and development, such as leaf abscission and fruit ripening.

eubacteria (yoo′′bak-teer′ee-ah) Prokaryotes other than the archaebacteria.

euchromatin (yoo-croh′mah-tin) A loosely coiled chromatin that is generally capable of transcription. Compare with *heterochromatin*.

euglenoids (yoo-glee′noids) A group of mostly freshwater, flagellated, unicellular algae that move by means of an anterior flagellum and are usually photosynthetic.

eukaryote (yoo′′kar′ee-ote) An organism whose cells possess nuclei and other membrane-bounded organelles. Includes protists, fungi, plants, and animals. Compare with *prokaryote*.

euphotic zone The upper reaches of the ocean, in which enough light penetrates to support photosynthesis.

eustachian tube (yoo-stay′shee-un) The auditory tube passing between the middle ear cavity and the pharynx in vertebrates; permits the equalization of pressure on the tympanic membrane.

eutrophic lake A lake enriched with nutrients such as nitrate and phosphate and consequently overgrown with plants or algae.

evergreen A term describing a plant that sheds leaves over a long period, so that some leaves are always present. Compare with *deciduous*.

evolution Any cumulative genetic changes in a population from generation to generation. Evolution leads to differences in populations and explains the origin of all of the organisms that exist today or have ever existed.

evolutionary systematics An approach to classification that considers both evolutionary relationships and the extent of divergence that has occurred since a group branched from an ancestral group. Compare with *cladistics* and *phenetics*.

excitatory postsynaptic potential (EPSP) A change in membrane potential that brings a neuron closer to the firing level. Compare with *inhibitory postsynaptic potential (IPSP)*.

excretion (ek-skree′shun) The discharge from the body of a waste product of metabolism (not to be confused with the elimination of undigested food materials). Compare with *elimination*.

excretory system The body system in animals that functions in osmoregulation and in the discharge of metabolic wastes.

exergonic reaction (ex′er-gon′′ik) A reaction characterized by a release of free energy. Also called spontaneous reaction. Compare with *endergonic reaction*.

exocrine gland (ex′oh-crin)   A gland that excretes its products through a duct that opens onto a free surface such as the skin (e.g., sweat glands). Compare with *endocrine gland*.

exocytosis (ex″oh-sy-toh′sis)   The active transport of materials out of the cell by fusion of cytoplasmic vesicles with the plasma membrane. Compare with *endocytosis*.

exon   (1) A protein-coding region of a eukaryotic gene; (2) The RNA transcribed from such a region. Compare with *intron*.

exoskeleton (ex″oh-skel′eh-ton)   An external skeleton, such as the shell of mollusks or outer covering of arthropods; provides protection and sites of attachment for muscles. Compare with *endoskeleton*.

exotoxin   A poisonous substance released by certain bacteria. Compare with *endotoxin*.

explicit memory   Factual knowledge of people, places, or objects; requires conscious recall of the information.

exploitation competition   An intraspecific competition in which all the individuals in a population "share" the limited resource equally, so that at high-population densities, none of them obtains an adequate amount. Also called scramble competition. Compare with *interference competition*.

exponential population growth   The accelerating population growth rate that occurs when optimal conditions allow a constant per capita growth rate. When the increase in number versus time is plotted on a graph, exponential growth produces a characteristic J-shaped curve. Compare with *logistic population growth*.

ex situ conservation   Conservation efforts that involve conserving biological diversity in human-controlled settings, such as zoos. Compare with *in situ conservation*.

exteroceptor (ex′tur-oh-sep″tor)   One of the sense organs that receives sensory stimuli from the outside world, such as the eyes or touch receptors. Compare with *interoceptor*.

extinction   The elimination of a species; occurs when the last individual member of a species dies.

extracellular matrix (ECM)   A network of proteins and carbohydrates that surrounds many animal cells.

extraembryonic membranes   Multicellular membranous structures that develop from the germ layers of a terrestrial vertebrate embryo but are not part of the embryo itself. See *chorion, amnion, allantois,* and *yolk sac*.

F₁ generation (first filial generation)   The first generation of hybrid offspring resulting from a cross between parents from two different true-breeding lines.

F₂ generation (second filial generation)   The offspring of the F₁ generation.

facilitated diffusion   The passive transport of ions or molecules by a specific carrier protein in a membrane. As in simple diffusion, net transport is down a concentration gradient, and no additional energy has to be supplied. Compare with *diffusion* and *active transport*.

facilitation   A process in which a neuron is brought closer to its threshold level by stimulation from various presynaptic neurons.

facultative anaerobe   An organism capable of carrying out aerobic respiration but able to switch to fermentation when oxygen is unavailable; e.g., yeast. Compare with *obligate anaerobe*.

FAD/FADH₂   Oxidized and reduced forms, respectively, of flavin adenine dinucleotide, a coenzyme that transfers electrons (as hydrogen) in metabolism, including cellular respiration.

fallopian tube   See *oviduct*.

family   A taxonomic category made up of related genera.

fatty acid   A lipid that is an organic acid containing a long hydrocarbon chain, with no double bonds (saturated fatty acid), one double bond (monounsaturated fatty acid), or two or more double bonds (polyunsaturated fatty acid); components of triacylglycerols, and phospholipids, as well as monoacylglycerols and diacylglycerols.

fecundity   The potential capacity of an individual to produce offspring.

feedback inhibition   A type of enzyme regulation in which the accumulation of the product of a reaction inhibits an earlier reaction in the sequence; also known as end product inhibition.

fermentation   An anaerobic process by which ATP is produced by a series of redox reactions in which organic compounds serve both as electron donors and terminal electron acceptors.

fern   One of a phylum of seedless vascular plants that reproduce by spores produced in sporangia usually borne on leaves in sori; ferns have an alternation of generations between the dominant sporophyte (fern plant) and the gametophyte (prothallus).

fertilization   The fusion of two *n* gametes; results in the formation of a 2*n* zygote. Compare with *double fertilization*.

fetus   The unborn human offspring from the third month of pregnancy to birth.

fiber   (1) In plants, a type of sclerenchyma cell; fibers are long, tapered cells with thick walls. Compare with *sclereid*. (2) In animals, an elongated cell such as a muscle or nerve cell. (3) In animals, the microscopic, threadlike protein and carbohydrate complexes scattered through the matrix of connective tissues.

fibrin   An insoluble protein formed from the plasma protein fibrinogen during blood clotting.

fibroblasts   Connective tissue cells that produce the fibers and the protein and carbohydrate complexes of the matrix of connective tissues.

fibronectins   Glycoproteins of the extracellular matrix that bind to integrins (receptor proteins in the plasma membrane).

fibrous root system   A root system consisting of several adventitious roots of approximately equal size that arise from the base of the stem. Compare with *taproot system*.

Fick's law of diffusion   A physical law governing rates of gas exchange in animal respiratory systems; states that the rate of diffusion of a substance across a membrane is directly proportional to the surface area and to the difference in pressure between the two sides.

filament   In flowering plants, the thin stalk of a stamen; the filament bears an anther at its tip.

first law of thermodynamics   The law of conservation of energy, which states that the total energy of any closed system (any object plus its surroundings, i.e., the universe) remains constant. Compare with *second law of thermodynamics*.

fitness   See *direct fitness*.

fixed action pattern (FAP)   An innate behavior triggered by a sign stimulus.

flagellum (flah-jel′um) (pl. *flagella*)   A long, whiplike structure extending from certain cells and used in locomotion. (1) Eukaryote flagella are composed of two central single microtubules surrounded by nine double microtubules (9 + 2 structure), all covered by a plasma membrane. (2) Prokaryote flagella are filaments rotated by special structures located in the plasma membrane and cell wall.

flame cells   Collecting cells that have cilia; part of the osmoregulatory system of flatworms.

flavin adenine dinucleotide   See *FAD/FADH₂*.

flowering plants See *angiosperms*.

flowing-water ecosystem A river or stream ecosystem.

fluid-mosaic model The currently accepted model of the plasma membrane and other cell membranes, in which protein molecules float in a phospholipid bilayer.

fluorescence The emission of light of a longer wavelength (lower energy) than the light originally absorbed.

follicle (fol'i-kl) (1) A simple, dry, dehiscent fruit that splits open at maturity along one suture to liberate the seeds; (2) A small sac of cells in the mammalian ovary that contains a maturing egg; (3) The pocket in the skin from which a hair grows.

follicle-stimulating hormone (FSH) A gonadotropic hormone secreted by the anterior lobe of the pituitary gland; stimulates follicle development in the ovaries of females and sperm production in the testes of males.

food chain The series of organisms through which energy flows in an ecosystem. Each organism in the series eats or decomposes the preceding organism in the chain. See *food web*.

food web A complex interconnection of all of the food chains in an ecosystem.

foram See *foraminiferan*.

foramen magnum The opening in the vertebrate skull through which the spinal cord passes.

foraminiferan (for''am-in-if'er-an) A marine protozoon that produces a shell, or test, that encloses an amoeboid body. Also called foram.

forebrain In the early embryo, one of the three divisions of the developing vertebrate brain; subdivides to form the telencephalon, which gives rise to the cerebrum, and the diencephalon, which gives rise to the thalamus and hypothalamus. Compare with *midbrain* and *hindbrain*.

forest decline A gradual deterioration (and often death) of many trees in a forest; may be caused by a combination of factors, such as acid precipitation, toxic heavy metals, and surface-level ozone.

fossil Parts or traces of an ancient organism usually preserved in rock.

fossil fuel Combustible deposits in Earth's crust that are composed of the remnants of prehistoric organisms that existed millions of years ago, e.g., oil, natural gas, and coal.

founder cell A cell from which a particular cell lineage is derived.

founder effect Genetic drift that results from a small population colonizing a new area.

fovea (foe'vee-ah) The area of sharpest vision in the retina; cone cells are concentrated here.

fragile site A weak point at a specific location on a chromosome where part of a chromatid appears to be attached to the rest of the chromosome by a thin thread of DNA.

fragile X syndrome A human genetic disorder caused by a fragile site that occurs near the tip on the X chromosome; effects range from mild learning disabilities to severe mental retardation and hyperactivity.

frameshift mutation A mutation that results when one or two nucleotide pairs are inserted into or deleted from the DNA. The change causes the mRNA transcribed from the mutated DNA to have an altered reading frame such that all codons downstream from the mutation are changed.

free energy The maximum amount of energy available to do work under the conditions of a biochemical reaction.

free radicals Toxic, highly reactive compounds that have un-paired electrons that can bond with other compounds in the cell, interfering with normal function.

frequency-dependent selection Selection in which the relative fitness of different genotypes is related to how frequently they occur in the population.

freshwater wetlands Land that is transitional between freshwater and terrestrial ecosystems and is covered with water for at least part of the year; e.g., marshes and swamps.

frontal lobes In mammals, the anterior part of the cerebrum.

fruit In flowering plants, a mature, ripened ovary. Fruits contain seeds and usually provide seed protection and dispersal.

fruiting body A multicellular structure that contains the sexual spores of certain fungi; refers to the ascocarp of an ascomycete and the basidiocarp of a basidiomycete.

fucoxanthin (few''koh-zan'thin) The brown carotenoid pigment found in brown algae, golden algae, diatoms, and dinoflagellates.

functional genomics The study of the roles of genes in cells.

functional group A group of atoms that confers distinctive properties on an organic molecule (or region of a molecule) to which it is attached, e.g., hydroxyl, carbonyl, carboxyl, amino, phosphate, and sulfhydryl groups.

fundamental niche The potential ecological niche that an organism could occupy if there were no competition from other species. Compare with *realized niche*.

fungus (pl. *fungi*) A heterotrophic eukaryote with chitinous cell walls and a body usually in the form of a mycelium of branched, threadlike hyphae. Most fungi are decomposers; some are parasitic.

G protein One of a group of proteins that bind GTP and are involved in the transfer of signals across the plasma membrane.

G_1 phase The first gap phase within the interphase stage of the cell cycle; G_1 occurs before DNA synthesis (S phase) begins. Compare with *S* and *G_2 phases*.

G_2 phase Second gap phase within the interphase stage of the cell cycle; G_2 occurs after DNA synthesis (S phase) and before mitosis. Compare with *S* and *G_1 phases*.

gallbladder A small sac that stores bile.

gametangium (gam''uh-tan'gee-um) Special multicellular or unicellular structure of plants, protists, and fungi in which gametes are formed.

gamete (gam'eet) A sex cell; in plants and animals, an egg or sperm. In sexual reproduction, the union of gametes results in the formation of a zygote. The chromosome number of a gamete is designated *n*. Species that are not polyploid have haploid gametes and diploid zygotes.

gametic isolation (gam-ee'tik) A prezygotic reproductive isolating mechanism in which sexual reproduction between two closely related species cannot occur because of chemical differences in the gametes.

gametogenesis The process of gamete formation. See *spermatogenesis* and *oogenesis*.

gametophyte generation (gam-ee'toh-fite) The *n*, gamete-producing stage in the life cycle of a plant. Compare with *sporophyte generation*.

gamma-aminobutyric acid (GABA) A neurotransmitter that has an inhibitory effect.

ganglion (gang'glee-on) (pl. *ganglia*) A mass of neuron cell bodies.

ganglion cell A type of neuron in the retina of the eye; receives input from bipolar cells.

gap junction Structure consisting of specialized regions of the plasma membrane of two adjacent cells; contains numerous pores that allow the passage of certain small molecules and ions between them.

gastrin (gas′trin)   A hormone released by the stomach mucosa; stimulates the gastric glands to secrete pepsinogen.

gastrovascular cavity   A central digestive cavity with a single opening that functions as both mouth and anus; characteristic of cnidarians and flatworms.

gastrula (gas′troo-lah)   A three-layered embryo formed by the process of gastrulation.

gastrulation (gas-troo-lay′shun)   Process in embryonic development during which the three germ layers (ectoderm, mesoderm, and endoderm) form.

gel electrophoresis   Procedure by which proteins or nucleic acids can be separated on the basis of size and charge as they migrate through a gel in an electrical field.

gene   A segment of DNA that serves as a unit of hereditary information; includes a transcribable DNA sequence (plus associated sequences regulating its transcription) that yields a protein or RNA product with a specific function. Most eukaryotic genes are in chromosomes.

gene amplification   The developmental process in which certain cells produce multiple copies of a gene by selective replication, thus allowing for increased synthesis of the gene product. Compare with *nuclear equivalence* and *genomic rearrangement*.

gene flow   The movement of alleles between local populations due to the migration of individuals; can have significant evolutionary consequences.

gene locus   See *locus*.

gene pool   All the alleles of all the genes present in a freely interbreeding population.

generation time   The time required for the completion of one cell cycle.

gene replacement therapy   Any of a variety of methods designed to correct a disease or alleviate its symptoms through the introduction of genes into the affected person's cells. Also known as gene transfer therapy.

gene transfer therapy   See *gene replacement therapy*.

genetic bottleneck   See *bottleneck*.

genetic code   See *codon*.

genetic counseling   Medical and genetic information provided to couples who are concerned about the risk of abnormality in their children.

genetic drift   A random change in allele frequency in a small breeding population.

genetic engineering   Manipulation of genes, often through recombinant DNA technology.

genetic equilibrium   The condition of a population that is not undergoing evolutionary change, i.e., in which allele and genotype frequencies do not change from one generation to the next. See *Hardy-Weinberg principle*.

genetic polymorphism (pol′′ee-mor′fizm)   The presence in a population of two or more alleles for a given gene locus.

genetic probe   A single-stranded nucleic acid (either DNA or RNA) that can be used to identify a complementary sequence by hydrogen-bonding to it.

genetic recombination   See *recombination, genetic*.

genetic screening   A systematic search through a population for individuals with a genotype or karyotype that might cause a serious genetic disease in them or their offspring.

genome (jee′nome)   Originally, all the genetic material in a cell or individual organism. The term is used more than one way, depending on context: e.g., an organism's haploid genome is all the DNA contained in one haploid set of its chromosomes, and its mitochondrial genome is all the DNA in a mitochondrion. See *human genome*.

genomic DNA library   A collection of recombinant plasmids in which all the DNA in the genome is represented. Compare with *cDNA library*.

genomic rearrangement   A physical change in the structure of one or more genes that occurs during the development of an organism and leads to an alteration in gene expression; compare with *nuclear equivalence* and *gene amplification*.

genotype (jeen′oh-type)   The genetic makeup of an individual. Compare with *phenotype*.

genotype frequency   The proportion of a particular genotype in the population.

genus (jee′nus)   A taxonomic category made up of related species.

germination   Resumption of growth of an embryo or spore; occurs when a seed or spore sprouts.

germ layers   In animals, three embryonic tissue layers: endoderm, mesoderm, and ectoderm.

germ line cell   In animals, a cell that is part of the line of cells that will ultimately undergo meiosis to form gametes. Compare with *somatic cell*.

germplasm   Any plant or animal material that may be used in breeding; includes seeds, plants, and plant tissues of traditional crop varieties and the sperm and eggs of traditional livestock breeds.

gibberellin (jib′′ur-el′lin)   A plant hormone involved in many aspects of plant growth and development, such as stem elongation, flowering, and seed germination.

gills   (1) The respiratory organs characteristic of many aquatic animals, usually thin-walled projections from the body surface or from some part of the digestive tract; (2) The spore-bearing, platelike structures under the caps of mushrooms.

ginkgo (ging′ko)   A member of an ancient gymnosperm group that consists of a single living representative (*Ginkgo biloba*), a hardy, deciduous tree with broad, fan-shaped leaves and naked, fleshy seeds (on female trees).

gland   See *endocrine gland* and *exocrine gland*.

glial cells (glee′ul)   In nervous tissue, cells that support and nourish neurons.

globulin (glob′yoo-lin)   One of a class of proteins in blood plasma, some of which (gamma globulins) function as antibodies.

glomerulus (glom-air′yoo-lus)   The cluster of capillaries at the proximal end of a nephron; the glomerulus is surrounded by Bowman's capsule.

glucagon (gloo′kah-gahn)   A hormone secreted by the pancreas that stimulates glycogen breakdown, thereby increasing the concentration of glucose in the blood. Compare with *insulin*.

glucose   A hexose aldehyde sugar that is central to many metabolic processes.

glutamate   An amino acid that functions as the major excitatory neurotransmitter in the vertebrate brain.

glyceraldehyde-3-phosphate (G3P)   Phosphorylated 3-carbon compound that is an important intermediate in glycolysis and in the Calvin cycle.

glycerol   A three-carbon alcohol with a hydroxyl group on each carbon; a component of triacylglycerols and phospholipids, as well as monoacylglycerols and diacylglycerols.

glycocalyx (gly''koh-kay'lix) A coating on the outside of an animal cell, formed by the polysaccharide portions of glycoproteins and glycolipids associated with the plasma membrane.

glycogen (gly'koh-jen) The principal storage polysaccharide in animal cells; formed from glucose and stored primarily in the liver and, to a lesser extent, in muscle cells.

glycolipid A lipid with covalently attached carbohydrates.

glycolysis (gly-kol'ih-sis) The first stage of cellular respiration, literally the "splitting of sugar." The metabolic conversion of glucose into pyruvate, accompanied by the production of ATP.

glycoprotein (gly'koh-pro-teen) A protein with covalently attached carbohydrates.

glycosidic linkage Covalent linkage joining two sugars; includes an oxygen atom bonded to a carbon of each sugar.

glyoxysomes (gly-ox'ih-somz) Membrane-bounded structures in cells of certain plant seeds; contain a large array of enzymes that convert stored fat to sugar.

gnetophyte (nee'toe-fite) One of a small phylum of unusual gymnosperms that possess some features similar to flowering plants.

goblet cells Unicellular glands that secrete mucus.

goiter (goy'ter) An enlargement of the thyroid gland.

golden alga A member of a phylum of algae, most of which are biflagellated, unicellular, and contain pigments, including chlorophyll *a* and *c* and carotenoids, including fucoxanthin.

Golgi complex (goal'jee) Organelle composed of stacks of flattened, membranous sacs. Mainly responsible for modifying, packaging, and sorting proteins that will be secreted or targeted to other organelles of the internal membrane system or to the plasma membrane; also called Golgi body or Golgi apparatus.

gonad (goh'nad) A gamete-producing gland; an ovary or a testis.

gonadotropin-releasing hormone (GnRH) A hormone secreted by the hypothalamus that stimulates the anterior pituitary to secrete the gonadotropic hormones: follicle-stimulating hormone (FSH) and luteinizing hormone (LH).

gonadotropic hormones (go-nad-oh-troh'pic) Hormones produced by the anterior pituitary gland that stimulate the testes and ovaries; include follicle-stimulating hormone (FSH) and luteinizing hormone (LH).

graded potential A local change in electrical potential that can vary in magnitude depending on the strength of the applied stimulus.

gradualism The idea that evolution occurs by a slow, steady accumulation of genetic changes over time. Compare with *punctuated equilibrium*.

graft rejection An immune response directed against a transplanted tissue or organ.

grain A simple, dry, one-seeded fruit in which the fruit wall is fused to the seed coat, making it impossible to separate the fruit from the seed, e.g., corn and wheat kernels.

granulosa cells In mammals, cells that surround the developing oocyte and are part of the follicle; produce estrogens and inhibin.

granum (pl. *grana*) A stack of thylakoids within a chloroplast.

gravitropism (grav''ih-troh'pizm) Growth of a plant in response to gravity.

gray crescent The grayish area of cytoplasm that marks the region where gastrulation begins in an amphibian embryo.

gray matter Nervous tissue in the brain and spinal cord that contains cell bodies, dendrites, and unmyelinated axons. Compare with *white matter*.

green alga A member of a diverse phylum of algae that contain the same pigments as plants (chlorophylls *a* and *b* and carotenoids).

greenhouse effect The natural global warming of Earth's atmosphere caused by the presence of carbon dioxide and other greenhouse gases, which trap the sun's radiation in much the same way that glass does in a greenhouse. The additional warming that may be produced by increased levels of greenhouse gases that absorb infrared radiation is known as the enhanced greenhouse effect.

greenhouse gases Trace gases in the atmosphere that allow the sun's energy to penetrate to Earth's surface but do not allow as much of it to escape as heat.

gross primary productivity The rate at which energy accumulates (is assimilated) in an ecosystem during photosynthesis. Compare with *net primary productivity*.

ground state The lowest energy state of an atom.

ground tissue system All tissues in the plant body other than the dermal tissue system and vascular tissue system; consists of parenchyma, collenchyma, and sclerenchyma.

growth factors A group of more than 50 extracellular peptides that signal certain cells to grow and divide.

growth hormone (GH) A hormone secreted by the anterior lobe of the pituitary gland; stimulates growth of body tissues; also called somatotropin.

growth rate The rate of change of a population's size on a per capita basis.

guanine (gwan'een) A nitrogenous purine base that is a component of nucleic acids and GTP.

guard cell One of a pair of epidermal cells that adjust their shape to form a stomatal pore for gas exchange.

guttation (gut-tay'shun) The appearance of water droplets on leaves, forced out through leaf pores by root pressure.

gymnosperm (jim'noh-sperm) Any of a group of seed plants in which the seeds are not enclosed in an ovary; gymnosperms frequently bear their seeds in cones. Includes four phyla: conifers, cycads, ginkgoes, and gnetophytes.

habitat The natural environment or place where an organism, population, or species lives.

habitat fragmentation The division of habitats that formerly occupied large, unbroken areas into smaller pieces by roads, fields, cities, and other human land-transforming activities.

habitat isolation A prezygotic reproductive isolating mechanism in which reproduction between similar species is prevented because they live and breed in different habitats

habituation (hab-it''yoo-ay'shun) A type of learning in which an animal becomes accustomed to a repeated, irrelevant stimulus and no longer responds to it.

hair cell A vertebrate mechanoreceptor found in the lateral line of fishes, the vestibular apparatus, semicircular canals, and cochlea.

half-life The period of time required for a radioisotope to change into a different material.

haploid (hap'loyd) The condition of having one set of chromosomes per nucleus. Compare with *diploid* and *polyploid*.

"hard-wiring" Refers to how neurons signal one another, how they connect, and how they carry out basic functions such as regulating heart rate, blood pressure, and sleep-wake cycles.

Hardy-Weinberg principle The mathematical prediction that allele frequencies do not change from generation to generation in a large population in the absence of microevolutionary processes (mutation, genetic drift, gene flow, natural selection).

Hatch-Slack pathway   See *C₄ plant*.

haustorium (hah-stor′ee-um) (pl. *haustoria*)   In parasitic fungi, a specialized hypha that penetrates a host cell and obtains nourishment from the cytoplasm.

Haversian canals (ha-vur′zee-un)   Channels extending through the matrix of bone; contain blood vessels and nerves.

heat   The total amount of kinetic energy in a sample of a substance.

heat energy   The thermal energy that flows from an object with a higher temperature to an object with a lower temperature.

heat of vaporization   The amount of heat energy that must be supplied to change one gram of a substance from the liquid phase to the vapor phase.

helicases   Enzymes that unwind the two strands of a DNA double helix.

heliotropism   The ability of leaves or flowers of certain plants to follow the sun by aligning themselves either perpendicular or parallel to the sun's rays; also called solar tracking.

helper T cell   T lymphocyte that activates B lymphocytes and can stimulate cytotoxic T cell production. Also known as CD4 T cell.

hemichordates   A phylum of sedentary, wormlike deuterostomes.

hemizygous (hem′′ih-zy′gus)   Possessing only one allele for a particular locus; a human male is hemizygous for all X-linked genes. Compare with *homozygous* and *heterozygous*.

hemocoel   Blood cavity characteristic of animals with an open circulatory system.

hemocyanin   A hemolymph pigment that transports oxygen in some mollusks and arthropods.

hemoglobin (hee′moh-gloh′′bin)   The red, iron-containing protein pigment in blood that transports oxygen and carbon dioxide and aids in regulation of pH.

hemolymph (hee′moh-limf)   The fluid that bathes the tissues in animals with an open circulatory system, e.g., arthropods and most mollusks.

hemophilia (hee′′-moh-feel′ee-ah)   A hereditary disease in which blood does not clot properly; the form known as hemophilia A has an X-linked, recessive inheritance pattern.

Hensen's node   See *primitive streak*.

hepatic (heh-pat′ik)   Pertaining to the liver.

hepatic portal system   The portion of the circulatory system that carries blood from the intestine through the liver.

herbivore (erb′uh-vore)   An animal that feeds on plants or algae. Also called primary consumer.

hermaphrodite (her-maf′roh-dite)   An organism that possesses both male and female sex organs.

heterochromatin (het′′ur-oh-kroh′mah-tin)   Highly coiled and compacted chromatin in an inactive state. Compare with *euchromatin*.

heterocyst (het′ur-oh-sist′′)   An oxygen-excluding cell of cyanobacteria that is the site of nitrogen fixation.

heterogametic   A term describing an individual that produces two classes of gametes with respect to their sex chromosome constitutions. Human males (XY) are heterogametic, producing X and Y sperm. Compare with *homogametic*.

heterospory (het′′ur-os′pur-ee)   Production of two types of *n* spores, microspores (male) and megaspores (female). Compare with *homospory*.

heterothallic (het′′ur-oh-thal′ik)   Pertaining to certain algae and fungi that have two mating types; only by combining a plus strain and a minus strain can sexual reproduction occur. Compare with *homothallic*.

heterotroph (het′ur-oh-trof)   An organism that cannot synthesize its own food from inorganic raw materials and therefore must obtain energy and body-building materials from other organisms. Also called consumer. Compare with *autotroph*. See *chemoheterotroph* and *photoheterotroph*.

heterozygote advantage   A phenomenon in which the heterozygous condition confers some special advantage on an individual that either homozygous condition does not (i.e., *Aa* has a higher degree of fitness than does *AA* or *aa*).

heterozygous (het-ur′oh-zye′gus)   Possessing a pair of unlike alleles for a particular locus. Compare with *homozygous*.

hexose   A monosaccharide containing six carbon atoms.

hibernation   Long-term torpor in response to winter cold and scarcity of food. Compare with *estivation*.

histamine (his′tah-meen)   Substance released from mast cells that is involved in allergic and inflammatory reactions.

hindbrain   In the early embryo, one of the three divisions of the developing vertebrate brain; subdivides to form the metencephalon, which gives rise to the cerebellum and pons, and the myelencephalon, which gives rise to the medulla. Compare with *forebrain* and *midbrain*.

histones (his′tones)   Small, positively charged (basic) proteins in the cell nucleus that bind to the negatively charged DNA. See *nucleosomes*.

holdfast   The basal structure for attachment to solid surfaces found in multicellular algae.

holoblastic cleavage   A cleavage pattern in which the entire embryo cleaves; characteristic of eggs with little or moderate yolk (isolecithal or moderately telolecithal), e.g., the eggs of echinoderms, amphioxus, and mammals. Compare with *meroblastic cleavage*.

homeobox   A DNA sequence of approximately 180 base pairs found in many homeotic genes and some other genes that are important in development; genes containing homeobox sequences code for certain transcription factors.

homeodomain   A functional region of certain transcription factor proteins; consists of approximately 60 amino acids specified by a homeobox DNA sequence and includes a recognition alpha helix, which can bind to specific DNA sequences and affect their transcription.

home range   A geographical area that an animal seldom or never leaves.

homeostasis (home′′ee-oh-stay′sis)   The balanced internal environment of the body; the automatic tendency of an organism to maintain such a steady state.

homeotic gene (home′′ee-ah′tik)   A gene that controls the formation of specific structures during development. Such genes were originally identified through insect mutants in which one body part is substituted for another.

hominid (hah′min-id)   Any of a group of extinct and living humans. Also called hominine.

hominoid (hah′min-oid)   The apes and hominids.

Homo erectus   An extinct hominid that lived between 2 million and 200,000 years ago; made stone tools and may have worn clothing, built fires, and lived in caves.

Homo ergaster   An extinct hominid that is recognized by some paleoanthropologists as separate from *Homo erectus*; other paleoanthropologists do not recognize *H. ergaster* as a separate species and instead consider it to be the African line of *H. erectus*.

homogametic   Term describing an individual that produces gametes with identical sex chromosome constitutions. Human females (XX) are homogametic, producing all X eggs. Compare with *heterogametic*.

Homo habilis An extinct hominid that lived between about 2.3 and 1.5 million years ago; lived in Africa and fashioned crude stone tools.

Homo heidelbergensis See *archaic Homo sapiens*.

homologous chromosomes (hom-ol′ah-gus) Chromosomes that are similar in morphology and genetic constitution. In humans there are 23 pairs of homologous chromosomes; one member of each pair is inherited from the mother, and the other from the father.

homologous features See *homology*.

homology Similarity in different species that results from their derivation from a common ancestor. The features that exhibit such similarity are called homologous features. Compare with *homoplasy*.

Homo neanderthalensis Primitive humans who lived in Europe and western Asia from about 230,000 to 30,000 years ago; possessed sophisticated stone tools, cared for the sick and elderly, and buried their dead; also called Neandertals.

homoplastic features See *homoplasy*.

homoplasy Similarity in the characters in different species that is due to convergent evolution, not common descent. Characters that exhibit such similarity are called homoplastic features. Compare with *homology*.

Homo sapiens The modern human species.

homospory (hoh′′mos′pur-ee) Production of one type of *n* spore that gives rise to a bisexual gametophyte. Compare with *heterospory*.

homothallic (hoh′′moh-thal′ik) Pertaining to certain algae and fungi that are self-fertile. Compare with *heterothallic*.

homozygous (hoh′′moh-zy′gous) Possessing a pair of identical alleles for a particular locus. Compare with *heterozygous*.

hormone An organic chemical messenger in multicellular organisms that is produced in one part of the body and often transported to another part where it signals cells to alter some aspect of metabolism.

hornwort A type of spore-producing, nonvascular, thallose plant with a life cycle similar to mosses.

horsetail A phylum of seedless vascular plants with a life cycle similar to ferns.

host mothering The introduction of an embryo from one species into the uterus of another species, where it implants and develops; the host mother subsequently gives birth and may raise the offspring as her own; also called embryo transfer.

human chorionic gonadotropin (hCG) A hormone secreted by cells surrounding the early embryo; signals the mother's corpus luteum to continue to function.

human genetics The science of inherited variation in humans.

human genome The totality of genetic information in human cells; includes the DNA content of both the nucleus and mitochondria. See *genome*.

human immunodeficiency virus (HIV) The retrovirus that causes AIDS (acquired immunodeficiency syndrome).

human leukocyte antigen (HLA) See *major histocompatibility complex*.

humus (hew′mus) Organic matter in various stages of decomposition in the soil; gives soil a dark brown or black color.

Huntington disease A genetic disease that has an autosomal dominant inheritance pattern and causes mental and physical deterioration.

hybrid The offspring of two genetically dissimilar parents.

hybrid breakdown A postzygotic reproductive isolating mechanism in which, although an interspecific hybrid is fertile and produces a second (F_2) generation, the F_2 has defects that prevent it from successfully reproducing.

hybrid inviability A postzygotic reproductive isolating mechanism in which the embryonic development of an interspecific hybrid is aborted.

hybridization (1) Interbreeding between members of two different taxa; (2) Interbreeding between genetically dissimilar parents; (3) In molecular biology, complementary base pairing between nucleic acid (DNA or RNA) strands from different sources.

hybrid sterility A postzygotic reproductive isolating mechanism in which an interspecific hybrid cannot reproduce successfully.

hybrid vigor The genetic superiority of an F_1 hybrid over either parent, due to the presence of heterozygosity for a number of different loci.

hybrid zone An area of overlap between two closely related populations, subspecies, or species, in which interbreeding occurs.

hydration Process of association of a substance with the partial positive and/or negative charges of water molecules.

hydrocarbon An organic compound composed solely of hydrogen and carbon atoms.

hydrogen bond A weak attractive force existing between a hydrogen atom with a partial positive charge and an electronegative atom (usually oxygen or nitrogen) with a partial negative charge. Compare with *covalent bond* and *ionic bond*.

hydrological cycle The water cycle, which includes evaporation, precipitation, and flow to the ocean. The hydrological cycle supplies terrestrial organisms with a continual supply of fresh water.

hydrolysis Reaction in which a covalent bond between two subunits is broken through the addition of the equivalent of a water molecule; a hydrogen atom is added to one subunit and a hydroxyl group to the other. Compare with *condensation synthesis*.

hydrophilic Interacting readily with water; having a greater affinity for water molecules than they have for each other. Compare with *hydrophobic*.

hydrophobic Not readily interacting with water; having less affinity for water molecules than they have for each other. Compare with *hydrophilic*.

hydroponics (hy′′dra-paun′iks) Growing plants in an aerated solution of dissolved inorganic minerals; i.e., without soil.

hydrostatic skeleton A type of skeleton found in some invertebrates in which contracting muscles push against a tube of fluid.

hydroxide ion An anion (negatively charged particle) consisting of oxygen and hydrogen; usually written OH⁻.

hydroxyl group (hy-drok′sil) Polar functional group; abbreviated —OH.

hyperpolarize To change the membrane potential so that the inside of the cell becomes more negative than its resting potential.

hypertonic A term referring to a solution having an osmotic pressure (or solute concentration) greater than that of the solution with which it is compared. Compare with *hypotonic* and *isotonic*.

hypha (hy′fah) (pl. *hyphae*) One of the threadlike filaments composing the mycelium of a water mold or fungus.

hypocotyl (hy′poh-kah′′tl)   The part of the axis of a plant embryo or seedling below the point of attachment of the cotyledons.

hypothalamus (hy-poh-thal′uh-mus)   Part of the mammalian brain that regulates the pituitary gland, the autonomic system, emotional responses, body temperature, water balance, and appetite; located below the thalamus.

hypothesis   A testable statement about the nature of an observation or relationship. Compare with *theory* and *principle*.

hypothetico-deductive approach   Emphasizes the use of deductive reasoning to test hypotheses. Compare with *hypothetico-inductive approach*. See *deductive reasoning*.

hypothetico-inductive approach   Emphasizes the use of inductive reasoning to discover new general principles. Compare with *hypothetico-deductive approach*. See *inductive reasoning*.

hypotonic   A term referring to a solution having an osmotic pressure (or solute concentration) less than that of the solution with which it is compared. Compare with *hypertonic* and *isotonic*.

hypotrichs   A group of dorsoventrally flattened ciliates that exhibt an unusual creeping-darting locomotion.

illuviation   The deposition of material leached from the upper layers of soil into the lower layers.

imaginal discs   Paired structures in an insect larva that develop into specific adult structures during complete metamorphosis.

imago (ih-may′go)   The adult form of an insect.

imbibition (im′′bi-bish′en)   The absorption of water by a seed prior to germination.

immigration   A type of migration in which individuals enter a population and thus increase its size. Compare with *emigration*.

immune response   Process of recognizing foreign macromolecules and mounting a response aimed at eliminating them. See *specific* and *nonspecific immune responses; primary* and *secondary responses*.

immunoglobulin (im-yoon′′oh-glob′yoo-lin)   See *antibody*.

imperfect flower   A flower that lacks either stamens or carpels. Compare with *perfect flower*.

imperfect fungi   See *deuteromycetes*.

implantation   The embedding of a developing embryo in the inner lining (endometrium) of the uterus.

implicit memory   The unconscious memory for perceptual and motor skills, e.g., riding a bicycle.

imprinting   (1) The expression of a gene based on its parental origin. (2) A type of learning by which a young bird or mammal forms a strong social attachment to an individual (usually a parent) or object within a few hours after hatching or birth.

inborn error of metabolism   A metabolic disorder cause by the mutation of a gene that codes for an enzyme needed for a biochemical pathway.

inbreeding   The mating of genetically similar individuals. Homozygosity increases with each successive generation of inbreeding. Compare with *outbreeding*.

inbreeding depression   The phenomenon in which inbred offspring of genetically similar individuals have lower fitness (e.g., decline in fertility and high juvenile mortality) than noninbred individuals.

inclusive fitness   The total of an individual's direct and indirect fitness; includes the genes contributed directly to offspring and those contributed indirectly by kin selection. Compare with *direct fitness*. See *kin selection*.

incomplete dominance   A condition in which neither member of a pair of contrasting alleles is completely expressed when the other is present.

incomplete flower   A flower that lacks one or more of the four parts: sepals, petals, stamens, and/or carpels. Compare with *complete flower*.

independent assortment, principle of   The genetic principle, first noted by Gregor Mendel, that states that the alleles of unlinked loci are randomly distributed to gametes.

indeterminate growth   Unrestricted growth, as for example, in stems and roots. Compare with *determinate growth*.

index fossils   Fossils restricted to a narrow period of geological time and found in the same sedimentary layers in different geographical areas.

indoleacetic acid   See *auxin*.

induced fit   Conformational change in the active site of an enzyme that occurs when it binds to its substrate.

inducer molecule   A substance that binds to a repressor protein, converting it to its inactive form, which is unable to prevent transcription.

inducible operon   An operon that is normally inactive because a repressor molecule is attached to its operator; transcription is activated when a specific inducer molecule binds to the repressor, making it incapable of binding to the operator, e.g., the lactose operon of *Escherichia coli*. Compare with *repressible operon*.

induction   The process by which the differentiation of a cell or group of cells is influenced by interactions with neighboring cells.

inductive reasoning   The reasoning that uses specific examples to draw a general conclusion or discover a general principle. Compare with *deductive reasoning*. See *hypothetico-inductive approach*.

infant mortality rate   The number of infant deaths per 1000 live births. (A child is an infant during its first two years of life.)

inflammatory response   The response of body tissues to injury or infection, characterized clinically by heat, swelling, redness, and pain, and physiologically by increased dilation of blood vessels and increased phagocytosis.

inflorescence   A cluster of flowers on a common floral stalk.

ingestion   The process of taking food (or other material) into the body.

inhibin   A hormone that inhibits FSH secretion; produced by Sertoli cells in the testes and by granulosa cells in the ovaries.

inhibitory postsynaptic potential (IPSP)   A change in membrane potential that takes a neuron farther from the firing level. Compare with *excitatory postsynaptic potential (EPSP)*.

initiation (of protein synthesis)   The first steps of protein synthesis, in which the large and small ribosomal subunits and other components of the translation machinery bind to the 5′ end of mRNA. See *elongation* and *termination*.

initiation codon   The codon AUG, which serves as the signal to begin translation of messenger RNA; also called a start codon. Compare with *termination codon*.

innate behavior   Behavior that is inherited and typical of the species; also called instinct.

innate immune responses   See *nonspecific immune responses*.

inner cell mass   The cluster of cells in the early mammalian embryo that gives rise to the embryo proper.

inorganic compound   A simple substance that does not contain a carbon backbone. Compare with *organic compound*.

inositol triphosphate (IP₃) A second messenger that increases intracellular calcium concentration and activates enzymes.

insight learning A complex learning process in which an animal adapts past experience to solve a new problem that may involve different stimuli.

in situ conservation Conservation efforts that concentrate on preserving biological diversity in the wild. Compare with *ex situ conservation*.

instinct See *innate behavior*.

instrumental conditioning See *operant conditioning*.

insulin (in'suh-lin) A hormone secreted by the pancreas that lowers blood-glucose concentration. Compare with *glucagon*.

insulin-like growth factors (IGF) Somatomedins; proteins that mediate responses to growth hormone.

insulin resistance A condition in which insulin is present, but insulin receptors on target cells do not bind with it; this condition is present in Type 2 diabetes.

insulin shock A condition in which the blood glucose concentration is so low that the individual may appear intoxicated, or may become unconscious, and even die; can be caused by the injection of too much insulin or by certain metabolic malfunctions.

integrins Receptor proteins that bind to specific proteins in the extracellular matrix and to membrane proteins on adjacent cells; transmit signals into the cell from the extracellular matrix.

integral membrane protein A protein that is tightly associated with the lipid bilayer of a biological membrane; a transmembrane integral protein spans the bilayer. Compare with *peripheral membrane protein*.

integration The process of summing (adding and subtracting) incoming neural signals.

integumentary system (in-teg''yoo-men'tar-ee) The body's covering, including the skin and its nails, glands, hair, and other associated structures.

integuments The outer cell layers that surround the megasporangium of an ovule; develop into the seed coat.

intercellular substance In connective tissues, the combination of matrix and fibers in which the cells are embedded.

interference competition Intraspecific competition in which certain dominant individuals obtain an adequate supply of the limited resource at the expense of other individuals in the population. Also called contest competition. Compare with *exploitation competition*.

interferons (in''tur-feer'on) Cytokines produced by animal cells when challenged by a virus; prevent viral reproduction and enable cells to resist a variety of viruses.

interkinesis The stage between meiosis I and meiosis II. Interkinesis is usually brief; the chromosomes may decondense, reverting at least partially to an interphase-like state, but DNA synthesis and chromosome duplication do not occur.

interleukins A diverse group of cytokines produced mainly by macrophages and lymphocytes.

intermediate-day plant A plant that flowers when it is exposed to days and nights of intermediate length but does not flower when the daylength is too long or too short. Compare with *long-day, short-day,* and *day-neutral plants*.

intermediate disturbance hypothesis In community ecology, the idea that species richness is greatest at moderate levels of disturbance, which create a mosaic of habitat patches at different stages of succession.

intermediate filaments Cytoplasmic fibers that are part of the cytoskeletal network and are intermediate in size between microtubules and microfilaments.

internal membrane system The group of membranous structures in eukaryotic cells that interact through direct connections or by means of vesicles; includes the endoplasmic reticulum, outer membrane of the nuclear envelope, Golgi complex, lysosomes, and the plasma membrane; also called endomembrane system.

interneuron (in''tur-noor'on) A nerve cell that carries impulses from one nerve cell to another and is not directly associated with either an effector or a sensory receptor. Also known as an association neuron.

internode The region on a stem between two successive nodes. Compare with *node*.

interoceptor (in'tur-oh-sep''tor) A sense organ within a body organ that transmits information regarding chemical composition, pH, osmotic pressure, or temperature. Compare with *exteroceptor*.

interphase The stage of the cell cycle between successive mitotic divisions; its subdivisions are the G_1 (first gap), S (DNA synthesis), and G_2 (second gap) phases.

interspecific competition The interaction between members of different species that vie for the same resource in an ecosystem (e.g., food or living space). Compare with *intraspecific competition*.

interstitial cells (of testis) The cells between the seminiferous tubules that secrete testosterone.

interstitial fluid The fluid that bathes the tissues of the body; also called tissue fluid.

intertidal zone The marine shoreline area between the high tide mark and the low tide mark.

intraspecific competition The interaction between members of the same species that vie for the same resource in an ecosystem (e.g., food or living space). Compare with *interspecific competition*.

intrinsic rate of increase The theoretical maximum rate of increase in population size occurring under optimal environmental conditions. Also called biotic potential.

intron A non–protein-coding region of a eukaryotic gene and also of the pre-mRNA transcribed from such a region. Introns do not appear in mRNA. Compare with *exon*.

invertebrate An animal without a backbone (vertebral column); invertebrates account for about 95% of animal species.

in vitro Occurring outside a living organism (literally "in glass"). Compare with *in vivo*.

in vitro evolution Test tube experiments that demonstrate that RNA molecules in the RNA world could have catalyzed the many different chemical reactions needed for life. Also called directed evolution.

in vivo Occurring in a living organism. Compare with *in vitro*.

ion An atom or group of atoms bearing one or more units of electrical charge, either positive (cation) or negative (anion).

ion channels Channels for the passage of ions through a membrane; formed by specific membrane proteins.

ionic bond The chemical attraction between a cation and an anion. Compare with *covalent bond* and *hydrogen bond*.

ionic compound A substance consisting of cations and anions, which are attracted by their opposite charges; ionic compounds do not consist of molecules. Compare with *covalent compound*.

ionization The dissociation of a substance to yield ions, e.g., the ionization of water yields H^+ and OH^-.

iris The pigmented portion of the vertebrate eye.

iron-sulfur world hypothesis The hypothesis that simple organic molecules that are the precursors of life originated at hydro-thermal vents in the deep-ocean floor. Compare with *prebiotic broth hypothesis*.

irreversible inhibitor   A substance that permanently inactivates an enzyme. Compare with *reversible inhibitor*.

islets of Langerhans (eye′lets of Lahng′er-hanz)   The endocrine portion of the pancreas that secretes glucagon and insulin, hormones that regulate the concentration of glucose in the blood.

isogamy (eye-sog′uh-me)   Sexual reproduction involving motile gametes of similar form and size. Compare with *anisogamy* and *oogamy*.

isogenic   A term describing a strain of organisms in which all individuals are genetically identical and homozygous at all loci.

isolecithal egg   An egg containing a relatively small amount of uniformly distributed yolk. Compare with *telolecithal egg*.

isomer (eye′soh-mer)   One of two or more chemical compounds having the same chemical formula, but different structural formulas, e.g., structural and geometric isomers and enantiomers.

isoprene units   Five-carbon hydrocarbon monomers that make up certain lipids such as carotenoids and steroids.

isotonic (eye″soh-ton′ik)   A term applied to solutions that have identical concentrations of solute molecules and hence the same osmotic pressure. Compare with *hypertonic* and *hypotonic*.

isotope (eye′suh-tope)   An alternate form of an element with a different number of neutrons, but the same number of protons and electrons. See *radioisotopes*.

iteroparity   The condition of having repeated reproductive cycles throughout a lifetime. Compare with *semelparity*.

jelly coat   One of the acellular coverings of the eggs of certain animals, such as echinoderms.

joint   The junction between two or more bones of the skeleton.

joule   A unit of energy, equivalent to 0.239 calorie.

juvenile hormone (JH)   An arthropod hormone that preserves juvenile structure during a molt. Without it, metamorphosis toward the adult form takes place.

juxtaglomerular apparatus (juks″tah-glo-mer′yoo-lar)   A structure in the kidney that secretes renin in response to a decrease in blood pressure.

***K* selection**   A reproductive strategy recognized by some ecologists in which a species typically has a large body size, slow development, long life span, and does not devote a large proportion of its metabolic energy to the production of offspring. Compare with *r selection*.

karyotype (kare′ee-oh-type)   The chromosomal constitution of an individual. Representations of the karyotype are generally prepared by photographing the chromosomes and arranging the homologous pairs according to size, centromere position, and pattern of bands.

keratin (kare′ah-tin)   A horny, water-insoluble protein found in the epidermis of vertebrates and in nails, feathers, hair, and horns.

ketone   An organic molecule containing a carbonyl group bonded to two carbon atoms. Compare with *aldehyde*.

keystone species   A species whose presence in an ecosystem largely determines the species composition and functioning of that ecosystem.

kidney   The paired vertebrate organ important in excretion of metabolic wastes and in osmoregulation.

killer T cell   See *cytotoxic T cell*.

kilobase (kb)   1000 bases or base pairs of a nucleic acid.

kilocalorie   The amount of heat required to raise the temperature of 1 kg of water 1°C; also called Calorie, which is equivalent to 1000 calories.

kilojoule   1000 joules. See *joule*.

kinases   Enzymes that catalyze the transfer of phosphate groups from ATP to acceptor molecules. Protein kinases activate or inactivate proteins through the addition of phosphates at specific locations.

kinetic energy   Energy of motion. Compare with *potential energy*.

kinetochore (kin-eh′toh-kore)   The portion of the chromosome centromere to which the mitotic spindle fibers attach.

kingdom   A broad taxonomic category made up of related phyla; many biologists currently recognize six kingdoms of living organisms.

kin selection   A type of natural selection that favors altruistic behavior toward relatives (kin), thereby ensuring that, although the chances of an individual's survival are lessened, some of its genes will survive through successful reproduction of close relatives; increases inclusive fitness.

Klinefelter syndrome   Inherited condition in which the affected individual is a sterile male with an XXY karyotype.

Koch's postulates   A set of guidelines used to demonstrate that a specific pathogen causes specific disease symptoms.

Krebs cycle   See *citric acid cycle*.

krummholz   The gnarled, shrublike growth habit found in trees at high elevations, near their upper limit of distribution.

labyrinth   The system of interconnecting canals of the inner ear of vertebrates.

labyrinthodonts   The first successful group of tetrapods.

lactation (lak-tay′shun)   The production or release of milk from the breast.

lacteal (lak′tee-al)   One of the many lymphatic vessels in the intestinal villi that absorb fat.

lactic acid (lactate)   A three-carbon organic acid.

lagging strand   A strand of DNA that is synthesized as a series of short segments, called Okazaki fragments, which are then covalently joined by DNA ligase. Compare with *leading strand*.

lamins   Proteins attached to the inner surface of the nuclear envelope that provide a type of skeletal framework.

landscape   A large land area (several to many square kilometers) composed of interacting ecosystems.

landscape ecology   The subdiscipline in ecology that studies the connections in a heterogenous landscape.

large intestine   The portion of the digestive tract of humans (and other vertebrates) consisting of the cecum, colon, rectum, and anus.

larva (pl. *larvae*)   An immature form in the life history of some animals; may be unlike the parent.

larynx (lare′inks)   The organ at the upper end of the trachea that contains the vocal cords.

lateral meristems   Areas of localized cell division on the side of a plant that give rise to secondary tissues. Lateral meristems, including the vascular cambium and the cork cambium, cause an increase in the girth of the plant body. Compare with *apical meristem*.

leaching   The process by which dissolved materials are washed away or carried with water down through the various layers of the soil.

leader sequence   Noncoding sequence of nucleotides in mRNA that is transcribed from the region that precedes (is upstream to) the coding region.

leading strand   Strand of DNA that is synthesized continuously. Compare with *lagging strand.*

learning   A change in the behavior of an animal that results from experience.

lectins   Sugar-binding proteins that were originally extracted from plant seeds, where they are found in large quantities; also occur in many other organisms.

legume (leg'yoom)   (1) A simple, dry fruit that splits open at maturity along two sutures to release seeds; (2) Any member of the pea family, e.g., pea, bean, peanut, alfalfa.

lek   A small territory in which males compete for females.

lens   The oval, transparent structure located behind the iris of the vertebrate eye; bends incoming light rays and brings them to a focus on the retina.

lenticels (len'tih-sels)   Porous swellings of cork cells in the stems of woody plants; facilitate the exchange of gases.

leptin   A hormone produced by adipose tissue that signals brain centers about the status of energy stores.

leukocytes (loo'koh-sites)   White blood cells; colorless amoeboid cells that defend the body against disease-causing organisms.

leukoplasts   Colorless plastids; include amyloplasts, which are used for starch storage in cells of roots and tubers.

lichen (ly'ken)   A compound organism composed of a symbiotic fungus and an alga or cyanobacterium.

life history traits   Significant features of a species' life cycle, particularly traits that influence survival and reproduction.

life span   The maximum duration of life for an individual of a species.

life table   A table showing mortality and survival data by age of a population or cohort.

ligament (lig'uh-ment)   A connective tissue cable or strap that connects bones to each other or holds other organs in place.

ligand   A molecule that binds to a specific site in a receptor or other protein.

light-dependent reactions   Reactions of photosynthesis in which light energy absorbed by chlorophyll is used to synthesize ATP and usually NADPH. Includes *cyclic electron transport* and *noncyclic electron transport.*

lignin (lig'nin)   A substance found in many plant cell walls that confers rigidity and strength, particularly in woody tissues.

limbic system   In vertebrates, an action system of the brain. In humans, plays a role in emotional responses, motivation, autonomic function, and sexual response.

limiting resource   An environmental resource that, because it is scarce or unfavorable, tends to restrict the ecological niche of an organism.

limnetic zone (lim-net'ik)   The open water away from the shore of a lake or pond extending down as far as sunlight penetrates. Compare with *littoral zone* and *profundal zone.*

linkage   The tendency for a group of genes located on the same chromosome to be inherited together in successive generations.

lipase (lip'ase)   A fat-digesting enzyme.

lipid   Any of a group of organic compounds that are insoluble in water but soluble in nonpolar solvents; lipids serve as energy storage and are important components of cell membranes.

lipoprotein (lip-oh-proh' teen)   A large molecular complex consisting of lipids and protein; transports lipids in the blood. High-density lipoproteins (HDLs) transport cholesterol to the liver; low-density lipoproteins (LDLs) deliver cholesterol to many cells of the body.

littoral zone (lit'or-ul)   The region of shallow water along the shore of a lake or pond. Compare with *limnetic zone* and *profundal zone.*

liver   A large, complex organ that secretes bile, helps maintain homeostasis by removing or adding nutrients to the blood, and performs many other metabolic functions.

liverworts   A phylum of spore-producing, nonvascular, thallose or leafy plants with a life cycle similar to mosses.

local hormones   See *local regulators.*

local regulators   Prostaglandins (a group of local hormones), growth factors, cytokines, and other soluble molecules that act on nearby cells by paracrine regulation or act on the cells that produce them (autocrine regulation).

locus   The place on the chromosome at which the gene for a given trait occurs, i.e., a segment of the chromosomal DNA containing information that controls some feature of the organism; also called gene locus.

logistic population growth   Population growth that initially occurs at a constant rate of increase over time (i.e., exponential) but then levels out as the carrying capacity of the environment is approached. When the increase in number versus time is plotted on a graph, logistic growth produces a characteristic S-shaped curve. Compare with *exponential population growth.*

long-day plant   A plant that flowers in response to shortening nights; also called short-night plant. Compare with *short-day, intermediate-day,* and *day-neutral plants.*

long-night plant   See *short-day plant.*

long-term potentiation (LTP)   Long-lasting increase in the strength of synaptic connections that occurs in response to a series of high frequency electrical stimuli. Compare with *long-term synaptic depresssion (LTD).*

long-term synaptic depression (LTD)   Long-lasting decrease in the strength of synaptic connections that occurs in response to low-frequency stimulation of neurons. Compare with *long-term potentiation (LTP).*

loop of Henle (Hen'lee)   The U-shaped loop of a mammalian kidney tubule, which extends down into the renal medulla.

loose connective tissue   A type of connective tissue that is widely distributed in the body; consists of fibers strewn through a semifluid matrix.

lophoporate phyla   Three related invertebrate protostome phyla, characterized by a ciliated ring of tentacles that surrounds the mouth.

Lophotrochozoa   A branch of the protostomes that includes the nemerteans (proboscis worms), mollusks, annelids, and the lophophorate phyla.

lumen (loo'men)   (1) The space enclosed by a membrane, such as the lumen of the endoplasmic reticulum or the thylakoid lumen; (2) The cavity or channel within a tube or tubular organ, such as a blood vessel or the digestive tract.

lung   An internal respiratory organ that functions in gas exchange; enables an animal to breathe air.

luteinizing hormone (LH) (loot'eh-ny-zing)   Gonadotropic hormone secreted by the anterior pituitary; stimulates ovulation and maintains the corpus luteum in the ovaries of females; stimulates testosterone production by interstitial cells in the testes of males.

lymph (limf)   The colorless fluid within the lymphatic vessels that is derived from blood plasma and resembles it closely in composition; contains white blood cells; ultimately lymph is returned to the blood.

lymph node   A mass of lymph tissue surrounded by a connective tissue capsule; manufactures lymphocytes and filters lymph.

lymphatic system   A subsystem of the cardiovascular system; returns excess interstitial fluid (lymph) to the circulation; defends the body against disease organisms.

lymphocyte (lim′foh-site)   White blood cell with nongranular cytoplasm that is responsible for immune responses. See *B cell* and *T cell*.

lysis (ly′sis)   The process of disintegration of a cell or some other structure.

lysogenic conversion   The change in properties of bacteria that results from the presence of a prophage.

lysosomes (ly′soh-somes)   Intracellular organelles present in many animal cells; contain a variety of hydrolytic enzymes.

lysozyme   An enzyme found in many tissues and in tears and other body fluids; attacks the cell wall of many gram-positive bacteria.

macroevolution   Large-scale evolutionary change over long time spans. Compare with *microevolution*.

macromolecule   A very large organic molecule, such as a protein or nucleic acid.

macronucleus   A large nucleus found, along with one or several micronuclei, in ciliates. The macronucleus regulates metabolism and growth. Compare with *micronucleus*.

macronutrient   An essential element that is required in fairly large amounts for normal growth. Compare with *micronutrient*.

macrophage (mak′roh-faje)   A large phagocytic cell capable of ingesting and digesting bacteria and cellular debris. Macrophages are also antigen-presenting cells.

major histocompatibility complex (MHC)   A group of membrane proteins, present on the surface of most cells, that are slightly different in each individual. In humans, the MHC is called the HLA (human leukocyte antigen) group.

malignant   The term used to describe cancer cells, tumor cells that are able to invade tissue and metastasize.

malnutrition   Poor nutritional status; can result from dietary intake that is either below or above required needs.

Malpighian tubules (mal-pig′ee-an)   The excretory organs of many arthropods.

mammals   The class of vertebrates characterized by hair, mammary glands, a diaphragm, and differentiation of teeth.

mandible (man′dih-bl)   (1) The lower jaw of vertebrates; (2) Jaw-like, external mouthparts of insects.

mangrove forest   A tidal wetland dominated by mangrove trees, in which the salinity fluctuates between that of sea water and fresh water.

mantle   In the mollusk, a fold of tissue that covers the visceral mass and that usually produces a shell.

marine snow   The organic debris (plankton, dead organisms, fecal material, etc.) that "rains" into the dark area of the oceanic province from the lighted region above; the primary food of most organisms that live in the ocean's depths.

marsupials (mar-soo′pee-uls)   A subclass of mammals, characterized by the presence of an abdominal pouch in which the young, which are born in a very undeveloped condition, are carried for some time after birth.

mass extinction   The extinction of numerous species during a relatively short period of geological time. Compare with *background extinction*.

mast cell   A type of cell found in connective tissue; contains histamine and is important in allergic reactions.

maternal effect genes   Genes of the mother that are transcribed during oogenesis and subsequently affect the development of the embryo. Compare with *zygotic genes*.

matrix (may′triks)   (1) In cell biology, the interior of the compartment enclosed by the inner mitochondrial membrane; (2) In zoology, nonliving material secreted by and surrounding connective tissue cells; contains a network of microscopic fibers.

matter   Anything that has mass and takes up space.

maxillae   Appendages used for manipulating food; characteristic of crustaceans.

mechanical isolation   A prezygotic reproductive isolating mechanism in which fusion of the gametes of two species is prevented by morphological or anatomical differences.

mechanoreceptor (meh-kan′oh-ree-sep′′tor)   A sensory cell or organ that perceives mechanical stimuli, e.g., touch, pressure, gravity, stretching, or movement.

medulla (meh-dul′uh)   (1) The inner part of an organ, such as the medulla of the kidney; compare with *cortex*. (2) The most posterior part of the vertebrate brain, lying next to the spinal cord.

medusa   A jellyfish-like animal; a free-swimming, umbrella-shaped stage in the life cycle of certain cnidarians. Compare with *polyp*.

megaphyll (meg′uh-fil)   Type of leaf found in horsetails, ferns, gymnosperms, and angiosperms; contains multiple vascular strands (i.e., complex venation). Compare with *microphyll*.

megaspore (meg′uh-spor)   The *n* spore in heterosporous plants that gives rise to a female gametophyte. Compare with *microspore*.

meiosis (my-oh′sis)   Process in which a 2*n* cell undergoes two successive nuclear divisions (meiosis I and meiosis II), potentially producing four *n* nuclei; leads to the formation of gametes in animals and spores in plants.

melanin   A dark pigment present in many animals; contributes to the color of the skin.

melanin concentrating hormone (MCH)   A neuropeptide signaling molecule that helps regulate energy homeostasis.

melanocortins   A group of peptides that appear to decrease appetite in response to increased fat stores.

melatonin (mel-ah-toh′ nin)   A hormone secreted by the pineal gland that plays a role in setting circadian rhythms.

memory cell   B or T lymphocyte that permits rapid mobilization of immune response on second or subsequent exposure to a particular antigen.

meninges (meh-nin′jeez) (sing. *meninx*)   The three membranes that protect the brain and spinal cord: the dura mater, arachnoid, and pia mater.

menopause   The period (usually occurring between 45 and 55 years of age) in women when the recurring menstrual cycle ceases.

menstrual cycle (men′stroo-ul)   In the human female, the monthly sequence of events that prepares the body for pregnancy; the cycle begins with the first day of menstruation; the first two weeks of the cycle are the preovulatory phase; ovulation takes place on about the 14th day of the cycle; the third and fourth weeks of the cycle are the postovulatory phase.

menstruation (men-stroo-ay′shun)   The monthly discharge of blood and degenerated uterine lining in the human female; marks the beginning of each menstrual cycle.

meristem (mer′ih-stem)   A localized area of mitotic cell division in the plant body. See *apical meristem* and *lateral meristems*.

meroblastic cleavage   Cleavage pattern observed in the telolecithal eggs of reptiles and birds, in which cleavage is restricted to a small disc of cytoplasm at the animal pole. Compare with *holoblastic cleavage*.

mesenchyme (mes'en-kime)   A loose, often jelly-like connective tissue containing undifferentiated cells; found in the embryos of vertebrates and the adults of some invertebrates.

mesoderm (mez'oh-derm)   The middle germ layer of the early embryo; gives rise to connective tissue, muscle, bone, blood vessels, kidneys, and many other structures. Compare with *ectoderm* and *endoderm*.

mesophyll (mez'oh-fil)   Photosynthetic tissue in the interior of a leaf; sometimes differentiated into palisade mesophyll and spongy mesophyll.

Mesozoic era   That part of geological time extending from roughly 248 to 65 million years ago.

messenger RNA (mRNA)   RNA that specifies the amino acid sequence of a protein; transcribed from DNA.

metabolic pathway   A series of chemical reactions in which the product of one reaction becomes the substrate of the next reaction.

metabolic rate   Energy production of an organism per unit time. See *basal metabolic rate*.

metabolism   The sum of all the chemical processes that occur within a cell or organism: the transformations by which energy and matter are made available for use by the organism. See *anabolism* and *catabolism*.

metamorphosis (met''ah-mor'fuh-sis)   Transition from one developmental stage to another, such as from a larva to an adult.

metanephridia (sing. *metanephridium*)   The excretory organs of annelids and mollusks; each metanephridium consists of a tubule open at both ends; at one end a ciliated funnel opens into the coelom, and the other end of the tube opens to the outside of the body.

metaphase (met'ah-faze)   The stage of mitosis, and of meiosis I and II, in which the chromosomes line up on the equatorial plane of the cell. Occurs after prophase and before anaphase.

metapopulation   A population that is divided into several local populations among which individuals occasionally disperse.

metastasis (met-tas'tuh-sis)   The spreading of cancer cells from one organ or part of the body to another.

methyl group   A nonpolar functional group; abbreviated —CH$_3$.

microclimate   Local variations in climate produced by differences in elevation, in the steepness and direction of slopes, and in exposure to prevailing winds.

microevolution   Small-scale evolutionary change due to changes in allele or genotype frequencies that occur within a population over successive generations. Compare with *macroevolution*.

microfilaments   Thin fibers composed of actin protein subunits; form part of the cytoskeleton.

microfossils   Ancient traces (fossils) of microscopic life.

microglia   Phagocytic glial cells found in the CNS.

micronucleus   One or more smaller nuclei found, along with the macronucleus, in ciliates. The micronucleus is involved in sexual reproduction. Compare with *macronucleus*.

micronutrient   An essential element that is required in trace amounts for normal growth. Compare with *macronutrient*.

microphyll (mi'kro-fil)   Type of leaf found in club mosses; contains one vascular strand (i.e., simple venation). Compare with *megaphyll*.

microsphere   A protobiont produced by adding water to abiotically formed polypeptides.

microspore (mi'kro-spor)   The *n* spore in heterosporous plants that gives rise to a male gametophyte. Compare with *megaspore*.

microtubules (my-kroh-too'bewls)   Hollow cylindrical fibers composed of tubulin protein subunits; major components of the cytoskeleton and found in mitotic spindles, cilia, flagella, centrioles, and basal bodies.

microtubule-associated proteins (MAPs)   Include structural proteins that help regulate microtubule assembly and cross-link microtubules to other cytoskeletal polymers; and motors, such as kinesin and dynein, that use ATP to produce movement.

microtubule-organizing center (MTOC)   The region of the cell from which microtubules are anchored and possibly assembled. The MTOCs of many organisms (including animals, but not flowering plants or most gymnosperms) contain a pair of centrioles.

microvilli (sing. *microvillus*)   Minute projections of the plasma membrane that increase the surface area of the cell; found mainly in cells concerned with absorption or secretion, such as those lining the intestine or the kidney tubules.

midbrain   In vertebrate embryos, one of the three divisions of the developing brain. Also called mesencephalon. Compare with *forebrain* and *hindbrain*.

middle lamella   The layer composed of pectin polysaccharides that serves to cement together the primary cell walls of adjacent plant cells.

midvein   The main, or central, vein of a leaf.

migration   The periodic or seasonal movement of an organism (individual or population) from one place to another, usually over a long distance. See *dispersal*.

mineralocorticoids (min''ur-al-oh-kor'tih-koidz)   Hormones produced by the adrenal cortex that regulate mineral metabolism and, indirectly, fluid balance. The principal mineralocorticoid is aldosterone.

minerals   Inorganic nutrients ingested as salts dissolved in food and water.

missense mutation   A type of base-substitution mutation that causes one amino acid to be substituted for another in the resulting protein product. Compare with *nonsense mutation*.

mitochondria (my''toh-kon'dree-ah) (sing. *mitochondrion*)   Intracellular organelles that are the sites of oxidative phosphorylation in eukaryotes; include an outer membrane and an inner membrane.

mitochondrial DNA (mtDNA)   DNA present in mitochondria that is transmitted maternally, from mothers to their offspring. Mitochondrial DNA mutates more rapidly than nuclear DNA.

mitosis (my-toh'sis)   The division of the cell nucleus resulting in two daughter nuclei, each with the same number of chromosomes as the parent nucleus; mitosis consists of four phases: prophase, metaphase, anaphase, and telophase. Cytokinesis usually overlaps the telophase stage.

mitosis-promoting factor (MPF)   A cyclin-dependent protein kinase that controls the transition of a cell from the G$_2$ stage of interphase to mitosis; formerly known as maturation promoting factor.

mitotic spindle   Structure consisting mainly of microtubules that provides the framework for chromosome movement during cell division.

mitral valve   See *atrioventricalar valve*.

mobile genetic element   See *transposon*.

mole   The atomic mass of an element or the molecular mass of a compound, expressed in grams; one mole of any substance has 6.02×10^{23} units (Avogadro's number).

molecular anthropology   The branch of science that compares genetic material from individuals of regional human populations to help unravel the origin and migrations of modern humans.

molecular chaperones Proteins that help other proteins fold properly. Although not dictating the folding pattern, chaperones make the process more efficient.

molecular clock analysis A comparison of the DNA nucleotide sequences of related organisms to estimate when they diverged from one another during the course of evolution.

molecular formula The type of chemical formula that gives the actual numbers of each type of atom in a molecule. Compare with *simplest formula* and *structural formula*.

molecular mass The sum of the atomic masses of the atoms that make up a single molecule of a compound; expressed in atomic mass units (amu) or daltons.

molecule The smallest particle of a covalently bonded element or compound that has the composition and properties of a larger part of the substance.

mollusks A phylum of coelomate protostome animals characterized by a soft body, visceral mass, mantle, and foot.

molting The shedding and replacement of an outer covering such as an exoskeleton.

molting hormone A steroid hormone that stimulates growth and molting in insects. Also called ecdysone.

monoacylglycerol (mon′′o-as′′-il-glis′er-ol) Lipid consisting of glycerol combined chemically with a single fatty acid. Also called monoglyceride. Compare with *diacylglycerol* and *triacylglycerol*.

monocot (mon′oh-kot) One of the two classes of flowering plants; monocot seeds contain a single cotyledon, or seed leaf. Compare with *dicot*.

monoclonal antibodies Identical antibody molecules produced by cells cloned from a single cell.

monocyte (mon′oh-site) A type of white blood cell; a large phagocytic, nongranular leukocyte that enters the tissues and differentiates into a macrophage.

monoecious (mon-ee′shus) Having male and female reproductive parts in separate flowers or cones on the same plant; compare with *dioecious*.

monogamy A mating system in which a male animal mates with a single female during a breeding season.

monoglyceride See *monoacylglycerol*.

monohybrid cross A genetic cross that takes into account the behavior of alleles of a single locus. Compare with *dihybrid cross*.

monokaryotic (mon′′o-kare-ee-ot′ik) The condition of having a single *n* nucleus per cell, characteristic of certain fungal hyphae. Compare with *dikaryotic*.

monomer (mon′oh-mer) A molecule that can be linked with other similar molecules; two monomers join to form a dimer, whereas many can be linked to form a polymer. Monomers can be small (e.g., sugars or amino acids) or they can be large (e.g., tubulin or actin proteins).

monophyletic group (mon′′oh-fye-let′ik) A group made up of organisms that evolved from a common ancestor. Compare with *polyphyletic group* and *paraphyletic group*.

monosaccharide (mon-oh-sak′ah-ride) A simple sugar that cannot be degraded by hydrolysis to a simpler sugar.

monosomy The condition in which only one member of a chromosome pair is present and the other is missing. Compare with *trisomy* and *disomy*.

monotremes (mon′oh-treems) Egg-laying mammals such as the duck-billed platypus of Australia.

monounsaturated fatty acid See *fatty acid*.

monozygotic twins Genetically identical twins that arise from the division of a single fertilized egg; commonly known as identical twins. Compare with *dizygotic twins*.

morphogen Any chemical agent thought to be responsible for the processes of cell differentiation and pattern formation that lead to morphogenesis.

morphogenesis (mor-foh-jen′eh-sis) The development of the form and structures of an organism and its parts; proceeds by a series of steps known as pattern formation.

mortality The rate at which individuals die; the average per capita death rate.

morula (mor′yoo-lah) An early embryo consisting of a solid ball of cells.

mosaic development A highly invariant developmental pattern in which the fate of each blastomere becomes determined at a very early stage. Compare with *regulative development*.

mosses A phylum of spore-producing nonvascular plants with an alternation of generations in which the dominant *n* gametophyte alternates with a 2*n* sporophyte that remains attached to the gametophyte.

motor neuron An efferent neuron that transmits impulses away from the central nervous system to skeletal muscle.

motor unit All the skeletal muscle fibers that are stimulated by a single motor neuron.

mRNA cap An unusual nucleotide, 7-methylguanylate, that is added to the 5′ end of a eukaryotic messenger RNA. Capping enables eukaryotic ribosomes to bind to mRNA.

mucosa (mew-koh′suh) See *mucous membrane*.

mucous membrane A type of epithelial membrane that lines a body cavity that opens to the outside of the body, eg., the digestive and respiratory tracts; also called mucosa.

mucus (mew′cus) A sticky secretion composed of covalently linked protein and carbohydrate; serves to lubricate body parts and trap particles of dirt and other contaminants. (The adjectival form is spelled *mucous*.)

Müllerian mimicry (mul-ler′ee-un mim′ih-kree) The resemblance of dangerous, unpalatable, or poisonous species to one another so that they are more easily recognized by potential predators, which learn to avoid all of them after tasting one. Compare with *Batesian mimicry*.

multiple alleles (al-leels′) Three or more alleles of a single locus (in a population), such as the alleles governing the ABO series of blood types.

multiple fruit A fruit that develops from many ovaries of many separate flowers, e.g., pineapple. Compare with *simple, aggregate*, and *accessory fruits*.

muscle (1) A tissue specialized for contraction; (2) An organ that produces movement by contraction.

mutagen (mew′tah-jen) Any agent capable of producing mutations.

mutation Any change in DNA; may include a change in the nucleotide base pairs of a gene, a rearrangement of genes within the chromosomes so that their interactions produce different effects, or a change in the chromosomes themselves.

mutualism (1) In ecology, a symbiotic relationship in which both partners benefit from the association. Compare with *parasitism* and *commensalism*. (2). In animal behavior, cooperative behavior in which each animal in the group benefits.

mycelium (my-seel′ee-um) (pl. *mycelia*) The vegetative body of most fungi and certain protists (water molds); consists of a branched network of hyphae.

mycorrhizae (my′′kor-rye′zee) Mutualistic associations of fungi and plant roots that aid in the plant's absorption of essential minerals from the soil.

mycotoxins Poisonous chemical compounds produced by fungi, e.g., aflatoxins that harm the liver and are known carcinogens.

myelin sheath (my′eh-lin) The white fatty material that forms a sheath around the axons of certain nerve cells, which are then called myelinated fibers.

myocardial infarction (MI) Heart attack; serious consequence occurring when the heart muscle receives insufficient oxygen.

myofibrils (my-oh-fy′brilz) Tiny threadlike structures in the cytoplasm of striated and cardiac muscle that are responsible for contractions of the cell; contain myofilaments.

myofilament (my-oh-fil′uh-ment) One of the filaments making up a myofibril; the structural unit of muscle proteins in a muscle cell. See *myosin filament* and *actin filament*.

myoglobin (my′oh-glob′′bin) A hemoglobin-like, oxygen-transferring protein found in muscle.

myosin (my′oh-sin) A protein that, together with actin, is responsible for muscle contraction.

myosin filaments Thick filaments composed mainly of the protein myosin; actin and myosin filaments make up the myofibrils of muscle fibers.

n The chromosome number of a gamete. The chromosome number of a zygote is 2*n*. If an organism is not polyploid, the *n* gametes are haploid and the 2*n* zygotes are diploid.

NAD$^+$/NADH Oxidized and reduced forms, respectively, of nicotinamide adenine dinucleotide, a coenzyme that transfers electrons (as hydrogen), particularly in catabolic pathways, including cellular respiration.

NADP$^+$/NADPH Oxidized and reduced forms, respectively, of nicotinamide adenine dinucleotide phosphate, a coenzyme that acts as an electron (hydrogen) transfer agent, particularly in anabolic pathways, including photosynthesis.

nanoplankton Extremely minute (< 50 μm in length) algae that are major producers in the ocean because of their great abundance; part of phytoplankton.

nastic movement A temporary, reversible movement of a plant organ in response to external stimuli; movement is caused by changes in the turgor of certain cells.

natality The rate at which individuals produce offspring; the average per capita birth rate.

natural selection The mechanism of evolution proposed by Charles Darwin; the tendency of organisms that possess favorable adaptations to their environment to survive and become the parents of the next generation. Evolution occurs when natural selection results in changes in allele frequencies in a population.

natural killer cell (NK cell) A large, granular lymphocyte that functions in both nonspecific and specific immune responses; releases cytokines and proteolytic enzymes that target tumor cells and cells infected with viruses and other pathogens.

Neandertal See *Homo neanderthalensis*.

necrosis Uncontrolled cell death that causes inflammation and damages other cells. Compare with *apoptosis*.

nectary (nek′ter-ee) A gland or other structure that secretes nectar.

negative feedback mechanism A homeostatic mechanism in which a change in some condition triggers a response that counteracts, or reverses, the changed condition, restoring homeostasis, e.g., how mammals maintain body temperature. Compare with *positive feedback mechanism*.

nekton (nek′ton) Free-swimming aquatic organisms such as fish and turtles. Compare with *plankton*.

nematocyst (nem-at′oh-sist) A stinging structure found within cnidocytes (stinging cells) in cnidarians; used for anchorage, defense, and capturing prey.

nematodes The phylum of animals commonly known as roundworms.

nemerteans The phylum of animals commonly known as ribbon worms; possess a proboscis for capturing prey.

neo-Darwinism See *synthetic theory of evolution*.

neonate Newborn individual.

neoplasm See *tumor*.

nephridial organ (neh-frid′ee-al) The excretory organ of many invertebrates; consists of simple or branching tubes that usually open to the outside of the body through pores; also called nephridia.

nephron (nef′ron) The functional, microscopic unit of the vertebrate kidney.

neritic province (ner-ih′tik) Ocean water that extends from the shoreline to where the bottom reaches a depth of 200 m. Compare with *oceanic province*.

nerve A bundle of axons (or dendrites) wrapped in connective tissue that conveys impulses between the central nervous system and some other part of the body.

nerve net A system of interconnecting nerve cells found in cnidarians and echinoderms.

nervous tissue A type of animal tissue specialized for transmitting electrical and chemical signals.

nest parasitism A behavior practiced by brown-headed cowbirds and certain other bird species in which females lay their eggs in the nests of other bird species and leave all parenting jobs to the hosts.

net primary productivity The energy that remains in an ecosystem (as biomass) after cellular respiration has occurred; net primary productivity equaly gross primary productivity minus respiration. Compare with *gross primary productivity*.

neural crest (noor′ul) The group of cells along the neural tube that migrate and form structures of the peripheral nervous system and certain other structures.

neural plasticity The ability of the nervous system to change in response to experience.

neural plate See *neural tube*.

neural transmission See *transmission, neural*.

neural tube The hollow, longitudinal structure in the early vertebrate embryo that gives rise to the brain and spinal cord. The neural tube forms from the neural plate, a flattened, thickened region of the ectoderm that rolls up and sinks below the surface.

neuroendocrine cells Neurons that produce neurohormones.

neurohormones Hormones produced by neuroendocrine cells; transported down axons and released into interstitial fluid; typically diffuse into capillaries and are transported by the blood; common in invertebrates; in vertebrates, neurohormones are produced by the hypothalamus.

neuron (noor′on) A nerve cell; a conducting cell of the nervous system that typically consists of a cell body, dendrites, and an axon.

neuropeptide The group of peptides produced in neural tissue that function as signaling molecules; many are neurotransmitters.

neuropeptide Y A signaling molecule produced by the hypothalamus that increases appetite and slows metabolism; helps restore energy homeostasis when leptin levels and food intake are low.

neurotransmitter A chemical signal used by neurons to transmit impulses across a synapse.

neutral solution A solution of pH 7; there are equal concentrations of hydrogen ions (H^+) and hydroxide ions (OH^-). Compare with *acidic solution* and *basic solution*.

neutral variation Variation that does not appear to confer any selective advantage or disadvantage to the organism.

neutron (noo′tron) An electrically neutral particle with a mass of one atomic mass unit (amu) found in the atomic nucleus. Compare with *proton* and *electron*.

neutrophil (new′truh-fil) A type of granular leukocyte important in immune responses; a type of phagocyte that engulfs and destroys bacteria and foreign matter.

niche (nich) The totality of an organism's adaptations, its use of resources, and the lifestyle to which it is fitted in its community. How an organism uses materials in its environment as well as how it interacts with other organisms; also called ecological niche. See *fundamental niche* and *realized niche*.

nicotinamide adenine dinucleotide See NAD$^+$/NADH.

nicotinamide adenine dinucleotide phosphate See NADP$^+$/NADPH.

nitric oxide (NO) A gaseous signaling molecule; a neurotransmitter.

nitrification (nie″tra-fuh-kay′shun) The conversion of ammonia to nitrate by certain bacteria (nitrifying bacteria) in the soil; part of the nitrogen cycle.

nitrogen cycle The worldwide circulation of nitrogen from the abiotic environment into living things and back into the abiotic environment.

nitrogen fixation The conversion of atmospheric nitrogen (N_2) to ammonia (NH_3) by certain bacteria; part of the nitrogen cycle.

nitrogenase (nie-traa′jen-ase) The enzyme responsible for nitrogen fixation under anaerobic conditions.

nociceptors (no′sih-sep-torz) Pain receptors; free endings of certain sensory neurons whose stimulation is perceived as pain.

node The area on a stem where each leaf is attached. Compare with *internode*.

nodules Swellings on the roots of plants, such as legumes, in which symbiotic nitrogen-fixing bacteria *(Rhizobium)* live.

noncompetitive inhibitor A substance that lowers the rate at which an enzyme catalyzes a reaction but does not bind to the active site. Compare with *competitive inhibitor*.

noncyclic electron transport In photosynthesis, the linear flow of electrons through Photosystems I and II; results in the formation of ATP (by chemiosmosis), NADPH, and O_2. Compare with *cyclic electron transport*.

nondisjunction Abnormal separation of sister chromatids or of homologous chromosomes caused by their failure to disjoin (move apart) properly during mitosis or meiosis.

nonpolar covalent bond Chemical bond formed by the equal sharing of electrons between atoms of approximately equal electronegativity. Compare with *polar covalent bond*.

nonpolar molecule Molecule that does not have a positively charged end and a negatively charged end; nonpolar molecules are generally insoluble in water. Compare with *polar molecule*.

nonsense mutation A base substitution mutation that results in an amino acid–specifying codon being changed to a termination (stop) codon; when the abnormal mRNA is translated, the resulting protein is usually truncated and nonfunctional. Compare with *missense mutation*.

nonspecific immune responses Mechanisms such as physical barriers (e.g., the skin) and phagocytosis that provide immediate and general protection against pathogens. Also called innate immunity. Compare with *specific immune responses*.

norepinephrine (nor-ep-ih-nef′rin) A neurotransmitter that is also a hormone secreted by the adrenal medulla.

Northern blot hybridization A technique in which RNA fragments, previously separated by gel electrophoresis, are transferred to a nitrocellulose membrane; a specific radioactive genetic probe is then allowed to hybridize to complementary fragments, thus marking their locations. Compare with *Southern blot hybridization* and *Western blotting*.

notochord (no′toe-kord) The flexible, longitudinal rod in the anteroposterior axis that serves as an internal skeleton in the embryos of all chordates and in the adults of some.

nuclear area Region of a bacterial cell that contains DNA but is not enclosed by a membrane.

nuclear envelope The double membrane system that encloses the cell nucleus of eukaryotes.

nuclear equivalence The concept that, with few exceptions, the nuclei of all differentiated cells of an adult organism are genetically identical to each other and to the nucleus of the zygote from which they were derived. Compare with *genomic rearrangement* and *gene amplification*.

nuclear pores Structures in the nuclear envelope that allow passage of certain materials between the cell nucleus and the cytoplasm.

nucleolus (new-klee′oh-lus) (pl. *nucleoli*) Specialized structure in the cell nucleus formed from regions of several chromosomes; site of assembly of the ribosomal subunits.

nucleoplasm The contents of the cell nucleus.

nucleoside triphosphate Molecule consisting of a nitrogenous base, a pentose sugar, and three phosphate groups, e.g., adenosine triphosphate (ATP).

nucleosomes (new′klee-oh-somz) Repeating units of chromatin structure, each consisting of a length of DNA wound around a complex of eight histone molecules. Adjacent nucleosomes are connected by a DNA linker region associated with another histone protein.

nucleotide (noo′klee-oh-tide) A molecule composed of one or more phosphate groups, a five-carbon sugar (ribose or deoxyribose), and a nitrogenous base (purine or pyrimidine).

nucleus (new′klee-us) (pl. *nuclei*) (1) The central region of an atom, containing the protons and neutrons; (2) A cellular organelle in eukaryotes that contains the DNA and serves as the control center of the cell; (3) A mass of nerve cell bodies in the central nervous system.

nut A simple, dry fruit that contains a single seed and is surrounded by a hard fruit wall.

nutrients The chemical substances in food that are used as components for synthesizing needed materials and/or as energy sources.

nutrition The process of taking in and using food (nutrients).

obesity Excess accumulation of body fat; a person is considered obese if the body mass index (BMI) is 30 or more.

obligate anaerobe Organism that grows only in the absence of oxygen. Compare with *facultative anaerobe*.

occipital lobes Posterior areas of the mammalian cerebrum; interpret visual stimuli from the retina of the eye.

oceanic province That part of the open ocean that overlies an ocean bottom deeper than 200 m. Compare with *neritic province*.

Okazaki fragment One of many short segments of DNA, each 100 to 1000 nucleotides long, that must be joined by DNA ligase to form the lagging strand in DNA replication.

olfactory epithelium   Tissue containing odor-sensing neurons.

oligodendrocyte   A type of glial cell that forms myelin sheaths around neurons in the CNS.

ommatidium (om″ah-tid′ee-um) (pl. *ommatidia*)   One of the light-detecting units of a compound eye, consisting of a lens and a crystalline cone that focus light onto photoreceptors called retinular cells.

omnivore (om′nih-vore)   An animal that eats a variety of plant and animal materials.

oncogene (on′koh-jeen)   An abnormally functioning gene implicated in causing cancer. Compare with *proto-oncogene* and *anti-oncogene*.

onycophorans (on″ih-kof′or-anz)   Phylum of rare, tropical, caterpillar-like animals, structurally intermediate between annelids and arthropods, possessing an annelid-like excretory system, and claw-tipped short legs.

oocytes (oh′oh-sites)   Meiotic cells that give rise to egg cells (ova).

oogamy (oh-og′uh-me)   The fertilization of a large, nonmotile female gamete by a small, motile male gamete. Compare with *isogamy* and *anisogamy*.

oogenesis (oh″oh-jen′eh-sis)   Production of female gametes (eggs) by meiosis. Compare with *spermatogenesis*.

oospore   A thick-walled, resistant spore formed from a zygote during sexual reproduction in water molds and certain algae.

open circulatory system   A type of circulatory system in which the blood bathes the tissues directly; characteristic of arthropods and many mollusks. Compare with *closed circulatory system*.

open system   An entity that can exchange energy and matter with its surroundings. Compare with *closed system*.

operant conditioning   A type of learning in which an animal is rewarded or punished for performing a behavior it discovers by chance; also called instrumental conditioning.

operator site   One of the control regions of an operon; the DNA segment to which a repressor binds, thereby inhibiting the transcription of the adjacent structural genes of the operon.

operculum   In bony fishes, a protective flap of the body wall that covers the gills.

operon (op′er-on)   In prokaryotes, a group of structural genes that are coordinately controlled and transcribed as a single message, plus their adjacent regulatory elements.

optimal foraging   The process of obtaining food in a manner that maximizes benefits and/or minimizes costs.

orbital   Region in which electrons occur in an atom or molecule.

order   A taxonomic category made up of related families.

organ   A specialized structure, such as the heart or liver, made up of tissues and adapted to perform a specific function or group of functions.

organ of Corti (kor′tie)   The structure within the inner ear of vertebrates that contains receptor cells that sense sound vibrations.

organ system   An organized group of tissues and organs that work together to perform a specialized set of functions, e.g., the digestive system or circulatory system.

organelle   One of the specialized structures within the cell, such as the mitochondria, Golgi complex, ribosomes, or contractile vacuole; many organelles are membrane-bounded.

organic compound   A compound composed of a backbone made up of carbon atoms. Compare with *inorganic compound*.

organism   Any living system composed of one or more cells.

organismic respiration   See *respiration*.

organogenesis   The process of organ formation.

orgasm (or′gazm)   The climax of sexual excitement.

origin of replication   A specific site on the DNA where replication can begin.

osmoconformer   An animal in which the salt concentration of body fluids varies with changes in surrounding seawater. Compare with *osmoregulator*.

osmoregulation (oz″moh-reg-yoo-lay′shun)   The active regulation of the osmotic pressure of body fluids so that they do not become excessively dilute or excessively concentrated.

osmoregulator   An animal that maintains an optimal salt concentration in its body fluids despite changes in salinity of its surroundings. Compare with *osmoconformer*.

osmosis (oz-moh′sis)   The net movement of water (the principal solvent in biological systems) by diffusion through a selectively permeable membrane from a region of higher concentration of water (a hypotonic solution) to a region of lower concentration of water (a hypertonic solution).

osmotic pressure   The pressure that must be exerted on the hypertonic side of a selectively permeable membrane to prevent diffusion of water (by osmosis) from the side containing pure water.

osteichthyes (os″tee-ick′thees)   Historically, the vertebrate class of bony fishes. Biologists now divide bony fishes into three classes: Actinopterygii, the ray-finned fishes; Actinistia, the coelacanths; and Sarcopterygii, the lobe-finned fishes.

osteoblast (os′tee-oh-blast)   A type of bone cell that secretes the protein matrix of bone. Also see *osteocyte*.

osteoclast (os′tee-oh-clast)   Large, multinucleate cell that helps sculpt and remodel bones by dissolving and removing part of the bony substance.

osteocyte (os′tee-oh-site)   A mature bone cell; an osteoblast that has become embedded within the bone matrix and occupies a lacuna.

osteon (os′tee-on)   The spindle-shaped unit of bone composed of concentric layers of osteocytes organized around a central Haversian canal containing blood vessels.

otoliths (oh′toe-liths)   Small calcium carbonate crystals in the saccule and utricle of the inner ear; sense gravity and are important in static equilibrium.

outbreeding   The mating of individuals of unrelated strains. Compare with *inbreeding*.

ovary (oh′var-ee)   (1) In animals, one of the paired female gonads responsible for producing eggs and sex hormones; (2) In flowering plants, the base of the carpel that contains ovules; ovaries develop into fruits after fertilization.

oviduct (oh′vih-dukt)   The tube that carries ova from the ovary to the uterus, cloaca, or body exterior. Also called fallopian tube or uterine tube.

oviparous (oh-vip′ur-us)   Bearing young in the egg stage of development; egg-laying. Compare with *viviparous* and *ovoviviparous*.

ovoviviparous (oh′voh-vih-vip″ur-us)   A type of development in which the young hatch from eggs incubated inside the mother's body. Compare with *viviparous* and *oviparous*.

ovulation (ov-u-lay′shun)   The release of an ovum from the ovary.

ovule (ov′yool)   The structure (i.e., megasporangium) in the plant ovary that develops into the seed following fertilization.

ovum (pl. *ova*)   Female gamete of an animal.

oxaloacetate   Four-carbon compound; important intermediate in the citric acid cycle and in the C_4 and CAM pathways of carbon fixation in photosynthesis.

oxidants Highly reactive molecules such as radicals, peroxides, and superoxides that are produced during normal cell processes that require oxygen; can damage DNA and other molecules by snatching electrons.

oxidation The loss of one or more electrons (or hydrogen atoms) by an atom, ion, or molecule. Compare with *reduction*.

oxidative phosphorylation (fos′′for-ih-lay′shun) The production of ATP using energy derived from the transfer of electrons in the electron transport system of mitochondria; occurs by chemiosmosis.

oxygen-carrying capacity The maximum amount of oxygen that can be transported by hemoglobin.

oxygen debt The oxygen necessary to metabolize the lactic acid produced during strenuous exercise.

oxygen-hemoglobin dissociation curve A curve depicting the percentage saturation of hemoglobin with oxygen, as a function of certain variables such as oxygen concentration, carbon dioxide concentration, or pH.

oxyhemoglobin Hemoglobin that has combined with oxygen.

oxytocin (ok′′see-tow′sin) Hormone secreted by the hypothalamus and released by the posterior lobe of the pituitary gland; stimulates contraction of the pregnant uterus and the ducts of mammary glands.

ozone A blue gas, O_3, with a distinctive odor that is a human-made pollutant near Earth's surface (in the troposphere) but a natural and essential component of the stratosphere.

P generation (parental generation) Members of two different true-breeding lines that are crossed to produce the F_1 generation.

P680 Chlorophyll *a* molecules that serve as the reaction center of Photosystem II, transferring photoexcited electrons to a primary acceptor; named by their absorption peak at 680 nm.

P700 Chlorophyll *a* molecules that serve as the reaction center of Photosystem I, transferring photoexcited electrons to a primary acceptor; named by their absorption peak at 700 nm.

pacemaker (of the heart) See *sinoatrial (SA) node*.

Pacinian corpuscle (pah-sin′-ee-an kor′pus-el) A receptor located in the dermis of the skin that responds to pressure.

paedomorphosis Retention of juvenile or larval features in a sexually mature animal.

pair bond A stable relationship between animals of opposite sex that ensures cooperative behavior in mating and rearing the young.

paleoanthropology (pay′′lee-o-an-thro-pol′uh-gee) The study of human evolution.

Paleozoic era That part of geological time extending from roughly 570 to 248 million years ago.

palindromic Reading the same forward and backward; some DNA sequences are palindromic because the base sequence of one strand is the reverse of the base sequence in its complement; for example, the complement of 5′-GAATTC-3′ is 3′-CTTAAG-5′.

palisade mesophyll (mez′oh-fil) The vertically stacked, columnar mesophyll cells near the upper epidermis in certain leaves. Compare with *spongy mesophyll*.

pancreas (pan′kree-us) Large gland located in the vertebrate abdominal cavity. The pancreas produces pancreatic juice containing digestive enzymes; also serves as an endocrine gland, secreting the hormones insulin and glucagon.

panspermia The idea that life did not originate on Earth, but began elsewhere in the galaxy and drifted through space to Earth.

parabronchi (sing. *parabronchus*) Thin-walled ducts in the lungs of birds; gases are exchanged across their walls.

paracrine regulation A type of regulation in which a signal molecule (e.g., certain hormones) diffuses through interstitial fluid and acts on nearby target cells. Compare with *autocrine regulation*.

paraphyletic group A group of organisms made up of a common ancestor and some, but not all, of its descendants. Compare with *monophyletic group* and *polyphyletic group*.

parapodia (par′′uh-poh′dee-ah) (sing. *parapodium*) Paired, thickly bristled paddle-like appendages extending laterally from each segment of polychaete worms.

parasite A heterotrophic organism that obtains nourishment from the living tissue of another organism (the host).

parasitism (par′uh-si-tiz′′m) A symbiotic relationship in which one member (the parasite) benefits and the other (the host) is adversely affected. Compare with *commensalism* and *mutualism*.

parasympathetic nervous system A division of the autonomic nervous system concerned with the control of the internal organs; functions to conserve or restore energy. Compare with *sympathetic nervous system*.

parathyroid glands Small, pea-sized glands closely adjacent to the thyroid gland; their secretion regulates calcium and phosphate metabolism.

parathyroid hormone (PTH) A hormone secreted by the parathyroid glands; regulates calcium and phosphate metabolism.

parenchyma (par-en′kih-mah) Highly variable living plant cells that have thin primary walls; function in photosynthesis, the storage of nutrients, and/or secretion.

parsimony The principle based on the experience that the simplest explanation is most probably the correct one.

parthenogenesis (par′′theh-noh-jen′eh-sis) The development of an unfertilized egg into an adult organism; common among honey bees, wasps, and certain other arthropods.

parturition (par′′to-rish′un) The birth process.

partial pressure (of a gas) The pressure exerted by gas in a mixture, which is the same pressure it would exert if alone. For example, the partial pressure of atmospheric oxygen (P_{O_2}) is 160 mm Hg at sea level.

passive immunity Temporary immunity that depends on the presence of immunoglobulins produced by another organism. Compare with *active immunity*.

passive ion channel A channel in the plasma membrane that permits the passage of specific ions such as Na^+, K^+, or Cl^-.

patch clamp technique A method that allows researchers to study the ion channels of a tiny patch of membrane by tightly sealing a micropipette to the patch and measuring the flow of ions through the channels.

patchiness See *clumped dispersion*.

pathogen (path′oh-gen) An organism, usually a microorganism, capable of producing disease.

pattern formation See *morphogenesis*.

pedigree A chart constructed to show an inheritance pattern within a family through multiple generations.

peduncle The stalk of a flower or inflorescence.

pellicle A flexible outer covering of protein; characteristic of certain protists, e.g., ciliates and euglenoids.

penis The male sexual organ of copulation in reptiles, mammals, and a few birds.

pentose A sugar molecule containing five carbons.

people overpopulation A situation in which there are too many people in a given geographical area; results in pollution, environmental degradation, and resource depletion. Compare with *consumption overpopulation*.

pepsin (pep'sin)   An enzyme produced in the stomach that initiates digestion of protein.

peptide (pep'tide)   A compound consisting of a chain of amino acid groups linked by peptide bonds. A dipeptide consists of two amino acids, a polypeptide of many.

peptide bond   A distinctive covalent carbon-to-nitrogen bond that links amino acids in peptides and proteins.

peptidoglycan (pep''tid-oh-gly'kan)   A modified protein or peptide possessing an attached carbohydrate; component of the eubacterial cell wall.

perennial plant (purr-en'ee-ul)   A woody or herbaceous plant that grows year after year, i.e., lives more than two years. Compare with *annual* and *biennial*.

perfect flower   A flower that has both stamens and carpels. Compare with *imperfect* flower.

pericentriolar material   Fibrils surrounding the centrioles in the microtubule organizing centers in cells of animals and other organisms possessing centrioles; chemically similar to the material in the microtubule organizing centers of organisms lacking centrioles.

pericycle (pehr'eh-sy''kl)   A layer of meristematic cells typically found between the endodermis and phloem in roots.

periderm (pehr'ih-durm)   The outer bark of woody stems and roots; composed of cork cells, cork cambium, and cork parenchyma, along with traces of primary tissues.

period   An interval of geological time that is a subdivision of an era. Each period is divided into epochs.

peripheral membrane protein   A protein associated with one of the surfaces of a biological membrane. Compare with *integral membrane protein*.

peripheral nervous system (PNS)   In vertebrates, the nerves and receptors that lie outside the central nervous system. Compare with *central nervous system (CNS)*.

peristalsis (pehr''ih-stal'sis)   Rhythmic waves of muscular contraction and relaxation in the walls of hollow tubular organs, such as the ureter or parts of the digestive tract, that serve to move the contents through the tube.

permafrost   Permanently frozen subsoil characteristic of frigid areas such as the tundra.

peroxisomes (pehr-ox'ih-somz)   Membrane-bounded organelles in eukaryotic cells containing enzymes that produce or degrade hydrogen peroxide.

persistence   A characteristic of certain chemicals that are extremely stable and may take many years to be broken down into simpler forms by natural processes.

petal   One of the parts of the flower attached inside the whorl of sepals; petals are usually colored.

petiole (pet'ee-ohl)   The part of a leaf that attaches to a stem.

pH   The negative logarithm of the hydrogen ion concentration of a solution (expressed as moles per liter). Neutral pH is 7, values less than 7 are acidic, and those greater than 7 are basic.

phage   See *bacteriophage*.

phagocytosis (fag''oh-sy-toh'sis)   Literally, "cell eating"; a type of endocytosis by which certain cells engulf food particles, microorganisms, foreign matter, or other cells.

pharmacogenomics   A new field of gene-based medicine in which drugs are personalized to match a patient's genetic makeup.

pharynx (fair'inks)   Part of the digestive tract. In complex vertebrates it is bounded anteriorly by the mouth and nasal cavities and posteriorly by the esophagus and larynx; the throat region in humans.

phenetics (feh-neh'tiks)   An approach to classification based on measurable similarities in phenotypic characters, without consideration of homology or other evolutionary relationships. Compare with *cladistics* and *evolutionary systematics*.

phenotype (fee'noh-type)   The physical or chemical expression of an organism's genes. Compare with *genotype*.

phenotype frequency   The proportion of a particular phenotype in the population.

phenylketonuria (PKU) (fee''nl-kee''toh-noor'ee-ah)   An inherited disease in which there is a deficiency of the enzyme that normally converts phenylalanine to tyrosine; results in mental retardation if untreated.

pheromone (fer'oh-mone)   A substance secreted by an organism to the external environment that influences the development or behavior of other members of the same species.

phloem (flo'em)   The vascular tissue that conducts dissolved sugar and other organic compounds in plants.

phosphate group   A weakly acidic functional group that can release one or two hydrogen ions.

phosphodiester linkage   Covalent linkage between two nucleotides in a strand of DNA or RNA; includes a phosphate group bonded to the sugars of two adjacent nucleotides.

phosphoenolpyruvate (PEP)   Three-carbon phosphorylated compound that is an important intermediate in glycolysis and is a reactant in the initial carbon fixation step in C_4 and CAM photosynthesis.

phosphoglycerate (PGA)   Phosphorylated three-carbon compound that is an important metabolic intermediate.

phospholipids (fos''foh-lip'idz)   Lipids in which there are two fatty acids and a phosphorus-containing group attached to glycerol; major components of cell membranes.

phosphorus cycle   The worldwide circulation of phosphorus from the abiotic environment into living things and back into the abiotic environment.

phosphorylation (fos''for-ih-lay'shun)   The introduction of a phosphate group into an organic molecule. See *kinases*.

photoautotroph   An organism that obtains energy from light and synthesizes organic compounds from inorganic raw materials; includes plants, algae, and some bacteria. Compare with *photoheterotroph, chemoautotroph,* and *chemoheterotroph*.

photoheterotroph   An organism that is able to carry out photosynthesis to obtain energy but is unable to fix carbon dioxide and therefore requires organic compounds as a carbon source; includes some bacteria. Compare with *photoautotroph, chemoautotroph,* and *chemoheterotroph*.

photolysis (foh-tol'uh-sis)   The photochemical splitting of water in the light-dependent reactions of photosynthesis, catalyzed by a specific enzyme.

photon (foh'ton)   A particle of electromagnetic radiation; one quantum of radiant energy.

photoperiodism (foh''teh-peer'ee-o-dizm)   The physiological response (such as flowering) of plants to variations in the length of daylight and darkness.

photophosphorylation (foh''toh-fos-for-ih-lay'shun)   The production of ATP in photosynthesis.

photoreceptor (foh''toh-ree-sep'tor)   (1) A sense organ specialized to detect light; (2) A pigment that absorbs light before triggering a physiological response.

photorespiration (foh''toh-res-pur-ay'shun)   The process that reduces the efficiency of photosynthesis in C_3 plants during hot spells in summer; consumes oxygen and produces carbon dioxide through the degradation of Calvin cycle intermediates.

photosynthesis The biological process that captures light energy and transforms it into the chemical energy of organic molecules (e.g., carbohydrates), which are manufactured from carbon dioxide and water; performed by plants, algae, and certain bacteria.

photosystem One of two photosynthetic units, consisting of chlorophyll molecules, accessory pigments, proteins, and associated electron acceptors, responsible for capturing light energy and transferring excited electrons; photosystem I best absorbs and uses light of about 700 nm, whereas photosystem II best absorbs and uses light of about 680 nm.

phototroph (foh´toh-trof) Organism that uses light as a source of energy. Compare with *chemotroph*. See *photoautotroph* and *photoheterotroph*.

phototropism (foh´´toh-troh´pizm) The growth of a plant in response to the direction of light.

phycocyanin (fy´´koh-sy-ah´nin) A blue pigment found in cyanobacteria and red algae.

phycoerythrin (fy´´koh-ee-rih´thrin) A red pigment found in cyanobacteria and red algae.

phyletic evolution See *anagenesis*.

phylogenetic systematics See *cladistics*.

phylogenetic tree A branching diagram that shows lines of descent among a group of related species.

phylogeny (fy-loj´en-ee) The complete evolutionary history of a group of organisms.

phylum (fy´lum) A taxonomic grouping of related, similar classes; a category beneath the kingdom and above the class.

phytochemicals Compounds found in plants that play important roles in preventing certain diseases; some function as antioxidants.

phytochrome (fy´toh-krome) A blue-green, proteinaceous pigment involved in a wide variety of physiological responses to light; occurs in two interchangeable forms depending on the ratio of red to far-red light.

phytoplankton (fy´´toh-plank´tun) Microscopic floating algae and cyanobacteria that are the base of most aquatic food webs. Compare with *zooplankton*. See *plankton* and *nanoplankton*.

pia mater (pee´a may´ter) The inner membrane covering the brain and spinal cord; the innermost of the meninges; also see *dura mater* and *arachnoid*.

pigment A substance that selectively absorbs light of different wavelengths.

pili (pie´lie) (sing. *pilus*) Hairlike structures on the surface of many bacteria. Function in conjugation or attachment.

pineal gland (pie-nee´al) Endocrine gland located in the brain.

pinocytosis (pin´´oh-sy-toh´sis) Cell drinking; a type of endocytosis by which cells engulf and absorb droplets of liquids.

pioneer The first organism to colonize an area and begin the first stage of succession.

pistil The female reproductive organ of a flower; consists of either a single carpel or two or more fused carpels. See *carpel*.

pith The innermost tissue in the stems and roots of many herbaceous plants; primarily a storage tissue.

pituitary gland (pi-too´ih-tehr´´ee) An endocrine gland located below the hypothalamus; secretes several hormones that influence a wide range of physiological processes.

placenta (plah-sen´tah) The partly fetal and partly maternal organ whereby materials are exchanged between fetus and mother in the uterus of placental mammals.

placoderms (plak´oh-durms) A group of extinct jawed fishes.

plankton Free-floating, mainly microscopic aquatic organisms found in the upper layers of the water; composed of phytoplankton and zooplankton. Compare with *nekton*.

planula larva (plan´yoo-lah) A ciliated larval form found in cnidarians.

plasma The fluid portion of blood in which red blood cells, white blood cells, and platelets are suspended.

plasma membrane The selectively permeable surface membrane that encloses the cell contents and through which all materials entering or leaving the cell must pass.

plasma cell Cell that secretes antibodies; a differentiated B lymphocyte (B cell).

plasma proteins Proteins such as albumins, globulins, and fibrinogen that circulate in the blood plasma.

plasmids (plaz´midz) Small circular double-stranded DNA molecules that carry genes separate from the main DNA of a cell.

plasmodesmata (sing. *plasmodesma*) Cytoplasmic channels connecting adjacent plant cells and allowing for the movement of molecules and ions between cells.

plasmodial slime mold (plaz-moh´dee-uhl) A fungus-like protist whose feeding stage consists of a plasmodium.

plasmodium (plaz-moh´dee-um) A multinucleate mass of living matter that moves and feeds in an amoeboid fashion.

plasmolysis (plaz-mol´ih-sis) The shrinkage of cytoplasm and the pulling away of the plasma membrane from the cell wall when a plant cell (or other walled cell) loses water, usually in a hypertonic environment.

plastids (plas´tidz) A family of membrane-bounded organelles occurring in photosynthetic eukaryotic cells; include chloroplasts, chromoplasts, and amyloplasts and other leukoplasts.

platelets (playt´lets) Cell fragments in vertebrate blood that function in clotting; also called thrombocytes.

platyhelminthes The phylum of acoelomate animals commonly known as flatworms.

plesiomorphic characters See *shared ancestral characters*.

pleiotropic (ply´´oh-troh´pik) A term referring to an allele that affects a number of characteristics of an individual.

pleural membrane (ploor´ul) The membrane that lines the thoracic cavity and envelops each lung.

ploidy The number of chromosome sets in a nucleus or cell. See *haploid*, *diploid*, and *polyploid*.

plumule (ploom´yool) The embryonic shoot apex, or terminal bud, located above the point of attachment of the cotyledon(s).

pluripotent (ploor-i-poh´tent) A term describing a stem cell that is able to divide to give rise to all tissues of the body. Compare with *totipotent*.

pneumatophore (noo-mat´uh-for´´) Roots that extend up out of the water in swampy areas and are thought to provide aeration between the atmosphere and submerged roots.

polar body A small *n* cell produced during oogenesis in female animals that does not develop into a functional ovum.

polar covalent bond Chemical bond formed by the sharing of electrons between atoms that differ in electronegativity; the end of the bond near the more electronegative atom has a partial negative charge, the other end has a partial positive charge. Compare with *nonpolar covalent bond*.

polar molecule Molecule that has one end with a partial positive charge and the other with a partial negative charge; polar molecules are generally soluble in water. Compare with *nonpolar molecule*.

polar nucleus   In flowering plants, one of two n cells in the embryo sac that fuse with a sperm during double fertilization to form the $3n$ endosperm.

pollen grain   The immature male gametophyte of seed plants (gymnosperms and angiosperms) that produces sperm capable of fertilization.

pollen tube   In gymnosperms and flowering plants, a tube or extension that forms after germination of the pollen grain and through which male gametes (sperm cells) pass into the ovule.

pollination (pol''uh-nay'shen)   In seed plants, the transfer of pollen from the male to the female part of the plant.

polyadenylation (pol''ee-a-den-uh-lay'shun)   That part of eukaryotic mRNA processing in which multiple adenine-containing nucleotides (a poly A tail) are added to the 3′ end of the molecule.

polyandry   A mating system in which a female mates with several males during a breeding season. Compare with *polygyny*.

polygyny   A mating system in which a male animal mates with many females during a breeding season. Compare with *polyandry*.

poly A tail   See *polyadenylation*.

polygenic inheritance (pol''ee-jen'ik)   Inheritance in which several independently assorting or loosely linked nonallelic genes modify the intensity of a trait or contribute to the phenotype in additive fashion.

polymer (pol'ih-mer)   A molecule built up from repeating subunits of the same general type (monomers), such as a protein, nucleic acid, or polysaccharide.

polymerase chain reaction (PCR)   A method by which a targeted DNA fragment can be amplified in vitro to produce millions of copies.

polymorphism (pol''ee-mor'fizm)   (1) The existence of two or more phenotypically different individuals within a population; (2) The presence of more than one allele for a given locus in a population.

polyp (pol'ip)   A hydra-like animal; the sessile stage of the life cycle of certain cnidarians. Compare with *medusa*.

polypeptide   See *peptide*.

polyphyletic group (pol''ee-fye-let'ik)   A group made up of organisms that evolved from two or more different ancestors. Compare with *monophyletic group* and *paraphyletic group*.

polyploid (pol'ee-ployd)   The condition of having more than two sets of chromosomes per nucleus. Compare with *diploid* and *haploid*.

polyribosome   A complex consisting of a number of ribosomes attached to an mRNA during translation; also known as a polysome.

polysaccharide (pol-ee-sak'ah-ride)   A carbohydrate consisting of many monosaccharide subunits, e.g., starch, glycogen, and cellulose.

polysome   See *polyribosome*.

polyspermy   The fertilization of an egg by more than one sperm.

polytene   A term describing a giant chromosome consisting of many (usually > 1000) parallel DNA double helices. Polytene chromosomes are typically found in cells of the salivary glands and some other tissues of certain insects, such as the fruit fly, *Drosophila*.

polyunsaturated fatty acid   See *fatty acid*.

pons (ponz)   The white bulge that is the part of the brain stem between the medulla and the midbrain; connects various parts of the brain.

population   A group of organisms of the same species that live in a defined geographical area at the same time.

population bottleneck   See *bottleneck*.

population crash   An abrupt decline in the size of a population.

population density   The number of individuals of a species per unit of area or volume at a given time.

population dynamics   The study of changes in populations, such as how and why population numbers change over time.

population ecology   That branch of biology that deals with the numbers of a particular species that are found in an area and how and why those numbers change (or remain fixed) over time.

population genetics   The study of genetic variability in a population and of the forces that act on it.

population growth momentum   The continued growth of a population after fertility rates have declined, as a result of a population's young age structure.

poriferans   Sponges; members of phylum Porifera.

positive feedback mechanism   A homeostatic mechanism in which a change in some condition triggers a response that intensifies the changing condition. Compare with *negative feedback mechanism*.

posterior   Toward the tail end of a bilaterally symmetrical animal. Compare with *anterior*.

postsynaptic neuron   A neuron that transmits an impulse away from a synapse. Compare with *presynaptic neuron*.

postzygotic barrier   One of several reproductive isolating mechanisms that prevent gene flow between species after fertilization has taken place; e.g., hybrid inviability, hybrid sterility, and hybrid breakdown. Compare with *prezygotic barrier*.

potential energy   Stored energy; energy that can do work as a consequence of its position or state. Compare with *kinetic energy*.

potentiation   A form of synaptic enhancement (increase in neurotransmitter release) that can last for several minutes; occurs when a presynaptic neuron continues to transmit action potentials at a high rate for a minute or longer.

preadaptation   A novel evolutionary change in a preexisting biological structure that enables it to have a different function; feathers, which evolved from reptilian scales, represent a preadaptation for flight

prebiotic broth hypothesis   The hypothesis that simple organic molecules that are the precursors of life originated and accumulated at Earth's surface, in shallow seas or on rock or clay surfaces. Compare with *iron-sulfur world hypothesis*.

Precambrian time   All of geological time before the Paleozoic era, encompassing approximately the first 4 billion years of Earth's history.

predation   Relationship in which one organism (the predator) kills and devours another organism (the prey).

pre-mRNA   RNA precursor to mRNA in eukaryotes; contains both introns and exons.

premise   Information supplied from which conclusions can be drawn in the process of deductive reasoning.

pressure-flow hypothesis   The mechanism by which dissolved sugar is thought to be transported in phloem; caused by a pressure gradient between the source (where sugar is loaded into the phloem) and the sink (where sugar is removed from phloem).

prenatal   A term referring to the time before birth.

presynaptic neuron   A neuron that transmits an impulse to a synapse. Compare with *postsynaptic neuron*.

prezygotic barrier One of several reproductive isolating mechanisms that interfere with fertilization between male and female gametes of different species; e.g., temporal isolation, habitat isolation, behavioral isolation, mechanical isolation, and gametic isolation. Compare with *postzygotic barrier*.

primary consumer See *herbivore*.

primary growth An increase in the length of a plant that occurs at the tips of the shoots and roots due to the activity of apical meristems. Compare with *secondary growth*.

primary mycelium A mycelium in which the cells are monokaryotic and haploid; a mycelium that grows from either an ascospore or a basidiospore. Compare with *secondary mycelium*.

primary producer See *autotroph*.

primary response The response of the immune system to first exposure to an antigen. Compare with *secondary response*.

primary structure (of a protein) The complete sequence of amino acids in a polypeptide chain, beginning at the amino end and ending at the carboxyl end. Compare with *secondary, tertiary,* and *quaternary protein structure*.

primary succession An ecological succession that occurs on land that has not previously been inhabited by plants; no soil is present initially. See *succession*. Compare with *secondary succession*.

primer See *RNA primer*.

primitive groove See *primitive streak*.

primitive streak Dynamic, constantly changing structure that forms at the midline of the blastodisc in birds, mammals, and some other vertebrates, and is active in gastrulation. Cells from the surface enter the interior through the furrow at its center (primitive groove), which is the functional equivalent of the blastopore. The anterior end of the primitive streak is Hensen's node.

primosome A complex of proteins responsible for synthesizing the RNA primers required in DNA synthesis.

principle A scientific theory that has withstood repeated testing and has the highest level of scientific confidence. Compare with *hypothesis* and *theory*.

prion An infectious agent that consists only of protein.

producer See *autotroph*.

product Substance formed by a chemical reaction. Compare with *reactant*.

product rule The rule for combining the probabilities of independent events by multiplying their individual probabilities. Compare with *sum rule*.

profundal zone (pro-fun′dl) The deepest zone of a large lake, located below the level of penetration by sunlight. Compare with *littoral zone* and *limnetic zone*.

progesterone (pro-jes′ter-own) A steroid hormone secreted by the ovary (mainly by the corpus luteum) and placenta; stimulates the uterus (to prepare the endometrium for implanation) and breasts (for milk secretion).

progymnosperm (pro-jim′noh-sperm) An extinct group of plants that are thought to have been the ancestors of gymnosperms.

prokaryote (pro-kar′ee-ote) A cell that lacks a nucleus and other membrane-bounded organelles; includes the bacteria, members of kingdoms Eubacteria and Archaebacteria. Compare with *eukaryote*.

promoter The nucleotide sequence in DNA to which RNA polymerase attaches to begin transcription.

prophage (pro′faj) Bacteriophage nucleic acid that is inserted into the bacterial DNA.

prophase The first stage of mitosis and of meiosis I and meiosis II. During prophase the chromosomes become visible as distinct structures, the nuclear envelope breaks down, and a spindle forms. Meiotic prophase I is complex and includes synapsis of homologous chromosomes and crossing-over.

proplastids Organelles that are plastid precursors; may mature into various specialized plastids, including chloroplasts, chromoplasts, or leukoplasts.

proprioceptors (pro′′pree-oh-sep′torz) Receptors in muscles, tendons, and joints that respond to changes in movement, tension, and position; enable an animal to perceive the position of its body.

prop root An adventitious root that arises from the stem and provides additional support for a plant such as corn.

prostaglandins (pros′′tah-glan′dinz) Derivatives of unsaturated fatty acids that produce a wide variety of hormone-like effects; synthesized by most cells of the body; sometimes called local hormones.

prostate gland A gland in male animals that produces an alkaline secretion that is part of the semen.

protein A large, complex organic compound composed of covalently linked amino acid subunits; contains carbon, hydrogen, oxygen, nitrogen, and sulfur.

prothallus (pro-thal′us) (pl. *prothalli*) The free-living, *n* gametophyte in ferns and other seedless vascular plants.

protist (pro′tist) One of a vast kingdom of eukaryotic organisms, primarily unicellular or simple multicellular; mostly aquatic.

protobionts (pro′′toh-by′ontz) Assemblages of organic polymers that spontaneously form under certain conditions. Protobionts may have been involved in chemical evolution.

proton A particle present in the nuclei of all atoms that has one unit of positive charge and a mass of one atomic mass unit (amu). Compare with *electron* and *neutron*.

protonema (pro′′toh-nee′mah) (pl. *protonemata*) In mosses, a filament of n cells that grows from a spore and develops into leafy moss gametophytes.

protonephridia (pro′′toh-nef-rid′ee-ah) (sing. *protonephridium*) The flame-cell excretory organs of flatworms and some other simple invertebrates.

proto-oncogene A gene that normally promotes cell division in response to the presence of certain growth factors; when mutated it may become an oncogene, possibly leading to the formation of a cancer cell. Compare with *oncogene*.

protostome (pro′toh-stome) A major division of the animal kingdom in which the blastopore develops into the mouth, and the anus forms secondarily; includes the annelids, arthropods, and mollusks. Compare with *deuterostome*.

protozoa (proh′′toh-zoh′a) (sing. *protozoon*) An informal group of unicellular, animal-like protists, including amoebas, foraminiferans, actinopods, ciliates, flagellates, and apicomplexans. (The adjectival form is *protozoan*.)

provirus (pro-vy′rus) A part of a virus, consisting of nucleic acid only, that has been inserted into a host genome. See *DNA provirus*.

proximal Closer to the point of reference. Compare with *distal*.

proximal convoluted tubule The part of the renal tubule that extends from Bowman's capsule to the loop of Henle. Compare with *distal convoluted tubule*.

proximate causes (of behavior) The immediate causes of behavior, such as genetic, developmental, and physiological processes that permit the animal to carry out a specific behavior. Compare with *ultimate causes of behavior*.

pseudocoelom (sue″doh-see′lom)   A body cavity between the mesoderm and endoderm; derived from the blastocoel. Compare with *coelom*.

pseudocoelomate (sue″doh-seel′oh-mate)   An animal possessing a pseudocoelom. Compare with *coelomate* and *acoelomate*.

pseudoplasmodium (sue″doe-plaz-moh′dee-um)   In cellular slime molds, an aggregation of amoeboid cells that forms a spore-producing fruiting body during reproduction.

pseudopodium (sue″doe-poe′dee-um) (pl. *pseudopodia*)   A temporary extension of an amoeboid cell that is used for feeding and locomotion.

puff   In a polytene chromosome, a decondensed region that is a site of intense RNA synthesis.

pulmonary circulation   The part of the circulatory system that delivers blood to and from the lungs for oxygenation. Compare with *systemic circulation*.

pulse, arterial   The alternate expansion and recoil of an artery.

pulvinus (pul-vy′nus)   A special structure, often located at the base of the petiole, that functions in leaf movement by changes in turgor.

punctuated equilibrium   The idea that evolution proceeds with periods of little or no genetic change, followed by very active phases, so that major adaptations or clusters of adaptations appear suddenly in the fossil record. Compare with *gradualism*.

Punnett square   The grid structure, first developed by Reginald Punnett, that allows direct calculation of the probabilities of occurrence of all possible offspring of a genetic cross.

pupa (pew′pah) (pl. *pupae*)   A stage in the development of an insect, between the larva and the imago (adult); a form that neither moves nor feeds, and may be in a cocoon.

pure line   See *true-breeding line*.

purines (pure′eenz)   Nitrogenous bases with carbon and nitrogen atoms in two attached rings, e.g., adenine and guanine; components of nucleic acids, ATP, GTP, NAD$^+$, and certain other biologically active substances. Compare with *pyrimidines*.

pyramid of biomass   An ecological pyramid that illustrates the total biomass, as, for example, the total dry weight, of all organisms at each trophic level in an ecosystem.

pyramid of energy   An ecological pyramid that shows the energy flow through each trophic level of an ecosystem.

pyramid of numbers   An ecological pyramid that shows the number of organisms at each trophic level in an ecosystem.

pyrimidines (pyr-im′ih-deenz)   Nitrogenous bases, each composed of a single ring of carbon and nitrogen atoms, e.g., thymine, cytosine, and uracil; components of nucleic acids. Compare with *purines*.

pyruvate (pyruvic acid)   A three-carbon compound; the end product of glycolysis.

quadrupedal (kwad′roo-ped″ul)   Walking on all fours.

quantitative trait   A trait that shows continuous variation in a population (e.g., human height) and typically has a polygenic inheritance pattern.

quaternary structure (of a protein)   The overall conformation of a protein produced by the interaction of two or more polypeptide chains. Compare with *primary, secondary,* and *tertiary protein structure*.

***r* selection**   A reproductive strategy recognized by some ecologists, in which a species typically has a small body size, rapid development, short life span, and devotes a large proportion of its metabolic energy to the production of offspring. Compare with *K selection*.

radial cleavage   The pattern of blastomere production in which the cells are located directly above or below one another; characteristic of early deuterostome embryos. Compare with *spiral cleavage*.

radial symmetry   A body plan in which any section through the mouth and down the length of the body divides the body into similar halves. Jellyfish and other cnidarians have radial symmetry. Compare with *bilateral symmetry*.

radicle (rad′ih-kl)   The embryonic root of a seed plant.

radioactive decay   The process in which a radioactive element emits radiation and, as a result, its nucleus changes into the nucleus of a different element.

radioisotopes   Unstable isotopes that spontaneously emit radiation; also called radioactive isotopes.

radiolarians   Those actinopods that secrete elaborate shells of silica (glass).

radula (rad′yoo-lah)   A rasplike structure in the digestive tract of chitons, snails, squids, and certain other mollusks.

rain shadow   An area that has very little precipitation, found on the downwind side of a mountain range. Deserts often occur in rain shadows.

random dispersion   The spatial distribution pattern of a population in which the presence of one individual has no effect on the distribution of other individuals. Compare with *clumped dispersion* and *uniform dispersion*.

range   The area where a particular species occurs.

ray   A chain of parenchyma cells (one to many cells thick) that functions for lateral transport in stems and roots of woody plants.

ray-finned fishes   A class (Actinopterygii) of modern bony fishes; contains about 95% of living fish species.

reabsorption   The selective removal of certain substances from the glomerular filtrate by the renal tubules and collecting ducts of the kidney, and their return into the blood.

reactant   Substance that participates in a chemical reaction. Compare with *product*.

reaction center   The portion of a photosystem that includes chlorophyll *a* molecules capable of transferring electrons to a primary electron acceptor, which is the first of several electron acceptors in a series; the reaction center of Photosystem I is P700 and of Photosystem II is P680. See *antenna complex* and *photosystem*.

realized niche   The lifestyle that an organism actually pursues, including the resources that it actually uses. An organism's realized niche is narrower than its fundamental niche because of interspecific competition. Compare with *fundamental niche*.

receptacle   The end of a flower stalk where the flower parts (sepals, petals, stamens, and carpels) are attached.

reception   Process of detecting a stimulus.

receptor down-regulation   The process by which some hormone receptors decrease in number, thereby suppressing the sensitivity of target cells to the hormone. Compare with *receptor up-regulation*.

receptor-mediated endocytosis   A type of endocytosis in which extracellular molecules become bound to specific receptors on the cell surface and then enter the cytoplasm enclosed in vesicles.

receptor up-regulation   The process by which some hormone receptors increase in number, thereby increasing the sensitivity of the target cells to the hormone. Compare with *receptor down-regulation*.

recessive allele (al-leel′)   An allele that is not expressed in the heterozygous state. Compare with *dominant allele*.

recombinant DNA Any DNA molecule made by combining genes from different organisms.

recombination, genetic The appearance of new gene combinations. Recombination in eukaryotes generally results from meiotic events, either crossing-over or shuffling of chromosomes.

red alga A member of a diverse phylum of algae that contain the pigments chlorophyll *a*, carotenoids, phycocyanin, and phycoerythrin.

red blood cell (RBC) See *erythrocyte*.

redox reaction (ree'dox) The chemical reaction in which one or more electrons are transferred from one substance (the substance that becomes oxidized) to another (the substance that becomes reduced). See *oxidation* and *reduction*.

red tide A red or brown coloration of ocean water caused by a population explosion, or bloom, of dinoflagellates.

reduction The gain of one or more electrons (or hydrogen atoms) by an atom, ion, or molecule. Compare with *oxidation*.

reflex action An automatic, involuntary response to a given stimulus that generally functions to restore homeostasis.

refractory period The brief period that must elapse after the response of a neuron or muscle fiber, during which it cannot respond to another stimulus.

regulative development The very plastic developmental pattern in which each individual blastomere retains totipotency. Compare with *mosaic development*.

regulon A group of operons that are coordinately controlled.

renal (ree'nl) Pertaining to the kidney.

renal pelvis The funnel-shaped chamber of the kidney that receives urine from the collecting ducts; urine then moves into the ureters.

renin (reh'nin) An enzyme released by the kidney in response to a decrease in blood pressure, which activates a pathway leading to production of angiotensin II, a hormone that increases aldosterone release.

replacement-level fertility The number of children a couple must produce to "replace" themselves. The average number is greater than two because some children die before reaching reproductive age.

replication fork Y-shaped structure produced during the semiconservative replication of DNA.

replication See *DNA replication*.

repolarization The process of returning membrane potential to its resting level.

repressible operon An operon that is normally active but can be controlled by a repressor protein, which becomes active when it binds to a corepressor; the active repressor binds to the operator, making the operon transcriptionally inactive, e.g., the tryptophan operons of *Escherichia coli* and *Salmonella*. Compare with *inducible operon*.

repressor protein A negative regulatory protein that inhibits transcription when bound to DNA; some repressors require a corepressor to be active; some other repressors become inactive when bound to an inducer molecule. Compare with *activator protein*.

reproduction The process by which new individuals are produced. See *asexual reproduction* and *sexual reproduction*.

reproductive isolating mechanisms The reproductive barriers that prevent a species from interbreeding with another species; as a result, each species' gene pool is isolated from other species. See *prezygotic barrier* and *postzygotic barrier*.

reptiles A class of vertebrates characterized by dry skin with horny scales and adaptations for terrestrial reproduction; include turtles, snakes, and alligators; reptiles are not a monophyletic group.

residual capacity The volume of air that remains in the lungs at the end of a normal exhalation.

resin A viscous organic material that certain plants produce and secrete into specialized ducts; may play a role in deterring disease organisms or plant-eating insects.

resolution See *resolving power*.

resolving power The ability of a microscope to show fine detail, defined as the minimum distance between two points at which they can be seen as separate images; also called resolution.

resource partitioning The reduction of competition for environmental resources such as food that occurs among coexisting species as a result of each species' niche differing from the others in one or more ways.

respiration (1) Cellular respiration is the process by which cells generate ATP through a series of redox reactions. In aerobic respiration the terminal electron acceptor is molecular oxygen; in anaerobic respiration the terminal acceptor is an inorganic molecule other than oxygen. (2) Organismic respiration is the process of gas exchange between a complex animal and its environment, generally through a specialized respiratory surface, such as a lung or gill.

respiratory centers Centers in the medulla and pons that regulate breathing.

resting potential The membrane potential (difference in electrical charge between the two sides of the plasma membrane) of a neuron in which no action potential is occurring. The typical resting potential is about −70 millivolts. Compare with *action potential*.

restoration ecology The scientific field that uses the principles of ecology to help return a degraded environment as closely as possible to its former undisturbed state.

restriction enzyme One of a class of enzymes that cleave DNA at specific base sequences; produced by bacteria to degrade foreign DNA; used in recombinant DNA technology.

restriction fragment length polymorphism (RFLP) analysis A technique that permits assessment of the degree of relatedness among individuals within a population; individuals are compared on the basis of the different patterns of DNA fragments generated when their DNA is cut with the same restriction enzyme.

restriction map A physical map of DNA in which sites cut by specific restriction enzymes serve as landmarks.

reticular activating system (RAS) (reh-tik'yoo-lur) A diffuse network of neurons in the brain stem responsible for maintaining consciousness.

retina (ret'ih-nah) The innermost of the three layers (retina, choroid layer, and sclera) of the eyeball, which is continuous with the optic nerve and contains the light-sensitive rod and cone cells.

retrovirus (ret'roh-vy''rus) An RNA virus that uses reverse transcriptase to produce a DNA intermediate, known as a DNA provirus, in the host cell. See *DNA provirus*.

reverse transcriptase An enzyme produced by retroviruses that catalyzes the production of DNA using RNA as a template.

reversible inhibitor A substance that forms weak bonds with an enzyme, temporarily interfering with its function; a reversible inhibitor can be competitive or noncompetitive. Compare with *irreversible inhibitor*.

Rh factors Red blood cell antigens, known as D antigens, first identified in *Rhesus* monkeys. Persons possessing these antigens are Rh⁺ those lacking them are Rh⁻ See *erythroblastosis fetalis*.

rhizome (ry'zome) A horizontal underground stem that bears leaves and buds and often serves as a storage organ and a means of asexual reproduction, e.g., iris.

rhodopsin (rho-dop′sin) Visual purple; a light-sensitive pigment found in the rod cells of the vertebrate eye; a similar molecule is employed by certain bacteria in the capture of light energy to make ATP.

ribonucleic acid (RNA) A family of single-stranded nucleic acids that function mainly in protein synthesis.

ribosomal RNA (rRNA) See *ribosomes*.

ribosomes (ry′boh-sohms) Organelles that are part of the protein synthesis machinery of both prokaryotic and eukaryotic cells; consist of a larger and smaller subunit, each composed of ribosomal RNA (rRNA) and ribosomal proteins.

ribozyme (ry′boh-zime) A molecule of RNA that has catalytic properties.

ribulose bisphosphate (RuBP) A five-carbon phosphorylated compound with a high energy potential that reacts with carbon dioxide in the initial step of the Calvin cycle.

ribulose bisphosphate carboxylase See *Rubisco*.

RNA polymerase An enzyme that catalyzes the synthesis of RNA from a DNA template. Also called DNA-dependent RNA polymerase.

RNA primer The sequence of about five RNA nucleotides that are synthesized during DNA replication to provide a 3′ end to which DNA polymerase can add nucleotides. The RNA primer is later degraded and replaced with DNA.

RNA world A model that proposes that, during the evolution of cells, RNA was the first informational molecule to evolve, followed at a later time by proteins and DNA.

rod One of the rod-shaped, light-sensitive cells of the retina that are particularly sensitive to dim light and mediate black and white vision. Compare with *cone*.

root cap A covering of cells over the root tip that protects the delicate meristematic tissue directly behind it.

root graft The process of roots from two different plants growing together and becoming permanently attached to one another.

root hair An extension, or outgrowth, of a root epidermal cell. Root hairs increase the absorptive capacity of roots.

root pressure The pressure in xylem sap that occurs as a result of the active absorption of mineral ions followed by the osmotic uptake of water into roots from the soil.

root system The underground portion of a plant that anchors it in the soil and absorbs water and dissolved minerals.

rough ER See *endoplasmic reticulum*.

Rubisco The common name of ribulose bisphosphate carboxylase, the enzyme that catalyzes the reaction of carbon dioxide with ribulose bisphosphate in the Calvin cycle.

rugae (roo′jee) Folds, such as those in the lining of the stomach.

runner See *stolon*.

S phase Stage in interphase of the cell cycle during which DNA and other chromosomal constituents are synthesized. Compare with G_1 *and* G_2 *phases*.

saccule The structure within the vestibule of the inner vertebrate ear that along with the utricle houses the receptors of static equilibrium.

salinity The concentration of dissolved salts (e.g., sodium chloride) in a body of water.

salivary glands Accessory digestive glands found in vertebrates and some invertebrates; in humans there are three pairs.

salt An ionic compound consisting of an anion other than a hydroxide ion and a cation other than a hydrogen ion. A salt can be formed by the reaction between an acid and a base.

salt marsh A wetland dominated by grasses in which the salinity fluctuates between that of sea water and fresh water; salt marshes are usually located in estuaries.

saltatory conduction The transmission of a neural impulse along a myelinated neuron; ion activity at one node depolarizes the next node along the axon.

saprobe See *decomposer*.

saprotroph (sap′roh-trof) See *decomposer*.

sarcolemma (sar′′koh-lem′mah) The muscle cell plasma membrane.

sarcomere (sar′koh-meer) A segment of a striated muscle cell located between adjacent **Z**-lines that serves as a unit of contraction.

sarcoplasmic reticulum The system of vesicles in a muscle cell that surrounds the myofibrils and releases calcium in muscle contraction; a modified endoplasmic reticulum.

saturated fatty acid See *fatty acid*.

savanna (suh-van′uh) A tropical grassland containing scattered trees; found in areas of low rainfall or seasonal rainfall with prolonged dry periods.

scaffolding proteins Nonhistone proteins that help maintain the structure of a chromosome.

schizocoely (skiz′oh-seely) The process of coelom formation in which the mesoderm splits into two layers, forming a cavity between them; characteristic of protostomes. Compare with *enterocoely*.

Schwann cells Supporting cells found in nervous tissue outside the central nervous system; produce the myelin sheath around peripheral neurons.

sclera (skler′ah) The outer coat of the eyeball; a tough, opaque sheet of connective tissue that protects the inner structures and helps maintain the rigidity of the eyeball.

sclereid (skler′id) In plants, a sclerenchyma cell that is variable in shape but typically not long and tapered. Compare with *fiber*.

sclerenchyma (skler-en′kim-uh) Cells that provide strength and support in the plant body, are often dead at maturity, and have extremely thick walls; includes fibers and sclereids.

scramble competition See *exploitation competition*.

scrotum (skroh′tum) The external sac of skin found in most male mammals that contains the testes and their accessory organs.

secondary consumer See *carnivore*.

secondary growth An increase in the girth of a plant due to the activity of the vascular cambium and cork cambium; secondary growth results in the production of secondary tissues, i.e., wood and bark. Compare with *primary growth*.

secondary mycelium A dikaryotic mycelium formed by the fusion of two primary hyphae. Compare with *primary mycelium*.

secondary response The rapid production of antibodies induced by a second exposure to an antigen several days, weeks, or even months after the initial exposure. Compare with *primary response*.

secondary structure (of a protein) A regular geometric shape produced by hydrogen bonding between the atoms of the uniform polypeptide backbone; includes the alpha helix and the beta-pleated sheet. Compare with *primary, tertiary,* and *quaternary protein structure*.

secondary succession An ecological succession that takes place after some disturbance destroys the existing vegetation; soil is already present. See *succession*. Compare with *primary succession*.

second law of thermodynamics   The physical law that states that the total amount of entropy in the universe continually increases. Compare with *first law of thermodynamics*.

second messenger   A substance within a cell that relays a message and (usually) triggers a response to a hormone combined with a receptor at the cell's surface, e.g., cyclic AMP and calcium ions.

secretory vesicles   Small cytoplasmic vesicles that move substances from an internal membrane system to the plasma membrane.

seed   A plant reproductive body composed of a young, multicellular plant and nutritive tissue (food reserves), enclosed by a seed coat.

seed coat   The outer protective covering of a seed.

seed fern   An extinct group of seed-bearing woody plants with fernlike leaves; seed ferns probably descended from progymnosperms and gave rise to cycads and possibly ginkgoes.

segregation, principle of   The genetic principle, first noted by Gregor Mendel, that states that two alleles of a locus become separated into different gametes.

selectively permeable membrane   A membrane that allows some substances to cross it more easily than others. Biological membranes are generally permeable to water, but restrict the passage of many solutes.

self-incompatibility   A genetic condition in which the pollen cannot effect fertilization in the same flower or in flowers on the same plant.

semelparity   The condition of having a single reproductive effort in a lifetime. Compare with *iteroparity*.

semen   The fluid composed of sperm suspended in various glandular secretions that is ejaculated from the penis during orgasm.

semicircular canals   The passages in the vertebrate inner ear containing structures that control the sense of equilibrium (balance).

semiconservative replication   See *DNA replication*.

semilunar valves   Valves between the ventricles of the heart and the arteries that carry blood away from the heart; aortic and pulmonary valves.

seminal vesicles   (1) In mammals, glandular sacs that secrete a component of seminal fluid; (2) In some invertebrates, structures that store sperm.

seminiferous tubules (sem-ih-nif′er-ous)   Coiled tubules in the testes in which spermatogenesis takes place in male vertebrates.

senescence (se-nes′cents)   The aging process.

sensory neuron   A neuron that transmits an impulse from a receptor to the central nervous system.

sensory receptor   A cell (or part of a cell) specialized to detect specific energy stimuli in the environment.

sepal (see′pul)   One of the outermost parts of a flower, usually leaflike in appearance, that protect the flower as a bud.

septum (pl. *septa*)   A cross wall or partition, e.g., the walls that divide a hypha into cells.

sequencing   See *DNA sequencing*.

serotonin   A neurotransmitter of the biogenic amine group.

Sertoli cells (sur-tole′ee)   Supporting cells of the tubules of the testis.

sessile (ses′sile)   Permanently attached to one location, e.g., coral animals.

setae (sing. *seta*)   Bristle-like structures that aid in annelid locomotion.

set point   A normal condition maintained by homeostatic mechanisms.

sex-influenced trait   A genetic trait that is expressed differently in males and females.

sex-linked gene   A gene carried on a sex chromosome. In mammals almost all sex-linked genes are borne on the X chromosome, i.e., are X-linked.

sexual dimorphism   Marked phenotypic differences between the two sexes of the same species.

sexual isolation   See *behavioral isolation*.

sexual reproduction   A type of reproduction in which two gametes (usually, but not necessarily, contributed by two different parents) fuse to form a zygote. Compare with *asexual reproduction*.

sexual selection   A type of natural selection that occurs when individuals of a species vary in their ability to compete for mates; individuals with reproductive advantages are selected over others of the same sex.

shade avoidance   The tendency of plants that are adapted to high light intensities to grow taller when they are closely surrounded by other plants.

shared ancestral characters   Traits that were present in an ancestral species that have remained essentially unchanged; suggest a distant common ancestor. Also called plesiomorphic characters. Compare with *shared derived characters*.

shared derived characters   Homologous traits found in two or more taxa that are present in their most recent common ancestor but not in earlier common ancestors. Also called synapomorphic characters. Compare with *shared ancestral characters*.

shoot system   The above-ground portion of a plant, such as the stem and leaves.

short-day plant   A plant that flowers in response to lengthening nights; also called long-night plant. Compare with *long-day, intermediate-day,* and *day-neutral plants*.

short-night plant   See *long-day plant*.

sickle cell anemia   An inherited form of anemia in which there is abnormality in the hemoglobin beta chains; the inheritance pattern is autosomal recessive.

sieve tube members   Cells that conduct dissolved sugar in the phloem of flowering plants.

signaling molecule   See *cell signaling*.

signal transduction   A process in which a cell converts and amplifies an extracellular signal into an intracellular signal that affects some function in the cell. Also see *cell signaling*.

sign stimulus   Any stimulus that elicits a fixed action pattern in an animal.

simple fruit   A fruit that develops from a single ovary. Compare with *aggregate, accessory,* and *multiple fruits*.

simplest formula   A type of chemical formula that gives the smallest whole number ratio of the component atoms. Compare with *molecular formula* and *structural formula*.

sink habitat   A lower quality habitat in which local reproductive success is less than local mortality. Compare with *source habitat*.

sinoatrial (SA) node   The mass of specialized cardiac muscle in which the impulse triggering the heartbeat originates; the pacemaker of the heart.

skeletal muscle   The voluntary striated muscle of vertebrates, so-called because it usually is directly or indirectly attached to some part of the skeleton. Compare with *cardiac muscle* and *smooth muscle*.

slash-and-burn agriculture   A type of agriculture in which tropical rain forest is cut down, allowed to dry, and burned. The crops that are planted immediately afterwards thrive because the ashes provide nutrients; in a few years, however, the soil is depleted and the land must be abandoned.

small intestine Portion of the vertebrate digestive tract that extends from the stomach to the large intestine.

small nuclear ribonucleoprotein complexes (snRNP) Aggregations of RNA and protein responsible for binding to pre-mRNA in eukaryotes and catalyzing the excision of introns and the splicing of exons.

smooth ER See *endoplasmic reticulum.*

smooth muscle Involuntary muscle tissue that lacks transverse striations; found mainly in sheets surrounding hollow organs, such as the intestine. Compare with *cardiac muscle* and *skeletal muscle.*

social behavior Interaction of two or more animals, usually of the same species.

sociobiology The branch of biology that focuses on the evolution of social behavior through natural selection.

sodium-potassium pump Active transport system that transports sodium ions out of, and potassium ions into, cells.

soil erosion The wearing away or removal of soil from the land; although soil erosion occurs naturally from precipitation and runoff, human activities (such as clearing the land) accelerate it.

solar tracking See *heliotropism.*

solute A dissolved substance. Compare with *solvent.*

solvent Substance capable of dissolving other substances. Compare with *solute.*

somatic cell In animals, a cell of the body not involved in formation of gametes. Compare with *germ line cell.*

somatic nervous system That part of the vertebrate peripheral nervous system that keeps the body in adjustment with the external environment; includes sensory receptors on the body surface and within the muscles, and the nerves that link them with the central nervous system. Compare with *autonomic nervous system.*

somatomedins See *insulin-like growth factors.*

somatotropin See *growth hormone.*

sonogram See *ultrasound imaging.*

soredium (sor-id′e-um) (pl. *soredia*) In lichens, a type of asexual reproductive structure that consists of a cluster of algal cells surrounded by fungal hyphae.

sorus (soh′rus) (pl. *sori*) In ferns, a cluster of spore-producing sporangia.

source habitat A good habitat in which local reproductive success is greater than local mortality. Surplus individuals in a source habitat may disperse to other habitats. Compare with *sink habitat.*

Southern blot hybridization A technique in which DNA fragments, previously separated by gel electrophoresis, are transferred to a nitrocellulose membrane. A specific radioactive genetic probe is then allowed to hybridize to complementary fragments, marking their locations. Compare with *Northern blot hybridization* and *Western blotting.*

speciation Evolution of a new species.

species According to the biological species concept, one or more populations whose members are capable of interbreeding in nature to produce fertile offspring and do not interbreed with members of other species.

species diversity A measure of the relative importance of each species within a comunity; represents a combination of species richness and species evenness.

species evenness The distribution of individuals of each species in the community.

species richness The number of species in a community.

specific immune responses Defense mechanisms that target specific macromolecules associated with a pathogen. Includes cell-mediated immunity and antibody-mediated immunity. Also known as acquired or adaptive immune responses.

specific epithet The second part of the name of a species; designates a specific species belonging to that genus.

specific heat The amount of heat energy that must be supplied to raise the temperature of 1 g of a substance 1°C.

sperm The motile, *n* male reproductive cell of animals and some plants and protists; also called spermatozoan.

spermatid (spur′ma-tid) An immature sperm cell.

spermatocyte (spur-mah′toh-site) A meiotic cell that gives rise to spermatids and ultimately to mature sperm cells.

spermatogenesis (spur′′mah-toh-jen′eh-sis) The production of male gametes (sperm) by meiosis and subsequent cell differentiation. Compare with *oogenesis.*

spermatozoan (spur-mah-toh-zoh′un) See *sperm.*

sphincter (sfink′tur) A group of circularly arranged muscle fibers, the contractions of which close an opening, e.g., the pyloric sphincter at the exit of the stomach.

spinal cord In vertebrates, the dorsal, tubular nerve cord.

spinal nerves In vertebrates, the nerves that emerge from the spinal cord.

spindle See *mitotic spindle.*

spine A leaf that is modified for protection, such as a cactus spine.

spiracle (speer′ih-kl) An opening for gas exchange, such as the opening of a trachea on the body surface of an insect.

spiral cleavage A distinctive spiral pattern of blastomere production in an early protostome embryo. Compare with *radial cleavage.*

spirillum (pl. *spirilla*) A long, rigid, helical bacterium. Compare with *spirochete, vibrio, bacillus,* and *coccus.*

spirochete A long, flexible, helical bacterium. Compare with *spirillum, vibrio, bacillus,* and *coccus.*

spleen An abdominal organ located just below the diaphragm that removes worn-out blood cells and bacteria from the blood and plays a role in immunity.

spongy mesophyll (mez′oh-fil) The loosely arranged mesophyll cells near the lower epidermis in certain leaves. Compare with *palisade mesophyll.*

spontaneous reaction See *exergonic reaction.*

sporangium (spor-an′jee-um) (pl. *sporangia*) A spore case, found in plants, certain protists, and fungi.

spore A reproductive cell that gives rise to individual offspring in plants, fungi, and certain algae and protozoa.

sporophyll (spor′oh-fil) A leaflike structure that bears spores.

sporophyte generation (spor′oh-fite) The 2*n*, spore-producing stage in the life cycle of a plant. Compare with *gametophyte generation.*

sporozoa See *apicomplexans.*

sporozoite The infective sporelike state in apicomplexans.

stabilizing selection Natural selection that acts against extreme phenotypes and favors intermediate variants; associated with a population well-adapted to its environment. Compare with *directional selection* and *disruptive selection.*

stamen (stay′men) The male part of a flower; consists of a filament and anther.

standing-water ecosystem A lake or pond ecosystem.

starch A polysaccharide composed of alpha glucose subunits; made by plants for energy storage.

start codon See *initiation codon*.

stasis Long periods in the fossil record in which there is little or no evolutionary change.

statocyst (stat′oh-sist) An invertebrate sense organ containing one or more granules (statoliths); senses gravity and motion.

statoliths (stat′uh-liths) Granules of loose sand or calcium carbonate found in statocysts.

stele The cylinder in the center of roots and stems that contains the vascular tissue.

stem cell A relatively undifferentiated cell capable of repeated cell division. At each division at least one of the daughter cells usually remains a stem cell, whereas the other may differentiate as a specific cell type.

sterilization A procedure that renders an individual incapable of producing offspring; the most common surgical procedures are vasectomy in the male and tubal ligation in the female.

stereocilia Hairlike projections of hair cells; microvilli that contain actin filaments.

steroids (steer′oids) Complex molecules containing carbon atoms arranged in four attached rings, three of which contain six carbon atoms each and the fourth of which contains five; e.g., cholesterol and certain hormones, including the male and female sex hormones of vertebrates.

stigma The portion of the carpel where pollen grains land during pollination (and before fertilization).

stipe A short stalk or stemlike structure that is a part of the body of certain multicellular algae.

stipule (stip′yule) One of a pair of scalelike or leaflike structures found at the base of certain leaves.

stolon (stow′lon) An above-ground, horizontal stem with long internodes; stolons often form buds that develop into separate plants, e.g., strawberry; also called runner.

stomach Muscular region of the vertebrate digestive tract, extending from the esophagus to the small intestine.

stomata (sing. *stoma*) Small pores located in the epidermis of plants that provide for gas exchange for photosynthesis; each stoma is flanked by two guard cells, which are responsible for its opening and closing.

stop codon See *termination codon*.

stratosphere The layer of the atmosphere between the troposphere and the mesosphere. It contains a thin ozone layer that protects life by filtering out much of the sun's ultraviolet radiation.

stratum basale (strat′um bah-say′lee) The deepest sublayer of the human epidermis, consisting of cells that continuously divide. Compare with *stratum corneum*.

stratum corneum The most superficial sublayer of the human epidermis. Compare with *stratum basale*.

strobilus (stroh′bil-us) (pl. *strobili*) In certain plants, a conelike structure that bears spore-producing sporangia.

stroke volume The volume of blood pumped by one ventricle during one contraction.

stroma A fluid space of the chloroplast, enclosed by the chloroplast inner membrane and surrounding the thylakoids; site of the reactions of the Calvin cycle.

stromatolite (stroh-mat′oh-lite) A column-like rock that is composed of many minute layers of prokaryotic cells, usually cyanobacteria.

structural formula A type of chemical formula that shows the spatial arrangement of the atoms in a molecule. Compare with *simplest formula* and *molecular formula*.

structural isomer One of two or more chemical compounds having the same chemical formula, but differing in the covalent arrangement of their atoms, e.g., glucose and fructose.

style The neck connecting the stigma to the ovary of a carpel.

subsidiary cell In plants, a structurally distinct epidermal cell associated with a guard cell.

substance P A peptide neurotransmitter released by certain sensory neurons in pain pathways; signals the brain regarding painful stimuli; also stimulates other structures including smooth muscle in the digestive tract.

substrate A substance on which an enzyme acts; a reactant in an enzymatically catalyzed reaction.

succession The sequence of changes in the species composition in a community over time. See *primary succession* and *secondary succession*.

sucker A shoot that develops adventitiously from a root; a type of asexual reproduction.

sulcus (sul′kus) (pl. *sulci*) A groove, trench, or depression, especially one occurring on the surface of the brain, separating the convolutions.

sulfhydryl group Functional group abbreviated —SH; found in organic compounds called thiols.

sum rule The rule for combining the probabilities of mutually exclusive events by adding their individual probabilities. Compare with *product rule*.

summation The process of adding together excitatory postsynaptic potentials (EPSPs).

suppressor T cell T lymphocyte that suppresses the immune response.

supraorbital ridge (soop′′rah-or′bit-ul) The prominent bony ridge above the eye socket; ape skulls have prominent supraorbital ridges.

surface tension The attraction that the molecules at the surface of a liquid may have for each other.

survivorship The probability that a given individual in a population or cohort will survive to a particular age; usually presented as a survivorship curve.

survivorship curve A graph of the number of surviving individuals of a cohort, from birth to the maximum age attained by any individual.

suspensor (suh-spen′sur) In plant embryo development, a multicellular structure that anchors the embryo and aids in nutrient absorption from the endosperm.

swim bladder The hydrostatic organ in bony fishes that permits the fish to hover at a given depth.

symbiosis (sim-bee-oh′sis) An intimate relationship between two or more organisms of different species. See *commensalism, mutualism,* and *parasitism*.

sympathetic nervous system A division of the autonomic nervous system; its general effect is to mobilize energy, especially during stress situations; prepares the body for fight-or-flight response. Compare with *parasympathetic nervous system*.

sympatric speciation (sim-pa′trik) The evolution of a new species within the same geographical region as the parental species. Compare with *allopatric speciation*.

symplast A continuum consisting of the cytoplasm of many plant cells, connected from one cell to the next by plasmodesmata. Compare with *apoplast*.

synapomorphic characters See *shared derived characters*.

synapse (sin′aps) The junction between two neurons or between a neuron and an effector (muscle or gland).

synapsis (sin-ap′sis)   The process of physical association of homologous chromosomes during prophase I of meiosis.

synaptic enhancement   An increase in neurotransmitter release thought to occur as a result of calcium ion accumulation inside the presynaptic neuron.

synaptic plasticity   The ability of synapses to change in response to certain types of stimuli. Synaptic changes occur during learning and memory storage.

synaptonemal complex   The structure, visible with the electron microscope, produced when homologous chromosomes undergo synapsis.

syngamy (sin′gah-mee)   The union of the gametes in sexual reproduction.

synthetic theory of evolution   The synthesis of previous theories, especially of Mendelian genetics, with Darwin's theory of evolution by natural selection to formulate a comprehensive explanation of evolution; also called neo-Darwinism.

systematics   The scientific study of the diversity of organisms and their evolutionary relationships. Taxonomy is an aspect of systematics. See *taxonomy*.

systemic anaphylaxis   A rapid, widespread allergic reaction that can lead to death.

systemic circulation   The part of the circulatory system that delivers blood to and from the tissues and organs of the body. Compare with *pulmonary circulation*.

systole (sis′tuh-lee)   The phase of the cardiac cycle when the heart is contracting. Compare with *diastole*.

T cell (T lymphocyte)   The type of white blood cell responsible for a wide variety of immune functions, particularly cell-mediated immunity. T cells are processed in the thymus. Compare with *B cell*.

T tubules   Transverse tubules; system of inward extensions of the muscle fiber plasma membrane.

taiga (tie′gah)   The northern coniferous forest biome found primarily in Canada, northern Europe, and Siberia; also called boreal forest.

taproot system   A root system consisting of a prominant main root with smaller lateral roots branching off it; a taproot develops directly from the embryonic radicle. Compare with *fibrous root system*.

target cell or tissue   A cell or tissue with receptors that bind a hormone.

TATA box   A component of a eukaryotic promoter region; consists of a sequence of bases located about 30 base pairs upstream from the transcription initiation site.

taxon   A formal taxonomic group at any level, e.g., phylum or genus.

taxonomy (tax-on′ah-mee)   The science of naming, describing, and classifying organisms; see *systematics*.

Tay-Sachs disease   A serious genetic disease in which abnormal lipid metabolism in the brain causes mental deterioration in affected infants and young children; inheritance pattern is autosomal recessive.

tectorial membrane (tek-tor′ee-ul)   The roof membrane of the organ of Corti in the cochlea of the ear.

telolecithal egg   An egg with a large amount of yolk, concentrated at the vegetal pole. Compare with *isolecithal egg*.

telophase (teel′oh-faze or tel′oh-faze)   The last stage of mitosis and of meiosis I and II when, having reached the poles, chromosomes become decondensed, and a nuclear envelope forms around each group.

temperate deciduous forest   A forest biome that occurs in temperate areas where annual precipitation ranges from about 75 cm to 125 cm.

temperate grassland   A grassland characterized by hot summers, cold winters, and less rainfall than is found in a temperate deciduous forest biome.

temperate rain forest   A coniferous biome characterized by cool weather, dense fog, and high precipitation, e.g., the north Pacific coast of North America.

temperate virus   A virus that can become integrated into the host DNA as a prophage.

temperature   The average kinetic energy of the particles in a sample of a substance.

temporal isolation   A prezygotic reproductive isolating mechanism in which genetic exchange is prevented between similar species because they reproduce at different times of the day, season, or year.

tendon   A connective tissue structure that joins a muscle to another muscle, or a muscle to a bone. Tendons transmit the force generated by a muscle.

tendril   A leaf or stem that is modified for holding or attaching onto objects.

tension-cohesion model   The mechanism by which water and dissolved inorganic minerals are thought to be transported in xylem; water is pulled upward under tension due to transpiration while maintaining an unbroken column in xylem due to cohesion; also called transpiration-cohesion model.

teratogen   Any agent capable of interfering with normal morphogenesis in an embryo, thereby causing malformations; examples include radiation, certain chemicals, and certain infectious agents.

terminal bud   A bud at the tip of a stem. Compare with *axillary bud*.

termination (of protein synthesis)   The final stage of protein synthesis, which occurs when a termination (stop) codon is reached, causing the completed polypeptide chain to be released from the ribosome. See *initiation* and *elongation*.

termination codon   Any of the three codons in mRNA that do not code for an amino acid (UAA, UAG, or UGA). This stops translation at that point. Also known as a stop codon. Compare with *initiation codon*.

territoriality   Behavior pattern in which one organism (usually a male) stakes out a territory of its own and defends it against intrusion by other members of the same species and sex.

tertiary consumer   See *carnivore*.

tertiary structure (of a protein) (tur′she-air″ee)   The overall three-dimensional shape of a polypeptide that is determined by interactions involving the amino acid side chains. Compare with *primary, secondary,* and *quaternary protein structure*.

test   A shell.

test cross   The genetic cross in which either an F_1 individual, or an individual of unknown genotype, is mated to a homozygous recessive individual.

testis (tes′tis) (pl. *testes*)   The male gonad that produces sperm and the male hormone testosterone; in humans and certain other mammals the testes are located in the scrotum.

testosterone (tes-tos′ter-own)   The principal male sex hormone (androgen); a steroid hormone produced by the interstitial cells of the testes; stimulates spermatogenesis and is responsible for primary and secondary sex characteristics in the male.

tetrad   The chromosome complex formed by the synapsis of a pair of homologous chromosomes (i.e., four chromatids) during meiotic prophase I; also known as a bivalent.

tetrapods (tet'rah-podz) Four-limbed vertebrates: the amphibians, reptiles, birds, and mammals.

thalamus (thal'uh-mus) The part of the vertebrate brain that serves as a main relay center, transmitting information between the spinal cord and the cerebrum.

thallus (thal'us) (pl. *thalli*) The simple body of an alga, fungus, or nonvascular plant that lacks root, stems, or leaves, e.g., a liverwort thallus or a lichen thallus.

theca cells The layer of connective tissue cells that surrounds the granulosa cells in an ovarian follicle; stimulated by luteinizing hormone (LH) to produce androgens which are converted to estrogen in the granulosa cells.

theory A widely accepted explanation supported by a large body of observations and experiments. A good theory relates facts that appear to be unrelated; it predicts new facts and suggests new relationships. Compare with *hypothesis* and *principle*.

therapsids (ther-ap'sids) A group of mammal-like reptiles of the Permian period; gave rise to the mammals.

thermal stratification The marked layering (separation into warm and cold layers) of temperate lakes during the summer. See *thermocline*.

thermocline (thur'moh-kline) A marked and abrupt temperature transition in temperate lakes between warm surface water and cold deeper water. See *thermal stratification*.

thermodynamics Principles governing energy transfer (often expressed in terms of heat transfer). See *first law of thermodynamics* and *second law of thermodynamics*.

thermoreceptor A sensory receptor that responds to heat.

thigmomorphogenesis (thig''moh-mor-foh-jen'uh-sis) An alteration of plant growth in response to mechanical stimuli such as wind, rain, hail, and contact with passing animals.

thigmotropism (thig'moh-troh'pizm) Plant growth in response to contact with a solid object, such as the twining of plant tendrils.

threatened species A species in which the population is small enough for it to be at risk of becoming extinct throughout all or part of its range, but not so small that it is in imminent danger of extinction. Compare with *endangered species*.

threshold level The potential that a neuron or other excitable cell must reach for an action potential to be initiated.

thrombocytes See *platelets*.

thylakoid lumen See *thylakoids*.

thylakoids (thy'lah-koidz) An interconnected system of flattened, saclike membranous structures inside the chloroplast; the thylakoid membranes contain chlorophyll and the electron transport chain and enclose a compartment, the thylakoid lumen.

thymine (thy'meen) A nitrogenous pyrimidine base found in DNA.

thymus gland (thy'mus) An endocrine gland that functions as part of the lymphatic system; important in the ability to make immune responses.

thyroid gland An endocrine gland that lies anterior to the trachea and releases hormones that regulate the rate of metabolism.

thyroid hormones Hormones, including thyroxin, secreted by the thyroid gland; stimulate rate of metabolism.

tidal volume The volume of air moved into and out of the lungs with each normal resting breath.

tight junctions Specialized structures that form between some animal cells, producing a tight seal that prevents materials from passing through the spaces between the cells.

tissue A group of closely associated, similar cells that work together to carry out specific functions.

tissue culture The growth of tissue or cells in a synthetic growth medium under sterile conditions.

tissue fluid See *interstitial fluid*.

tolerance A decreased response to a drug over time.

tonoplast The membrane surrounding a vacuole.

topoisomerases (toe-poe-eye-sahm'er-ases) Enzymes that relieve twists and kinks in a DNA molecule by breaking and rejoining the strands.

torpor An energy-conserving state of low metabolic rate and inactivity. See *estivation* and *hibernation*.

torsion The twisting of the visceral mass characteristic of gastropod mollusks.

total fertility rate The average number of children born to a woman during her lifetime.

totipotent (toh-ti-poh'tent) A term describing a cell or nucleus that contains the complete set of genetic instructions required to direct the normal development of an entire organism. Compare with *pleuripotent*.

trace element An element required by an organism in very small amounts.

trachea (tray'kee-uh)(pl. *tracheae*) (1) Principal thoracic air duct of terrestrial vertebrates; windpipe; (2) One of the microscopic air ducts (or tracheal tubes) branching throughout the body of most terrestrial arthropods and some terrestrial mollusks.

tracheal tubes See *trachea*.

tracheid (tray'kee-id) A type of water-conducting and supporting cell in the xylem of vascular plants.

tract A bundle of nerve fibers within the central nervous system.

transcription The synthesis of RNA from a DNA template.

transcription factors DNA-binding proteins that regulate transcription in eukaryotes; include positively acting activators and negatively acting repressors.

transduction (1) The transfer of a genetic fragment from one cell to another, e.g., from one bacterium to another, by a virus. (2) In the nervous system, the conversion of energy of a stimulus to electrical signals.

transfer RNA (tRNA) RNA molecules that bind to specific amino acids and serve as adapter molecules in protein synthesis. The tRNA anticodons bind to complementary mRNA codons.

transformation (1) The incorporation of genetic material into a cell, thereby changing its phenotype; (2) The conversion of a normal cell to a malignant cell.

transgenic organism A plant or animal that has foreign DNA incorporated into its genome.

translation The conversion of information provided by mRNA into a specific sequence of amino acids in a polypeptide chain; process also requires transfer RNA and ribosomes.

translocation (1) The movement of organic materials (dissolved food) in the phloem of a plant; (2) Chromosome abnormality in which part of one chromosome has become attached to another; (3) Part of the elongation cycle of protein synthesis in which a transfer RNA attached to the growing polypeptide chain is transferred from the A site to the P site.

transmembrane protein An integral membrane protein that spans the lipid bilayer.

transmission, neural The conduction of a neural impulse along a neuron or from one neuron to another.

transpiration   The loss of water vapor from the aerial surfaces of a plant (i.e., leaves and stems).

transpiration-cohesion model   See *tension-cohesion model*.

transport vesicles   Small cytoplasmic vesicles that move substances from one membrane system to another.

transposable element   See *transposon*.

transposon (tranz-poze′on)   A DNA segment that is capable of moving from one chromosome to another or to different sites within the same chromosome; also called a transposable element or mobile genetic element.

transverse tubules   See *T tubules*.

triacylglycerol (try-ace′′il-glis′er-ol)   The main storage lipid of organisms, consisting of a glycerol combined chemically with three fatty acids; also called triglyceride. Compare with *monoacylglycerol* and *diacylglycerol*.

tricarboxylic acid (TCA) cycle   See *citric acid cycle*.

trichocyst (trik′oh-sist)   A cellular organelle found in certain ciliates that can discharge a threadlike structure that may aid in trapping and holding prey.

trichome (try′kohm)   A hair or other appendage growing out from the epidermis of a plant.

tricuspid valve   See *atrioventricular valve*.

triglyceride   See *triacylglycerol*.

triose   A sugar molecule containing three carbons.

triplet   A sequence of three nucleotides that serves as the basic unit of genetic information.

triplet code   The sequences of three nucleotides that compose the codons, the units of genetic information in mRNA that specify the order of amino acids in a polypeptide chain.

trisomy (try′sohm-ee)   The condition in which each chromosome has two copies, except for one, which is present in triplicate. Compare with *monosomy* and *disomy*.

trochophore larva (troh′koh-for)   A larval form found in mollusks and many polychaetes.

trophic level (troh′fik)   Each sequential step of matter and energy in a food web, from producers to primary, secondary, or tertiary consumers; each organism is assigned to a trophic level based on its primary source of nourishment.

trophoblast (troh′foh-blast)   The outer cell layer of a late blastocyst which, in placental mammals, gives rise to the chorion and to the fetal contribution to the placenta.

tropic hormone (trow′pic)   A hormone, produced by one endocrine gland, that targets another endocrine gland.

tropical dry forest   A tropical forest where enough precipitation falls to support trees but not enough to support the lush vegetation of a tropical rain forest; often occurs in areas with pronounced rainy and dry seasons.

tropical rain forest   A lush, species-rich forest biome that occurs in tropical areas where the climate is very moist throughout the year. Tropical rain forests are also characterized by old, infertile soils.

tropism (troh′pizm)   In plants, a directional growth response that is elicited by an environmental stimulus.

tropomyosin (troh-poh-my′oh-sin)   A regulatory muscle protein involved in contraction.

true-breeding line   A genetically pure strain of organism, i.e., one in which all individuals are homozygous for the traits under consideration; also called a pure line.

tube feet   Structures characteristic of echinoderms; function in locomotion and feeding.

tuber   A thickened end of a rhizome that is fleshy and enlarged for food storage, e.g., white potato.

tubular transport maximum (Tm)   The maximum rate at which a substance can be reabsorbed from the renal tubules of the kidney.

tumor   A mass of tissue that grows in an uncontrolled manner; a neoplasm.

tumor necrosis factors (TNF)   Cytokines that can kill tumor cells and can stimulate immune cells to initiate an inflammatory response.

tumor suppressor gene   See *anti-oncogene*.

tundra (tun′dra)   A treeless biome between the taiga in the south and the polar ice cap in the north that consists of boggy plains covered by lichens and small plants. Characterized by harsh, very cold winters and extremely short summers. Also called arctic tundra. Compare with *alpine tundra*.

tunicates   Chordates belonging to subphylum Urochordata; sea squirts.

turgor pressure (tur′gor)   Hydrostatic pressure that develops within a walled cell, such as a plant cell, when the osmotic pressure of the cell's contents is greater than the osmotic pressure of the surrounding fluid.

Turner syndrome   An inherited condition in which only one sex chromosome (an X chromosome) is present in cells; karyotype is designated XO; affected individuals are sterile females.

tyrosine kinase   An enzyme that phosphorylates the tyrosine part of proteins.

tyrosine kinase receptor   A plasma membrane receptor that phosphorylates the tyrosine part of proteins; when a ligand binds to the receptor, the conformation of the receptor changes and it may phosphorylate itself as well as other molecules; important in immune function and serves as a receptor for insulin.

ultimate causes (of behavior)   Evolutionary explanations for why a certain behavior occurs. Compare with *proximate causes of behavior*.

ultrasound imaging   A technique in which high-frequency sound waves (ultrasound) are used to provide an image (sonogram) of an internal structure.

ultrastructure   The fine detail of a cell, generally only observable by use of an electron microscope.

umbilical cord   In placental mammals, the organ that connects the embryo to the placenta.

uniform dispersion   The spatial distribution pattern of a population in which individuals are regularly spaced. Compare with *random dispersion* and *clumped dispersion*.

unsaturated fatty acid   See *fatty acid*.

upstream promoter elements (UPE)   Components of a eukaryotic promoter, found upstream of the RNA polymerase-binding site; the strength of a promoter is affected by the number and type of UPEs present.

upwelling   An upward movement of water that brings nutrients from the ocean depths to the surface. Where upwelling occurs, the ocean is very productive.

uracil (yur′ah-sil)   A nitrogenous pyrimidine base found in RNA.

urea (yur-ee′ah)   The principal nitrogenous excretory product of mammals; one of the water-soluble end products of protein metabolism.

ureter (yur′ih-tur)   One of the paired tubular structures that conducts urine from the kidney to the bladder.

urethra (yoo-ree′thruh)   The tube that conducts urine from the bladder to the outside of the body.

uric acid (yoor′ik)   The principal nitrogenous excretory product of insects, birds, and reptiles; a relatively insoluble end product of protein metabolism; also occurs in mammals as an end product of purine metabolism.

urinary bladder An organ that receives urine from the ureters and temporarily stores it.

urinary system The body system in vertebrates that consists of kidneys, urinary bladder, and associated ducts.

urochordates A subphylum of chordates; includes the tunicates.

uterine tube (yoo'tur-in) See *oviduct*.

uterus (yoo'tur-us) The hollow, muscular organ of the female reproductive tract in which the fetus undergoes development.

utricle The structure within the vestibule of the vertebrate inner ear that, along with the saccule, houses the receptors of static equilibrium.

vaccine (vak-seen') A commercially produced, weakened or killed antigen associated with a particular disease that stimulates the body to make antibodies.

vacuole (vak'yoo-ole) A fluid-filled, membrane-bounded sac found within the cytoplasm; may function in storage, digestion, or water elimination.

vagina The elastic, muscular tube, extending from the cervix to its orifice, that receives the penis during sexual intercourse and serves as the birth canal.

valence electrons The electrons in the outer electron shell, known as the valence shell, of an atom; in the formation of a chemical bond an atom can accept electrons into its valence shell, or donate or share valence electrons.

van der Waals forces Weak attractive forces between atoms; caused by interactions among fluctuating charges.

vas deferens (vas def'ur-enz) (pl. *vasa deferentia*) One of the paired sperm ducts that connects the epididymis of the testis to the ejaculatory duct.

vascular cambium A lateral meristem that produces secondary xylem (wood) and secondary phloem (inner bark). Compare with *cork cambium*.

vascular tissue system The tissues specialized for translocation of materials throughout the plant body, i.e., the xylem and phloem.

vasoconstriction Narrowing of the diameter of blood vessels.

vasodilation Expansion of the diameter of blood vessels.

vector (1) Any carrier or means of transfer; (2) Agent, e.g., a plasmid or virus, that transfers genetic information; (3) Agent that transfers a parasite from one host to another.

vegetal pole The yolky pole of a vertebrate or echinoderm egg. Compare with *animal pole*.

vein (1) A blood vessel that carries blood from the tissues toward a chamber of the heart; compare with *artery*. (2) A strand of vascular tissue that is part of the network of conducting tissue in a leaf.

veliger larva The larval stage of many marine gastropods (snails) and bivalves (e.g., clams); often is a second larval stage that develops after the trochophore larva.

ventilation The process of actively moving air or water over a respiratory surface.

ventral Toward the lowermost surface or belly of an animal. Compare with *dorsal*.

ventricle (1) A cavity in an organ; (2) One of the several cavities of the brain; (3) One of the chambers of the heart that receives blood from an atrium.

vernalization (vur''nul-uh-zay'shun) The induction of flowering by a low temperature treatment.

vertebrates A subphylum of chordates; possess a bony vertebral column; include fishes, amphibians, reptiles, birds, and mammals.

vesicle (ves'ih-kl) Any small sac, especially a small spherical membrane-bounded compartment, within the cytoplasm.

vessel element A type of water-conducting cell in the xylem of vascular plants.

vestibular apparatus Collectively, the saccule, utricle, and semicircular canals of the inner ear.

vestigial (ves-tij'ee-ul) Rudimentary; an evolutionary remnant of a formerly functional structure.

vibrio A spiral-shaped bacterium that has the form of a short helix. Compare with *spirillum, spirochete, bacillus,* and *coccus*.

villus (pl. *villi*) A multicellular, minute, elongated projection, from the surface of an epithelial membrane, e.g., villi of the mucosa of the small intestine.

viroid (vy'roid) A tiny, naked infectious particle consisting only of nucleic acid.

virulent Able to cause disease in a host. Compare with *avirulent*.

virus A tiny pathogen composed of a core of nucleic acid usually encased in protein and capable of infecting living cells; a virus is characterized by total dependence on a living host.

viscera (vis'ur-uh) The internal body organs, especially those located in the abdominal or thoracic cavities.

visceral mass The concentration of body organs (viscera) located above the foot in mollusks.

vital capacity The maximum volume of air a person can expire after filling the lungs to the maximum extent.

vitamin A complex organic molecule required in very small amounts for normal metabolic functioning.

vitelline envelope An acellular covering of the eggs of certain animals (e.g., echinoderms), located just outside the plasma membrane.

viviparous (vih-vip'er-us) Bearing living young that develop within the body of the mother. Compare with *oviparous* and *ovoviviparous*.

voltage-activated ion channels Ion channels in the plasma membrane of neurons that are regulated by changes in voltage. Also called voltage-gated channels.

vomeronasal organ In mammals, an organ in the epithelium of the nose, made up of specialized chemoreceptor cells that detect pheromones.

vulva The external genital structures of the female.

warning coloration See *aposematic coloration*.

water mold A fungus-like protist with a body consisting of a coenocytic mycelium that reproduces asexually by forming motile zoospores and sexually by forming oospores.

water potential Free energy of water; the water potential of pure water is zero and that of solutions is a negative value. Differences in water potential are used to predict the direction of water movement (always from a region of less negative water potential to a region of more negative water potential).

water vascular system Unique hydraulic system of echinoderms; functions in locomotion and feeding.

wavelength The distance from one wave peak to the next; the energy of electromagnetic radiation is inversely proportional to its wavelength.

weathering processes Chemical or physical processes that help form soil from rock; during weathering processes, the rock is gradually broken into smaller and smaller pieces.

Western blotting A technique in which proteins, previously separated by gel electrophoresis, are transferred to paper. A specific labeled antibody is generally used to mark the location of a particular protein. Compare with *Southern blot hybridization* and *Northern blot hybridization*.

whisk ferns One of a phylum of seedless vascular plants with a life cycle similar to ferns.

white matter Nervous tissue in the brain and spinal cord that contains myelinated axons. Compare with *gray matter*.

wild type The phenotypically normal (naturally occurring) form of a gene or organism.

wobble The ability of some tRNA anticodons to associate with more than one mRNA codon; in these cases the 5′ base of the anticodon is capable of forming hydrogen bonds with more than one kind of base in the 3′ position of the codon.

work Any change in the state or motion of matter.

X-linked gene A gene carried on an X chromosome.

x-ray diffraction A technique for determining the spatial arrangement of the components of a crystal.

xylem (zy′lem) The vascular tissue that conducts water and dissolved minerals in plants.

XYY karyotype Chromosome constitution that causes affected individuals (who are fertile males) to be unusually tall, with severe acne.

yeast A unicellular fungus (ascomycete) that reproduces asexually by budding or fission and sexually by ascospores.

yolk sac One of the extraembryonic membranes; a pouchlike outgrowth of the digestive tract of embryos of certain vertebrates (e.g., birds) that grows around the yolk and digests it. Embryonic blood cells are formed in the mammalian yolk sac, which lacks yolk.

zero population growth Point at which the birth rate equals the death rate. A population with zero population growth does not change in size.

zona pellucida (pel-loo′sih-duh) The thick, transparent covering that surrounds the plasma membrane of a mammalian ovum.

zooflagellate A unicellular, nonphotosynthetic protozoon that possesses one or more long, whiplike flagella.

zooplankton (zoh″oh-plank′tun) The nonphotosynthetic organisms present in plankton, e.g., protozoa, tiny crustaceans, and the larval stages of many animals. See *plankton*. Compare with *phytoplankton*.

zoospore (zoh′oh-spore) A flagellated motile spore produced asexually by certain algae, chytrids, water molds, and other protists.

zooxanthellae (zoh″oh-zan-thel′ee) (sing. *zooxanthella*) Endosymbiotic, photosynthetic dinoflagellates found in certain marine invertebrates; their mutualistic relationship with corals enhances the corals′ reef-building ability.

zygomycetes (zy″gah-my′seats) Fungi characterized by the production of nonmotile asexual spores and sexual zygospores.

zygosporangium (zy′gah-spor-an′gee-um) A thick-walled sporangium containing a zygospore.

zygospore (zy′gah-spor) A sexual spore produced by a zygomycete.

zygote The 2*n* cell that results from the union of *n* gametes in sexual reproduction. Species that are not polyploid have haploid gametes and diploid zygotes.

zygotic genes Genes that are transcribed after fertilization, either in the zygote or in the embryo. Compare with *maternal effect genes*.

zygotic segmentation genes In *Drosophila*, genes transcribed in the embryo that are responsible for controlling formation of the segmented body.

Index

secondary cell wall of, 677
secondary growth of, 687–688, 688il
self-incompatibility of, 754
sexual reproduction of, 586–588, 589il, 751–752, 752il, 753il, 766–767. *See also* Pollination
shoot system of, 676, 677il
sieve tube members of, 584, 682, 683t, 684il
size of, 675, 675il
sporophyte generation of, 751
stems of, 710–725. *See also* Stem(s)
subsidiary cells of, 695
tracheids of, 682, 683t, 684il
trichomes of, 684, 685t, 686
tropism of, 779–781, 780il, 781il
vascular tissue system of, **676,** 678il, 678t, 682, 683t, 684il
vernalization of, 775, 778
vessel elements of, 583–584, 682, 683t, 684il
woody, **675**
xylem of, 682, 683t, 684il
Angiotensins, **930,** 1027t, **1028**
Animal pole, **1090**
Animalia, **11,** 12il, **472,** 473il, 473t, **596,** A-9–A-10
Animals, 595–613, 602t. *See also* Deuterostomes; Protostomes
body symmetry of, **597,** 598il
classification of, 597–601, 601il, 602t
environments for, 596
phylogeny of, 597–601, 601il, 602t
Anion, **31–33,** 32il
Anisogamous sexual reproduction, **524,** 525il
Ankylosaurus, 441, 442il
Annelida, 602t, **622–625,** 623il, 623t, 640t, A-9
Annelids, **622–625,** 623il, 623t
development of, 1092il
nervous system of, 857, 857il
skeleton of, 820–821
Annual plants, **675**
Annual rings, **718,** 718il, 720f–721f
Anolis carolinensis (green anole), 1160–1161, 1161il
Anolis sagrei (brown anole), 1160–1161, 1161il
Anoplura, 636t
Ant, 637t, 743
in seed dispersal, 763–764, 764il
Antagonist, **820, 830,** 831il
Anteater *(Myrmecophagg tridactyla),* 379, 380il
Antenna complexes, 182, 182il
Antennae, in arthropods, **630**
Antennal glands, **634**
Antennapedia locus, of *Drosophila melanogaster,* 348, 354il
Anterior cavity, of eye, **904,** 905il
Anterior direction, **597,** 598il
Anther, **586,** 586il, **751,** 752il
Antheridium, **555,** 556il
Anthoceros natans (common hornwort), 559il, 561
Anthocerotophyta, 557il, 558t, 559il, **561,** A-8
Anthophyta, **583–590,** A-9. *See also* Angiosperms
Anthozoa, 604il, 604t, **605,** 607–608
Anthrax, 12il, 498, 503
Anthropoidea, 451, 451il, 451t, **452–453,** 453il
Anthropology, molecular, 460–461
Anti-anxiety drugs, 880t
Antibiotics, 150, 385, 503–504
Antibody (antibodies), **941,** 948–952. *See also* Immunoglobulin
affinity of, 950
classes of, 951
diversity of, 952–954, 955il
fluorescent, 76
monoclonal, **952,** 957

production of, 948–949, 948il, 949il
structure of, 949–950, 950il, 951il
Anticodon, **264–265, 269,** 270il
Antidepressants, 880t
Antidiuretic hormone (ADH), **1026–1028,** 1027il, 1027t, 1034il, 1035, 1042t, **1043**
Antigen, **941,** 950
Antigen D, 961–962, 962il
Antigen-antibody complex, **950,** 950il, 951–952, 951il
Antigenic determinant, **950,** 950il
Antigen-presenting cells, **945,** 948, 948il, 965
Antihistamines, 964
Antimicrobial peptides, 941
Anti-oncogenes, 353
Antioxidants, **1004**
Antipsychotic medications, 880t
Antiteuchus melanoleucus (coca shield bug), 1127il
Antrum, **1067,** 1068il
Anura, **658**
Anus, of earthworm, 624
Aorta, **922, 931**
Aortic arch, 932il
Aortic bodies, 981
Aortic valve, **924,** 924il
Aotus evingatus (owl monkey), 904il
Apes, 450il, 453–456, 453il, 454il, 455il, 456il
Aphids, 637t
Aphotic region, **1226**
Apical dominance, **785**
Apical meristem, **570,** 686–687, 687il, **711,** 714t
Apicomplexa, 511t, **516–517,** 517il, A-7
Apicomplexans, **516–517,** 517il, 530
Apis mellifera (honeybee), 831il, 832, 832il, 1126–1128, 1128il, 1171, 1172il
Aplysia, 870–873, 871il, 872il, 873il
Apoda, **658**
Apoenzyme, **145**
Apomixis, **766**
Apoplast, 733il, **734**
Apoptosis, **93,** 357, 947, 965, 1067, **1088,** 1107
Aposematic coloration, **1167,** 1168il
Appendages, in arthropods, **630,** 631t, **632**
Appendicitis, 999
Appendix, vermiform, **999**
Aquaporin-1, 115
Aquatic ecosystems, 1215–1227
estuary, **1222–1223,** 1222il
freshwater, **1217–1222,** 1217il, 1220il, 1221il
freshwater flowing-water, **1217–1219,** 1217il
freshwater standing-water, **1219–1221,** 1220il, 1221il
freshwater wetland, **1221–1222,** 1221il
marine, 1223–1227, 1223il, 1224il, 1225il, 1227il
organisms of, 1216–1217
salinity and, **1215–1216**
Aqueous humor, **904–905**
Arabidopsis thaliana (mouse-ear cress), 677il
development of, 359–360, 360il
genome of, 309
phytochrome in, **773–774,** 774il
Arachnids, 602t, 631t, **632–633,** 633il, 640t
population ecology of, 1144–1145, 1145il
Arachnoid, **861,** 862il
Arboreal mammal, **449,** 450, 450il, **665**
Archaea, **11,** 12il, **472,** 472il, 493, **498–499,** 499il, 499t, 501t. *See also* Bacteria
Archaeanthus linnenbergeri, 592il
Archaebacteria, **11,** 12il, **472,** 473il, 473t, 493, A-7
Archaefructus, 591il
Archaeopteris, 590, 591il
Archaeopteryx, 443, 662il, 663
Archegonium (archegonia), **555,** 556il

Archenteron, **1094,** 1094il
Archosaurs, mass extinction of, 423, 424il
Arctic tundra, **1206,** 1207, 1208il, 1209il
Arctium minus (burdock), 763il
Ardipithecus, 457
Argentinosaurus, 441, 442il
Arginine, 60il
Argyroxyphium sandwicense, 423il
Aristotle, 369
Arrhythmia, 934f
Art, career resources in, A-12
Arterioles, **919,** 920il, 921, 921il, **1020,** 1021il
Artery, **919,** 920il, 928–929, 930il
Arthropoda, 602t, **629–639,** 629il, 630il, 631t, 640t, A-9
Arthropods, **629–639,** 629il, 630il, 631t
muscles of, 825
nervous system of, 857, 857il
skeleton of, 821, 822il
tracheal tube systems of, 970, 971il
Articulated insect, **638**
Artificial insemination, 1076f, **1239**
Artificial pacemaker, 927
Artificial selection, **371,** 371il
Artiodactyla, 669t
Arum maculatum, 164
Ascaris, 627–628, 628il
Ascidiacea, **649,** 649il
Asclepias syriaca (milkweed), 763il, 1167–1168, 1168il
Ascocarp, **540,** 543il
Ascomycetes, 536t, **540–543,** 540il, 542il, 543il
edible, 549, 549il
in plant diseases, 550, 551il
Ascomycota, 536t, **540–543,** 540il, 542il, 543il, A-8
Ascorbic acid, 1005t
Ascospore, **541,** 542il
Ascus (asci), **540**
Asexual reproduction, **6,** 7il, **207, 1058,** 1059, 1059il
Asparagine, 60il
Aspartate, 846t
Aspartic acid, 60il
Aspergillosis, 551
Aspergillus fumigatus, 551
Aspergillus tamarii, 548–549
Assimilation, in nitrogen cycle, 1191il, 1192
Association area, **865,** 867il
Association for Tropical Biology, A-11
Association for Women in Science, A-11
Association neuron, **837**
Association of Medical Illustrators, A-12
Association of Systematic Collections, A-16
Assortative mating, **394**
Aster, **201**
Asteroidea, **644,** 645il, 646il
Asthma, **963–964**
Astigmatism, 906, 906il
Astrocytes, **837**
Atherosclerosis, 934f–935f
Athlete's foot, 551
Atlantic puffin *(Fratercula arctica),* 663il
Atlas, **822**
Atmosphere, 1137, 1196–1198, 1198il
circulation of, 1197, 1198il
horizontal movements of, 1197–1198, 1198il
ocean interaction with, 1199, 1200il
pollution of, 1244–1249, 1244il, 1245t, 1246il, 1248il
Atom(s), **8,** 9il, **24–28**
chemical bonds of, **29–33,** 30il, 32il, 33il
electron orbitals of, **27–28,** 27il
electronegativity of, **30–31,** 31il
ground state of, **176**
Lewis structure of, 29, **29**

Soil *(continued)*
  macronutrients of, 743, 744t
  micronutrients of, 743, 744t
  minerals of, 743–745, 744t, 745il
  nutrient depletion of, 745–746
  organic matter of, 741, 741il
  organisms of, 742–743, 742il
  pH of, 743, 743il
  pore spaces of, 741, 742il
  salinization of, 746
Solanum, 1164–1165
Solar energy, **1195**–1196, 1195il
Solar tracking, **780**–781
Solute, **32**
Solution
  acidic, **38**, 39il
  basic, **38**, 39il
  buffer, **38**–39
  hypertonic, **113**–114, 114t, 115il
  hypotonic, **114**, 114t, 115il
  isotonic, **113**, 114t, 115il
  neutral, **38**, 39il
  pH of, **36**, 38–39, 38t, 39il
Solvent, **32**, 34, 112
Somatic cell, 341il, **342**, 342n
Somatic cell gene therapy, 335
Somatic nervous system, **874**–876, 876t, 877il
Somatomedins, **1044**
Somites, **1096**, 1096il
Song, in birds, 664
Sonogram, of embryo, 1104
Sooty tern *(Sterna fuscata),* 812il
Sordeium (soredia), 546il, 547
Sorghastrum nutans, 548, 548t
Sorus (sori), **563**
Sources, ecological, **1149**, 1150il
Southern, E.M., 308
Southern blot, **308**
Soy sauce, fungi in, 548–549
Spanish moss, 560, 1171il
Spartina (cordgrass), 1222il
Spatial summation, **850**
Speciation, 411–417
  allopatric, **411**–413, 412il, 413il
  anagenic, **411**
  cladogenic, **411**
  hybrid zone and, **416**–417
  stasis and, **417**
  sympatric, **413**–416, 414il, 415il, 416il
Species, **10**, 11il, **368**, **407**, 468n, 470il, 471t
  behavioral isolation of, **409**, 409il
  biological concept of, 407–408
  center of origin of, **1227**
  concept of, 407–408
  cosmopolitan, **1227**
  diversity of, **1172**–1175, 1173il, 1174il, 1175il
  ecological niche of, 1160–1162, 1161il, 1162il
  endangered, **1233**–1234
  endemic, **1227**
  evolution of, 411–417. *See also* Evolution;
    Speciation
  exotic, **1235**–1237, 1235t, 1237t
  extinction of, **1233**–1242, 1233il, 1235t, 1241t
  gametic isolation of, **409**, 410il
  global warming effects on, 1247–1248, 1248il
  habitat isolation of, **408**–409, 409il
  hybrid, 410, 410il, **414**, 414il, 416–417
  interspecific competition among, **1163**–1165,
    1163t, 1164il, 1165il
  intraspecific competition among, **1143**, 1143il
  keystone, **1172**
  K-selected, **1146**–1147
  local populations of, **1148**–1149, 1149il
  mechanical isolation of, **409**, 410il
  morphological concept of, 407

naming of, 10–12, 11il, 11t
ozone depletion effects on, 1251
postzygotic barriers between, **410**–411, 410il,
  411t
preservation of, 1238–1242, 1240il, 1241il
prezygotic barriers between, **408**–409, 408il,
  409il, 410il, 411, 411t
range of, **1227**, **1234**
r-selected, **1146**
sexual isolation of, **409**, 409il
succession of, **1175**–1176, 1176il
temporal isolation of, **408**, 408il
threatened, **1234**
ultraviolet radiation effects on, 1251
Species diversity, **1172**–1175, 1173il, 1174il,
  1175il
Species evenness, **1173**, 1173il
Species richness, 411, **1172**–1175, 1173il, 1174il,
  1175il, **1233**
  community stability and, 1175–1176
Species richness–energy hypothesis, 1174, 1175il
Specific epithet, **10**, 11t, **469**
Specific (adaptive, acquired) immune response,
  941–944, 942il
Speckled cowbird *(Molothrus ater),* 1236f
Speech, functional magnetic resonance imaging
  during, 855il, 856
Sperm, **1058**, 1062, 1064il
  abnormalities of, 1063–1064
  capacitation of, 1075, **1089**
  flagella of, 75
  structure of, 1062, 1064il
Spermatids, **1061**, 1062il
Spermatocyte, **1061**, 1062il
Spermatogenesis, 213, **1061**, 1062il
Spermatogonium (spermatogonia), **1061**, 1062il
Spermicides, 1080t
Sphagnum (peat mosses), 560
Sphenophyta, 558t, **566**, 569, 569il, A-8
Spicules, of sponge, **602**
Spiders, 602t, 631t, **632**–633, 633il, 640t
  population ecology of, 1144–1145, 1145il
Spike, of action potential, 841, 843il
Spike moss *(Selaginella),* 570, 571il
Spiller, David, 1144
Spinal accessory nerve, 876t
Spinal cord, **861**–863, 861t, 863il, 866il
  injury to, 3
  structure of, 863il
Spinal nerves, **876**, 877il
Spinal tracts, **861**–861, 863il
Spindle, of tubulin subunits, 96
Spines, **704**, 705il
Spinosella plicifera, 603il
Spiny anteater *(Tachyglossus aculeatus),* 666il,
  667
Spiracles, **638**, **970**, 971il
Spiral cleavage, **598**, 600il, **1090**
Spirochetes, **494**, 500t
Spirodela sp. (duckweeds), 675il
Spirogyra, 179–180, 180il, 511t, 525il
Spiroplasma, 494, 494il
Splitleaf philodendron, 164
Sponge(s), 597, **601**–604, 602t, 603il
  feeding by, 602–603
  food processing by, 989
  reproduction of, 603–604
  skeleton of, 602
  structure of, 603il
Sponge crab *(Criptodromia octodenta),* 629il
Spongin, 602
Spongocoel, **602**, 603il
Spongy body, 1061il, **1064**, 1065il
Spongy bone, 801, 804il
Spongy mesophyll, 695il, **696**

Spontaneous abortion, **1082**
Sporangium (sporangia)
  of hornworts, **561**
  of plasmodial slime mold, **526**, 527il
  of zygomycetes, **537**–539, 538il
Spores
  of fungi, 534il, 535, 536il
  of seedless plants, **556**, 558–559, 560il, 561il,
    563–564, 566il, 570, 570il, 571il
Sporogenous cells, **556**, 560il, 561il
Sporophyll, **580**
Sporophyte generation, **213**, 213il, **555**, 555il,
  751
Sporozoa, 511t, **516**
Sporozoites, **516**
Spotted hyena *(Crocuta crocuta),* 988, 988il
Spring peeper frog *(Hyla crucifer),* 1120il
Spring turnover, **1220**, 1221il
Springwood, 718, 719il
Squamata, 661il, **662**
Squamous epithelium, **797**, 798t, 799t
Squash *(Cucurbita pepo),* 702il
Squids, 602t, 618, 618t, 619il, 622, 640t
Srinivasan, Mandyam, 1128
Stabilizing selection, **397**, 398il
Stachys byzantina (lamb's ear), 695il
Staghorn fern *(Platycerium bifurcatum),*
  565il
Stahl, Franklin, 250
Stamen, **586**, 586il, 587il, 590, **751**, 752il
Standing-water ecosystem, **1219**–1221, 1220il,
  1221il
Stapes, **894**, 894il
Staphylococci, 501t
Staphylococcus, 17, 501t
Star coral *(Montastrea annularis),* 608
Starch, **52**, 53il
Starling's law, **927**–928
Stasis, speciation and, **417**
Statocysts, **634**, **891**–892, 892il
Statolith, **891**, 892il
Stele, of dicot root, 732il, 734
Stem(s), 710–725
  auxin effect on, 784–785
  cork cambium of, 713, 715–717, 718il
  dicot, **711**–712, 712il
  external structure of, 711, 711il
  gibberellin effect on, 785–786, 786il
  growth of, 711
  internal structure of, 711–713, 712il, 713il
  monocot, **712**–713, 713il
  origin of, 711
  periderm of, 713, 715–717, 718il
  secondary growth of, 713–719, 714il, 714t,
    715il, 716il
  sugar translocation in, 723–725, 723il, 724il
  vascular cambium of, 713–715, 714il, 715il, 716il
  water transport in, 719–723, 722il
  woody, 713–719, 714il, 715il, 716il, 727il, 728il
Stem cells, **3**, 312, 314, **343**, 346, 346f, 957, **1088**
Stentor, 511t, 515, 515il
Steppan, Claire M., 1051
Stereocilia, **892**
Sterility, male, **1062**
Sterilization, **1081**–1082, 1081t, 1082il
Sterna fuscata (sooty tern), 812il
Steroid hormones, **56**–57, 59il, **1034**–1035,
  1034il, 1037, 1037il, 1052–1054
  anabolic, 1035f
Steward, F.C., 342, 787
Sticklebacks, 373–374, 1166–1167
Stictocephala bubalus (buffalo treehopper), 637t
Stigma, **586**, 586il, 588il, **751**, 752il
Stigmatella aurantiaca, 500t
Stimulus (stimuli), **5**, 836